CHEVROLET | CORSICA / BERETTA
1988-92 REPAIR MANUAL

CHILTON'S

Senior Vice President	Ronald A. Hoxter
Publisher and Editor-In-Chief	Kerry A. Freeman, S.A.E.
Executive Editors	Dean F. Morgantini, S.A.E., W. Calvin Settle, Jr., S.A.E.
Managing Editor	Nick D'Andrea
Special Products Manager	Ken Grabowski, A.S.E., S.A.E.
Senior Editors	Jacques Gordon, Michael L. Grady, Debra McCall, Kevin M. G. Maher, Richard J. Rivele, S.A.E., Richard T. Smith, Jim Taylor, Ron Webb
Project Managers	Martin J. Gunther, Will Kessler, A.S.E., Richard Schwartz
Production Manager	Andrea Steiger
Product Systems Manager	Robert Maxey
Director of Manufacturing	Mike D'Imperio
Editor	Martin J. Gunther

CHILTON BOOK COMPANY

ONE OF THE *DIVERSIFIED PUBLISHING COMPANIES,*
A PART OF *CAPITAL CITIES/ABC, INC.*

Manufactured in USA
© 1992 Chilton Book Company
Chilton Way, Radnor, PA 19089
ISBN 0-8019-8254-5
Library of Congress Catalog Card No. 91-058820
5678901234 5432109876

Contents

Contents

SAFETY NOTICE

Proper service and repair procedures are vital to the safe, reliable operation of all motor vehicles, as well as the personal safety of those performing repairs. This manual outlines procedures for servicing and repairing vehicles using safe, effective methods. The procedures contain many NOTES, CAUTIONS and WARNINGS which should be followed along with standard safety procedures to eliminate the possibility of personal injury or improper service which could damage the vehicle or compromise its safety.

It is important to note that the repair procedures and techniques, tools and parts for servicing motor vehicles, as well as the skill and experience of the individual performing the work vary widely. It is not possible to anticipate all of the conceivable ways or conditions under which vehicles may be serviced, or to provide cautions as to all of the possible hazards that may result. Standard and accepted safety precautions and equipment should be used when handling toxic or flammable fluids, and safety goggles or other protection should be used during cutting, grinding, chiseling, prying, or any other process that can cause material removal or projectiles.

Some procedures require the use of tools specially designed for a specific purpose. Before substituting another tool or procedure, you must be completely satisfied that neither your personal safety, nor the performance of the vehicle will be endangered.

Although information in this manual is based on industry sources and is complete as possible at the time of publication, the possibility exists that some car manufacturers made later changes which could not be included here. While striving for total accuracy, Chilton Book Company cannot assume responsibility for any errors, changes or omissions that may occur in the compilation of this data.

PART NUMBERS

Part numbers listed in this reference are not recommendations by Chilton for any product by brand name. They are references that can be used with interchange manuals and aftermarket supplier catalogs to locate each brand supplier's discrete part number.

SPECIAL TOOLS

Special tools are recommended by the vehicle manufacturer to perform their specific job. Use has been kept to a minimum, but where absolutely necessary, they are referred to in the text by the part number of the tool manufacturer. These tools can be purchased, under the appropriate part number, from your General Motors dealer or regional distributor, or an equivalent tool can be purchased locally from a tool supplier or parts outlet. Before substituting any tool for the one recommended, read the SAFETY NOTICE at the top of this page.

ACKNOWLEDGMENTS

The Chilton Book Company expresses appreciation to General Motors Corp., Detroit, MI for their generous assistance.

1

GENERAL INFORMATION AND MAINTENANCE

HOW TO USE THIS BOOK

Chilton's Total Car Care Manual for Corsica/Beretta is intended to help you learn more about the inner workings of your vehicle and save you money on its upkeep and operation.

The first two sections will be the most used, since they contain maintenance and tune-up information and procedures. Studies have shown that a properly tuned and maintained car can get at least 10% better gas mileage than an out-of-tune car. The other sections deal with the more complex systems of your car. Operating systems from engine through brakes are covered to the extent that the average do-it-yourselfer becomes mechanically involved.

A secondary purpose of this book is a reference for owners who want to understand their car and/or their mechanics better. In this case, no tools at all are required.

Before removing any bolts, read through the entire procedure. This will give you the overall view of what tools and supplies will be required. There is nothing more frustrating than having to walk to the bus stop on Monday morning because you were short one bolt on Sunday afternoon. So read ahead and plan ahead. Each operation should be approached logically and all procedures thoroughly understood before attempting any work.

All sections contain adjustments, maintenance, removal and installation procedures, and repair or overhaul procedures. When repair is not considered practical, we tell you how to remove the part and then how to install the new or rebuilt replacement. In this way, you at least save the labor costs. Backyard repair of such components as the alternator is just not practical.

Two basic mechanic's rules should be mentioned here. One, whenever the left side of the car or engine is referred to, it is meant to specify the driver's side of the car. Conversely, the right side of the car means the passenger's side. Secondly, most screws and bolts are removed by turning counterclockwise, and tightened by turning clockwise.

Safety is always the most important rule. Constantly be aware of the dangers involved in working on an automobile and take the proper precautions. See the section in this section Servicing Your Vehicle Safely and the SAFETY NOTICE on the acknowledgment page.

Pay attention to the instructions provided. There are 3 common mistakes in mechanical work:

1. Incorrect order of assembly, disassembly or adjustment. When taking something apart or putting it together, doing things in the wrong order usually justs cost you extra time; however, it CAN break something. Read the entire procedure before beginning disassembly. Do everything in the order in which the instructions say you should do it, even if you can't immediately see a reason for it. When you're taking apart something that is very intricate (for example, a carburetor), you might want to draw a picture of how it looks when assembled at one point in order to make sure you get everything back in its proper position. (We will supply exploded view whenever possible). When making adjustments, especially tune-up adjustments, do them in order; often, one adjustment affects another, and you cannot expect even satisfactory results unless each adjustment is made only when it cannot be changed by any order.

2. Overtorquing (or undertorquing). While it is more common for over-torquing to cause damage, undertorquing can cause a fastener to vibrate loose causing serious damage. Especially when dealing with aluminum parts, pay attention to torque specifications and utilize a torque wrench in assembly. If a torque figure is not available, remember that if you are using the right tool to do the job, you will probably not have to strain yourself to get a fastener tight enough. The pitch of most threads is so slight that the tension you put on the wrench will be multiplied many, many times in actual force on

what you are tightening. A good example of how critical torque is can be seen in the case of spark plug installation, especially where you are putting the plug into an aluminum cylinder head. Too little torque can fail to crush the gasket, causing leakage of combustion gases and consequent overheating of the plug and engine parts. Too much torque can damage the threads, or distort the plug which changes the spark gap.

There are many commercial products available for ensuring that fasteners won't come loose, even if they are not torqued just right (a very common brand is Loctite®). If you're worried about getting something together tight enough to hold, but loose enough to avoid mechanical damage during assembly, one of these products might offer substantial insurance. Read the label on the package and make sure the products is compatible with the materials, fluids, etc. involved before choosing one.

3. Crossthreading. This occurs when a part such as a bolt is screwed into a nut or casting at the wrong angle and forced. Cross threading is more likely to occur if access is difficult. It helps to clean and lubricate fasteners, and to start threading with the part to be installed going straight in. Then, start the bolt, spark plug, etc. with your fingers. If you encounter resistance, unscrew the part and start over again at a different angle until it can be inserted and turned several turns without much effort. Keep in mind that many parts, especially spark plugs, used tapered threads so that gentle turning will automatically bring the part you're treading to the proper angle if you don't force it or resist a change in angle. Don't put a wrench on the part until its's been turned a couple of turns by hand. If you suddenly encounter resistance, and the part has not seated fully, don't force it. Pull it back out and make sure it's clean and threading properly.

Always take your time and be patient; once you have some experience, working on your car will become an enjoyable hobby.

TOOLS AND EQUIPMENT

Naturally, without the proper tools and equipment it is impossible to properly service you vehicle. It would be impossible to catalog each tool that you would need to perform each or any operation in this book. It would also be unwise for the amateur to rush out and buy an

expensive set of tool on the theory that he may need on or more of them at sometime.

The best approach is to proceed slowly gathering together a good quality set of those tools that are used most frequently. Don't be misled by the low cost of bargain tools. It is far

better to spend a little more for better quality. Forged wrenches, 6- or 12-point sockets and fine tooth ratchets are by far preferable to their less expensive counterparts. As any good mechanic can tell you, there are few worse experiences than trying to work on a car with bad

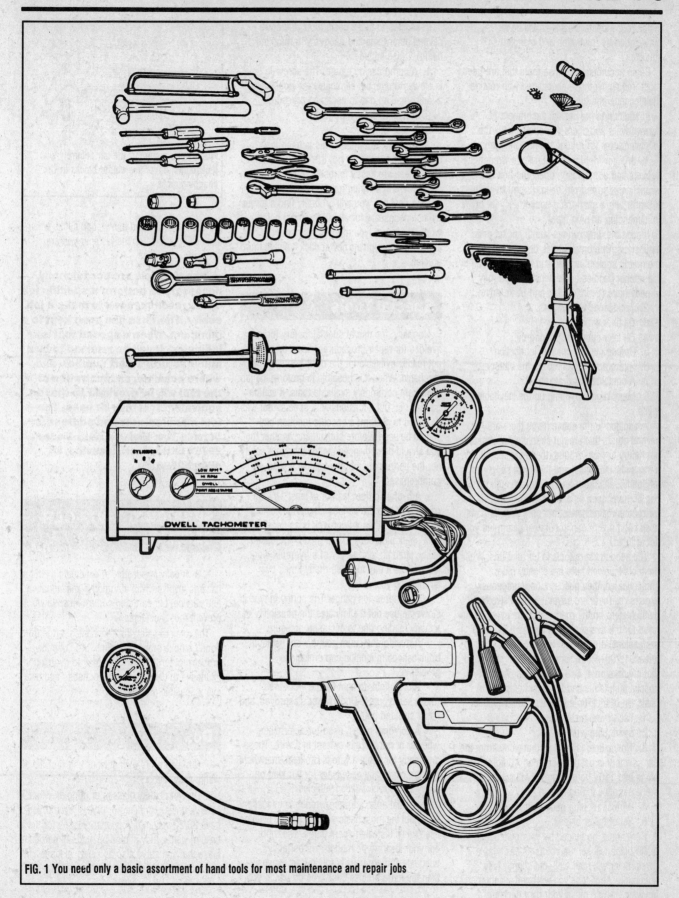

FIG. 1 You need only a basic assortment of hand tools for most maintenance and repair jobs

tools. Your monetary savings will be far outweighed by frustration and mangled knuckles.

Begin accumulating those tools that are used most frequently; those associated with routine maintenance and tune-up.

In addition to the normal assortment of screwdrivers and pliers you should have the following tools for routine maintenance jobs:

1. SAE (or Metric) or SAE/Metric wrenches-sockets and combination open end-box end wrenches in sizes from 1/8 in. (3mm) to 3/4 in. (19mm) and a spark plug socket (13/16 in. or 5/8 in. depending on plug type).

If possible, buy various length socket drive extensions. One break in this department is that the metric sockets available in the U.S. will all fit the ratchet handles and extensions you may already have (1/4 in., 3/8 in., and 1/2 in. drive).

2. Jackstands for support.
3. Oil filter wrench.
4. Oil filler spout for pouring oil.
5. Grease gun for chassis lubrication.
6. Hydrometer for checking the battery.
7. A container for draining oil.
8. Many rags for wiping up the inevitable mess.

In addition to the above items there are several others that are not absolutely necessary, but handy to have around. these include oil dry, a transmission funnel and the usual supply of lubricants, antifreeze and fluids, although these can be purchased as needed. This is a basic list for routine maintenance, but only your personal needs and desire can accurately determine you list of tools.

The second list of tools is for tune-ups. While the tools involved here are slightly more sophisticated, they need not be outrageously expensive. There are several inexpensive tach/dwell meters on the market that are every bit as good for the average mechanic as a $100.00 professional model. Just be sure that it goes to a least 1,200–1,500 rpm on the tach scale and that it works on 4, 6, 8 cylinder engines. (A special tach is needed for diesel engines). A basic list of tune-up equipment could include:

1. Tach/dwell meter.
2. Spark plug wrench.
3. Timing light (a DC light that works from the car's battery is best, although an AC light that plugs into 110V house current will suffice at some sacrifice in brightness).
4. Wire spark plug gauge/adjusting tools.
5. Set of feeler blades.

Here again, be guided by your own needs. A feeler blade will set the points as easily as a dwell meter will read well, but slightly less accurately. And since you will need a tachometer anyway. . . well, make your own decision.

In addition to these basic tools, there are several other tools and gauges you may find useful. These include:

1. A compression gauge. The screw-in type is slower to use, but eliminates the possibility of a faulty reading due to escaping pressure.
2. A manifold vacuum gauge.
3. A test light.
4. An induction meter. This is used for determining whether or not there is current in a wire. These are handy for use if a wire is broken somewhere in a wiring harness.

As a final not, you will probably find a torque wrench necessary for all but the most basic work. The beam type models are perfectly adequate, although the newer click type are more precise.

Special Tools

Normally, the use of special factory tools is avoided for repair procedures, since these are not readily available for the do-it-yourself mechanic. When it is possible to preform the job with more commonly available tools, it will be pointed out, but occasionally, a special tool was designed to perform a specific function and should be used. Before substituting another tool, you should be convinced that neither your safety nor the performance of the vehicle will be compromised.

• A hydraulic floor jack of at least 1 1/2 ton capacity. If you are serious about maintaining your own car, then a floor jack is as necessary as a spark plug socket. The greatly increased utility, strength, and safety of a hydraulic floor jack makes it pay for itself many times over through the years.

• A compression gauge. The screw-in type is slower to use but it eliminates the possibility of a faulty reading due to escaping pressure.

• A manifold vacuum gauge, very useful in troubleshooting ignition and emissions problems.

• A drop light, to light up the work area (make sure yours is Underwriter's approved, and has a shielded bulb).

• A volt/ohm meter, used for determining whether or not there is current in a wire. These are handy for use if a wire is broken somewhere and are especially necessary for working on today's electronics-laden vehicles.

As a final note, a torque wrench is necessary for all but the most basic work. It should even be used when installing spark plugs. The more common beam-type models are perfectly adequate and are usually much less expensive than the more precise click type on which you

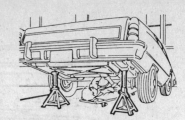

FIG. 2 Always support the car securely with jackstands; never use cinder blocks or tire changing jacks

pre-set the torque and the wrench clicks when that setting arrives on the fastener you are torquing).

➡ **Special tools are occasionally necessary to perform a specific job or are recommended to make a job easier. Their use has been kept to a minimum. When a special tool is indicated, it will be referred to by a manufacturer's part number. and, where possible, an illustration of the tool will be provided so that an equivalent tool may be used. The tool manufacturer and address is: Service Tool Division Kent-Moore 29784 Little Mack Roseville, MI 48066-2298**

SERVICING YOUR CAR SAFELY

It is virtually impossible to anticipate all of the hazards involved with automotive maintenance and service, but care and common sense will prevent most accidents.

The rules of safety for mechanics range from "don't smoke around gasoline," to "use the proper tool for the job." The trick to avoiding injuries is to develop safe work habits and take every possible precaution.

Dos

• Do keep a fire extinguisher and first aid kit within easy reach.

• Do wear safety glasses or goggles when cutting, drilling, grinding or prying, even if you have 20/20 vision. If you wear glasses for the sake of vision, they should be made of hardened glass that can serve also as safety glasses, or wear safety goggles over your regular glasses.

• Do shield your eyes whenever you work around the battery. Batteries contain sulphuric acid. In case of contact with the eyes or skin, flush the area with water or a mixture of water and baking soda and get medical attention immediately.

• Do use safety stands for any undercar service. Jacks are for raising vehicles; safety stands are for making sure the vehicle stays raised until you want it to come down. Whenever the car is raised, block the wheels remaining on the ground and set the parking brake.

• Do use adequate ventilation when working with any chemicals or hazardous materials. Like carbon monoxide, the asbestos dust resulting from brake lining wear can be poisonous in sufficient quantities.

• Do disconnect the negative battery cable when working on the electrical system. The secondary ignition system can contain up to 40,000 volts.

• Do follow manufacturer's directions whenever working with potentially hazardous materials. Both brake fluid and antifreeze are poisonous if taken internally.

• Do properly maintain your tools. Loose hammerheads, mushroomed punches and chisels, frayed or poorly grounded electrical cords, excessively worn screwdrivers, spread wrenches (open end), cracked sockets, slipping ratchets, or faulty droplight sockets can cause accidents.

• Likewise, keep your tools clean; a greasy wrench can slip off a bolt head, ruining the bolt and often ruining your knuckles in the process.

• Do use the proper size and type of tool for the job being done.

• Do when possible, pull on a wrench handle rather than push on it, and adjust you stance to prevent a fall.

• Do be sure that adjustable wrenches are tightly closed on the nut or bolt and pulled so that the face is on the side of the fixed jaw.

• Do select a wrench or socket that fits the nut or bolt. The wrench or socket should sit straight, not cocked.

• Do strike squarely with a hammer; avoid glancing blows.

• Do set the parking brake and block the drive wheels if the work requires the engine running.

Don'ts

• Don't run the engine in a garage or anywhere else without proper ventilation — EVER! Carbon monoxide is poisonous; it takes a long time to leave the human body and you can build up a deadly supply of it in your system by simply breathing in a little every day. You may not realize you are slowly poisoning yourself. Always use power vents, windows, fans or open the garage doors.

• Don't work around moving parts while wearing a necktie or other loose clothing. Short sleeves are much safer than long, loose sleeves; hard-toed shoes with neoprene soles protect your toes and give a better grip on slippery surfaces. Jewelry such as watches, fancy belt buckles, beads or body adornment of any kind is not safe working around a car. Long hair should be tied back under a hat or cap.

• Don't use pockets for toolboxes. A fall or bump can drive a screwdriver deep into your body. Even a wiping cloth hanging from the back pocket can wrap around a spinning shaft or fan.

• Don't smoke when working around gasoline, cleaning solvent or other flammable material.

• Don't smoke when working around the battery. When the battery is being charged, it gives off explosive hydrogen gas.

• Don't use gasoline to wash your hands; there are excellent soaps available. Gasoline may contain lead, and lead can enter the body through a cut, accumulating in the body until you are very ill. Gasoline also remove all the natural oils from the skin so that bone dry hands will such up oil and grease.

• Don't service the air conditioning system unless you are equipped with the necessary tools and training. The refrigerant, R-12, is extremely cold when compressed, and when released into the air will instantly freeze any surface it contacts, including your eyes. Although the refrigerant is normally non-toxic, R-12 becomes a deadly poisonous gas in the presence of an open flame. One good whiff of the vapors from burning refrigerant can be fatal.

• Don't use screwdrivers for anything other than driving screws! A screwdriver used as an prying tool can snap when you least expect it, causing injuries. At the very least, you'll ruin a good screwdriver.

• Don't use a bumper jack (that little ratchet, scissors, or pantograph jack supplied with the car) for anything other than chaining a flat! These jacks are only intended for emergency use out on the road; they are NOT designed as a maintenance tool. If you are serious about maintaining your car yourself, invest in a hydraulic floor jack of a least 1$\frac{1}{2}$ ton capacity, and at least two sturdy jackstands.

SERIAL NUMBER IDENTIFICATION

Vehicle

♦ SEE FIG. 3

The vehicle identification number (V.I.N.) is a seventeen place sequence stamped on a plate attached to the left front of the instrument panel, visible through the windshield. This is the legal identification of the vehicle. The eighth digit indicates the engine code and the tenth digit indicates the model year. The engine code (VIN) is specified in all the engine specification charts.

Body

♦ SEE FIG. 4

There is a Body Identification Plate located on the upper horizontal surface of the radiator shroud, the upper radiator support or the motor campartment front panel on the right hand side of the vehicle near the radiator support.

Engine

♦ SEE FIGS. 5-9

The engine VIN code is stamped on a pad at various locations on the cylinder block.

Transaxle

♦ SEE FIGS. 10-13

The manual transaxle identification number is stamped on a pad on the forward side of the

FIG. 3 Vehicle identification number location

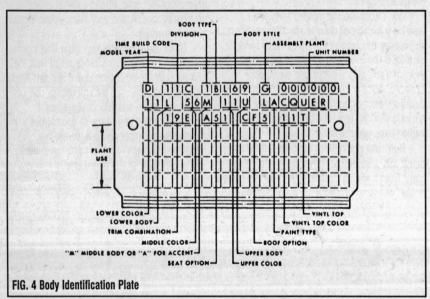

FIG. 4 Body Identification Plate

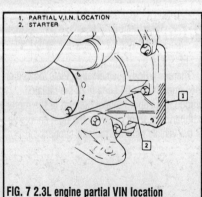

1. PARTIAL V.I.N. LOCATION
2. STARTER

FIG. 7 2.3L engine partial VIN location

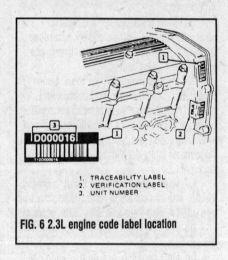

FIG. 5 2.0L, 2.2L engine date code and partial VIN location

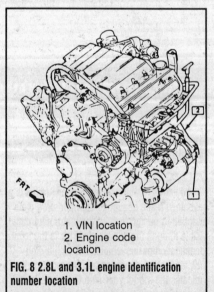

1. TRACEABILITY LABEL
2. VERIFICATION LABEL
3. UNIT NUMBER

FIG. 6 2.3L engine code label location

1. VIN location
2. Engine code location

FIG. 8 2.8L and 3.1L engine identification number location

transaxle case, between the upper and middle transaxle-to-engine mounting bolts or on a paper label attached to the transaxle case. If the label is missing or unreadable, use the service parts information label to determine which transaxle was installed. The automatic transaxle identification number is stamped on the oil flange pad to the right of the oil dipstick, at the rear of the transaxle. The automatic transaxle model code tag is on top of the case, next to the shift lever.

VEHICLE IDENTIFICATION CHART

It is important for servicing and ordering parts to be certain of the vehicle and engine identification. The VIN (vehicle identification number) is a 17 digit number visible through the windshield on the driver's side of the dash and contains the vehicle and engine identification codes. The tenth digit indicates model year and the eighth digit indicates engine code. It can be interpreted as follows:

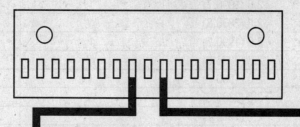

Engine Code						Model Year	
Code	Cu. In.	Liter	Cyl.	Fuel Sys.	Eng. Mfg.	Code	Year
1	121	2.0	4	TBI	Chevrolet	I	1987
4	133	2.2	4	PFI	Chevrolet	J	1988
G	133	2.2	4	TBI	Chevrolet	K	1989
A	138	2.3	4	PFI	Chevrolet	L	1990
W	173	2.8	V6	PFI	Chevrolet	M	1991
T	191	3.1	V6	PFI	Chevrolet	N	1992

TBI—Throttle Body Injection
PFI—Port Fuel Injection

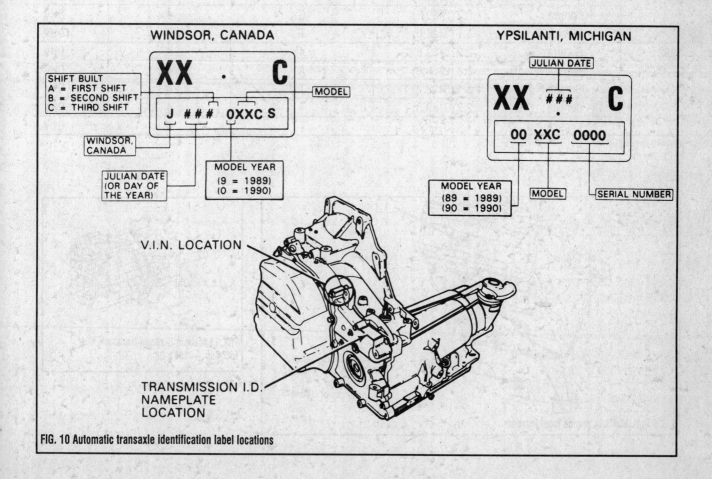

FIG. 10 Automatic transaxle identification label locations

ENGINE IDENTIFICATION

Year	Model	Engine Displacement Liter (cc)	Engine Series Identification (VIN)	No. of Cylinders	Engine Type
1987	Beretta	2.0 (1990.7)	1	4	OHV
	Beretta	2.8 (2836.8)	W	6	OHV
	Corsica	2.0 (1990.7)	1	4	OHV
	Corsica	2.8 (2836.8)	W	6	OHV
1988	Beretta	2.0 (1990.7)	1	4	OHV
	Beretta	2.8 (2836.8)	W	6	OHV
	Corsica	2.0 (1990.7)	1	4	OHV
	Corsica	2.8 (2836.8)	W	6	OHV
1989	Beretta	2.0 (1990.7)	1	4	OHV
	Beretta	2.8 (2836.8)	W	6	OHV
	Corsica	2.0 (1990.7)	1	4	OHV
	Corsica	2.8 (2836.8)	W	6	OHV
1990	Beretta	2.2 (2189.8)	G	4	OHV
	Beretta	2.3 (2260.0)	A	4	OHC
	Beretta	3.1 (3128.0)	T	6	OHV
	Corsica	2.2 (2189.8)	G	4	OHV
	Corsica	3.1 (3128.0)	T	6	OHV
1991	Beretta	2.2 (2189.8)	G	4	OHV
	Beretta	2.3 (2260.0)	A	4	OHC
	Beretta	3.1 (3128.0)	T	6	OHV
	Corsica	2.2 (2189.8)	G	4	OHV
	Corsica	3.1 (3128.0)	T	6	OHV
1992	Beretta	2.2 (2189.8)	4	4	OHV
	Beretta	2.3 (2260.0)	A	4	OHC
	Beretta	3.1 (3128.0)	T	6	OHV
	Corsica	2.2 (2189.8)	4	4	OHV
	Corsica	3.1 (3128.0)	T	6	OHV

OHV—Overhead Valves
OHC—Overhead Cam

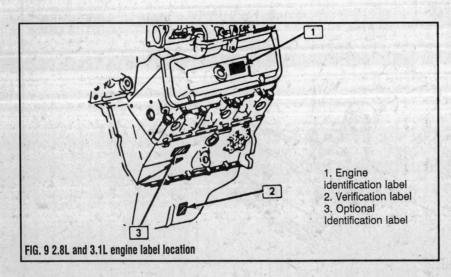

1. Engine identification label
2. Verification label
3. Optional Identification label

FIG. 9 2.8L and 3.1L engine label location

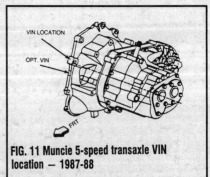

FIG. 11 Muncie 5-speed transaxle VIN location — 1987-88

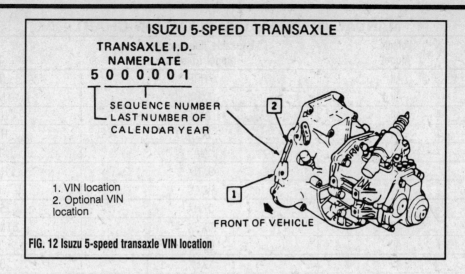

FIG. 12 Isuzu 5-speed transaxle VIN location

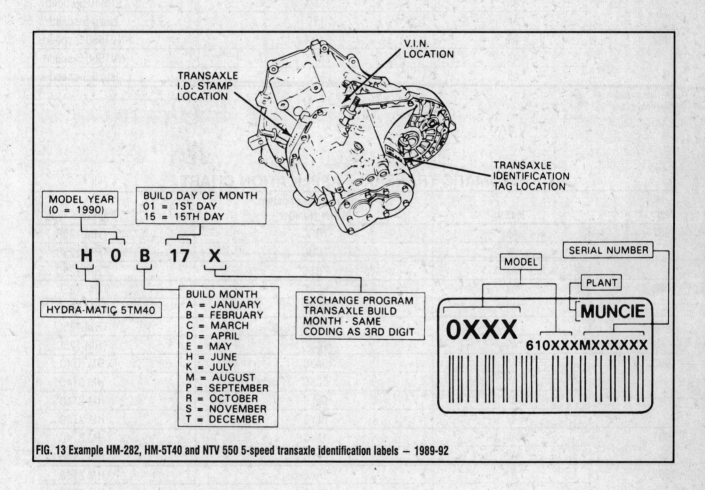

FIG. 13 Example HM-282, HM-5T40 and NTV 550 5-speed transaxle identification labels — 1989-92

MANUAL TRANSAXLE APPLICATION CHART

Year	Vehicle Model	Transaxle Identification Model Number	Transaxle Type
1987	All	7RRB	Muncie 5-speed
	All	7XBX	Muncie 5-speed
1988	All	8XN	HM-282 5-speed
	All	8ZN	HM-282 5-speed
	All	NA	Isuzu 5-speed
1989	All	9XNX	HM-282 5-speed
	All	9DAC	Isuzu 5-speed
1990	All	0XNX	5TM40 5-speed
	All	0XEX	5TM40 (HD) 5-speed
	All	0DHH	Isuzu 5-speed
1991	All	1XEX	5TM40 5-speed
	All	1XNX	5TM40 5-speed
	All	1LYC	Isuzu 5-speed
1992	All	2XNX	NVT550 5-speed
	All	2NFX	NVT550 5-speed
	All	NA	Isuzu 5-speed

NA—Not available
HD—Heavy Duty

AUTOMATIC TRANSAXLE APPLICATION CHART

Year	Model	Transaxle Identification Model Number	Transaxle Type
1987	All	7CRC	THM 125C
	All	7CUC	THM 125C
	All	7CSC	THM 125C
1988	All	8CRC	THM 125C
	All	8CUC	THM 125C
1989	All	9CRC	THM 125C
	All	9CUC	THM 125C
1990	All	0AYC	HM 3T40
	All	0LKC	HM 3T40
	All	0LLC	HM 3T40
	All	0LYC	HM 3T40
1991	All	1LYC	HM 3T40
	All	1LLC	HM 3T40
1992	All	2AKC	HM 3T40
	All	2LFC	HM 3T40
	All	2LLC	HM 3T40

ROUTINE MAINTENANCE

Routine maintenance is the self-explanatory term used to describe the sort of periodic work necessary to keep a car in safe and reliable working order. A regular program aimed at monitoring essential systems ensures that the car's components are functioning correctly (and will continue to do so until the next inspection, one hopes), and can prevent small problems from developing into major headaches. Routine maintenance also pays off big dividends in keeping major repair costs at a minimum, extending the life of the car, and enhancing resale value, should you ever desire to part with your Corsica or Beretta.

The newer GM cars require less in the way of routine maintenance than any cars in recent memory. However, a very definite maintenance schedule is provided by General Motors, and must be followed not only to keep the new car warranty in effect, but also to keep the car working properly. The Maintenance Intervals chart in this section outlines the routine maintenance which must be performed according to intervals based on either accumulated mileage or time. Your Corsica or Beretta also came with a maintenance schedule provided by G.M. Adherence to these schedules will result in a longer life for your car, and will, over the long run, save you money and time.

The checks and adjustments in the following sections generally require only a few minutes of attention every few weeks; the services to be performed can be easily accomplished in a morning. The most important part of any maintenance program is regularity. The few minutes or occasional morning spent on these seemingly trivial tasks will forestall or eliminate major problems later.

Air Cleaner

All the dust present in the air is kept out of the engine by means of the air cleaner filter element. Proper maintenance is vital, as a clogged element not only restricts the air-flow, and thus the power, but may also cause premature engine wear.

The filter element should be replaced every 30,000 miles or 36 months. Change the filter more often if the car is driven in dry, dusty areas. The condition of the element should be checked periodically; if it appears to be overly dirty or clogged, shake it, if this does not help, the element should be replaced.

FIG. 13A Air cleaner cover retainer–1992 2.2L engine

➡ **The paper element should never be cleaned or soaked with gasoline, cleaning solvent or oil.**

CLEANING OR REPLACING THE FILTER ELEMENT

1. Remove either the the wing nut, upper cover retaining bolts or release clips from the upper top of the air cleaner and either lift off or separate the upper air cleaner housing.
2. Remove the air filter and replace it with a new one.
3. Before reinstalling the filter element, wipe out the housing with a damp cloth. Check the lid gasket, if equipped, to ensure that it has a tight seal.
4. Position the filter element, replace the lid or housing cover and tighten the retaining bolts or clips.

Fuel Filter

REPLACEMENT

▶ SEE FIGS. 14-16

❄ CAUTION

Never smoke when working around gasoline! Avoid all sources of sparks or ignition. Gasoline vapors are EXTREMELY volatile! An inline filter can be found in the fuel feed line attached to the rear crossmember of the vehicle.

1987–89

1. Release the fuel system pressure.
2. Place absorbent rags under the connections and disconnect the fuel lines.

FIG. 13B Lift the cover and remove the filter—1992 2.2L engine

➡ **Always use a back-up wrench anytime the fuel filter is removed or installed.**

3. Remove the fuel filter from the retainer or mounting bolt.

4. When installing, always use a good O-ring at the coupling locations and torque the fittings at 22 ft. lbs. Start the engine and check for leaks.

➡ **The filter has an arrow (fuel flow direction) on the side of the case, be sure to install it correctly in the system, the with arrow facing away from the fuel tank.**

1990–92

1. Release the fuel system pressure as outlined in this section.

2. Make sure the negative battery cable is disconnected and raise and support the vehicle safely.

3. Remove the filter attaching screw and filter.

➡ **Kinked nylon fuel feed or return lines cannot be straightened and must be replaced.**

4. Grasp the filter and one nylon fuel connecting line fitting. Twist the quick connect fitting 1/4 turn in each direction to loosen any dirt

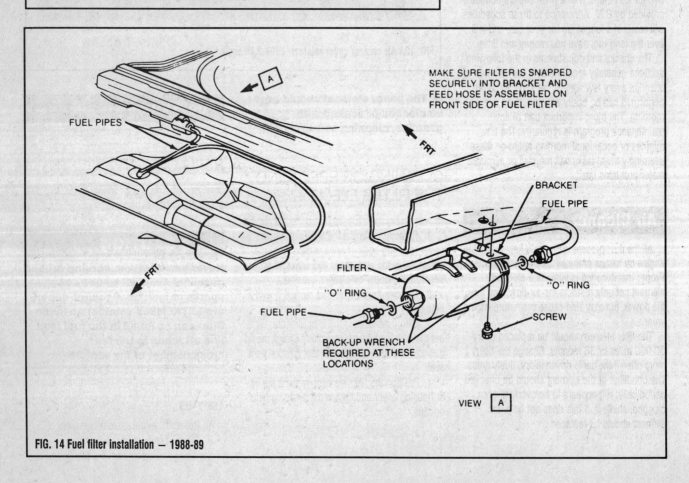

MAKE SURE FILTER IS SNAPPED SECURELY INTO BRACKET AND FEED HOSE IS ASSEMBLED ON FRONT SIDE OF FUEL FILTER

FUEL PIPES

FRT

FRT

BRACKET

FUEL PIPE

FILTER

"O" RING

FUEL PIPE

"O" RING

SCREW

BACK-UP WRENCH REQUIRED AT THESE LOCATIONS

VIEW A

FIG. 14 Fuel filter installation — 1988-89

within the fitting. Repeat for the other nylon fuel connecting line fitting.

5. Disconnect the quick connect fittings by squeezing the plastic tabs of the male end connector and pulling the connection apart. Repeat for the other fitting and remove the fuel filter.

To install:

6. Remove the protective caps from the ends of the new filter.

7. Install the new plastic connector retainers on the filter inlet and outlet tubes.

8. Apply a few drops of clean engine oil to both tube ends of the filter and O-rings.

9. Push the connectors together to cause the retaining the retaining tabs/fingers to snap into place. Pull on both ends of each connection to make sure they are secure.

10. Install the fuel filter to the frame with the attaching screws.

11. Tighten the fuel filler cap.

12. Connect the negative battery cable.

13. Turn the ignition switch to the **ON** position for 2 seconds, then turn to the **OFF** position for 10 seconds. Again turn the ignition switch to the **ON** position and check for leaks.

14. For vehicles equipped with the 3.1L engine, the ECM will need to relearn the IAC pintle valve position following the reconnection of the battery.

Fuel Pressure Release

❄ CAUTION

To reduce the risk of fire or personal injury, it is necessary to relieve the fuel system pressure before servicing the fuel system.

2.0L and 2.2L engines

1988–91

The TBI Model 700 used on these models uses a constant bleed feature to relieve fuel pressure. Therefore, no special procedures are required for relieving fuel pressure.

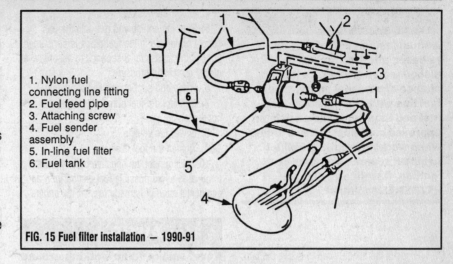

1. Nylon fuel connecting line fitting
2. Fuel feed pipe
3. Attaching screw
4. Fuel sender assembly
5. In-line fuel filter
6. Fuel tank

FIG. 15 Fuel filter installation — 1990-91

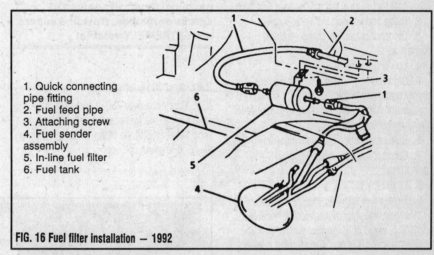

1. Quick connecting pipe fitting
2. Fuel feed pipe
3. Attaching screw
4. Fuel sender assembly
5. In-line fuel filter
6. Fuel tank

FIG. 16 Fuel filter installation — 1992

FIG. 16A Fuel filter location–1992 2.2L engine

❋❋❋ CAUTION

A small amount of fuel may be released after the fuel line is disconnected. To reduce the chance of personal injury, cover the fuel line with cloth to collect the fuel and then place the cloth in an approved container. Never smoke when working around gasoline! Avoid all sources of sparks or ignition. Gasoline vapors are EXTREMELY volatile!

1992

1. Loosen the full filler cap to relieve the tank vapor pressure. Leave the cap loose at this time.
2. Raise and support the vehicle safely.
3. Disconnect the fuel pump electrical connector.
4. Lower the vehicle.
5. Start the engine and run until the fuel supply remaining in the fuel pipes is consumed. Engage the starter for 3 seconds to assure relief of any remaining pressure.
6. Raise and support the vehicle safely.
7. Connect the fuel pump electrical connector.
8. Lower the vehicle.
9. Tighten the fuel filler cap.
10. Disconnect the negative battery cable terminal to avoid possible fuel discharge if an accidental attempt is made to start the engine.

2.3L engine

1990

1. Connect a J–34730–1 fuel gage or equivalent to the fuel pressure valve. Wrap a shop towel around the fitting while connecting the gage to avoid spillage.
2. Install a bleed hose into an approved container and open the valve to bleed the system pressure.

❋❋❋ CAUTION

Never smoke when working around gasoline! Avoid all sources of sparks or ignition. Gasoline vapors are EXTREMELY volatile!

1991–92

1. Loosen the full filler cap to relieve the tank vapor pressure. Leave the cap loose at this time.
2. Raise and support the vehicle safely.
3. Disconnect the fuel pump electrical connector.

4. Lower the vehicle.
5. Start the engine and run until the fuel supply remaining in the fuel pipes is consumed. Engage the starter for 3 seconds to assure relief of any remaining pressure.
6. Raise and support the vehicle safely.
7. Connect the fuel pump electrical connector.
8. Lower the vehicle.
9. Tighten the fuel filler cap.
10. Disconnect the negative battery cable terminal to avoid possible fuel discharge if an accidental attempt is made to start the engine.

❋❋❋ CAUTION

Never smoke when working around gasoline! Avoid all sources of sparks or ignition. Gasoline vapors are EXTREMELY volatile!

2.8L and 3.1L engines

1. Connect a J–34730–1 fuel gage or equivalent to the fuel pressure valve. Wrap a shop towel around the fitting while connecting the gage to avoid spillage.

2. Install a bleed hose into an approved container and open the valve to bleed the system pressure.

❋❋❋ CAUTION

Never smoke when working around gasoline! Avoid all sources of sparks or ignition. Gasoline vapors are EXTREMELY volatile!

PCV Valve

REMOVAL & INSTALLATION

◆ SEE FIGS. 17-20

All engines, except the 2.3L VIN A engine, use a Positive Crankcase Ventilation (PCV) valve to regulate crankcase ventilation during various engine running conditions. At high vacuum (idle speed and partial load range) it will open slightly and at low vacuum (full throttle) it will open fully.

FIG. 17A Disconnect the hose and remove the PCV valve cover–1992 2.2L engine

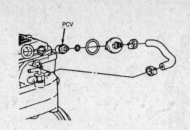

FIG. 17 PCV system — 2.0L and 2.2L engine

This causes vapors to be drawn from the crankcase by engine vacuum and then sucked into the combustion chamber where they are dissipated. The crankcase ventilation system used on the 2.3L engine does not use a PCV valve. This system requires no regular scheduled maintenance. Details on all PCV system, including system tests, are given in Section Four.

The PCV valve must be replaced every 30,000 miles.

On most engines the valve is located in a rubber grommet in the valve cover, connected to the air cleaner housing by a large diameter rubber hose. To replace the valve:

All Except 2.2L VIN 4 Engine

1. Pull the valve (with the hose attached) from the rubber grommet in the valve cover.
2. Remove the valve from the hose.
3. Install a new valve into the hose.
4. Press the valve back into the rubber grommet in the valve cover.

2.2L VIN 4 Engine

1. Pull the hose from the threaded PCV valve cover which is screwed into the valve cover.
2. Using a suitable wrench, remove the PCV valve cover and seal from the valve cover.
3. Using a needle nose pliers, reach into the valve cover opening and pull out the PCV valve and seals.
4. Inspect the seals and replace as necessary. Reverse the removal procedure to install. Tighten the PCV valve cover to 89 inch lbs. (10 Nm).

Evaporative Emissions System

Check the evaporative emission control system every 15,000 miles. Check the fuel vapor lines and the vacuum hoses for proper connections and correct routing, as well as

FIG. 17B Unscrew the PCV valve cover from the rocker cover–1992 2.2L engine

FIG. 17C Pull the PCV valve from the rocker cover opening–1992 2.2L engine

condition. Replace clogged, damaged or deteriorated parts as necessary. Refer to the Vehicle Emission Control Information Label, located under the hood, for routing of the canister hoses.

For more details on the evaporative emissions system, please refer to section Four.

Battery

♦ SEE FIG. 21

The Corsica's and Beretta's have a maintenance free battery as standard equipment, eliminating the need for fluid level checks and the possibility of specific gravity tests. Nevertheless, the battery does require some attention.

Once a year, the battery terminals and the cable clamps should be cleaned. Remove the side terminal bolts and the cables and the battery terminals with a wire brush until all corrosion, grease, etc. is removed and the metal is shiny. It is especially important to clean the inside of the clamp thoroughly,

since a small deposit of foreign material or oxidation there will prevent a sound electrical connection and inhibit either starting or charging. Special tools are available for cleaning the side terminal clamps and terminals.

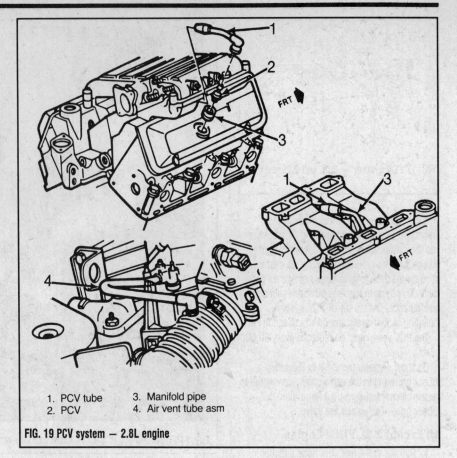

1. PCV tube
2. PCV
3. Manifold pipe
4. Air vent tube asm

FIG. 19 PCV system — 2.8L engine

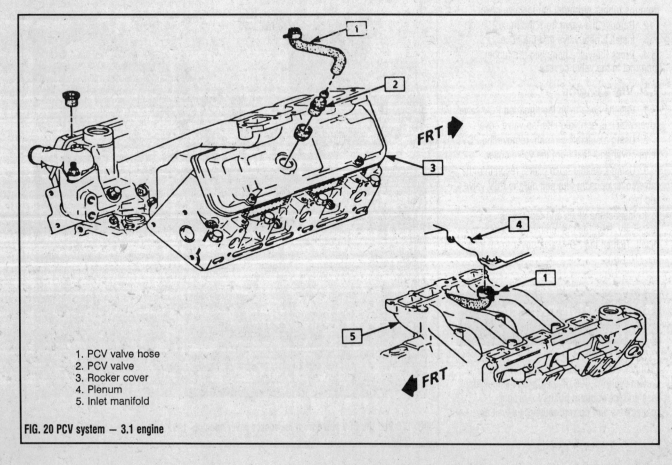

1. PCV valve hose
2. PCV valve
3. Rocker cover
4. Plenum
5. Inlet manifold

FIG. 20 PCV system — 3.1 engine

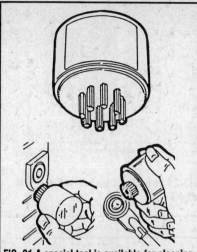

FIG. 21 A special tool is available for cleaning the side terminals and clamps

Before installing the cables, loosen the battery hold-down retainer, remove the battery, and check the battery tray. Clear it of any debris and check it for soundness. Rust should be wire brushed away, and the metal given a coat of anti-rust paint. Replace the battery and tighten the hold-down clamp securely, but be careful not to overtighten, which will crack the battery case.

After the clamps and terminals are clean, reinstall the cables, negative cables last. Give the clamps and terminals a thin external coat of grease after installation, to retard corrosion.

Check the cables at the same time that the terminals are cleaned. If the cable insulation is cracked or broken, or if the ends are frayed, the cable should be replaced with a new cable of the same length and gauge.

➡ **Keep flame or sparks away from the battery; it gives off explosive hydrogen gas. Battery electrolyte contains sulphuric acid. If you should get any on your skin or in your eyes, flush the affected areas with plenty of clear water; if it lands in your eyes, get medical help immediately.**

Drive Belts

◆ SEE FIGS. 22-28

All engines are equipped with a single (serpentine belt) to drive all engine accessories with the exception of the power steering pump on the 2.3L engine which is driven by a poly-groove belt. The poly-groove belt is not self adjusting and therefore may require service. The serpentine belt driven accessories are rigidly mounted with belt tension maintained by a spring loaded tensioner assembly. The belt tensioner has the ability to control belt tension over a fairly broad range of belt lengths. However, there are limits to the tensioner's ability to compensate for varying lengths of belts. Poor tension control and/or damage to the tensioner could result with the tensioner operating outside of its range.

INSPECTION

1. If fraying of the belt is noticed, check to make sure both the belt and the tensioner assembly are properly aligned and that the belt edges are not in contact with the flanges of the tensioner pulley.

2. If, while adjusting belt tension, tensioner runs out of travel, the belt is stretched beyond adjustment and should be replaced.

3. If a whining is heard around the tensioner or idler assemblies, check for possible bearing failure.

➡ **Routine inspection of the belt may reveal cracks in the belt ribs. These cracks will not impair belt performance and therefore should not be considered a problem requiring belt replacement. However, the belt should be replaced if belt slip occurs or if sections of the belt ribs are missing.**

REPLACEMENT

Serpentine Belt

To replace the belt push (rotate) the belt tensioner and remove the belt. Use a 15mm socket on the 2.0L, 2.2L and 3.1L engines. On the 2.8L V6 engine use a $3/4$ in. open end wrench socket.

On the 2.3L 4 cyl. engine a serpentine belt is used to drive the alternator and air conditioner compressor. To replace the belt push (rotate) the belt tensioner, using a 13 mm socket, and remove the belt.

Poly-Groove Belt

On the 2.3L 4 cyl. engine, the power steering pump is driven by a poly-groove belt and can be replace as follows:

1. Loosen the pump bracket adjustment bolts.
2. Loosen the belt tension adjustment stud.
3. Remove the belt from the vehicle.

To install:

4. Place the belt into position.
5. Set the belt tension by turning the adjustment stud to the following:
   - New belt — 191 lbs. (850 N)
   - Used belt — 100 lbs. (450 N)

If installing a new belt, set the belt tension to the new belt specification. Start the engine and run for a minimum of 2 minutes then readjust the belt to the used belt specification.

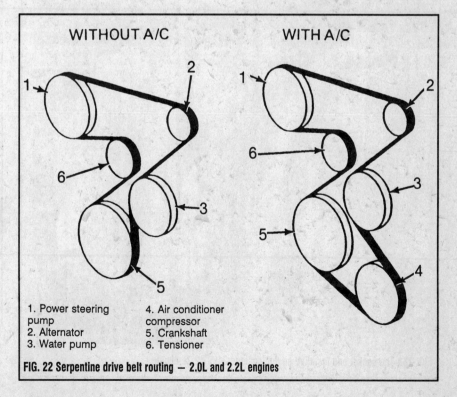

WITHOUT A/C   WITH A/C

1. Power steering pump
2. Alternator
3. Water pump
4. Air conditioner compressor
5. Crankshaft
6. Tensioner

FIG. 22 Serpentine drive belt routing — 2.0L and 2.2L engines

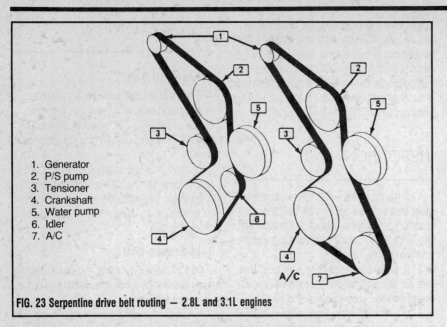

1. Generator
2. P/S pump
3. Tensioner
4. Crankshaft
5. Water pump
6. Idler
7. A/C

FIG. 23 Serpentine drive belt routing — 2.8L and 3.1L engines

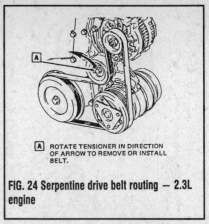

A ROTATE TENSIONER IN DIRECTION OF ARROW TO REMOVE OR INSTALL BELT.

FIG. 24 Serpentine drive belt routing — 2.3L engine

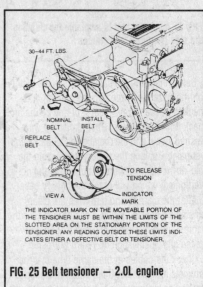

30-44 FT. LBS.

A

NOMINAL BELT
INSTALL BELT
REPLACE BELT

TO RELEASE TENSION

VIEW A

INDICATOR MARK

THE INDICATOR MARK ON THE MOVEABLE PORTION OF THE TENSIONER MUST BE WITHIN THE LIMITS OF THE SLOTTED AREA ON THE STATIONARY PORTION OF THE TENSIONER. ANY READING OUTSIDE THESE LIMITS INDICATES EITHER A DEFECTIVE BELT OR TENSIONER.

FIG. 25 Belt tensioner — 2.0L engine

FIG. 26A The socket end installed on the tensioner–1992 2.2L engine

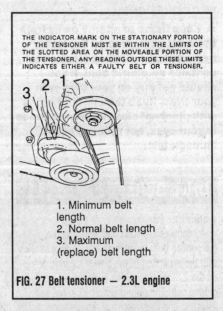

THE INDICATOR MARK ON THE STATIONARY PORTION OF THE TENSIONER MUST BE WITHIN THE LIMITS OF THE SLOTTED AREA ON THE MOVEABLE PORTION OF THE TENSIONER. ANY READING OUTSIDE THESE LIMITS INDICATES EITHER A FAULTY BELT OR TENSIONER.

1. Minimum belt length
2. Normal belt length
3. Maximum (replace) belt length

FIG. 27 Belt tensioner — 2.3L engine

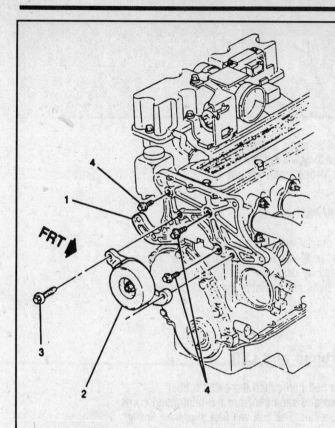

1. ENGINE LIFT BRACKET
2. BELT TENSIONER
3. BOLT
4. BOLTS

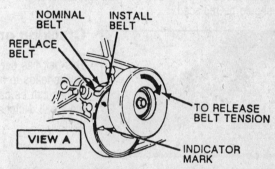

NOMINAL BELT
INSTALL BELT
REPLACE BELT
TO RELEASE BELT TENSION
INDICATOR MARK

VIEW A

THE INDICATOR MARK ON THE MOVABLE PORTION OF THE TENSIONER MUST BE WITHIN THE LIMITS OF THE SLOTTED AREA (NOMINAL BELT) ON THE STATIONARY PORTION OF THE TENSIONER. ANY READING OUTSIDE THESE LIMITS INDICATES EITHER A DEFECTIVE BELT OR TENSIONER.

FIG. 26 Belt tensioner — 2.2L engine

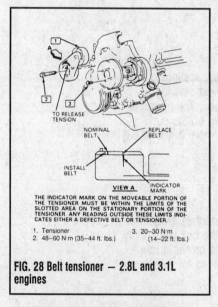

TO RELEASE TENSION
NOMINAL BELT
REPLACE BELT
INSTALL BELT
VIEW A
INDICATOR MARK

THE INDICATOR MARK ON THE MOVEABLE PORTION OF THE TENSIONER MUST BE WITHIN THE LIMITS OF THE SLOTTED AREA ON THE STATIONARY PORTION OF THE TENSIONER. ANY READING OUTSIDE THESE LIMITS INDICATES EITHER A DEFECTIVE BELT OR TENSIONER.

1. Tensioner
2. 48–60 N·m (35–44 ft. lbs.)
3. 20–30 N·m (14–22 ft. lbs.)

FIG. 28 Belt tensioner — 2.8L and 3.1L engines

6. Tighten the pump bracket bolts to 72 ft. lbs. (98 Nm) for the rear bolts and 19 ft. lbs. (26 Nm) for the front bolts.

Hoses

Upper and lower radiator hoses and all heater hoses should be checked for deterioration, leaks

FIG. 26B With the tensioner rotated clockwise, remove the serpentine belt–1992 2.2L engine

HOW TO SPOT WORN V-BELTS

V–Belts are vital to efficient engine operation—they drive the fan, water pump and other accessories. They require little maintenance (occasional tightening) but they will not last forever. Slipping or failure of the V–belt will lead to overheating. If your V–belt looks like any of these, it should be replaced.

Cracking or Weathering

This belt has deep cracks, which cause it to flex. Too much flexing leads to heat build–up and premature failure. These cracks can be caused by using the belt on a pulley that is too small. Notched belts are available for small diameter pulleys.

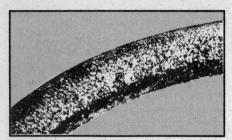

Softening (Grease and Oil)

Oil and grease on a belt can cause the belt's rubber compounds to soften and separate from the reinforcing cords that hold the belt together. The belt will first slip, then finally fail altogether.

Glazing

Glazing is caused by a belt that is slipping. A slipping belt can cause a run-down battery, erratic power steering, overheating or poor accessory performance. The more the belt slips, the more glazing will be built up on the surface of the belt. The more the belt is glazed, the more it will slip. If the glazing is light, tighten the belt.

Worn Cover

The cover of this belt is worn off and is peeling away. The reinforcing cords will begin to wear and the belt will shortly break. When the belt cover wears in spots or has a rough jagged appearance, check the pulley grooves for roughness.

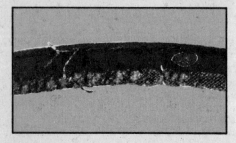

Separation

This belt is on the verge of breaking and leaving you stranded. The layers of the belt are separating and the reinforcing cords are exposed. It's just a matter of time before it breaks completely.

HOW TO SPOT BAD HOSES

Both the upper and lower radiator hoses are called upon to perform difficult jobs in an inhospitable environment. They are subject to nearly 18 psi at under hood temperatures often over 280°F, and must circulate nearly 7500 gallons of coolant an hour—3 good reasons to have good hoses.

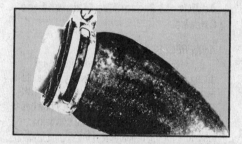

Swollen Hose

A good test for any hose is to feel it for soft or spongy spots. Frequently these will appear as swollen areas of the hose. The most likely cause is oil soaking. This hose could burst at any time, when hot or under pressure.

Cracked Hose

Cracked hoses can usually be seen but feel the hoses to be sure they have not hardened; a prime cause of cracking. This hose has cracked down to the reinforcing cords and could split at any of the cracks.

Frayed Hose End (Due to Weak Clamp)

Weakened clamps frequently are the cause of hose and cooling system failure. The connection between the pipe and hose has deteriorated enough to allow coolant to escape when the engine is hot.

Debris In Cooling System

Debris, rust and scale in the cooling system can cause the inside of a hose to weaken. This can usually be felt on the outside of the hose as soft or thinner areas.

and loose hose clamps every 15,000 miles. To remove the hoses:

1. Drain the radiator as detailed later in this section.

2. Loosen the hose clamps at each end of the hose to be removed.

3. Working the hose back and forth, slide it off its connection and then install a new hose if necessary.

4. Position the hose clamps at least 1/4 in. (6mm) from the end of the hose and tighten them.

➡ **Always make sure that the hose clamps are beyond the bead and placed in the center of the clamping surface before tightening them.**

Air Conditioning

GENERAL SERVICING PROCEDURES

♦ SEE FIGS. 29-52

The most important aspect of air conditioning service is the maintenance of a pure and adequate charge of refrigerant in the system. A refrigeration system cannot function properly if a significant percentage of the charge is lost. Leaks are common because the severe vibration encountered in an automobile can easily cause a sufficient cracking or loosening of the air conditioning fittings; as a result, the extreme operating pressures of the system force refrigerant out.

The problem can be understood by considering what happens to the system as it is operated with a continuous leak. Because the expansion valve regulates the flow of refrigerant to the evaporator, the level of refrigerant there is fairly constant. The receiver/drier stores any excess of refrigerant, and so a loss will first appear there as a reduction in the level of liquid. As this level nears the bottom of the vessel, some refrigerant vapor bubbles will begin to appear in the stream of liquid supplied to the expansion valve. This vapor decreases the capacity of the expansion valve very little as the valve opens to compensate for its presence. As the quantity of liquid in the condenser decreases, the operating pressure will drop there and throughout the high side of the system. As the R-12 continues to be expelled, the pressure available to force the liquid through the expansion valve will continue to decrease, and,

eventually, the valve's orifice will prove to be too much of a restriction for adequate flow even with the needle fully withdrawn.

At this point, low side pressure will start to drop, and severe reduction in cooling capacity, marked by freeze-up of the evaporator coil, will result. Eventually, the operating pressure of the evaporator will be lower than the pressure of the atmosphere surrounding it, and air will be drawn into the system wherever there are leaks in the low side.

Because all atmospheric air contains at least some moisture, water will enter the system and mix with the R-12 and the oil. Trace amounts of moisture will cause sludging of the oil, and corrosion of the system. Saturation and clogging of the filter/drier, and freezing of the expansion valve orifice will eventually result. As air fills the system to a greater and greater extent, it will interfere more and more with the normal flows of refrigerant and heat.

From this description, it should be obvious that much of the repairman's time will be spent detecting leaks, repairing them, and then restoring the purity and quantity of the refrigerant charge. A list of general precautions that should be observed while doing this follows:

1. Keep all tools as clean and dry as possible.
2. Thoroughly purge the service gauges and hoses of air and moisture before connecting them to the system. Keep them capped when not in use.
3. Thoroughly clean any refrigerant fitting before disconnecting it, in order to minimize the entrance of dirt into the system.
4. Plan any operation that requires opening the system beforehand, in order to minimize the length of time it will be exposed to open air. Cap or seal the open ends to minimize the entrance of foreign material.
5. When adding oil, pour it through an extremely clean and dry tube or funnel. Keep the oil capped whenever possible. Do not use oil that has not been kept tightly sealed.
6. Use only refrigerant 12. Purchase refrigerant intended for use in only automatic air conditioning systems. Avoid the use of refrigerant 12 that may be packaged for another use, such as cleaning, or powering a horn, as it is impure.
7. Completely evacuate any system that has been opened to replace a component, or that has leaked sufficiently to draw in moisture and air. This requires evacuating air and moisture with a good vacuum pump for at least one hour. If a system has been open for a considerable length of time it may be advisable to evacuate the system for up to 12 hours (overnight).
8. Use a wrench on both halves of a fitting that is to be disconnected, so as to avoid placing torque on any of the refrigerant lines.

9. When overhauling a compressor, pour some of the oil into a clean glass and inspect it. If there is evidence of dirt or metal particles, or both, flush all refrigerant components with clean refrigerant before evacuating and recharging the system. In addition, if metal particles are present, the compressor should be replaced.

10. Schrader valves may leak only when under full operating pressure. Therefore, if leakage is suspected but cannot be located, operate the system with a full charge of refrigerant and look for leaks from all Schrader valves. Replace any faulty valves.

Additional Preventive Maintenance Checks

ANTIFREEZE

In order to prevent heater core freeze-up during A/C operation, it is necessary to maintain permanent type antifreeze protection of +15°F, or lower. A reading of −15°F is ideal since this protection also supplies sufficient corrosion inhibitors for the protection of the engine cooling system.

➡ **The same antifreeze should not be used longer than the manufacturer specifies.**

RADIATOR CAP

For efficient operation of an air conditioned car's cooling system, the radiator cap should have a holding pressure which meets manufacturer's specifications. A cap which fails to hold these pressures should be replaced.

CONDENSER

Any obstruction of or damage to the condenser configuration will restrict the air flow which is essential to its efficient operation. It is therefore a good rule to keep this unit clean and in proper physical shape.

➡ **Bug screens are regarded as obstructions.**

CONDENSATION DRAIN TUBE

This single molded drain tube expels the condensation, which accumulates on the bottom of the evaporator housing, into the engine compartment. If this tube is obstructed, the air conditioning performance can be restricted and condensation buildup can spill over onto the vehicle's floor.

SAFETY PRECAUTIONS

Because of the importance of the necessary safety precautions that must be exercised when working with air conditioning systems and R-12 refrigerant, a recap of the safety precautions are outlined.

1. Avoid contact with a charged refrigeration system, even when working on another part of the air conditioning system or vehicle. If a heavy tool comes into contact with a section of copper tubing or a heat exchanger, it can easily cause the relatively soft material to rupture.

2. When it is necessary to apply force to a fitting which contains refrigerant, as when checking that all system couplings are securely tightened, use a wrench on both parts of the fitting involved, if possible. This will avoid putting torque on refrigerant tubing. (It is advisable, when possible, to use tube or line wrenches when tightening these flare nut fittings.)

3. Do not attempt to discharge the system by merely loosening a fitting, or removing the service valve caps and cracking these valves. Precise control is possible only when using the service gauges. Place a rag under the open end of the center charging hose while discharging the system to catch any drops of liquid that might escape. Wear protective gloves when connecting or disconnecting service gauge hoses.

4. Discharge the system only in a well ventilated area, as high concentrations of the gas can exclude oxygen and act as an anesthetic. When leak testing or soldering, this is particularly important, as toxic gas is formed when R-12 contacts any flame. If possible dicharge the system in an approved R12 recovery machine. See the caution under the Discharging procedure.

5. Never start a system without first verifying that both service valves are back-seated, if equipped, and that all fittings throughout the system are snugly connected.

6. Avoid applying heat to any refrigerant line or storage vessel. Charging may be aided by using water heated to less than 125° to warm the refrigerant container. Never allow a refrigerant storage container to sit out in the sun, or near any other source of heat, such as a radiator.

7. Always wear goggles when working on a system to protect the eyes. If refrigerant contacts the eyes, it is advisable in all cases to see a physician as soon as possible.

8. Frostbite from liquid refrigerant should be treated by first gradually warming the area with cool water, and then gently applying petroleum jelly. A physician should be consulted.

9. Always keep refrigerant drum fittings capped when not in use. Avoid sudden shock to the drum, which might occur from dropping it, or from banging a heavy tool against it. Never carry a drum in the passenger compartment of a car.

10. Always completely discharge the system before painting the vehicle (if the paint is to be baked on), or before welding anywhere near refrigerant lines.

Air Conditioning Tools and Gauges

Test Gauges

Most of the service work performed in air conditioning requires the use of a set of two gauges, one for the high (head) pressure side of the system, the other for the low (suction) side.

The low side gauge records both pressure and vacuum. Vacuum readings are calibrated from 0 to 30 inches and the pressure graduations read from 0 to no less than 60 psi.

The high side gauge measures pressure from 0 to at least 600 psi.

Both gauges are threaded into a manifold that contains two hand shut-off valves. Proper manipulation of these valves and the use of the attached test hoses allow the user to perform the following services:

1. Test high and low side pressures.
2. Remove air, moisture, and contaminated refrigerant.

3. Purge the system (of refrigerant).
4. Charge the system (with refrigerant).

The manifold valves are designed so they have no direct effect on gauge readings, but serve only to provide for, or cut off, flow of refrigerant through the manifold. During all testing and hook-up operations, the valves are kept in a closed position to avoid disturbing the refrigeration system. The valves are opened only to purge the system of refrigerant or to charge it.

When purging the system, the center hose is uncapped at the lower end, and both valves are cracked open slightly. This allows refrigerant pressure to force the entire contents of the system out through the center hose. During charging, the valve on the high side of the manifold is closed, and the valve on the low side is cracked open. Under these conditions, the low pressure in the evaporator will draw refrigerant from the relatively warm refrigerant storage container into the system.

Service Valves

For the user to diagnose an air conditioning system he or she must gain "entrance" to the system in order to observe the pressures. The Corsica and Beretta uses the familar Schrader valve.

The Schrader valve is similar to a tire valve stem and the process of connecting the test hoses is the same as threading a hand pump outlet hose to a bicycle tire. As the test hose is threaded to the service port the valve core is depressed, allowing the refrigerant to enter the test hose outlet. Removal of the test hose automatically closes the system.

Extreme caution must be observed when removing test hoses from the Schrader valves as some refrigerant will normally escape, usually under high pressure. Observe safety precautions.

REFRIGERANT — 12
PRESSURE — TEMPERATURE
RELATIONSHIP

The table below indicates the pressure of Refrigerant — 12 at various temperatures. For instance, a drum of Refrigerant at a temperature of 80°F (26.6°C) will have a pressure of 84.1 PSI (579.9 kPa). If it is heated to 125°F (51.6°C), the pressure will increase to 167.5 PSI (1154.9 kPa). It also can be used conversely to determine the temperature at which Refrigerant — 12 boils under various pressures. For example, at a pressure of 30.1 PSI (207.5 kPa), Refrigerant — 12 boils at 32°F (0°C).

(°F)(°C)		(PSIG)(kPa)		(°F)(°C)		(PSIG)(kPa)	
− 21.7	− 29.8C	0(ATMOSPHERIC 0(kPa)		55	12.7C	52.0	358.5
		PRESSURE)		60	15.5C	57.7	397.8
− 20	− 28.8C	2.4	16.5	65	18.3C	63.7	439.2
− 10	− 23.3C	4.5	31.0	70	21.1C	70.1	482.7
− 5	− 20.5C	6.8	46.9	75	23.8C	76.9	530.2
0	− 17.7C	9.2	63.4	80	26.6C	84.1	579.9
5	− 15.0C	11.8	81.4	85	29.4C	91.7	632.3
10	− 12.2C	14.7	101.4	90	32.2C	99.6	686.7
15	− 9.4C	17.7	122.0	95	35.0C	108.1	745.3
20	− 6.6C	21.1	145.5	100	37.7C	116.9	805.0
25	− 3.8C	24.6	169.6	105	40.5C	126.2	870.2
30	− 1.1C	28.5	196.5	110	43.3C	136.0	937.7
32	0C	30.1	207.5	115	46.1C	146.5	1010.1
35	1.6C	32.6	224.8	120	48.8C	157.1	1083.2
40	4.4C	37.0	255.1	125	51.6C	167.5	1154.9
45	7.2C	41.7	287.5	130	54.4C	179.0	1234.2
50	10.0C	46.7	322.0	140	60.0C	204.5	1410.0

FIG. 29 Pressure temperature relationship of R-12

USING THE MANIFOLD GAUGES

The following are step-by-step procedures to guide the user to correct gauge usage.

1. WEAR GOGGLES OR FACE SHIELD DURING ALL TESTING OPERATIONS. BACKSEAT HAND SHUT-OFF TYPE SERVICE VALVES.

2. Remove caps from high and low side service ports. Make sure both gauge valves are closed.

3. Connect low side test hose to service valve that leads to the evaporator (located between the evaporator outlet and the compressor).

4. Attach high side test hose to service valve that leads to the condenser.

5. Mid-position hand shutoff type service valves.

6. Start engine and allow for warm-up. All testing and charging of the system should be done after engine and system have reached normal operation temperatures (except when using certain charging stations).

7. Adjust air conditioner controls to maximum cold.

8. Observe gauge readings.

When the gauges are not being used it is a good idea to:

a. Keep both hand valves in the closed position.

b. Attach both ends of the high and low service hoses to the manifold, if extra outlets are present on the manifold, or plug them if not. Also, keep the center charging hose attached to an empty refrigerant can. This extra precaution will reduce the possibility of moisture entering the gauges. If air and moisture have gotten into the gauges, purge the hoses by supplying refrigerant under pressure to the center hose with both gauge valves open and all openings unplugged.

SYSTEM CHECKS

✳✳ CAUTION

Do not attempt to charge or discharge the refrigerant system unless you are thoroughly familiar with its operation and the hazards involved. The compressed refrigerant used in the air conditioning system expands and evaporates (boils) into the atmosphere at a temperature of –21.7°F (–29.8°C) or less. This will freeze any surface that it comes in contact with, including your eyes. In addition, the refrigerant decomposes into a poisonous gas in the presence of flame.

All models utilize a V-5 variable displacement compressor that can match the automotive air conditioning demand under all conditions without cycling.

On 1992 models, along with the V-5 variable displacement compressor, a Thermal Expansion Valve (TXV) was added as a flow control device. The valve, with its monitoring bulb and attaching capillary, mesh screen, and variable orfice is located in the evaporator inlet pipe. While sensing the temperature of the evaporator outlet pipe, the monitoring bulb's internal pressure raises or lowers in direct proportion, opening or closing the valve to allow more or less R-12 into the evaporator.

➡ **If your car is equipped with an aftermarket air conditioner, the following system checks may not apply. Contact the manufacturer of the unit for instructions on system checks.**

The air conditioning system on these cars has no sight glass.

1. Run the engine until it reaches normal operating temperature.

2. Open the hood and all doors.

3. Turn the air conditioning on, move the temperature selector to the first detent to the right of COLD (outside air) and then turn the blower on HI.

4. Idle the engine at 1,000 rpm.

5. Hand feel feel the temperature of the evaporator inlet pipe after orifice, and the accumulator surface with the compressor engaged.

6. Both should be the same temperature and both some degree cooler than ambient. If not leak check the system and if a leak is found, discharge and repair as required. Evacuate and recharge. If no leak is found refer to the diagnostic chart.

DISCHARGING THE SYSTEM

✳✳ CAUTION

R-12 refrigerant is a chlorofluorocarbon which, when released into the atmosphere, can contrubute to the depletion of the ozone layer in the upper atmosphere. Ozone filters out harmful radiation from the sun. If possible, an approved R-12 Recovery/recycling machine that meets SAE standards should be employed when discharging the system. Follow the operating instructions provided with the approved equippment exactly to properly discharge the system. Perform the following operation in a well-ventilated area.

When it is necessary to remove (purge) the refrigerant pressurized in the system, follow this procedure:

1. Operate air conditioner for at least 10 minutes.

2. Attach gauges, shut off engine and air conditioner.

3. Place a container or rag at the outlet of the center charging hose on the gauge. The refrigerant will be discharged there and this precaution will avoid its uncontrolled exposure.

4. Open low side hand valve on gauge slightly.

5. Open high side hand valve slightly.

➡ **Too rapid a purging process will be identified by the appearance of an oily foam. If this occurs, close the hand valves a little more until this condition stops.**

6. Close both hand valves on the gauge set when the pressures read 0 and all the refrigerant has left the system.

EVACUATING THE SYSTEM

Before charging any system it is necessary to purge the refrigerant and draw out the trapped moisture with a suitable vacuum pump. Failure to do so will result in ineffective charging and possible damage to the system.

Use this hook-up for the proper evacuation procedure:

1. Connect both service gauge hoses to the high and low service outlets.

2. Open high and low side hand valves on gauge manifold.

3. Open both service valves a slight amount (from back seated position), allow refrigerant to discharge from system.

4. Install center charging hose of gauge set to vacuum pump.

5. Operate vacuum pump for at least one hour. (If the system has been subjected to open conditions for a prolonged period of time it may be necessary to "pump the system down" overnight. Refer to "System Sweep" procedure.)

➡ **If low pressure gauge does not show at least 28 in.Hg within 5 minutes, check the system for a leak or loose gauge connectors.**

6. Close hand valves on gauge manifold.

7. Shut off pump.

8. Observe low pressure gauge to determine if vacuum is holding. A vacuum drop may indicate a leak.

SYSTEM SWEEP

An efficient vacuum pump can remove all the air contained in a contaminated air conditioning system very quickly, because of its vapor state. Moisture, however, is far more difficult to remove because the vacuum must force the liquid to evaporate before it will be able to remove it from the system. If a system has become severely contaminated, as, for example, it might become after all the charge was lost in conjunction with vehicle accident damage, moisture removal is extremely time consuming. A vacuum pump could remove all of the moisture only if it were operated for 12 hours or more.

Under these conditions, sweeping the system with refrigerant will speed the process of moisture removal considerably. To sweep, follow the following procedure:

1. Connect vacuum pump to gauges, operate it until vacuum ceases to increase, then continue operation for 10 more minutes.

2. Charge system with 50% of its rated refrigerant capacity.

3. Operate system at fast idle for 10 minutes.

4. Discharge the system.

5. Repeat twice the process of charging to 50% capacity, running the system for 10 minutes, and discharging it, for a total of 3 sweeps.

6. Replace drier.

7. Pump system down as in Step 1.

8. Charge system.

CHARGING THE SYSTEM

☀ CAUTION

Never attempt to charge the system by opening the high pressure gauge control while the compressor is operating. The compressor accumulating pressure can burst the refrigerant container, causing severe personal injuries.

When charging the system, attach only the low pressure line to the low pressure gauge port, located on the accumulator. Do not attach the high pressure line to any service port or allow it to remain attached to the vacuum pump after evacuation. Be sure both the high and the low pressure control valves are closed on the gauge set. To complete the charging of the system, follow the outline supplied.

1. Start the engine and allow to run at idle, with the cooling system at normal operating temperature and set the A/C mode control button on "OFF".

2. Attach the center gauge hose to a single or multi-can dispenser.

3. With the multi-can dispenser inverted, allow one pound or the contents of one or two 14 oz. cans to enter the system through the low pressure side by opening the gauge low pressure control valve.

4. Close the low pressure gauge control valve and turn the A/C system to NORM to engage the compressor. Place the blower motor in its HI mode.

5. Open the low pressure gauge control valve and draw the remaining charge into the system. Refer to the capacity chart at the end of this section for the individual vehicle or system capacity.

6. Close the low pressure gauge control valve and the refrigerant source valve, on the multi-can dispenser. Remove the low pressure hose from the accumulator quickly to avoid loss of refrigerant through the Schrader valve.

7. Install the protective cap on the gauge port and check the system for leakage.

8. Test the system for proper operation.

FREON CAPACITIES:
- 1988: 2.75 lbs. (1.25 kg)
- 1988–91: 2.25 lbs. (1.02 kg)
- 1992: 2.63 lbs. (1.20 kg)

LEAK TESTING THE SYSTEM

There are several methods of detecting leaks in an air conditioning system; among them, the two most popular are (1) halide leak-detection or the "open flame method," and (2) electronic leak-detection.

The halide leak detection is a torch like device which produces a yellow-green color when refrigerant is introduced into the flame at the burner. A purple or violet color indicates the presence of large amounts of refrigerant at the burner.

An electronic leak detector is a small portable electronic device with an extended probe. With the unit activated the probe is passed along those components of the system which contain refrigerant. If a leak is detected, the unit will sound an alarm signal or activate a display signal depending on the manufacturer's design. It is advisable to follow the manufacturer's instructions as the design and function of the detection may vary significantly.

☀ CAUTION

Care should be taken to operate either type of detector in well ventilated areas, so as to reduce the chance of personal injury, which may result from coming in contact with poisonous gases produced when R-12 is exposed to flame or electric spark.

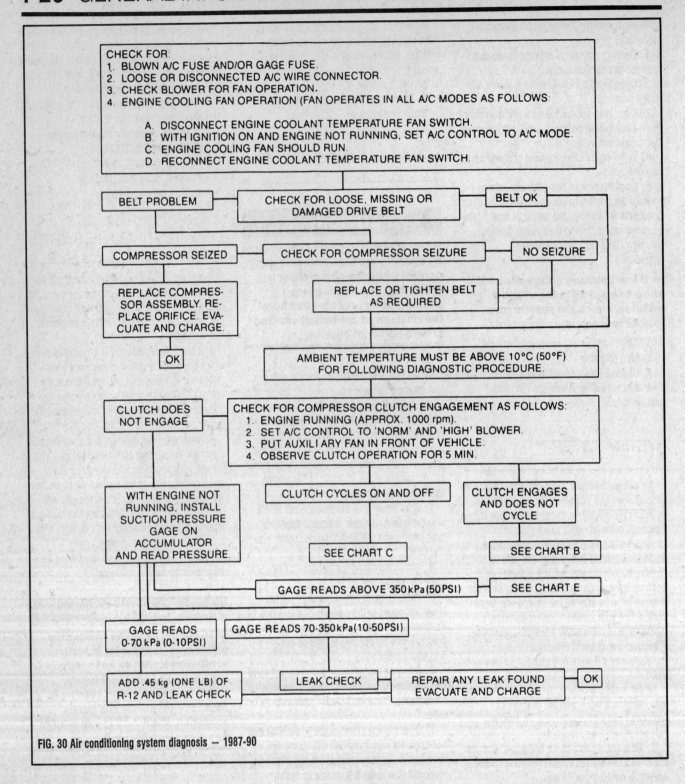

CHECK FOR:
1. BLOWN A/C FUSE AND/OR GAGE FUSE.
2. LOOSE OR DISCONNECTED A/C WIRE CONNECTOR.
3. CHECK BLOWER FOR FAN OPERATION.
4. ENGINE COOLING FAN OPERATION (FAN OPERATES IN ALL A/C MODES AS FOLLOWS:

   A. DISCONNECT ENGINE COOLANT TEMPERATURE FAN SWITCH.
   B. WITH IGNITION ON AND ENGINE NOT RUNNING, SET A/C CONTROL TO A/C MODE.
   C. ENGINE COOLING FAN SHOULD RUN.
   D. RECONNECT ENGINE COOLANT TEMPERATURE FAN SWITCH.

BELT PROBLEM

CHECK FOR LOOSE, MISSING OR DAMAGED DRIVE BELT

BELT OK

COMPRESSOR SEIZED

CHECK FOR COMPRESSOR SEIZURE

NO SEIZURE

REPLACE COMPRESSOR ASSEMBLY. REPLACE ORIFICE. EVACUATE AND CHARGE.

REPLACE OR TIGHTEN BELT AS REQUIRED

OK

AMBIENT TEMPERTURE MUST BE ABOVE 10°C (50°F) FOR FOLLOWING DIAGNOSTIC PROCEDURE.

CLUTCH DOES NOT ENGAGE

CHECK FOR COMPRESSOR CLUTCH ENGAGEMENT AS FOLLOWS:
1. ENGINE RUNNING (APPROX. 1000 rpm).
2. SET A/C CONTROL TO 'NORM' AND 'HIGH' BLOWER.
3. PUT AUXILIARY FAN IN FRONT OF VEHICLE.
4. OBSERVE CLUTCH OPERATION FOR 5 MIN.

WITH ENGINE NOT RUNNING, INSTALL SUCTION PRESSURE GAGE ON ACCUMULATOR AND READ PRESSURE.

CLUTCH CYCLES ON AND OFF

CLUTCH ENGAGES AND DOES NOT CYCLE

SEE CHART C

SEE CHART B

GAGE READS ABOVE 350 kPa (50 PSI)

SEE CHART E

GAGE READS 0-70 kPa (0-10 PSI)

GAGE READS 70-350 kPa (10-50 PSI)

ADD .45 kg (ONE LB) OF R-12 AND LEAK CHECK

LEAK CHECK

REPAIR ANY LEAK FOUND EVACUATE AND CHARGE

OK

FIG. 30 Air conditioning system diagnosis — 1987-90

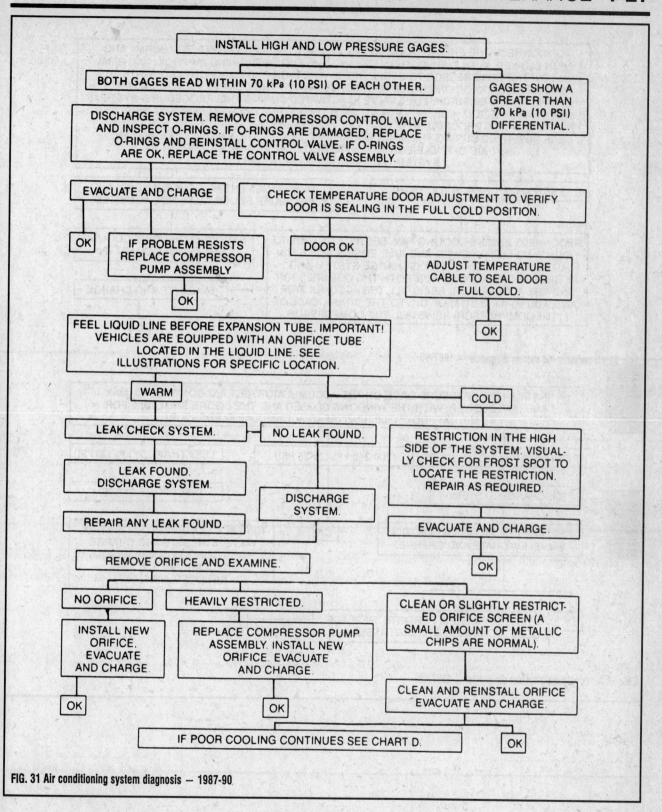

FIG. 31 Air conditioning system diagnosis — 1987-90

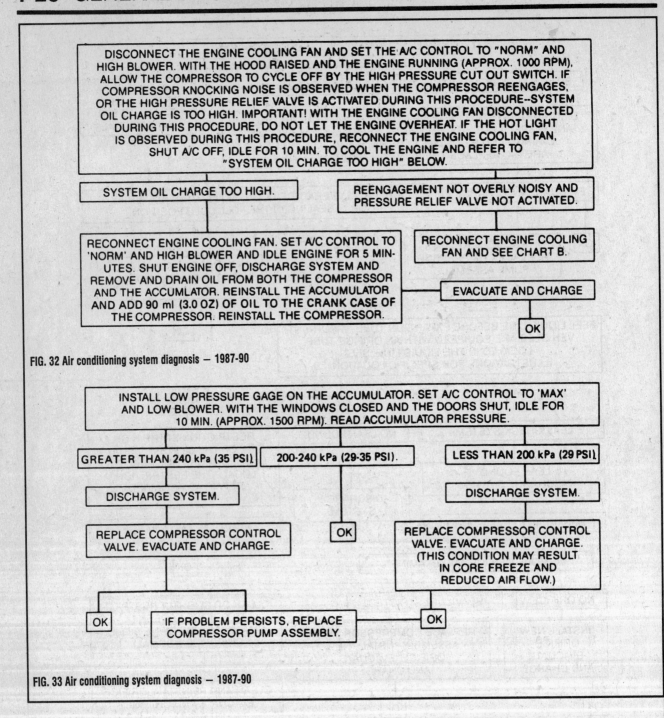

DISCONNECT THE ENGINE COOLING FAN AND SET THE A/C CONTROL TO "NORM" AND HIGH BLOWER. WITH THE HOOD RAISED AND THE ENGINE RUNNING (APPROX. 1000 RPM), ALLOW THE COMPRESSOR TO CYCLE OFF BY THE HIGH PRESSURE CUT OUT SWITCH. IF COMPRESSOR KNOCKING NOISE IS OBSERVED WHEN THE COMPRESSOR REENGAGES, OR THE HIGH PRESSURE RELIEF VALVE IS ACTIVATED DURING THIS PROCEDURE--SYSTEM OIL CHARGE IS TOO HIGH. IMPORTANT! WITH THE ENGINE COOLING FAN DISCONNECTED DURING THIS PROCEDURE, DO NOT LET THE ENGINE OVERHEAT. IF THE HOT LIGHT IS OBSERVED DURING THIS PROCEDURE, RECONNECT THE ENGINE COOLING FAN, SHUT A/C OFF, IDLE FOR 10 MIN. TO COOL THE ENGINE AND REFER TO "SYSTEM OIL CHARGE TOO HIGH" BELOW.

SYSTEM OIL CHARGE TOO HIGH.

REENGAGEMENT NOT OVERLY NOISY AND PRESSURE RELIEF VALVE NOT ACTIVATED.

RECONNECT ENGINE COOLING FAN. SET A/C CONTROL TO 'NORM' AND HIGH BLOWER AND IDLE ENGINE FOR 5 MINUTES. SHUT ENGINE OFF, DISCHARGE SYSTEM AND REMOVE AND DRAIN OIL FROM BOTH THE COMPRESSOR AND THE ACCUMLATOR. REINSTALL THE ACCUMULATOR AND ADD 90 ml (3.0 OZ) OF OIL TO THE CRANK CASE OF THE COMPRESSOR. REINSTALL THE COMPRESSOR.

RECONNECT ENGINE COOLING FAN AND SEE CHART B.

EVACUATE AND CHARGE

OK

FIG. 32 Air conditioning system diagnosis — 1987-90

INSTALL LOW PRESSURE GAGE ON THE ACCUMULATOR. SET A/C CONTROL TO 'MAX' AND LOW BLOWER. WITH THE WINDOWS CLOSED AND THE DOORS SHUT, IDLE FOR 10 MIN. (APPROX. 1500 RPM). READ ACCUMULATOR PRESSURE.

GREATER THAN 240 kPa (35 PSI).

200-240 kPa (29-35 PSI).

LESS THAN 200 kPa (29 PSI).

DISCHARGE SYSTEM.

DISCHARGE SYSTEM.

REPLACE COMPRESSOR CONTROL VALVE. EVACUATE AND CHARGE.

OK

REPLACE COMPRESSOR CONTROL VALVE. EVACUATE AND CHARGE. (THIS CONDITION MAY RESULT IN CORE FREEZE AND REDUCED AIR FLOW.)

OK

IF PROBLEM PERSISTS, REPLACE COMPRESSOR PUMP ASSEMBLY.

OK

FIG. 33 Air conditioning system diagnosis — 1987-90

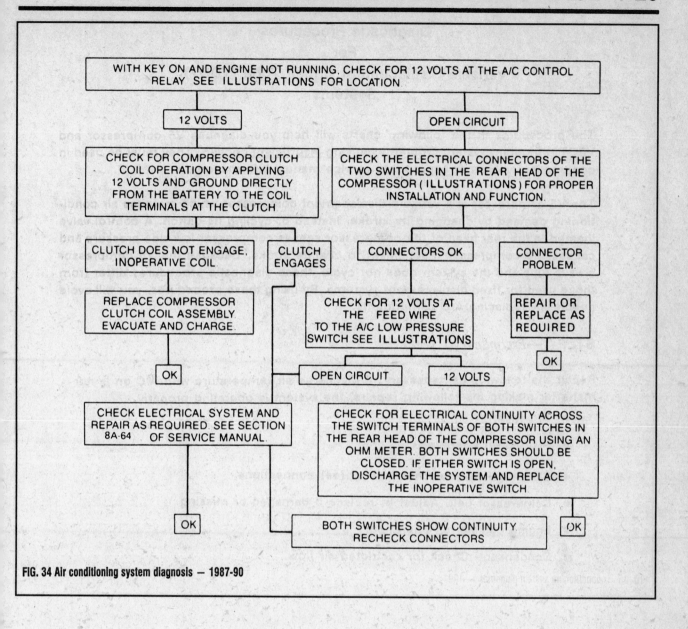

FIG. 34 Air conditioning system diagnosis — 1987-90

Diagnostic Procedures
For
Variable Displacement Orifice Tube (VDOT)
Systems

The procedures in the following charts will help you diagnose V5 compressor and VDOT refrigerant system problems causing insufficient cooling. They must be used in conjunction with other appropriate service manual information.

The V5 compressor is a variable displacement compressor which matches air conditioning demand by changing its stroke, instead of cycling its clutch. A control valve located in the rear head of the compressor senses compressor low side pressure and causes the compressor mechanism to change stroke. Because the V5 compressor always runs and the system does not cycle, these diagnostic procedures differ from those used for fixed displacement systems. By using these procedures, you will avoid needlessly replacing A/C components.

STEP 1--*Preliminary Checks*

Repair the following as necessary. If discharge air temperature with A/C on is normal after making the following repairs, the system is operating properly.

- A/C fuse.

- A/C blower operation.

- Clutch coil and rear head switch(es) connections.

- Compressor belt. Adjust or replace if damaged or missing.

- Engine cooling fan operation.

- Condenser – Check for restricted air flow.

FIG. 35 Air conditioning system diagnosis — 1991

STEP 2--*Checking Refrigerant Charge*

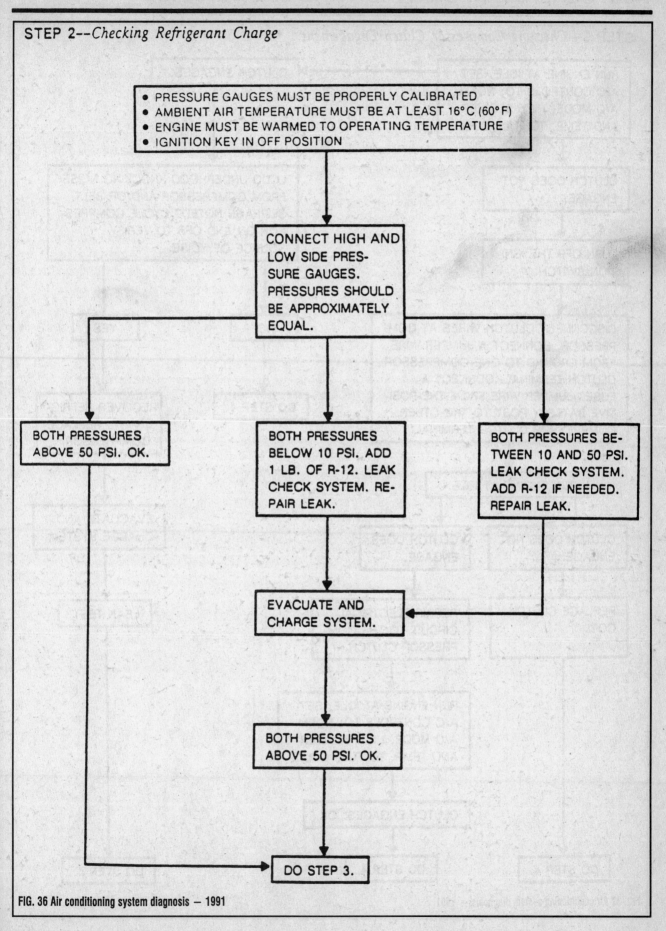

- PRESSURE GAUGES MUST BE PROPERLY CALIBRATED
- AMBIENT AIR TEMPERATURE MUST BE AT LEAST 16°C (60°F)
- ENGINE MUST BE WARMED TO OPERATING TEMPERATURE
- IGNITION KEY IN OFF POSITION

CONNECT HIGH AND LOW SIDE PRESSURE GAUGES. PRESSURES SHOULD BE APPROXIMATELY EQUAL.

BOTH PRESSURES ABOVE 50 PSI. OK.

BOTH PRESSURES BELOW 10 PSI. ADD 1 LB. OF R-12. LEAK CHECK SYSTEM. REPAIR LEAK.

BOTH PRESSURES BETWEEN 10 AND 50 PSI. LEAK CHECK SYSTEM. ADD R-12 IF NEEDED. REPAIR LEAK.

EVACUATE AND CHARGE SYSTEM.

BOTH PRESSURES ABOVE 50 PSI. OK.

DO STEP 3.

FIG. 36 Air conditioning system diagnosis — 1991

STEP 3--_Checking Compressor Clutch Engagement_

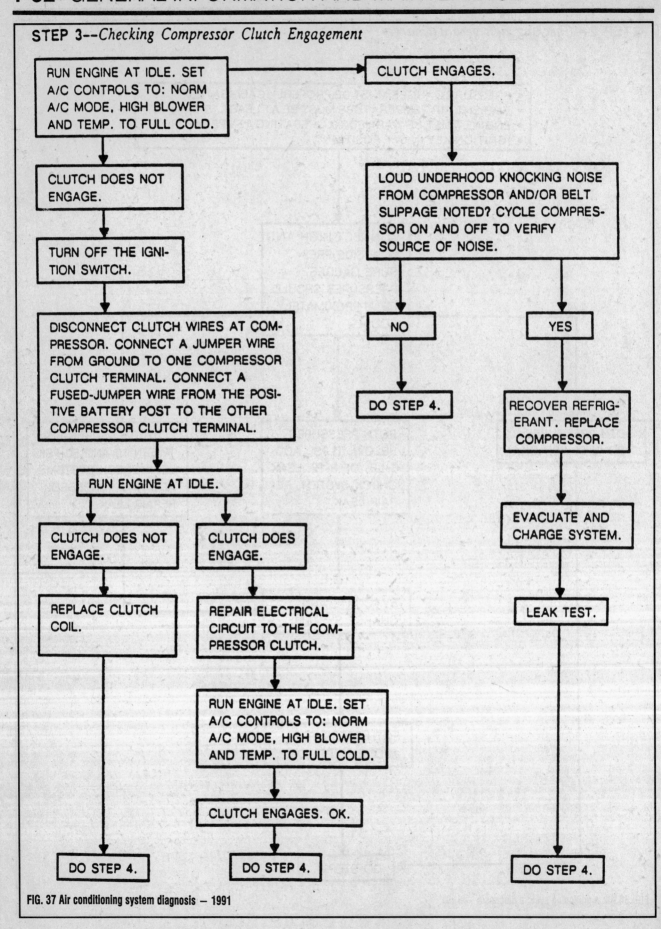

FIG. 37 Air conditioning system diagnosis — 1991

STEP 4--*Continued*

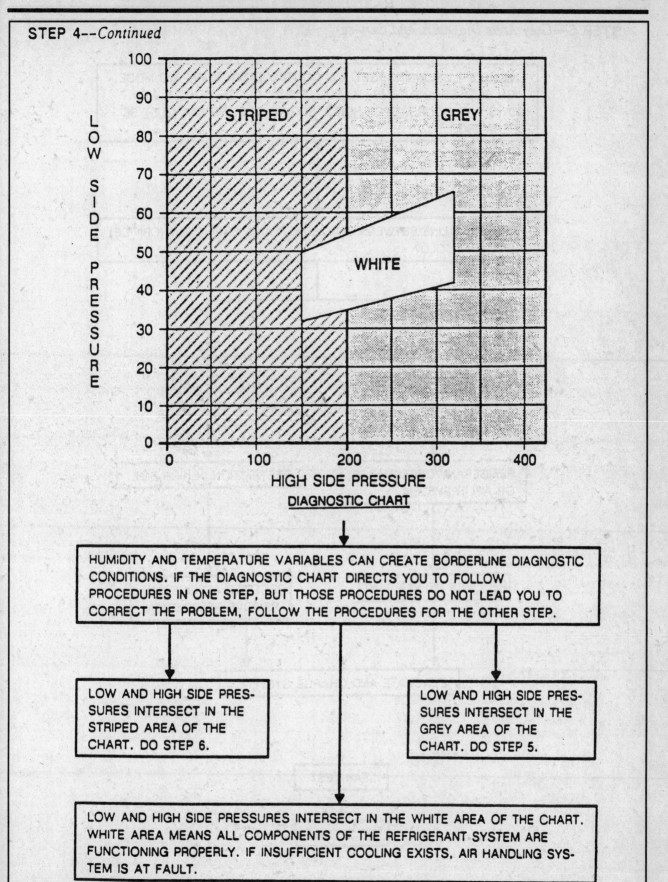

FIG. 38 Air conditioning system diagnosis — 1991

STEP 5--*Grey Area Diagnosis And Service*

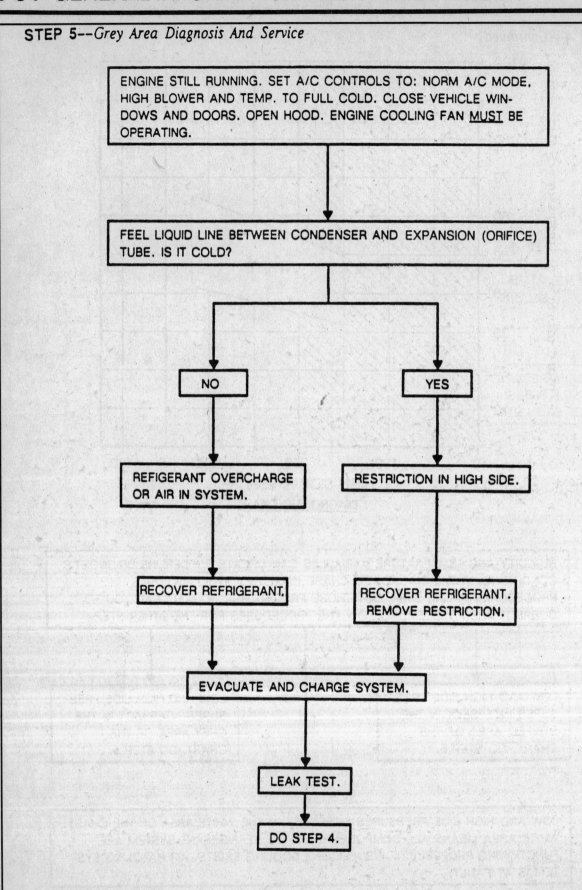

ENGINE STILL RUNNING. SET A/C CONTROLS TO: NORM A/C MODE, HIGH BLOWER AND TEMP. TO FULL COLD. CLOSE VEHICLE WINDOWS AND DOORS. OPEN HOOD. ENGINE COOLING FAN MUST BE OPERATING.

FEEL LIQUID LINE BETWEEN CONDENSER AND EXPANSION (ORIFICE) TUBE. IS IT COLD?

NO

YES

REFIGERANT OVERCHARGE OR AIR IN SYSTEM.

RESTRICTION IN HIGH SIDE.

RECOVER REFRIGERANT.

RECOVER REFRIGERANT. REMOVE RESTRICTION.

EVACUATE AND CHARGE SYSTEM.

LEAK TEST.

DO STEP 4.

FIG. 39 Air conditioning system diagnosis — 1991

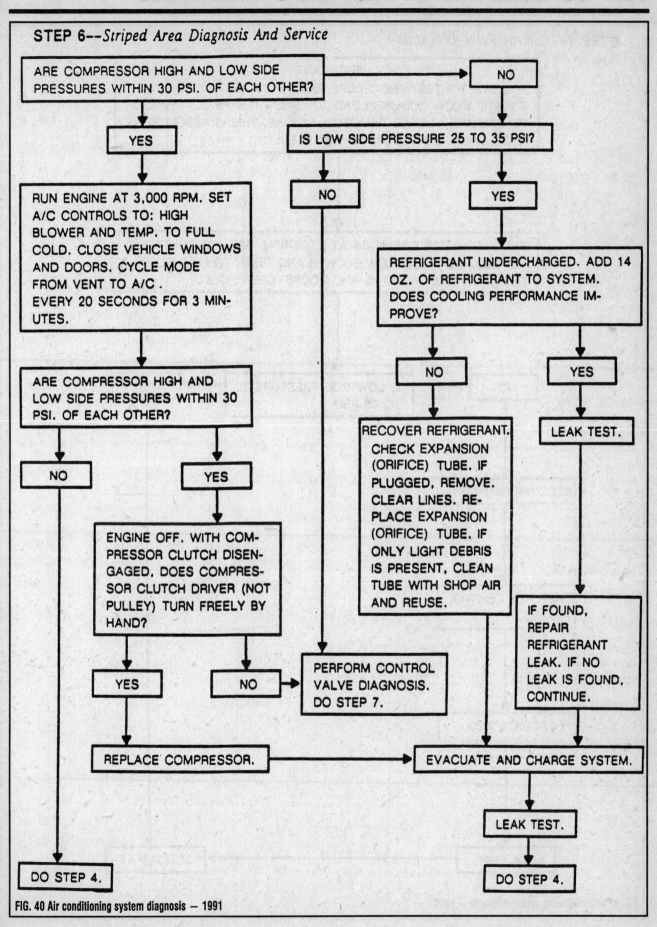

STEP 6--*Striped Area Diagnosis And Service*

FIG. 40 Air conditioning system diagnosis — 1991

STEP 7--*Control Valve Diagnosis*

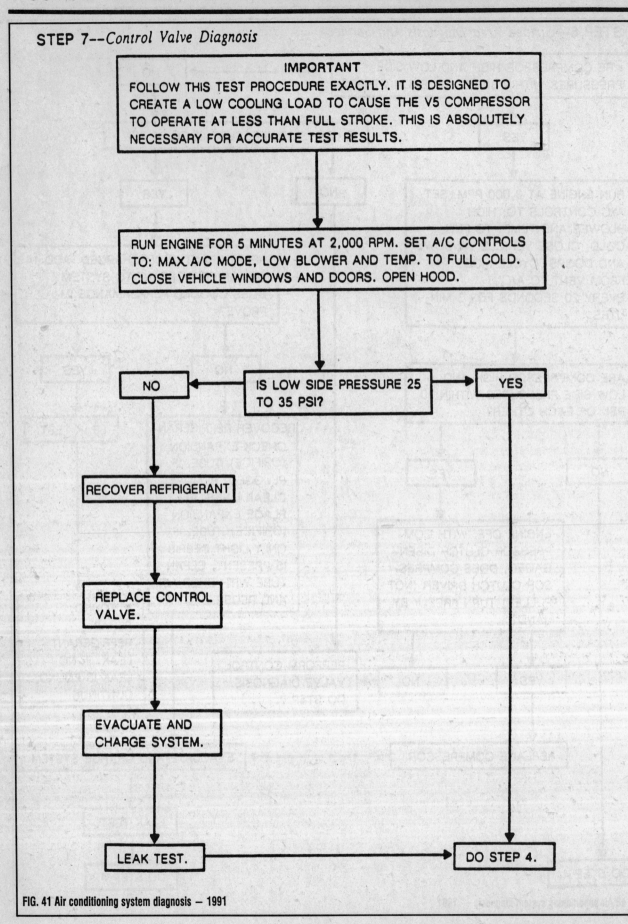

IMPORTANT
FOLLOW THIS TEST PROCEDURE EXACTLY. IT IS DESIGNED TO CREATE A LOW COOLING LOAD TO CAUSE THE V5 COMPRESSOR TO OPERATE AT LESS THAN FULL STROKE. THIS IS ABSOLUTELY NECESSARY FOR ACCURATE TEST RESULTS.

RUN ENGINE FOR 5 MINUTES AT 2,000 RPM. SET A/C CONTROLS TO: MAX A/C MODE, LOW BLOWER AND TEMP. TO FULL COLD. CLOSE VEHICLE WINDOWS AND DOORS. OPEN HOOD.

IS LOW SIDE PRESSURE 25 TO 35 PSI?

NO — RECOVER REFRIGERANT — REPLACE CONTROL VALVE. — EVACUATE AND CHARGE SYSTEM. — LEAK TEST.

YES — DO STEP 4.

FIG. 41 Air conditioning system diagnosis — 1991

V5/TXV SYSTEM DIAGNOSTICS

Diagnostic Flow Chart

This chart is the starting point for verifying and diagnosing all air conditioning and HVAC control related complaints. It represents the correct path to follow from a customer complaint or condition through delivery of the vehicle back to the customer.

Preliminary Checks

This step covers all physical and visual inspections of interior and underhood components. Many problems can be detected by a thorough inspection. Failure to perform this step could result in wasted time proceeding further down the flow chart.

Vehicle Set Up and Performance Test

To run an air conditioning performance test the vehicle must be set-up according to the service manual instructions. The instructions include manifold gauge set installation and controller settings. Improper vehicle set up will result in inaccurate pressure and temperature readings.

General and Specific System Condition Charts

These charts were developed in a wind tunnel by producing known system problems and recording pressures and temperatures at various ambient temperatures. The tests were then validated using the same vehicle set up in a service environment. To find your system problem, compare the performance test readings to the readings on the charts for your ambient temperature and humidity. When all pressure and temperature readings fall within the limits of a given chart, use that chart to repair the vehicle. There is some variance in readings between systems of different vehicles; however the target areas have been developed to accommodate these changes.

Compressor Control Test

This is designed to evaluate the compressor's ability to change displacement with varying heat loads.

Step 1 — *Preliminary Checks*

Repair the following as necessary. If discharge temperature with A/C on is normal after making the following repairs, the system is operating properly.

- A/C fuse
- A/C blower operation
- Temperature door. Move temperature door lever from cold to hot. Listen for temperature door movement.

- Clutch coil connection
- Transducer connection
- Compressor belt. Replace if damaged or missing
- Engine cooling fan operation (at idle, cooling fan must be on at any A/C mode except 3.1L/V6 engines) cooling fan must be operating in correct direction (drawing outside air through the condenser toward engine)
- Condenser — Check for restricted air flow
- Dealer technical bulletins for updates on A/C system

FIG. 42 Air conditioning system diagnosis — 1992

Step 2 — *Checking Refrigerant Charge*

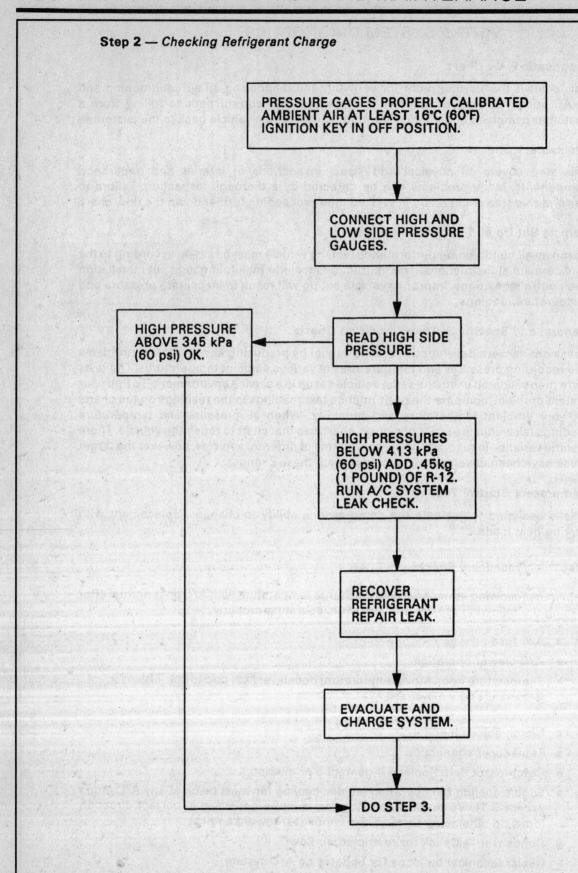

FIG. 43 Air conditioning system diagnosis — 1992

Step 3 — *Checking Compressor Clutch Engagement*

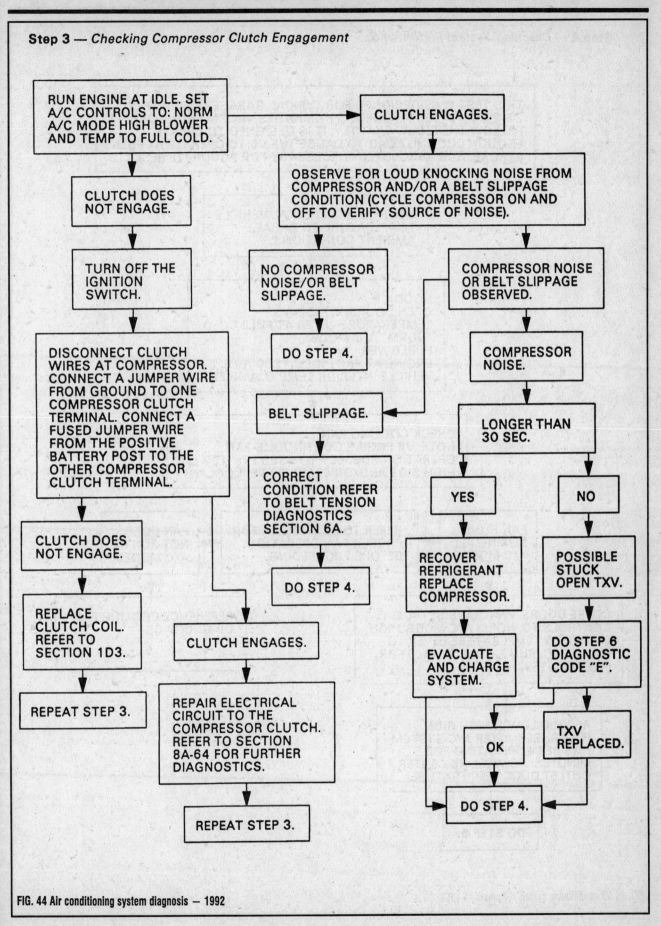

FIG. 44 Air conditioning system diagnosis — 1992

Step 4 — *Checking System Performance*

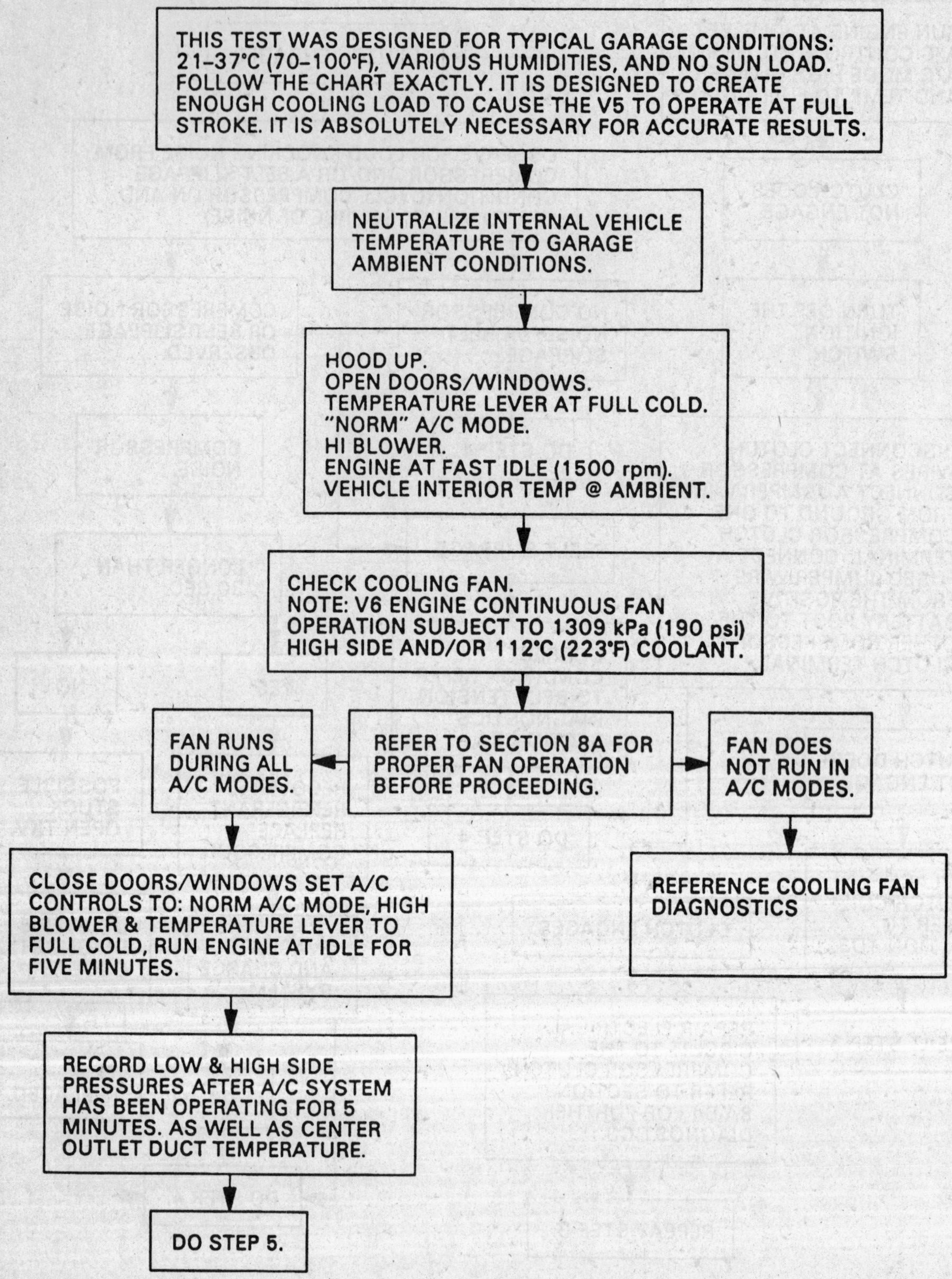

THIS TEST WAS DESIGNED FOR TYPICAL GARAGE CONDITIONS: 21–37°C (70–100°F), VARIOUS HUMIDITIES, AND NO SUN LOAD. FOLLOW THE CHART EXACTLY. IT IS DESIGNED TO CREATE ENOUGH COOLING LOAD TO CAUSE THE V5 TO OPERATE AT FULL STROKE. IT IS ABSOLUTELY NECESSARY FOR ACCURATE RESULTS.

↓

NEUTRALIZE INTERNAL VEHICLE TEMPERATURE TO GARAGE AMBIENT CONDITIONS.

↓

HOOD UP.
OPEN DOORS/WINDOWS.
TEMPERATURE LEVER AT FULL COLD.
"NORM" A/C MODE.
HI BLOWER.
ENGINE AT FAST IDLE (1500 rpm).
VEHICLE INTERIOR TEMP @ AMBIENT.

↓

CHECK COOLING FAN.
NOTE: V6 ENGINE CONTINUOUS FAN OPERATION SUBJECT TO 1309 kPa (190 psi) HIGH SIDE AND/OR 112°C (223°F) COOLANT.

↓

FAN RUNS DURING ALL A/C MODES. ← REFER TO SECTION 8A FOR PROPER FAN OPERATION BEFORE PROCEEDING. → FAN DOES NOT RUN IN A/C MODES.

↓ CLOSE DOORS/WINDOWS SET A/C CONTROLS TO: NORM A/C MODE, HIGH BLOWER & TEMPERATURE LEVER TO FULL COLD, RUN ENGINE AT IDLE FOR FIVE MINUTES.

↓ REFERENCE COOLING FAN DIAGNOSTICS

↓

RECORD LOW & HIGH SIDE PRESSURES AFTER A/C SYSTEM HAS BEEN OPERATING FOR 5 MINUTES. AS WELL AS CENTER OUTLET DUCT TEMPERATURE.

↓

DO STEP 5.

FIG. 45 Air conditioning system diagnosis — 1992

Step 5 — *Diagnostic Chart*

1. USE THE CHART BELOW WHICH CORRESPONDS TO THE PRESENT AMBIENT TEMPERATURE.

2. READ THE HIGH SIDE AND LOW SIDE PRESSURES AND NOTE THE LETTER CODED AREA IN WHICH THEY INTERSECT.

3. MATCH THE LETTER CODE WITH THE CORRESPONDING LETTER CODE ON THE FOLLOWING PAGE AND CONTINUE WITH THE DIAGNOSTIC CODE PROCEDURES.

A. – NORMAL SYSTEM

B. – LOW REFRIGERANT CHARGE

C. – REFRIGERANT OVERCHARGE / OR RD RESTRICTED

D. – TXV CLOSED

E. – TXV STUCK OPEN

F. – NO PUMP

} GO TO STEP 6

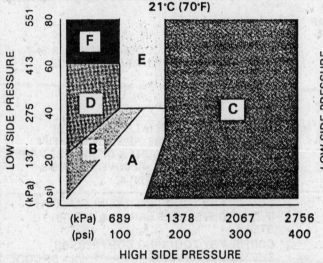

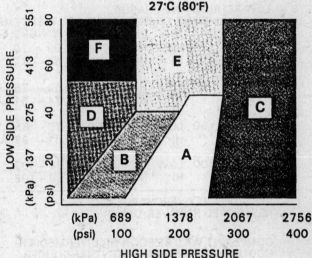

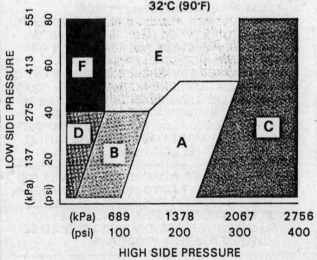

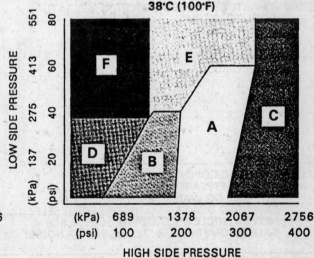

FIG. 46 Air conditioning system diagnosis — 1992

Step 6 — *Diagnostic Code Procedures*

Refer to appropriate diagnostic code chart for ambient garage conditions. NOTE: High humidity is above 60% relative. (Obtain humidity level from local radio weather report.)

A – NORMAL SYSTEM PERFORMANCE
AMBIENT TEMPERATURE – OUTLET TEMP RANGES:

ADDITIONAL INDICATORS

70	LOW HUMIDITY	45 – 50	SYSTEM WITHIN SPECS.
	HI HUMIDITY	51 – 56	
80	LOW HUMIDITY	50 – 57	NOTE: IF LOW SIDE PRESSURE IS LESS THAN 172 kPa (25 psi), MAY INDICATE POSSIBLE CONTROL VALVE PROBLEM — GO TO STEP 8.
	HI HUMIDITY	58 – 65	
90	LOW HUMIDITY	60 – 65	
	HI HUMIDITY	66 – 70	
100	LOW HUMIDITY	67 – 75	
	HI HUMIDITY	76 – 80	

B – LOW REFRIGERANT CHARGE
AMBIENT TEMPERATURE – OUTLET TEMP RANGES:

70	LOW HUMIDITY	63 – 70	SYSTEM SLIGHTLY COOLER THAN AMBIENT DEPENDING UPON REMAINING CHARGE.
	HI HUMIDITY	63 – 77	
80	LOW HUMIDITY	64 – 75	
	HI HUMIDITY	74 – 81	
90	LOW HUMIDITY	75 – 85	CONFIRM BY TOUCHING COMPRESSOR SUCTION/DISCHARGE PIPE. SUCTION PIPE WILL BE COOL TO WARM & DISCHARGE WARM TO HOT. LEAK CHECK, RECOVER REPAIR & RECHARGE. REPEAT STEP 4.
	HI HUMIDITY	81 – 88	
100	LOW HUMIDITY	85 – 102	
	HI HUMIDITY	90 – 105	

C – REFRIGERANT OVERCHARGE OR RESTRICTED RECEIVER/DRYER

COMPLAINT WILL BE POOR OR INTERMEDIATE COOLING AT HIGH AMBIENTS (TRANSDUCER SHUTS SYSTEM DOWN BECAUSE OF EXCESSIVE HIGH SIDE SYSTEM PRESSURE)

CONFIRM BY TOUCHING R/D INLET/ OUTLET IF TEMP DIFFERENCE R&R RD & RETURN TO STEP 4.
CONFIRM BY TOUCHING COMPRESSOR SUCTION/DISCHARGE PIPE — IT WILL BE COOL & DISCHARGE PIPE WILL BE HOT.

D – TXV STUCK CLOSED OUTLET TEMPERATURE COOL TO WARM

CONFIRM BY THOROUGH PHYSICAL INSPECTION OF ALL LINES AND COMPONENTS. PRIOR TO FRONT OF DASH. IF INLET LINE IS COOL AT FOD CHECK FOR RESTRICTION ON HIGH SIDE. (NOTICEABLE WARM/COLD TEMPERATURE DIFFERENCE AT GIVEN POINT ON LIQUID LINE OR RD) IF NO RESTRICTION FOUND, CONFIRM BY LISTENING FOR 'HISS' ON NORM A/C, LOW BLOWER. VERIFY BY RUNNING ENGINE AT 2000 rpm; IF PRESSURES DO NOT CHANGE BY MORE THAN 20 psi AND OUTLET AIR DOESN'T FEEL COOL, REPLACE TXV.

E – TXV STUCK OPEN
SYSTEM APPEARS TO PERFORM NORMALLY, BUT MAY GO WARM TEMPORARILY ON EXTENDED DRIVES AND RECORRECT ITSELF AFTER VEHICLE SHUT DOWN. MAY ALSO CAUSE COMPRESSOR "SLUGGING" — NOISE

RUN HI BLOWER, NORMAL A/C FAST IDLE FOR 2 MIN. ENGINE OFF FOR 3 MIN. RESTART ENGINE WITH A/C OFF. LET ENGINE RPM STABALIZE. ON LOW BLOWER RUN A/C AND LISTEN FOR SLUGGING. REPLACE TXV. HOOD SHOULD BE LOWERED FOR THIS PROCEDURE.

F – COMPRESSOR NO PUMP
OUTLET TEMPERATURE IS AMBIENT

CONFIRM BY FOLLOWING DIAGNOSTIC TREE SECTION STEP 7.

NOTE: IF NONE OF THE ABOVE CONDITIONS CAN BE VERIFIED, RECOVER, EVACUATE AND RECHARGE WITH PROPER CHARGE AND PREFORM STEP 4 AGAIN.

FIG. 47 Air conditioning system diagnosis – 1992

Step 7— *Checking For No Stroke Compressor*

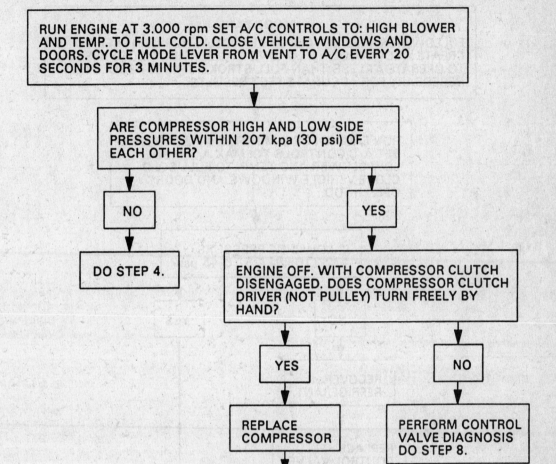

RUN ENGINE AT 3.000 rpm SET A/C CONTROLS TO: HIGH BLOWER AND TEMP. TO FULL COLD. CLOSE VEHICLE WINDOWS AND DOORS. CYCLE MODE LEVER FROM VENT TO A/C EVERY 20 SECONDS FOR 3 MINUTES.

ARE COMPRESSOR HIGH AND LOW SIDE PRESSURES WITHIN 207 kpa (30 psi) OF EACH OTHER?

NO → DO STEP 4.

YES → ENGINE OFF. WITH COMPRESSOR CLUTCH DISENGAGED. DOES COMPRESSOR CLUTCH DRIVER (NOT PULLEY) TURN FREELY BY HAND?

YES → REPLACE COMPRESSOR → RECOVER REFRIGERANT EVACUATE AND CHARGE SYSTEM. → LEAK TEST. → DO STEP 4.

NO → PERFORM CONTROL VALVE DIAGNOSIS DO STEP 8.

NOTE: FAILED TXV **CAN** CAUSE INTERNAL COMPRESSOR FAILURE. AFTER REPLACING FAILED COMPRESSOR, PAY PARTICULAR ATTENTION TO TXV OPERATION. IF PROBLEM INDICATED, PERFORM APPROPRIATE REPAIR PROCEDURE.

FIG. 48 Air conditioning system diagnosis — 1992

Step 8— *Control Valve Diagnosis*

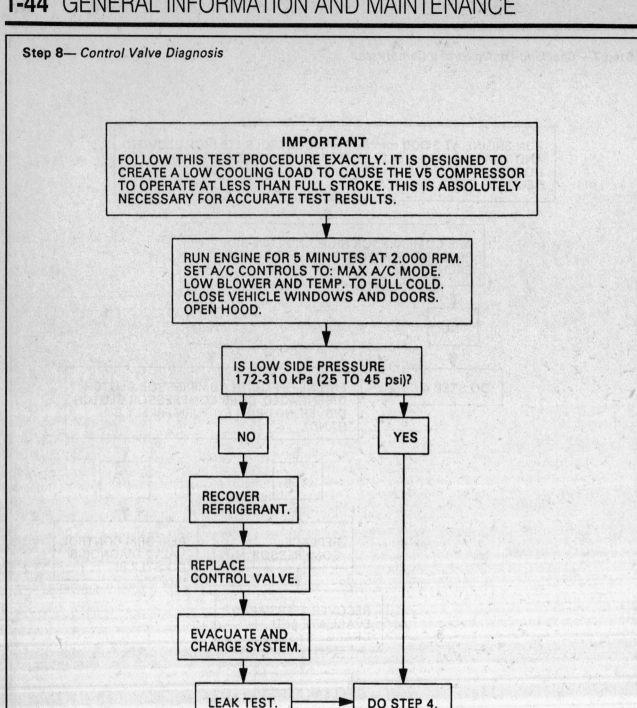

```
┌─────────────────────────────────────────────┐
│                  IMPORTANT                    │
│ FOLLOW THIS TEST PROCEDURE EXACTLY. IT IS     │
│ DESIGNED TO CREATE A LOW COOLING LOAD TO      │
│ CAUSE THE V5 COMPRESSOR TO OPERATE AT LESS    │
│ THAN FULL STROKE. THIS IS ABSOLUTELY          │
│ NECESSARY FOR ACCURATE TEST RESULTS.          │
└─────────────────────────────────────────────┘
```

RUN ENGINE FOR 5 MINUTES AT 2.000 RPM.
SET A/C CONTROLS TO: MAX A/C MODE.
LOW BLOWER AND TEMP. TO FULL COLD.
CLOSE VEHICLE WINDOWS AND DOORS.
OPEN HOOD.

IS LOW SIDE PRESSURE
172-310 kPa (25 TO 45 psi)?

NO → RECOVER REFRIGERANT. → REPLACE CONTROL VALVE. → EVACUATE AND CHARGE SYSTEM. → LEAK TEST. → DO STEP 4.

YES → DO STEP 4.

FIG. 49 Air conditioning system diagnosis — 1992

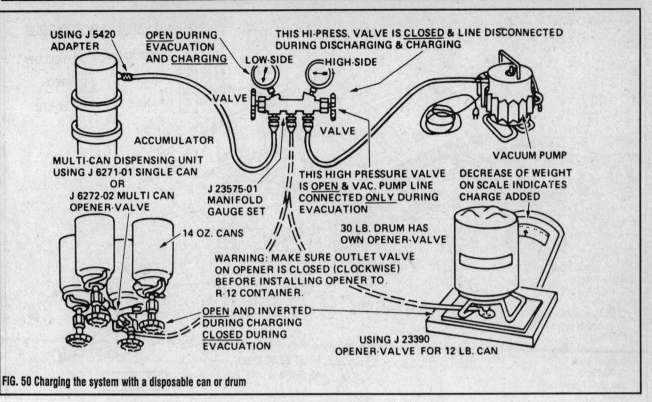

FIG. 50 Charging the system with a disposable can or drum

VACUUM VALVE LOGIC		MODE LEVER POSITION						
PORT	CONNECTION	OFF	MAX	NORM	BI-LEVEL	VENT	HEAT	DEFROST
1	INPUT	3, 5	2, 3, 4	3, 4	3	3, 4	3, 5	5
2	OSA RECIRC	VENT	VAC	VENT	VENT	VENT	VENT	VENT
3	DEFROST	VAC	VAC	VAC	VAC	VAC	VAC	VENT
4	A/C MODE	VENT	VAC	VAC	VENT	VAC	VENT	VENT
5	HEAT MODE	VAC	VENT	VENT	VENT	VENT	VAC	VAC

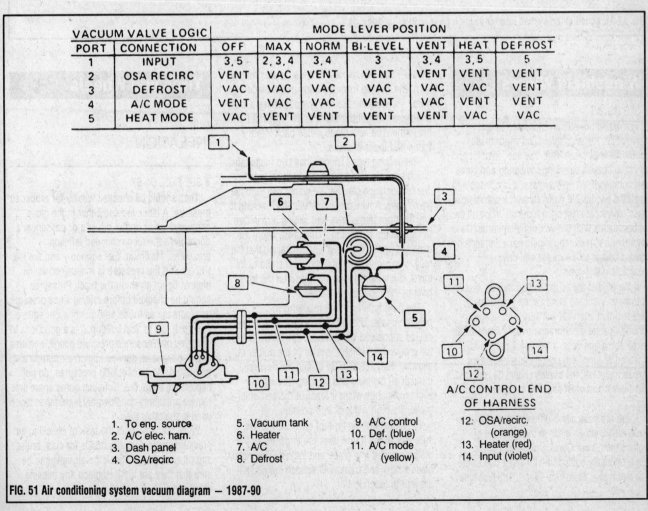

1. To eng. source
2. A/C elec. harn.
3. Dash panel
4. OSA/recirc
5. Vacuum tank
6. Heater
7. A/C
8. Defrost
9. A/C control
10. Def. (blue)
11. A/C mode (yellow)
12. OSA/recirc. (orange)
13. Heater (red)
14. Input (violet)

A/C CONTROL END OF HARNESS

FIG. 51 Air conditioning system vacuum diagram — 1987-90

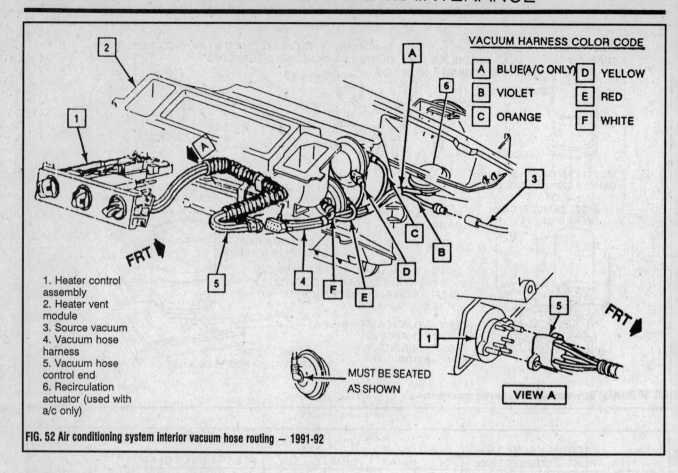

VACUUM HARNESS COLOR CODE

A	BLUE(A/C ONLY)	D	YELLOW
B	VIOLET	E	RED
C	ORANGE	F	WHITE

1. Heater control assembly
2. Heater vent module
3. Source vacuum
4. Vacuum hose harness
5. Vacuum hose control end
6. Recirculation actuator (used with a/c only)

MUST BE SEATED AS SHOWN

VIEW A

FIG. 52 Air conditioning system interior vacuum hose routing — 1991-92

Windshield Wipers

♦ SEE FIG. 53

For maximum effectiveness and longest element lift, the windshield and wiper blades should be kept clean. Dirt, tree sap, road tar and so on will cause streaking, smearing and blade deterioration if left on the glass. It is advisable to wash the windshield carefully with a commercial glass cleaner at least once a month. Wipe off the rubber blades with the wet rag afterwards. Do not attempt to move the wipers back and forth by hand; damage to the motor and drive mechanism will result.

If the blades are found to be cracked, broken or torn, they should be replaced immediately. Replacement intervals will vary with usage, although ozone deterioration usually limits blade life to about one year. If the wiper pattern is smeared or streaked, or if the blade chatters across the glass, the blades should be replaced. It is easiest and most sensible to replace them in pairs.

There are basically 3 different types of wiper blade refills, which differ in their method of replacement. Your Corsica or Beretta could come originally equipped with either one of the first two types, Anco® or Trico®. The first type

(Anco®) has two release buttons, approximately 1/3 of the way up from the ends of the blade frame. Pushing the buttons down releases a lock and allows the rubber blade to be removed from the frame. The new blade slides back into the frame and locks in place.

The second type (Trico®), has two metal tabs which are unlocked by squeezing them together. The rubber blade can then be withdrawn from the frame jaws. A new one is installed by inserting it into the front frame jaws and sliding it rearward to engage the remaining frame jaws. There are usually 4 jaws; be certain when installing that the refill is engaged in all of them. At the end of its travel, the tabs will lock into place on the front jaws of the wiper blade frame.

The third type is a refill made from polycarbonate. The refill has a simple locking device at one end which flexes downward out of the groove into which the jaws of the holder fit, allowing easy release. By sliding the new refill through all the jaws and pushing through the slight resistance when it reaches the end of its travel, the refill will lock into position.

Regardless of the type of refill used, make sure that all the frame jaws are engaged as the refill is pushed into place and locked. The metal blade holder and frame will scratch the glass if allowed to touch it.

Tires and Wheels

INFLATION

♦ SEE FIGS. 54-67

Tires should be checked weekly for proper air pressure. A label, located either in the glove compartment or on the driver's or passenger's door, gives the recommended inflation pressures. Maximum fuel economy and tire life will result if the pressure is maintained at the highest figure given on the label. Pressures should be checked before driving since pressure can increase as much as 6 pounds per square inch (psi) due to heat buildup. It is a good idea to have you own accurate pressure gauge, because not all gauges on service station air pumps can be trusted. When checking pressures, do not neglect the spare tire. Note that some spare tires require pressures considerably higher than those used in the other tires.

While you are about the task of checking air pressure, inspect the tire treads for cuts, bruises and other damage. Check the air valves to be sure that they are tight. Replace any missing valve caps.

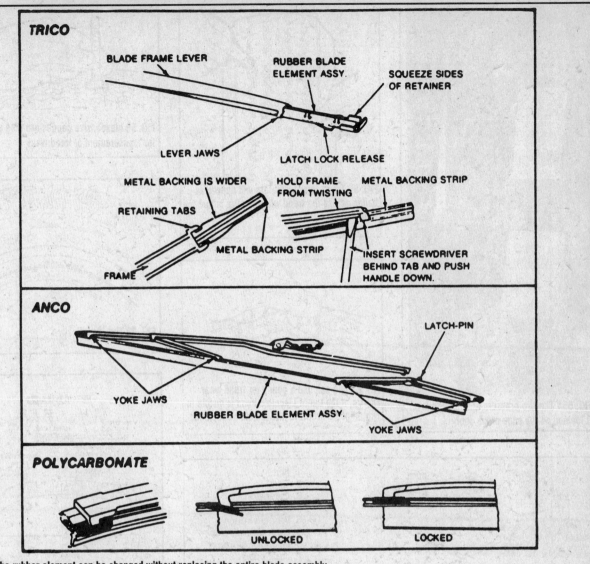

FIG. 53 The rubber element can be changed without replacing the entire blade assembly

Check the tires for uneven wear that might indicate the need for front end alignment or tire rotation. Tires should be replaced when a tread wear indicator appears as a solid band across the tread.

TIRE DESIGN

When buying new tires, give some thought to the following points, especially if you are considering a switch to larger tires or a different profile series:

1. All 4 tires must be of the same construction type. This rule cannot be violated, Radial, bias, and bias-belted tires must not be mixed.

2. The wheels should be the correct width for the tire. Tire dealers have charts of tire and rim compatibility. A mis-match will cause sloppy

FIG. 54 Don't judge a radial tire's pressure by its appearance. An improperly inflated radial tire looks similar to a properly inflated one

handling and rapid tire wear. The tread width should match the rim width (inside bead to inside bead) within an inch. For radial tires, the rim should be 80% or less of the tire (not tread) width.

3. The height (mounted diameter) of the new tires can change speedometer accuracy, engine speed at a given road speed, fuel mileage, acceleration, and ground clearance. Tire

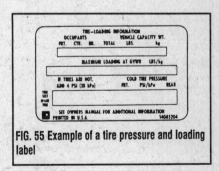

FIG. 55 Example of a tire pressure and loading label

manufacturers furnish full measurement specifications.

4. The spare tire should be usable, at least for short distance and low speed operation, with the new tires.

5. There shouldn't be any body interference when loaded, on bumps, or in turns.

FIG. 55A The tire pressure and loading label is located on the edge of the door

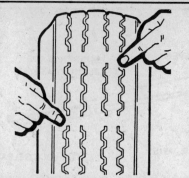

FIG. 56 Tread wear indicators will appear as bands across the tread when the tire is due for replacement

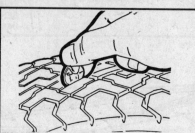

FIG. 57 You can use a penny for tread wear checks; if the top of Lincoln's head is visible in two adjacent grooves, tire should be replaced

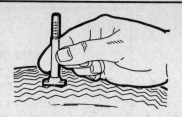

FIG. 58 Inexpensive gauges are also available for measurement of tread wear

FIG. 59 Tire identification

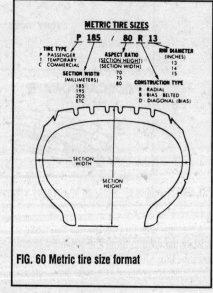

FIG. 60 Metric tire size format

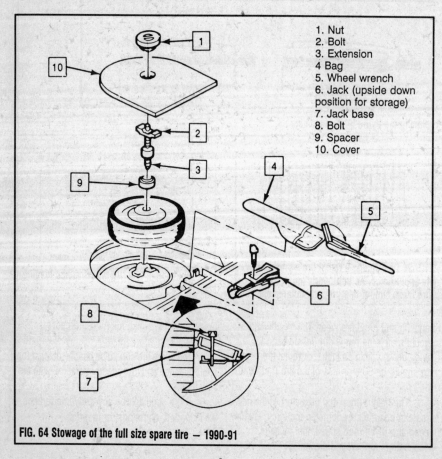

1. Nut
2. Bolt
3. Extension
4 Bag
5. Wheel wrench
6. Jack (upside down position for storage)
7. Jack base
8. Bolt
9. Spacer
10. Cover

FIG. 64 Stowage of the full size spare tire — 1990-91

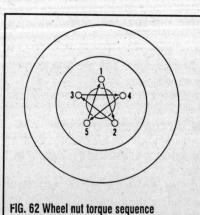

FIG. 62 Wheel nut torque sequence

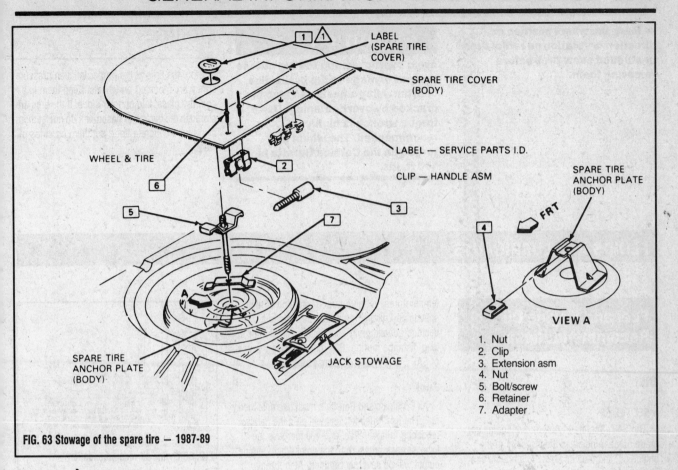

1. Nut
2. Clip
3. Extension asm
4. Nut
5. Bolt/screw
6. Retainer
7. Adapter

FIG. 63 Stowage of the spare tire — 1987-89

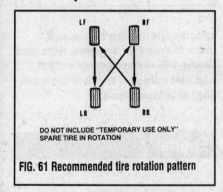

DO NOT INCLUDE "TEMPORARY USE ONLY" SPARE TIRE IN ROTATION

FIG. 61 Recommended tire rotation pattern

TIRE ROTATION

Tire rotation is recommended every 6,000 miles or so, to obtain maximum tire wear. The pattern you use depends on whether or not you car has a usable spare. Radial tires should not be cross-switched (from one side of the car to the other); they last longer if their direction of rotation is not changed. Snow tires sometimes have directional arrows molded into the side of the carcass; the arrow shows the direction of rotation. They will wear very rapidly if the rotation is reversed. Studded tires will lose their studs if their rotational direction is reversed.

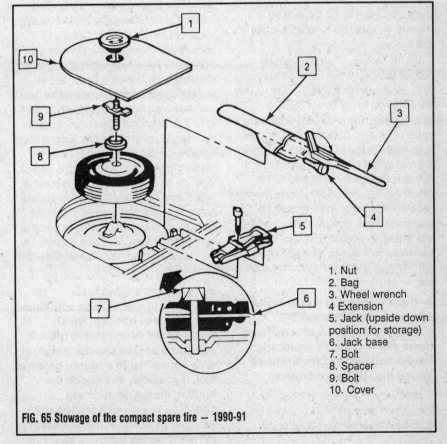

1. Nut
2. Bag
3. Wheel wrench
4 Extension
5. Jack (upside down position for storage)
6. Jack base
7. Bolt
8. Spacer
9. Bolt
10. Cover

FIG. 65 Stowage of the compact spare tire — 1990-91

➡ **Mark the wheel position or direction or rotation on radial tires or studded snow tires before removing them.**

STORAGE

Store the tires at the proper inflation pressure if they are mounted on wheels. Keep them in a cool dry place, laid on their sides. If the tires are stored in the garage or basement, do not let them stand on a concrete floor; set them on strips of wood.

FLUIDS AND LUBRICANTS

Fuel and Engine Oil Recommendations

Oil

◆ SEE FIG. 68

The SAE (Society of Automotive Engineers) grade number indicates the viscosity of the engine oil, and thus its ability to lubricate at a given temperature. The lower the SAE grade number, the lighter the oil; the lower the viscosity, the easier it is to crank the engine in cold weather.

The API (American Petroleum Institute) designation indicates the classification of engine oil for use under given operating conditions. Only oils designated for use Service SG/CC or SG/CD should be used. Oils of the SG type perform a variety of functions inside the engine in addition to the basic function as a lubricant. Through a balanced system of metallic detergents and polymeric dispersants, the oil prevents the formation of high and low temperature deposits, and also keeps sludge and dirt particles in suspension. Acids, particularly sulfuric acid, as well as other by products of combustion, are neutralized. Both the SAE grade number and the API designation can be found on the top of the oil can.

➡ **Non-detergent or straight mineral oils must never be used. Oil viscosities should be chosen from those oils recommended for the lowest anticipated temperatures during the oil change interval.**

Multi-viscosity oils offer the important advantage of being adaptable to temperature extremes. They allow easy starting at low

temperatures, yet give good protection at high speeds and engine temperatures. This is a decided advantage in changeable climates or in long distance touring. GM recommends the use of SAE 5W–30, Energy-Conserving oil.

Fuel

All Corsica's and Beretta's must use unleaded fuel. The use of leaded fuel will plug the catalyst rendering it inoperative, and will increase the exhaust back pressure to the point where engine output will be severely reduced. Also it may damage the Oxygen sensor, and may effect emission control, driveability, and fuel economy.

Use of a fuel too low in octane (a measurement of anti-knock quality) will result in spark knock. Since many factors affect operating efficiency, such as altitude, terrain, and air temperature and humidity, knocking may result even though the recommended fuel is being used. If persistent knocking occurs, it may be necessary to switch to a slightly higher grade of unleaded gasoline. Continuous or heavy knocking may result in serious engine damage, for which the manufacturer is not responsible. Federal regulations require that the fuel octane ratings be posted on the pumps. The octane rating shown is an average of the Research(R) octane and the Motor(M) octane numbers. The Corsica/Beretta should use unleaded fuel with an octane rating of at least 87.

➡ **Your car's engine fuel requirement can change with time, due to carbon buildup, which changes the compression ratio. If your car's engine knocks, pings, or runs on, switch to a higher grade of fuel, if possible, and check the ignition timing. Sometimes changing brands of gasoline will cure the problem. If it is necessary to retard timing from**

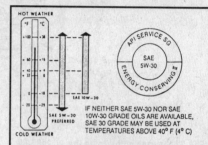

FIG. 68 Engine oil recommendation

specifications, don't change it more than a few degrees. Retarded timing will reduce power output and fuel mileage, and will increase engine temperature.

Engine

OIL LEVEL CHECK

The engine oil level should be checked at every fuel stop, or once a week, whichever occurs more regularly. The best time to check is when the engine is warm, although checking immediately after the engine has been shut off will result in an inaccurate reading, since it takes a few minutes for all of the oil to drain back down into the crankcase. If the engine is cold, the engine should not be run before the level is checked. The oil level is checked by means of a dipstick, located at the front of the engine compartment:

1. If the engine is warm, it should be allowed to sit for a few minutes after being shut off to

allow the oil to drain down into the oil pan. The car should be parked on a level surface.

2. Pull out the dipstick located in front of the engine, wipe it clean with a rag, and reinsert it firmly. Be sure it is pushed all the way home, or the reading you're about to take will be incorrect.

3. Pull the dipstick again and hold it horizontally to prevent the oil from running. The dipstick is marked with Add and Full lines. The oil level should be above the Add line.

4. Reinstall the dipstick.

Add oil as needed. One quart of oil will raise the level from Add to Full. Only oils labeled SG should be used; select a viscosity that will be compatible with the temperatures expected until the next drain interval. See the Oil and Fuel Recommendations section later in this section if you are not sure what type of oil to use. Check the oil level again after any additions. Be careful not to overfill, which will lead to leakage and seal damage.

OIL AND FILTER CHANGE

♦ SEE FIGS. 69-71

❄ CAUTION

The EPA warns that prolonged contact with used engine oil may cause a number of skin disorders, including cancer! You should make every effort to minimize your exposure to used engine oil. Protective gloves should be worn when changing the oil. Wash your hands and any other exposed skin areas as soon as possible after exposure to used engine oil. Soap and water, or waterless hand cleaner should be used.

FIG. 69 The oil drain plug is located at the lowest point of the engine oil pan

FIG. 69A Engine oil dipstick location–1992 2.2L engine

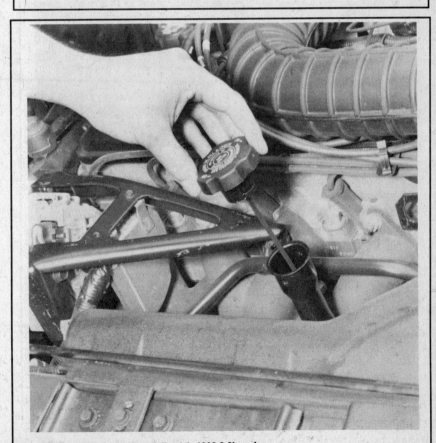

FIG. 69B Removing the engine oil dipstick–1992 2.2L engine

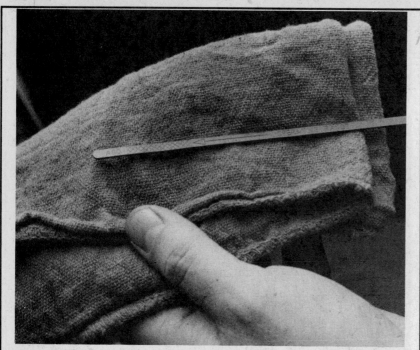

FIG. 69C Make sure the oil level is in the hatchmark area. Do not overfill—1992 2.2L engine shown

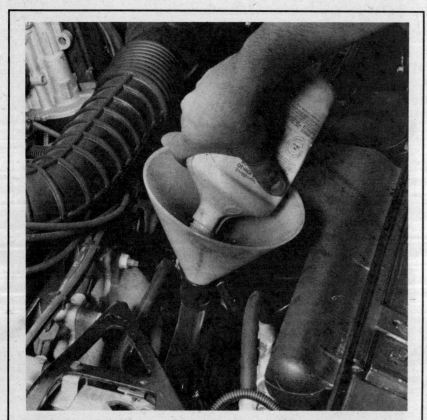

FIG. 69D Add engine oil through the dipstick tube, as necessary—1992 2.2L engine shown

✱✱✱ WARNING

If you purchased your Corsica or Beretta new, the engine oil and filter should be changed at the first 7,500 miles or 12 months (whichever comes first), and every 7,500 miles or 12 months thereafter. You should make it a practice to change the oil filter at every oil change; otherwise, a quart of dirty oil remains in the engine every other time the oil is changed. The change interval should be halved when the car is driven under severe conditions, such as in extremely dusty weather, or when the car is used for trailer towing, prolonged high speed driving, or repeated short trips in freezing weather.

1. Drive the car until the engine is at normal operating temperature. A run to the parts store for oil and a filter should accomplish this. If the engine is not hot when the oil is changed, most of the acids and contaminants will remain inside the engine.

2. Shut off the engine, and slide a pan of at least 6 quarts capacity under the oil pan. Throwaway aluminum roasting pans can be used for this.

3. Remove the drain plug from the engine oil pan, after wiping the plug area clean. The drain plug is the bolt inserted at an angle into the lowest point of the oil pan.

4. The oil from the engine will be HOT. It will probably not be possible to hold onto the drain plug. You may have to let it fall into the pan and fish it out later. Allow all the oil to drain completely. This will take a few minutes.

5. Wipe off the drain plug, removing any traces of metal particles. Pay particular attention to the threads. Replace it, and tighten it snugly.

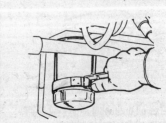

FIG. 70 Use an oil filter strap wrench to remove the oil filter; install the new oil filter by hand

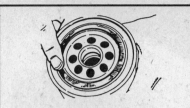

FIG. 71 Apply a thin film of oil to the new gasket to prevent it from tearing upon installation

6. The oil filter is at the back of the engine. It is impossible to reach from above, and almost as inaccessible from below. It may be easiest to remove the right front wheel and reach through the fender opening to get at the 4 cylinder oil filter. Use an oil filter strap wrench to loosen the oil filter; these are available at auto parts stores. It is recommended that you purchase one with as thin a strap as possible, to get into tight areas. Place the drain pan on the ground, under the filter. Unscrew and discard the old filter. It will be VERY HOT, so be careful.

7. If the oil filter is on so tightly that it collapses under pressure from the wrench, drive a long punch or a nail through it, across the diameter and as close to the base as possible, and use this as a lever to unscrew it. Make sure you are turning it counterclockwise.

8. Clean off the oil filter mounting surface with a rag. Apply a thin film of clean engine oil to the filter gasket.

9. Screw the filter on by hand until the gasket makes contact. Then tighten it by hand an additional 1/2–3/4 turn. Do not overtighten.

10. Remove the filler cap, after wiping the area clean.

11. Add the correct number of quarts of oil specified in the Capacities chart. If you don't have an oil can spout, you will need a funnel. Be certain you do not overfill the engine, which can cause serious damage. Replace the cap.

12. Check the oil level on the dipstick. It is normal for the level to be a bit above the full mark. Start the engine and allow it to idle for a few minutes.

❉ CAUTION

Do not run the engine above idle speed until it has built up oil pressure, indicated when the oil light goes out.

Check around the filter and drain plug for any leaks.

13. Shut off the engine, allow the oil to drain for a minute, and check the oil level.

After completing this job, you will have several quarts of filthy oil to dispose of. The best thing to do with it is to funnel it into old plastic milk containers or bleach bottles. Then, you can pour it into a recycling barrel at either your dealer or gas station.

Manual Transaxle

FLUID RECOMMENDATION AND LEVEL CHECK

▶ SEE FIGS. 72-74

The fluid level in the manual transaxle should be checked every 12 months or 7,500 miles, whichever comes first.

The fluid level indicator is on the driver's side of the case above the axle shaft. On 1987–88 models, the fluid level indicator is in the filler tube on the 4 cylinder engines and on the V6 engines, the fluid level indicator and washer are separate from the filler tube. The filler tube cap must be removed to add fluid on V6 engines. On 1989–92 models the fluid level indicator and filler plug are one in the same.

1. Park the car on a level surface. The transaxle should be cool to the touch. If it is hot, check the level later, when it has cooled.

2. Remove the fluid level indicator and be sure the fluid level is at the "Full Cold" mark.

➡ **Oil may appear at the bottom of the dipstick even when the fluid is several pints low.**

3. If lubricant is needed, add GM part No. 12345349 Manual Transaxle Fluid, or equivalent, until the level is at the "Full Cold" mark.

4. When the level is correct, seat the level indicator and/or filler plug fully.

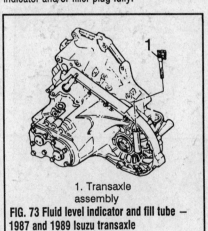

1. Transaxle assembly

FIG. 73 Fluid level indicator and fill tube — 1987 and 1989 Isuzu transaxle

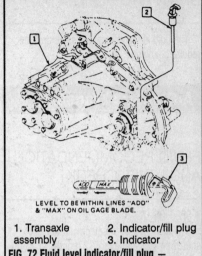

LEVEL TO BE WITHIN LINES "ADD" & "MAX" ON OIL GAGE BLADE.

1. Transaxle assembly
2. Indicator/fill plug
3. Indicator

FIG. 72 Fluid level indicator/fill plug — HM-282, 5TM40 and NVT550 transaxles

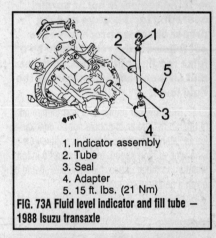

1. Indicator assembly
2. Tube
3. Seal
4. Adapter
5. 15 ft. lbs. (21 Nm)

FIG. 73A Fluid level indicator and fill tube — 1988 Isuzu transaxle

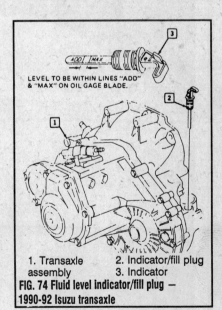

LEVEL TO BE WITHIN LINES "ADD" & "MAX" ON OIL GAGE BLADE.

1. Transaxle assembly
2. Indicator/fill plug
3. Indicator

FIG. 74 Fluid level indicator/fill plug — 1990-92 Isuzu transaxle

DRAIN AND REFILL

The fluid in the manual transaxle does not require changing.

Automatic Transaxle

FLUID RECOMMENDATION AND LEVEL CHECK

◆ SEE FIGS. 75-79

The fluid level in the automatic transaxle should be checked every 12 months or 7,500 miles, whichever comes first. The transaxle has a dipstick for fluid level checks.

➡ **If the vehicle is not at normal operating temperature and the proper checking procedures are not followed, the result could be a false reading of the fluid indicator and an incorrect adjustment of the fluid level.**

1. Drive the car until it is at normal operating temperature. The level should not be checked immediately after the car has been driven for a long time at high speed, or in city traffic in hot weather; in those cases, the transaxle should be given a half hour to cool down.

FIG. 75A Automatic transaxle fluid dipstick location–1992 2.2L engine

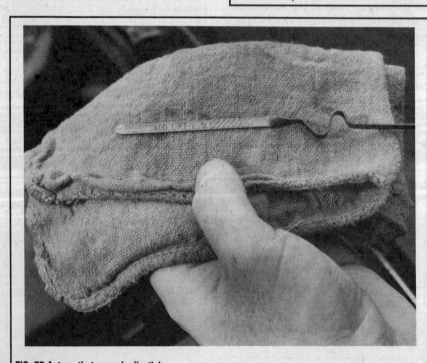

FIG. 75 Automatic transaxle dipstick

2. Stop the car, apply the parking brake, then shift slowly through all gear positions, ending in Park. Let the engine idle for about two minutes with the selector in Park. The car should be on a level surface.

3. With the engine still running, remove the dipstick, wipe it clean, then reinsert it, pushing it fully home.

4. Pull the dipstick again and, holding it horizontally, read the fluid level.

5. Cautiously feel the end of the dipstick to determine the temperature. It should be at room temperature or hotter and the fluid should be in the cross-hatch area. If the level is not in the correct area, more will have to be added.

6. Fluid is added through the dipstick tube. You will probably need the aid of a spout or a long-necked funnel. Be sure that whatever you pour through is perfectly clean and dry. Use an automatic transmission fluid marked DEXRON®II. Add fluid slowly, and in small amounts, checking the level frequently between additions. Do not overfill, which will cause foaming, fluid loss, slippage, and possible

transaxle damage. It takes only one pint to raise the level from Add to Full when the transaxle is hot.

DRAIN AND REFILL

The fluid should be changed according to the schedule in the Maintenance Intervals chart. If the car is normally used in severe service, such as stop and start driving, trailer towing, or the like, the interval should be halved. If the car is driven under especially nasty conditions, such as in heavy city traffic where the temperature normally reaches 90 °F, or in very hilly or mountainous areas, or in police, taxi, or delivery service, the fluid should be changed every 15,000 miles (24,000 km.).

The fluid must be hot before it is drained; a 20 minute drive should accomplish this.

1. There is no drain plug; the fluid pan must be removed. Place a drain pan underneath the transaxle pan and remove the pan attaching bolts at the front and sides of the pan.

2. Loosen the rear pan attaching bolts approximately 4 turns each.

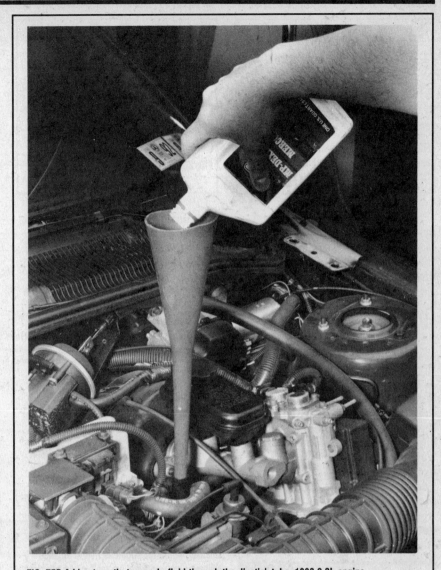

FIG. 75B Add automatic transaxle fluid through the dipstick tube–1992 2.2L engine

FIG. 76 Loosen the pan bolts and allow one corner of the pan to tilt slightly to drain the fluid

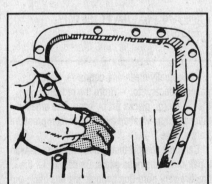

FIG. 77 Clean the pan thoroughly with gasoline and allow it to air dry completely

3. Very carefully pry the pan loose. You can use a small prybar for this if you work CAREFULLY. Do not distort the pan flange, or score the mating surface of the transaxle case. You'll be very sorry later if you do. As the pan is pried loose, all of the fluid is going to come pouring out.

4. Remove the remaining bolts and remove the pan and gasket. Throw away the gasket.

5. Clean the pan with solvent and allow it to air dry. If you use a rag to wipe out the pan, you risk leaving bits of lint behind, which will clog the dinky hydraulic passages in the transaxle.

6. Remove and discard the filter and the O-ring seal.

7. Install a new filter and O-ring, locating the filter against the dipstick stop.

8. Install a new gasket on the pan and install the pan. Tighten the bolts evenly and in rotation to 15 ft. lbs. (20 Nm) for 1987–88 vehicles and

FIG. 78 Install a new gasket on the pan

8 ft. lbs. (11 Nm) for 1989–92 vehicles. Do not overtighten.

9. Add approximately 4 qts. (1987–89) or 7 qts. (1990–92) of DEXRON®II automatic transmission fluid to the transaxle through the dipstick tube. You will need a long necked funnel, or a funnel and tube to do this.

FIG. 79 Fill the transaxle with the required amount of fluid. Do not overfill. Check the fluid level and add fluid as necessary

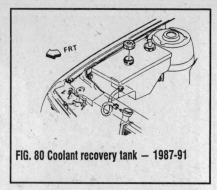

FIG. 80 Coolant recovery tank — 1987-91

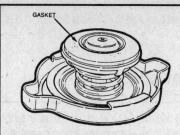

FIG. 81 Check the condition of the radiator cap gasket

10. With the transaxle in Park, put on the parking brake, block the front wheels, start the engine and let it idle. DO NOT RACE THE ENGINE. DO NOT MOVE THE LEVER THROUGH ITS RANGES.

11. With the lever in Park, check the fluid level. If it's OK, take the car out for a short drive, park on a level surface, and check the level again, as outlined earlier in this section. Add more fluid if necessary. Be careful not to overfill, which will cause foaming and fluid loss.

➡ **Normal fluid is usually red (sometimes dark green) in color. If the drained fluid is discolored (brown, black or pink), thick, or smells burnt, serious transmission troubles, probably due to overheating, should be suspected. Your car's transaxle should be inspected by a reliable transmission specialist to determine the problem.**

Cooling System

FLUID RECOMMENDATION AND LEVEL CHECK

♦ SEE FIGS. 80-83

✳ CAUTION

Never remove the radiator cap under any conditions while the engine is running! Failure to follow these instructions could result in damage to the cooling system or engine and/or personal injury. To avoid having scalding hot coolant or steam blow out of the radiator, use extreme care when removing the radiator cap from a hot radiator.

Wait until the engine has cooled, then wrap a thick cloth around the radiator cap and turn it slowly to the first stop. Step back while the pressure is released from the cooling system. When you are sure the pressure has been released, press down on the radiator cap (still have the cloth in position) turn and remove the radiator cap.

Dealing with the cooling system can be a dangerous matter unless the proper precautions are observed. It is best to check the coolant level in the radiator when the engine is cold. The cooling system has, as one of its components, a coolant recovery tank. If the coolant level is at or near the FULL COLD line (engine cold) or the FULL HOT line (engine hot), the level is satisfactory. Always be certain that the filler caps on both the radiator and the recovery tank are closed tightly.

In the event that the coolant level must be checked when the engine is hot on engines without a coolant recovery tank, place a thick rag over the radiator cap and slowly turn the cap counterclockwise until it reaches the first detent. Allow all hot steam to escape. This will allow the pressure in the system to drop gradually, preventing an explosion of hot coolant. When the hissing noise stops, remove the cap the rest of the way.

If the coolant level is found to be low, add a 50/50 mixture of ethylene glycol-based antifreeze and clean water. On older models, coolant must be added through the radiator filler neck. On newer models with the recovery tank, coolant may be added either through the filler neck on the radiator or directly into the recovery tank.

✳ CAUTION

Never add coolant to a hot engine unless it is running. If it is not running you run the risk of cracking the engine block.

If the coolant level is chronically low or rusty, refer to Cooling System Troubleshooting Chart at the end of this section.

At least once every 2 years, the engine cooling system should be inspected, flushed, and refilled with fresh coolant. If the coolant is left in the system too long, it loses its ability to prevent rust and corrosion. If the coolant has too much water, it won't protect against freezing.

The pressure cap should be looked at for signs of age or deterioration. Fan belt and other drive belts should be inspected and adjusted to the proper tension. (See checking belt tension).

Hose clamps should be tightened, and soft or cracked hoses replaced. Damp spots, or accumulations of rust or dye near hoses, water pump or other areas, indicate possible leakage, which must be corrected before filling the system with fresh coolant.

CHECK THE RADIATOR CAP

While you are checking the coolant level, check the radiator cap for a worn or cracked gasket. It the cap doesn't seal properly, fluid will be lost and the engine will overheat.

Worn caps should be replaced with a new one.

CLEAN RADIATOR OF DEBRIS

Periodically clean any debris — leaves, paper, insects, etc. — from the radiator fins. Pick the large pieces off by hand. The smaller pieces can be washed away with water pressure from a hose.

Carefully straighten any bent radiator fins with a pair of needle nose pliers. Be careful — the fins are very soft. Don't wiggle the fins back and forth too much. Straighten them once and try not to move them again.

FIG. 82 Clean the front of the radiator of any bugs, leaves or other debris at every change

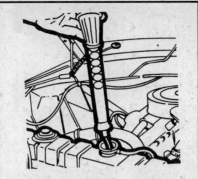

FIG. 83 You can use an inexpensive tester to check anti-freeze protection

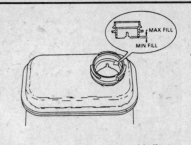

FIG. 84 Master cylinder fluid level indicator

DRAIN AND REFILL

Completely draining and refilling the cooling system every two years at least will remove accumulated rust, scale and other deposits. Coolant in late model cars is a 50/50 mixture of ethylene glycol and water for year round use. Use a good quality antifreeze with water pump lubricants, rust inhibitors and other corrosion inhibitors along with acid neutralizers.

1. Drain the existing antifreeze and coolant. Open the radiator and engine drain petcocks, or disconnect the bottom radiator hose, at the radiator outlet.

❊❊ CAUTION

When draining the coolant, keep in mind that cats and dogs are attracted by the ethylene glycol antifreeze, and are quite likely to drink any that is left in an uncovered container or in puddles on the ground. This will prove fatal in sufficient quantity. Always drain the coolant into a sealable container. Coolant should be reused unless it is contaminated or several years old.

2. Close the petcock or reconnect the lower hose and fill the system with water.
3. Add a can of quality radiator flush.
4. Idle the engine until the upper radiator hose gets hot.
5. Drain the system again.
6. Repeat this process until the drained water is clear and free of scale.
7. Close all petcocks and connect all the hoses.
8. If equipped with a coolant recovery system, flush the reservoir with water and leave empty.

9. Determine the capacity of your coolant system (see capacities specifications). Add a 50/50 mix of quality antifreeze (ethylene glycol) and water to provide the desired protection.
10. Run the engine to operating temperature.
11. Stop the engine and check the coolant level.
12. Check the level of protection with an antifreeze tester, replace the cap and check for leaks.

Brake Master Cylinder

FLUID RECOMMENDATION AND LEVEL CHECK

▶ SEE FIG. 84

Twice a year, the fluid level in the brake master cylinder should be checked.
1. Park the car on a level surface.
2. Clean off the top of the master cylinder and remove the cap.

❊❊ WARNING

Be careful not to drip any brake fluid on painted surfaces; the stuff eats paint. Brake fluid absorbs moisture from the air, which reduces effectiveness, and will corrode brake parts once in the system. Never leave the master cylinder or the brake fluid container uncovered for any longer than necessary.

3. The fluid level should be as shown.
4. If fluid addition is necessary, use only extra heavy duty disc brake fluid meeting DOT 3 specifications. The fluid should be reasonably fresh because brake fluid deteriorates with age.
5. Replace the cap.

If the brake fluid level is constantly low, the system should be checked for leaks. However, it is normal for the fluid level to fall gradually as the disc brake pads wear; expect the fluid level to drop not more than 1/8 in. (3mm) for every 10,000 miles of wear.

Clutch Master Cylinder

FLUID RECOMMENDATION AND LEVEL CHECK

Twice a year, the fluid level in the clutch master cylinder should be checked. When adding fluid, use GM Delco Supreme No. II® brake fluid, or an equivalent that meets DOT 3 specifications.

Steering Gear

The rack and pinion steering gear used on the Corsica/Beretta is a sealed unit; no fluid level checks or additions are ever necessary.

Power Steering Pump

▶ SEE FIG. 85

The power steering hydraulic fluid reservoir is attached to the firewall at the back of the engine compartment. It is a translucent plastic container with fluid level markings on the outside. Check the fluid level at least twice a year. When the fluid is cool (about 70°F), the fluid level should be between the "ADD" and "Cold" marks If the level is low, add power steering fluid until it is correct. Be careful not to overfill as this will cause fluid loss and seal damage. A large loss in the system may indicate a problem. This should be inspected and repaired at once.

➡ **Some people still believe you can use automatic transmission fluid in GM power steering systems. This is not true. Automatic transmission fluid is not compatible with the seals and hoses used in the power steering system. Using Dexron®II in the system can cause seepage past the seals. Use only power fluid GM part No. 1050017, or equivalent.**

Windshield Washer Fluid

Check the fluid level in the windshield washer tank at every oil level check. The fluid can be mixed in a 50% solution with water, if desired, as long as temperatures remain above freezing. Below freezing, the fluid should be used full strength. Never add engine coolant antifreeze to the washer fluid, because it will damage the car's paint.

Chassis Greasing

◆ SEE FIG. 86

There are only 2 areas which require regular chassis greasing: the lower ball joint fittings and the tie rod end to strut fittings. These parts should be greased every 12 months or 7,500 miles (12,000 Km.) with an EP grease meeting G.M. specification 6031M.

If you choose to do this job yourself, you will need to purchase a hand operated grease gun, if you do not own one already, and a long flexible extension hose to reach the various grease fittings. You will also need a cartridge of the appropriate grease.

FIG. 84A Brake master cylinder reservoir fill cap–1992 2.2L engine

FIG. 86 Chassis Lubrication points

FIG. 85 Power steering reservoir filler and level indicator cap

Press the fitting on the grease gun hose onto the grease fitting on the suspension or steering linkage component. Pump a few shots of grease into the fitting, until the rubber boot on the joint begins to expand, indicating that the joint is full. Remove the gun from the fitting. Be careful not to overfill the joints, which will rupture the rubber boots, allowing the entry of dirt. You can keep the grease fittings clean by covering them with a small square of tin foil.

Chassis Lubrication

Every 12 months or 7,500 miles (12,000 km.), the various linkages and hinges on the chassis and body should be lubricated, as follows:

TRANSAXLE SHIFT LINKAGE

Lubricate the manual transaxle shift linkage contact points with the EP grease used for chassis greasing, which should meet G.M. specification 6031M. The automatic transaxle linkage should be lubricated with clean engine oil.

HOOD LATCH AND HINGES

Clean the latch surfaces and apply clean engine oil to the latch pilot bolts and the spring anchor. Use the engine oil to lubricate the hood hinges as well. Use a chassis grease to lubricate all the pivot points in the latch release mechanism.

DOOR HINGES

The gas tank filler door, car door, and rear hatch or trunk lid hinges should be wiped clean and lubricated with clean engine oil. Silicone

FIG. 85A Removing the filler cap/level indicator on the power steering reservoir–1992 2.2L engine

spray also works well on these parts, but must be applied more often. Use engine oil to lubricate the trunk or hatch lock mechanism and the lock bolt and striker. The door lock cylinders can be lubricated easily with a shot of silicone spray or one of the may dry penetrating lubricants commercially available.

PARKING BRAKE LINKAGE

Use chassis grease on the parking brake cable where it contacts the guides, links, levers, and pulleys. The grease should be a water resistant one for durability under the car.

ACCELERATOR LINKAGE

Lubricate the carburetor stud, carburetor lever, and the accelerator pedal lever at the support inside the car with clean engine oil.

TRAILER TOWING

General Recommendations

Your car was primarily designed to carry passengers and cargo. It is important to remember that towing a trailer will place additional loads on your vehicle's engine, drive train, steering, braking and other systems. However, if you find it necessary to tow a trailer, using the proper equipment is a must.

Local laws may require specific equipment such as trailer brakes or fender mounted mirrors. Check your local laws.

➡ A trailering brochure with information on trailer towing, special equipment required and optional equipment available can be obtained from your Chevrolet dealer

Trailer Weight

The weight of the trailer is the most important factor. A good weight-to-horsepower ratio is about 35:1, i.e. 35 lbs. (16kg) of GCW (Gross Combined Weight) for every horsepower your engine develops. Multiply the engine's rated horsepower by 35 and subtract the weight of the car passengers and luggage. The result is the approximate ideal maximum weight you should tow, although a numerically higher axle ratio can help compensate for heavier weight.

Hitch Weight

Figure the hitch weight to select a proper hitch. Hitch weight is usually 9–11% of the trailer gross weight and should be measured with the trailer loaded. Hitches fall into 3 types: those that mount on the frame and rear bumper or the bolt-on or weld-on distribution type used for larger trailers. Axle mounted or clamp-on bumper hitches should never be used.

Check the gross weight rating of your trailer. Tongue weight is usually figured as 10% of gross trailer weight. Therefore, a trailer with a maximum gross weight of 2,000 lb. (907kg) will have a maximum tongue weight of 200 lb. (90.7kg). Class I trailers fall into this category. Class II trailers are those with a gross weight rating of 2,000–3,500 lb. (907–1588kg), while Class III trailers fall into the 3,500–6,000 lb.

(1588–2722kg) category. Class IV trailers are those over 6,000 lb. (2722kg) and are for use with fifth wheel trucks, only.

When you've determined the hitch that you'll need, follow the manufacturer's installation instructions, exactly, especially when it comes to fastener torques. The hitch will subjected to a lot of stress and good hitches come with hardened bolts. Never substitute an inferior bolt for a hardened bolt.

Cooling

ENGINE

One of the most common, if not THE most common, problems associated with trailer towing is engine overheating.

If you have a standard cooling system, without an expansion tank, you'll definitely need to get an aftermarket expansion tank kit, preferably one with at least a 2 quart capacity. These kits are easily installed on the radiator's overflow hose, and come with a pressure cap designed for expansion tanks.

Another helpful accessory is a Flex Fan. These fan are large diameter units are designed to provide more airflow at low speeds, with blades that have deeply cupped surfaces. The blades then flex, or flatten out, at high speed, when less cooling air is needed. These fans are far lighter in weight than stock fans, requiring less horsepower to drive them. Also, they are far quieter than stock fans.

If you do decide to replace your stock fan with a flex fan, note that if your car has a fan clutch, a spacer between the flex fan and water pump hub will be needed.

Aftermarket engine oil coolers are helpful for prolonging engine oil life and reducing overall engine temperatures. Both of these factors increase engine life.

While not absolutely necessary in towing Class I and some Class II trailers, they are recommended for heavier Class II and all Class III towing.

Engine oil cooler systems consist of an adapter, screwed on in place of the oil filter, a remote filter mounting and a multi-tube, finned heat exchanger, which is mounted in front of the radiator or air conditioning condenser.

TRANSMISSION

An automatic transmission is usually recommended for trailer towing. Modern automatics have proven reliable and, of course, easy to operate, in trailer towing.

The increased load of a trailer, however, causes an increase in the temperature of the automatic transmission fluid. Heat is the worst enemy of an automatic transmission. As the temperature of the fluid increases, the life of the fluid decreases.

It is essential, therefore, that you install an automatic transmission cooler.

The cooler, which consists of a multi-tube, finned heat exchanger, is usually installed in front of the radiator or air conditioning compressor, and hooked inline with the transmission cooler tank inlet line. Follow the cooler manufacturer's installation instructions.

Select a cooler of at least adequate capacity, based upon the combined gross weights of the car and trailer.

Cooler manufacturers recommend that you use an aftermarket cooler in addition to, and not instead of, the present cooling tank in your radiator. If you do want to use it in place of the radiator cooling tank, get a cooler at least 2 sizes larger than normally necessary.

➡ A transmission cooler can, sometimes, cause slow or harsh shifting in the transmission during cold weather, until the fluid has a chance to come up to normal operating temperature. Some coolers can be purchased with or retrofitted with a temperature bypass valve which will allow fluid flow through the cooler only when the fluid has reached operating temperature, or above.

Handling A Trailer

Towing a trailer with ease and safety requires a certain amount of experience. It's a good idea to learn the feel of a trailer by practicing turning, stopping and backing in an open area such as an empty parking lot.

PUSHING AND TOWING

The Corsica/Beretta may not be pushed or towed to start, because doing so may cause the catalytic converter to explode. If the battery is weak, the engine may be jump started, using the procedure outlined in the following section.

Do not tow your Corsica/Beretta on all 4 wheels. If your car is equipped with automatic transaxle at, it may be towed on the drive wheels at speeds less than 35 mph (60 km/h) for distances up to 50 miles (80 km).

JUMP STARTING A DEAD BATTERY

The chemical reaction in a battery produces explosive hydrogen gas. This is the safe way to jump start a dead battery, reducing the chances of an accidental spark that could cause an explosion.

Jump Starting Precautions

1. Be sure both batteries are of the same voltage.
2. Be sure both batteries are of the same polarity (have the same grounded terminal).
3. Be sure the vehicles are not touching.
4. Be sure the vent cap holes are not obstructed.
5. Do not smoke or allow sparks around the battery.
6. In cold weather, check for frozen electrolyte in the battery. Do not jump start a frozen battery.
7. Do not allow electrolyte on your skin or clothing.
8. Be sure the electrolyte is not frozen.

CAUTION: Make certin that the ignition key, in the vehicle with the dead battery, is in the OFF position. Connecting cables to vehicles with on-board computers will result in computer destruction if the key is not in the OFF position.

Jump Starting Procedure

1. Determine voltages of the two batteries; they must be the same.
2. Bring the starting vehicle close (they must not touch) so that the batteries can be reached easily.
3. Turn off all accessories and both engines. Put both vehicles in Neutral or Park and set the handbrake.
4. Cover the cell caps with a rag—do not cover terminals.
5. If the terminals on the run-down battery are heavily corroded, clean them.
6. Identify the positive and negative posts on both batteries and connect the cables in the order shown.
7. Start the engine of the starting vehicle and run it at fast idle. Try to start the car with the dead battery. Crank it for no more than 10 seconds at a time and let it cool for 20 seconds in between tries.
8. If it doesn't start in 3 tries, there is something else wrong.
9. Disconnect the cables in the reverse order.
10. Replace the cell covers and dispose of the rags.

MAKE CERTAIN VEHICLES DO NOT TOUCH

1 CONNECT JUMPER CABLE TO DEAD BATTERY (+ TERMINAL)

2 CONNECT OTHER + END OF JUMPER CABLE TO GOOD BATTERY (+ TERMINAL)

BATTERY IN VEHICLE THAT IS DISCHARGED/DEAD

BATTERY IN VEHICLE WITH CHARGED/GOOD BATTERY

ENGINE

JUMPER CABLE

JUMPER CABLE

ENGINE

4 MAKE LAST CONNECTION OF SECOND JUMPER CABLE (–) TO ENGINE IN CAR WITH DEAD BATTERY; MAKE CONNECTION AWAY FROM BATTERY.

3 CONNECT SECOND JUMPER CABLE TO GOOD BATTERY (– TERMINAL)

FOR NEGATIVE GROUND VEHICLES

Side terminal batteries occasionally pose a problem when connecting jumper cables. There frequently isn't enough room to clamp the cables without touching sheet metal. Side terminal adaptors are available to alleviate this problem and should be removed after use

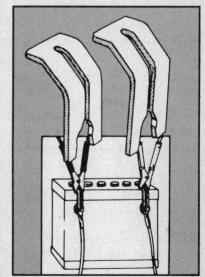

JACKING AND HOISTING

◆ SEE FIGS. 87-89

The Corsica/Beretta is supplied with a jack for changing tires. This jack is satisfactory for its intended purpose; it is not meant to support the car while you go crawling around underneath it. Never crawl under the car when it is supported by only a jack.

The car may also be jacked at the rear axle between the spring seats, or at the front end at the engine cradle crossbar or lower control arm. The car must never be lifted by the rear lower control arms.

The car can be raised on a 4 point hoist which contacts the chassis at points just behind the front wheels and just ahead of the rear wheels, as shown in the accompanying diagram. Be certain that the lift pads do not contact the catalytic converter.

It is imperative that strict safety precautions be observed both while raising the car and in the subsequent support after the car is raised. If a jack is used to raise the car, the transaxle should be shifted to Park (automatic) or First (manual), the parking brake should be set, and the opposite wheel should be blocked. Jacking should only be attempted on a hard level surface.

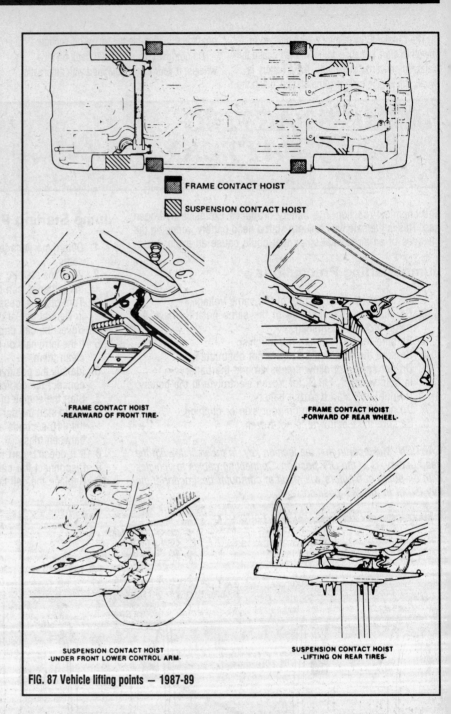

■ FRAME CONTACT HOIST

▨ SUSPENSION CONTACT HOIST

FRAME CONTACT HOIST
-REARWARD OF FRONT TIRE-

FRAME CONTACT HOIST
-FORWARD OF REAR WHEEL-

SUSPENSION CONTACT HOIST
-UNDER FRONT LOWER CONTROL ARM-

SUSPENSION CONTACT HOIST
-LIFTING ON REAR TIRES-

FIG. 87 Vehicle lifting points — 1987-89

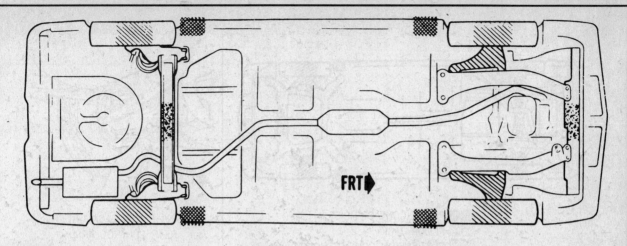

 FRAME CONTACT HOIST   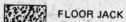 FLOOR JACK   SUSPENSION CONTACT HOIST

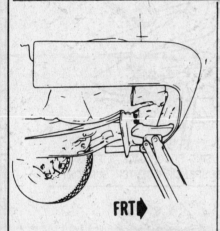

WHEN USING FLOOR JACK, LIFT
ON CENTER OF FRONT SUPPORT

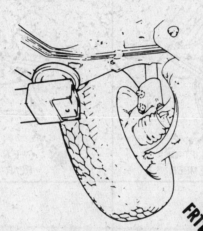

FRAME CONTACT HOIST
(REARWARD OF FRONT TIRE)

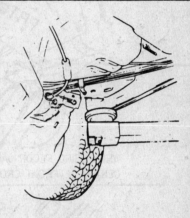

FRAME CONTACT HOIST
(FORWARD OF REAR TIRE)

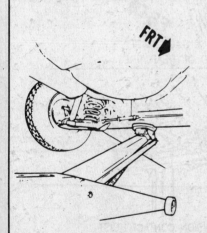

WHEN USING FLOOR JACK, LIFT
ON CENTER OR REAR TORQUE ARM

SUSPENSION CONTACT HOIST
(UNDER FRONT LOWER CONTROL ARM)

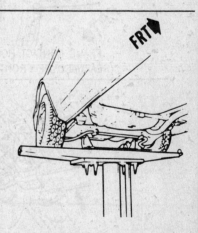

SUSPENSION CONTACT HOIST
(LIFTING ON REAR TIRES)

FIG. 88 Vehicle lifting points — 1990-91

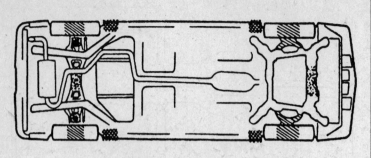

■ FRAME CONTACT HOIST
▨ FLOOR JACK
▧ SUSPENSION CONTACT HOIST

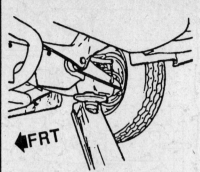

USING FLOOR JACK UNDER
REAR CONTROL ARM

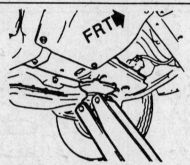

WHEN USING FLOOR JACK, LIFT ON
CENTER OF FRONT CROSSMEMBER

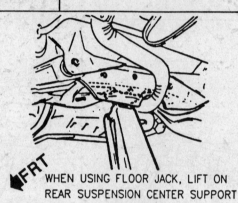

WHEN USING FLOOR JACK, LIFT ON
REAR SUSPENSION CENTER SUPPORT

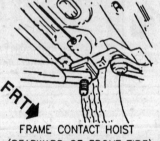

FRAME CONTACT HOIST
(REARWARD OF FRONT TIRE)

FRAME CONTACT HOIST
(FORWARD OF REAR TIRE)

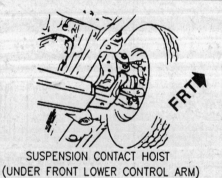

SUSPENSION CONTACT HOIST
(UNDER FRONT LOWER CONTROL ARM)

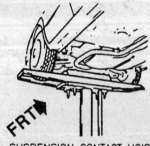

SUSPENSION CONTACT HOIST
(LIFTING ON REAR TIRES)

FIG. 89 Vehicle lifting points — 1992

FIG. 89A Floor jack front lifting point–1992 Corsica shown

FIG. 89B Floor jack rear lifting point–1992 Corsica shown

FIG. 89C Position the jackstands just to the rear of the front wheel opening as shown–1992 2.2L engine

FIG. 89D Position the jackstands just to the front of the rear wheel opening as shown–1992 2.2L engine

MAINTENANCE INTERVALS CHART

Maintenance	Service Interval
Air cleaner element (Replace)	3,000 miles
Cooling system (Check)	Weekly
(Flush and refill)	30,000 miles (24 months)
Chassis lubrication	7,500 (12 months)
Automatic Transaxle	
(Check)	Weekly
(Fluid and filter change)	100,000 miles (Heavy duty service—15,000 miles)
Fuel filter (Replacement)	30,000 miles
PCV valve and filter (Replacement)	30,000 miles
Spark plug (Replacement)	30,000 miles
Spark plug wire (Inspection)	60,000 miles
Engine oil (Check)	Weekly
Engine oil and filter (Replacement)	7,500 miles
Throttle body mounting torque (Check—18 ft. lbs.)	After the 1st 7,500 miles
Tire pressure (Check)	Every month
Tire and wheel (rotation)	1st 7,500 miles and every 15,000 miles thereafter

CAPACITIES

Year	Model	Engine ID/VIN	Engine Displacement filter (cc)	Engine Crankcase with Filter	Transmission (pts.) 5-Spd	Transmission (pts.) Auto.	Fuel Tank (gal.)	Cooling System (qt.) w/AC	Cooling System (qt.) wo/AC
1987	All	1	2.0 (1990.7)	4.0①	5.4	8.0②	14.0	9.8	9.6
	All	W	2.8 (2836.8)	4.0①	4.5	8.0②	14.0	11.1	11.0
1988	All	1	2.0 (1990.7)	4.0①	5.4	8.0②	14.0	9.8	9.6
	All	W	2.8 (2836.8)	4.0①	4.5	8.0②	14.0	11.1	11.0
1989	All	1	2.0 (1990.7)	4.0①	4.0	8.0②	13.6	14.1	13.2
	All	W	2.8 (2836.8)	4.0①	4.0	8.0②	13.6	16.7	16.6
1990	All	G	2.2 (2189.8)	4.0①	4.0	14.0③	13.6	14.1	13.2
	All	A	2.3 (2260.0)	4.0①	4.0	14.0③	15.6	9.5	9.6
	All	T	3.1 (3128.0)	4.0①	4.0	14.0③	15.6	12.4	12.4
1991	All	G	2.2 (2189.8)	4.0①	4.0	14.0③	13.6	14.1	13.2
	Beretta	A	2.3 (2260.0)	4.0①	4.0	14.0③	15.6	9.5	9.6
	All	T	3.1 (3128.0)	4.0①	4.0	14.0③	15.6	12.4	12.4
1992	All	4	2.2 (2189.8)	4.0①	4.0	14.0③	15.6	9.2	9.2
	Beretta	A	2.3 (2260.0)	4.0①	4.0	14.0③	15.6	10.3	10.3
	All	T	3.1 (3128.0)	4.0①	4.0	14.0③	15.6	13.1	13.1

① When changing filter, add oil as necessary to bring to correct level.
② This figure is for drain and refill. Complete overhaul capacity is 12.0 pts.
③ This figure is for drain and refill. Complete overhaul capacity is 18.0 pts.

TORQUE SPECIFICATIONS

Component	English	Metric
Automatic Transaxle		
Oil pan retaining nuts		
1987-88:	15 ft. lbs	20 Nm
1989-92:	8 ft. lbs.	11 Nm
Fuel Filter		
Fitting Conncection nuts		
1987-89:	22 ft. lbs.	30 Nm
Power Steering Pump Bracket (belt installation)		
2.3L engine		
Front:	19 ft. lbs.	26 Nm
Rear:	72 ft. lbs.	98 Nm
Wheel lug nuts:	100 ft. lbs.	138 Nm

Troubleshooting Basic Air Conditioning Problems

Problem	Cause	Solution
There's little or no air coming from the vents (and you're sure it's on)	• The A/C fuse is blown • Broken or loose wires or connections • The on/off switch is defective	• Check and/or replace fuse • Check and/or repair connections • Replace switch
The air coming from the vents is not cool enough	• Windows and air vent wings open • The compressor belt is slipping • Heater is on • Condenser is clogged with debris • Refrigerant has escaped through a leak in the system • Receiver/drier is plugged	• Close windows and vent wings • Tighten or replace compressor belt • Shut heater off • Clean the condenser • Check system • Service system
The air has an odor	• Vacuum system is disrupted • Odor producing substances on the evaporator case • Condensation has collected in the bottom of the evaporator housing	• Have the system checked/repaired • Clean the evaporator case • Clean the evaporator housing drains
System is noisy or vibrating	• Compressor belt or mountings loose • Air in the system	• Tighten or replace belt; tighten mounting bolts • Have the system serviced

Sight glass condition
  Constant bubbles, foam or oil streaks
  Clear sight glass, but no cold air
  Clear sight glass, but air is cold
  Clouded with milky fluid
	• Undercharged system
	• No refrigerant at all
	• System is OK
	• Receiver drier is leaking dessicant
		• Charge the system
		• Check and charge the system
		• Have system checked

Large difference in temperature of lines	• System undercharged	• Charge and leak test the system
Condensation dripping in the passenger compartment	• Drain hose plugged or improperly positioned • Insulation removed or improperly installed	• Clean the drain hose and check for proper installation • Replace the insulation on the expansion valve and hoses

Troubleshooting Basic Air Conditioning Problems (cont.)

Problem	Cause	Solution
Compressor noise	• Broken valves	• Replace the valve plate
	• Overcharged	• Discharge, evacuate and install the correct charge
	• Incorrect oil level	• Isolate the compressor and check the oil level. Correct as necessary.
	• Piston slap	• Replace the compressor
	• Broken rings	• Replace the compressor
	• Drive belt pulley bolts are loose	• Tighten with the correct torque specification
Excessive vibration	• Incorrect belt tension	• Adjust the belt tension
	• Clutch loose	• Tighten the clutch
	• Overcharged	• Discharge, evacuate and install the correct charge
	• Pulley is misaligned	• Align the pulley
Frozen evaporator coil	• Faulty thermostat	• Replace the thermostat
	• Thermostat capillary tube improperly installed	• Install the capillary tube correctly
	• Thermostat not adjusted properly	• Adjust the thermostat
Low side low—high side low	• System refrigerant is low	• Evacuate, leak test and charge the system
	• Expansion valve is restricted	• Replace the expansion valve
Low side high—high side low	• Internal leak in the compressor—worn	• Remove the compressor cylinder head and inspect the compressor. Replace the valve plate assembly if necessary. If the compressor pistons, rings or
Low side high—high side low (cont.)		cylinders are excessively worn or scored replace the compressor
	• Cylinder head gasket is leaking	• Install a replacement cylinder head gasket
	• Expansion valve is defective	• Replace the expansion valve
	• Drive belt slipping	• Adjust the belt tension
Low side high—high side high	• Condenser fins obstructed	• Clean the condenser fins
	• Air in the system	• Evacuate, leak test and charge the system
	• Expansion valve is defective	• Replace the expansion valve
	• Loose or worn fan belts	• Adjust or replace the belts as necessary
Low side low—high side high	• Expansion valve is defective	• Replace the expansion valve
	• Restriction in the refrigerant hose	• Check the hose for kinks—replace if necessary
Low side low—high side high	• Restriction in the receiver/drier	• Replace the receiver/drier
	• Restriction in the condenser	• Replace the condenser
Low side and high normal (inadequate cooling)	• Air in the system	• Evacuate, leak test and charge the system
	• Moisture in the system	• Evacuate, leak test and charge the system

Troubleshooting Basic Wheel Problems

Problem	Cause	Solution
The car's front end vibrates at high speed	• The wheels are out of balance • Wheels are out of alignment	• Have wheels balanced • Have wheel alignment checked/adjusted
Car pulls to either side	• Wheels are out of alignment • Unequal tire pressure • Different size tires or wheels	• Have wheel alignment checked/adjusted • Check/adjust tire pressure • Change tires or wheels to same size
The car's wheel(s) wobbles	• Loose wheel lug nuts • Wheels out of balance • Damaged wheel • Wheels are out of alignment • Worn or damaged ball joint • Excessive play in the steering linkage (usually due to worn parts) • Defective shock absorber	• Tighten wheel lug nuts • Have tires balanced • Raise car and spin the wheel. If the wheel is bent, it should be replaced • Have wheel alignment checked/adjusted • Check ball joints • Check steering linkage • Check shock absorbers
Tires wear unevenly or prematurely	• Incorrect wheel size • Wheels are out of balance • Wheels are out of alignment	• Check if wheel and tire size are compatible • Have wheels balanced • Have wheel alignment checked/adjusted

Troubleshooting Basic Tire Problems

Problem	Cause	Solution
The car's front end vibrates at high speeds and the steering wheel shakes	• Wheels out of balance • Front end needs aligning	• Have wheels balanced • Have front end alignment checked
The car pulls to one side while cruising	• Unequal tire pressure (car will usually pull to the low side) • Mismatched tires • Front end needs aligning	• Check/adjust tire pressure • Be sure tires are of the same type and size • Have front end alignment checked
Abnormal, excessive or uneven tire wear See "How to Read Tire Wear"	• Infrequent tire rotation • Improper tire pressure • Sudden stops/starts or high speed on curves	• Rotate tires more frequently to equalize wear • Check/adjust pressure • Correct driving habits
Tire squeals	• Improper tire pressure • Front end needs aligning	• Check/adjust tire pressure • Have front end alignment checked

Tire Size Comparison Chart

"Letter" sizes			Inch Sizes	Metric-inch Sizes		
"60 Series"	"70 Series"	"78 Series"	1965–77	"60 Series"	"70 Series"	"80 Series"
		Y78-12	5.50-12, 5.60-12 6.00-12	165/60-12	165/70-12	155-12
		W78-13	5.20-13	165/60-13	145/70-13	135-13
		Y78-13	5.60-13	175/60-13	155/70-13	145-13
			6.15-13	185/60-13	165/70-13	155-13, P155/80-13
A60-13	A70-13	A78-13	6.40-13	195/60-13	175/70-13	165-13
B60-13	B70-13	B78-13	6.70-13	205/60-13	185/70-13	175-13
			6.90-13			
C60-13	C70-13	C78-13	7.00-13	215/60-13	195/70-13	185-13
D60-13	D70-13	D78-13	7.25-13			
E60-13	E70-13	E78-13	7.75-13			195-13
			5.20-14	165/60-14	145/70-14	135-14
			5.60-14	175/60-14	155/70-14	145-14
			5.90-14			
A60-14	A70-14	A78-14	6.15-14	185/60-14	165/70-14	155-14
	B70-14	B78-14	6.45-14	195/60-14	175/70-14	165-14
	C70-14	C78-14	6.95-14	205/60-14	185/70-14	175-14
D60-14	D70-14	D78-14				
E60-14	E70-14	E78-14	7.35-14	215/60-14	195/70-14	185-14
F60-14	F70-14	F78-14, F83-14	7.75-14	225/60-14	200/70-14	195-14
G60-14	G70-14	G77-14, G78-14	8.25-14	235/60-14	205/70-14	205-14
H60-14	H70-14	H78-14	8.55-14	245/60-14	215/70-14	215-14
J60-14	J70-14	J78-14	8.85-14	255/60-14	225/70-14	225-14
L60-14	L70-14		9.15-14	265/60-14	235/70-14	
	A70-15	A78-15	5.60-15	185/60-15	165/70-15	155-15
B60-15	B70-15	B78-15	6.35-15	195/60-15	175/70-15	165-15
C60-15	C70-15	C78-15	6.85-15	205/60-15	185/70-15	175-15
	D70-15	D78-15				
E60-15	E70-15	E78-15	7.35-15	215/60-15	195/70-15	185-15
F60-15	F70-15	F78-15	7.75-15	225/60-15	205/70-15	195-15
G60-15	G70-15	G78-15	8.15-15/8.25-15	235/60-15	215/70-15	205-15
H60-15	H70-15	H78-15	8.45-15/8.55-15	245/60-15	225/70-15	215-15
J60-15	J70-15	J78-15	8.85-15/8.90-15	255/60-15	235/70-15	225-15
	K70-15		9.00-15	265/60-15	245/70-15	230-15
L60-15	L70-15	L78-15, L84-15	9.15-15			235-15
	M70-15	M78-15				255-15
		N78-15				

NOTE: Every size tire is not listed and many size comaprisons are approximate, based on load ratings. Wider tires than those supplied new with the vehicle should always be checked for clearance

2

ENGINE PERFORMANCE AND TUNE-UP

GASOLINE ENGINE TUNE-UP SPECIFICATIONS

Year	Engine ID/VIN	Engine Displacement Liter (cc)	Spark Plugs Gap (in.)	Ignition Timing (deg.) MT	AT	Fuel Pump (psi)	Idle Speed (rpm) MT	AT	Valve Clearance In.	Ex.
1987	1	2.0 (1990.7)	0.035	①	①	9–13	①	①	Hyd.	Hyd.
	W	2.8 (2836.8)	0.045	①	①	40.5–47	①	①	Hyd.	Hyd.
1988	1	2.0 (1990.7)	0.035	①	①	9–13	①	①	Hyd.	Hyd.
	W	2.8 (2836.8)	0.045	①	①	40.5–47	①	①	Hyd.	Hyd.
1989	1	2.0 (1990.7)	0.035	①	①	9–13	①	①	Hyd.	Hyd.
	W	2.8 (2836.8)	0.045	①	①	40.5–47	①	①	Hyd.	Hyd.
1990	G	2.2 (2189.8)	0.035	①	①	9–13	①	①	Hyd.	Hyd.
	A	2.3 (2260.0)	0.035	①	①	40–47	①	①	Hyd.	Hyd.
	T	3.1 (3128.0)	0.045	①	①	40.5–47	①	①	Hyd.	Hyd.
1991	G	2.2 (2189.8)	0.035	①	①	9–13	①	①	Hyd.	Hyd.
	A	2.3 (2260.0)	0.035	①	①	40.5–47	①	①	Hyd.	Hyd.
	T	3.1 (3128.0)	0.045	①	①	40.5–47	①	①	Hyd.	Hyd.
1992	4	2.2 (2189.8)	0.035	①	①	41–47	①	①	Hyd.	Hyd.
	A	2.3 (2260.0)	0.045	①	①	41–47	①	①	Hyd.	Hyd.
	T	3.1 (3128.0)	0.045	①	①	41–47	①	①	Hyd.	Hyd.

NOTE: The lowest cylinder pressure should be within 75% of the highest cylinder pressure reading. For example, if the highest cylinder is 134 psi, the lowest should be 101. Engine should be at normal operating temperature with throttle valve in the wide open position.
The underhood specifications sticker often reflects tune-up specification changes in production. Sticker figures must be used if they disagree with those in this chart.
① The ignition timing and idle speed are controlled by the Electronic Control Module (ECM). No Adjustments are necessary. See underhood sticker.

TUNE-UP PROCEDURES

In order to extract the full measure of performance and economy from your car's engine it is essential that it be properly tuned at regular intervals. Although the tune-up intervals have been stretched to limits which would have been thought impossible a few years ago, periodic maintenance is still required. A regularly scheduled tune-up will keep your car's engine running smoothly and will prevent the annoying minor breakdowns and poor performance associated with an untuned engine.

A complete tune-up should be performed at the interval specified in the Maintenance Intervals chart in Section 1. This interval should be halved if the car is operated under severe conditions, such as trailer towing, prolonged idling, continual stop-and-start driving, or if starting and running problems are noticed. It is assumed that the routine maintenance described in Section One has been kept up, as this will have a decided effect on the results of a tune-up. All of the applicable steps should be followed in order, as the result is a cumulative one.

If the specifications on the tune-up label in the engine compartment of your Corsica/Beretta disagree with the Tune-Up Specifications chart in this section, the figures on the sticker must be used. The label often reflects changes made during the production run.

Spark Plugs

▶ SEE FIGS. 1-7

Spark plugs ignite the air and fuel mixture in the cylinder as the piston reaches the top of the compression stroke. The controlled explosion that results forces the piston down, turning the crankshaft and the rest of the drive train.

The average life of a spark plug in a Corsica/Beretta is 30,000 miles (48,300km). Part of the reason for this extraordinarily long life is the exclusive use of unleaded fuel, which reduces the amount of deposits within the combustion chamber and on the spark plug electrodes themselves, compared with the deposits left by

the leaded gasoline used in the past. An additional contribution to long life is made by the HEI (High Energy Ignition) System, which fires the spark plugs with over 35,000 volts of electricity. The high voltage serves to keep the electrodes clear, and because it is a cleaner blast of electricity than that produced by old style breaker-points ignitions, the electrodes suffer less pitting and wear.

Nevertheless, the life of a spark plug is dependent on a number of factors, including the mechanical condition of the engine, driving conditions, and the driver's habits.

When you remove the plugs, check the condition of the electrodes; they are a good indicator of the internal state of the engine. Since the spark plug wires must be checked every 15,000 miles (24,100km), the spark plugs can be removed and examined at the same time. This will allow you to keep an eye on the mechanical status of the engine.

A small deposit of light tan or rust-red material on a spark plug that has been used for any period of time is to be considered normal. Any other color, or abnormal amounts of wear or deposits, indicates that there is something amiss in the engine.

The gap between the center electrode and the side or ground electrode can be expected to increase not more than 0.001 in. (0.025mm) every 1,000 miles (1609km) under normal conditions.

When a spark plug is functioning normally or, more accurately, when the plug is installed in an engine that is functioning properly, the plugs can be taken out, cleaned, regapped, and reinstalled in the engine without doing the engine any harm.

When, and if, a plug fouls and begins to misfire, you will have to investigate, correct the cause of the fouling, and either clean or replace the plug.

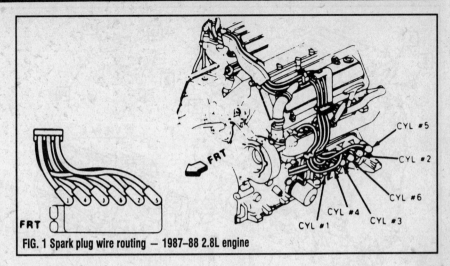

FIG. 1 Spark plug wire routing — 1987–88 2.8L engine

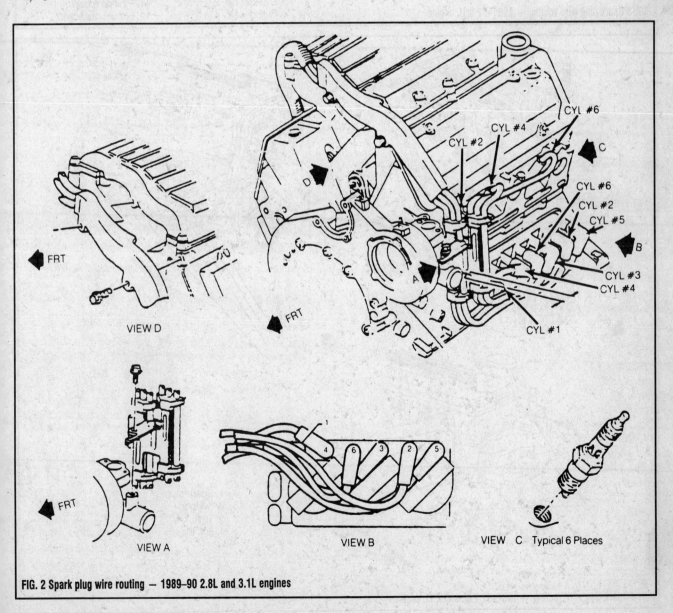

VIEW D

VIEW A

VIEW B

VIEW C Typical 6 Places

FIG. 2 Spark plug wire routing — 1989–90 2.8L and 3.1L engines

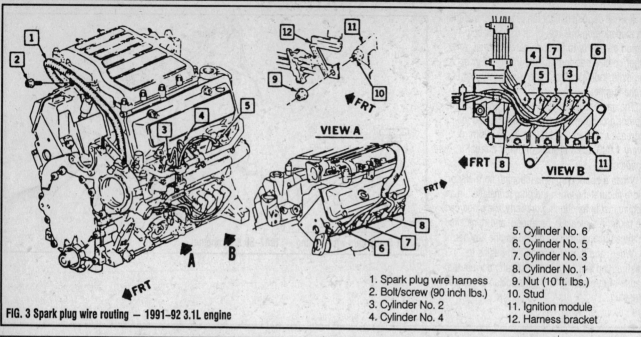

VIEW A

VIEW B

1. Spark plug wire harness
2. Bolt/screw (90 inch lbs.)
3. Cylinder No. 2
4. Cylinder No. 4
5. Cylinder No. 6
6. Cylinder No. 5
7. Cylinder No. 3
8. Cylinder No. 1
9. Nut (10 ft. lbs.)
10. Stud
11. Ignition module
12. Harness bracket

FIG. 3 Spark plug wire routing — 1991–92 3.1L engine

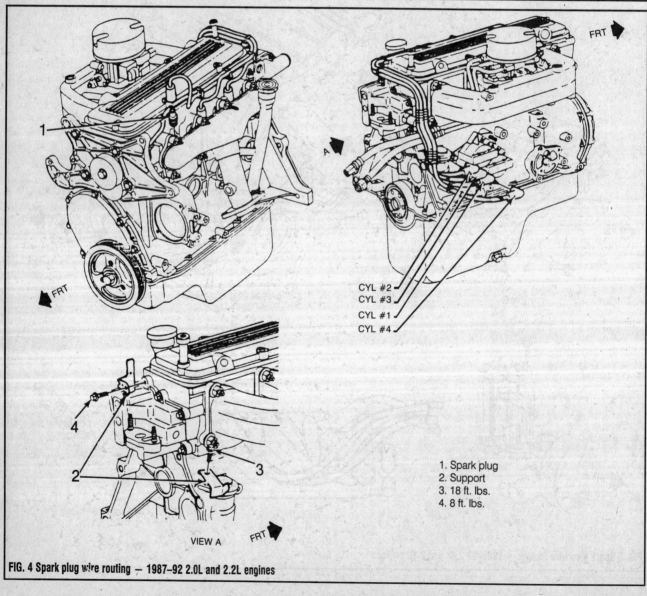

CYL #2
CYL #3
CYL #1
CYL #4

VIEW A

1. Spark plug
2. Support
3. 18 ft. lbs.
4. 8 ft. lbs.

FIG. 4 Spark plug wire routing — 1987–92 2.0L and 2.2L engines

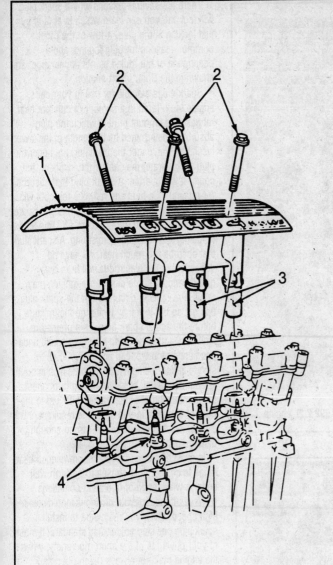

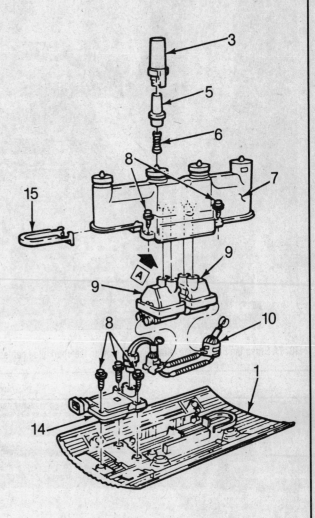

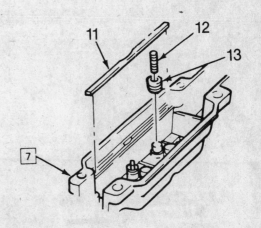

1. Ignition cover
2. 19 ft. lbs.
3. Retainer
4. Spark plug
5. Boot
6. Spring
7. Housing
8. 35 inch lbs.
9. Coil (s)
10. Harness assembly
11. Insulator
12. Contact
13. Seal
14. Module
15. Retainer

FIG. 5 Spark plugs and ignition assembly — 2.3L engine

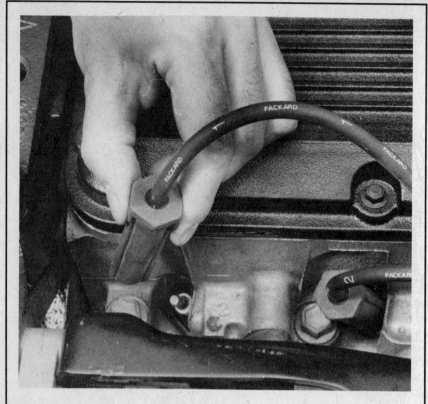

FIG. 7A Grasp the boot not the wires when removing the spark plug cables—1992 2.2L engine

FIG. 7B Spark plug removal—1992 2.2L engine

There are several reasons why a spark plug will foul and you can learn which is at fault by just looking at the plug. A few of the most common reasons for plug fouling, and a description of the fouled plug's appearance, are shown in the Color Insert section.

Spark plugs suitable for use in your car's engine are offered in a number of different heat ranges. The amount of heat which the plug absorbs is determined by the length of the lower insulator. The longer the insulator, the hotter the plug will operate; the shorter the insulator, the cooler it will operate. A spark plug that absorbs (or retains) little heat and remains too cool will accumulate deposits of oil and carbon, because it is not hot enough to burn them off. This leads to fouling and consequent misfiring. A spark plug that absorbs too much heat will have no deposits, but the electrodes will burn away quickly and, in some cases, pre-ignition may result. Pre-ignition occurs when the spark plug tips get so hot that they ignite the fuel/mixture before the actual spark fires. This premature ignition will usually cause a pinging sound under conditions of low speed and heavy load. In severe cases, the heat may become high enough to start the fuel/air mixture burning throughout the combustion chamber rather than just to the front of the plug. In this case, the resultant explosion (detonation) will be strong enough to damage pistons, rings, and valves.

In most cases the factory recommended heat range is correct; it is chosen to perform well under a wide range of operating conditions. However, if most of your driving is long distance, high speed travel, you may want to install a spark plug one step colder than standard. If most of your driving is of the short trip variety, when the engine may not always reach operating temperature, a hotter plug may help burn off the deposits normally accumulated under those conditions.

REMOVAL

1. Number the wires with pieces of adhesive tape so that you won't cross them when you replace them.
2. The spark plug boots have large grips to aid in removal. Grasp the wire by the rubber boot and twist the boot 1/2 turn in either direction to break the tight seal between the boot and the plug. Then twist and pull on the boot to remove the wire from the spark plug. Do not pull on the wire itself or you will damage the carbon cord conductor.
3. Use a 5/8 in. spark plug socket to loosen all of the plugs about two turns. A universal joint installed at the socket end of the extension will ease the process.

If removal of the plugs is difficult, apply a few drops of penetrating oil or silicone spray to the area around the base of the plug, and allow it a few minutes to work.

4. If compressed air is available, apply it to the area around the spark plug holes. Otherwise, use a rag or a brush to clean the area. Be careful not to allow any foreign material to drop into the spark plug holes.

5. Remove the plugs by unscrewing them the rest of the way.

INSPECTION

Check the plugs for deposits and wear. If they are not going to be replaced, clean the plugs thoroughly. Remember that any kind of deposit will decrease the efficiency of the plug. Plugs can be cleaned on a spark plug cleaning machine, which can sometimes be found in service stations, or you can do an acceptable job of cleaning with a stiff brush. If the plugs are cleaned, the electrodes must be filed flat. use an ignition points file, not an emery board or the like, which will leave deposits. The electrodes must be filed perfectly flat with sharp edges; rounded edges reduce the spark plug voltage by as much as 50%.

Check spark plug gap before installation. The ground electrode (the L-shaped one connected to the body of the plug) must be parallel to the center electrode and the specified size wire gauge (see Tune-Up Specifications) should pass through the gap with a slight drag. Always check the gap on new plugs, too; they are not always set correctly at the factory. Do not use a flat feeler gauge when measuring the gap, because the reading will be inaccurate. Wire gapping tools usually have a bending tool attached. Use that to adjust the side electrode until the proper distance is obtained. Absolutely never bend the center electrode. Also, be careful not to bend the side electrode too far or too often; it may weaken and break off within the engine, requiring removal of the cylinder head to retrieve it.

INSTALLATION

1. Lubricate the threads of the spark plugs with a drop of oil or a shot of silicone spray. Install the plugs and tighten them hand tight. Take care not to cross-thread them.

2. Tighten the spark plugs with the socket. Do not apply the same amount of force you would use for a bolt; just snug them in. These spark plugs do nut use gaskets, and over-tightening

FIG. 7C Spark plug removal–1992 2.2L engine

will make future removal difficult. If a torque wrench is available, tighten to the correct specification.

➡ **While over-tightening the spark plug is to be avoided, under-tightening is just as bad. If combustion gases leak past the threads, the spark plug will overheat and rapid electrode wear will result.**

3. Install the wires on their respective plugs. Make sure the wires are firmly connected. You will be able to feel them click into place.

CHECKING AND REPLACING SPARK PLUG WIRES

Every 15,000 miles (24,100km), inspect the spark plug wires for burns, cuts, or breaks in the insulation. Check the boots and the nipples on the distributor cap. Replace any damaged wiring.

Every 45,000 miles (72,400km) or so, the resistance of the wires should be checked with an ohmmeter. Wires with excessive resistance will cause misfiring, and may make the engine difficult to start in damp weather. Generally, the useful life of the cables is 45,000–60,000 miles (72,400–96,500km).

To check resistance, remove the distributor cap, leaving the wires in place. Connect one lead of an ohmmeter to an electrode within the cap; connect the other lead to the corresponding spark plug terminal (remove it from the spark plug for this test). Replace any wire which shows a resistance over 30,000Ω. The following chart gives resistance values as a function of length. Generally speaking, however, resistance should not be considered the outer limit of acceptability.

- 0–15 in. (0–38mm): 3,000–10,000Ω
- 15–25 in. (38–64mm): 4,000–15,000Ω
- 25–35 in. (64–89mm): 6,000–20,000Ω
- Over 35 in. (89mm): 25,000Ω

It should be remembered that resistance is also a function of length; the longer the wire, the greater the resistance. Thus, if the wires on your car are longer than the factory originals, resistance will be higher, quite possible outside these limits.

When installing new wires, replace them one at a time to avoid mixups. Start by replacing the longest one first. Install the boot firmly over the spark plug. Route the wire over the same path as the original. Insert the nipple firmly onto the tower on the distributor cap, then install the cap cover and latches to secure the wires.

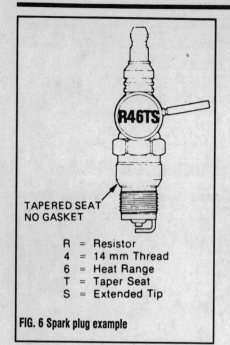

TAPERED SEAT
NO GASKET

R = Resistor
4 = 14 mm Thread
6 = Heat Range
T = Taper Seat
S = Extended Tip

FIG. 6 Spark plug example

Firing Orders

▶ SEE FIGS. 8-10

To avoid confusion, replace the spark plug wires one at a time.

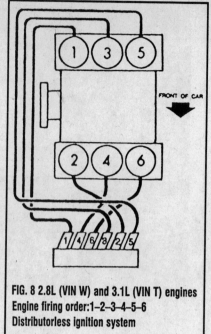

FIG. 8 2.8L (VIN W) and 3.1L (VIN T) engines
Engine firing order:1–2–3–4–5–6
Distributorless ignition system

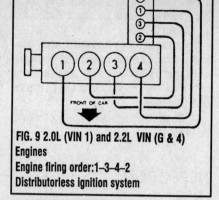

FIG. 9 2.0L (VIN 1) and 2.2L VIN (G & 4) Engines
Engine firing order:1–3–4–2
Distributorless ignition system

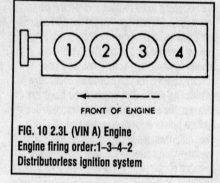

FRONT OF ENGINE

FIG. 10 2.3L (VIN A) Engine
Engine firing order:1–3–4–2
Distributorless ignition system

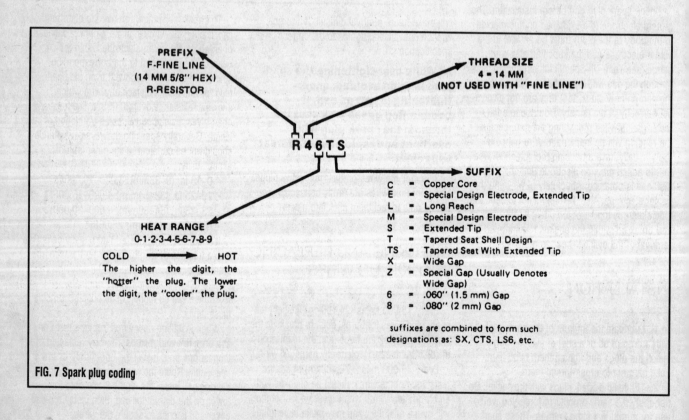

PREFIX
F-FINE LINE
(14 MM 5/8" HEX)
R-RESISTOR

THREAD SIZE
4 = 14 MM
(NOT USED WITH "FINE LINE")

R 4 6 T S

HEAT RANGE
0-1-2-3-4-5-6-7-8-9

COLD ⟶ HOT
The higher the digit, the "hotter" the plug. The lower the digit, the "cooler" the plug.

SUFFIX

C = Copper Core
E = Special Design Electrode, Extended Tip
L = Long Reach
M = Special Design Electrode
S = Extended Tip
T = Tapered Seat Shell Design
TS = Tapered Seat With Extended Tip
X = Wide Gap
Z = Special Gap (Usually Denotes Wide Gap)
6 = .060" (1.5 mm) Gap
8 = .080" (2 mm) Gap

suffixes are combined to form such designations as: SX, CTS, LS6, etc.

FIG. 7 Spark plug coding

GENERAL MOTORS DIRECT IGNITION SYSTEM AND ELECTRONIC SPARK TIMING

General Information

The Direct Ignition System (DIS), used on all vehicles, except those equipped the 2.3L VIN A engine, does not use the conventional distributor and ignition coil. The system consists of ignition module, crankshaft sensor or combination sensor, along with the related connecting wires and Electronic Spark Timing (EST) portion of the Electronic Control Module (ECM).

The DIS system uses a "waste spark" method of spark distribution. Companion cylinders are paired and the spark occurs simultaneously in the cylinder with the piston coming up on the compression stroke and in the companion cylinder with the piston coming up on the exhaust stroke.

1. Example of firing order and companion cylinders: 1–2–3–4–5–6; 1/4, 2/5, 3/6.
2. Example of firing order and companion cylinders: 1–6–5–4–3–2; 1/4, 6/3, 5/2.
3. Example of firing order and companion cylinders: 1–3–4–2; 1/4, 2/3

➡ **Notice the companion cylinders in the V6 engine firing order remain the same, but the cylinder firing order sequence differs.**

The cylinder on the exhaust stroke requires very little of the available voltage to arc, so the remaining high voltage is used by the cylinder in the firing position (TDC compression). This same process is repeated when the companion cylinders reverse roles.

It is possible in an engine no-load condition, for one plug to fire, even though the spark plug lead from the same coil is disconnected from the other spark plug. The disconnected spark plug lead acts as one plate of a capacitor, with the engine being the other plate. These two capacitors plates are charged as a current surge (spark) jumps across the gap of the connected spark plug.

These plates are then discharged as the secondary energy is dissipated in an oscillating current across the gap of the spark plug still connected. Because of the direction of current flow in the primary windings and thus in the secondary windings, one spark plug will fire from the center electrode to the side electrode, while the other will fire from the side electrode to the center electrode.

These systems utilize the EST signal from the ECM, as do the convention distributor type ignition systems equipped with the EST system to control timing.

In the Direct Ignition system and while under 400 rpm, the DIS ignition module controls the spark timing through a module timing mode. Over 400 rpm, the ECM controls the spark timing through the EST mode. In the Direct Ignition system, to properly control the ignition timing, the ECM relies on the the following information from the various sensors.

1. Engine load (manifold pressure or vacuum).
2. Atmospheric (barometric) pressure.
3. Engine temperature.
4. Manifold air temperature.
5. Crankshaft position.
6. Engine speed (rpm).

Direct Ignition System Components

➡ **The Direct Ignition System/EST is used with TBI and Ported fuel injection systems.**

CRANKSHAFT SENSOR

A magnetic crankshaft sensor (Hall Effect switch) is used and is remotely mounted on the opposite side of the engine from the DIS module. The sensor protrudes in to the engine block, within 0.050 in. (1.3mm) of the crankshaft reluctor.

The reluctor is a special wheel cast into the crankshaft with seven slots machined into it, six of them being evenly spaced at 60° apart. A seventh slot is spaced 10° from one of the other slots and serves as a generator of a "sync-pulse". As the reluctor rotates as part of the crankshaft, the slots change the magnetic field of the sensor, creating an induced voltage pulse.

Based on the crankshaft sensor pulses, the DIS module sends reference signals to the ECM, which are used to indicate crankshaft position and engine speed. The DIS module will continue to send these reference pulses to the ECM at a rate of one per each 120° of crankshaft rotation. The ECM actvates the fuel injectors, based on the recognition of every other reference pulse, beginning at a crankshaft position 120° after piston top dead center (TDC). By comparing the time between the pulses, the DIS module can

recognize the pulse representing the seventh slot (sync-pulse) which starts the calculation of ignition coil sequencing. The second crankshaft pulse following the sync-pulse signals the DIS module to fire the No.2–5 ignition coil, the fourth crankshaft pulse signals the module to fire No.3–6 ignition coil and the sixth crankshaft pulse signals the module to fire the 1–4 ignition coil.

IGNITION COILS

There are two separate coils for the four cylinder engines and three separate coils for the V6 engines, mounted to the coil/module assembly. Spark distribution is synchronized by a signal from the crankshaft sensor which the ignition module uses to trigger each coil at the proper time. Each coil provides the spark for two spark plugs.

Two types of ignition coil assemblies are used, Type I and Type II During the diagnosis of the systems, the correct type of ignition coil assembly must be identified and the diagnosis directed to that system.

Type I module/coil assembly has three twin tower ignition coils, combined into a single coil pack unit. This unit is mounted to the DIS module. ALL THREE COILS MUST BE REPLACED AS A UNIT. A separate current source through a fused circuit to the module terminal **P** is used to power the ignition coils.

Type II coil/module assembly has three separate coils that are mounted to the DIS module. EACH COIL CAN BE REPLACED SEPARATELY. A fused low current source to the module terminal **M**, provides power for the sensors, ignition coils and internal module circuitry.

DIS MODULE

The DIS module monitors the crankshaft sensor signal and based on these signals, sends a reference signal to the ECM so that correct spark and fuel injector control can be maintained during all driving conditions. During cranking, the DIS module monitors the sync-pulse to begin the ignition firing sequence. Below 400 rpm, the module controls the spark advance by triggering each of the ignition coils at a predetermined interval, based on engine speed only. Above 400 rpm, the ECM controls the spark timing (EST) and compensates for all driving conditions. The DIS module must receive a sync-pulse and then a crank signal, in that order, to enable the engine to start.

The DIS module is not repairable. When a module is replaced, the remaining DIS components must be transferred to the new module.

DIRECT IGNITION ELECTRONIC SPARK TIMING (EST) CIRCUITS

This system uses the same EST to ECM circuits that the distributor type systems with EST use. The following is a brief description for the EST circuits.

DIS REFERENCE, CIRCUIT 430

The crankshaft sensor generates a signal to the ignition module, which results in a reference pulse being sent to the ECM. The ECM uses this signal to calculate crankshaft position and engine speed for injector pulse width.

➡ **The crankshaft sensor is mounted to the base of the DIS module on the 2.0L and 2.2L four cylinder engines and is mounted directly into the side of the engine block. On the 2.8L and 3.1L engine the sensor is mounted remotely on the opposite side of the engine from the DIS module.**

REFERENCE GROUND CIRCUIT 453

This wire is grounded through the module and insures that the ground circuit has no voltage drop between the ignition module and the ECM, which can affect performance.

BY-PASS, CIRCUIT 424

At approximately 400 rpm, the ECM applies 5 volts to this circuit to switch spark timing control from the DIS module to the ECM. An open or grounded by pass circuit will set a code 42 and result in the engine operating in a back-up ignition timing mode (module timing) at a calculated timing value. This may cause poor performance and reduced fuel economy.

ELECTRONIC SPARK TIMING (EST), CIRCUIT 423

The DIS module sends a reference signal to the ECM when the engine is cranking. While the engine is under 400 rpm, the DIS module controls the ignition timing. When the engine speed exceeds 400 rpm, the ECM applies 5 volts to the By-pass line to switch the timing to the ECM control (EST).

An open or ground in the EST circuit will result in the engine continuing to run, but in a back-up ignition timing mode (module timing mode) at a calculated timing value and the SERVICE ENGINE SOON light will not be on. If the EST fault is still present, the next time the engine is restarted, a code 42 will be set and the engine will operate in the module timing mode. This may cause poor performance and reduced fuel economy.

Diagnosis

DIRECT IGNITION SYSTEM

➡ **The following diagnostic aids are quick checks. Should more in-depth diagnosis of the system be needed, refer to the diagnostic charts.**

The ECM uses information from the MAP and Coolant sensors, in addition to rpm to calculate spark advance as follows:

1. Low MAP output voltage = More spark advance.
2. Cold engine = More spark advance.
3. High MAP output voltage = Less spark advance.
4. Hot engine = Less spark advance.

Therefore, detonation could be caused by low MAP output or high resistance in the coolant sensor circuit.

Poor performance could be caused by high MAP output or low resistance in the coolant sensor circuit.

If the engine cranks but will not operate, or starts, then immediately stalls, Chart A-3 diagnosis, located in Section 4, must be accomplished to determine if the failure is in the DIS system or the fuel system.

CODE 42

If code 42 is set, that code chart must be used for diagnosis. If the symptom is that the engine is missing, and the ignition system is suspected, refer to CHART C4-D ""DIS Misfire"" , located in this Section for diagnosis.

CODE 12

Code 12 is used during the diagnostic circuit check procedure to test the diagnostic and code display ability of the ECM. This code indicates that the ECM is not receiving the engine rpm (reference) signal. This occurs with the ignition key in the ON position and the engine not operating.

SETTING IGNITION TIMING

Because the reluctor wheel is an integral part of the crankshaft and the crankshaft sensor is mounted in a fixed position, timing adjustment is not possible.

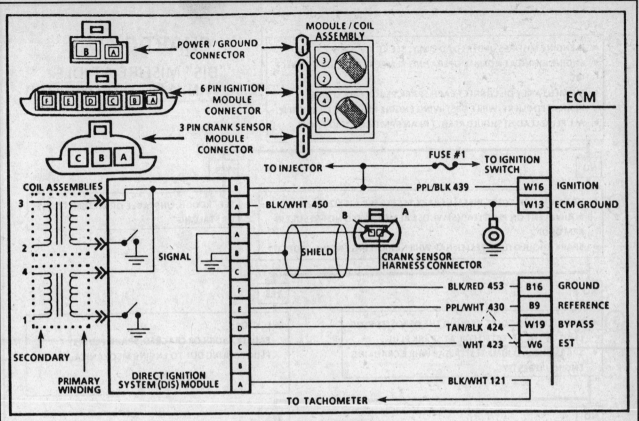

CHART C-4D-1

"DIS" MISFIRE AT IDLE
2.0L (VIN 1) "L" CARLINE (TBI)

Circuit Description:

The "direct ignition system" (DIS) uses a waste spark method of distribution. In this type of system, the ignition module triggers the #1/4 coil pair resulting in both #1 and #4 spark plugs firing at the same time. #1 cylinder is on the compression stroke at the same time #4 is on the exhaust stroke, resulting in a lower energy requirement to fire #4 spark plug. This leaves the remainder of the high voltage to be used to fire #1 spark plug. The crank sensor is remotely mounted beside the module/coil assembly and protrudes through the block to within approximately .050" of the crankshaft reluctor. Since the reluctor is a machined portion of the crankshaft and the crankshaft sensor is mounted in a fixed position on the block, timing adjustments are not possible or necessary.

Test Description: Numbers below refer to circled numbers on the diagnostic chart.

1. If the "Misfire" complaint exists <u>under load only</u>, the diagnostic chart on page 2 must be used. Engine rpm should drop approximately equally on all plug leads.

2. A spark tester, such as a ST-125, must be used because it is essential to verify adequate available secondary voltage at the spark plug (25,000 volts).

3. If the spark jumps the tester gap after grounding the opposite plug wire, it indicates excessive resistance in the plug which was bypassed. A faulty or poor connection at that plug could also result in the miss condition. Also, check for carbon deposits inside the spark plug boot.

4. If carbon tracking is evident, replace coil and be sure plug wires relating to that coil are clean and tight. Excessive wire resistance or faulty connections could have caused the coil to be damaged.

5. If the no spark condition follows the suspected coil, that coil is faulty. Otherwise, the ignition module is the cause of no spark. This test could also be performed by substituting a known good coil for the one causing the no spark condition.

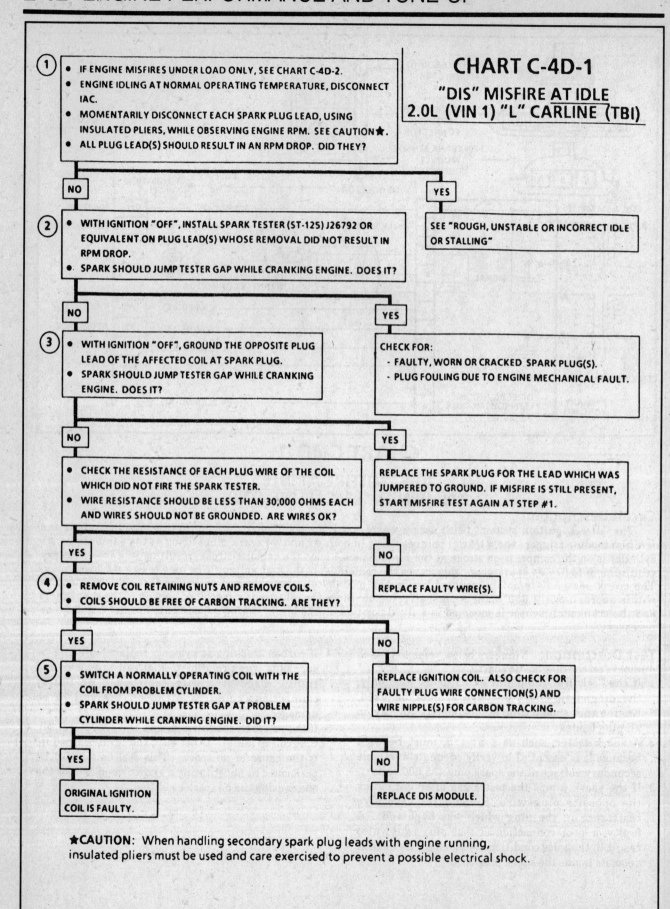

CHART C-4D-1

"DIS" MISFIRE AT IDLE
2.0L (VIN 1) "L" CARLINE (TBI)

(1)
- IF ENGINE MISFIRES UNDER LOAD ONLY, SEE CHART C-4D-2.
- ENGINE IDLING AT NORMAL OPERATING TEMPERATURE, DISCONNECT IAC.
- MOMENTARILY DISCONNECT EACH SPARK PLUG LEAD, USING INSULATED PLIERS, WHILE OBSERVING ENGINE RPM. SEE CAUTION ★.
- ALL PLUG LEAD(S) SHOULD RESULT IN AN RPM DROP. DID THEY?

NO

YES → SEE "ROUGH, UNSTABLE OR INCORRECT IDLE OR STALLING"

(2)
- WITH IGNITION "OFF", INSTALL SPARK TESTER (ST-125) J26792 OR EQUIVALENT ON PLUG LEAD(S) WHOSE REMOVAL DID NOT RESULT IN RPM DROP.
- SPARK SHOULD JUMP TESTER GAP WHILE CRANKING ENGINE. DOES IT?

NO

YES → CHECK FOR:
- FAULTY, WORN OR CRACKED SPARK PLUG(S).
- PLUG FOULING DUE TO ENGINE MECHANICAL FAULT.

(3)
- WITH IGNITION "OFF", GROUND THE OPPOSITE PLUG LEAD OF THE AFFECTED COIL AT SPARK PLUG.
- SPARK SHOULD JUMP TESTER GAP WHILE CRANKING ENGINE. DOES IT?

NO

YES → REPLACE THE SPARK PLUG FOR THE LEAD WHICH WAS JUMPERED TO GROUND. IF MISFIRE IS STILL PRESENT, START MISFIRE TEST AGAIN AT STEP #1.

- CHECK THE RESISTANCE OF EACH PLUG WIRE OF THE COIL WHICH DID NOT FIRE THE SPARK TESTER.
- WIRE RESISTANCE SHOULD BE LESS THAN 30,000 OHMS EACH AND WIRES SHOULD NOT BE GROUNDED. ARE WIRES OK?

YES

NO → REPLACE FAULTY WIRE(S).

(4)
- REMOVE COIL RETAINING NUTS AND REMOVE COILS.
- COILS SHOULD BE FREE OF CARBON TRACKING. ARE THEY?

YES

NO → REPLACE IGNITION COIL. ALSO CHECK FOR FAULTY PLUG WIRE CONNECTION(S) AND WIRE NIPPLE(S) FOR CARBON TRACKING.

(5)
- SWITCH A NORMALLY OPERATING COIL WITH THE COIL FROM PROBLEM CYLINDER.
- SPARK SHOULD JUMP TESTER GAP AT PROBLEM CYLINDER WHILE CRANKING ENGINE. DID IT?

YES

NO → REPLACE DIS MODULE.

YES → ORIGINAL IGNITION COIL IS FAULTY.

★**CAUTION:** When handling secondary spark plug leads with engine running, insulated pliers must be used and care exercised to prevent a possible electrical shock.

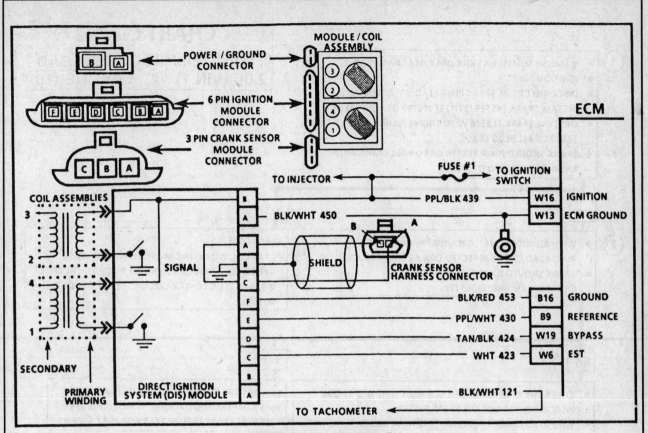

CHART C-4D-2

"DIS" MISFIRE UNDER LOAD
2.0L (VIN 1) "L" CARLINE (TBI)

Circuit Description:

The "direct ignition system" (DIS) uses a waste spark method of distribution. In this type of system, the ignition module triggers the #1/4 coil pair resulting in both #1 and #4 spark plugs firing at the same time. #1 cylinder is on the compression stroke at the same time #4 is on the exhaust stroke, resulting in a lower energy requirement to fire #4 spark plug. This leaves the remainder of the high voltage to be used to fire #1 spark plug. The crank sensor is remotely mounted beside the module/coil assembly and protrudes through the block to within approximately .050" of the crankshaft reluctor. Since the reluctor is a machined portion of the crankshaft, and the crankshift sensor is mounted in a fixed position on the block, timing adjustments are not possible or necessary.

Test Description: Numbers below refer to circled numbers on the diagnostic chart.

1. If the "Misfire" complaint exists <u>at idle only</u>, the diagnostic chart on page 1 must be used. A spark tester such as a ST-125 must be used because it is essential to verify adequate available secondary voltage at the spark plug. (25,000 volts). Spark should jump the test gap on all 4 leads. This simulates a "load" condition.

2. If the spark jumps the tester gap after grounding the opposite plug wire, it indicates excessive resistance in the plug which was bypassed.

A faulty or poor connection at that plug could also result in the miss condition. Also, check for carbon deposits inside the spark plug boot.

3. If carbon tracing is evident replace coil and be sure plug wires relating to that coil are clean and tight. Excessive wire resistance or faulty connections could have caused the coil to be damaged.

4. If the no spark condition follows the suspected coil, that coil is faulty. Otherwise, the ignition module is the cause of no spark. This test could also be performed by substituting a known good coil for the one causing the no spark condition.

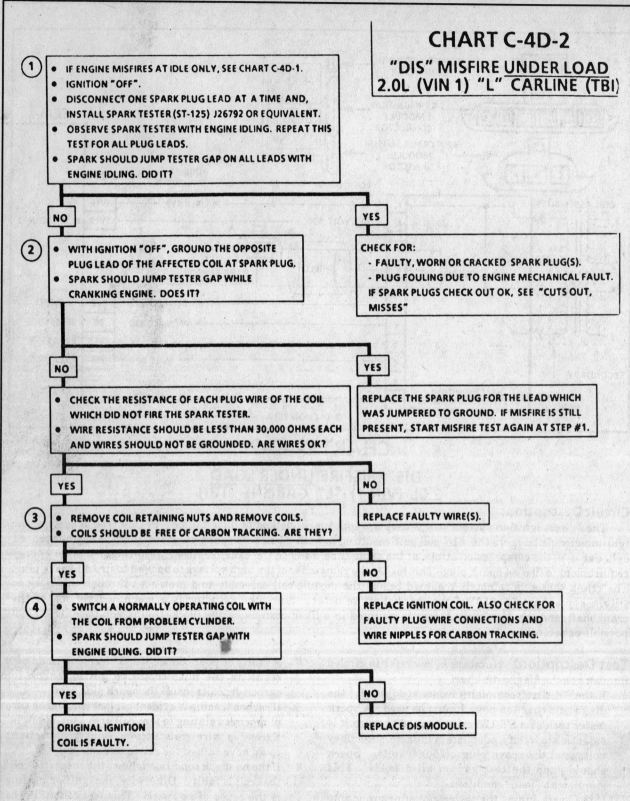

CHART C-4D-2
"DIS" MISFIRE UNDER LOAD
2.0L (VIN 1) "L" CARLINE (TBI)

1
- IF ENGINE MISFIRES AT IDLE ONLY, SEE CHART C-4D-1.
- IGNITION "OFF".
- DISCONNECT ONE SPARK PLUG LEAD AT A TIME AND, INSTALL SPARK TESTER (ST-125) J26792 OR EQUIVALENT.
- OBSERVE SPARK TESTER WITH ENGINE IDLING. REPEAT THIS TEST FOR ALL PLUG LEADS.
- SPARK SHOULD JUMP TESTER GAP ON ALL LEADS WITH ENGINE IDLING. DID IT?

NO

2
- WITH IGNITION "OFF", GROUND THE OPPOSITE PLUG LEAD OF THE AFFECTED COIL AT SPARK PLUG.
- SPARK SHOULD JUMP TESTER GAP WHILE CRANKING ENGINE. DOES IT?

YES

CHECK FOR:
- FAULTY, WORN OR CRACKED SPARK PLUG(S).
- PLUG FOULING DUE TO ENGINE MECHANICAL FAULT.
IF SPARK PLUGS CHECK OUT OK, SEE "CUTS OUT, MISSES"

NO

- CHECK THE RESISTANCE OF EACH PLUG WIRE OF THE COIL WHICH DID NOT FIRE THE SPARK TESTER.
- WIRE RESISTANCE SHOULD BE LESS THAN 30,000 OHMS EACH AND WIRES SHOULD NOT BE GROUNDED. ARE WIRES OK?

YES

REPLACE THE SPARK PLUG FOR THE LEAD WHICH WAS JUMPERED TO GROUND. IF MISFIRE IS STILL PRESENT, START MISFIRE TEST AGAIN AT STEP #1.

YES

3
- REMOVE COIL RETAINING NUTS AND REMOVE COILS.
- COILS SHOULD BE FREE OF CARBON TRACKING. ARE THEY?

NO

REPLACE FAULTY WIRE(S).

YES

4
- SWITCH A NORMALLY OPERATING COIL WITH THE COIL FROM PROBLEM CYLINDER.
- SPARK SHOULD JUMP TESTER GAP WITH ENGINE IDLING. DID IT?

NO

REPLACE IGNITION COIL. ALSO CHECK FOR FAULTY PLUG WIRE CONNECTIONS AND WIRE NIPPLES FOR CARBON TRACKING.

YES

ORIGINAL IGNITION COIL IS FAULTY.

NO

REPLACE DIS MODULE.

★CAUTION: When handling secondary spark plug leads with engine running, insulated pliers must be used and care exercised to prevent a possible electrical shock.

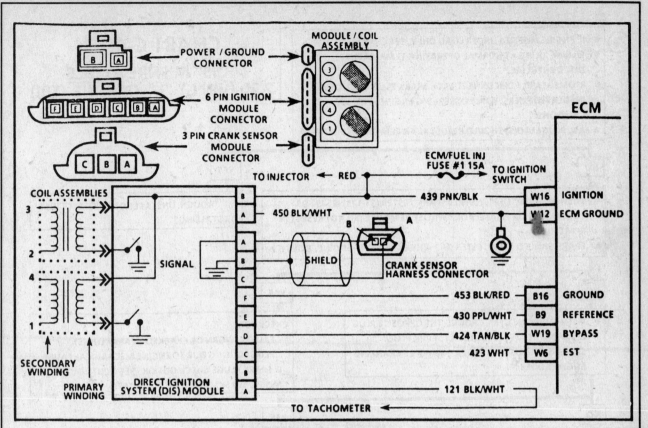

CHART C-4D-1

"DIS" MISFIRE AT IDLE
2.2L (VIN G) "L" CARLINE (TBI)

Circuit Description:

The Direct Ignition System (DIS) uses a waste spark method of distribution. In this type of system, the ignition module triggers the #1/4 coil pair resulting in both #1 and #4 spark plugs firing at the same time. #1 cylinder is on the compression stroke at the same time #4 is on the exhaust stroke, resulting in a lower energy requirement to fire #4 spark plug. This leaves the remainder of the high voltage to be used to fire #1 spark plug. The crank sensor is remotely mounted beside the module/coil assembly and protrudes through the block to within approximately .050" of the crankshaft reluctor. Since the reluctor is a machined portion of the crankshaft and the crankshaft sensor is mounted in a fixed position on the block, timing adjustments are not possible or necessary.

Test Description: Numbers below refer to circled numbers on the diagnostic chart.

1. If the "Misfire" complaint exists under load only, the diagnostic chart on page 2 must be used. Engine rpm should drop approximately equally on all plug leads.
2. A spark tester, such as a ST-125, must be used because it is essential to verify adequate available secondary voltage at the spark plug (25,000 volts).
3. If the spark jumps the tester gap after grounding the opposite plug wire, it indicates excessive resistance in the plug which was bypassed. A faulty or poor connection at that plug could also result in the miss condition. Also, check for carbon deposits inside the spark plug boot.

4. If carbon tracking is evident, replace coil and be sure plug wires relating to that coil are clean and tight. Excessive wire resistance or faulty connections could have caused the coil to be damaged.
5. If the no spark condition follows the suspected coil, that coil is faulty. Otherwise, the ignition module is the cause of no spark. This test could also be performed by substituting a known good coil for the one causing the no spark condition.

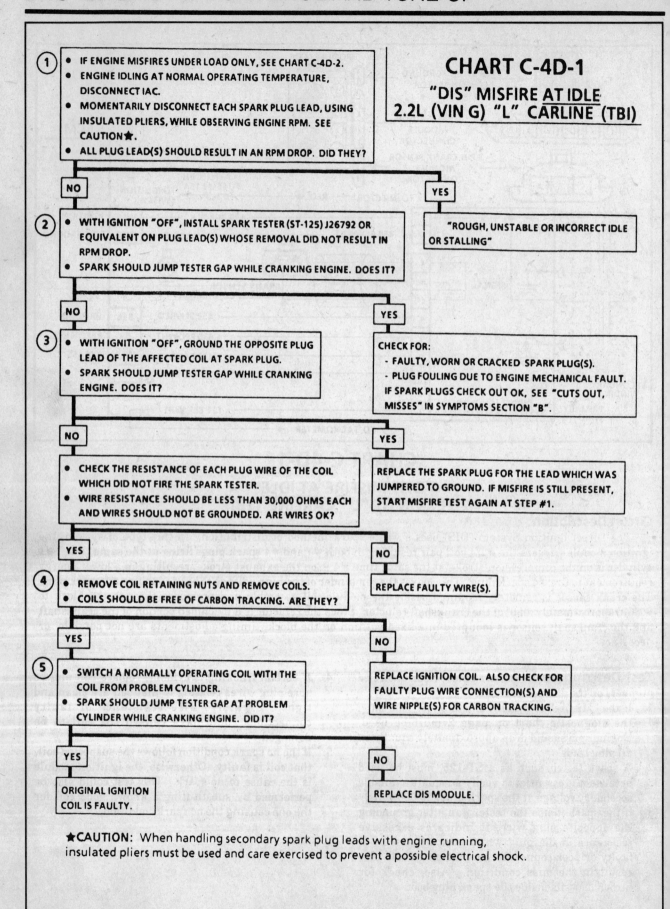

CHART C-4D-1
"DIS" MISFIRE AT IDLE
2.2L (VIN G) "L" CARLINE (TBI)

1
- IF ENGINE MISFIRES UNDER LOAD ONLY, SEE CHART C-4D-2.
- ENGINE IDLING AT NORMAL OPERATING TEMPERATURE, DISCONNECT IAC.
- MOMENTARILY DISCONNECT EACH SPARK PLUG LEAD, USING INSULATED PLIERS, WHILE OBSERVING ENGINE RPM. SEE CAUTION★.
- ALL PLUG LEAD(S) SHOULD RESULT IN AN RPM DROP. DID THEY?

NO

YES

"ROUGH, UNSTABLE OR INCORRECT IDLE OR STALLING"

2
- WITH IGNITION "OFF", INSTALL SPARK TESTER (ST-125) J26792 OR EQUIVALENT ON PLUG LEAD(S) WHOSE REMOVAL DID NOT RESULT IN RPM DROP.
- SPARK SHOULD JUMP TESTER GAP WHILE CRANKING ENGINE. DOES IT?

NO

YES

CHECK FOR:
- FAULTY, WORN OR CRACKED SPARK PLUG(S).
- PLUG FOULING DUE TO ENGINE MECHANICAL FAULT.
IF SPARK PLUGS CHECK OUT OK, SEE "CUTS OUT, MISSES" IN SYMPTOMS SECTION "B".

3
- WITH IGNITION "OFF", GROUND THE OPPOSITE PLUG LEAD OF THE AFFECTED COIL AT SPARK PLUG.
- SPARK SHOULD JUMP TESTER GAP WHILE CRANKING ENGINE. DOES IT?

NO

YES

REPLACE THE SPARK PLUG FOR THE LEAD WHICH WAS JUMPERED TO GROUND. IF MISFIRE IS STILL PRESENT, START MISFIRE TEST AGAIN AT STEP #1.

- CHECK THE RESISTANCE OF EACH PLUG WIRE OF THE COIL WHICH DID NOT FIRE THE SPARK TESTER.
- WIRE RESISTANCE SHOULD BE LESS THAN 30,000 OHMS EACH AND WIRES SHOULD NOT BE GROUNDED. ARE WIRES OK?

YES

NO

REPLACE FAULTY WIRE(S).

4
- REMOVE COIL RETAINING NUTS AND REMOVE COILS.
- COILS SHOULD BE FREE OF CARBON TRACKING. ARE THEY?

YES

NO

REPLACE IGNITION COIL. ALSO CHECK FOR FAULTY PLUG WIRE CONNECTION(S) AND WIRE NIPPLE(S) FOR CARBON TRACKING.

5
- SWITCH A NORMALLY OPERATING COIL WITH THE COIL FROM PROBLEM CYLINDER.
- SPARK SHOULD JUMP TESTER GAP AT PROBLEM CYLINDER WHILE CRANKING ENGINE. DID IT?

YES

NO

ORIGINAL IGNITION COIL IS FAULTY.

REPLACE DIS MODULE.

★CAUTION: When handling secondary spark plug leads with engine running, insulated pliers must be used and care exercised to prevent a possible electrical shock.

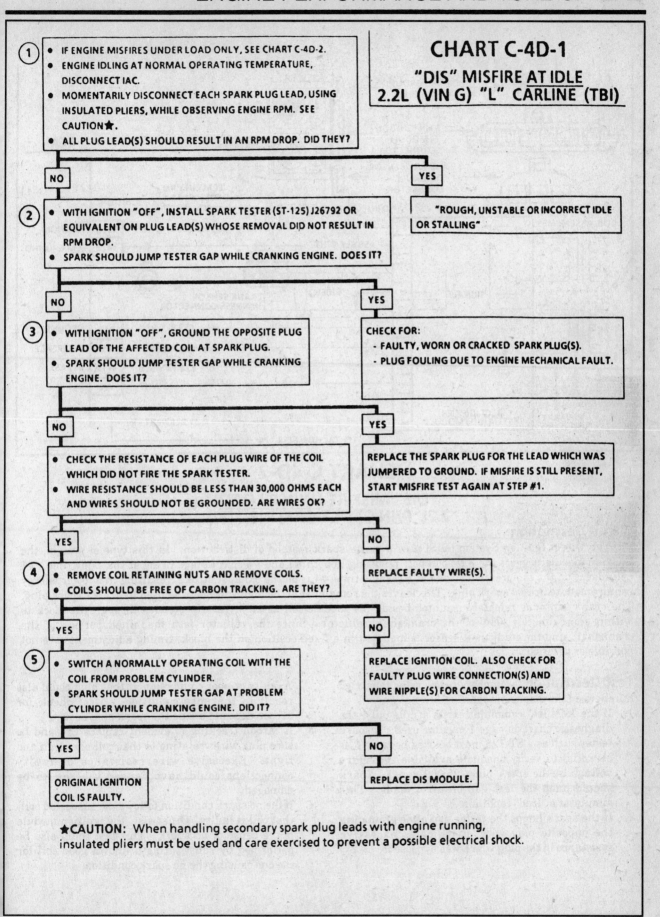

CHART C-4D-1
"DIS" MISFIRE AT IDLE
2.2L (VIN G) "L" CARLINE (TBI)

1
- IF ENGINE MISFIRES UNDER LOAD ONLY, SEE CHART C-4D-2.
- ENGINE IDLING AT NORMAL OPERATING TEMPERATURE, DISCONNECT IAC.
- MOMENTARILY DISCONNECT EACH SPARK PLUG LEAD, USING INSULATED PLIERS, WHILE OBSERVING ENGINE RPM. SEE CAUTION ★.
- ALL PLUG LEAD(S) SHOULD RESULT IN AN RPM DROP. DID THEY?

NO

YES

"ROUGH, UNSTABLE OR INCORRECT IDLE OR STALLING"

2
- WITH IGNITION "OFF", INSTALL SPARK TESTER (ST-125) J26792 OR EQUIVALENT ON PLUG LEAD(S) WHOSE REMOVAL DID NOT RESULT IN RPM DROP.
- SPARK SHOULD JUMP TESTER GAP WHILE CRANKING ENGINE. DOES IT?

NO

YES

CHECK FOR:
- FAULTY, WORN OR CRACKED SPARK PLUG(S).
- PLUG FOULING DUE TO ENGINE MECHANICAL FAULT.

3
- WITH IGNITION "OFF", GROUND THE OPPOSITE PLUG LEAD OF THE AFFECTED COIL AT SPARK PLUG.
- SPARK SHOULD JUMP TESTER GAP WHILE CRANKING ENGINE. DOES IT?

NO

YES

REPLACE THE SPARK PLUG FOR THE LEAD WHICH WAS JUMPERED TO GROUND. IF MISFIRE IS STILL PRESENT, START MISFIRE TEST AGAIN AT STEP #1.

- CHECK THE RESISTANCE OF EACH PLUG WIRE OF THE COIL WHICH DID NOT FIRE THE SPARK TESTER.
- WIRE RESISTANCE SHOULD BE LESS THAN 30,000 OHMS EACH AND WIRES SHOULD NOT BE GROUNDED. ARE WIRES OK?

YES

NO

REPLACE FAULTY WIRE(S).

4
- REMOVE COIL RETAINING NUTS AND REMOVE COILS.
- COILS SHOULD BE FREE OF CARBON TRACKING. ARE THEY?

YES

NO

REPLACE IGNITION COIL. ALSO CHECK FOR FAULTY PLUG WIRE CONNECTION(S) AND WIRE NIPPLE(S) FOR CARBON TRACKING.

5
- SWITCH A NORMALLY OPERATING COIL WITH THE COIL FROM PROBLEM CYLINDER.
- SPARK SHOULD JUMP TESTER GAP AT PROBLEM CYLINDER WHILE CRANKING ENGINE. DID IT?

YES

NO

REPLACE DIS MODULE.

ORIGINAL IGNITION COIL IS FAULTY.

★**CAUTION:** When handling secondary spark plug leads with engine running, insulated pliers must be used and care exercised to prevent a possible electrical shock.

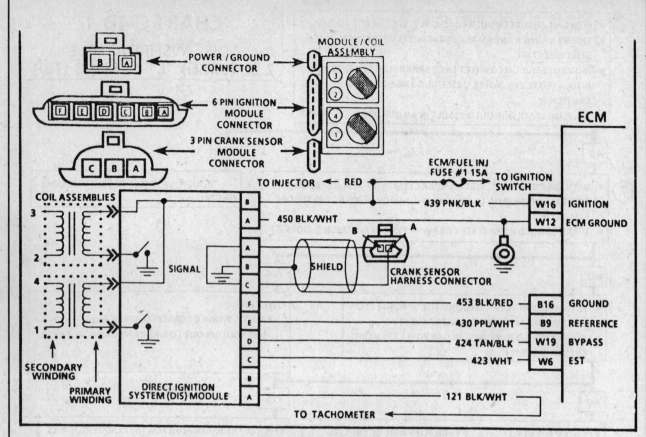

CHART C-4D-2

"DIS" MISFIRE UNDER LOAD
2.2L (VIN G) "L" CARLINE (TBI)

Circuit Description:

The Direct Ignition System (DIS) uses a waste spark method of distribution. In this type of system, the ignition module triggers the #1/4 coil pair resulting in both #1 and #4 spark plugs firing at the same time. #1 cylinder is on the compression stroke at the same time #4 is on the exhaust stroke, resulting in a lower energy requirement to fire #4 spark plug. This leaves the remainder of the high voltage to be used to fire #1 spark plug. The crank sensor is remotely mounted beside the module/coil assembly and protrudes through the block to within approximately .050" of the crankshaft reluctor. Since the reluctor is a machined portion of the crankshaft, and the crankshaft sensor is mounted in a fixed position on the block, timing adjustments are not possible or necessary.

Test Description: Numbers below refer to circled numbers on the diagnostic chart.

1. If the "Misfire" complaint exists at idle only, the diagnostic chart on page 1 must be used. A spark tester such as a ST-125 must be used because it is essential to verify adequate available secondary voltage at the spark plug (25,000 volts). Spark should jump the test gap on all 4 leads. This simulates a "load" condition.

2. If the spark jumps the tester gap after grounding the opposite plug wire, it indicates excessive resistance in the plug which was bypassed.

A faulty or poor connection at that plug could also result in the miss condition. Also, check for carbon deposits inside the spark plug boot.

3. If carbon tracking is evident replace coil and be sure plug wires relating to that coil are clean and tight. Excessive wire resistance or faulty connections could have caused the coil to be damaged.

4. If the no spark condition follows the suspected coil, that coil is faulty. Otherwise, the ignition module is the cause of no spark. This test could also be performed by substituting a known good coil for the one causing the no spark condition.

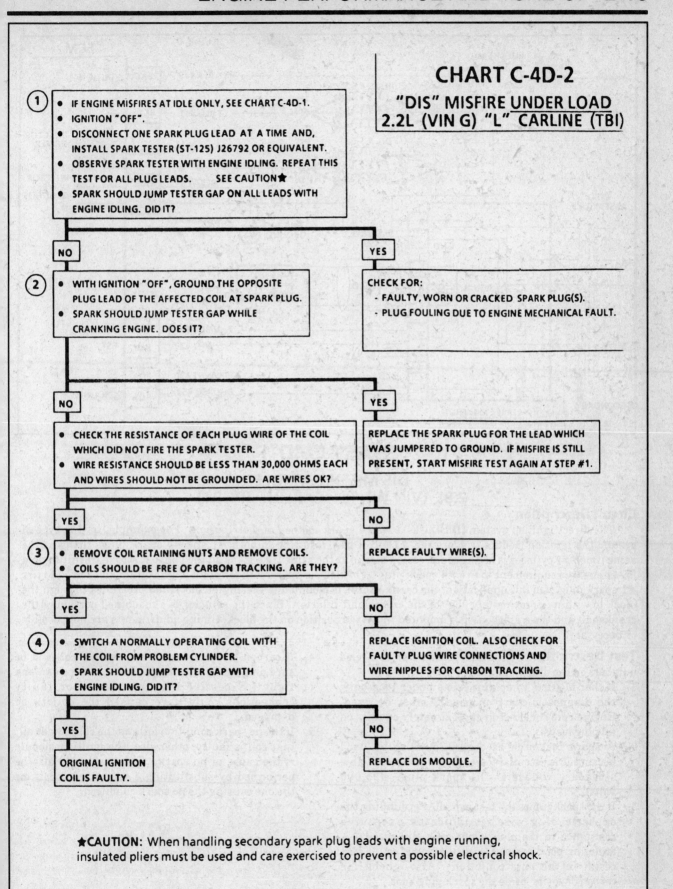

CHART C-4D-2
"DIS" MISFIRE UNDER LOAD
2.2L (VIN G) "L" CARLINE (TBI)

① (Step 1)
- IF ENGINE MISFIRES AT IDLE ONLY, SEE CHART C-4D-1.
- IGNITION "OFF".
- DISCONNECT ONE SPARK PLUG LEAD AT A TIME AND, INSTALL SPARK TESTER (ST-125) J26792 OR EQUIVALENT.
- OBSERVE SPARK TESTER WITH ENGINE IDLING. REPEAT THIS TEST FOR ALL PLUG LEADS.   SEE CAUTION★
- SPARK SHOULD JUMP TESTER GAP ON ALL LEADS WITH ENGINE IDLING. DID IT?

NO

YES

② (Step 2)
- WITH IGNITION "OFF", GROUND THE OPPOSITE PLUG LEAD OF THE AFFECTED COIL AT SPARK PLUG.
- SPARK SHOULD JUMP TESTER GAP WHILE CRANKING ENGINE. DOES IT?

CHECK FOR:
- FAULTY, WORN OR CRACKED SPARK PLUG(S).
- PLUG FOULING DUE TO ENGINE MECHANICAL FAULT.

NO

YES

- CHECK THE RESISTANCE OF EACH PLUG WIRE OF THE COIL WHICH DID NOT FIRE THE SPARK TESTER.
- WIRE RESISTANCE SHOULD BE LESS THAN 30,000 OHMS EACH AND WIRES SHOULD NOT BE GROUNDED. ARE WIRES OK?

REPLACE THE SPARK PLUG FOR THE LEAD WHICH WAS JUMPERED TO GROUND. IF MISFIRE IS STILL PRESENT, START MISFIRE TEST AGAIN AT STEP #1.

YES

NO

③ (Step 3)
- REMOVE COIL RETAINING NUTS AND REMOVE COILS.
- COILS SHOULD BE FREE OF CARBON TRACKING. ARE THEY?

REPLACE FAULTY WIRE(S).

YES

NO

④ (Step 4)
- SWITCH A NORMALLY OPERATING COIL WITH THE COIL FROM PROBLEM CYLINDER.
- SPARK SHOULD JUMP TESTER GAP WITH ENGINE IDLING. DID IT?

REPLACE IGNITION COIL. ALSO CHECK FOR FAULTY PLUG WIRE CONNECTIONS AND WIRE NIPPLES FOR CARBON TRACKING.

YES

NO

ORIGINAL IGNITION COIL IS FAULTY.

REPLACE DIS MODULE.

★**CAUTION:** When handling secondary spark plug leads with engine running, insulated pliers must be used and care exercised to prevent a possible electrical shock.

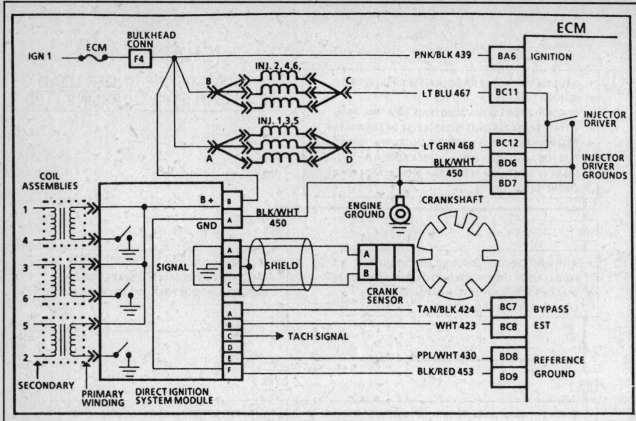

CHART C-4D-1

DIS MISFIRE AT IDLE
2.8L (VIN W) "L" CARLINE (PORT)

Circuit Description:

The direct ignition system (DIS) uses a waste spark method of distribution. For example, in this type of system the ignition module triggers the #1/4 coil pair resulting in both #1 and #4 spark plugs firing at the same time. #1 cylinder is on the compression stroke at the same time #4 is on the exhaust stroke, resulting in a lower energy requirement to fire #4 spark plug. This leaves the remainder of the high voltage to be used to fire #1 spark plug. On this application, the crank sensor is mounted to the engine block and protrudes through the block to within approximately 050" of the crankshaft reluctor. Since the reluctor is a machined portion of the crankshaft and the crank sensor is mounted in a fixed position on the block, timing adjustments are not possible or necessary.

Test Description: Numbers below refer to circled numbers on the diagnostic chart.

1. If the "Misfire" complaint exists <u>under load only</u>, the diagnostic chart on page 2 must be used. Engine rpm should drop approximately equally on all plug leads.
2. A spark test such as a ST-125 must be used because it is essential to verify adequate available secondary voltage at the spark plug. (25,000 volts).
3. If the spark jumps the test gap after grounding the opposite plug wire, it indicates excessive resistance in the plug which was Bypassed. A faulty or poor connection at that plug could also result in the miss condition. Also, check for carbon deposits inside the spark plug boot.

4. If carbon tracking is evident, replace coil and be sure plug wires relating to that coil are clean and tight. Excessive wire resistance or faulty connections could have caused the coil to be damaged.
5. If the no spark condition follows the suspected coil, that coil is faulty, otherwise, the ignition module is the cause of no spark. This test could also be performed by substituting a known good coil for the one causing the no spark condition.

CHART C-4D-1
DIS MISFIRE AT IDLE
2.8L (VIN W) "L" CARLINE (PORT)

①
- IF ENGINE MISFIRES UNDER LOAD ONLY, SEE CHART C-4D-2.
- ENGINE IDLING AT NORMAL OPERATING TEMPERATURE, DISCONNECT IAC.
- MOMENTARILY DISCONNECT EACH SPARK PLUG LEAD, USING INSULATED PLIERS, WHILE OBSERVING ENGINE RPM. SEE CAUTION★.
- ALL PLUG LEAD(S) SHOULD RESULT IN AN RPM DROP. DID THEY?

NO → **YES** → "ROUGH, UNSTABLE OR INCORRECT IDLE OR STALLING"

②
- WITH IGNITION "OFF", INSTALL SPARK TESTER (ST-125) J-26792 OR EQUIVALENT ON PLUG LEAD(S) WHOSE REMOVAL DID NOT RESULT IN RPM DROP.
- SPARK SHOULD JUMP TESTER GAP WHILE CRANKING ENGINE. DOES IT?

NO → **YES** → CHECK FOR:
- FAULTY, WORN OR CRACKED SPARK PLUG(S).
- PLUG FOULING DUE TO ENGINE MECHANICAL FAULT.

③
- WITH IGNITION "OFF", GROUND THE OPPOSITE PLUG LEAD OF THE AFFECTED COIL AT SPARK PLUG.
- SPARK SHOULD JUMP TESTER GAP WHILE CRANKING ENGINE. DOES IT?

NO → **YES** → REPLACE THE SPARK PLUG FOR THE LEAD WHICH WAS JUMPERED TO GROUND. IF MISFIRE IS STILL PRESENT, START MISFIRE TEST AGAIN AT STEP #1.

- CHECK THE RESISTANCE OF EACH PLUG WIRE OF THE COIL WHICH DID NOT FIRE THE SPARK TESTER.
- WIRE RESISTANCE SHOULD BE LESS THAN 30,000 OHMS EACH AND WIRES SHOULD NOT BE GROUNDED. ARE WIRES OK?

YES → **NO** → REPLACE FAULTY WIRE(S).

④
- REMOVE COIL RETAINING NUTS AND REMOVE COILS.
- COILS SHOULD BE FREE OF CARBON TRACKING. ARE THEY?

YES → **NO** → REPLACE IGNITION COIL. ALSO CHECK FOR FAULTY PLUG WIRE CONNECTION(S) AND WIRE NIPPLE(S) FOR CARBON TRACKING.

⑤
- SWITCH A NORMALLY OPERATING COIL WITH THE COIL FROM PROBLEM CYLINDER.
- SPARK SHOULD JUMP TESTER GAP AT PROBLEM CYLINDER WHILE CRANKING ENGINE. DID IT?

YES → **NO** → REPLACE DIS MODULE.

ORIGINAL IGNITION COIL IS FAULTY.

★CAUTION: When handling secondary spark plug leads with engine running, insulated pliers must be used and care exercised to prevent a possible electrical shock.

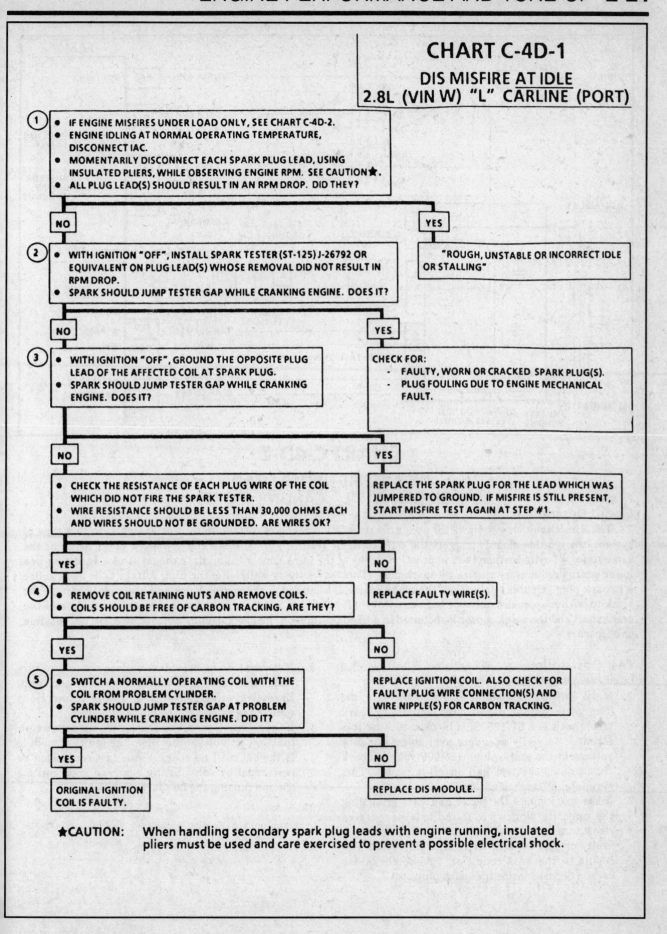

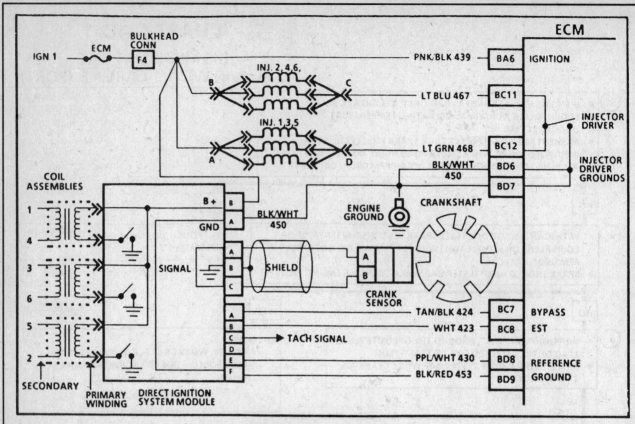

CHART C-4D-2

DIS MISFIRE UNDER LOAD
2.8L (VIN W) "L" CARLINE (PORT)

Circuit Description:

The direct ignition system (DIS) uses a waste spark method of distribution. For example, in this type of system, the ignition module triggers the #1/4 coil pair resulting in both #1 and #4 spark plugs firing at the same time. #1 cylinder is on the compression stroke at the same time #4 is on the exhaust stroke, resulting in a lower energy requirement to fire #4 spark plug. This leaves the remainder of the high voltage to be used to fire #1 spark plug. On this application, the crank sensor is mounted to the engine block and protrudes through the block to within approximately 050" of the crankshaft reluctor. Since the reluctor is a machined portion of the crankshaft and the crank sensor is mounted in a fixed position on the block, timing adjustments are not possible or necessary.

Test Description: Numbers below refer to circled numbers on the diagnostic chart.

1. If the "Misfire" complaint exists <u>at idle only</u>, the diagnostic chart on page 1 must be used. A spark tester such as a ST-125 must be used because it is essential to verify adequate available secondary voltage at the spark plug. (25,000 volts). Spark should jump the test gap on all 4 leads. This simulates a "load" condition.

2. If the spark jumps the tester gap after grounding the opposite plug wire, it indicates excessive resistance in the plug which was Bypassed. A faulty or poor connection at that plug could also result in the miss condition. Also, check for carbon deposits inside the spark plug boot.

3. If carbon tracing is evident replace coil and be sure plug wires relating to that coil are clean and tight. Excessive wire resistance or faulty connections could have caused the coil to be damaged.

4. If the no spark condition follows the suspected coil, that coil is faulty, otherwise, the ignition module is the cause of no spark. This test could also be performed by substituting a known good coil for the one causing the no spark condition.

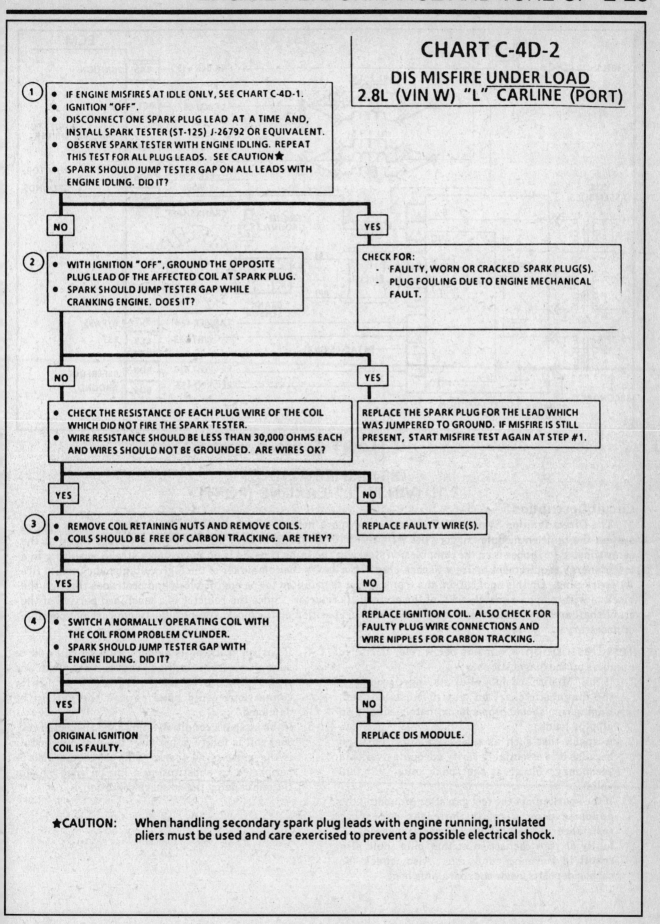

CHART C-4D-2
DIS MISFIRE UNDER LOAD
2.8L (VIN W) "L" CARLINE (PORT)

1
- IF ENGINE MISFIRES AT IDLE ONLY, SEE CHART C-4D-1.
- IGNITION "OFF".
- DISCONNECT ONE SPARK PLUG LEAD AT A TIME AND, INSTALL SPARK TESTER (ST-125) J-26792 OR EQUIVALENT.
- OBSERVE SPARK TESTER WITH ENGINE IDLING. REPEAT THIS TEST FOR ALL PLUG LEADS. SEE CAUTION★
- SPARK SHOULD JUMP TESTER GAP ON ALL LEADS WITH ENGINE IDLING. DID IT?

NO | **YES**

YES →
CHECK FOR:
- FAULTY, WORN OR CRACKED SPARK PLUG(S).
- PLUG FOULING DUE TO ENGINE MECHANICAL FAULT.

2
- WITH IGNITION "OFF", GROUND THE OPPOSITE PLUG LEAD OF THE AFFECTED COIL AT SPARK PLUG.
- SPARK SHOULD JUMP TESTER GAP WHILE CRANKING ENGINE. DOES IT?

NO | **YES**

YES →
REPLACE THE SPARK PLUG FOR THE LEAD WHICH WAS JUMPERED TO GROUND. IF MISFIRE IS STILL PRESENT, START MISFIRE TEST AGAIN AT STEP #1.

- CHECK THE RESISTANCE OF EACH PLUG WIRE OF THE COIL WHICH DID NOT FIRE THE SPARK TESTER.
- WIRE RESISTANCE SHOULD BE LESS THAN 30,000 OHMS EACH AND WIRES SHOULD NOT BE GROUNDED. ARE WIRES OK?

YES | **NO**

NO →
REPLACE FAULTY WIRE(S).

3
- REMOVE COIL RETAINING NUTS AND REMOVE COILS.
- COILS SHOULD BE FREE OF CARBON TRACKING. ARE THEY?

YES | **NO**

NO →
REPLACE IGNITION COIL. ALSO CHECK FOR FAULTY PLUG WIRE CONNECTIONS AND WIRE NIPPLES FOR CARBON TRACKING.

4
- SWITCH A NORMALLY OPERATING COIL WITH THE COIL FROM PROBLEM CYLINDER.
- SPARK SHOULD JUMP TESTER GAP WITH ENGINE IDLING. DID IT?

YES | **NO**

ORIGINAL IGNITION COIL IS FAULTY.

REPLACE DIS MODULE.

★CAUTION: When handling secondary spark plug leads with engine running, insulated pliers must be used and care exercised to prevent a possible electrical shock.

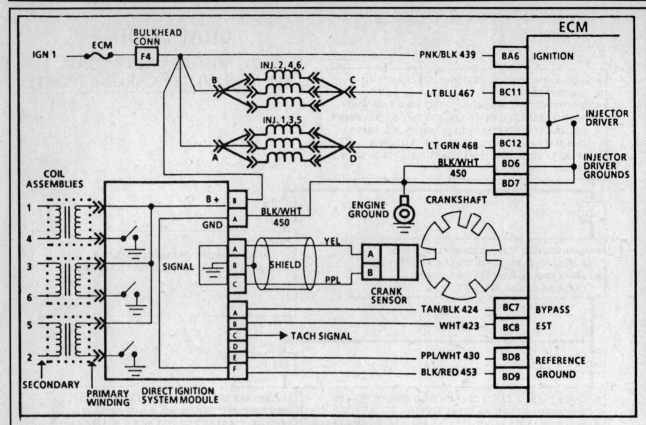

CHART C-4D-1

DIS MISFIRE AT IDLE
3.1L (VIN T) "L" CARLINE (PORT)

Circuit Description:

The Direct Ignition System (DIS) uses a waste spark method of distribution. For example, in this type of system the ignition module triggers the #1/4 coil pair resulting in both #1 and #4 spark plugs firing at the same time. #1 cylinder is on the compression stroke at the same time #4 is on the exhaust stroke, resulting in a lower energy requirement to fire #4 spark plug. This leaves the remainder of the high voltage to be used to fire #1 spark plug. On this application, the crank sensor is mounted to the engine block and protrudes through the block to within approximately 050" of the crankshaft reluctor. Since the reluctor is a machined portion of the crankshaft and the crank sensor is mounted in a fixed position on the block, timing adjustments are not possible or necessary.

Test Description: Numbers below refer to circled numbers on the diagnostic chart.

1. If the "Misfire" complaint exists <u>under load only</u>, the diagnostic chart on page 2 must be used. Engine rpm should drop approximately equally on all plug leads.
2. A spark test such as a ST-125 must be used because it is essential to verify adequate available secondary voltage at the spark plug. (25,000 volts).
3. If the spark jumps the test gap after grounding the opposite plug wire, it indicates excessive resistance in the plug which was Bypassed. A faulty or poor connection at that plug could also result in the miss condition. Also, check for carbon deposits inside the spark plug boot.

4. If carbon tracking is evident, replace coil and be sure plug wires relating to that coil are clean and tight. Excessive wire resistance or faulty connections could have caused the coil to be damaged.
5. If the no spark condition follows the suspected coil, that coil is faulty, otherwise, the ignition module is the cause of no spark. This test could also be performed by substituting a known good coil for the one causing the no spark condition.

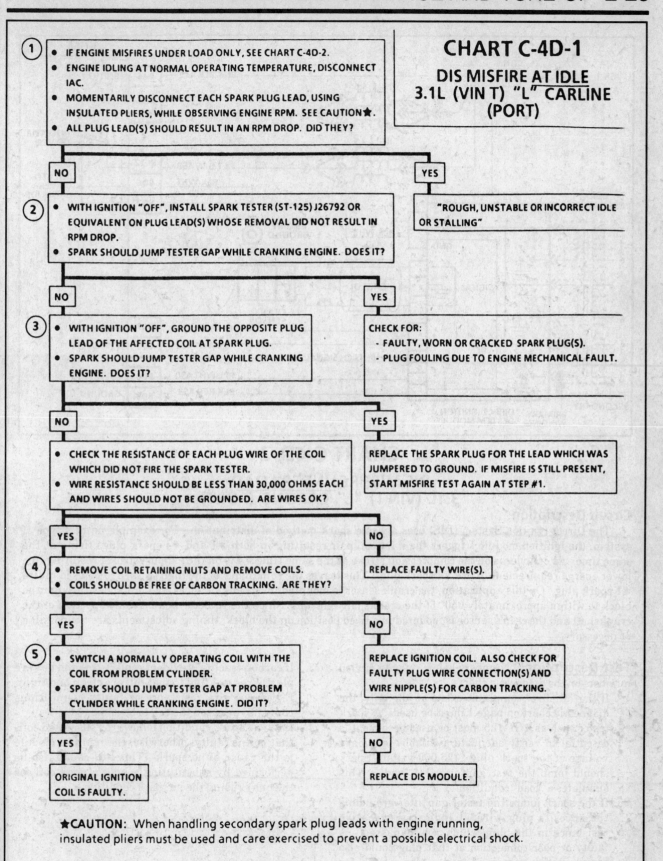

CHART C-4D-1
DIS MISFIRE AT IDLE
3.1L (VIN T) "L" CARLINE (PORT)

1
- IF ENGINE MISFIRES UNDER LOAD ONLY, SEE CHART C-4D-2.
- ENGINE IDLING AT NORMAL OPERATING TEMPERATURE, DISCONNECT IAC.
- MOMENTARILY DISCONNECT EACH SPARK PLUG LEAD, USING INSULATED PLIERS, WHILE OBSERVING ENGINE RPM. SEE CAUTION★.
- ALL PLUG LEAD(S) SHOULD RESULT IN AN RPM DROP. DID THEY?

NO → | **YES** → "ROUGH, UNSTABLE OR INCORRECT IDLE OR STALLING"

2
- WITH IGNITION "OFF", INSTALL SPARK TESTER (ST-125) J26792 OR EQUIVALENT ON PLUG LEAD(S) WHOSE REMOVAL DID NOT RESULT IN RPM DROP.
- SPARK SHOULD JUMP TESTER GAP WHILE CRANKING ENGINE. DOES IT?

NO → | **YES** →
CHECK FOR:
- FAULTY, WORN OR CRACKED SPARK PLUG(S).
- PLUG FOULING DUE TO ENGINE MECHANICAL FAULT.

3
- WITH IGNITION "OFF", GROUND THE OPPOSITE PLUG LEAD OF THE AFFECTED COIL AT SPARK PLUG.
- SPARK SHOULD JUMP TESTER GAP WHILE CRANKING ENGINE. DOES IT?

NO → | **YES** →
REPLACE THE SPARK PLUG FOR THE LEAD WHICH WAS JUMPERED TO GROUND. IF MISFIRE IS STILL PRESENT, START MISFIRE TEST AGAIN AT STEP #1.

- CHECK THE RESISTANCE OF EACH PLUG WIRE OF THE COIL WHICH DID NOT FIRE THE SPARK TESTER.
- WIRE RESISTANCE SHOULD BE LESS THAN 30,000 OHMS EACH AND WIRES SHOULD NOT BE GROUNDED. ARE WIRES OK?

YES → | **NO** → REPLACE FAULTY WIRE(S).

4
- REMOVE COIL RETAINING NUTS AND REMOVE COILS.
- COILS SHOULD BE FREE OF CARBON TRACKING. ARE THEY?

YES → | **NO** →
REPLACE IGNITION COIL. ALSO CHECK FOR FAULTY PLUG WIRE CONNECTION(S) AND WIRE NIPPLE(S) FOR CARBON TRACKING.

5
- SWITCH A NORMALLY OPERATING COIL WITH THE COIL FROM PROBLEM CYLINDER.
- SPARK SHOULD JUMP TESTER GAP AT PROBLEM CYLINDER WHILE CRANKING ENGINE. DID IT?

YES → ORIGINAL IGNITION COIL IS FAULTY. | **NO** → REPLACE DIS MODULE.

★**CAUTION:** When handling secondary spark plug leads with engine running, insulated pliers must be used and care exercised to prevent a possible electrical shock.

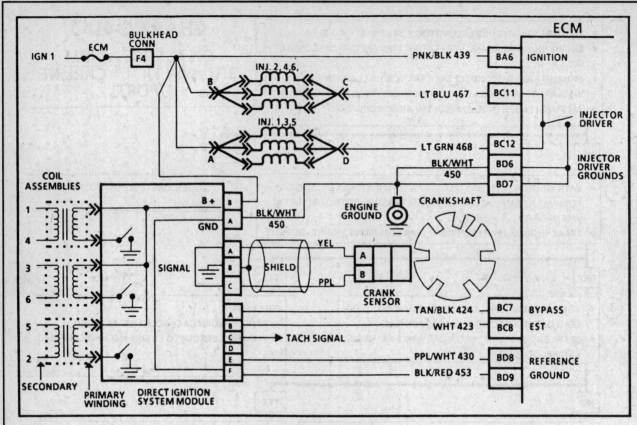

CHART C-4D-2

DIS MISFIRE UNDER LOAD
3.1L (VIN T) "L" CARLINE (PORT)

Circuit Description:

The Direct Ignition System (DIS) uses a waste spark method of distribution. For example, in this type of system, the ignition module triggers the #1/4 coil pair resulting in both #1 and #4 spark plugs firing at the same time. #1 cylinder is on the compression stroke at the same time #4 is on the exhaust stroke, resulting in a lower energy requirement to fire #4 spark plug. This leaves the remainder of the high voltage to be used to fire #1 spark plug. On this application, the crank sensor is mounted to the engine block and protrudes through the block to within approximately 050" of the crankshaft reluctor. Since the reluctor is a machined portion of the crankshaft and the crank sensor is mounted in a fixed position on the block, timing adjustments are not possible or necessary.

Test Description: Numbers below refer to circled numbers on the diagnostic chart.

1. If the "Misfire" complaint exists at idle only, the diagnostic chart on page 1 must be used. A spark tester such as a ST-125 must be used because it is essential to verify adequate available secondary voltage at the spark plug. (25,000 volts). Spark should jump the test gap on all 4 leads. This simulates a "load" condition.

2. If the spark jumps the tester gap after grounding the opposite plug wire, it indicates excessive resistance in the plug which was bypassed. A faulty or poor connection at that plug could also result in the miss condition. Also, check for carbon deposits inside the spark plug boot.

3. If carbon tracing is evident replace coil and be sure plug wires relating to that coil are clean and tight. Excessive wire resistance or faulty connections could have caused the coil to be damaged.

4. If the no spark condition follows the suspected coil, that coil is faulty, otherwise, the ignition module is the cause of no spark. This test could also be performed by substituting a known good coil for the one causing the no spark condition.

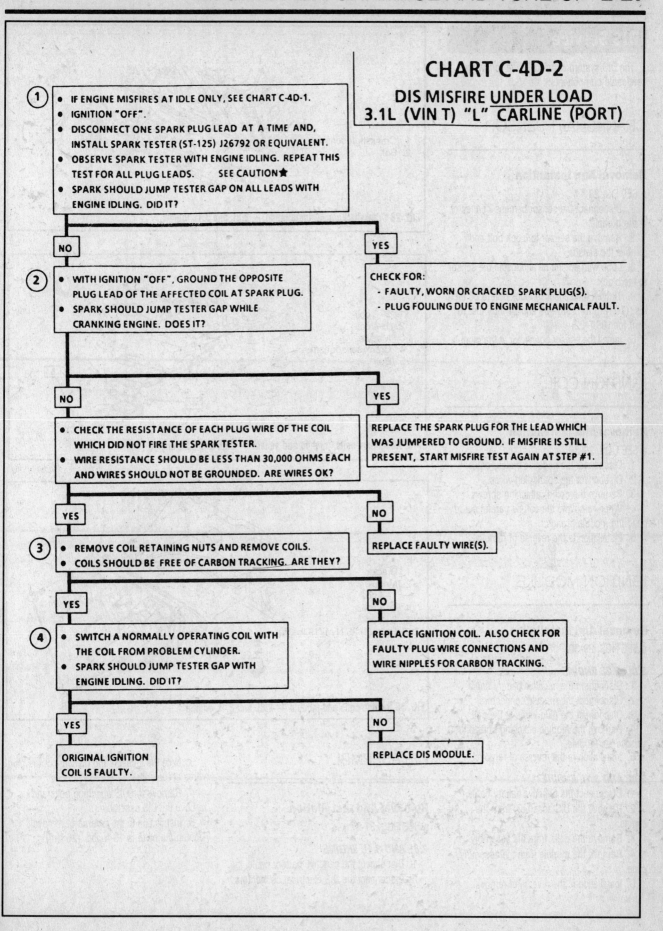

CHART C-4D-2
DIS MISFIRE UNDER LOAD
3.1L (VIN T) "L" CARLINE (PORT)

1
- IF ENGINE MISFIRES AT IDLE ONLY, SEE CHART C-4D-1.
- IGNITION "OFF".
- DISCONNECT ONE SPARK PLUG LEAD AT A TIME AND, INSTALL SPARK TESTER (ST-125) J26792 OR EQUIVALENT.
- OBSERVE SPARK TESTER WITH ENGINE IDLING. REPEAT THIS TEST FOR ALL PLUG LEADS.   SEE CAUTION ★
- SPARK SHOULD JUMP TESTER GAP ON ALL LEADS WITH ENGINE IDLING. DID IT?

NO → **YES**

2
- WITH IGNITION "OFF", GROUND THE OPPOSITE PLUG LEAD OF THE AFFECTED COIL AT SPARK PLUG.
- SPARK SHOULD JUMP TESTER GAP WHILE CRANKING ENGINE. DOES IT?

YES (from step 1)
CHECK FOR:
- FAULTY, WORN OR CRACKED SPARK PLUG(S).
- PLUG FOULING DUE TO ENGINE MECHANICAL FAULT.

NO → **YES**

- CHECK THE RESISTANCE OF EACH PLUG WIRE OF THE COIL WHICH DID NOT FIRE THE SPARK TESTER.
- WIRE RESISTANCE SHOULD BE LESS THAN 30,000 OHMS EACH AND WIRES SHOULD NOT BE GROUNDED. ARE WIRES OK?

YES (from step 2)
REPLACE THE SPARK PLUG FOR THE LEAD WHICH WAS JUMPERED TO GROUND. IF MISFIRE IS STILL PRESENT, START MISFIRE TEST AGAIN AT STEP #1.

YES → **NO**

3
- REMOVE COIL RETAINING NUTS AND REMOVE COILS.
- COILS SHOULD BE FREE OF CARBON TRACKING. ARE THEY?

NO
REPLACE FAULTY WIRE(S).

YES → **NO**

4
- SWITCH A NORMALLY OPERATING COIL WITH THE COIL FROM PROBLEM CYLINDER.
- SPARK SHOULD JUMP TESTER GAP WITH ENGINE IDLING. DID IT?

NO
REPLACE IGNITION COIL. ALSO CHECK FOR FAULTY PLUG WIRE CONNECTIONS AND WIRE NIPPLES FOR CARBON TRACKING.

YES → **NO**

YES
ORIGINAL IGNITION COIL IS FAULTY.

NO
REPLACE DIS MODULE.

DIS Service

The DIS system consists of the following servicable components:

CRANKSHAFT SENSOR

Removal And Installtion

▶ SEE FIG. 28

1. Disconnect the sensor harness connector at the module.
2. Remove the sensor to block bolt and remove the sensor.
3. Lube with engine oil and install the sensor to the block.
4. Tighten the sensor to block bolt to 88 inch lbs. (10 Nm) for 1987–89 and 71 inch lbs. (8 Nm) for 1990–92.
5. Install the sensor connector at the module.

IGNITION COIL

Removal And Installation

▶ SEE FIGS. 29-30

1. Disconnect the negative battery cable.
2. Disconnect the spark plug wires.
3. Remove the coil(s) attaching screws.
4. When removing the coil be careful not to bend the module prongs.
5. Installation is the reverse of removal.

IGNITION MODULE

Removal And Installation

▶ SEE FIGS. 29-30

2.0L, 2.2L ENGINE

1. Disconnect the negative battery cable.
2. Disconnect the module connectors.
3. Disconnect the plug wires at the coil.
4. Remove the module attaching bolts and remove the module.
5. Installation is the reverse of removal.

2.8L AND 3.1L ENGINE

1. Disconnect the negative battery cable.
2. Remove the DIS assembly from the engine.
3. Remove the coils from the assembly.
4. Remove the module from the assembly plate.
5. Installation is the reverse of removal.

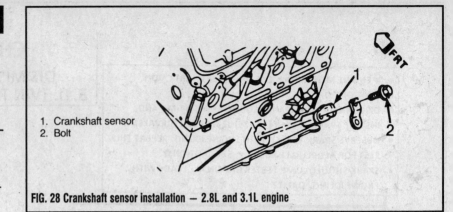

1. Crankshaft sensor
2. Bolt

FIG. 28 Crankshaft sensor installation — 2.8L and 3.1L engine

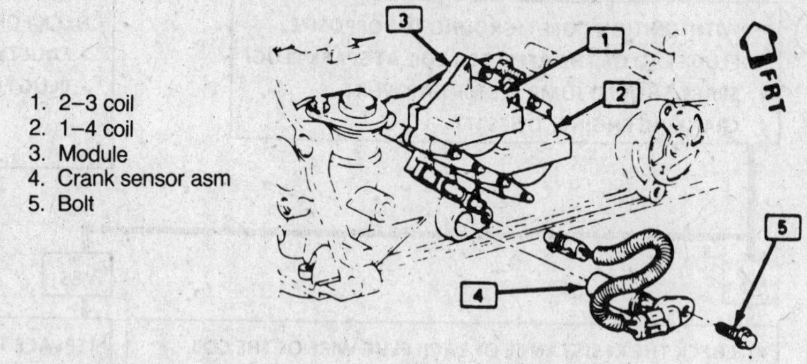

1. 2–3 coil
2. 1–4 coil
3. Module
4. Crank sensor asm
5. Bolt

FIG. 29 Ignition coils, module and sensor — 2.0L and 2.2L engine

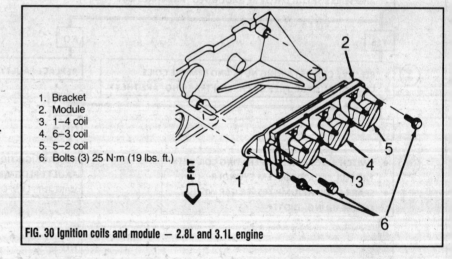

1. Bracket
2. Module
3. 1–4 coil
4. 6–3 coil
5. 5–2 coil
6. Bolts (3) 25 N·m (19 lbs. ft.)

FIG. 30 Ignition coils and module — 2.8L and 3.1L engine

DIS ASSEMBLY

Removal And Installation

▶ SEE FIGS. 31-32

2.8L AND 3.1L ENGINE

1. Disconnect the negative battery cable.
2. Disconnect the DIS electrical connectors.
3. Note the location and disconnect the plug wires at the coils.
4. Remove the DIS attaching bolts and remove the DIS assembly.
5. Installation is the reverse of removal. Tighten the bolts to 19 ft. lbs. (26 Nm).

INTEGRATED DIRECT IGNITION SYSTEM

The Integrated Direct Ignition System (IDIS) is used on vehicles equipped with the 2.3L VIN A engine and consist of 2 separate ignition coils an ignition module and a secondary conductor housing mounted to an aluminum cover plate. A crankshaft sensor, related connecting wires and an Electronic Spark Timing (EST) portion of the Electronic Control Module (ECM) make up the remainder of the system.

This system, being a distributorless ignition system, uses a waste spark method of spark distribution. Each cylinder is paired with its companion cylinder in the firing order. This places 1 cylinder on the compression stroke with the companion cylinder on the exhaust stroke. The cylinder that is on the exhaust stroke uses very little spark allowing most of the spark to go to the cylinder on the compression stroke. This process reverses when the cylinder roles reverse.

Because of the direction of current flow in the primary winding and thus, into the secondary winding, 1 plug will fire from the center electrode to the side electrode while the other fires from the side electrode.

The magnetic pick-up sensor is mounted on the side of engine block, in proximity to the crankshaft reluctor ring. Notches in the crankshaft reluctor ring trigger the magnetic pick-up sensor to provide timing information to the Electronic Control Module. The magnetic pick-up sensor provides a cam signal to identify correct firing sequence and crank signals to trigger each coil at the proper time.

The Electronic Control Module (ECM) sends a signal from the Electronic Spark Control (EST) to control spark timing. Under 700 rpm, the ignition module controls spark timing when the system is in the module or bypass timing mode. When over 700 rpm, the Electronic Control Module controls spark timing, when the system is in the EST mode.

Since no distributor is used, the timing references are gathered from the engine sensors.

INDIGRATED DIRECT IGNITION ELECTRONIC SPARK TIMING (EST) CIRCUITS

This system uses the same EST to ECM circuits that the distributor type systems with

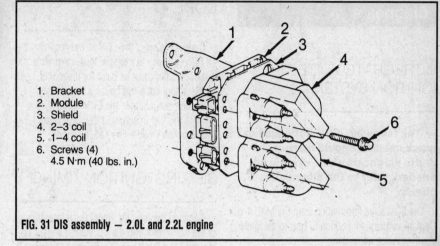

1. Bracket
2. Module
3. Shield
4. 2–3 coil
5. 1–4 coil
6. Screws (4)
   4.5 N·m (40 lbs. in.)

FIG. 31 DIS assembly — 2.0L and 2.2L engine

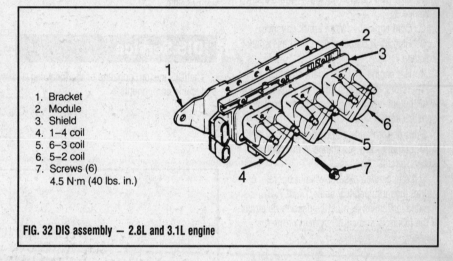

1. Bracket
2. Module
3. Shield
4. 1–4 coil
5. 6–3 coil
6. 5–2 coil
7. Screws (6)
   4.5 N·m (40 lbs. in.)

FIG. 32 DIS assembly — 2.8L and 3.1L engine

EST use. The following is a brief description for the EST circuits.

IDIS REFERENCE, CIRCUIT 430

The crankshaft sensor generates a signal to the ignition module, which results in a reference pulse being sent to the ECM. The ECM uses this signal to calculate crankshaft position and engine speed for injector pulse width.

REFERENCE GROUND, CIRCUIT 453

This wire is grounded through the module and insures that the ground circuit has no voltage drop between the ignition module and the ECM, which can affect performance.

BY-PASS, CIRCUIT 424

At approximately 700 rpm, the ECM applies 5 volts to this circuit to switch spark timing control from the DIS module to the ECM. An open or grounded by pass circuit will set a code 42 and result in the engine operating in a back-up ignition timing mode (module timing) at a calculated timing value. This may cause poor performance and reduced fuel economy.

ELECTRONIC SPARK TIMING (EST), CIRCUIT 423

The IDIS module sends a reference signal to the ECM when the engine is cranking. While the engine is under 400 rpm, the DIS module controls the ignition timing. When the engine speed exceeds 400 rpm, the ECM applies 5 volts to the By-pass line to switch the timing to the ECM control (EST).

An open or ground in the EST circuit will result in the engine continuing to run, but in a back-up ignition timing mode (module timing mode) at a calculated timing value and the SERVICE ENGINE SOON light will not be on. If the EST fault is still present, the next time the engine is restarted, a code 42 will be set and the engine will operate in the module timing mode. This may cause poor performance and reduced fuel economy.

Diagnosis

INTREGRATED DIRECT IGNITION SYSTEM

➡ **The following diagnostic aids are quick checks. Should more in-depth diagnosis of the system be needed, refer to the diagnostic charts.**

The ECM uses information from the MAP and Coolant sensors, in addition to rpm to calculate spark advance as follows;

1. Low MAP output voltage = More spark advance.
2. Cold engine = More spark advance.
3. High MAP output voltage = Less spark advance.
4. Hot engine = Less spark advance.

Therefore, detonation could be caused by low MAP output or high resistance in the coolant sensor circuit.

Poor performance could be caused by high MAP output or low resistance in the coolant sensor circuit.

If the engine cranks but will not operate, or starts, then immediately stalls, Chart A-3, located in Section 4, must be used to determine if the failure is in the IDIS system or the fuel system.

CODE 42

If code 42 is set, that code chart must be used for diagnosis. If the symptom is that the engine is missing, and the ignition system is suspected, refer to CHART C4-M ""IDI Misfire"", located in this Section, for diagnosis.

CODE 12

Code 12 is used during the diagnostic circuit check procedure to test the diagnostic and code display ability of the ECM. This code indicates that the ECM is not receiving the engine rpm (reference) signal. This occurs with the ignition key in the ON position and the engine not operating.

CODE 41

Code 41 is set if the ECM is not receiving the 1X reference signal from the ignition module and that code chart must be used for diagnosis. Loss of this signal does not cause a drivability symptom, but disables the ECM's ability to activate the fuel injectors in the Alternating Synscronous Double Fire (ASDF) mode.

SETTING IGNITION TIMING

Because the reluctor wheel is an integral part of the crankshaft and the crankshaft sensor is mounted in a fixed position, timing adjustment is not possible.

IDIS Service

The IDIS system consists of the following servicable components:

IGNITION ASSEMBLY

Removal and Installation

▸ SEE FIG. 35
1. Disconnect the negative battery cable.
2. Disconnect the harness connector from the coil and module assembly.
3. Remove the ignition assembly-to-camshaft housing attaching bolts.
4. Carefully remove the ignition assembly from the the engine.

➡ **If the spark plug boots present a problem coming off, it may be necessary to use a special removal tool, first twisting and pulling upward on the retainers.**

To install:
5. Install the spark plug boots and retainers on the ignition assembly housing secondary terminals.

➡ **If the boots and retainers are not in place on the housing secondary terminals prior to installing the ignition assembly, damage to the ignition system may result.**

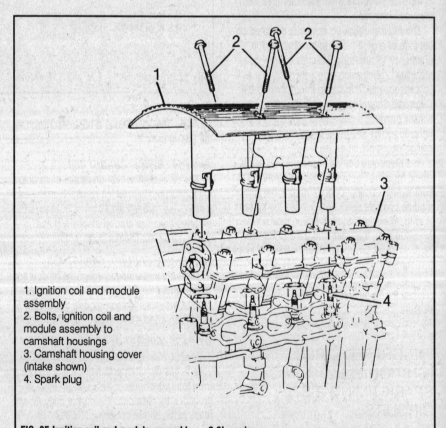

1. Ignition coil and module assembly
2. Bolts, ignition coil and module assembly to camshaft housings
3. Camshaft housing cover (intake shown)
4. Spark plug

FIG. 35 Ignition coil and module assembly — 2.3L engine

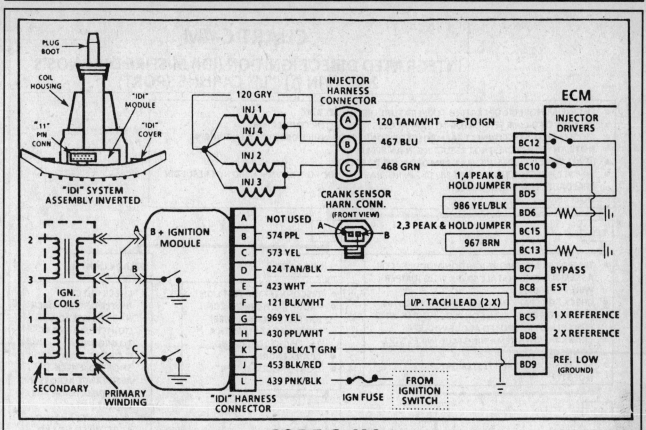

CODE C-4M

INTEGRATED DIRECT IGNITION (IDI) MISFIRE DIAGNOSIS
2.3L (VIN A) "L" CARLINE (PORT)

Circuit Description:

The Integrated Direct Ignition (IDI) system uses a waste spark method of distribution. In this type of system the ignition module triggers the #1-4 coil pair resulting in both #1 and #4 spark plugs firing at the same time. #1 cylinder is on the compression stroke at the same time #4 is on the exhaust stroke, resulting in a lower energy requirement to fire # 4 spark plug. This leaves the remainder of the high voltage to be used to fire #1 spark plug. On this application, the crank sensor is mounted to, and protrudes through the block to within approximately 0.050" of the crankshaft reluctor. Since the reluctor is a machined portion of the crankshaft and the sensor is mounted in a fixed position on the block, timing adjustments are not possible or necessary.

Test Description:
Numbers below refer to circled numbers on the diagnostic chart.

1. This checks for equal relative power output between the cylinders. Any injector which when disconnected did not result in an rpm drop approximately equal to the others, is located on the misfiring cylinder.
2. If a plug boot is burned, the other plug on that coil may still fire at idle. This step tests the system's ability to produce at least 25,000 volts at each spark plug.
3. No spark, on one coil, may be caused by an open secondary circuit. Therefore, the coil's secondary resistance should be checked. Resistance readings above 20,000 ohms, but not infinite, will probably not cause a no start but may cause an engine miss under certain conditions.

4. If the no spark condition is caused by coil connections, a coil or a secondary boot assembly, the test light will blink. If the light does not blink, the fault is module connections or the module.
5. Checks for ignition voltage feed to injector and for an open injector driver circuit.
6. An injector driver circuit shorted to ground would result in the test light "ON" steady, and possibly a flooded condition which could damage engine. A shorted injector (less than 2 ohms) could cause incorrect ECM operation.

Diagnostic Aid:

Verify IDI connector terminal "J", CKT 450 resistance to ground is less than .5 ohm.

CHART C-4M

INTEGRATED DIRECT IGNITION (IDI) MISFIRE DIAGNOSIS
2.3L (VIN A) "L" CARLINE (PORT)

**① **
- ENGINE AT NORMAL OPERATING TEMPERATURE DISCONNECT IAC.
- REMOVE CV OIL/AIR SEPARATOR TO GAIN ACCESS TO INJECTOR CONNECTORS.
- MOMENTARILY DISCONNECT EACH INJECTOR CONNECTOR WHILE OBSERVING ENGINE RPM.
- NOTE ANY INJECTOR(S) NOT RESULTING IN AN RPM DROP.
- (IF ALL INJECTORS RESULT IN AN RPM DROP, GO TO STEP 2).
- INSTALL INJECTOR TEST LIGHT J-34730-2 IN INJ. HARN. CONN. FOR INJ. WHICH DID NOT RESULT IN RPM DROP. LIGHT SHOULD BLINK. DOES IT?

YES   **NO**

②
- TEMPORARILY REMOVE IGNITION MODULE / COIL ASSEMBLY AND INSTALL SPARK PLUG JUMPER WIRES (J-36012)
- CHECK FOR SPARK WITH SPARK TESTER J-26792, (ST-125) OR EQUIVALENT ON PLUG JUMPER WIRE FOR CYLINDER(S) NOTED ABOVE WHILE CRANKING WITH <u>REMAINING PLUG WIRES STILL CONNECTED.</u>
- SPARK SHOULD JUMP TESTER GAP. DOES IT?

LIGHT "OFF"   **STEADY LIGHT**

⑤
- DISCONNECT INJ. TEST LIGHT.
- PROBE INJ. HARNESS CONN. IGN FEED (PNK/BLK WIRE) TERMINAL AT INJ. WITH A TEST LIGHT TO GROUND.
- CRANK ENGINE.
- LIGHT SHOULD BE "ON". IS IT?

⑥
- CHECK INJECTOR DRIVER CIRCUIT WHICH HAD THE STEADY LIGHT, FOR A SHORT TO GROUND.
- IF CIRCUIT IS NOT SHORTED, CHECK RESISTANCE ACROSS EACH INJECTOR IN THE CIRCUIT.
- RESISTANCE SHOULD BE BETWEEN 1.8 AND 2.2 OHMS FOR EACH INJECTOR. IS IT?

NO   **YES**

③
- REMOVE BOOT ASSYS. FOR AFFECTED COIL (1-4 OR 2-3)
- CONNECT DVM (20K OHMS SCALE) BETWEEN SECONDARY "IDI" COIL TERMINALS AND THEN FROM ONE COIL TERMINAL TO COVER PLATE.
- RESISTANCE SHOULD BE LESS THAN 10K OHMS BETWEEN TERMINALS AND INFINITE (OPEN CIRCUIT) TO COVER. IS IT?

INSPECT SPARK PLUG AND BOOT FOR DAMAGE. IF OK, SUBSTITUTE A KNOWN GOOD INJ.,

YES   **NO**

CHECK CKT 467 OR 468 FOR SHORT TO VOLTAGE, OPEN OR POOR CONNECTIONS AT ECM TERMINAL "BC10" OR "BC12". IF OK, CHECK FOR OPEN PEAK AND HOLD JUMPER. IF OK, REPLACE ECM.

REPAIR OPEN OR GROUNDED CIRCUIT BETWEEN CAVITY "A" OF 3 TERMINAL INJECTOR HARNESS CONNECTOR AND INJECTOR CONNECTOR.

NO   **YES**

REPLACE ANY INJECTOR THAT MEASURES UNDER 1.8 OHMS AND RECHECK FOR MISFIRE BEGINNING WITH STEP 1 AGAIN.

FAULTY ECM.

YES   **NO**

④
- REMOVE COIL HOUSING AND DISCONNECT COIL HARNESS AT MODULE.
- OBSERVE A TEST LIGHT CONNECTED BETWEEN MODULE TO COIL POWER TERMINAL "A" (PURPLE WIRE) & DRIVER TERMINAL ("B" OR "C") FOR AFFECTED COIL, WHILE CRANKING ENGINE.
- SHOULD BLINK. DOES IT?

CHECK FOR CORROSION AT COIL SECONDARY TERMINALS. IF TERMINALS ARE OK, THE IGNITION COIL IS FAULTY.

NO   **YES**

POOR CONNECTION OR FAULTY IDI MODULE.

OPEN OR SHORTED COIL HARNESS, POOR COIL CONNECTION, FAULTY COIL OR BOOT ASSEMBLY.

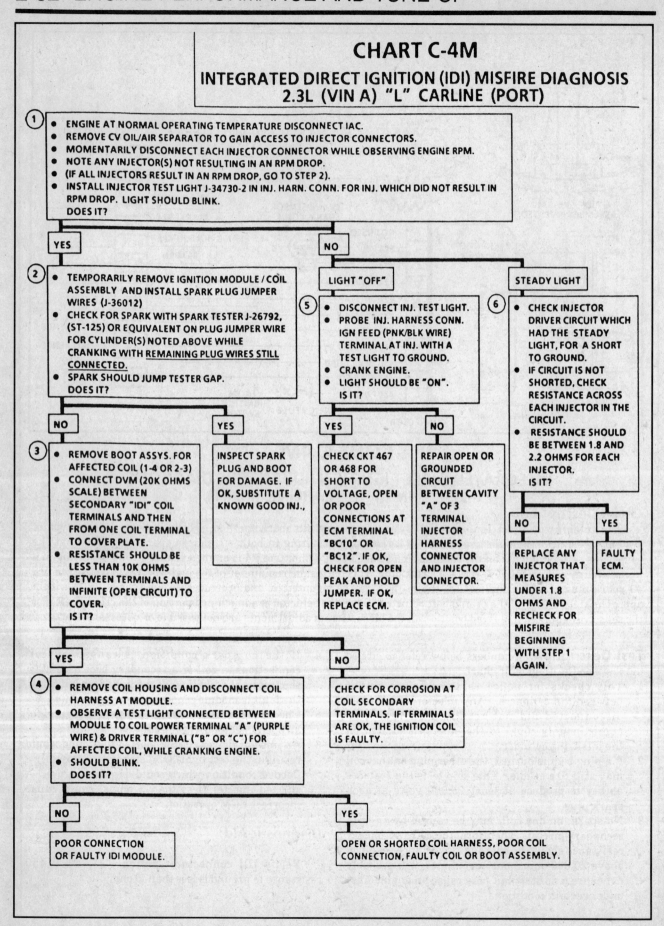

6. Position the ignition assembly to the engine while carefully aligning the boots to the spark plug terminals.

7. Coat the ignition assembly-to-camshaft housing attaching bolts with an approved lubricant and install them into the housing.

8. Tighten the attaching bolts to 19 ft. lbs. (26 Nm).

9. Connect the harness connector to the ignition coil module assembly.

10. Connect the negative battery cable.

11. Start the engine and test the engine performance.

CRANKSHAFT SENSOR

Removal and Installation

♦ SEE FIG. 36

1. Disconnect the negative battery cable.

2. Disconnect the harness connector at the crankshaft sensor.

3. Remove the sensor attaching bolt.

4. Remove the crankshaft sensor from the engine.

5. Inspect the sensor O-ring for wear, cracks or signs of leakage. Replace it if necessary.

To install:

6. Lubricate the O-ring with engine oil and install it on the sensor.

7. Position the sensor to the engine block and install the attaching bolt. Tighten the attaching bolt to 88 inch lbs. (10 Nm).

8. Connect the sensor harness connector.

9. Connect the negative battery cable.

10. Start the engine and test engine performance.

IGNITION COIL

Removal and Installation

♦ SEE FIG. 37

1. Disconnect the negative battery cable.

2. Disconnect the harness connector from the coil and module assembly.

3. Remove the ignition assembly-to-camshaft housing attaching bolts.

4. Carefully remove the ignition assembly from the engine.

➡ **If the spark plug boots present a problem coming off, it may be necessary to use a special removal tool, first twisting and pulling upward on the retainers.**

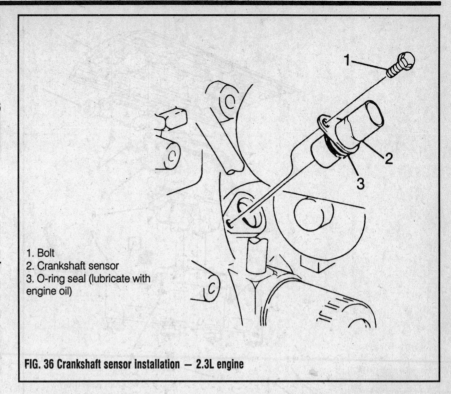

1. Bolt
2. Crankshaft sensor
3. O-ring seal (lubricate with engine oil)

FIG. 36 Crankshaft sensor installation — 2.3L engine

5. Remove the ignition coil housing-to-cover bolts.

6. Remove the cover from the coil housing.

7. Disconnect the ignition coil harness connectors from the coil pack assembly.

8. Carefully lift the coil pack out and remove the contacts and seals from the housing.

To install:

9. Install new coil seals into the coil housing.

10. Install the coil contacts to the coil housing and retain with petroleum jelly.

11. Place the coil pack into the housing and connect the harness connectors.

12. Assemble the cover to the coil housing and install the attaching bolts. Tighten the attaching bolts to 35 inch lbs. (4 Nm).

13. Install the spark plug boots and retainers on the ignition assembly housing secondary terminals.

➡ **If the boots and retainers are not in place on the housing secondary terminals prior to installing the ignition assembly, damage to the ignition system may result.**

14. Position the ignition assembly to the engine while carefully aligning the boots to the spark plug terminals.

15. Coat the ignition assembly-to-camshaft housing attaching bolts with an approved lubricant and install them into the housing.

16. Tighten the attaching bolts to 19 ft. lbs. (26 Nm).

17. Connect the harness connector to the ignition coil module assembly.

18. Connect the negative battery cable.

19. Start the engine and test the engine performance.

IGNITION MODULE

Removal and Installation

♦ SEE FIG. 37

1. Disconnect the negative battery cable.

2. Disconnect the harness connector from the coil and module assembly.

3. Remove the ignition assembly-to-camshaft housing attaching bolts.

4. Carefully remove the ignition assembly from the engine.

➡ **If the spark plug boots present a problem coming off, it may be necessary to use a special removal tool, first twisting and pulling upward on the retainers.**

5. Remove the ignition coil housing-to-cover bolts.

6. Remove the cover from the coil housing.

7. Disconnect the coil harness connector from the module.

8. Remove the screws attaching the module to the ignition assembly cover.

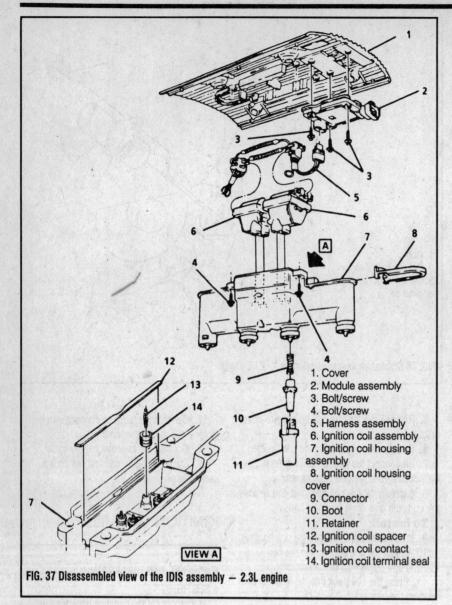

1. Cover
2. Module assembly
3. Bolt/screw
4. Bolt/screw
5. Harness assembly
6. Ignition coil assembly
7. Ignition coil housing assembly
8. Ignition coil housing cover
9. Connector
10. Boot
11. Retainer
12. Ignition coil spacer
13. Ignition coil contact
14. Ignition coil terminal seal

VIEW A

FIG. 37 Disassembled view of the IDIS assembly — 2.3L engine

➡ **If the same module is going to be replaced, take care not to remove the grease from the module or coil. If a new module is to be installed, a package of silicone grease will be included with it. This grease aids in preventing the module from overheating.**

To Install:

9. Place the module on the ignition cover and install the attaching bolts. Tighten the attaching bolts to 35 inch lbs. (4 Nm).

10. Connect the coil harness connector to the module.

11. Assemble the module cover to the coil housing and install the attaching bolts. Tighten the attaching bolts to 35 inch lbs. (4 Nm).

12. Install the spark plug boots and retainers on the ignition assembly housing secondary terminals.

➡ **If the boots and retainers are not in place on the housing secondary terminals prior to installing the ignition assembly, damage to the ignition system may result.**

13. Position the ignition assembly to the engine while carefully aligning the boots to the spark plug terminals.

14. Coat the ignition assembly-to-camshaft housing attaching bolts with an approved lubricant and install them into the housing.

15. Tighten the attaching bolts to 19 ft. lbs. (26 Nm).

16. Connect the harness connector to the ignition coil module assembly.

17. Connect the negative battery cable.

18. Start the engine and test the engine performance.

Valve Lash

All engines use hydraulic valve lifters. No adjustments are necessary.

Minimum Idle Speed Adjustment

Various engine sensors send signals to the ECM. The ECM then sends signals to the (IAC) Idle Air Control Valve and the (TPS) Throttle Position Sensor to control the idle speed. The throttle stop screw, used for regulating minimum idle speed, is adjusted at the factory. The screw is covered with a plug to discourage unauthorized adjustments. The only time it may necessary to adjust the screw is when the throttle body is being replaced. The engine should be at normal operating temperature before making adjustments. This procedure is not necessary on 1992 vehicles equipped with the 2.2L engine.

2.0L Engine

1987–88

1. Remove the TBI bonnet and gasket.

2. Pierce the idle stop screw plug with an awl and apply leverage to remove it.

3. Connect a tachometer to the engine.

4. Set the parking brake and block the drive wheels.

5. Start the engine, put the transmission in park (neutral on manual transmission) and allow the engine rpm to stabilize.

6. Disconnect the idle air control connector.

7. Install tool J–36377, or equivalent in the idle air passage of the TBI unit. Verify that no air leaks exist around tool J–36377.

8. On vehicles with automatic transmission, place the selector lever in **D** (drive) before making a adjustment.

9. Adjust the idle stop screw to obtain 650 ± 25 rpm.

10. On vehicles with automatic transmission, place the selector lever in **P** (park). Turn the ignition **OFF**, remove the IAC passage plug tool and reconnect IAC valve electrical connector.

11. Use silicone sealant, or equivalent, to cover the minimum air adjustment screw.

12. Install the TBI bonnet. Replace the gasket if necessary.

1989

1. Block the drive wheels and apply the parking brake. Run the engine to normal operating temperature.

2. Remove the air cleaner assembly or air duct.

3. Remove the hoses and plug any possible air sources on the tube manifold assembly.

4. Disconnect the throttle cable.

5. Ground the diagnostic test terminal in the ALDL connector.

6. Turn the ignition **ON**, leaving the engine **OFF**. Wait at least 30 seconds to allow the IAC pintle to seat in the throttle body.

7. With the ignition **ON**, the engine stopped, test terminal still grounded, disconnect the IAC valve electrical terminal.

8. Connect a tachometer to the engine or use a scan tool, if available, to monitor the engine speed.

9. Remove the ground from the diagnostic test terminal, place the transmission in **PARK** or **NEUTRAL** and start the engine. It may be necessary to depress the accelerator in order to start the engine. Allow the engine speed to stabilize.

➡ **Before proceeding, make sure all the accessories are turned OFF** and the engine cooling fan is not in operation.

10. If the idle speed is not 450–550 rpm, adjust as necessary.

11. Install the throttle cable and make sure the idle speed is not affected.

12. Turn the ignition **OFF** and reconnect the IAC valve electrical connection.

13. Unplug and reconnect any vacuum ports which were plugged.

14. Install the air cleaner assembly or air duct.

2.2L Engine

1990–91

➡ **This procedure requires the use of a scan tool to plug into the ALDL terminal.**

1. Block the drive wheels and apply the parking brake. Run the engine to normal operating temperature.

2. Connect a scan tool to the ALDL connector.

3. Select the "Field Service Mode" on the scan tool. This will cause the IAC valve pintle to seat in the throttle body, closing the air passage. Wait at least 45 seconds, disconnect the IAC valve connector then exit the "Field Service Mode".

4. Place the transmission in **PARK** or **NEUTRAL** and start the engine. It may be necessary to depress the accelerator in order to start the engine. Allow the engine speed to stabilize.

➡ **Before proceeding, make sure all the accessories are turned OFF** and the engine cooling fan is not in operation.

5. If the idle speed is not 450–550 rpm, adjust as necessary.

6. Turn the ignition **OFF** and reconnect the IAC valve electrical connection.

7. Reset the IAC valve pintle position as follows:

   a. Select "Engine rpm" on the scan tool.

   b. Start the engine and hold the speed above 2000 rpm.

   c. Select the "Field Service Mode" on the scan tool, for 10 seconds. This will reset the IAC pintle position.

   d. Exit the "Field Service Mode", and allow the engine to return to idle.

   e. Turn the ignition **OFF**, then restart and check for proper operation.

   f. Unblock the drive wheels.

2.8L Engine

1987–88

Various engine sensors send signals to the ECM. The ECM then sends signals to the (IAC) Idle Air Control Valve and the (TPS) Throttle Position Sensor to control the idle speed. The throttle stop screw, used for regulating minimum idle speed, is adjusted at the factory. The screw is covered with a plug to discourage unauthorized adjustments. Adjustment should not be necessary, however if it is necessary to gain access to the idle stop screw assembly use the following procedure:

➡ **Foreign material accumulating in the throttle body bore, on the throttle valve or on the throttle shaft, may result in a minimum idle speed that is not at specification. Clean the throttle body assembly as required and check the throttle assembly for smooth operation through the entire range of travel. Correct any problems found. Then, if necessary, adjust the minimum idle speed.**

The engine should be at normal operating temperature before making adjustments.

1. With the IAC valve connected, ground the diagnostic **TEST** terminal.

2. Turn **ON** the ignition, but do not start the engine. Wait at least 30 seconds.

3. With the ignition**ON**, disconnect the IAC electrical connector.

4. Remove the ground from the diagnostic lead and start the engine. Allow the system to go to closed loop.

5. Adjust the idle stop screw to:

   • Automatic transmission — 550 rpm in drive

   • Manual transmission — 650 rpm in neutral

6. Turn the ignition **OFF** and reconnect the connector at the IAC valve.

7. Start the engine and check the idle operation.

1989

➡ **This procedure requires the use of a scan tool to plug into the ALDL terminal.**

1. Back the throttle stop screw out until an air gap between the screw and the throttle lever can be seen by looking downward from above the throttle body.

2. Turn the stop screw until it just contacts the throttle lever.

3. Turn the stop screw in $1^1/_2$ turns further.

4. Place the transmission in **PARK** or **NEUTRAL**.

5. Block the drive wheel and apply the parking brake.

6. Connect the scan tool to the ALDL connector.

7. Start the engine and allow it to reach normal operating temperature and "Closed Loop". Run the engine until the IAC has relearned its controlled idle position.

8. Using the scan tool, observe the idle air control (IAC) valve counts. With the engine satbilized, the IAC valve should be 10–15 counts.

➡ **The IAC valve counts should be check with all accesories and cooling fan OFF.**

9. If the IAC counts are out of the acceptable range, the adjustment may be tailored as follows:

   a. For more throttle valve opening, lower the IAC valve counts.

   b. For less throttle valve opening, higher the IAC valve counts.

   c. If it is necessary to change the adjustment more than one half turn either way, check for other causes of incorrect idle speed.

3.1L Engine

1990–92

➡ **This procedure requires the use of a scan tool to plug into the ALDL terminal.**

1. Back the throttle stop screw out until an air gap between the screw and the throttle lever can be seen by looking downward from above the throttle body.

2. Turn the stop screw until it just contacts the throttle lever.

3. Turn the stop screw in $1^1/_2$ turns further.

➡ **The ECM will need to relearn the IAC pintle position following battery reconnect. Refer to the Idle Learn Procedure for inputing this information immediately.**

4. Place the transmission in **PARK** or **NEUTRAL**.

5. Block the drive wheel and apply the parking brake.

6. Connect the scan tool to the ALDL connector.

7. Start the engine and allow it to reach normal operating temperature and "Closed Loop". Run the engine until the IAC has relearned its controlled idle position.

8. Using the scan tool, observe the idle air control (IAC) valve counts. With the engine satbilized, the IAC valve should be 10–20 counts.

➡ The IAC valve counts should be check with all accesories and cooling fan OFF.

9. If the IAC counts are out of the acceptable range, repeat adjustment.

IDLE LEARN PROCEDURE

3.1L Engine

Any time the battery is disconnected, the programmed position of the IAC valve pintle is lost, and replaced with a default value until the vehicle is driven and has time to relearn the correct IAC pintle position. To return the IAC valve pintle to the correct position immediately, perform the following:

1. Reconnect the battery.

2. Install a Tech 1 scan tool.

3. Select **IAC SYSTEM**, then **IDLE LEARN** in the **MISC TEST** mode.

4. Proceed with the idle learn as directed by the scan tool.

TORQUE SPECIFICATIONS

Component	U.S.	Metric
Spark Plugs		
1987-88		
2.0L engine:	11-18 ft. lbs.	15-22 Nm
2.8L engine:	20 ft. lbs.	27 Nm
1989		
2.0L engine:	7-20 ft. lbs.	10-27 Nm
2.8L engine:	20 ft. lbs.	27 Nm
1990		
2.2L engine:	11 ft. lbs.	15 Nm
2.3L engine:	17 ft. lbs.	22 Nm
3.1L engine:	20 ft. lbs.	27 Nm
1991		
2.2L engine:	11 ft. lbs.	15 Nm
2.3L engine:	22 ft. lbs.	18 Nm
3.1L engine:	18 ft. lbs.	24 Nm
1992		
2.2L engine:	11 ft. lbs.	15 Nm
2.3L engine:	20 ft. lbs.	27 Nm
3.1L engine:	11 ft. lbs.	15 Nm
Direct Ignition System		
Crankshaft sensor:	71 inch lbs.	8 Nm
DIS assembly:	19 ft. lbs.	26 Nm
Indirect Ignition System		
Crankshaft sensor:	88 inch lbs.	10 Nm
Ignition assembly:	19 ft. lbs.	26 Nm
Ignition coil:	35 inch lbs.	4 Nm
Ignition module:	35 inch lbs.	4 Nm

3

ENGINE AND ENGINE OVERHAUL

THE ENGINE ELECTRICAL SYSTEM

The engine electrical system can be broken down into three separate and distinct systems:
1. The starting system
2. The charging system
3. The ignition system

Battery and Starting System

The battery is the first link in the chain of mechanisms which work together to provide cranking of the automobile engine. In most modern cars, the battery is a lead-acid electrochemical device consisting of six 2 volt (2V) subsections connected in series so the unit is capable of producing approximately 12V of electrical pressure. Each subsection, or sell, consists of a series of positive and negative plates held a short distance apart in a solution of sulfuric acid and water. The two types of plates are of dissimilar metals. This causes a chemical reaction to be set up, and it is this reaction which produces current flow from the battery when its positive and negative terminals are connected to an electrical appliance such as a lamp or motor. The continued transfer of electrons would eventually convert the sulfuric acid in the electrolyte to water, and make the two plates identical in chemical composition. As electrical energy is removed from the battery, its voltage output tend to drop. Thus, measuring battery voltage and battery electrolyte composition are two ways of checking the ability of the unit to supply power. During the starting of the engine, electrical energy is removed from the battery. However, if the charging circuit is in good condition and the operating conditions are normal, the power removed from the battery will be replaced by the generator (or alternator) which will force electrons back through the battery, reversing the normal flow, and restoring the battery to its original chemical state.

The battery and starting motor are linked by very heavy electrical cables designed to minimize resistance to the flow of current. Generally, the major power supply cable that leaves the battery goes directly to the starter, while other electrical system needs are supplied by a smaller cable. During the starter operation, power flows from the battery to the starter and is grounded through the car's frame and the battery's negative ground strap.

The starting motor is a specially designed, direct current electric motor capable of producing a very great amount of power for its size. One thing that allows the motor to produce a great deal of power is its tremendous rotating speed. It drives the engine through a tiny pinion gear (attached to the starter's armature), which drives the very large flywheel ring gear at a greatly reduced speed. Another factor allowing it to produce so much power is that only intermittent operation is required of it. Thus, little allowance for air circulation is required, and the windings can be built into a very small space.

The starter solenoid is a magnetic device which employs the small current supplied by the starting switch circuit of the ignition switch. This magnetic action moves a plunger which mechanically engages the starter and electrically closes the heavy switch which connects it to the battery. The starting switch circuit consists of the starting switch contained within the ignition switch, a transmission neutral safety switch or clutch pedal switch, and the wiring necessary to connect these with the starter solenoid or relay.

A pinion, which is a small gear, is mounted to a one-way drive clutch. this clutch is splined to the starter armature shaft. When the ignition switch is moved to the start position, the solenoid plunger slides the pinion toward the flywheel ring gear via a collar and spring. If the teeth on the pinion and flywheel match properly, the pinion will engage the flywheel immediately. IF the gear teeth butt one another, the spring will be compressed and will force the gears to mesh as soon as the starter turns far enough to allow them to do so. As the solenoid plunger reaches the end of its travel, it closes the contacts that connect the battery and starter and then the engine is cranked.

As soon as the engine starts, the flywheel ring gear begins turning fast enough to drive the pinion at an extremely high rate of speed. At this point, the one-way clutch begins allowing the pinion to spin faster that the starter shaft so that the starter will not operate at excessive speed. When the ignition switch is released from the starter position, the solenoid is de-energized, and a spring contained within the solenoid assembly pulls the gear out of mesh and interrupts the current flow to the starter.

Some starters employ a separate relay, mounted away from the starter, to switch the motor and solenoid current on and off. The relay thus replaces the solenoid electrical switch, but does not eliminate the need for a solenoid mounted on the starter used to mechanically engage the starter drive gears. The relay is used to reduce the amount of current the starting switch must carry.

The Charging System

The automobile charging system provides electrical power for operation of the vehicle's ignition and starting systems and all the electrical accessories. The battery serves as an electrical surge of storage tank, storing (in chemical form) the energy originally produced by the engine driven generator. The system also provides a means of regulating generator output to protect the battery from being overcharged and to avoid excessive voltage to the accessories.

The storage battery is a chemical device incorporating parallel lead plates in a tank containing a sulfuric acid-water solution. Adjacent plates are slightly dissimilar, and the chemical reaction of the two dissimilar plates produces electrical energy when the battery is connected to a load such as the starter motor. The chemical reaction is reversible, so that when the generator is producing a voltage (electrical pressure) greater then that produced by the battery, electricity is forced into the battery, and the battery is returned to its fully charged state.

The vehicle's generator is driven mechanically, through V-belts, by the engine crankshaft. It consists of two coils of fine wire, one stationary (the stator), and one movable (the rotor). The rotor may also be known as the armature and consists of fine wire wrapped around an iron core which is mounted on a shaft. The electricity which flows through the two coils of wire (provided initially by the battery in some cases) creates an intense magnetic field around both rotor and stator, and the interaction between the two fields creates voltage, allowing the generator to power the accessories and charge the battery.

There are two types of generators; the earlier is the direct current (DC) type. The current produced by the DC generator is generated in the armature and carried off the spinning armature by stationary brushes contacting the commutator. The commutator is a series of smooth metal contact plates on the end of the armature. The commutator plates, which are separated from one another by a very short gap, are connected to the armature circuits so that current will flow in one direction only in wires carrying the generator output. The generator stator consists of two stationary coils of wire which draw some of the output current of the generator to form a powerful magnetic field and create the interaction of fields which generates the voltage. The generator field is wired in series with the regulator.

Newer automobiles use alternating current generators or alternators because they are more efficient, can be rotated at higher speeds, and have fewer brush problems, In an alternator, the field rotates while all the current produced passes only through the stator windings. The brushes bear against continuous slip rings rather than a commutator. This causes the current produced to periodically reverse the direction of its flow. Diodes (electrical one-way switches) block the flow of current from traveling in the wrong direction. A series of diodes is wired together to permit the alternating flow of the stator to be converted to a pulsating, but unidirectional flow of current from traveling in the wrong direction. A series of diodes is wires together to permit the alternating flow of the stator to be converted to a pulsating, but unidirectional flow at the alternator output. The alternator's field is wires in series with the voltage regulator.

The regulator consist of several circuits. Each circuit has a core, or magnetic coil of wire, which operates a switch. Each switch is connected to ground through on or more resistors. The coil of wire responds directly to system voltage. When the voltage reaches the required level, the magnetic field created by the winding of wire closes the switch and inserts a resistance into the generator field circuit, thus reducing the output. The contacts of the switch cycle open and close many times each second to precisely control voltage.

While alternators are self-limiting as far as maximum current is concerned. DC generators employ a current regulating circuit which responds directly to the total amount of current flowing through the generator circuit rather than to the output voltage. The current regulator is similar to the voltage regulator except all system current must flow through the energizing coil on its way to the various accessories.

SAFETY PRECAUTIONS

Observing these precautions will ensure safe handling of the electrical system components, and will avoid damage to the vehicle's electrical system:

a. Be absolutely sure of the polarity of a booster battery before making connections. Connect the cables positive to positive, and negative to negative. Connect positive cables first and then make the last connection to ground on the body of the booster vehicle so that arcing cannot ignite hydrogen gas that may have accumulated near the battery. Even momentary connection of a booster battery with the polarity reversed will damage alternator diodes.

b. Disconnect both vehicle battery cables before attempting to charge a battery.

c. Never ground the alternator or generator output or battery terminal. Be cautious when using metal tools around a battery to avoid creating a short circuit between the terminals.

d. Never ground the field circuit between the alternator and regulator.

e. Never run an alternator or generator without load unless the field circuit is disconnected.

f. Never attempt to polarize an alternator.

g. Keep the regulator cover in place when taking voltage and current limiter readings.

h. Use insulated tools when adjusting the regulator.

i. Whenever DC generator-to-regulator wires have been disconnected, the generator must be repolarized. To do this with an externally grounded, light duty generator, momentarily place a jumper wires between the battery terminal and the generator terminal of the regulator. With an internally grounded heavy duty unit, disconnect the wire to the regulator field terminal and touch the regulator battery terminal with it.

ENGINE ELECTRICAL

Ignition Coil

2.0L, 2.2L, 2.8L and 3.1L Engines

All models, except those equipped with the 2.3L VIN A engine, are equipped with a Direct Ignition System (DIS) which does not use the conventional distributor and ignition coil. The system consists of ignition module, crankshaft sensor or combination sensor, along with the related connecting wires and Electronic Spark Timing (EST) portion of the Electronic Control Module (ECM).

There are two separate twin tower coils for the 4-cylinder engines and three separate twin tower coils for the V6 engines, mounted to the coil/module assembly. Spark distribution is synchronized by a signal from the crankshaft sensor which the ignition module uses to trigger each coil at the proper time. Each coil provides the spark for two spark plugs simultaneously (Waste Spark Distribution). Each coil can be replaced separately.

2.3L Engine

All models, equipped the 2.3L engine, are equipped with the Integrated Direct Ignition System (IDIS) which consist of 2 separate ignition coils, an ignition module and a secondary conductor housing mounted to an aluminum cover plate. A crankshaft sensor, related connecting wires and an Electronic Spark Timing (EST) portion of the Electronic Control Module (ECM) make up the remainder of the system.

This system, being a distributorless ignition system, uses a waste spark method of spark distribution. Each cylinder is paired with its companion cylinder in the firing order. This places 1 cylinder on the compression stroke with the companion cylinder on the exhaust stroke. The cylinder that is on the exhaust stroke uses very little spark allowing most of the spark to go to the cylinder on the compression stroke. This process reverses when the cylinder roles reverse.

➡ **For servicing and testing the DIS and IDIS systems, please refer to Section 2.**

Alternator

The alternating current generator (alternator) supplies a continuous output of electrical energy at all engine speeds. The alternator generates electrical energy for the engine and all electrical components, and recharges the battery by supplying it with current. This unit consists of four main assemblies: two end frame assemblies, a rotor assembly, and a stator assembly. The rotor is supported in the drive end frame by a ball bearing and at the other end by a roller bearing. These bearings are lubricated during manufacture and require no maintenance. There are six diodes in the end frame assembly. Diodes are electrical check valves that change the alternating current supplied from the stator windings to a direct current (DC), delivered to the output (BAT) terminal. Three diodes are negative and are mounted flush with the end frame; the other three are positive and are mounted into a strip called a heat sink. The positive diodes are easily identified as the ones within small cavities or depressions. A capacitor, or condenser, mounted on the end frame protects the rectifier bridge and diode trio from high voltages, and suppresses radio noise. This capacitor requires no maintenance.

Two sizes of the CS series alternator are used on the Corsica/Beretta cars, the CS–121 and CS–130, denoting the OD in mm of the stator laminations.

➡ **The alternator is serviced as a complete assembly.**

ALTERNATOR PRECAUTIONS

1. When installing a battery, make sure that the positive and negative cables are not reversed.
2. When jump-starting the car, be sure that like terminals are connected. This also applies to using a battery charger. Reversed polarity will burn out the alternator and regulator in a matter of seconds.
3. Never operate the alternator with the battery disconnected or on an otherwise uncontrolled open circuit.
4. Do not short across or ground any alternator or regulator terminals.
5. Do not try to polarize the alternator.
6. Do not apply full battery voltage to the field (brown) connector.
7. Always disconnect the battery ground cable before disconnecting the alternator lead.
8. Always disconnect the battery (negative cable first) when charging it.
9. Never subject the alternator to excessive heat or dampness. If you are steam cleaning the engine, cover the alternator.
10. Never use arc-welding equipment on the car with the alternator connected.

CHARGING SYSTEM TROUBLESHOOTING

There are many possible ways in which the charging system can malfunction. Often the source of a problem is difficult to diagnose, requiring special equipment and a good deal of experience. This is usually not the case, however, where the charging system fails completely and causes the dash board warning light to come on or the battery to become dead. To troubleshoot a complete system failure only two pieces of equipment are needed: a test light, to determine that current is reaching a certain point; and a current indicator (voltmeter), to determine the direction of the current flow and its measurement in Volts.

This test works under three assumptions:
1. The battery is known to be good and fully charged.
2. The alternator belt is in good condition and adjusted to the proper tension.
3. All connections in the system are clean and tight.

➡ **In order for the current indicator to give a valid reading, the car must be equipped with battery cables which are of the same gauge size and quality as original equipment battery cables.**

4. For vehicles without charge indicator lamp, go to step 7.
5. With the switch **ON**, engine stopped, the lamp should be on. If not, detach the harness at the alternator and ground the **L** terminal.
• If the lamp lights, replace or repair the alternator.
• If the lamp does not light, locate the open circuit between the grounding lead and the ignition switch. Lamp may be open.
6. With the switch on and the engine running at moderate speed, the lamp should be off. If not, detach the wiring harness at the alternator.
• If the lamp goes off, replace or repair the alternator.
• If the lamp stays on, check for a grounded **L** terminal in the wiring harness.
7. Battery undercharged or overcharged.
• Detach the wiring harness connector from the alternator.
• With the switch on, engine not running, connect the voltmeter from ground to the **L** terminal.
• A zero reading indicates an open circuit between the terminal and the battery. Correct as required.
• Reconnect the harness connector to the alternator and run the engine at moderate speed.

• Measure the voltage across the battery. If above 16V, replace or repair alternator
8. Turn on the accessories, load the battery with a carbon pile (variable rheostat that controls the flow of electric current) to obtain maximum amperage. Maintain voltage at 13V or below.
• If within 15 amperes of rated output, the alternator is ok.
• If not within 15 amperes of rated output, replace or repair alternator.

REMOVAL & INSTALLATION

➡ **All alternators are serviced as a complete assembly.**

2.0 and 2.2L Engines

1. Disconnect the negative battery cable at the battery.

✳✳ CAUTION

Failure to disconnect the negative cable may result in injury from the positive battery lead at the alternator, and may short the alternator and regulator during the removal process.

2. Disconnect and label the two terminal plug and the battery leads from the rear of the alternator.
3. Remove the 3 bolts to generator brace.
4. Remove the upper bracket nut at the exhaust manifold.
5. Remove the upper bracket bolt.
6. Remove the upper bracket with the heat shield and remove the alternator.
To install:
6. Position the alternator and connect the electrical connections.
7. Install the upper bracket with the heat.
8. Install the upper bracket bolt and nut.
9. Install the 3 alternator mounting bolts.
10. Tighten the upper bracket bolt and bracket nut to 22 ft. lbs. (30 Nm).
11. Tighten the 2 upper alternator mounting bolts to 22 ft. lbs. (30 Nm).
12. Tighten the lower alternator mounting bolt and nut to 33 ft. lbs. (45 Nm).

2.8L and 3.1L Engines

1. Disconnect the negative battery cable.
2. Remove the serpentine drive belt.
3. Label and disconnect the electrical connectors from the back of the alternator.
4. Remove the alternator mounting bolts.

5. Remove the alternator-to-bracket bolts and the alternator.

To install:

6. Position the alternator to the mounting bracket and install the attaching bolts.

7. Tighten the rear stud and bolt to 18 ft. lbs. (25 Nm).

8. Tighten the front bolt to 18 ft. lbs. (25 Nm).

9. Tighten the rear bolt to support to 37 ft. lbs. (50 Nm).

10. Connect the alternator electrical connectors to the rear of the alternator.

11. Install the serpentine drive belt.

12. Connect the negative battery cable.

13. Start the engine and perform a charging system test.

2.3L Engine

1. Disconnect the negative battery cable.
2. Remove the serpentine drive belt.

✖ CAUTION

To avoid personal injury when rotating the serpentine belt tensioner, be sure to use a tight fitting 13mm wrench at least 24 in. (610mm) long.

3. Remove the coolant and washer reservoir attaching screws.

4. Disconnect the washer pump electrical connector and position the reservoir to the side.

5. Remove the air conditioner line rail clip.

6. Disconnect the 2 vacuum lines at the front of the engine and remove vacuum harness attaching bracket, as required.

7. Disconnect and tag electrical connections from injector harness and alternator.

8. Remove the rear alternator mounting bolts.

9. Remove the front alternator mounting bolt and engine harness clip.

10. Carefully remove the alternator from between the mounting bracket and the air conditioning and condenser hose.

➡ **Extreme care must be taken when removing or installing the alternator as not to damage the air conditioner compressor and condenser hoses.**

To install:

11. Place the alternator between the air conditioner compressor and condenser hoses and install it on the bracket.

12. Install the rear mounting bolt. Tighten the mounting bolt to 19 ft. lbs. (26 Nm).

FIG. 1A Use a small prying tool to unlock the alternator wiring connector–1992 2.2L engine

FIG. 1B Alternator removal–1992 2.2L engine

FIG. 1C Alternator removal–1992 2.2L engine

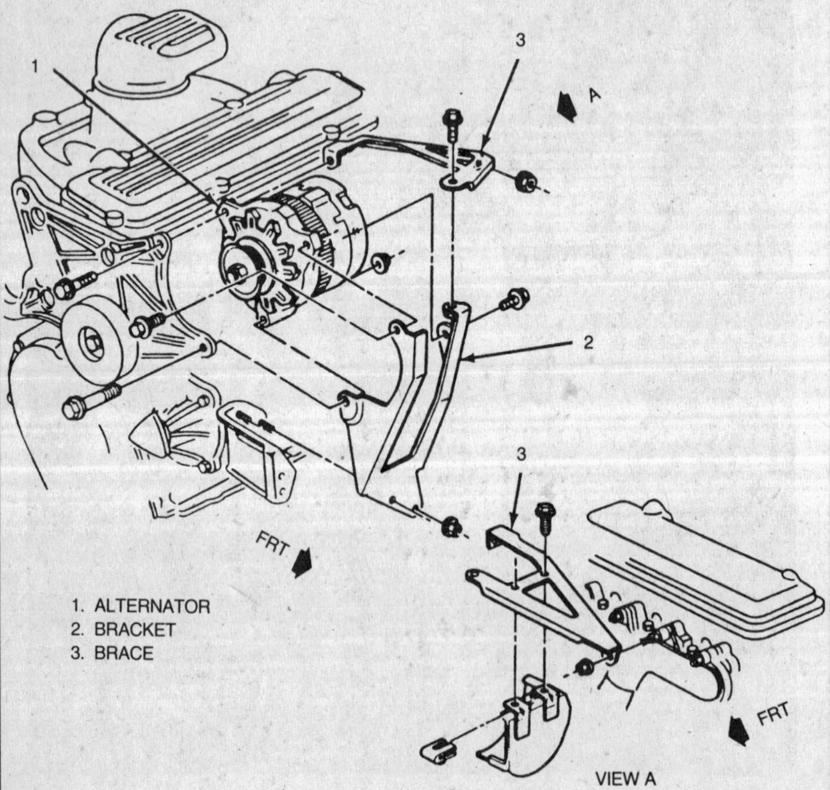

1. ALTERNATOR
2. BRACKET
3. BRACE

VIEW A

FIG. 1 Alternator mounting — 2.0L and 2.2L engines

13. Install the front mounting bolts. Tighten the upper mounting bolt to 37 ft. lbs. (50 Nm) and the lower mounting bolt to 19 ft. lbs. (26 Nm).

14. Install the serpentine drive belt.

> ❊❊ **CAUTION**
>
> **To avoid personal injury when rotating the serpentine belt tensioner, be sure to use a tight fitting 13mm wrench at least 24 in. (610mm) long.**

15. Install the air conditioner rail clip.

16. Connect the washer pump electrical connector.

17. Install the coolant and washer pump reservoir.

18. Connect the electrical connections for the alternator and injector harness.

19. If removed, install the vacuum harness attaching bracket and connect the vacuum lines at the front of the engine.

20. Connect the negative battery cable.

21. Start the engine and perform a charging system test.

Regulator

A solid state regulator is mounted within the alternator. All regulator components are enclosed in a solid mold. The regulator is non-adjustable and requires no maintenance.

Battery

Refer to Section 1 for details on battery maintenance.

REMOVAL & INSTALLATION

1. Disconnect the negative (ground) cable first, then the positive cable. The side terminal cables are retained only by the center bolt.

> ❊❊ **CAUTION**
>
> **To avoid sparks, always disconnect the negative cable first, and connect it last.**

2. Remove the battery holddown clamp.

3. Remove the battery.

4. Before installing the battery, clean the

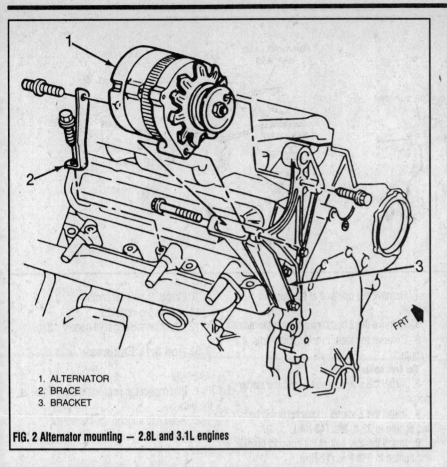

1. ALTERNATOR
2. BRACE
3. BRACKET

FIG. 2 Alternator mounting — 2.8L and 3.1L engines

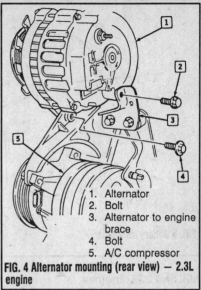

1. Alternator
2. Bolt
3. Alternator to engine brace
4. Bolt
5. A/C compressor

FIG. 4 Alternator mounting (rear view) — 2.3L engine

battery terminals and the cables thoroughly.

5. Check the battery tray to be sure it is clear of any debris. If it is rusty, it should be wire-brushed clean and given a coat of anti-rust paint, or replaced.

6. Install the battery in the tray, being sure it is centered in the lip.

7. Install the holddown clamp. Tighten to 6 ft. lbs., which is tight enough to hold the battery in place, but loose enough to prevent the case from cracking.

8. Connect the positive, then the negative battery cables. Installation torque for the cables is 19 ft. lbs. Give the terminals a light external coat of grease after installation to retard corrosion.

Starter

REMOVAL & INSTALLATION

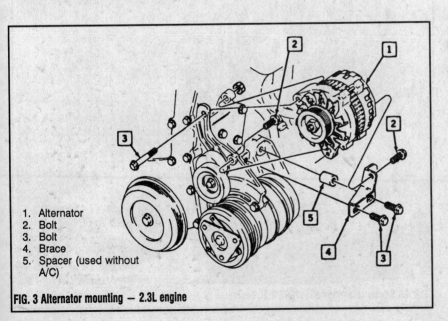

1. Alternator
2. Bolt
3. Bolt
4. Brace
5. Spacer (used without A/C)

FIG. 3 Alternator mounting — 2.3L engine

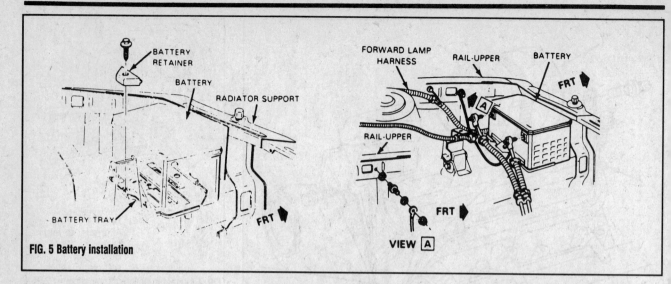

FIG. 5 Battery installation

2.0L and 2.2L Engines

1987–88

1. Disconnect the negative battery cable at the battery.

2. Raise and support the car safely.

3. Remove the solenoid wires and the battery cable.

4. Remove the rear motor support bracket.

5. Remove the air conditioning compressor support rod (if so equipped).

4. Remove the two starter-to-engine bolts, and allow the starter to drop down. Note the location and number of any shims (if used). Remove the starter.

5. Installation is the reverse of removal. Torque the 2 mounting bolts to 26–37 ft. lbs. (30–50 Nm).

1989–92

1. Disconnect the negative battery cable at the battery.

2. Raise and support the car safely.

3. Remove the solenoid wires and the battery cable.

4. Remove the one bolt at the support bracket.

5. Remove the 2 bolts from the starter motor.

6. Remove the starter motor and shims, if equipped.

To Install:

7. Install the shims, if used, and the starter motor.

8. Install the 2 starter motor retaining bolts and tighten to 32 ft. lbs. (43 Nm).

9. Install the one bolt at the support bracket and tighten to 9 ft. lbs. (12 Nm).

10. Install the starter motor wiring.

11. Lower the vehicle.

12. Connect the negative battery cable.

2.8L and 3.1L Engines

1987–88

1. Disconnect the negative battery cable at the battery.

2. Raise and support the car safely.

3. Remove the solenoid wires and the battery cable.

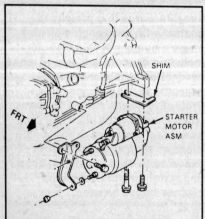

FIG. 6 Starter mounting — 2.0L and 2.2L engines

FIG. 6A Starter retaining bolts–1992 2.2L engine

4. Remove the 2 starter motor to engine bolts and remove the starter. Note the location and number of any shims (if used).

5. Installation is the reverse of removal. Tighten the 2 retaining bolts to 32 ft. lbs. (43 Nm).

1989

1. Disconnect the negative battery cable at the battery.

2. Raise and support the car safely.

3. Remove the solenoid wires and the battery cable.

5. Place a drain pan under the engine oil pan and remove the oil filter.

6. Remove the 2 starter motor to engine bolts and remove the starter. Note the location and number of any shims (if used).

7. Installation is the reverse of removal. Tighten the 2 retaining bolts to 32 ft. lbs. (43 Nm).

1990

1. Disconnect the negative battery cable.

2. Remove the air cleaner assembly, as required.

3. Raise and safely support the vehicle.

➡ **If equipped with an oil cooler, remove the oil filter and position the hose next to the starter to the side.**

4. Remove the air conditioning compressor brace attaching nuts and remove the brace from the engine, as required.

5. Remove flywheel inspection cover bolts and remove the inspection cover, as required.

6. Remove the starter attaching bolts.

7. Carefully lower the starter and remove the shims. Note the number and position of any shims.

8. Disconnect the electrical wiring connections at the starter.

To install:

9. Connect the electrical connections to the starter.

10. Position the shims in place and install the starter and mounting bolts. Tighten the bolts to 32 ft. lbs. (43 Nm).

➡ **If equipped with an oil cooler, position the cooler hose next to the starter motor and install the oil filter.**

11. If removed, install the flywheel inspection cover and attaching bolts.

12. If removed, install the air conditioning compressor brace and attaching nuts.

13. Lower vehicle and connect the negative battery cable.

14. If removed, install the air cleaner assembly.

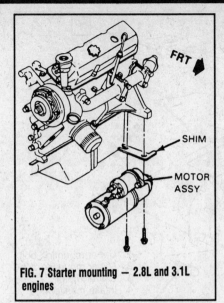

FIG. 7 Starter mounting — 2.8L and 3.1L engines

15. Crank the engine and check the starter operation.

1991–92

1. Disconnect the negative battery cable at the battery.

2. Raise and support the car safely.

3. Remove the solenoid wires and the battery cable.

4. Remove the 2 starter motor to engine bolts and remove the starter. Note the location and number of any shims (if used).

5. Installation is the reverse of removal. Tighten the 2 retaining bolts to 32 ft. lbs. (43 Nm).

2.3L ENGINE

1990

1. Disconnect the negative battery cable.

2. Disconnect the electrical connector from the cooling fan.

3. Remove the cooling fan mounting bolts and remove the fan assembly.

4. Remove the intake manifold-to-engine brace bolts and remove the brace from the engine.

5. Remove the starter mounting bolts.

6. Carefully lift the starter away from the engine with the solenoid harness attached to it.

7. When the starter is clear, disconnect the solenoid harness connections and lift the starter up and out toward the front of the vehicle.

To install:

8. Connect the solenoid harness connections to the starter, while supporting the starter toward the mounting position.

9. Rotate the starter so the solenoid faces the engine at a slight angle to clear the bottom of the intake manifold.

10. Install the starter to the engine and install the mounting bolts. Tighten the bolts to 32 ft. lbs. (43 Nm).

11. Install the intake manifold-to-engine brace and the attaching bolts.

12. Install the cooling fan and attaching bolts. Tighten bolts to 89 inch lbs. (10 Nm).

13. Connect the negative battery cable.

14. Crank the engine and check starter operation.

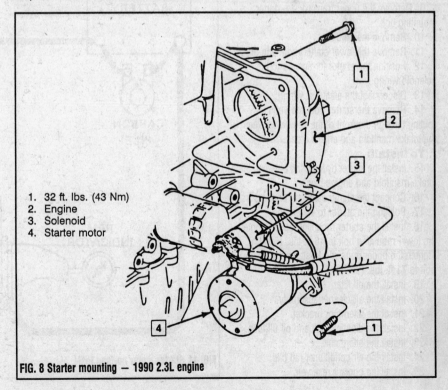

1. 32 ft. lbs. (43 Nm)
2. Engine
3. Solenoid
4. Starter motor

FIG. 8 Starter mounting — 1990 2.3L engine

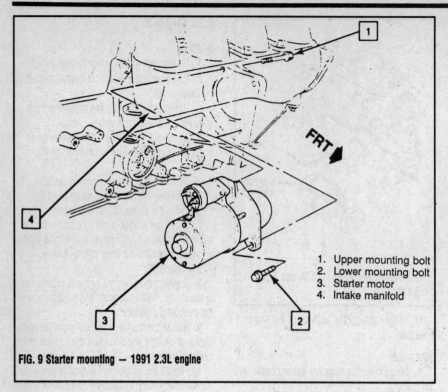

FIG. 9 Starter mounting — 1991 2.3L engine

1. Upper mounting bolt
2. Lower mounting bolt
3. Starter motor
4. Intake manifold

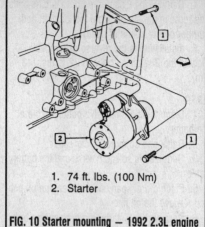

1. 74 ft. lbs. (100 Nm)
2. Starter

FIG. 10 Starter mounting — 1992 2.3L engine

1991

1. Disconnect the negative battery cable.
2. Remove the serpentine drive belt.
3. Remove the coolant reservoir.
4. Remove the air conditioner rail clip.
5. Remove the alternator.
6. Remove the dipstick, bolt and oil filler tube.
7. Remove the alternator bracket.
8. Remove the air cleaner assembly.
9. Remove the upper transaxle-to-starter mounting bolt.
10. Remove the oil filter.
11. Remove the lower starter mounting bolt.
12. Position the starter for access to the solenoid wiring.
13. Disconnect the electrical wiring.
14. Remove the starter from the vehicle, routing through the front of the engine between the intake manifold and engine block.

To Install:

15. Install the starter by lowering between the intake manifold and engine block.
16. Connect the starter electrical connectors.
17. Position the starter to the engine.
18. Install the starter mounting bolts. Tighten the lower mounting bolt to 46 ft. lbs. (63 Nm). Tighten the upper transaxle-to-starter mounting bolt to 71 ft. lbs. (96 Nm).
19. Install the oil filter.
20. Install the air cleaner assembly.
21. Install the alternator bracket.
22. Install the dipstick, bolt and oil fill tube.
23. Install the alternator.
24. Install the air conditioner rail clip.
25. Install the coolant reservoir.
26. Install the serpentine belt.
27. Connect the negative battery cable.
28. Refill the engine oil as necessary and check for leaks.

1992

1. Disconnect the negative battery cable.
2. Disconnect the air induction tubing, as necessary.
3. Remove the oil filter.
4. Remove the starter mounting bolts.
5. Disconnect the electrical wiring and remove the starter.

To Install:

1. Position the starter to the engine and connect the electrical wiring.

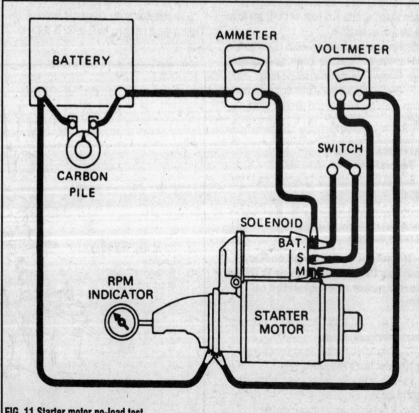

FIG. 11 Starter motor no-load test

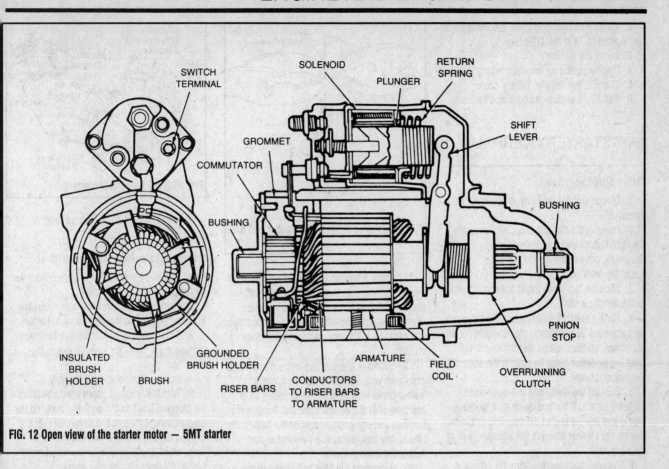

FIG. 12 Open view of the starter motor — 5MT starter

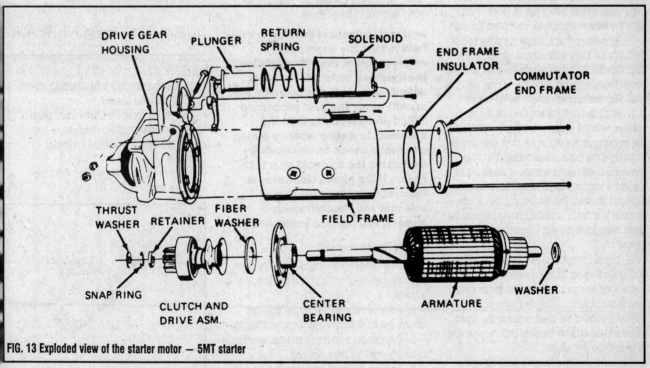

FIG. 13 Exploded view of the starter motor — 5MT starter

2. Install the upper and lower mounting bolts and tighten to 74 ft lbs. (100 Nm).

3. Install the oil filter.

4. Reconnect the air induction tubing.

5. Connect the negative battery cable.

6. Refill with engine oil and check for leaks.

5MT STARTER OVERHAUL

Drive Replacement

1. Disconnect the field coil straps from the solenoid.

2. Remove the through-bolts, and separate the commutator end frame, field frame assembly, drive housing, and armature assembly from each other.

3. Slide the two piece thrust collar off the end of the armature shaft.

4. Slide a suitably sized metal cylinder, such as a standard 1/2 in. (13mm) pipe coupling, or an old pinion, on the shaft so that the end of the coupling or pinion butts up against the edge of the pinion retainer.

5. Support the lower end of the armature securely on a soft surface, such as a wooden block, and tap the end of the coupling or pinion, driving the retainer towards the armature end of the snapring.

6. Remove the snapring from the groove in the armature shaft with a pair of pliers. Then, slide the retainer and starter drive from the shaft.

7. To reassemble, lubricate the drive end of the armature shaft with silicone lubricant, and then slide the starter drive onto the shaft with the pinion facing outward. Slide the retainer onto the shaft with the cupped surface facing outward.

8. Again support the armature on a soft surface, with the pinion at the upper end. Center the snapring on the top of the shaft (use a new snapring if the original was damaged during removal). Gently place a block of wood flat on top of the snapring so as not to move it from a centered position. Tap the wooden block with a hammer in order to force the snapring around the shaft. Then, slide the ring down into the snapring groove.

9. Lay the armature down flat on the surface you're working on. Slide the retainer close up on to the shaft and position it and the thrust collar next to the snapring. Using two pairs of pliers on opposite sides of the shaft, squeeze the thrust collar and the retainer together until the snapring is forced into the retainer.

10. Lube the drive housing bushing with a silicone lubricant. Then, install the armature and clutch assembly into the drive housing, engaging the solenoid shift lever with the clutch, and positioning the front end of armature shaft into the bushing.

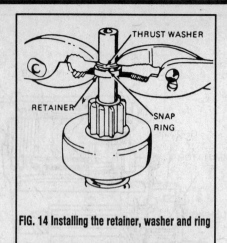

FIG. 14 Installing the retainer, washer and ring

11. Apply a sealing compound approved for this application onto the drive housing; then position the field frame around the armature shaft and against the drive housing. Work slowly and carefully to prevent damaging the starter brushes.

12. Lubricate the bushing in the commutator end frame with a silicone lubricant, place the leather brake washer onto the armature shaft, and then slide the commutator end frame over the shaft and into position against the field frame. Line up the bolt holes, and then install and tighten the through-bolts.

13. Reconnect the field coil straps to the motor terminal of the solenoid.

➡ **If replacement of the starter drive fails to cure the improper engagement of the starter pinion to the flywheel, there are probably defective parts in the solenoid and/or shift lever. The best procedure would probably be to take the assembly to a shop where a pinion clearance check can be made by energizing the solenoid on a test bench. If the pinion clearance is incorrect, disassemble the solenoid and the shift lever, inspect, and replace worn parts.**

Brush Replacement

1. After removing the starter from the engine, disconnect the field coil from the motor solenoid terminal.

2. Remove the starter through-bolts and remove the commutator end frame and washer.

3. Remove the field frame and the armature assembly from the drive housing.

4. Remove the brush holder from the brush support.

5. Remove the screw from the brush holder and separate the brush and holder.

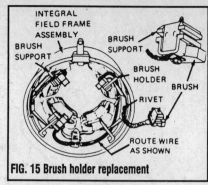

FIG. 15 Brush holder replacement

6. Installation is in the reverse order of removal.

Starter Solenoid Replacement

1. Remove the screw and washer from the motor connector strap terminal.

2. Remove the 2 screws which retain the solenoid housing to the end frame assembly.

3. Twist the solenoid clockwise to remove the flange key from the keyway slot in the housing.

4. Remove the solenoid assembly.

5. With the solenoid return spring installed on the plunger, position the solenoid body on the drive housing and turn it counterclockwise to engage the flange key in the keyway slot.

6. Install the 2 screws which retain the solenoid housing to the end frame.

SD200 STARTER OVERHAUL

◆ SEE FIG. 17

1. Remove the field lead attaching screw from the solenoid terminal.

2. Note the locations(bolts have different heads) and remove the through bolts and commutator end frame from the motor assembly.

3. Remove the brake washer from the armature shaft.

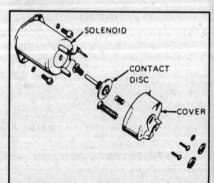

FIG. 16 The starter solenoid switch is serviced as an assembly. The cover may be removed to inspect the contacts and contact disc, if necessary

4. Remove the frame and field assembly from the drive end housing and armature.

5. Remove the armature with the drive assembly from the drive end frame by tilting to disengage the drive collar from the lever.

6. Remove the solenoid attaching screws and the solenoid from the drive end housing.

7. Remove the lever shaft retaining ring and lever shaft from the drive end housing. Remove the plunger and lever with return spring from the drive end housing.

8. Remove the thrust collar from the armature shaft, then snap the pinion stop collar off of the retainer ring. The collar will remain on the shaft next to the drive pinion.

9. Remove the retainer from the groove in the armature shaft. If the ring is not used bend the ring enough to avoid scratching the armature shaft surface as the ring is removed.

10. Remove the pinion stop collar and drive from the shaft.

To assemble:

11. Install the drive assembly to armature shaft as follows:

   a. Lightly lubricate the area on the armature shaft that will be under the drive assembly with GM 1960954 or equivalent.

   b. Install the drive assembly onto the armature shaft with the pinion away from the armature.

   c. Install the pinion stop collar onto the armature shaft.

   d. Install a new pinion stop retainer ring into the groove on the shaft. Do not reuse the old ring.

12. Inspect the bushing on the drive end housing and if damaged, replace the drive end housing. Lightly lubricate the bushing, if dry, with GM 1960954 or equivalent.

13. Install the shift lever yoke to the drive collar, then armature/drive/lever assembly into the drive end housing.

14. Install the shift lever shaft through the holes in the drive end housing and shift lever, then secure with the retainer. Place the return spring onto the plunger.

15. Install the solenoid over the plunger by depressing the spring, aligning to the drive end housing. Install the attaching screws and tighten to 60 inch lbs. (6.5 Nm).

16. Inspect and replace the brushes as necessary.

17. Install the frame and field assembly as follows:

   a. Apply sealer, GM 1050026 or equivalent, to the solenoid flange where the frame and field will contact it.

   b. Push the brushes into the brush holders and hold.

   c. Install the frame and field assembly over the armature, aligning properly to the drive end housing.

   d. Release the brushes onto the commutator. Be sure all 4 brushes move freely in the holders and are in contact with the commutator.

18. Install the brake washer onto the armature.

19. Inspect the bushing on the commutator end frame and if damaged, replace the commutator end frame. Lightly lubricate the bushing, if dry, with GM 1960954 or equivalent.

20. Install the commutator end frame onto the armature shaft, aligning with the frame and field assembly.

21. Install the identification tag onto the 1 through bolt, then install the 2 through bolts to the motor. If the through bolts have different heads place as noted during disassembly.

22. Tighten the through bolts to 75 inch lbs. (8.5 Nm).

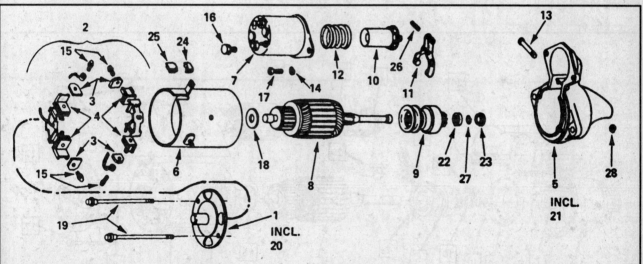

1. Commutator end frame	7. Solenoid switch	15. Brush attaching screw	21. Drive end bushing
2. Brush and holder package	8. Armature	16. Field lead to switch screw	22. Pinion stop collar
3. Brush	9. Drive assembly	17. Switch attaching screw	23. Thrust collar
4. Brush holder	10. Plunger	18. Brake washer	24. Grommet
5. Drive end housing	11. Shift lever	19. Through-bolt	25. Grommet
6. Frame and field assembly	12. Plunger return spring	20. Commutator end bushing	26. Plunger pin
	13. Shift lever shaft		27. Pinion stop retainer spring
	14. Lock washer		28. Lever shaft retaining ring

FIG. 17 Exploded view of the starter motor — SD200 starter

SD210 STARTER OVERHAUL

♦ SEE FIG. 18

1. Remove the field lead attaching screw from the solenoid terminal.

2. Note the locations and remove the through bolts and commutator end frame from the motor assembly.

3. Remove the brake washer from the armature shaft.

4. Remove the frame and field assembly from the drive end housing and armature.

5. Remove the heat shield attaching nuts and heat shield, if used, from the solenoid attaching screws.

6. Remove the solenoid attaching screws, clamp and the solenoid from the drive end housing.

7. Remove the plug from the slot in the drive end housing.

8. Remove the armature with drive, shift lever and plunger with spring, as an assembly from the drive end housing.

9. Remove the plunger and spring from the lever, then the lever from the drive by spreading the plastic arms just enough to disengage from the buttons on the drive collar.

10. Remove the thrust collar from the armature shaft, then snap the pinion stop collar

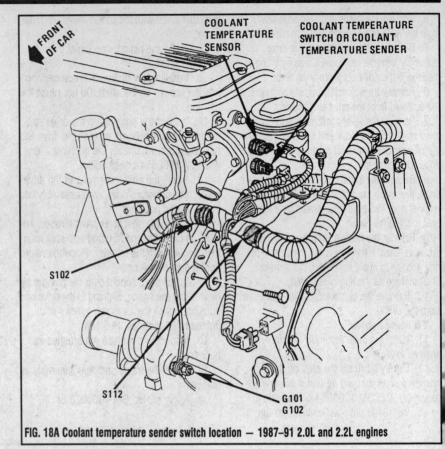

FIG. 18A Coolant temperature sender switch location — 1987–91 2.0L and 2.2L engines

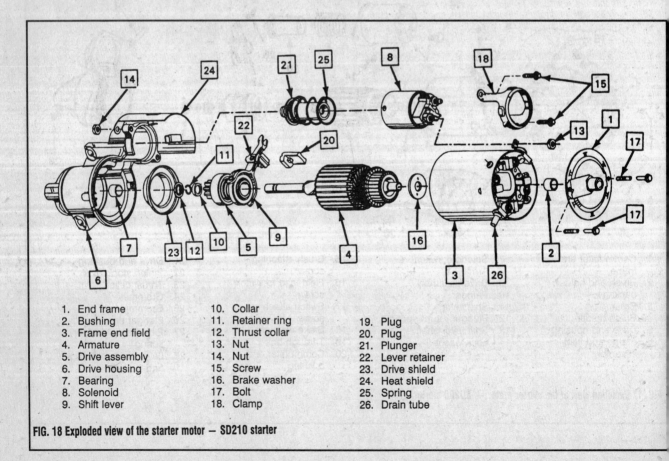

1. End frame	10. Collar	
2. Bushing	11. Retainer ring	
3. Frame end field	12. Thrust collar	19. Plug
4. Armature	13. Nut	20. Plug
5. Drive assembly	14. Nut	21. Plunger
6. Drive housing	15. Screw	22. Lever retainer
7. Bearing	16. Brake washer	23. Drive shield
8. Solenoid	17. Bolt	24. Heat shield
9. Shift lever	18. Clamp	25. Spring
		26. Drain tube

FIG. 18 Exploded view of the starter motor — SD210 starter

off of the retainer ring. The collar will remain on the shaft next to the drive pinion.

11. Remove the retainer from the groove in the armature shaft. If the ring is not used bend the ring enough to avoid scratching the armature shaft surface as the ring is removed.

12. Remove the pinion stop collar and drive from the shaft.

To assemble:

➡ The SD210 uses special life long brushes that do no require replacement for the life of the motor.

13. Install the drive assembly to armature shaft as follows:

   a. Lightly lubricate the area on the armature shaft that will be under the drive assembly with GM 1960954 or equivalent.

   b. Install the drive assembly onto the armature shaft with the pinion away from the armature.

   c. Install the pinion stop collar onto the armature shaft.

   d. Install a new pinion stop retainer ring into the groove on the shaft. Do not reuse the old ring.

14. Inspect the bushing on the drive end housing and if damaged, replace the drive end housing. Lightly lubricate the bushing, if dry, with GM 1960954 or equivalent.

15. Install the shift lever yoke to the drive collar, then armature/drive/lever assembly into the drive end housing.

16. Install the plug to the slot in the drive end housing. Snap the plunger with the spring onto the lever.

17. Install the solenoid over the plunger by depressing the spring, aligning the locator button with the slot in the drive end frame.

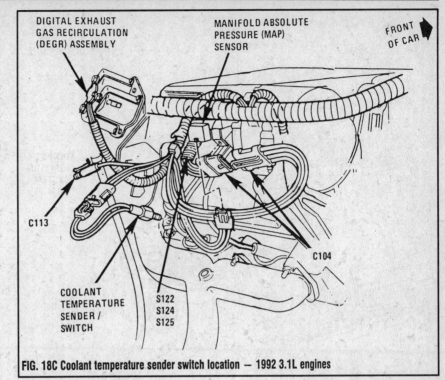

FIG. 18C Coolant temperature sender switch location — 1992 3.1L engines

Install the attaching bracket to the solenoid and align to the drive end housing. Install the attaching screws and tighten to 95 inch lbs. (11 Nm).

18. Install the frame and field assembly as follows:

   a. Use a soft cloth and clean the contact face of the brushes in the frame and field assembly. Long life brushes are permanently attached to the brush rigging. If brushes are damaged, replace the frame and field assembly.

   b. Push the brushes into the brush holders and hold.

   c. Install the frame and field assembly over the armature, aligning properly to the drive end housing.

   d. Release the brushes onto the commutator. Be sure all 4 brushes move freely in the holders and are in contact with the commutator.

19. Install the brake washer onto the armature.

20. Inspect the bushing on the commutator end frame and if damaged, replace the commutator end frame. Lightly lubricate the bushing, if dry, with GM 1960954 or equivalent.

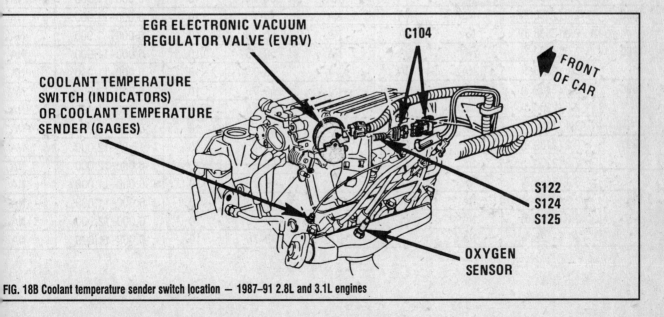

FIG. 18B Coolant temperature sender switch location — 1987–91 2.8L and 3.1L engines

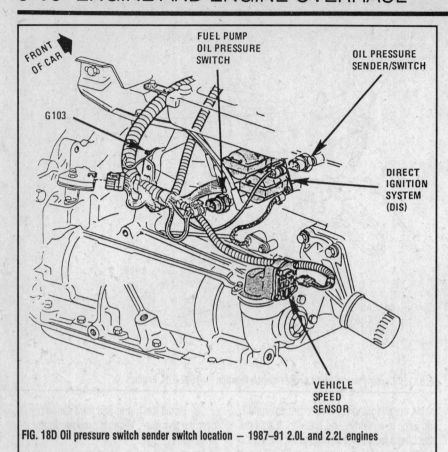

FIG. 18D Oil pressure switch sender switch location — 1987–91 2.0L and 2.2L engines

21. Install the commutator end frame onto the armature shaft, aligning with the frame and field assembly.

22. Install the identification tag onto the 1 through bolt, then install the 2 through bolts to the motor. If the through bolts have different heads place as noted during disassembly.

23. If used, install the heat shield and attaching nuts to the ends of the solenoid attaching screws.

24. Tighten the through bolts to 75 inch lbs. (8.5 Nm) and the nuts to 70 inch lbs. (8 Nm).

Gauge Sending Switches

REMOVAL & INSTALLATION

The oil pressure and coolant temperature sending switches are screw-in type switches which when replaced, require Teflon tape or its equivalent, on the threads. Refer to the illustrations for the various locations.

STARTER SPECIFICATIONS

| Year | Engine Displacement Liters (cc) | Lock Test | | | No-Load Test | | | Brush Spring Tension oz. |
		Amps	Volts	Torque (ft. lbs.)	Amps	Volts	RPM	
1987	2.0 (1990.7)	NA	NA	NA	50–75	10	6,000–11,900	NA
	2.8 (2836.8)	NA	NA	NA	50–75	10	6,000–11,900	NA
1988	2.0 (1990.7)	NA	NA	NA	50–75	10	6,000–11,900	NA
	2.8 (2836.8)	NA	NA	NA	50–75	10	6,000–11,900	NA
1989	2.0 (1990.7)	NA	NA	NA	50–75	10	6,000–11,900	NA
	2.8 (2836.8)	NA	NA	NA	50–75	10	6,000–11,900	NA
1990	2.2 (2189.8)	NA	NA	NA	50–75	10	6,000–11,900	NA
	2.3 (2260.0)	NA	NA	NA	50–75	10	6,000–11,900	NA
	3.1 (3128.0)	NA	NA	NA	50–75	10	6,000–11,900	NA
1991	2.2 (2189.8)	NA	NA	NA	55–85	10	7,500–12,000	NA
	2.3 (2260.0)	NA	NA	NA	52–76	10	6,000–12,000	NA
	3.1 (3128.0)	NA	NA	NA	45–75	10	6,000–11,000	NA
1992	2.2 (2189.8)	NA	NA	NA	45–75	10	6,000–11,000	NA
	2.3 (2260.0)	NA	NA	NA	52–76	10	6,000–12,000	NA
	3.1 (3128.0)	NA	NA	NA	45–75	10	6,000–11,000	NA

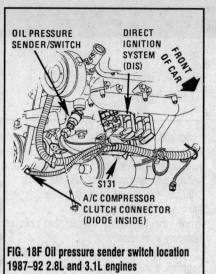

FIG. 18F Oil pressure sender switch location 1987–92 2.8L and 3.1L engines

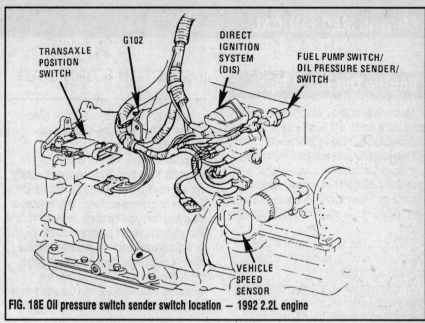

FIG. 18E Oil pressure switch sender switch location — 1992 2.2L engine

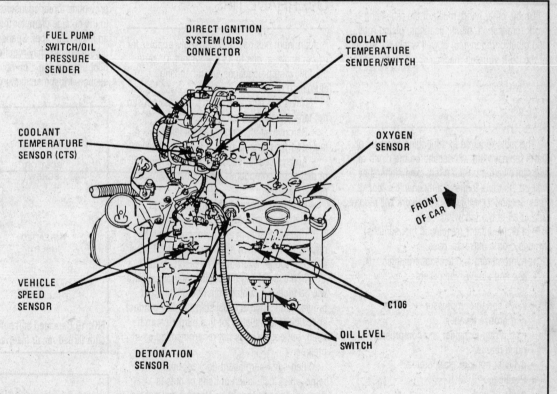

FIG. 18G Oil pressure and coolant temperature sender switch location — 1990–92 2.3L engine

ENGINE MECHANICAL

Engine Overhaul Tips

Most engine overhaul procedures are fairly standard. In addition to specific parts replacement procedures and complete specifications for your individual engine, this section also is a guide to accept rebuilding procedures. Examples of standard rebuilding practice are shown and should be used along with specific details concerning your particular engine.

Competent and accurate machine shop services will ensure maximum performance, reliability and engine life.

In most instances it is more profitable for the do-it-yourself mechanic to remove, clean and inspect the component, buy the necessary parts and deliver these to a shop for actual machine work.

On the other hand, much of the rebuilding work (crankshaft, block, bearings, piston rods, and other components) is well within the scope of the do-it-yourself mechanic.

TOOLS

The tools required for an engine overhaul or parts replacement will depend on the depth of your involvement. With a few exceptions, they will be the tools found in a mechanic's tool kit (see Section 1). More in-depth work will require any or all of the following:
- a dial indicator (reading in thousandths) mounted on a universal base
- micrometers and telescope gauges
- jaw and screw-type pullers
- scraper
- valve spring compressor
- ring groove cleaner
- piston ring expander and compressor
- ridge reamer
- cylinder hone or glaze breaker
- Plastigage®
- engine stand

The use of most of these tools is illustrated in this section. Many can be rented for a one-time use from a local parts jobber or tool supply house specializing in automotive work.

Occasionally, the use of special tools is called for. See the information on Special Tools and Safety Notice in the front of this book before substituting another tool.

INSPECTION TECHNIQUES

Procedures and specifications are given in this section for inspecting, cleaning and assessing the wear limits of most major components. Other procedures such as Magnaflux® and Zyglo® can be used to locate material flaws and stress cracks. Magnaflux® is a magnetic process applicable only to ferrous materials. The Zyglo® process coats the material with a fluorescent dye penetrant and can be used on any material Check for suspected surface cracks can be more readily made using spot check dye. The dye is sprayed onto the suspected area, wiped off and the area sprayed with a developer. Cracks will show up brightly.

OVERHAUL TIPS

Aluminum has become extremely popular for use in engines, due to its low weight. Observe the following precautions when handling aluminum parts:
- Never hot tank aluminum parts (the caustic hot tank solution will eat the aluminum.
- Remove all aluminum parts (identification tag, etc.) from engine parts prior to the tanking.
- Always coat threads lightly with engine oil or anti-seize compounds before installation, to prevent seizure.
- Never overtorque bolts or spark plugs especially in aluminum threads.

Stripped threads in any component can be repaired using any of several commercial repair kits (Heli-Coil®, Microdot®, Keenserts®, etc.).

When assembling the engine, any parts that will be frictional contact must be prelubed to provide lubrication at initial start-up. Any product specifically formulated for this purpose can be used, but engine oil is not recommended as a prelube.

When semi-permanent (locked, but removable) installation of bolts or nuts is desired, threads should be cleaned and coated with Loctite® or other similar, commercial non-hardening sealant.

REPAIRING DAMAGED THREADS

Several methods of repairing damaged threads are available. Heli-Coil® (shown here), Keenserts® and Microdot® are among the most widely used. All involve basically the same principle—drilling out stripped threads, tapping the hole and installing a prewound insert—making welding, plugging and oversize fasteners unnecessary.

Two types of thread repair inserts are usually supplied: a standard type for most Inch Coarse, Inch Fine, Metric Course and Metric Fine thread sizes and a spark lug type to fit most spark plug port sizes. Consult the individual manufacturer's catalog to determine exact applications. Typical thread repair kits will contain a selection of prewound threaded inserts, a tap (corresponding to the outside diameter threads of the insert) and an installation tool. Spark plug inserts usually differ because they require a tap equipped with pilot threads and a combined reamer/tap section. Most manufacturers also supply blister-

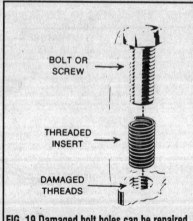

FIG. 19 Damaged bolt holes can be repaired with thread repair inserts.

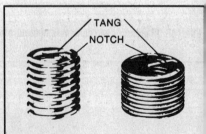

FIG. 20 Standard thread repair insert (left) and spark plug thread insert (right)

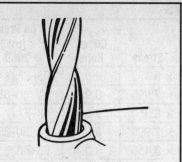

FIG. 21 Drill out the damaged threads with specified drill. Drill completely through the hole or to the bottom of the blind hole

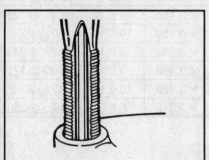

FIG. 22 With the tap supplied, tap the hole to receive the thread insert. Keep the tap well oiled and back it out frequently to avoid clogging the threads

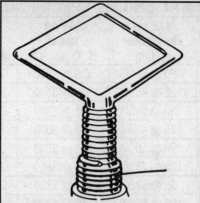

FIG. 23 Screw the threaded insert onto the installation tool until the tang engages the slot. Screw the insert into the tapped hole until it is 1/4–1/2 turn below the top surface. After installation break off the tang with a hammer and punch

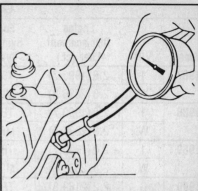

FIG. 24 The screw-in type compression gauge is more accurate

packed thread repair inserts separately in addition to a master kit containing a variety of taps and inserts plus installation tools.

Before effecting a repair to a threaded hole, remove any snapped, broken or damaged bolts or studs. Penetrating oil can be used to free frozen threads. The offending item can be removed with locking pliers or with a screw or stud extractor. After the hole is clear, the thread can be repaired, as shown in the series of accompanying illustrations.

Checking Engine Compression

A noticeable lack of engine power, excessive oil consumption and/or poor fuel mileage measured over an extended period are all indicators of internal engine war. Worn piston rings, scored or worn cylinder bores, blown head gaskets, sticking or burnt valves and worn valve seats are all possible culprits here. A check of each cylinder's compression will help you locate the problems.

As mentioned in the Tools and Equipment section of Section 1, a screw-in type compression gauge is more accurate that the type you simply hold against the spark plug hole, although it takes slightly longer to use. It's worth it to obtain a more accurate reading. Follow the procedures below.

1. Warm up the engine to normal operating temperature.
2. Remove all the spark plugs.
3. Disconnect the ECM fuse.
4. Fully open the throttle either by operating the throttle linkage by hand or by having an assistant floor the accelerator pedal.
5. Screw the compression gauge into the no.1 spark plug hole until the fitting is snug.

✳ WARNING

Be careful not to crossthread the plug hole. On aluminum cylinder heads use extra care, as the threads in these heads are easily ruined.

6. Ask an assistant to depress the accelerator pedal fully on both carbureted and fuel injected vehicles. Then, while you read the compression gauge, ask the assistant to crank the engine two or three times in short bursts using the ignition switch.
7. Read the compression gauge at the end of each series of cranks, and record the highest of these readings. Repeat this procedure for each of the engine's cylinders. Compare the highest reading of each cylinder to the compression pressure specification in the Tune-Up Specifications chart in Section 2. The specs in this chart are maximum values.

A cylinder's compression pressure is usually acceptable if it is not less than 70% of maximum. And no cylinder should be less than 100 lbs.

8. If a cylinder is unusually low, pour a tablespoon of clean engine oil into the cylinder through the spark plug hole and repeat the compression test. If the compression comes up after adding the oil, it appears that the cylinder's piston rings or bore are damaged or worn. If the pressure remains low, the valves may not be seating properly (a valve job is needed), or the head gasket may be blown near that cylinder. If compression in any two adjacent cylinders is low, and if the addition of oil doesn't help the compression, there is leakage past the head gasket. Oil and coolant water in the combustion chamber can result from this problem. There may be evidence of water droplets on the engine dipstick when a head gasket has blown.

Engine

REMOVAL & INSTALLATION

✳ CAUTION

When draining the coolant, keep in mind that cats and dogs are attracted by the ethylene glycol antifreeze, and are quite likely to drink any that is left in an uncovered container or in puddles on the ground. This will prove fatal in sufficient quantity. Always drain the coolant into a sealable container. Coolant should be reused unless it is contaminated or several years old.

GENERAL ENGINE SPECIFICATIONS

Year	VIN	Engine Displacement Liter (cc)	Fuel System Type	SAE net Horsepower @ rpm	SAE net Torque ft. lb. @ rpm	Bore × Stroke	Comp. Ratio	Oil Press. (psi.) @ 2000 rpm
1987	1	2.0 (1990.7)	TBI	90 @ 5600	108 @ 3200	3.500 × 3.150	9.0:1	63–77 @ 1200
	W	2.8 (2836.8)	MFI	125 @ 4500	160 @ 3600	3.503 × 2.990	8.9:1	50–65
1988	1	2.0 (1990.7)	TBI	90 @ 5600	108 @ 3200	3.500 × 3.150	9.0:1	63–77 @ 1200
	W	2.8 (2836.8)	MFI	125 @ 4500	160 @ 3600	3.503 × 2.990	8.9:1	50–65
1989	1	2.0 (1990.7)	TBI	90 @ 5600	108 @ 3200	3.500 × 3.150	9.0:1	63–77 @ 1200
	W	2.8 (2836.8)	MFI	125 @ 4500	160 @ 3600	3.503 × 2.990	8.9:1	50–65 @ 1200
1990	G	2.2 (2189.8)	TBI	95 @ 5200	120 @ 3200	3.500 × 3.460	9.0:1	63–77 @ 1200
	A	2.3 (2260.0)	MFI	180 @ 6200	160 @ 5200	3.622 × 3.460	10.0:1	30 @ 2000
	T	3.1 (3128.0)	MFI	135 @ 4200	180 @ 3600	3.503 × 3.312	8.8:1	50–65 @ 2400
1991	G	2.2 (2189.8)	TBI	110 @ 5200	120 @ 3200	3.500 × 3.460	9.0:1	63–77 @ 1200
	A	2.3 (2260.0)	MFI	180 @ 6200	160 @ 5200	3.622 × 3.460	10.0:1	30 @ 2000
	T	3.1 (3128.0)	MFI	140 @ 4200	185 @ 3600	3.503 × 3.312	8.8:1	50–65 @ 2400
1992	4	2.2 (2189.8)	TBI	110 @ 5200	120 @ 3200	3.500 × 3.460	9.0:1	63–77 @ 1200
	A	2.3 (2260.0)	MFI	180 @ 6200	160 @ 5200	3.622 × 3.460	10.0:1	30 @ 2000
	T	3.1 (3128.0)	MFI	140 @ 4200	185 @ 3600	3.503 × 3.312	8.8:1	50–65 @ 2400

TBI—Throttle Body Injection
MFI—Multi-port Fuel Injection

VALVE SPECIFICATIONS

Year	Engine VIN	Engine Displacement Liter (cc)	Seat Angle (deg)	Face Angle (deg)	Spring Test Pressure (lbs. @ in.)	Spring Installed Height (in.)	Stem-to-Guide Clearance (in.) Intake	Exhaust	Stem Diameter (in.) Intake	Exhaust
1987	1	2.0 (1990.7)	46	45	176–188① @ 1.33	1.60②	0.0011–0.0026	0.0014–0.0030	NA	NA
	W	2.8 (2836.8)	46	45	215 @ 1.29①	1.70②	0.0010–0.0027	0.0010–0.0027	NA NA	NA NA
1988	1	2.0 (1990.7)	46	45	176–188① @ 1.33	1.60②	0.0011–0.0026	0.0014–0.0030	NA	NA
	W	2.8 (2836.8)	46	45	215 @ 1.29①	1.70②	0.0010–0.0027	0.0010–0.0027	NA NA	NA NA
1989	1	2.0 (1990.7)	46	45	208–222① @ 1.33	1.61②	0.0011–0.0026	0.0014–0.0030	NA	NA
	W	2.8 (2836.8)	46	45	215 @ 1.29①	1.70②	0.0010–0.0027	0.0010–0.0027	NA NA	NA NA
1990	G	2.2 (2189.8)	46	45	208–222① @ 1.33	1.61②	0.0011–0.0026	0.0014–0.0030	NA	NA
	A	2.3 (2260.0)	45	44	193–207① @ 1.04	1.44②	0.0010–0.0027	0.0015–0.0032	NA 0.274–0.275	NA 0.274–0.275
	T	3.1 (3128.0)	46	45	215 @ 1.29①	1.57②	0.0010–0.0027	0.0010–0.0027	NA NA	NA NA

VALVE SPECIFICATIONS

Year	Engine VIN	Engine Displacement Liter (cc)	Seat Angle (deg)	Face Angle (deg)	Spring Test Pressure (lbs. @ in.)	Spring Installed Height (in.)	Stem-to-Guide Clearance (in.) Intake	Exhaust	Stem Diameter (in.) Intake	Exhaust
1991	G	2.2 (2189.8)	46	45	208–222① @ 1.33	1.61②	0.0011–0.0026	0.0014–0.0030	NA	NA
	A	2.3 (2260.0)	45	44	193–207① @ 1.04	1.44②	0.0010–0.0027	0.0015–0.0032	NA 0.274–0.275	NA 0.274–0.275
	T	3.1 (3128.0)	46	45	215 @ 1.29①	1.57②	0.0010–0.0027	0.0010–0.0027	NA NA	NA NA
1992	4	2.2 (2189.8)	46	45	208–222① @ 1.33	1.61②	0.0011–0.0026	0.0014–0.0030	NA	NA
	A	2.3 (2260.0)	45	44	193–207① @ 1.04	1.44②	0.0010–0.0027	0.0015–0.0032	NA 0.274–0.275	NA 0.274–0.275
	T	3.1 (3128.0)	46	45	215 @ 1.29①	1.57②	0.0010–0.0027	0.0010–0.0027	NA NA	NA NA

NA—Not Available
① With valve open
② With valve open

CAMSHAFT SPECIFICATIONS
(All specifications in inches)

Year	Engine VIN	Engine Displacement Liter (cc)	Journal Diameter 1	2	3	4	5	Bearing Clearance	Elevation Int.	Exh.	End Play
1987	1	2.0 (1990.7)	1.867–1.869	1.867–1.869	1.867–1.869	1.867–1.869	1.867–1.869	0.001–0.004	0.260	0.260	NA
	W	2.8 (2836.8)	1.867–1.881	1.867–1.881	1.867–1.881	1.867–1.881	1.867–1.881	0.001–0.004	0.262	0.273	NA
1988	1	2.0 (1990.7)	1.867–1.869	1.867–1.869	1.867–1.869	1.867–1.869	1.867–1.869	0.001–0.004	0.260	0.260	NA
	W	2.8 (2836.8)	1.867–1.881	1.867–1.881	1.867–1.881	1.867–1.881	1.867–1.881	0.001–0.004	0.262	0.273	NA
1989	1	2.0 (1990.7)	1.867–1.869	1.867–1.869	1.867–1.869	1.867–1.869	1.867–1.869	0.001–0.004	0.260	0.260	NA
	W	2.8 (2836.8)	1.867–1.881	1.867–1.881	1.867–1.881	1.867–1.881	1.867–1.881	0.001–0.004	0.262	0.273	NA
1990	G	2.2 (2189.8)	1.867–1.869	1.867–1.869	1.867–1.869	1.867–1.869	1.867–1.869	0.001–0.004	0.259	0.259	NA
	A	2.3 (2260.0)	1.572–1.573	1.375–1.376	1.375–1.376	1.375–1.376	1.375–1.376	0.001–0.004	0.410	0.410	.0009
	T	3.1 (3128.0)	1.867–1.881	1.867–1.881	1.867–1.881	1.867–1.881	1.867–1.881	0.001–0.004	0.262	0.273	NA
1991	G	2.2 (2189.8)	1.867–1.869	1.867–1.869	1.867–1.869	1.867–1.869	1.867–1.869	0.001–0.004	0.259	0.259	NA
	A	2.3 (2260.0)	1.572–1.573	1.375–1.376	1.375–1.376	1.375–1.376	1.375–1.376	0.001–0.004	0.410	0.410	.0009
	T	3.1 (3128.0)	1.867–1.881	1.867–1.881	1.867–1.881	1.867–1.881	1.867–1.881	0.001–0.004	0.262	0.273	NA

CAMSHAFT SPECIFICATIONS

(All specifications in inches)

Year	Engine VIN	Engine Displacement Liter (cc)	Journal Diameter					Bearing Clearance	Elevation		End Play
			1	2	3	4	5		Int.	Exh.	
1992	4	2.2 (2189.8)	1.867–1.869	1.867–1.869	1.867–1.869	1.867–1.869	1.867–1.869	0.001–0.004	0.259	0.259	NA
	A	2.3 (2260.0)	1.572–1.573	1.375–1.376	1.375–1.376	1.375–1.376	1.375–1.376	0.001–0.004	0.410	0.410	.0009
	T	3.1 (3128.0)	1.867–1.881	1.867–1.881	1.867–1.881	1.867–1.881	1.867–1.881	0.001–0.004	0.262	0.273	NA

CRANKSHAFT AND CONNECTING ROD SPECIFICATIONS

All specifications in inches.

Year	Engine VIN	Engine Displacement Liter (cc)	Crankshaft				Connecting Rod		
			Main Brg. Journal Dia.	Main Brg. Oil Clearance	Shaft End-play	Thrust on No.	Journal Diameter	Oil Clearance	Side Clearance
1987	1	2.0 (1990.7)	2.4945–2.4954	0.0006–0.0019	0.002–0.008	1	1.9983–1.9994	0.0010–0.0030	0.0040–0.0150
	W	2.8 (2836.8)	2.6473–2.6483	0.0016–0.0033	0.002–0.008	4	1.9983–1.9993	0.0010–0.0030	0.0060–0.0170
1988	1	2.0 (1990.7)	2.4945–2.4954	0.0006–0.0019	0.002–0.008	1	1.9983–1.9994	0.0010–0.0030	0.0040–0.0150
	W	2.8 (2836.8)	2.6473–2.6483	0.0016–0.0033	0.002–0.008	4	1.9983–1.9993	0.0010–0.0030	0.0060–0.0170
1989	1	2.0 (1990.7)	2.4945–2.4954	0.0006–0.0019	0.002–0.008	1	1.9983–1.9994	0.0010–0.0030	0.0040–0.0150
	W	2.8 (2836.8)	2.6473–2.6483	0.0016–0.0033	0.002–0.008	4	1.9983–1.9993	0.0010–0.0030	0.0060–0.0170
1990	G	2.2 (2189.8)	2.4945–2.4954	0.0006–0.0019	0.002–0.007	1	1.9983–1.9994	0.0010–0.0030	0.0040–0.0150
	A	2.3 (2260.0)	2.0470–2.0480	0.0005–0.0023	0.003–0.009	3	1.8887–1.8897	0.0005–0.0020	0.0059–0.0177
	T	3.1 (3128.0)	2.6473–2.6483	0.0012–0.0030	0.002–0.008	3	1.9983–1.9994	0.0010–0.0040	0.0140–0.0270
1991	G	2.2 (2189.8)	2.4945–2.4954	0.0006–0.0019	0.002–0.007	1	1.9983–1.9994	0.0010–0.0030	0.0040–0.0150
	A	2.3 (2260.0)	2.0470–2.0480	0.0005–0.0023	0.003–0.009	3	1.8887–1.8897	0.0005–0.0020	0.0059–0.0177
	T	3.1 (3128.0)	2.6473–2.6483	0.0012–0.0030	0.002–0.008	3	1.9983–1.9994	0.0010–0.0040	0.0140–0.0270
1992	4	2.2 (2189.8)	2.4945–2.4954	0.0006–0.0019	0.002–0.007	1	1.9983–1.9994	0.0010–0.0030	0.0040–0.0150
	A	2.3 (2260.0)	2.0470–2.0480	0.0005–0.0023	0.003–0.009	3	1.8887–1.8897	0.0005–0.0020	0.0059–0.0177
	T	3.1 (3128.0)	2.6473–2.6483	0.0012–0.0030	0.002–0.008	3	1.9983–1.9994	0.0010–0.0040	0.0140–0.0270

PISTON AND RING SPECIFICATIONS

(All specifications in inches)

| Year | Engine VIN | Engine Displacement Liter (cc) | Ring Gap | | | Ring Side Clearance | | | Piston Clearance |
			#1 Compression	#2 Compression	Oil Control	#1 Compression	#2 Compression	Oil Control	
1987	1	2.0 (1990.7)	0.010–0.020	0.010–0.020	0.010–0.050	0.001–0.003	0.001–0.003	0.0080	0.0010–0.0022
	W	2.8 (2836.8)	0.010–0.020	0.010–0.020	0.020–0.055	0.001–0.003	0.001–0.003	0.0080	0.0010–0.0029
1988	1	2.0 (1990.7)	0.010–0.020	0.010–0.020	0.010–0.050	0.001–0.003	0.001–0.003	0.0080	0.0010–0.0022
	W	2.8 (2836.8)	0.010–0.020	0.010–0.020	0.020–0.055	0.001–0.003	0.001–0.003	0.0080	0.0010–0.0029
1989	1	2.0 (1990.7)	0.010–0.020	0.010–0.020	0.010–0.050	0.001–0.003	0.001–0.003	0.0080	0.0010–0.0022
	W	2.8 (2836.8)	0.010–0.020	0.010–0.020	0.020–0.055	0.001–0.003	0.001–0.003	0.0080	0.0009–0.0029
1990	G	2.2 (2189.8)	0.010–0.020	0.010–0.020	0.010–0.050	0.002–0.003	0.002–0.003	0.0020–0.0082	0.0007–0.0017
	A	2.3 (2260.0)	0.014–0.024	0.016–0.026	0.016–0.055	0.003–0.005	0.002–0.003	—	0.0007–0.0022
	T	3.1 (3128.0)	0.010–0.020	0.020–0.028	0.010–0.030	0.002–0.003	0.002–0.003	0.0080	0.0009–0.0022
1991	G	2.2 (2189.8)	0.010–0.020	0.010–0.020	0.010–0.050	0.002–0.003	0.002–0.003	0.0020–0.0082	0.0007–0.0017
	A	2.3 (2260.0)	0.014–0.024	0.016–0.026	0.016–0.055	0.003–0.005	0.002–0.003	—	0.0007–0.0022
	T	3.1 (3128.0)	0.010–0.020	0.020–0.028	0.010–0.030	0.002–0.003	0.002–0.003	0.0080	0.0009–0.0022
1992	4	2.2 (2189.8)	0.010–0.020	0.010–0.020	0.010–0.050	0.002–0.003	0.002–0.003	0.0020–0.0082	0.0007–0.0017
	A	2.3 (2260.0)	0.014–0.024	0.016–0.026	0.016–0.055	0.003–0.005	0.002–0.003	—	0.0007–0.0022
	T	3.1 (3128.0)	0.010–0.020	0.020–0.028	0.010–0.030	0.002–0.003	0.002–0.003	0.0080	0.0009–0.0022

TORQUE SPECIFICATIONS

(All specifications in ft. lbs.)

| Year | Engine VIN | Engine Displacement Liter (cc) | Cylinder Head | Conn. Rod | Main Bearing | Crankshaft Damper | Flywheel | Mainfold | | Spark Plugs | Lug Nuts |
								Intake	Exhaust		
1987	1	2.0 (1990.7)	①	34–43	63–77	66–89	②	15–22	6–13	11–18	100
	W	2.8 (2836.8)	③	34–44	63–83	67–85	②	18	15–23	20	100
1988	1	2.0 (1990.7)	①	34–43	63–77	66–89	②	15–22	6–13	11–18	100
	W	2.8 (2836.8)	③	34–44	63–83	67–85	②	18	15–23	20	100
1989	1	2.0 (1990.7)	①	34–43	63–77	66–89	②	15–22	6–13	7–20	100
	W	2.8 (2836.8)	③	34–44	63–83	67–85	②	18	15–23	20	100
1990	G	2.2 (2189.8)	④	38	70	⑨	⑯	18	6–13	11	100
	A	2.3 (2260.0)	⑥	⑦	⑩	⑧	⑪	18	⑫	17	100
	T	3.1 (3128.0)	③	39	73	76	52	⑬	18	20	100

TORQUE SPECIFICATIONS

(All specifications in ft. lbs.)

Year	Engine VIN	Engine Displacement Liter (cc)	Cylinder Head	Conn. Rod	Main Bearing	Crankshaft Damper	Flywheel	Mainfold Intake	Mainfold Exhaust	Spark Plugs	Lug Nuts
1991	G	2.2 (2189.8)	⑭	38	70	⑮	⑯	18	⑤	11	100
	A	2.3 (2260.0)	⑥	⑦	⑩	⑧	⑪	18	⑰	22	100
	T	3.1 (3128.0)	③	39	73	76	52	⑬	18	18	100
1992	4	2.2 (2189.8)	⑭	38	70	⑮	⑯	22	⑤	11	100
	A	2.3 (2260.0)	⑥	⑦	⑩	⑧	⑪	18	⑰	20	100
	T	3.1 (3128.0)	③	39	73	76	52	⑬	18	11	100

① Short head bolts: 62–70 ft. lbs.
Long head bolts: 73–83 ft. lbs.
② Manual transaxle: 47–63 ft.lbs.
Automatic transaxle: 45–59 ft. lbs.
③ Cylinder head bolts should first be torqued to 33 ft. lbs., then tighten the bolts by rotating the torque wrench an additional 90 degrees.
④ 1st step: Tighten all bolts in sequence to 41 ft. lbs.
2nd step: Tighten all bolts 45 degrees in sequence.
3nd step: Tighten all bolts an additional 45 degrees in seuence.
4nd step: Tighten the long bolts (intake side) 8, 4, 1, 5, and 9 an additional 20 degrees. Tighten the short bolts (exhaust side) 7, 3, 2, 6, and 10 an additional 10 degrees.

⑤ Tighten the nuts to 115 inch lbs. and the studs to 89 inch lbs.
⑥ Tighten all bolts in sequence to 26 ft. lbs., plus an additional 100 degree turn of the torque wrench for the two short bolts and an additional 110 degree turn for the eight longer bolts.
⑦ Tighten the bolts to 18 ft. lbs., plus an additional 80 degree turn.
⑧ Torque the balancer to crankshaft bolt to 74 ft. lbs. plus an additional 90 degree turn.
⑨ Torque the crankshaft center bolt to 85 ft. lbs. and the pulley to hub bolts to 37 ft. lbs.
⑩ 15 ft. lbs. plus an additional 90 degree turn.
⑪ 22 ft. lbs. plus an additional 45 degree turn.

⑫ Tighten the nuts to 27 ft. lbs. and the studs to 106 inch lbs.
⑬ Tighten all bolts in sequence to 15 ft. lbs., then tighten all bolts to 24 ft. lbs.
⑭ Tighten all bolts in sequence to: long bolts (intake side) 8, 4, 1, 5, and 9 to 46 ft. lbs. Tighten the short bolts (exhaust side) 7, 3, 2, 6, and 10 to 43 ft. lbs., then all bolts an additional 90 degrees in sequence.
⑮ Torque the crankshaft center bolt to 77 ft. lbs. and the pulley to hub bolts to 37 ft. lbs.
⑯ Manual transaxle: 55 ft. lbs.
Automatic Transaxle: 52 ft. lbs.
⑰ Tighten the nuts to 31 ft. lbs. and the studs to 106 inch lbs.

Troubleshooting Basic Charging System Problems

Problem	Cause	Solution
Noisy alternator	• Loose mountings • Loose drive pulley • Worn bearings • Brush noise • Internal circuits shorted (High pitched whine)	• Tighten mounting bolts • Tighten pulley • Replace alternator • Replace alternator • Replace alternator
Squeal when starting engine or accelerating	• Glazed or loose belt	• Replace or adjust belt
Indicator light remains on or ammeter indicates discharge (engine running)	• Broken fan belt • Broken or disconnected wires • Internal alternator problems • Defective voltage regulator	• Install belt • Repair or connect wiring • Replace alternator • Replace voltage regulator
Car light bulbs continually burn out— battery needs water continually	• Alternator/regulator overcharging	• Replace voltage regulator/alternator

Troubleshooting Basic Starting System Problems

Problem	Cause	Solution
Car lights flare on acceleration	• Battery low • Internal alternator/regulator problems	• Charge or replace battery • Replace alternator/regulator
Low voltage output (alternator light flickers continually or ammeter needle wanders)	• Loose or worn belt • Dirty or corroded connections • Internal alternator/regulator problems	• Replace or adjust belt • Clean or replace connections • Replace alternator or regulator
Starter motor rotates engine slowly	• Battery charge low or battery defective • Defective circuit between battery and starter motor • Low load current • High load current	• Charge or replace battery • Clean and tighten, or replace cables • Bench-test starter motor. Inspect for worn brushes and weak brush springs. • Bench-test starter motor. Check engine for friction, drag or coolant in cylinders. Check ring gear-to-pinion gear clearance.
Starter motor will not rotate engine	• Battery charge low or battery defective • Faulty solenoid • Damage drive pinion gear or ring gear • Starter motor engagement weak • Starter motor rotates slowly with high load current • Engine seized	• Charge or replace battery • Check solenoid ground. Repair or replace as necessary. • Replace damaged gear(s) • Bench-test starter motor • Inspect drive yoke pull-down and point gap, check for worn end bushings, check ring gear clearance • Repair engine
Starter motor drive will not engage (solenoid known to be good)	• Defective contact point assembly • Inadequate contact point assembly ground • Defective hold-in coil	• Repair or replace contact point assembly • Repair connection at ground screw • Replace field winding assembly
Starter motor drive will not disengage	• Starter motor loose on flywheel housing • Worn drive end busing • Damaged ring gear teeth • Drive yoke return spring broken or missing	• Tighten mounting bolts • Replace bushing • Replace ring gear or driveplate • Replace spring
Starter motor drive disengages prematurely	• Weak drive assembly thrust spring • Hold-in coil defective	• Replace drive mechanism • Replace field winding assembly
Low load current	• Worn brushes • Weak brush springs	• Replace brushes • Replace springs

Troubleshooting Engine Mechanical Problems

Problem	Cause	Solution
External oil leaks	• Fuel pump gasket broken or improperly seated	• Replace gasket
	• Cylinder head cover RTV sealant broken or improperly seated	• Replace sealant; inspect cylinder head cover sealant flange and cylinder head sealant surface for distortion and cracks
	• Oil filler cap leaking or missing	• Replace cap
External oil leaks	• Oil filter gasket broken or improperly seated	• Replace oil filter
	• Oil pan side gasket broken, improperly seated or opening in RTV sealant	• Replace gasket or repair opening in sealant; inspect oil pan gasket flange for distortion
	• Oil pan front oil seal broken or improperly seated	• Replace seal; inspect timing case cover and oil pan seal flange for distortion
	• Oil pan rear oil seal broken or improperly seated	• Replace seal; inspect oil pan rear oil seal flange; inspect rear main bearing cap for cracks, plugged oil return channels, or distortion in seal groove
	• Timing case cover oil seal broken or improperly seated	• Replace seal
	• Excess oil pressure because of restricted PCV valve	• Replace PCV valve
	• Oil pan drain plug loose or has stripped threads	• Repair as necessary and tighten
	• Rear oil gallery plug loose	• Use appropriate sealant on gallery plug and tighten
	• Rear camshaft plug loose or improperly seated	• Seat camshaft plug or replace and seal, as necessary
	• Distributor base gasket damaged	• Replace gasket
Excessive oil consumption	• Oil level too high	• Drain oil to specified level
	• Oil with wrong viscosity being used	• Replace with specified oil
	• PCV valve stuck closed	• Replace PCV valve
	• Valve stem oil deflectors (or seals) are damaged, missing, or incorrect type	• Replace valve stem oil deflectors
	• Valve stems or valve guides worn	• Measure stem-to-guide clearance and repair as necessary
	• Poorly fitted or missing valve cover baffles	• Replace valve cover
	• Piston rings broken or missing	• Replace broken or missing rings
	• Scuffed piston	• Replace piston
	• Incorrect piston ring gap	• Measure ring gap, repair as necessary
	• Piston rings sticking or excessively loose in grooves	• Measure ring side clearance, repair as necessary
	• Compression rings installed upside down	• Repair as necessary
	• Cylinder walls worn, scored, or glazed	• Repair as necessary

Troubleshooting Engine Mechanical Problems (cont.)

Problem	Cause	Solution
	• Piston ring gaps not properly staggered	• Repair as necessary
	• Excessive main or connecting rod bearing clearance	• Measure bearing clearance, repair as necessary
No oil pressure	• Low oil level	• Add oil to correct level
	• Oil pressure gauge, warning lamp or sending unit inaccurate	• Replace oil pressure gauge or warning lamp
	• Oil pump malfunction	• Replace oil pump
	• Oil pressure relief valve sticking	• Remove and inspect oil pressure relief valve assembly
	• Oil passages on pressure side of pump obstructed	• Inspect oil passages for obstruction
	• Oil pickup screen or tube obstructed	• Inspect oil pickup for obstruction
	• Loose oil inlet tube	• Tighten or seal inlet tube
Low oil pressure	• Low oil level	• Add oil to correct level
	• Inaccurate gauge, warning lamp or sending unit	• Replace oil pressure gauge or warning lamp
	• Oil excessively thin because of dilution, poor quality, or improper grade	• Drain and refill crankcase with recommended oil
	• Excessive oil temperature	• Correct cause of overheating engine
	• Oil pressure relief spring weak or sticking	• Remove and inspect oil pressure relief valve assembly
	• Oil inlet tube and screen assembly has restriction or air leak	• Remove and inspect oil inlet tube and screen assembly. (Fill inlet tube with lacquer thinner to locate leaks.)
	• Excessive oil pump clearance	• Measure clearances
	• Excessive main, rod, or camshaft bearing clearance	• Measure bearing clearances, repair as necessary
High oil pressure	• Improper oil viscosity	• Drain and refill crankcase with correct viscosity oil
	• Oil pressure gauge or sending unit inaccurate	• Replace oil pressure gauge
	• Oil pressure relief valve sticking closed	• Remove and inspect oil pressure relief valve assembly
Main bearing noise	• Insufficient oil supply	• Inspect for low oil level and low oil pressure
	• Main bearing clearance excessive	• Measure main bearing clearance, repair as necessary
	• Bearing insert missing	• Replace missing insert
	• Crankshaft end play excessive	• Measure end play, repair as necessary
	• Improperly tightened main bearing cap bolts	• Tighten bolts with specified torque
	• Loose flywheel or drive plate	• Tighten flywheel or drive plate attaching bolts
	• Loose or damaged vibration damper	• Repair as necessary

Troubleshooting Engine Mechanical Problems (cont.)

Problem	Cause	Solution
Connecting rod bearing noise	• Insufficient oil supply	• Inspect for low oil level and low oil pressure
	• Carbon build-up on piston	• Remove carbon from piston crown
	• Bearing clearance excessive or bearing missing	• Measure clearance, repair as necessary
	• Crankshaft connecting rod journal out-of-round	• Measure journal dimensions, repair or replace as necessary
	• Misaligned connecting rod or cap	• Repair as necessary
	• Connecting rod bolts tightened improperly	• Tighten bolts with specified torque
Piston noise	• Piston-to-cylinder wall clearance excessive (scuffed piston)	• Measure clearance and examine piston
	• Cylinder walls excessively tapered or out-of-round	• Measure cylinder wall dimensions, rebore cylinder
	• Piston ring broken	• Replace all rings on piston
	• Loose or seized piston pin	• Measure piston-to-pin clearance, repair as necessary
	• Connecting rods misaligned	• Measure rod alignment, straighten or replace
	• Piston ring side clearance excessively loose or tight	• Measure ring side clearance, repair as necessary
	• Carbon build-up on piston is excessive	• Remove carbon from piston
Valve actuating component noise	• Insufficient oil supply	• Check for: (a) Low oil level (b) Low oil pressure (c) Plugged push rods (d) Wrong hydraulic tappets (e) Restricted oil gallery (f) Excessive tappet to bore clearance
	• Push rods worn or bent	• Replace worn or bent push rods
	• Rocker arms or pivots worn	• Replace worn rocker arms or pivots
	• Foreign objects or chips in hydraulic tappets	• Clean tappets
	• Excessive tappet leak-down	• Replace valve tappet
	• Tappet face worn	• Replace tappet; inspect corresponding cam lobe for wear
	• Broken or cocked valve springs	• Properly seat cocked springs; replace broken springs
	• Stem-to-guide clearance excessive	• Measure stem-to-guide clearance, repair as required
	• Valve bent	• Replace valve
	• Loose rocker arms	• Tighten bolts with specified torque
	• Valve seat runout excessive	• Regrind valve seat/valves
	• Missing valve lock	• Install valve lock
	• Push rod rubbing or contacting cylinder head	• Remove cylinder head and remove obstruction in head
	• Excessive engine oil (four-cylinder engine)	• Correct oil level

2.0L Engine

1. Disconnect the battery terminals (negative terminal first) from the battery. Remove the battery from the vehicle.

2. Position a clean drain pan under the radiator, open the drain cock and drain the cooling system. Remove the air intake hose.

3. From the throttle body, disconnect the T.V. and accelerator cables. Disconnect the ECM electrical harness connector from the engine.

4. Remove all vacuum hoses (not a part of the engine assembly), the upper/lower radiator hoses and the heater hoses from the engine.

5. Remove the heat shield from the exhaust manifold. Disconnect and label the engine wiring harness from the firewall.

6. Disconnect the windshield washer hoses and the bottle. Rotate the tensioner pulley (to reduce the belt tension) and remove the serpentine drive belt.

7. Disconnect and plug the fuel hoses. Raise and support front of the vehicle.

8. Remove the right-side inner fender splash shield.

9. Remove the air conditioning compressor-to-bracket bolts and move it aside (so it will not interfere with the engine removal); DO NOT disconnect the refrigerant lines.

10. Remove the flywheel splash shield. Label and disconnect electrical wires from the starter.

11. Remove the front starter brace, the starter-to-engine bolts and the starter.

12. If equipped with an automatic transaxle, remove the torque converter-to-flywheel bolts and push the converter back into the transaxle.

13. Remove the crankshaft pulley-to-crankshaft bolt. Using the Crankshaft Pulley Hub Remover tool No. J-24420 or equivalent, press the pulley from the crankshaft.

14. Remove the oil filter. Remove the engine-to-transaxle support bracket.

15. Disconnect the right-rear engine mount.

16. Remove the exhaust pipe-to-exhaust manifold bolts, the exhaust pipe from the center hanger and loosen the muffler hanger.

17. Remove the T.V. and shift cable bracket. Remove the two lower engine-to-transaxle bolts.

18. Lower the vehicle. From the intake manifold, remove the T.V. and accelerator cable bracket.

19. Remove the right-front engine mount nuts. Disconnect the electrical connectors. Remove the alternator-to-bracket bolts and the alternator.

20. Remove the master cylinder-to-booster nuts, move the master cylinder and support it out of the way; DO NOT disconnect the brake lines.

21. Using a vertical lifting device, install to the engine and lift it slightly.

22. Remove the right-front engine mount bracket. Remove the remaining engine-to-transaxle bolts.

23. Remove the power steering pump-to-engine bolts and move it aside; DO NOT disconnect the high pressure hoses.

24. Carefully lift and remove the engine from the vehicle.

To Install

25. Install the engine.

26. Install the power steering pump while lowering the engine.

27. Install the upper bellhousing bolts.

28. Install the right front motor mount bracket.

29. Remove the lifting device.

30. Connect the master cylinder to the booster.

31. Install the alternator and if removed, the adjusting brace.

32. Install the right front motor mount nuts.

33. Raise the car.

34. Install the remaining two bell housing bolts.

35. Connect the T.V. and shift cable bracket.

36. Connect the exhaust pipe at the center hanger and loosen the muffler hanger.

37. Connect the exhaust pipe at the manifold.

38. Connect the right rear motor mount. If the rear engine mount bracket is removed, the following procedure should be used to ensure proper engine mount bracket locations:

   a. Loosely install the engine mount bracket.

   b. Raise the engine and transaxle.

   c. Torque the engine mount nuts and bolts to the specifications shown.

39. Connect the engine to transmission support bracket.

40. Install the oil filter.

41. Install the crankshaft pulley using Tool J 24420.

42. Install the torque converter bolts.

43. Install the front starter brace and starter.

44. Connect the starter wires.

45. Install the flywheel splash shield.

46. If equipped with air conditioning, install the air conditioning compressor.

47. Install the inner fender splash shield.

48. If equipped with air conditioning, install the air conditioning brace.

49. Lower the vehicle.

50. Connect the fuel hoses.

51. Install the alternator belt or serpentine belt, if so equipped.

52. Install the windshield washer bottle.

53. Connect the engine wiring harness at the bulkhead.

54. Install the exhaust heat shield.

55. Connect the heater hoses at the engine.

56. Connect the radiator hoses at the engine.

57. Connect all vacuum hoses.

58. Connect the ECM harness at the engine.

59. Connect the accelerator cable and T.V. cables.

60. Install the air cleaner.

61. Fill the cooling system.

62. Connect the battery.

2.2L Engine

➡ **The following procedure is for the engine and transaxle assembly.**

1. Disconnect the battery.

2. Drain the cooling system.

3. Relieve the fuel system pressure.

4. Disconnect the hood lamp wiring, if so equipped and remove the hood.

5. Disconnect the throttle body intake duct.

6. Remove the rear sight shields.

7. Disconnect the upper radiator hose.

8. Disconnect the brake booster vacuum hose.

9. Disconnect the alternator top brace and wiring.

10. Disconnect and tag the upper engine harness from the engine.

11. Discharge the A/C system as outlined in Section One.

12. Disconnect the A/C compressor-to-condenser and accumulator lines.

13. Raise and support the vehicle safely.

14. Remove the left splash shield.

15. Disconnect the exhaust system.

16. Disconnect and tag the lower engine wiring.

17. Remove the flywheel inspection cover.

18. Remove the front wheels.

19. Disconnect the lower radiator hose.

20. Disconnect the heater hoses from the heater core.

21. Remove the brake calipers from the steering knuckle and wire up out of the way as outlined in Section 9.

22. Disconnect the tie rods from the struts.

23. Lower the vehicle.

24. Remove the clutch slave cylinder.

25. With the fuel system pressure released, place an absorbent shop towel around the connections and disconnect the fuel lines.

26. Disconnect the transaxle linkage at the transaxle.

27. Disconnect the accelerator cables from the TBI unit.

28. Disconnect the cruise control cables from the TBI unit.

29. Disconnect the throttle valve cables from the TBI, on vehicles equipped with an automatic transaxle.

30. Disconnect the automatic transaxle cooling lines.

31. Disconnect the power steering hoses from the power steering pump.

32. Remove the center suspension support bolts.

33. Align Engine/Transaxle Frame Handler tool No. J 36295 under the suspension supports, engine and transaxle; lower vehicle to dolly and add support under the engine.

34. Safely support the rear of the vehicle.

35. Disconnect the upper transaxle mount.

36. Remove the upper strut bolts and nuts.

37. Disconnect the front engine mount.

38. Disconnect the rear engine mount.

39. Remove the 4 rear suspension support bolts.

40. Remove the 4 front suspension support bolts and wire the bolt holes together to prevent axle separation.

41. Raise the vehicle and remove the engine and transaxle assembly on tool No. J 36295.

To install:

42. Lower the vehicle and install the engine and transaxle assembly using tool No. J 36295.

43. Install the suspension supports bolts and tighten to 65 ft. lbs. for the front and rear suspension supports and 66 ft. lbs. for the center suspension support.

44. Install the transaxle mount but do not tighten.

45. Install the rear engine mount but do not tighten.

46. Install the front engine mount but do not tighten.

47. Torque the manual transaxle mounting bolts as follows:
• Front transaxle strut to body bolts to 40 ft. lbs.
• Rear transaxle mount to body bolts to 23 ft. lbs.

48. Torque the automatic transaxle mount bolts to 22 ft. lbs.

49. Torque the front and rear engine mount bolts.

➡ **All engine mount bolts that have been removed must be cleaned and a new thread locking compound applied to the threads before reinstallation.**

50. Install the power steering hoses.

51. Connect the accelerator, cruise control and T.V. cables to the TBI.

52. Connect the transaxle cooling lines to the automatic transaxle.

53. Connect the transaxle linkage.

54. Reconnect the fuel lines.

55. Reconnect the clutch slave cylinder.

56. Raise and support the vehicle safely.

57. Install the tie rods.

58. Install the calipers to the steering knuckle.

59. Install the heater hoses to the heater core.

60. Install the lower radiator hose.

61. Install the A/C compressor.

62. Install the flywheel inspection cover.

63. Install the engine splash shield.

64. Install the front wheel and torque the wheel stud nuts to 100 ft. lbs.

65. Lower the vehicle.

66. Install the upper engine wiring.

67. Install the compressor to condenser and accumulator lines.

68. Install the brake booster vacuum hose.

69. Install the upper radiator hose.

70. Raise and support the vehicle safely.

71. Install the lower engine wiring.

72. Reconnect the exhaust system.

73. Lower the vehicle.

74. Connect the TBI wiring.

75. Install the air cleaner assembly.

76. Recharge the A/C system.

77. Check and adjust the wheel alignment.

78. Install the hood and connect the battery.

2.3L Engine

➡ SEE FIGS. 24A-24B

1. Disconnect the negative battery cable. Drain the cooling system and remove the air cleaner assembly.

2. Remove the front tire and wheel assemblies.

3. Remove the air cleaner assembly.

4. Disconnect the heater hoses.

5. Disconnect the upper radiator hose.

6. Disconnect the coolant fan.

7. Discharge the A/C system as outlined in Section One.

8. Remove the oil filter.

9. Disconnect the compressor/condenser hose assembly.

10. Disconnect and tag all vacuum lines and electrical connections.

11. Disconnect the negative battery cable from the block.

12. Disconnect the shift cable from the bracket assembly and power brake hose.

13. Disconnect the throttle cable and bracket.

14. Remove the power steering bracket with the pump and lines attached.

15. Disconnect the oil/air separator.

16. Relieve the fuel system pressure as outlined in Section One and disconnect the fuel lines.

17. Disconnect the clutch actuator.

18. Disconnect the engine oil cooler lines at the adapter.

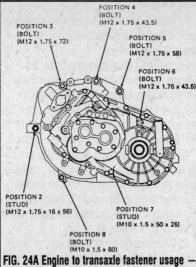

FIG. 24A Engine to transaxle fastener usage — 1990–92 2.3L engine

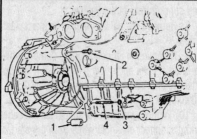

1. Spacer
2. Bolt/screw (41 ft. Lbs.)
3. Nut (41 ft. lbs.)
4. Stud (115 inch lbs.)

FIG. 24B Engine to transaxle attachment, rear side — 1990–92 2.3L engine

19. Remove the exhaust manifold heat shield.

20. Remove the exhaust manifold.

21. Remove the front engine mount nut.

22. Disconnect the lower radiator hose and heater hose.

23. Install engine support J 28467 or equivalent, disconnect the vacuum lines and pull the vacuum harness back through the front lift bracket.

24. Remove the left and right splash shields.

25. Separate the ball joints from the steering knuckles.

26. Support the suspension support, crossmember and stabilizer shaft with a suitable holding fixture and remove the suspension support retaining bolts.

27. Remove the suspension support, crossmember and stabilizer shaft as an assembly.

28. Install drive axle boot protectors J 34754 or equivalent, and remove the drive axles from the transaxle.

29. Position a suitable support below the engine and lower the car onto the support.

30. Remove the engine mount strut and transaxle brackets.

31. Mark the threads on the support fixture hooks so that the setting can be duplicated when reinstalling the engine. Remove the engine support fixture.

32. Raise the vehicle slowly off the engine and transaxle assembly.

To Install

➡ **Make certain the correct bolts are installed in their correct positions.**

33. Position the engine and transaxle assembly under the engine compartment and slowly lower the vehicle over the assembly until the transaxle is indexed and install the bolt.

34. Install the engine support fixture J 28467–A or equavlent and adjust to the previous setting.

35. Raise the vehicle off of the support fixture.

36. Install the engine mount strut and transaxle brackets.

37. Install drive axle boot protectors J 34754 or equivalent, and install the drive axles to the transaxle.

38. Install the suspension support, crossmember and stabilizer shaft as an assembly. Install and tighten the rear bolts first to 66 ft. lbs. (90 Nm), then the front bolts to 65 ft. lbs. (90 Nm).

39. Install the ball joint nuts.

40. Install the left and right splash shields.

41. Connect the lower radiator hose and heater hose.

42. Install the front engine mount nut.

43. Lower the vehicle.

44. Remove the engine support fixture J 28467–A or equavlent.

45. Install the exhaust manifold and heat shield.

46. Connect the engine oil cooler lines at the adapter.

47. Connect the clutch actuator.

48. Connect the fuel lines.

49. Connect the oil/air separator.

50. Install the power steering bracket with the pump and lines.

51. Connect the throttle cable and bracket.

52. Connect the shift cable to the bracket assembly and power brake hose.

53. Connect the negative battery cable to the block.

54. Connect all vacuum lines and electrical connections.

55. Connect the compressor/condenser hose assembly.

56. Install the oil filter.

57. Charge the A/C system as outlined in Section One.

58. Connect the coolant fan.

59. Connect the upper radiator hose.

60. Connect the heater hoses.

61. Install the air cleaner assembly.

62. Fill the cooling system, oil crankcase and connect the battery.

2.8L and 3.1L Engine

1. Relieve the fuel pressure. Disconnect the battery cables (negative cable first). Remove the battery from the vehicle.

2. Remove the air cleaner, the air inlet hose and the mass air flow sensor.

3. Position a clean drain pan under the radiator, open the drain cock and drain the cooling system. Remove the exhaust manifold crossover assembly bolts and separate the assembly from the exhaust manifolds.

4. Remove the serpentine belt tensioner and the drive belt. Remove the power steering pump-to-bracket bolts and support the pump aside.

5. Disconnect the radiator hose from the engine.

6. Disconnect the TV and accelerator cables from the throttle valve bracket on the plenum.

7. Disconnect the electrical connectors. Remove the alternator-to-bracket bolts and the alternator. Label and disconnect the electrical wiring harness from the engine.

8. Disconnect and plug the fuel hoses. Remove the coolant overflow and bypass hoses from the engine.

9. From the charcoal canister, disconnect the purge hose. Label and disconnect all the necessary vacuum hoses.

10. Using a engine holding fixture tool, support the engine.

11. Raise and safely support the vehicle.

12. Remove the right inner fender splash shield. Remove the crankshaft pulley-to-crankshaft bolt. Using a wheel puller, press the crankshaft pulley from the crankshaft.

13. Remove the flywheel cover. Label and disconnect the starter wires. Remove the starter-to-engine bolts and the starter.

14. Disconnect the wires from the oil pressure sending unit.

15. Remove the air conditioning compressor-to-bracket bolts and the bracket-to-engine bolts. Support the compressor so it will not interfere with the engine; do not disconnect the refrigerant lines.

16. Disconnect the exhaust pipe from the rear of the exhaust manifold.

17. If equipped with an automatic transaxle, remove the torque converter-to-flywheel bolts and push the converter into the transaxle.

18. Remove the front and rear engine mount bolts along with the mount brackets.

19. Remove the intermediate shaft bracket from the engine.

20. Disconnect the shifter cable from the transaxle.

21. Remove the lower engine-to-transaxle bolts and lower the vehicle.

22. Disconnect the heater hoses from the engine.

23. Using an vertical engine lift, install it to the engine and lift it slightly. Remove the engine holding fixture. Using a floor jack, support the transaxle.

24. Remove the upper engine-to-transaxle bolts. Remove the front engine mount bolts and transaxle mounting bracket.

25. Remove the engine from the vehicle.

To Install:

26. Secure the engine on a engine suitable lifting device.

27. Carefully lower the engine into the vehicle, aligning it to the transaxle.

28. Install the upper engine-to-transaxle bolts. Tighten bolts to 55 ft. lbs. (75 Nm).

29. Install the transaxle mount bracket and front engine mount attaching bolts. Tighten the bolts to 65 ft. lbs. (88 Nm).

30. Using a floor jack, support the transaxle and remove the engine lifting device from the engine.

31. Install the lower engine-to-transaxle.

32. Connect the heater hoses to the engine.

33. Connect the shifter cable to the transaxle.

34. Install the intermediate shaft bracket to the engine.

35. Install the front and rear engine mount bolts along with the mount brackets.

36. Lower the jack and remove it from the transaxle.

37. Raise the vehicle and support it safely.

38. If equipped with an automatic transaxle, install the torque converter-to-flywheel bolts.

39. Install the flywheel cover and attaching bolts.

40. Connect the exhaust pipe to the exhaust manifold and install the attaching bolts.

41. Lower the vehicle.

42. Position the air conditioning compressor, with the lines attached, in place and install the compressor-to-bracket bolts.

43. Install the compressor bracket-to-engine bolts.

44. Connect the wires to the oil pressure sending unit.

45. Connect the starter wires. Position the starter in place and install the starter-to-engine bolts.

46. Install the crankshaft pulley and install the pulley-to-crankshaft bolt. Install the right inner fender splash shield.

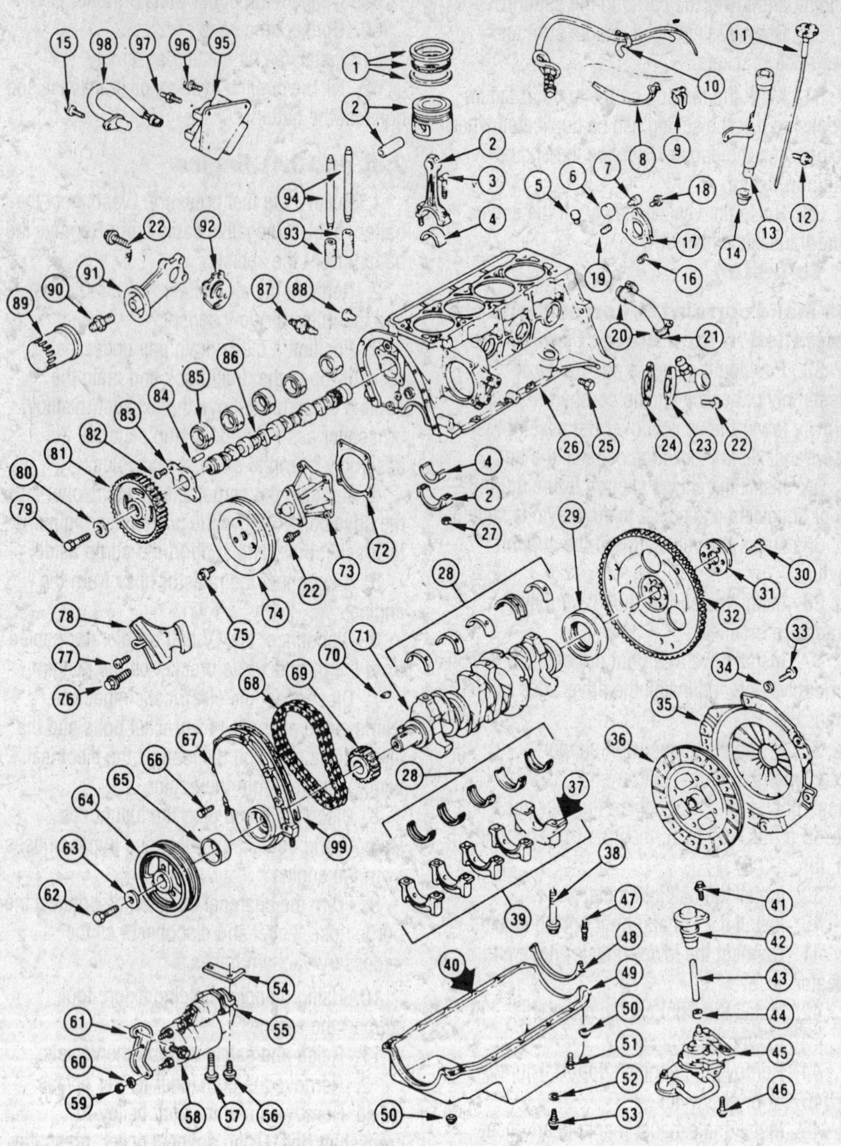

1. Ring, piston
2. Piston, w pin
3. Bolt, connecting rod
4. Bearing, connecting rod
5. Pin, cylinder head dowel
6. Plug, cylinder water jacket hole
7. Pin, clutch housing
8. Cord, engine block-heater
9. Heater, engine block
10. Retainer
11. Cap, oil fil & gage
12. Bolt, (M8 × 1.25 × 12)
13. Tube, oil fil
14. Seal, oil fil tube
15. Bolt, (m6 × 1 × 16)
16. Plug
17. Cover, camshaft rear
18. Bolt, (M6 × 1 × 13)
19. Plug
20. Clamp
21. Hose, coolant inlet
22. Bolt, (8 × 1.25 × 25)
23. Inlet, coolant
24. Gasket, coolant inlet
25. Plug, hex (1 4–18 × .56)
26. Engine, partial
27. Nut, connecting rod
28. Bearing, crankshaft
29. Seal, crankshaft rear oil
30. Bolt, flywheel
31. Retainer, flywheel
32. Flywheel, crankshaft
33. Bolt, clutch cover & pressure plate
34. Washer, spring lock (5 16)
35. Cover, plate, clutch pressure
36. Plate, clutch driven
37. Sealant
38. Bolt, crankshaft bearing cap
39. Cap, crankshaft bearing
40. Sealer
41. Bolt, (M8 × 1.25 × 25)
42. Drive, oil pump
43. Shaft, distributor to oil pump
44. Retainer
45. Pump, w screen
46. Bolt, oil pump & screen
47. Stud
48. Seal, oil pan rear
49. Pan, oil
50. Nut, (M6 × 1 × 6.5)
51. Bolt, (M6 × 1 × 13)
52. Gasket, oil pan drain screw
53. Screw, oil pan drain (M12 × 1.75)
54. Shim, starter motor
55. Motor, starter
56. Bolt, starter motor outboard (M10 × 46)
57. Bolt, starter motor inboard (M10 × 118)
58. Bolt, (M10 × 1.5 × 20)
59. Nut, (#10–24)
60. Washer, flat
61. Bracket, starter motor
62. Bolt, crankshaft pulley hub (M12 × 1.5 × 50)
63. Washer
64. Pulley, crankshaft
65. Seal, crankshaft front oil
66. Screw, hex (M6 × 1 × 30)
67. Cover, crankcase front end
68. Chain, camshaft timing

69. Sprocket, crankshaft
70. Key
71. Crankshaft, engine
72. Gasket, water pump
73. Pump, coolant
74. Pulley, water pump
75. Bolt, (M8 × 1.25 × 16)
76. Bolt, (M8 × 1.25 × 20)
77. Bolt, tensioner timing chain (M8 × 1.25 × 23)
78. Tensioner, timing chain
79. Bolt, hex (M12 × 1.75 × 35)
80. Washer, camshaft sprocket
81. Sprocket, camshaft
82. Screw, camshaft thrust plate
83. Plate, camshaft thrust

84. Pin, (M6 × 16)
85. Bearing, camshaft
86. Camshaft, engine
87. Switch, fuel pump
88. Valve, oil filter by-pass
89. Filter, oil (PF52)
90. Connector, oil filter adapter
91. Adapter, oil filter
92. Gasket, oil filter adapter
93. Lifter, hydraulic valve
94. Rod, push
95. Coil, w module ignition
96. Bolt, (M8 × 1.25 × 18)
97. Stud, ignition coil
98. Sensor
99. Gasket

FIG. 25 Exploded view of the lower engine assembly — 1988 2.0L engine

1. Air cleaner, TBI
2. Screw, (M6.3 × 1.81 × 20)
3. Washer
4. Duct, air intake front
5. Bolt, (M6 × 1 × 25)
6. Support, spark plug wire front
7. Support, spark plug wire rear
8. Bolt, (M8 × 1.25 × 25)
9. Support, ignition wire
10. Bolt, valve rocker cover
11. Tube, crankcase vent
12. Bolt, valve rocker cover
13. Cover, valve rocker
14. Gasket, valve rocker cover
15. Nut, valve rocker arm
16. Ball, rocker arm
17. Arm, valve rocker
18. Stud, valve rocker arm ball
19. Guide, push rod
20. Seat, valve spring
21. Control, heater coolant hose
22. Seal, valve stem oil
23. Spring, valve
24. Cap, valve spring
25. Key, valve stem
26. Plug, spark
27. Wire, spark plug
28. Nut, (M8 × 1.25 × 7.5)
29. Valve, EGR
30. Gasket, EGR valve
31. Plug, water outlet (3 8-18 × .42)
32. Sensor, coolant temperature
33. Stud, EGR valve (M8 × 1.25 × 45)
34. Adapter, coolant outlet
35. Thermostat, engine coolant outlet
36. Outlet, coolant
37. Stud
38. Nut, (M6 × 1)
39. Gasket, coolant outlet
40. Nut, (M10 × 1.5)
41. Bracket, engine lift
42. Stud, cylinder head
43. Stud, exhaust manifold
44. Gasket, exhaust manifold
45. Manifold, exhaust
46. Nut, (m8-1.25)
47. Valve, exhaust
48. Valve, inlet
49. Gasket, cylinder head
50. Head, w guide and insert
51. Bolt (M11 × 1.5 × 98)
52. Bolt, spl (M11 × 1.5 × 130) (5)
53. Switch, coolant temperature
54. Bracket, drive belt tensioner
55. Bolt, (M10 × 1.5 × 30)
56. Stud
57. Bracket, accelerator control cable
58. Stud
59. Nut, (M6 × 1 × 5.5)
60. Stud
61. Stud, intake manifold (M8 × 1.25)
62. Stud, intake manifold (M8 × 1.25)
63. Gasket, intake manifold
64. Manifold, intake

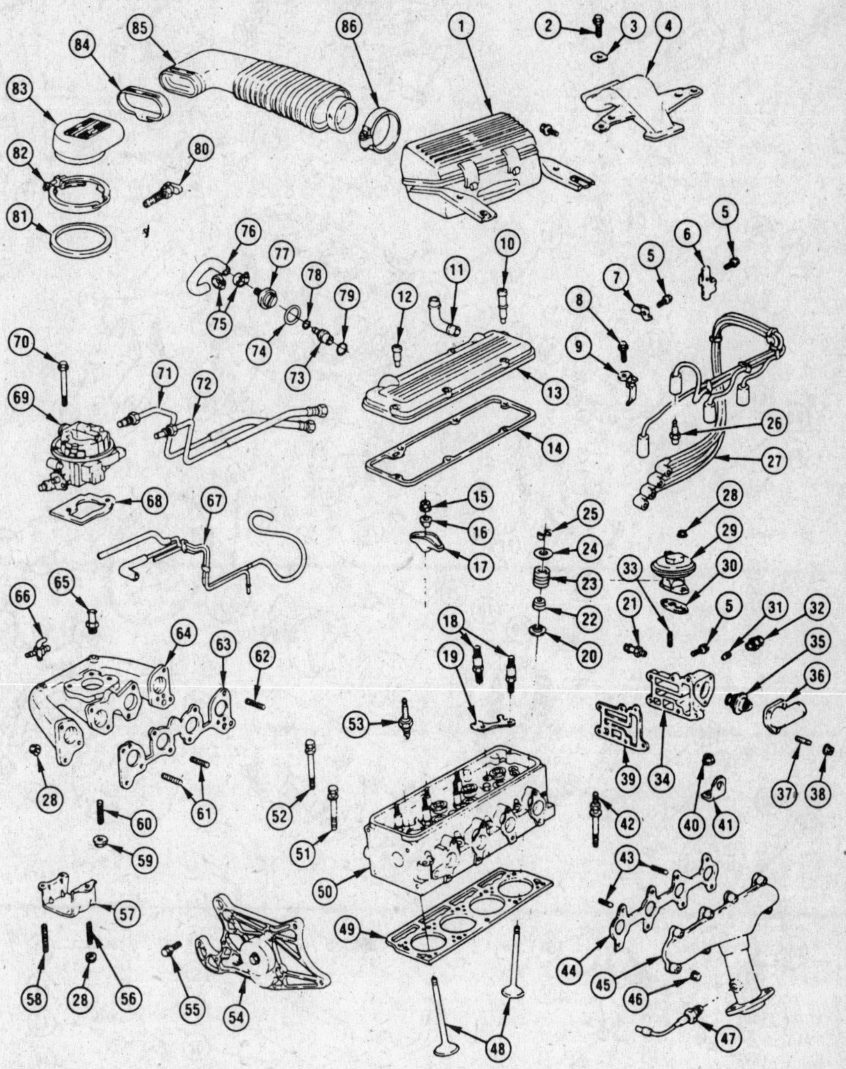

65. Fitting, vacuum power brake
66. Fitting, inlet manifold vacuum
67. Tube, EGR vacuum & evaporator canister
68. Gasket, TBI
69. Throttle body injection
70. Bolt, TBI
71. Pipe, fuel injection—fuel return
72. Pipe, fuel injection—fuel feed
73. Valve, crankcase vent
74. Seal, crankcase vent valve cap
75. Clamp, (1 2–13 16)

76. Hose, crankcase vent
77. Cap, crankcase vent valve
78. Seal, crankcase vent valve (top)
79. Seal, crankcase vent valve (bottom)
80. Sensor, manifold air temperature
81. Seal, air intake duct adapter front
82. Clamp, front air intake duct adapter
82. Adapter, air intake duct front
84. Clamp
85. Duct
86. Clamp

FIG. 27 Exploded view of the upper engine assembly — 1988–89 2.0L engine

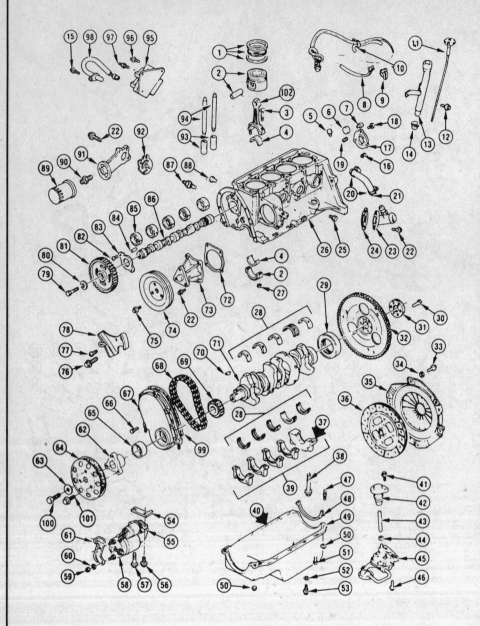

35. Cover, plate, clutch pressure
36. Plate, clutch driven
37. Sealant
38. Bolt, crankshaft bearing cap
39. Cap, crankshaft bearing
40. Sealer
41. Bolt
42. Drive, oil pump
43. Shaft, distributor to oil pump
44. Retainer
45. Pump, w screen
46. Bolt, oil pump & screen
47. Stud
48. Seal, oil pan rear
49. Pan, oil
50. Nut
51. Bolt
52. Gasket, oil pan drain screw
53. Screw, oil pan drain
54. Shim, starter motor
55. Motor, starter
56. Bolt, starter motor outboard
57. Bolt, starter motor inboard
58. Bolt
59. Nut
60. Washer, flat
61. Bracket, starter motor
62. Hub, crankshaft pulley
63. Washer
64. Pulley, crankshaft
65. Seal, crankshaft front oil
66. Screw, hex
67. Cover, crankcase front end
68. Chain, camshaft timing
69. Sprocket, crankshaft
70. Key
71. Crankshaft, engine
72. Gasket, water pump
73. Pump, coolant
74. Pulley, water pump
75. Bolt
76. Bolt
77. Bolt, tensioner timing chain
78. Tensioner, timing chain
79. Bolt, hex
80. Washer, camshaft sprocket
81. Sprocket, camshaft
82. Screw, camshaft thrust plate
83. Plate, camshaft thrust
84. Pin
85. Bearing, camshaft
86. Camshaft, engine
87. Switch, fuel pump
88. Valve, oil filter by-pass
89. Filter, oil (PF52)
90. Connector, oil filter adapter
91. Adapter, oil filter
92. Gasket, oil filter adapter
93. Lifter, hydraulic valve
94. Rod, push
95. Coil, w module ignition
96. Bolt
97. Stud, ignition coil
98. Sensor, crankshaft
99. Gasket
100. Bolt, crankshaft pulley hub
101. Bolt, crankshaft pulley
102. Connecting rod

1. Ring, piston
2. Piston, w pin
3. Bolt, connecting rod
4. Bearing, connecting rod
5. Pin, cylinder head dowel
6. Plug, cylinder water jacket hole
7. Pin, clutch housing
8. Cord, engine block heater
9. Heater, engine block
10. Retainer
11. Cap, oil fil & gage
12. Bolt
13. Tube, oil fil
14. Seal, oil fil tube
15. Bolt
16. Plug
17. Cover, camshaft rear

18. Bolt
19. Plug
20. Clamp
21. Hose, coolant inlet
22. Bolt
23. Inlet, coolant
24. Gasket, coolant inlet
25. Plug
26. Engine, partial
27. Nut, connecting rod
28. Bearing, crankshaft
29. Seal, crankshaft rear oil
30. Bolt, flywheel
31. Retainer, flywheel
32. Flywheel, crankshaft
33. Bolt, clutch cover & pressure plate
34. Washer, spring lock

FIG. 28 Exploded view of the lower engine assembly — 1989-92 2.0L and 2.2L engine

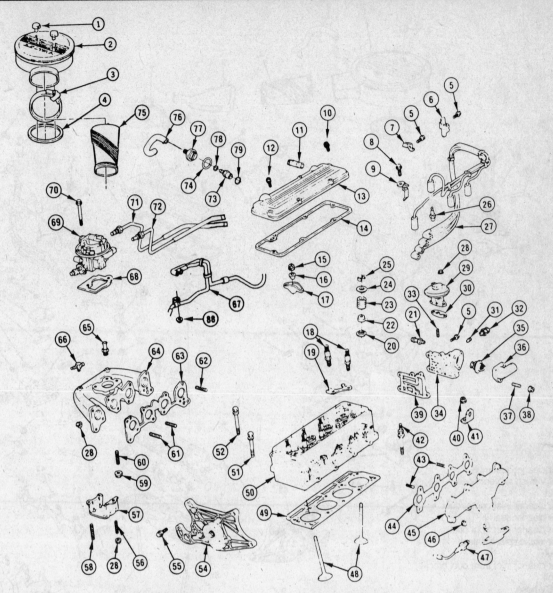

FIG. 29 Exploded view of the upper engine assembly — 1990 2.2L engine

1. Nut
2. Air cleaner assembly
3. Clamp
4. Seal
5. Bolt
6. Spark wire support
7. Spark wire support
8. Bolt
9. Ignition wire support
10. Rocker cover bolt
11. Crankcase vent tube
12. Rocker cover bolt
13. Valve rocker cover
14. Gasket
15. Rocker arm nut
16. Rocker arm ball
17. Rocker arm
18. Stud
19. Push rod guide
20. Valve spring seat
21. Coolant hose fitting
22. Valve stem oil seal
23. Valve spring
24. Valve spring cap
25. Valve stem key
26. Spark plug
27. Spark plug wire
28. Nut
29. EGR valve
30. Gasket
31. Water outlet plug
32. Coolant temperature sensor
33. EGR valve stud
34. Coolant outlet adapter
35. Thermostat
36. Coolant outlet
37. Stud
38. Nut
39. Coolant outlet gasket
40. Nut
41. Engine lift bracket
42. Cylinder head bolt
43. Exhaust manifold stud
44. Exhaust manifold gasket
45. Exhaust manifold
46. Nut
47. Oxygen sensor
48. Inlet valve
49. Cylinder head gasket
50. Cylinder head
51. Cylinder head short bolt
52. Cylinder head long bolt
54. Drive belt tensioner bracket
55. Bolt
56. Stud
57. Accelerator cable bracket
58. Stud
59. Nut
60. Stud
61. Stud
62. Stud
63. Gasket
64. Intake manifold
65. Vacuum power brake fitting
66. Intake manifold vacuum fitting
67. EGR vacuum tube
68. TBI gasket
69. Throttle body injector
70. TBI bolt
71. Pipe
72. Pipe
73. PCV valve
74. PCV cap seal
75. Air cleaner intake duct
76. PCV hose
77. PCV cap
78. PCV seal

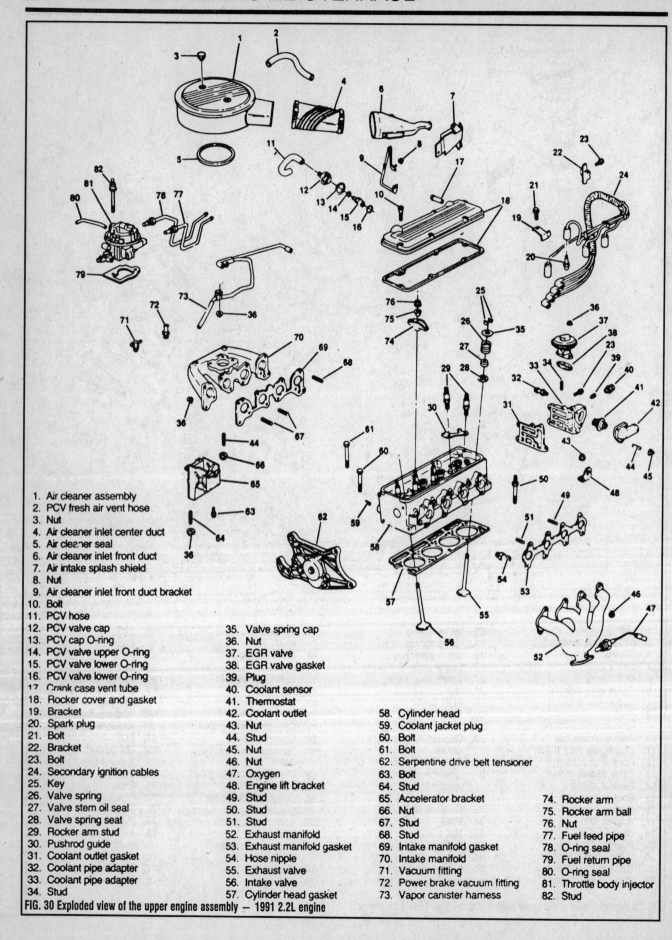

1. Air cleaner assembly
2. PCV fresh air vent hose
3. Nut
4. Air cleaner inlet center duct
5. Air cleaner seal
6. Air cleaner inlet front duct
7. Air intake splash shield
8. Nut
9. Air cleaner inlet front duct bracket
10. Bolt
11. PCV hose
12. PCV valve cap
13. PCV cap O-ring
14. PCV valve upper O-ring
15. PCV valve lower O-ring
16. PCV valve lower O-ring
17. Crank case vent tube
18. Rocker cover and gasket
19. Bracket
20. Spark plug
21. Bolt
22. Bracket
23. Bolt
24. Secondary ignition cables
25. Key
26. Valve spring
27. Valve stem oil seal
28. Valve spring seat
29. Rocker arm stud
30. Pushrod guide
31. Coolant outlet gasket
32. Coolant pipe adapter
33. Coolant pipe adapter
34. Stud

35. Valve spring cap
36. Nut
37. EGR valve
38. EGR valve gasket
39. Plug
40. Coolant sensor
41. Thermostat
42. Coolant outlet
43. Nut
44. Stud
45. Nut
46. Nut
47. Oxygen
48. Engine lift bracket
49. Stud
50. Stud
51. Stud
52. Exhaust manifold
53. Exhaust manifold gasket
54. Hose nipple
55. Exhaust valve
56. Intake valve
57. Cylinder head gasket

58. Cylinder head
59. Coolant jacket plug
60. Bolt
61. Bolt
62. Serpentine drive belt tensioner
63. Bolt
64. Stud
65. Accelerator bracket
66. Nut
67. Stud
68. Stud
69. Intake manifold gasket
70. Intake manifold
71. Vacuum fitting
72. Power brake vacuum fitting
73. Vapor canister harness

74. Rocker arm
75. Rocker arm ball
76. Nut
77. Fuel feed pipe
78. O-ring seal
79. Fuel return pipe
80. O-ring seal
81. Throttle body injector
82. Stud

FIG. 30 Exploded view of the upper engine assembly — 1991 2.2L engine

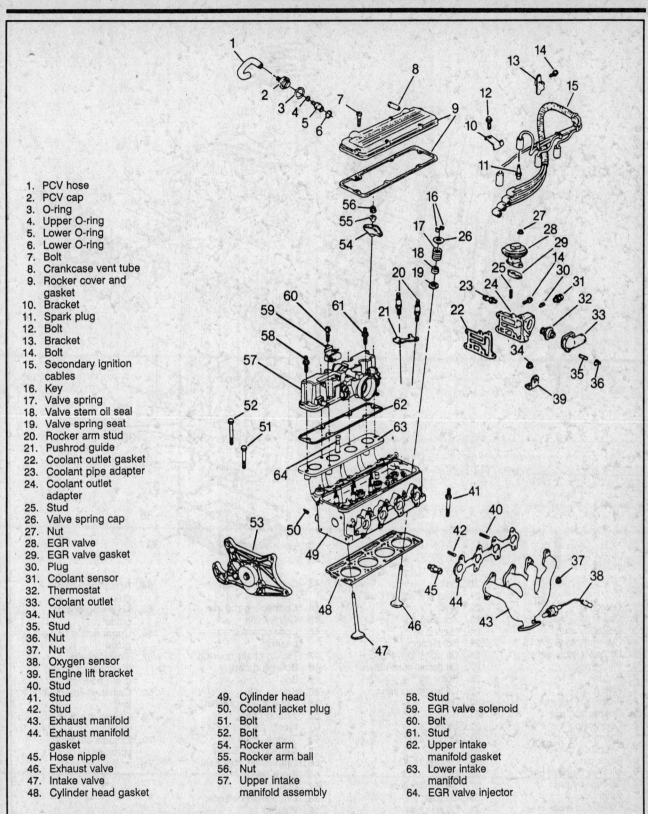

1. PCV hose
2. PCV cap
3. O-ring
4. Upper O-ring
5. Lower O-ring
6. Lower O-ring
7. Bolt
8. Crankcase vent tube
9. Rocker cover and gasket
10. Bracket
11. Spark plug
12. Bolt
13. Bracket
14. Bolt
15. Secondary ignition cables
16. Key
17. Valve spring
18. Valve stem oil seal
19. Valve spring seat
20. Rocker arm stud
21. Pushrod guide
22. Coolant outlet gasket
23. Coolant pipe adapter
24. Coolant outlet adapter
25. Stud
26. Valve spring cap
27. Nut
28. EGR valve
29. EGR valve gasket
30. Plug
31. Coolant sensor
32. Thermostat
33. Coolant outlet
34. Nut
35. Stud
36. Nut
37. Nut
38. Oxygen sensor
39. Engine lift bracket
40. Stud
41. Stud
42. Stud
43. Exhaust manifold
44. Exhaust manifold gasket
45. Hose nipple
46. Exhaust valve
47. Intake valve
48. Cylinder head gasket

49. Cylinder head
50. Coolant jacket plug
51. Bolt
52. Bolt
54. Rocker arm
55. Rocker arm ball
56. Nut
57. Upper intake manifold assembly

58. Stud
59. EGR valve solenoid
60. Bolt
61. Stud
62. Upper intake manifold gasket
63. Lower intake manifold
64. EGR valve injector

FIG. 31 Exploded view of the upper engine assembly — 1992 2.2L engine

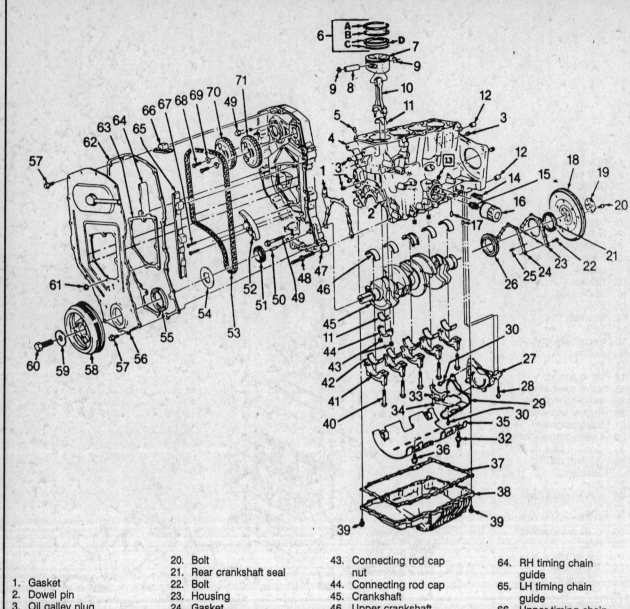

FIG. 32 Exploded view of the lower engine assembly — 1990–92 2.3L engine

1. Gasket
2. Dowel pin
3. Oil galley plug
4. Cylinder block
5. Oil flow check valve
6. Piston rings
7. Piston
8. Piston pin
9. Piston pin retainer
10. Connecting rod
11. Connecting rod bearing
12. Transaxle to cylinder block pin
13. Oil filter by-pass plug
14. Oil filter by-pass valve
15. Oil filter to block connector
16. Oil filter
17. Dowel pin
18. Flywheel
19. Flywheel retainer (automatic transaxle)
20. Bolt
21. Rear crankshaft seal
22. Bolt
23. Housing
24. Gasket
25. Dowel pin
26. Oil pump drive gear
27. Oil pump assembly
28. Bolt
29. Oil pump screen
30. Bolt
31. Bolt
32. Stud
33. Brace
34. Nut
35. Oil pan baffle
36. Bolt
37. Oil pan gasket
38. Oil pan
39. Oil pan bolt
40. Crankshaft bearing cap bolt
41. Crankshaft bearing cap
42. Lower crankshaft bearing
43. Connecting rod cap nut
44. Connecting rod cap
45. Crankshaft
46. Upper crankshaft bearing
47. Timing chain housing
48. Bolt (stud end)
49. Bolt
50. Key
51. Crankshaft sprocket
52. Timing chain tensioner and shoe
53. Timing chain
54. Crankshaft slinger
55. Crankshaft front seal
56. Front cover
57. Bolt
58. Crankshaft balancer
59. Washer
60. Bolt
61. Nut
62. Front cover outer gasket
63. Front cover inner gasket
64. RH timing chain guide
65. LH timing chain guide
66. Upper timing chain guide
67. Timing chain tensioner to timing chain housing bolt
68. Camshaft sprocket bolt
69. Camshaft sprocket washer
70. Exhaust camshaft sprocket
71. Intake camshaft sprocket

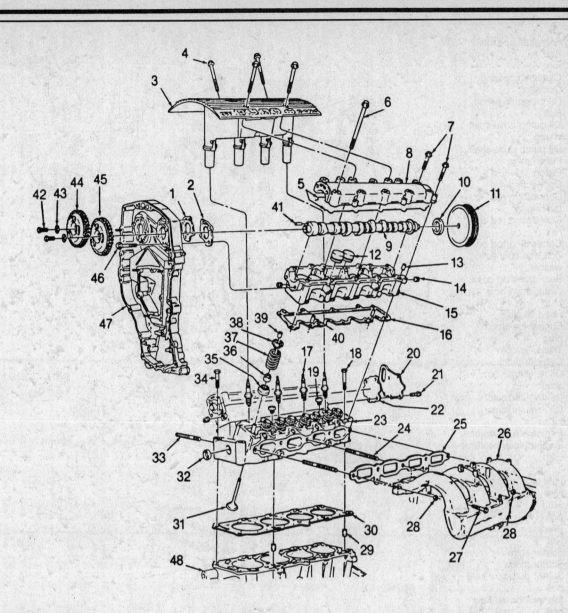

1. Timing chain housing gasket to exhaust camshaft housing
2. Timing chain housing gasket to intake camshaft housing
3. Ignition coil and module assembly
4. Bolts
5. Seal
6. Bolt
7. Bolt
8. Cover (intake shown)
9. Camshaft (intake shown)
10. Seal
11. Power steering pump drive pulley
12. Valve lifter
13. Dowel pin
14. Plug
15. Camshaft housing (intake shown)
16. Gasket
17. Spark plug
18. Cylinder head to block bolt (M12 × 1.75mm × 100mm)
19. Cylinder head threaded plug
20. Exhaust camshaft cover
21. Bolt
22. Gasket
23. Cylinder head
24. Intake manifold to cylinder head stud
25. Gasket
26. Intake manifold
27. Bolt
28. Nut
29. Cylinder head locating pin
30. Gasket
31. Intake valve shown
32. Cylinder head plug
33. Stud
34. Cylinder head to block bolt (M12 × 1.75mm × 100mm)
35. Rotator assembly
36. Valve stem seal
37. Spring
38. Retainer
39. Key
40. Dowel pin
41. Dowel pin
42. Bolt
43. Washer
44. Exhaust camshaft gear
45. Intake camshaft gear
46. Bolt
47. Cover
48. Block

FIG. 33 Exploded view of the upper engine assembly — 1990–92 2.3L engine

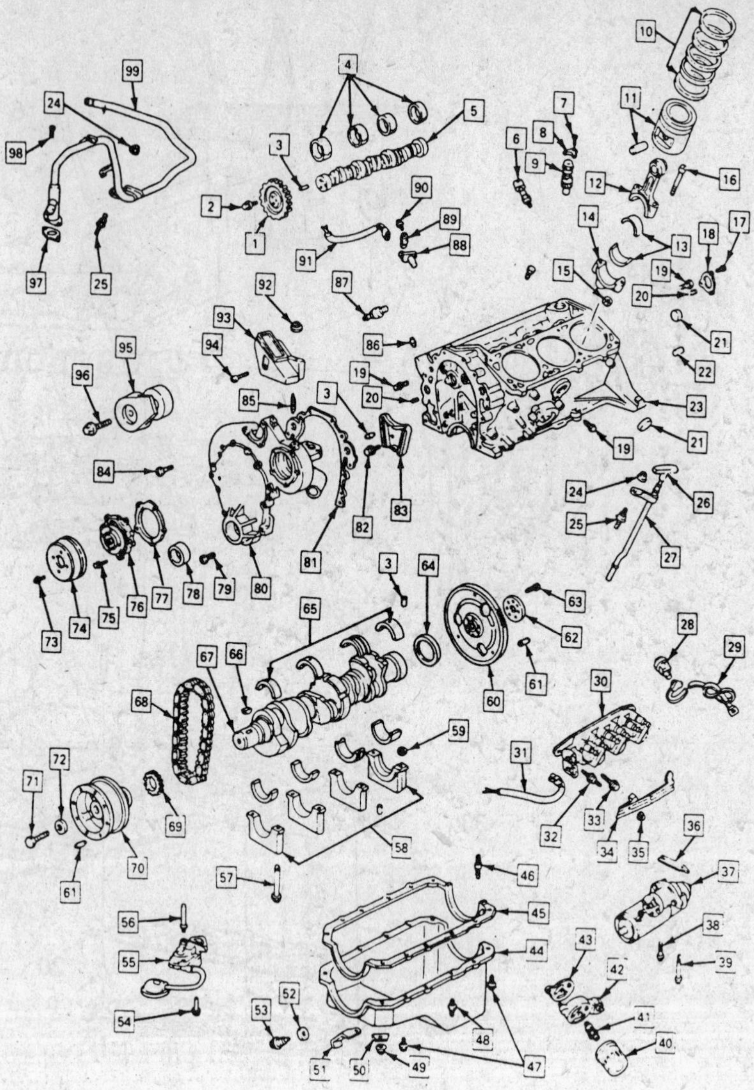

1. Camshaft sprocket
2. Bolt
3. Pin
4. Camshaft bearing
5. Camshaft
6. Oil pressure switch
7. Bolt
8. Oil pump drive shaft clamp
9. Oil pump drive shaft
10. Piston rings
11. Piston
12. Connecting rod
13. Connecting rod bearing kit
14. Connecting rod cap
15. Nut
16. Connecting rod bolt
17. Bolt with connecting washer
18. Rear camshaft cover
19. Water drain hole plug
20. Head fill plug
21. Engine expansion plug
22. Trans. line pin
23. Cylinder block
24. Oil level tube nut
25. Stud
26. Oil level indicator
27. Oil level indicator tube
28. Engine block heater
29. Engine block heater cord
30. Ignition coil
31. Ignition timing sensor wire
32. Stud
33. Bolt
34. Bracket
35. Nut
36. Starter shim
37. Starter motor
38. Starter outboard hole bolt
39. Starter inboard hole bolt
40. Oil filter
41. Oil cooler adapter retainer
42. Oil filter adapter
43. Oil filter adapter gasket
44. Engine oil pan
45. Oil pan gasket
46. Oil pan stud
47. Oil pan bolt
48. Oil pan stud
49. Nut
50. oil pan reinforcement
51. Wire harness clip
52. Gasket
53. Drain plug
54. Bolt
55. Oil pump
56. Distributor to oil pump shaft
57. Crankshaft bearing cap bolt

58. Crankshaft bearing cap
59. Cap
60. Flywheel
61. Groove pin
62. Flywheel retainer
63. Flywheel bolt
64. Crankshaft rear oil seal
65. Crankshaft bearing kit
66. Key
67. Crankshaft
68. Timing chain
69. Crankshaft sprocket
70. Torsional damper
71. Torsional bolt
72. Washer

73. Bolt
74. Coolant pump pulley
75. Coolant pump bolt
76. Coolant pump kit
77. Coolant pump gasket
78. Crankshaft front oil seal
79. Crankcase bolt
80. Engine front cover
81. Front engine cover gasket
82. Bolt
83. Timing chain damper
84. Crankcase front end cover bolt
85. Crankcase front end cover stud
86. Cylinder head pin

87. ECS knock sensor
88. Crankcase positioner sensor
89. Wiring clip retainer
90. Bolt
91. Ignition timing sensor wire
92. Nut
93. Drive belt shield
94. Drive belt shield bolt
95. Drive belt tensioner
96. Drive belt tensioner bolt
97. Engine cooling filler gasket
98. Screw
99. Coolant by-pass pipe
100. Pin

FIG. 34 Exploded view of the lower engine assembly — 1990–92 3.1L engine

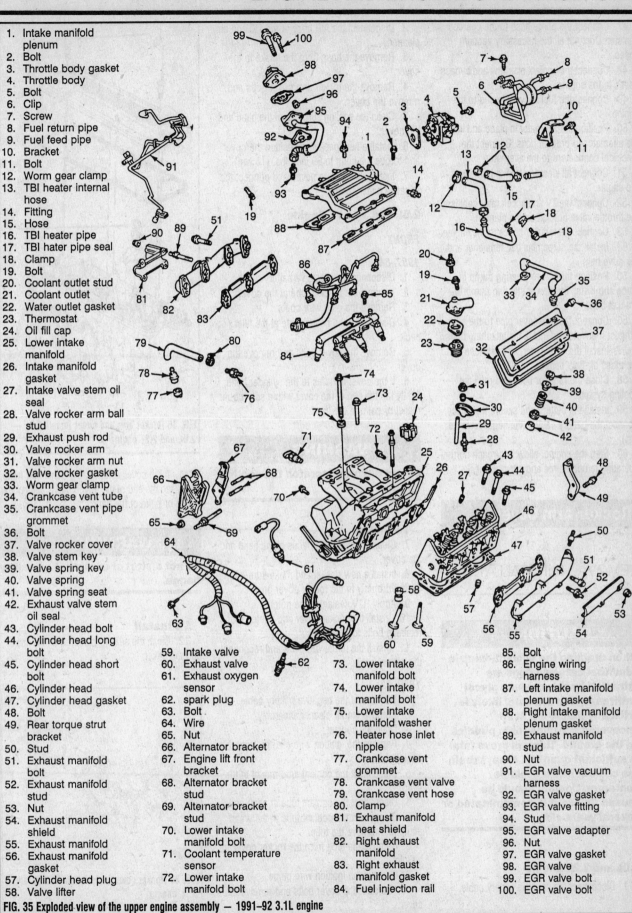

1. Intake manifold plenum
2. Bolt
3. Throttle body gasket
4. Throttle body
5. Bolt
6. Clip
7. Screw
8. Fuel return pipe
9. Fuel feed pipe
10. Bracket
11. Bolt
12. Worm gear clamp
13. TBI heater internal hose
14. Fitting
15. Hose
16. TBI heater pipe
17. TBI hater pipe seal
18. Clamp
19. Bolt
20. Coolant outlet stud
21. Coolant outlet
22. Water outlet gasket
23. Thermostat
24. Oil fill cap
25. Lower intake manifold
26. Intake manifold gasket
27. Intake valve stem oil seal
28. Valve rocker arm ball stud
29. Exhaust push rod
30. Valve rocker arm
31. Valve rocker arm nut
32. Valve rocker gasket
33. Worm gear clamp
34. Crankcase vent tube
35. Crankcase vent pipe grommet
36. Bolt
37. Valve rocker cover
38. Valve stem key
39. Valve spring key
40. Valve spring
41. Valve spring seat
42. Exhaust valve stem oil seal
43. Cylinder head bolt
44. Cylinder head long bolt
45. Cylinder head short bolt
46. Cylinder head
47. Cylinder head gasket
48. Bolt
49. Rear torque strut bracket
50. Stud
51. Exhaust manifold bolt
52. Exhaust manifold stud
53. Nut
54. Exhaust manifold shield
55. Exhaust manifold
56. Exhaust manifold gasket
57. Cylinder head plug
58. Valve lifter
59. Intake valve
60. Exhaust valve
61. Exhaust oxygen sensor
62. spark plug
63. Bolt
64. Wire
65. Nut
66. Alternator bracket
67. Engine lift front bracket
68. Alternator bracket stud
69. Alternator bracket stud
70. Lower intake manifold bolt
71. Coolant temperature sensor
72. Lower intake manifold bolt
73. Lower intake manifold bolt
74. Lower intake manifold bolt
75. Lower intake manifold washer
76. Heater hose inlet nipple
77. Crankcase vent grommet
78. Crankcase vent valve
79. Crankcase vent hose
80. Clamp
81. Exhaust manifold heat shield
82. Right exhaust manifold
83. Right exhaust manifold gasket
84. Fuel injection rail
85. Bolt
86. Engine wiring harness
87. Left intake manifold plenum gasket
88. Right intake manifold plenum gasket
89. Exhaust manifold stud
90. Nut
91. EGR valve vacuum harness
92. EGR valve gasket
93. EGR valve fitting
94. Stud
95. EGR valve adapter
96. Nut
97. EGR valve gasket
98. EGR valve
99. EGR valve bolt
100. EGR valve bolt

FIG. 35 Exploded view of the upper engine assembly — 1991–92 3.1L engine

47. Connect the purge hose to the charcoal canister. Connect all the necessary vacuum hoses.

48. Connect the coolant overflow and bypass hoses to the engine.

49. Connect the fuel delivery hoses to the engine.

50. Position the alternator in place and install the alternator-to-bracket bolts. Connect the electrical connectors to the alternator.

51. Connect all electrical wiring harnesses to the engine.

52. Connect the TV and accelerator cables to the throttle valve bracket on the plenum.

53. Connect the radiator hoses to the engine.

54. Install the serpentine belt tensioner and the drive belt.

55. Position the power steering pump in place and install the power steering pump-to-bracket bolts.

56. Connect the crossover pipe to the exhaust manifold and install the attaching bolts.

57. Install the air cleaner, air inlet hose and the mass air flow sensor.

58. Close the radiator cock and refill the cooling system.

59. Install the battery and secure it in place. Connect the battery cables (the negative cable last).

60. Start the engine, allow it to reach normal operating temperatures and check for leaks.

Rocker Arm Cover

REMOVAL & INSTALLATION

> ❄ **CAUTION**
>
> **When draining the coolant, keep in mind that cats and dogs are attracted by the ethylene glycol antifreeze, and are quite likely to drink any that is left in an uncovered container or in puddles on the ground. This will prove fatal in sufficient quantity. Always drain the coolant into a sealable container. Coolant should be reused unless it is contaminated or several years old.**

2.0L and 2.2L Engine

1. Disconnect the negative battery cable.

2. Disconnect the AIR hose at the TBI and air cleaner.

3. Remove the hose from the intake to the cover.

4. Remove the rocker arm cover bolts and remove the cover.

5. Clean the sealing surfaces of the head and the cover.

6. Install a new gasket, reposition the cover and torque the bolts to 89 inch lbs. (10 Nm).

7. Install all hoses removed and connect the negative battery cable.

2.8L and 3.1L V6 Engine

FRONT

1987–88

1. Disconnect the negative battery cable.

2. Remove the bracket tube at the cover.

3. Remove the plug wire cover.

4. Disconnect the heater hose at the filler neck.

5. Remove the cover bolts and remove the cover.

6. If the cover adheres to the cylinder head, lightly tap the end of the cover with a soft rubber mallet or palm of the hand.

> ❄ **WARNING**
>
> **Do not distort or scratch the sealing flange.**

To Install

7. Clean the sealing surfaces of the head and the cover.

8. Install a new gasket and make sure it is seated properly in the rocker cover groove.

9. Apply RTV sealant in the notch.

10. Install the rocker cover and tighten the retaining bolts to 6–9 ft. lbs.

11. Install the remaining parts and reconnect the battery cable.

1989–92

1. Disconnect the negative battery cable.

2. Remove the air cleaner assembly

3. Drain the coolant.

4. Remove the ignition wire clamps from the coolant tube.

5. Disconnect the coolant tube mount at the head.

6. Disconnect the coolant tube at each end.

7. Disconnect the coolant tube at the water pump and remove the tube.

8. Remove the tube from the rocker cover to air inlet.

9. Remove the ignition wire guide.

10. Remove the cover bolts and remove the cover.

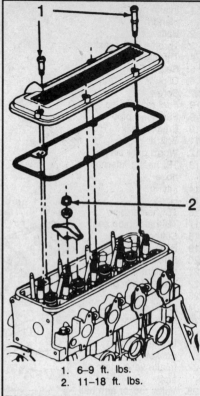

1. 6–9 ft. lbs.
2. 11–18 ft. lbs.

FIG. 36 Rocker arm and cover installation — 2.0L and 2.2L engine

11. If the cover adheres to the cylinder head, lightly tap the end of the cover with a soft rubber mallet or palm of the hand.

> ❄ **WARNING**
>
> **Do not distort or scratch the sealing flange.**

To Install

12. Clean the sealing surfaces of the head and the cover.

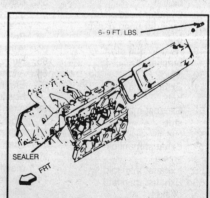

6–9 FT. LBS.

SEALER   FRT

FIG. 37 Rocker cover installation — 2.8L and 3.1L engine

13. Install a new gasket and make sure it is seated properly in the rocker cover groove.

14. Apply RTV sealant in the notch.

15. Install the rocker cover and tighten the retaining bolts to 89 inch lbs. (10 Nm).

16. Install the remaining parts and reconnect the battery cable.

REAR

1. Disconnect the negative battery cable.

2. Disconnect the brake booster vacuum line at the bracket.

3. Disconnect the cable bracket at the plenum.

4. Remove the vacuum line bracket at the cable bracket.

5. Disconnect the lines at the alternator brace stud.

6. Disconnect the rear alternator brace.

7. Remove the serpentine belt.

8. Disconnect the alternator and lay to one side.

9. Remove the PCV valve.

10. Loosen the alternator bracket.

11. Remove the rocker cover bolts, plug wires and rocker cover.

12. If the cover adheres to the cylinder head, lightly tap the end of the cover with a soft rubber mallet or palm of the hand.

❈❈ WARNING

Do not distort or scratch the sealing flange.

To Install

13. Clean the sealing surfaces of the head and the cover.

14. Install a new gasket and make sure it is seated properly in the rocker cover groove.

15. Apply RTV sealant in the notch.

16. Install the rocker cover and tighten the retaining bolts to 89 inch lbs.

17. Install the remaining parts and reconnect the battery cable.

Rocker Arms and Pushrods

REMOVAL, INSTALLATION AND ADJUSTMENT

2.0L and 2.2L Engine

1. Disconnect the negative battery cable.

2. Remove the rocker arm cover bolts and the cover.

3. Remove the rocker arm nuts, balls arms and push rods.

➡ **Be sure to keep the components in order for installation purposes.**

To install:

4. Coat the bearing surfaces of the rocker arms and the rocker arm balls with Molykote® or its equivalent.

5. Seat the push rods in the lifters.

6. Install the rocker arms, balls and nuts and tighten the rocker arm nuts to 7–11 ft. lbs. (10–15 Nm) for 1988 and 14 ft. lbs. (20 Nm) for 1989–92.

7. Install the rocker arm cover.

8. Connect the negative battery cable.

2.3L Engine

The valve train consists of 2 chain driven overhead camshafts with direct acting lifters.

2.8L and 3.1L V6 Engine

1988

1. Remove the rocker arm covers as outlined earlier.

2. Remove the rocker arm nuts, rocker arm balls, rocker arms, push rod guides and push rods and place in a rack so that they may be re installed in the same location.

3. Coat the bearing surfaces of the rocker arms and the rocker arm balls with Molykote® or its equivalent.

4. Install the pushrods making sure that they seat properly in the lifter.

5. Install the pushrod guides, rocker arms, pivot balls and nuts.

6. Tighten the rocker arm nuts to 18 ft.lbs. (25 Nm).

1989–92

1. Remove the rocker arm covers as outlined earlier.

2. Remove the rocker arm nuts, rocker arm balls, rocker arms and push rods and place in a rack so that they may be reinstalled in the same location.

➡ **Intake pushrods are marked orange and are 6 in. (152mm) long. Exhaust pushrods are marked blue and are 6³/₈ in. (162mm) long.**

3. Coat the bearing surfaces of the rocker arms and the rocker arm balls with Molykote® or its equivalent.

4. Install the pushrods making sure that they seat properly in the lifter.

5. Install the pushrods, rocker arms, pivot balls and nuts.

6. Tighten the rocker arm nuts to 18 ft. lbs. (25 Nm).

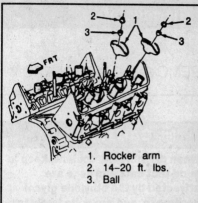

1. Rocker arm
2. 14–20 ft. lbs.
3. Ball

FIG. 38 Rocker arm installation — 2.8L and 3.1L engine

VALVE LASH ADJUSTMENT

2.8L and 3.1L engines

➡ **The following adjustment procedure should be used when reconditioning a valve seat, and a new adjustable rocker arm stud has been installed.**

1. Install the rocker arms, balls and nuts. Tighten the rocker arm nuts until all lash is eliminated.

2. Adjust the valves when the lifter is on the base circle of a camshaft lobe:

a. Crank the engine until the mark on the crankshaft pulley lines up with the **O** mark on the timing tab. Make sure that the engine is in the No. 1 firing position. Place your fingers on the No. 1 rocker arms as the mark on the crank pulley comes near the **O** mark. If the valves are not moving, the engine is in the No. 1 firing position. If the valves move, the engine is in the No. 4 firing position; rotate the engine 1 complete revolution and it will be in the No. 1 position.

b. When the engine is in the No. 1 firing position, adjust the following valves:

- Exhaust—1,2,3
- Intake—1,5,6

c. Back the adjusting nut out until lash can be felt at the pushrod, then turn the nut until all lash is removed (this can be determined by rotating the pushrod while turning the adjusting nut). When all lash has been removed, turn the nut in 1¹/₂ additional turns, this will center the lifter plunger.

d. Crank the engine 1 complete revolution until the timing tab and the **O** mark are again in alignment. Now the engine is in the No. 4 firing position. Adjust the following valves:

- Exhaust—4,5,6
- Intake—2,3,4

Thermostat

REMOVAL & INSTALLATION

❄ CAUTION

When draining the coolant, keep in mind that cats and dogs are attracted by the ethylene glycol antifreeze, and are quite likely to drink any that is left in an uncovered container or in puddles on the ground. This will prove fatal in sufficient quantity. Always drain the coolant into a sealable container. Coolant should be reused unless it is contaminated or several years old.

2.0L AND 2.2L Engine

The thermostat is located inside a housing on the back of the cylinder head. It is not necessary to remove the radiator hose from the thermostat housing when removing the thermostat.

1. Disconnect the negative battery cable.
2. Drain the cooling system and remove the air cleaner.
3. On some models it may be necessary to disconnect the A.I.R. pipe at the upper check valve and the bracket at the water outlet.
4. Disconnect the electrical lead.
5. Remove the two retaining bolts from the thermostat housing and lift up the housing with the house attached. Lift out the thermostat.
6. Insert the new thermostat, spring toward the engine. Apply a thin bead of silicone sealer to the housing mating surface and install the housing while the sealer is still wet. Tighten the housing retaining bolts to 6–9 ft. lbs. (8–10 Nm).

➡ Poor heater output and slow warmup is often caused by a thermostat stuck in the open position; occasionally one sticks shut causing immediate overheating. Do not attempt to correct a chronic overheating condition by permanently removing the thermostat. Thermostat flow restriction is designed into the system; without it, localized overheating (due to coolant turbulence) may occur, causing expensive troubles.

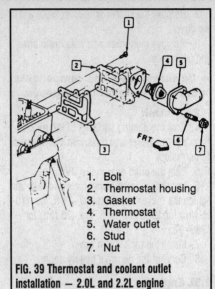

1. Bolt
2. Thermostat housing
3. Gasket
4. Thermostat
5. Water outlet
6. Stud
7. Nut

FIG. 39 Thermostat and coolant outlet installation — 2.0L and 2.2L engine

7. Installation of the remaining components is in the reverse order of removal.

2.3L Engine

1. Disconnect the negative battery cable.
2. Drain the engine coolant level below the thermostat housing.
3. Remove the upper radiator hose from the thermostat water outlet and position it to the side.
4. Remove the heater and throttle body coolant hoses from the thermostat housing and disconnect the electrical connector from the coolant temperature sensor.
5. Remove the thermostat attaching bolts.
6. Remove the thermostat housing gasket and thermostat.

To Install:

7. Throughly clean the mating surfaces of the engine and thermostat.
8. Install the new thermostat, gasket and housing, being careful not to allow the thermostat to slip out of position.
9. Install the attaching bolts and tighten to 19 ft. lbs. (26 Nm).
10. Connect the heater and throttle body coolant hoses the thermostat housing and connect the coolant temperature sensor connector.
11. Connect the upper radiator hose to the thermostat housing water outlet.
12. Refill and bleed the cooling system. Start the engine, allow it to reach normal operating temperature and check for leaks.
15. Allow time for the thermostat to open, recheck the coolant level and top up, as required.

2.8L and 3.1L V6 Engine

1. Disconnect the negative battery cable.

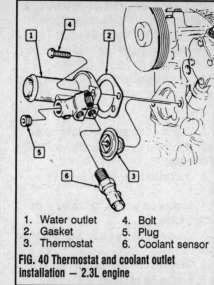

1. Water outlet
2. Gasket
3. Thermostat
4. Bolt
5. Plug
6. Coolant sensor

FIG. 40 Thermostat and coolant outlet installation — 2.3L engine

2. Drain the cooling system.
3. Some models with cruise control have a vacuum modulator attached to the thermostat housing with a bracket. If your vehicle is equipped as such, remove the bracket from the housing.
4. Unbolt the water outlet from the intake manifold, remove the outlet and lift the thermostat out of the manifold.
5. Clean both of the mating surfaces and run a 1/8 in. (3mm) wide bead of R.T.V. (room

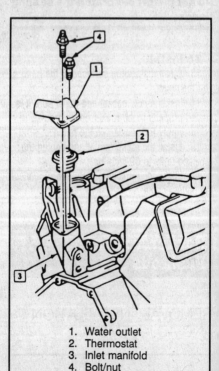

1. Water outlet
2. Thermostat
3. Inlet manifold
4. Bolt/nut

FIG. 41 Thermostat and coolant outlet installation — 2.8L and 3.1L engine

temperature vulcanizing) sealer in the groove of the water outlet.

6. Install the thermostat (spring towards engine) and bolt the water outlet into place while the R.T.V. sealer is still wet. Torque the bolts to 18 ft. lbs. (25 Nm). The remainder of the installation is the reverse of removal. Check for leaks after the car is started and correct as required.

Intake Manifold

REMOVAL & INSTALLATION

❋❋ CAUTION

When draining the coolant, keep in mind that cats and dogs are attracted by the ethylene glycol antifreeze, and are quite likely to drink any that is left in an uncovered container or in puddles on the ground. This will prove fatal in sufficient quantity. Always drain the coolant into a sealable container. Coolant should be reused unless it is contaminated or several years old.

2.0L and 2.2L Engine

1988-91
▶ SEE FIG. 42
1. Disconnect the negative battery cable.

2. Remove the TBI cover. Drain the cooling system.
3. Tag and disconnect all necessary vacuum lines and wires.
4. Disconnect the fuel lines at the TBI unit. Disconnect the TBI linkage and then remove the TBI unit.

❋❋ CAUTION

The fuel lines are pressurized (especially with fuel injection). Removal may cause fuel spray resulting in personal injury. Do not remove before bleeding the pressure from the fuel system. See Section 1 for the procedure.

5. Disconnect the serpentine drive belt. Remove the power steering pump-to-bracket bolts and support the pump out of the way; DO NOT disconnect the pressure hoses.
6. Raise and support the front of the vehicle.
7. Disconnect the T.V. cable, accelerator cable and brackets.
8. Remove the heater hose from the bottom of the intake manifold.
9. Remove the lower manifold bolts then lower the vehicle.
10. Remove the intake manifold-to-cylinder head nuts/bolts and the manifold.
To Install:
11. Using a gasket scraper, clean the gasket mounting surfaces.
12. Use new gaskets and torque the intake manifold-to-cylinder heads bolts (in the proper sequence) to 15–22 ft. lbs.
13. Raise the vehicle and support it safely.

14. Install the heater hoses.
15. Connect the T.V. cable, accelerator cable and brackets.
16. Lower the vehicle.
17. Install the TBI unit then connect the fuel lines and linkage at the TBI unit.
18. Connect all vacuum lines and wires.
19. Install the TBI cover.
20. Connect the battery cable.
21. Fill with coolant.

1992
▶ SEE FIG. 43
1. Disconnect the negative battery cable.
2. Relieve the fuel system pressure.
3. Remove the air intake duct.
4. Drain the cooling system.
5. Tag and disconnect all necessary vacuum lines and wires.
6. Disconnect the throttle linkage.
7. Remove the power steering pump and lay it aside without disconnecting the fluid lines.
8. Disconnect the MAP sensor and EGR solenoid valve.
9. Remove the upper intake manifold assembly.
10. Remove the EGR valve injector.
11. Remove the fuel injector retainer bracket, regulator and injectors.
12. Disconnect the accelerator and T.V. cables and cable bracket.
13. Raise the vehicle and support it safely.
14. Remove the 6 intake manifold lower nuts.
15. Lower the vehicle.
16. Remove the intake manifold upper nuts and remove the manifold.
To Install:
17. Clean the gasket mounting surfaces.
18. Install a new gasket and position the lower intake manifold.

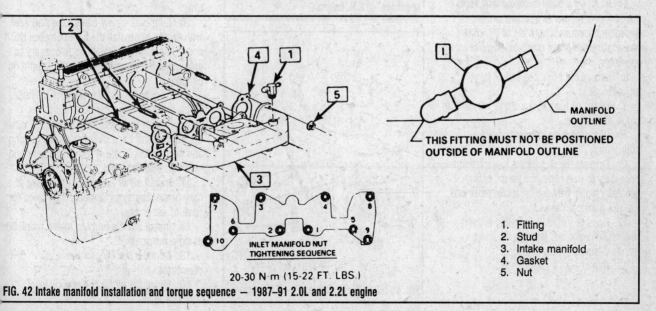

INLET MANIFOLD NUT TIGHTENING SEQUENCE

20-30 N·m (15-22 FT. LBS.)

1. Fitting
2. Stud
3. Intake manifold
4. Gasket
5. Nut

MANIFOLD OUTLINE

THIS FITTING MUST NOT BE POSITIONED OUTSIDE OF MANIFOLD OUTLINE

FIG. 42 Intake manifold installation and torque sequence — 1987-91 2.0L and 2.2L engine

19. Install the fuel injectors, regulator and injector retainer bracket and tighten the retaining bolts to 22 inch lbs. (3.5 Nm).

20. Tighten the upper intake manifold nuts in the proper sequence to 22 ft. lbs. 30 Nm).

21. Connect the accelerator and T.V. cables and cable bracket.

22. Raise the vehicle and support it safely.

23. Tighten the lower intake manifold nuts in the proper sequence to 22 ft. lbs. 30 Nm).

24. Lower the vehicle.

25. Install the EGR valve injector so that the port is facing directly towards the throttle body.

26. Install the upper intake manifold assembly.

27. Connect the MAP sensor and EGR solenoid valve.

28. Connect the vacuum lines and wires.

29. Install the air intake duct.

30. Install the power steering pump.

31. Connect the negative battery cable.

32. Refill the coolant system.

2.3L Engine

♦ SEE FIGS. 44-46

1. Disconnect the negative terminal from the battery. Drain the cooling system.

2. Remove the coolant fan shroud, vacuum hose and electrical connector from the MAP sensor.

3. Disconnect the throttle body to air cleaner duct.

4. Remove the throttle cable bracket.

5. Remove the power brake vacuum hose, including the retaining bracket to power steering bracket and position it to the side.

6. Remove the throttle body from the intake manifold with electrical harness, coolant hoses, vacuum hoses and throttle cable attached. Position these components aside.

7. Remove the oil/air separator bolts and hoses. Leave the hoses attached to the separator, disconnect from the oil fill, chain housing and the intake manifold. Remove as an assembly.

8. Remove the oil fill cap and oil level indicator stick.

9. Pull the oil tube fill upward to unseat from block and remove.

10. Disconnect the injector harness connector.

11. Remove the fill tube out top, rotating as necessary to gain clearance for the oil/air separator nipple between the intake tubes and fuel rail electrical harness.

12. Remove the intake manifold support bracket bolts and nut. Remove the intake manifold attaching nuts and bolts.

13. Remove the intake manifold.

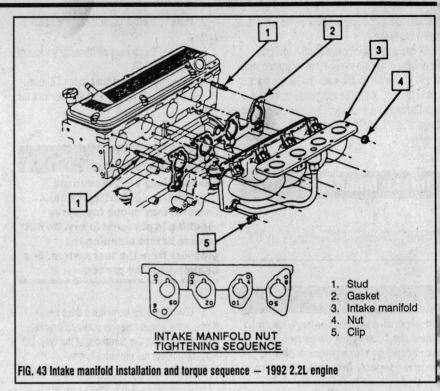

1. Stud
2. Gasket
3. Intake manifold
4. Nut
5. Clip

INTAKE MANIFOLD NUT TIGHTENING SEQUENCE

FIG. 43 Intake manifold installation and torque sequence — 1992 2.2L engine

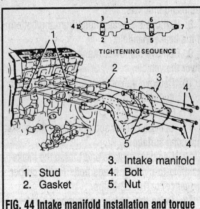

TIGHTENING SEQUENCE

1. Stud   3. Intake manifold
2. Gasket   4. Bolt
          5. Nut

FIG. 44 Intake manifold installation and torque sequence — 2.3L engine

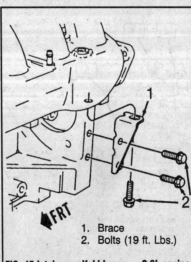

1. Brace
2. Bolts (19 ft. Lbs.)

FIG. 45 Intake manifold brace — 2.3L engine

➡ **Intake manifold mounting hole closest to chain housing is slotted for additional clearance.**

To install:

14. Install the intake manifold and gasket. Tightening the intake manifold bolts/nuts in sequence and to 18 ft. lbs. (25 Nm). Tighten intake manifold brace and retainers hand tight. Tighten to specifications in the following sequence:

a. Nut to stud bolt—18 ft. lbs. (25 Nm).

b. Bolt to intake manifold—40 ft. lbs. (55 Nm).

c. Bolt to cylinder block—40 ft. lbs. (55 Nm).

15. Lubricate a new oil fill tube ring seal with engine oil. Install the tube between No. 1 and 2 intake tubes. Rotate as necessary to gain clearance for oil/air separator nipple on fill tube.

16. Locate the oil fill tube in its cylinder block opening. Align the fill tube so it is approximately in its installed position. Place the palm of the hand over the oil fill opening and press straight down to seat fill tube and seal into cylinder block.

17. Install oil/air separator assembly, it may be necessary to lubricate the hoses for ease of assembly.

18. Install throttle body to intake manifold using a new gasket.

19. Connect the injector harness connector.

20. Install the oil fill cap and oil level indicator stick.

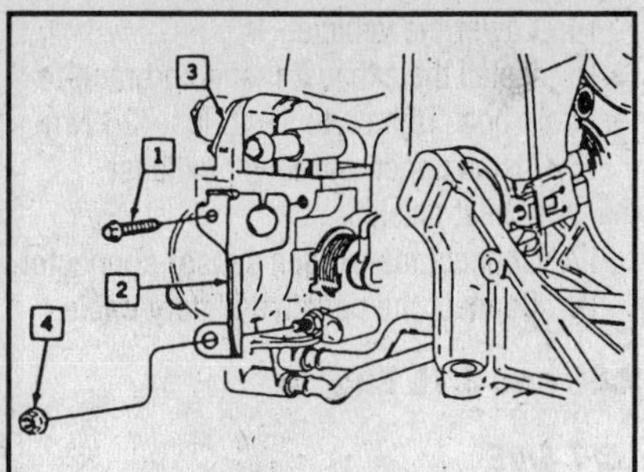

1. Bolt/screw (9 ft. lbs.)
2. Throttle cable bracket
3. Throttle body
4. Nut (19 ft. Lbs.)

FIG. 46 Throttle cable bracket installation — 2.3L engine

21. Install the power brake vacuum hose.
22. Install the throttle cable bracket.
23. Connect the throttle body to air cleaner duct.
24. Install the cooling fan shroud, vacuum hose and electrical connector to the MAP sensor.
25. Connect the negative battery cable.

2.8L and 3.1L Engine

♦ SEE FIG. 47

1. Disconnect the negative terminal from the battery. Drain the cooling system.
2. Disconnect the T.V. and accelerator cables from the plenum.
3. Remove the throttle body-to-plenum bolts and the throttle body. Remove the EGR valve.
4. Remove the plenum-to-intake manifold bolts and the plenum. Disconnect and plug the fuel lines and return pipes at the fuel rail.
5. Remove the serpentine drive belt. Remove the power steering pump-to-bracket bolts and support the pump out of the way; DO NOT disconnect the pressure hoses.
6. Remove the alternator-to-bracket bolts and support the alternator out of the way.
7. Loosen the alternator bracket. From the throttle body, disconnect the idle air vacuum hose.
8. Label and disconnect the electrical connectors from the fuel injectors. Remove the fuel rail.
9. Remove the breather tube. Disconnect the runners.
10. Remove both rocker arm cover-to-cylinder head bolts and the covers. Remove the radiator hose from the thermostat housing.
11. Label and disconnect the electrical connectors from the coolant temperature sensor and oil pressure sending unit. Remove the coolant sensor.

12. Remove the bypass hose from the filler neck and cylinder head.
13. Remove the intake manifold-to-cylinder head bolts and the manifold.
14. Loosen the rocker arm nuts, turn them 90° and remove the pushrods; be sure to keep the components in order for installation purposes.
15. Using a gasket scraper and degreaser, clean all gasket mounting surfaces.

To Install

1. Use new gaskets and place a 3/16 in. (5mm) bead of RTV sealant on the ridges of the manifold.
2. Install the pushrods and tighten the rocker arm nuts to 18 ft. lbs. (25 Nm).
3. Install the intake manifold and torque (following the torquing sequence) the intake manifold-to-cylinder head bolts to 15 ft. lbs. (20 Nm) and retighten to 24 ft. lbs. (33 Nm).
4. Install the heater inlet pipe.
5. Install the coolant sensor.
6. Connect the wires to the coolant sensor and oil sending unit.
7. Install the radiator hose at the thermostat outlet.
8. Fill the cooling system.
9. Install the rocker arm cover.
10. Install the breather tube.
11. Install the fuel rail.

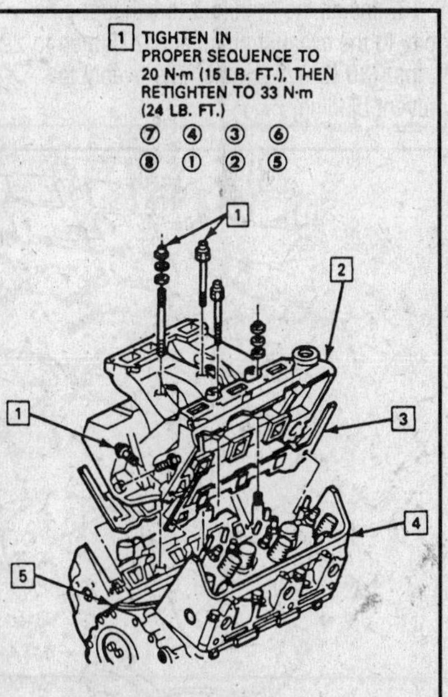

1 TIGHTEN IN PROPER SEQUENCE TO 20 N·m (15 LB. FT.), THEN RETIGHTEN TO 33 N·m (24 LB. FT.)

⑦ ④ ③ ⑥
⑧ ① ② ⑤

1. Tighten in sequence
2. Intake manifold
3. Gasket
4. Cylinder head
5. Sealer

FIG. 47 Intake manifold installation and torque sequence — 2.8L and 3.1L engine

12. Install the wires at the injectors.
13. Connect the idle air vacuum hose to the throttle body.
14. Install the alternator bracket and the alternator.
15. Install the power steering pump.
16. Install the serpentine belt.
17. Install the fuel inlet and return lines at the fuel rail.
18. Install the plenum.
19. Install the EGR valve.
20. Install the throttle body at the plenum.
21. Install the accelerator and T.V. cable bracket at the plenum.
22. Connect the battery.
23. Refill the cooling system.

Exhaust Manifold

REMOVAL & INSTALLATION

❀❀ CAUTION

When draining the coolant, keep in mind that cats and dogs are attracted by the ethylene glycol antifreeze, and are quite likely to drink any that is left in an uncovered container or in puddles on the ground. This will prove fatal in sufficient quantity. Always drain the coolant into a sealable container. Coolant should be reused unless it is contaminated or several years old.

2.0L and 2.2L Engine

♦ SEE FIG. 48-49

1. Disconnect the negative terminal from the battery.
2. Disconnect the oxygen sensor wire.
3. Remove the serpentine belt.
4. Remove the alternator-to-bracket bolts and support the alternator (with the wires attached) out of the way.
5. Raise and support the front of the vehicle.
6. Disconnect the exhaust pipe-to-exhaust manifold bolts and lower the vehicle.
7. Remove the exhaust manifold-to-cylinder head bolts.
8. Remove the exhaust manifold from the exhaust pipe flange and the manifold from the vehicle.

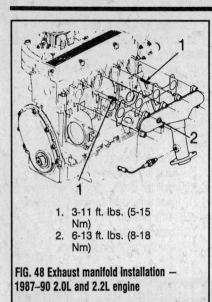

1. 3-11 ft. lbs. (5-15 Nm)
2. 6-13 ft. lbs. (8-18 Nm)

FIG. 48 Exhaust manifold installation — 1987–90 2.0L and 2.2L engine

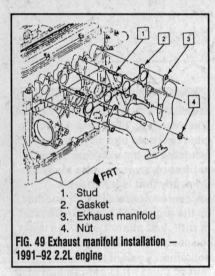

FRT

1. Stud
2. Gasket
3. Exhaust manifold
4. Nut

FIG. 49 Exhaust manifold installation — 1991–92 2.2L engine

9. Using a gasket scraper, clean the gasket mounting surfaces.

10. To install, use new gaskets and reverse the removal procedures. Torque the exhaust manifold-to-cylinder head nuts to 3–11 ft. lbs. (5–15 Nm) for 1988–90, and 115 inch lbs. (13 Nm) for 1991–92 and the bolts to 6–13 ft. lbs. (8–18 Nm) for 1988–90, and studs to 89 inch lbs. (10 Nm) for 1991–92. Start the engine and check for leaks.

2.3L Engine

♦ SEE FIG. 49A

1. Disconnect the negative battery cable and oxygen sensor connector.

2. Remove upper and lower exhaust manifold heat shields.

3. Remove exhaust manifold brace to manifold bolt.

4. Break loose the manifold to exhaust pipe spring loaded bolts using a 13mm box wrench.

5. Raise and support vehicle safely.

6. Remove the manifold-to-exhaust pipe bolts from the exhaust pipe flange, using a $\frac{7}{32}$ in. (5.5mm) socket. Rotate clockwise as if tightening a bolt with right hand threads or removing a bolt with left hand threads. It is necessary to relieve the spring pressure from 1 bolt prior to removing the second bolt. If the spring pressure is not relieved, it will cause the exhaust pipe to twist and bind the bolt as it is removed. Relieve the spring pressure by:

  a. Thread 1 bolt out 4 turns.

  b. Move to the other bolt and turn it all the way out of the exhaust pipe flange.

  c. Return to the first bolt and rotate it the rest of the way out of the exhaust pipe flange.

7. Pull down and back on the exhaust pipe to disengage it from the exhaust manifold bolts.

8. Lower vehicle.

9. Remove exhaust manifold to cylinder head attaching nuts and remove exhaust manifold.

To install:

10. Clean all sealing surfaces. Install a new exhaust manifold gasket, the exhaust manifold and the exhaust manifold-to-cylinder head attaching nuts. Tighten, in sequence, to 27 ft. lbs. (37 Nm).

11. Raise and safely support the vehicle.

12. Connect the exhaust pipe to the exhaust manifold flange.

13. Install the manifold to exhaust pipe bolts to the exhaust pipe flange. Tighten to 22 ft. lbs. (30 Nm). Turn the nuts evenly to prevent binding.

14. Lower the vehicle.

15. Install the exhaust manifold brace-to-manifold bolt. Tighten to 19 ft. lbs. (26 Nm).

16. Install upper and lower exhaust manifold heat shields.

17. Connect the oxygen sensor connector.

18. Connect the negative battery cable.

2.8L and 3.1L Engine

LEFT SIDE

1. Disconnect the negative terminal from the battery. Drain the cooling system.

2. Remove the air cleaner, air inlet hose and the mass air flow sensor.

3. Remove the coolant bypass pipe. Remove the manifold heat shield.

4. Disconnect the exhaust manifold crossover assembly at the right manifold.

5. Remove the exhaust manifold-to-cylinder head attaching bolts.

6. From the right manifold, remove the exhaust manifold with the crossover assembly.

7. Using a gasket scraper, clean the gasket mounting surfaces.

8. To install, use new gaskets and reverse the removal procedures. Torque the exhaust manifold-to-cylinder head bolts to 22–30 ft lbs. (30–40 Nm) for 1988 and 18 ft. lbs. (25 Nm) for 1989–92. Torque the crossover bolts to 18 ft. lbs. (25 Nm). Start the engine and check for exhaust leaks.

RIGHT SIDE

1. Disconnect the negative terminal from the battery.

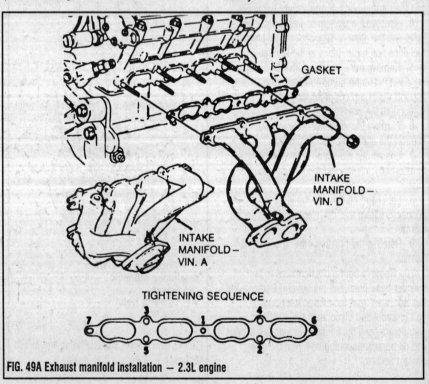

GASKET

INTAKE MANIFOLD — VIN. D

INTAKE MANIFOLD — VIN. A

TIGHTENING SEQUENCE

FIG. 49A Exhaust manifold installation — 2.3L engine

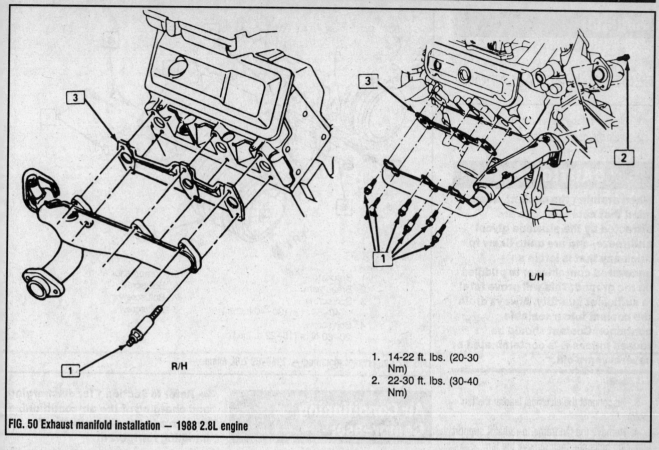

1. 14-22 ft. lbs. (20-30 Nm)
2. 22-30 ft. lbs. (30-40 Nm)

FIG. 50 Exhaust manifold installation — 1988 2.8L engine

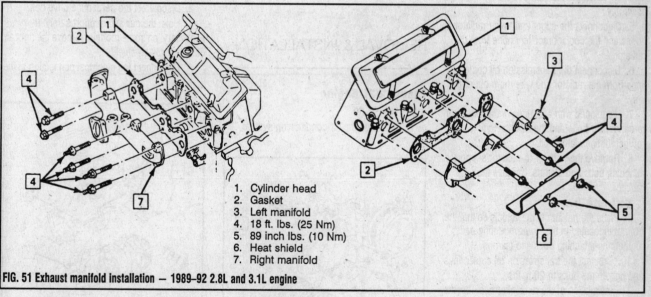

1. Cylinder head
2. Gasket
3. Left manifold
4. 18 ft. lbs. (25 Nm)
5. 89 inch lbs. (10 Nm)
6. Heat shield
7. Right manifold

FIG. 51 Exhaust manifold installation — 1989–92 2.8L and 3.1L engine

2. Raise and support the front of the vehicle.

3. Remove the heat shield.

4. Remove the exhaust pipe-to-exhaust manifold bolts and the crossover pipe-to-exhaust manifold bolts.

5. Remove the EGR pipe-to-exhaust manifold bolts and the pipe.

6. Disconnect the oxygen sensor wire.

7. Remove the exhaust manifold-to-cylinder head bolts and the exhaust manifold from the vehicle.

8. Using a gasket scraper, clean the gasket mounting surfaces.

9. To install, use new gaskets and reverse the removal procedures. Torque the exhaust manifold-to-cylinder head bolts to 14–22 ft. lbs. (20–30 Nm) for 1988 and 89 inch lbs. (10 Nm) for 1989–92. Tighten crossover pipe bolts to 18 ft. lbs. (25 Nm). Start the engine and check for leaks.

Radiator

REMOVAL & INSTALLATION

1. Disconnect the negative battery cable.
2. Drain the cooling system.

❄❄ CAUTION

When draining the coolant, keep in mind that cats and dogs are attracted by the ethylene glycol antifreeze, and are quite likely to drink any that is left in an uncovered container or in puddles on the ground. This will prove fatal in sufficient quantity. Always drain the coolant into a sealable container. Coolant should be reused unless it is contaminated or several years old.

3. Disconnect the electrical lead at the fan motor.

4. Remove the fan frame-to-radiator support attaching bolts and then remove the fan assembly.

5. Disconnect the upper and lower radiator hoses and the coolant recovery hose from the radiator.

6. Disconnect the transmission oil cooler lines from the radiator and wire them out of the way.

7. If equipped with A/C, remove the 4 radiator to condenser bolts and the radiator tank to refrigerant line clamp bolt.

8. Remove the radiator-to-radiator support attaching bolts and clamps. Remove the radiator.

To install:

9. Place the radiator in the vehicle so that the bottom is located in the lower mounting pads. Tighten the attaching bolts and clamps.

10. Connect the transmission oil cooler lines and tighten the bolts to 20 ft. lbs.

11. Installation of the remaining components is in the reverse order of removal. Fill the coolant system, check for leaks.

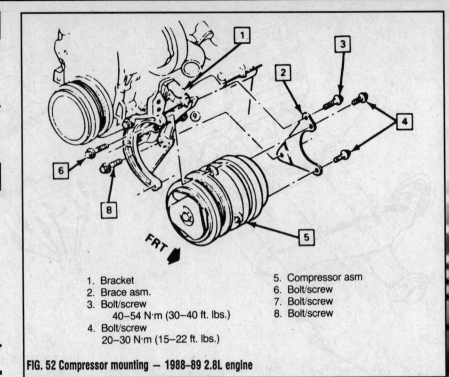

1. Bracket
2. Brace asm.
3. Bolt/screw
   40–54 N·m (30–40 ft. lbs.)
4. Bolt/screw
   20–30 N·m (15–22 ft. lbs.)
5. Compressor asm.
6. Bolt/screw
7. Bolt/screw
8. Bolt/screw

FIG. 52 Compressor mounting — 1988–89 2.8L engine

Air Conditioning Compressor

REMOVAL & INSTALLATION

Except 2.3L Engine

▶ SEE FIG. 52-59
1. Discharge the air conditioning system.

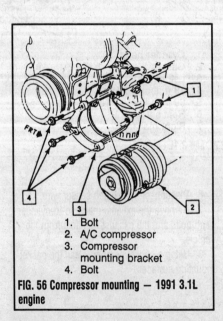

1. Bolt
2. A/C compressor
3. Compressor mounting bracket
4. Bolt

FIG. 56 Compressor mounting — 1991 3.1L engine

➡ **Refer to Section 1 for discharging and charging of the air conditioning system and the precautions of handling refrigerant.**

2. Disconnect the serpentine drive belt.

3. Hoist the car and support safely. If necessary, on some models, remove the right air dam and splash shield.

4. Disconnect the electrical connection at the

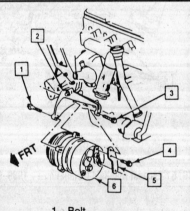

1. Bolt
2. Compressor mounting bracket
3. Bolt
4. Bolt
5. Rear compressor mounting bracket
6. A/C compressor

FIG. 57 Compressor mounting — 1991 2.2L engine

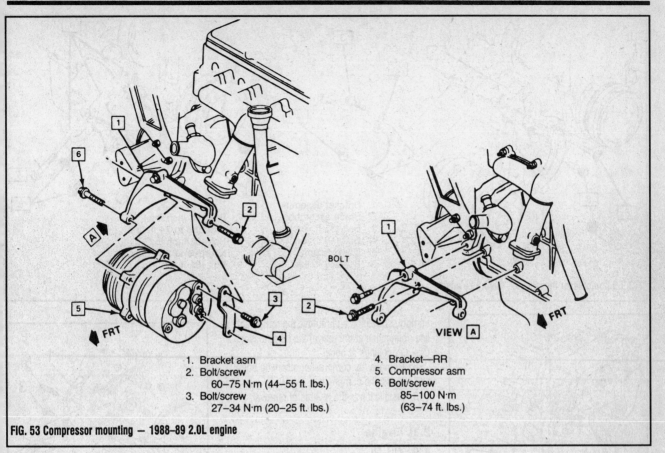

1. Bracket asm
2. Bolt/screw
   60–75 N·m (44–55 ft. lbs.)
3. Bolt/screw
   27–34 N·m (20–25 ft. lbs.)
4. Bracket—RR
5. Compressor asm
6. Bolt/screw
   85–100 N·m
   (63–74 ft. lbs.)

FIG. 53 Compressor mounting — 1988–89 2.0L engine

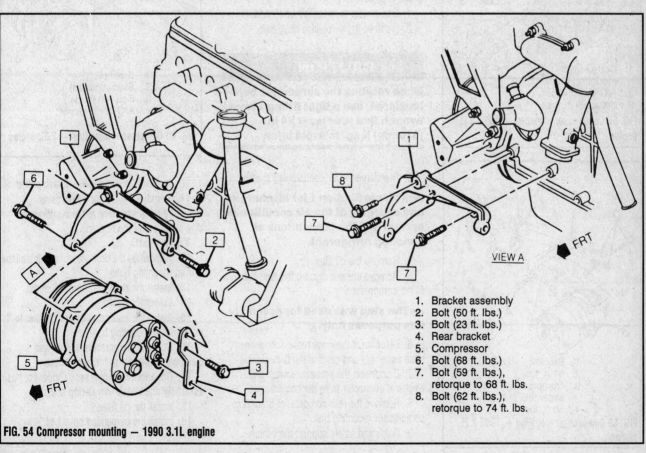

1. Bracket assembly
2. Bolt (50 ft. lbs.)
3. Bolt (23 ft. lbs.)
4. Rear bracket
5. Compressor
6. Bolt (68 ft. lbs.)
7. Bolt (59 ft. lbs.),
   retorque to 68 ft. lbs.
8. Bolt (62 ft. lbs.),
   retorque to 74 ft. lbs.

FIG. 54 Compressor mounting — 1990 3.1L engine

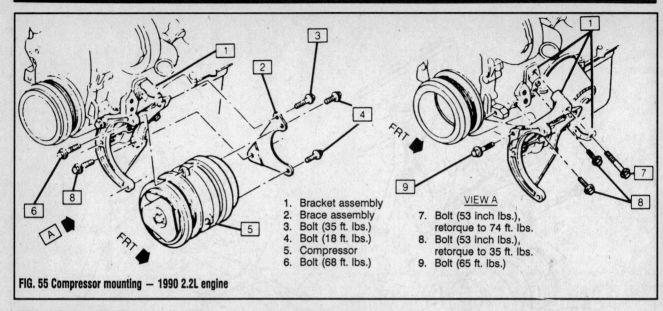

1. Bracket assembly
2. Brace assembly
3. Bolt (35 ft. lbs.)
4. Bolt (18 ft. lbs.)
5. Compressor
6. Bolt (68 ft. lbs.)

VIEW A

7. Bolt (53 inch lbs.), retorque to 74 ft. lbs.
8. Bolt (53 inch lbs.), retorque to 35 ft. lbs.
9. Bolt (65 ft. lbs.)

FIG. 55 Compressor mounting — 1990 2.2L engine

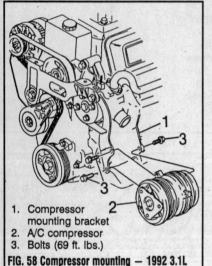

1. Compressor mounting bracket
2. A/C compressor
3. Bolts (69 ft. lbs.)

FIG. 58 Compressor mounting — 1992 3.1L engine

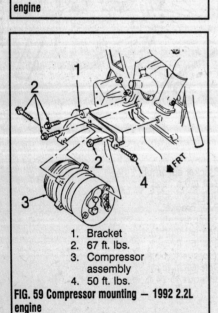

1. Bracket
2. 67 ft. lbs.
3. Compressor assembly
4. 50 ft. lbs.

FIG. 59 Compressor mounting — 1992 2.2L engine

compressor clutch and remove the refrigerant line connection at the rear of the compressor. Cap all openings at once!

5. Remove the compressor attaching bolts and remove the compressor.

6. Installation is the reverse of removal.

2.3L Engine

♦ SEE FIG. 60

1. Disconnect the negative battery cable.
2. Remove the serpentine drive belt.

❄ CAUTION

When rotating the serpentine belt tensioner, use a tight fitting 13mm wrench that is at least 24 in. (610mm) long, to avoid injury.

3. Discharge the air conditioning system.

➡ **Refer to Section 1 for discharging and charging of the air conditioning system and the precautions of handling refrigerant.**

4. Remove the oil filter.
5. Remove the and discard the stud in back of the compressor.

➡ **The stud was used for assembly line purposes only.**

6. Disconnect the compressor/condenser hose assembly and discard the O-ring seals.
7. Disconnect the pressure switch and electrical connector from the compressor.
8. Remove the rear compressor bracket to compressor mounting bolt.
9. Raise and safely support the vehicle.

1. Bracket
2. Stud (discard)
3. Bolt (40 ft. lbs.)
4. A/C compressor

FIG. 60 Compressor mounting — 2.3L engine

10. Remove the right lower splash shield.
11. Remove the 3 front compressor mounting bolts and remove the compressor down and out of the bottom.

To Install:

12. Reposition the compressor and install the 3 front mounting bolts.
13. Install the right lower splash shield.
14. Lower the vehicle.
15. Install the rear compressor bracket to compressor mounting bolt.
16. Connect the pressure switch and electrical connector to the compressor.
17. Connect the compressor/condenser hose assembly and install new O-ring seals.
18. Install the oil filter.
19. Install the serpentine drive belt.

When rotating the serpentine belt tensioner, use a tight fitting 13 mm wrench that is at least 24 in. (610mm) long, to avoid injury.

20. Connect the negative battery cable.
21. Evacuate and charge the air conditioning system.

➡ Refer to Section 1 for evacuating, charging and leak testing of the air conditioning system and the precautions of handling refrigerant.

Water Pump

REMOVAL & INSTALLATION

When draining the coolant, keep in mind that cats and dogs are attracted by the ethylene glycol antifreeze, and are quite likely to drink any that is left in an uncovered container or in puddles on the ground. This will prove fatal in sufficient quantity. Always drain the coolant into a sealable container. Coolant should be reused unless it is contaminated or several years old.

Except 2.3L Engine
▶ SEE FIGS. 61-62
1. Disconnect the negative battery cable.
2. Drain the engine coolant into a clean container for reuse.
3. Remove the serpentine drive belt.
4. If equipped with the 2.0L engine, remove the alternator and bracket with wires attached and position it aside.
5. If equipped with the 3.1L engine, remove the radiator and heater hoses.
6. Remove the water pump pulley bolts and the pulley.
7. Remove the water pump-to-engine bolts and the pump.

To install:
8. Clean the gasket mounting surfaces.

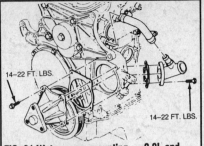

FIG. 61 Water pump mounting — 2.0L and 2.2L engine

14–22 FT. LBS.

14–22 FT. LBS.

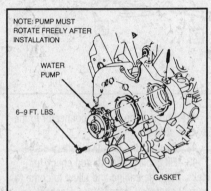

NOTE: PUMP MUST ROTATE FREELY AFTER INSTALLATION

WATER PUMP

6–9 FT. LBS.

GASKET

FIG. 62 Water pump mounting — 2.8L and 3.1L engine

9. Install the water pump and the water pump attaching bolts. Tighten the water pump-to-engine bolts to 14–22 ft. lbs. (19–30 Nm) on the 2.0L and 2.2L engines or to 6–9 ft. lbs. (8–12 Nm) on the 2.8L and 3.1L engines.
10. Install the water pump pulley and attaching bolts.
11. If equipped with the 3.1L engine, install the radiator and heater hoses.
12. If equipped with the 2.0L engine, install the alternator and bracket.
13. Install the serpentine drive belt.
14. Connect the negative battery cable.
15. Fill cooling system and check for leaks. Start the engine and allow to come to normal operating temperature. Recheck for leaks. Top-up coolant.

2.3L ENGINE
▶ SEE FIG. 63
1. Disconnect the negative battery cable.
2. Drain the engine coolant into a clean container for reuse.

➡ Remove the heater hose from the thermostat housing for additional draining.

3. Remove the oxygen sensor connector.
4. Remove the upper and lower exhaust manifold heat shield attaching bolts and remove the shields.

5. Remove the exhaust manifold brace-to-manifold attaching bolt.
6. Using a 13mm box wrench, loosen the exhaust pipe-to-manifold spring bolts from the engine compartment.
7. Raise and safely support the vehicle.
8. Remove the bolts from the exhaust flange using a ⁷⁄₃₂ in. (5.5mm) socket an 1 bolt rotate clockwise first.

➡ Rotating the bolt clockwise is necessary to relieve the spring pressure from 1st bolt prior to removing the 2nd bolt otherwise the exhaust pipe will twist and bind the bolt as it is removed.

9. Thread the bolt with least pressure on it out 4 turns.
10. Move the other bolt and turn it all the way out of the exhaust pipe flange.
11. Return to the 1st bolt and rotate it the rest of the way out.
12. Pull the exhaust pipe back from the exhaust manifold.
13. Remove the radiator outlet pipe from the oil pan and transaxle.
14. Remove the exhaust manifold brace.
15. Pull down on the radiator outlet pipe to disengage it from the water pump.
16. Lower the vehicle.
17. Remove the exhaust manifold-to-cylinder head attaching nuts.
18. Remove the exhaust manifold, seals and gaskets.
19. Remove the water pump cover-to-engine attaching bolts.
20. Remove the water pump-to-timing chain housing attaching nuts.
21. Remove the water pump and cover assembly from the engine.
22. Remove the water pump cover-to-radiator pump assembly.

To install:

➡ Before installing the water pump it is important to first read over the entire procedure. Pay special attention to the tightening sequence, to avoid part damage and to insure proper sealing.

23. Clean all mating surfaces thoroughly and use new gaskets.
24. Position the water pump cover to the radiator pump assembly and install the attaching bolts. Do not tighten.
25. Lubricate the splines of the radiator pump drive with the an approved chassis grease and install the pump and cover assembly.
26. Install the pump cover-to-engine attaching bolts. Do not tighten.

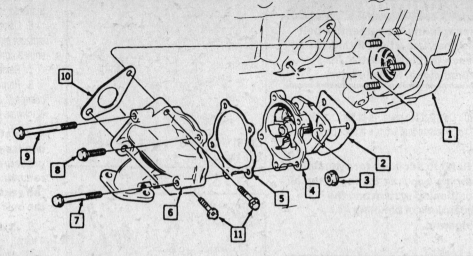

1. Timing chain housing
2. Timing chain housing gasket
3. Nut
4. Water pump body
5. Water pump body to cover gasket
6. Water pump cover
7. Bolt (3 lower positions)
8. Bolt
9. Bolt
10. Water pump cover to block gasket
11. Bolts (2)

FIG. 63 Water pump mounting — 2.3L engine

27. Install the timing chain housing nuts. Do not tighten.

28. Lubricate the O-ring on the radiator outlet pipe with a solution of antifreeze and slide the pipe into the radiator pump cover. Install the attaching bolts. Do not tighten.

29. Tighten the bolts and nuts in following order:

a. Pump assembly-to-timing chain housing nuts — 19 ft. lbs. (26 Nm).

b. Water pump-to-pump cover assembly — 106 inch lbs. (12 Nm).

c. Water Pump cover-to-engine (tighten the bottom bolt first) — 19 ft. lbs. (26 Nm).

d. Radiator outlet pipe assembly-to-pump cover — 125 ft. lbs. (14 Nm).

30. Install the exhaust manifold with new gaskets.

31. Install the exhaust manifold-to-cylinder head attaching nuts. Tighten the attaching nuts in sequence to 22 ft. lbs. (30 Nm).

32. Raise and safely support the vehicle.

33. Seat the exhaust manifold bolts into the exhaust pipe flange.

34. Using a $\frac{7}{32}$ in. (5.5mm) socket start both bolts. Rotate the bolts counterclockwise.

35. Turn both bolts in evenly to avoid cocking the exhaust pipe and binding the bolts. Turn the bolts in until fully seated.

36. Install the radiator outlet pipe to the transaxle and to the oil pan and install the exhaust manifold brace.

37. Lower the vehicle.

38. Install the exhaust manifold brace-to-manifold attaching bolt.

39. Using a 13mm wrench, tighten the exhaust pipe-to-manifold nuts to 22 ft. lbs. (30 Nm).

40. Install the lower heat shields.

41. Connect the oxygen connector to the oxygen sensor.

42. Connect the negative battery cable.

43. Fill cooling system and check for leaks. Start the engine and allow to come to normal operating temperature. Recheck for leaks. Top-up coolant.

Electric Cooling Fan

REMOVAL & INSTALLATION

◆ SEE FIGS. 64-68

1. Disconnect the negative terminal from the battery.

3. On some models, it may be necessary to remove the air cleaner assembly.

3. Disconnect the electrical wiring harness from the cooling fan frame.

4. Remove the fan assembly from the radiator support.

5. To install, reverse the removal procedures. Torque the fan assembly-to-radiator support bolts to 7 ft. lbs.

TESTING

The electric cooling fans are controlled by the Electronic Control Module. The coolant temperature sensor in the engine sends a signal to the ECM when the engine coolant temperature reaches 223°F (106°C). The ECM grounds the

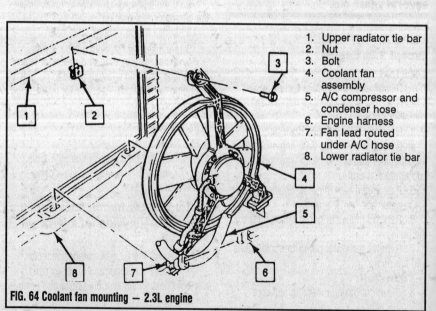

1. Upper radiator tie bar
2. Nut
3. Bolt
4. Coolant fan assembly
5. A/C compressor and condenser hose
6. Engine harness
7. Fan lead routed under A/C hose
8. Lower radiator tie bar

FIG. 64 Coolant fan mounting — 2.3L engine

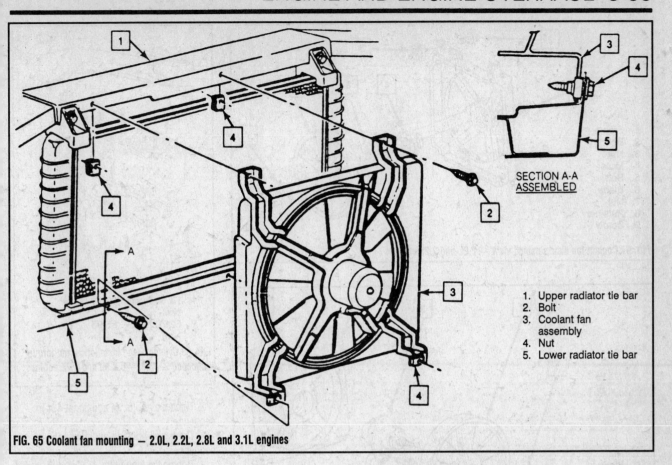

FIG. 65 Coolant fan mounting — 2.0L, 2.2L, 2.8L and 3.1L engines

1. Upper radiator tie bar
2. Bolt
3. Coolant fan assembly
4. Nut
5. Lower radiator tie bar

cooling fan relay which turns On the fan. The cooling fan will also turn On if the air conditioning pressure switch detects a pressure more than 200 psi and the vehicle speed is less than 70 mph. If the cooling fan is turned On by the ECM for any reason, the fan will cycle for no less than 30 seconds.

Cylinder Head

REMOVAL & INSTALLATION

❋❋ CAUTION

When draining the coolant, keep in mind that cats and dogs are attracted by the ethylene glycol antifreeze, and are quite likely to drink any that is left in an uncovered container or in puddles on the ground. This will prove fatal in sufficient quantity. Always drain the coolant into a sealable container. Coolant should be reused unless it is contaminated or several years old.

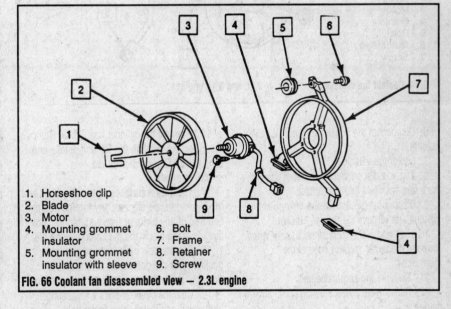

1. Horseshoe clip
2. Blade
3. Motor
4. Mounting grommet insulator
5. Mounting grommet insulator with sleeve
6. Bolt
7. Frame
8. Retainer
9. Screw

FIG. 66 Coolant fan disassembled view — 2.3L engine

2.0L and 2.2L Engine

▶ SEE FIGS. 69-70

➡ **The engine should be overnight cold before removing the cylinder head.**

1. Disconnect the negative battery cable.

2. Drain the cooling system.

3. Remove the TBI cover. Raise and safely support the vehicle.

4. Remove the exhaust shield. Disconnect the exhaust pipe.

5. Remove the heater hose from the intake manifold. Lower the vehicle.

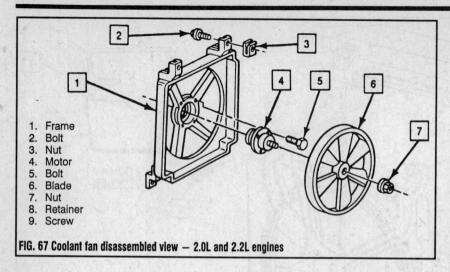

1. Frame
2. Bolt
3. Nut
4. Motor
5. Bolt
6. Blade
7. Nut
8. Retainer
9. Screw

FIG. 67 Coolant fan disassembled view — 2.0L and 2.2L engines

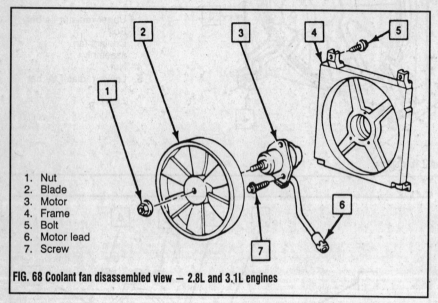

1. Nut
2. Blade
3. Motor
4. Frame
5. Bolt
6. Motor lead
7. Screw

FIG. 68 Coolant fan disassembled view — 2.8L and 3.1L engines

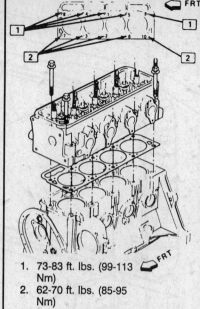

1. 73-83 ft. lbs. (99-113 Nm)
2. 62-70 ft. lbs. (85-95 Nm)

FIG. 69 Cylinder head installation and torque sequence — 1987–89 2.0L and 2.2L engines

6. Disconnect the accelerator and TV cable bracket.

7. Lower the vehicle.

8. Tag and disconnect the vacuum lines at the intake manifold and thermostat.

9. Disconnect the accelerator linkage at the TBI unit and remove the linkage bracket.

10. Tag and disconnect all necessary wires. Remove the upper radiator hose at the thermostat.

11. Remove the serpentine belt.

12. Remove the power steering pump and lay aside.

13. Make sure the fuel system pressure is released and disconnect and plug the fuel lines.

14. Remove the alternator. Remove the alternator brace from the head and remove the upper mounting bracket.

15. Remove the cylinder head cover. Remove the rocker arms and pushrods keeping all parts in order for correct installation.

16. Remove the cylinder head bolts. Remove the cylinder head with the TBI unit, intake and exhaust manifolds still attached.

To install:

17. The gasket surfaces on both the head and the block must be clean of any foreign matter and free of any nicks or heavy scratches. Bolt threads in the block and the bolts must be clean.

18. Place a new cylinder head gasket in position over the dowel pins on the block. Carefully guide the cylinder head into position.

19. Coat the cylinder bolts with sealing compound and install them finger tight.

20. Using a torque wrench, torque as follows:

a. 1988–89—tighten the long bolts to 73–83 ft lbs. in the sequence shown in the illustration and tighten the short bolts to 62–70 ft lbs. in the sequence shown in the illustration.

b. 1990—Tighten in 4 steps as follows:

• Tighten all bolts in sequence to 41 ft. lbs.

• Tighten all bolts an additional 45° in sequence.

• Tighten all bolts an additional 45° in sequence.

• Tighten the long bolts — 8, 4, 1, 1, 5 and 9 an additional 20° and tighten the short bolts — 7, 3, 2, 6 and 10 an additional 10°.

➡ **The short bolts, exhaust side, should end up with a total rotation of 100° and the long bolts, intake side, should end up with a total rotation of 110°.**

c. 1991–92—Tighten in 3 steps as follows:

• Tighten the long bolts in sequence to 46 ft. lbs.

• Tighten the short bolts in sequence to 43 ft. lbs.

• Tighten all bolts in sequence an additional 90°.

21. Reinstall the alternator. Install the power steering pump and brackets.

22. Reconnect the fuel lines and the hoses. Connect the exhaust pipe to the manifold.

23. Install the valve cover and connect the linkage at the TBI unit. Install the air cleaner and fill all the fluids.

24. Run the engine and check for leaks.

2.3L Engine

♦ SEE FIG. 71

1. Relieve the fuel system pressure. Disconnect the negative battery cable. Drain the engine coolant into a clean container for reuse.

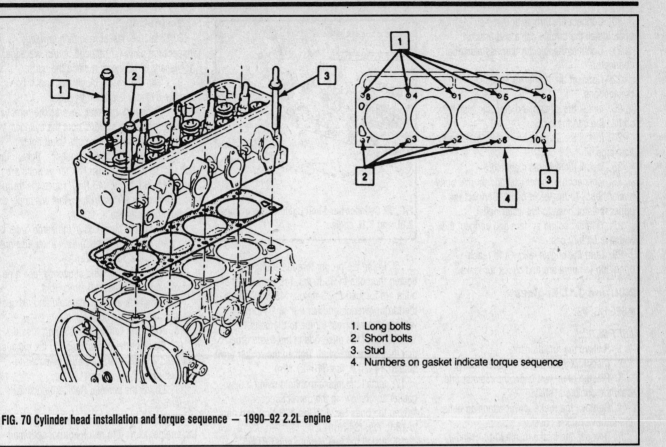

1. Long bolts
2. Short bolts
3. Stud
4. Numbers on gasket indicate torque sequence

FIG. 70 Cylinder head installation and torque sequence — 1990–92 2.2L engine

2. Disconnect heater inlet and throttle body heater hoses from water outlet. Disconnect upper radiator hose from water outlet.

3. Remove exhaust manifold.

4. Remove intake and exhaust camshaft housings.

5. Remove oil cap and dipstick. Pull oil fill tube upward to unseat from block.

6. Disconnect and tag injector harness electrical connector.

7. Disconnect throttle body to air cleaner duct. Remove throttle cable and bracket and position aside.

8. Remove throttle body from intake manifold with electrical harness, hoses, cable attached and position aside.

9. Disconnect and tag MAP sensor vacuum hose from intake manifold.

10. Remove intake manifold bracket to block bolt.

11. Disconnect and tag 2 coolant sensor connections.

12. Remove cylinder head to block bolts.

→ **When removing cylinder head to block bolts follow reverse of tighten sequence.**

13. Remove cylinder head and gasket.

→ **Clean all gasket surfaces with plastic or wood scraper. Do not use any sealing material.**

To install:

14. Install the cylinder head gasket to the cylinder block and carefully position the cylinder head in place.

15. Coat the head bolt threads with clean engine oil and allow the oil to drain off before installing.

16. Tighten the cylinder head bolts in sequence in 2 steps as follows:

Step 1: in sequence, tighten the long and short cylinder head to block bolts — 26 ft. lbs. (35 Nm).

Step 2: in sequence, tighten the 2 short bolts — an additional 100° turn and the 8 long bolts — an additional 110° turn.

17. Install the intake manifold-to-block bracket bolt and bracket.

18. Connect the MAP sensor vacuum hose to the intake manifold.

19. Install the throttle body on the intake manifold with electrical harness, hoses and cable attached.

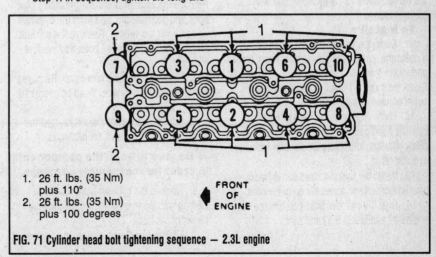

1. 26 ft. lbs. (35 Nm) plus 110°
2. 26 ft. lbs. (35 Nm) plus 100 degrees

FRONT OF ENGINE

FIG. 71 Cylinder head bolt tightening sequence — 2.3L engine

20. Connect the throttle body-to-air cleaner duct. Install the throttle cable and bracket.

21. Connect the injector harness electrical connector.

22. Connect the 2 coolant sensor connections.

23. Install the oil cap and dipstick. Install the oil fill tube into the block.

24. Install the exhaust and intake camshaft housings.

25. Install the exhaust manifold.

26. Connect the heater inlet and throttle body heater hoses to the water outlet. Connect the upper radiator hose to the water outlet.

27. Fill the cooling system and connect the negative battery cable.

28. Start the engine, allow it to reach operating temperature and check for leaks.

2.8L and 3.1L Engines

♦ SEE FIG. 72

LEFT SIDE

1. Relieve the fuel pressure.

2. Disconnect the negative battery cable.

3. Place a drain pan under the radiator and drain the cooling system.

4. Remove the rocker cover attaching bolts and remove rocker cover.

5. Remove the intake manifold-to-cylinder head bolts and the remove the intake manifold.

6. Remove the fuel plenum and fuel rail assembles.

7. Disconnect the exhaust crossover from the right exhaust manifold.

8. Disconnect the oil level indicator tube bracket.

9. Loosen the rocker arms nuts, turn the rocker arms and remove the pushrods.

➡ **Be sure to keep the parts in order for installation purposes.**

10. Remove the cylinder head-to-engine bolts; start with the outer bolts and work toward the center. Remove the cylinder head with the exhaust manifold.

To install:

11. Clean the gasket mounting surfaces. Inspect the surfaces of the cylinder head, block and intake manifold damage and/or warpage. Clean the threaded holes in the block and the cylinder head bolt threads.

12. Using new gaskets, align the new cylinder head gasket over the dowels on the block with the note **This Side Up** facing the cylinder head.

13. Install the cylinder head and exhaust manifold crossover assembly on the engine.

14. Coat the cylinder head bolt threads with engine oil and install the hand tight.

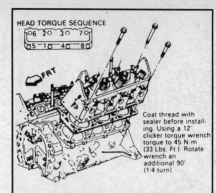

HEAD TORQUE SEQUENCE

FRT

Coat thread with sealer before installing. Using a 12" clicker torque wrench torque to 45 N·m (33 Lbs. Ft.). Rotate wrench an additional 90° (1/4 turn).

FIG. 72 Cylinder head bolt tightening sequence 2.8L and 3.1L engine

15. Using the proper torque sequence, tighten the bolts to 33 ft. lbs. (45 Nm). After all bolts are torqued to 33 ft. lbs. (45 Nm), rotate the torque wrench another 90° or 1/4 turn. This will apply the correct torque to the bolts.

16. Install the pushrods in the same order that they were removed. Tighten the rocker arm nuts to 14–20 ft. lbs. (19–27 Nm).

17. Install the intake manifold using a new gasket and following the correct sequence, tighten the bolts to 24 ft. lbs. (33 Nm) and nuts to 18 ft. lbs. (24 Nm).

18. Install the fuel plenum and fuel rail. Tighten the plenum bolts to 16 ft. lbs. (22 Nm).

19. Connect the exhaust crossover to the right exhaust manifold.

20. Connect the oil level indicator tube bracket.

21. Refill the cooling system. Connect the negative battery cable.

22. Operate the engine until normal operating temperatures are reached and check for leaks.

RIGHT SIDE

1. Relieve the fuel pressure. Disconnect the negative battery cable. Drain the cooling system.

2. Raise and safely support the vehicle. Remove the exhaust manifold-to-exhaust pipe bolts and separate the pipe from the manifold.

3. Lower the vehicle. Remove the exhaust manifold-to-cylinder head bolts and exhaust manifold.

4. Remove the rocker arm cover. Remove the intake manifold-to-cylinder head bolts and the intake manifold.

5. Loosen the rocker arms nuts, turn the rocker arms and remove the pushrods.

➡ **Be sure to keep the components in order for reassembly purposes.**

6. Remove the cylinder head-to-engine bolts, starting with the outer bolts, working towards the center of the head.

7. Lift the cylinder head from the engine.

To install:

8. Clean the gasket mounting surfaces. Inspect the parts for damage and/or warpage; if necessary, machine or replace the parts.

9. Clean the engine block's threaded holes and the cylinder head bolt threads.

10. Using new gaskets, reverse the removal procedures. Using sealant, coat the cylinder head bolts and install the bolts hand tight.

11. Using the torquing sequence, tighten the bolts to 33 ft. lbs. (45 Nm). After all bolts are torqued to 33 ft. lbs. (45 Nm), rotate the torque wrench another 90° or 1/4 turn; this will apply the correct torque to the bolts.

12. Install the pushrods in the same order as they were removed. Tighten the rocker arm nuts to 14–20 ft. lbs. (19–27 Nm).

13. Follow the torquing sequence, use a new gasket and install the intake manifold.

14. Install the exhaust manifold and exhaust manifold-to-cylinder head bolts.

15. Raise the vehicle and support it safely.

16. Connect the exhaust pipe to the exhaust manifold and install the exhaust manifold-to-exhaust pipe bolts.

17. Lower the vehicle. Refill the cooling system.

18. Connect the negative battery cable. Start the engine, allow it to reach normal operating temperatures and check for leaks.

RESURFACING

Cylinder Head Flatness

♦ SEE FIG. 73

When the cylinder head is removed, check the flatness of the cylinder head gasket surfaces.

1. Place a straightedge across the gasket surface of the cylinder head. Using feeler gauges, determine the clearance at the center of the straightedge.

2. If warpage exceeds 0.003 in. (0.076mm) in a 6 in. (152mm) span, or 0.006 in. (0.152mm) over the total length, the cylinder head must be resurfaced.

3. If necessary to refinish the cylinder head gasket surface, do not plane or grind off more than 0.254mm (0.010 in.) from the original gasket surface.

➡ **When milling the cylinder heads of V6 engines, the intake manifold mounting position is altered, and must be corrected by milling the manifold flange a proportionate amount. Consult an experienced machinist about this.**

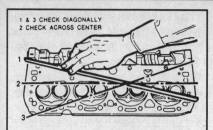

FIG. 73 Check the cylinder head mating surface for warpage with a precision straight edge

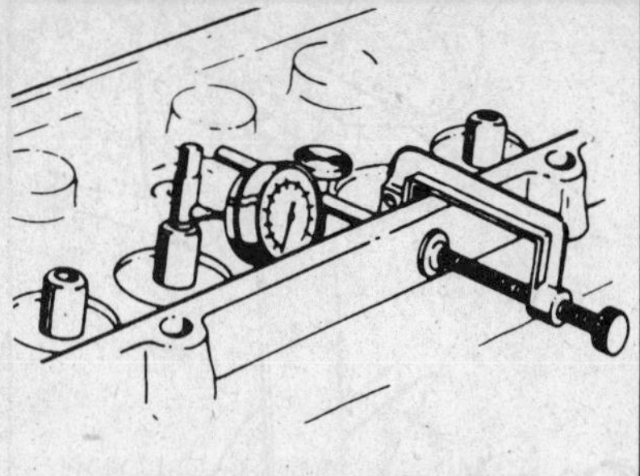

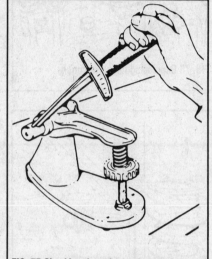

FIG. 74 Measuring valve guide clearance

CLEANING AND INSPECTION

♦ SEE FIGS. 74-75

1. Clean all carbon from the combustion chambers and valve ports.
2. Thoroughly clean the valve guides.
3. Clean all carbon and sludge from the pushrods, rocker arms and pushrod guides.
4. Clean the valve stems and heads on a buffing wheel.
5. Clean the carbon deposits from the head gasket mating surface.
6. Inspect the cylinder head for cracks in the exhaust ports, combustion chambers or external cracks to the water jacket.
7. Inspect the valves for burned heads, cracked faces or damaged stems.
8. Measure the valve stem clearance as follows:

   a. Clamp a dial indicator on ones side of the cylinder head. Locate the indicator so that movement of the valve stem from side to side (crosswise to the head) will cause direct movement of the indicator stem. The indicator stem must contact the side of the valve stem just above the guide.

   b. Drop the valve head 1.5mm off the valve seat.

   c. Move the stem of the valve from side to side, using light pressure to obtain a clearance reading. If the clearance exceeds specifications, it will be necessary to ream the valve guides for oversize valves. Service valves are available in standard, 0.089mm, 0.394mm and 0.775mm O.S. sizes.

➡ **If valve guides must be reamed this service is available at most machine shops.**

9. Check the valve spring tension with tool J-8056, spring tester. Springs should be compressed to the specified height and checked against the specifications chart. Springs should be replaced if not within (10 lbs. of the specified load (without dampers).
10. Inspect the rocker arms studs for wear or damage.

FIG. 75 Checking the valve spring tension

➡ **If a dial indicator is not available to you, take your cylinder head to a qualified machine shop for inspection**

Valves and Springs

REMOVAL & INSTALLATION

♦ SEE FIGS. 76–78

1. Block the head on its side, or install a pair of head-holding brackets made especially for valve removal.
2. Use a socket slightly larger than the valve stem and keepers, place the socket over the valve stem and gently hit the socket with a plastic hammer to break loose any varnish buildup.
3. Remove the valve keepers, retainer, spring shield and valve spring using a valve spring compressor (the locking C-clamp type is the easiest kind to use).

4. Put the parts in a separate container numbered for the cylinder being worked on; do not mix them with other parts removed.
5. Remove and discard the valve stem oil seals. A new seal will be used at assembly time.
6. Remove the valves from the cylinder head and place them, in order, through numbered holes punched in a stiff piece of cardboard or wood valve holding stick.

➡ **The exhaust valve stems, on some engines, are equipped with small metal caps. Take care not to lose the caps. Make sure to reinstall them at assembly time. Replace any caps that are worn.**

7. Use an electric drill and rotary wire brush to clean the intake and exhaust valve ports, combustion chamber and valve seats. In some cases, the carbon will need to be chipped away. Use a blunt pointed drift for carbon chipping. Be careful around the valve seat areas.
8. Use a wire valve guide cleaning brush and safe solvent to clean the valve guides.
9. Clean the valves with a revolving wires brush. Heavy carbon deposits may be removed with the blunt drift.

➡ **When using a wire brush to clean carbon on the valve ports, valves etc., be sure that the deposits are actually removed, rather than burnished.**

10. Wash and clean all valve springs, keepers, retaining caps etc., in safe solvent.
11. Clean the head with a brush and some safe solvent and wipe dry.
12. Check the head for cracks. Cracks in the cylinder head usually start around an exhaust valve seat because it is the hottest part of the combustion chamber. If a crack is suspected but cannot be detected visually have the area checked with dye penetrant or other method by the machine shop.
13. After all cylinder head parts are reasonably clean, check the valve stem-to-guide clearance. If a dial indicator is not on hand, a visual inspection can give you a fairly good idea if the guide, valve stem or both are worn.
14. Insert the valve into the guide until slight away from the valve seat. Wiggle the valve sideways. A small amount of wobble is normal, excessive wobble means a worn guide or valve stem. If a dial indicator is on hand, mount the indicator so that the stem of the valve is at 90° to the valve stem, as close to the valve guide as possible. Move the valve off the seat, and measure the valve guide-to-stem clearance by rocking the stem back and forth to actuate the dial indicator. Measure the valve stem using a

micrometer and compare to specifications to determine whether stem or guide wear is causing excessive clearance.

15. The valve guide, if worn, must be repaired before the valve seats can be resurfaced. Ford supplies valves with oversize stems to fit valve guides that are reamed to oversize for repair. The machine shop will be able to handle the guide reaming for you. In some cases, if the guide is not too badly worn, knurling may be all that is required.

16. Reface, or have the valves and valve seats refaced. The valve seats should be a true 45° angle. Remove only enough material to clean up any pits or grooves. Be sure the valve seat is not too wide or narrow. Use a 60° grinding wheel to remove material from the bottom of the seat for raising and a 30° grinding wheel to remove material from the top of the seat to narrow.

17. After the valves are refaced by machine, hand lap them to the valve seat. Clean the grinding compound off and check the position of face-to-seat contact. Contact should be close to the center of the valve face. If contact is close to the top edge of the valve, narrow the seat; if too close to the bottom edge, raise the seat.

18. Valves should be refaced to a true angle of 44°. Remove only enough metal to clean up the valve face or to correct runout. If the edge of a valve head, after machining, is $1/32$ in. (0.8mm) or less replace the valve. The tip of the valve stem should also be dressed on the valve grinding machine, however, do not remove more than 0.010 in. (0.254mm).

19. After all valve and valve seats have been machined, check the remaining valve train parts (springs, retainers, keepers, etc.) for wear. Check the valve springs for straightness and tension.

20. Install the valves in the cylinder head and metal caps.

21. Install new valve stem oil seals.

22. Install the valve keepers, retainer, spring shield and valve spring using a valve spring compressor (the locking C-clamp type is the easiest kind to use).

23. Check the valve spring installed height, shim or replace as necessary.

CHECKING VALVE SPRINGS

Place the valve spring on a flat surface next to a carpenter's square. Measure the height of the spring, and rotate the spring against the edge of the square to measure distortion. If the spring height varies (by comparison) by more than $1/16$ in. (1.6mm) or if the distortion exceeds $1/16$ in. (1.6mm), replace the spring.

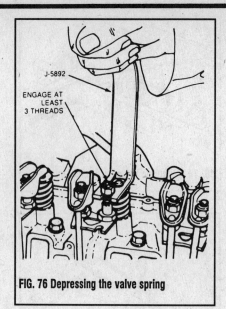

FIG. 76 Depressing the valve spring

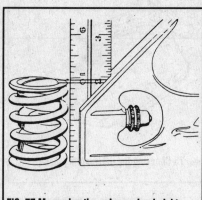

FIG. 77 Measuring the valve spring height

Have the valve springs tested for spring pressure at the installed and compressed (installed height minus valve lift) height using a valve spring tester. Springs should be within 1 pound, plus or minus each other. Replace springs as necessary.

VALVE SPRING INSTALLED HEIGHT

After installing the valve spring, measure the distance between the spring mounting pad and the lower edge of the spring retainer. Compare the measurement to specifications. If the installed height is incorrect, add shim washers between the spring mounting pad and the spring. Use only washers designed for valve springs, available at most parts houses.

Check the installed height of the valve springs, using a narrow thin scale. On the OHV 4-cylinder engine, measure from the top of the spring seat to the bottom of the cap.

On the V6 engine measure from the top of the spring damper "feet" to the bottom inside of the oil shedder for exhaust and from the top of the spring shim to the bottom of the valve cap for the intake. If this is found to exceed the specified height, install an additional valve spring seat shim approximately 0.7mm thick.

➡ **At no time should the valve spring be shimmed to give an installed height under the minimum specified.**

VALVE STEM OIL SEALS

When installing valve stem oil seals, ensure that a small amount of oil is able to pass the seal to lubricate the valve stems and guide walls, otherwise, excessive wear will occur.

On the V6 engine, check each valve stem oil seal by placing the valve stem leak detector tool J-23994, over the end of the valve stem and against the cap. Operate the vacuum pump and make sure no air leaks past the seal.

VALVE SEATS

If the valve seat is damaged or burnt and cannot be serviced by refacing, it may be possible to have the seat machined and an insert installed. Consult an automotive machine shop for their advice.

VALVE GUIDES

Worn valve guides can, in most cases, be reamed to accept a valve with an oversized stem. Valve guides that are not excessively worn or distorted may, in some cases, be knurled rather than reamed. However, if the valve stem is worn reaming for an oversized valve stem is the answer since a new valve would be required.

Knurling is a process in which metal is displaced and raised, thereby reducing clearance. Knurling also produces excellent oil control. The possibility of knurling instead of reaming the valve guides should be discussed with a reputable machinist or engine specialist.

Valve Lifter

REMOVAL & INSTALLATION

> ❄ **CAUTION**
>
> When draining the coolant, keep in mind that cats and dogs are attracted by the ethylene glycol antifreeze, and are quite likely to drink any that is left in an uncovered container or in puddles on the ground. This will prove fatal in sufficient quantity. Always drain the coolant into a sealable container. Coolant should be reused unless it is contaminated or several years old.

2.0L and 2.2L Engine

➧ SEE FIG. 79

1. Remove the rocker arm cover.
2. Loosen the rocker arm nut and swing the rocker arm aside.
3. Remove the pushrod.
4. With a flexible magnetic wand, remove the valve lifter.

Whenever new valve lifters are being installed, coat the foot of the valve lifters with camshaft assembly lube GM No. 1052365, or equivalent.

The lifter foot is slightly convex. This can be detected by holding a good straight edge to the surface while looking into a light source. If the lifter foot is worn flat or grooved, it must be replaced.

To install

5. With a flexible magnetic wand, install the valve lifter.
6. Install the pushrod and rocker arm.
7. Tighten the rocker arm nut to 22 ft. lbs. (30 Nm).
8. Install the rocker cover.

2.8L and 3.1L Engine

1. Drain the cooling system.
2. Remove the intake manifold assembly.
3. Remove the rocker arms and remove the valve lifter.

Whenever new valve lifters are being installed, coat the foot of the valve lifters with camshaft assembly lube GM No. 1052365, or equivalent.

To install

4. With a flexible magnetic wand, install the valve lifter.

5. Install the rocker arm.
6. Install the intake manifold assembly.
7. Tighten the rocker arm nut to 18 ft. lbs. (25 Nm).
8. Install the rocker cover.

Oil Pan

REMOVAL & INSTALLATION

> ❄ **CAUTION**
>
> The EPA warns that prolonged contact with used engine oil may cause a number of skin disorders, including cancer! You should make every effort to minimize your exposure to used engine oil. Protective gloves should be worn when changing the oil. Wash your hands and any other exposed skin areas as soon as possible after exposure to used engine oil. Soap and water, or waterless hand cleaner should be used.

When draining the coolant, keep in mind that cats and dogs are attracted by the ethylene glycol antifreeze, and are quite likely to drink any that is left in an uncovered container or in puddles on the ground. This will prove fatal in sufficient quantity. Always drain the coolant into a sealable container. Coolant should be reused unless it is contaminated or several years old.

2.0L and 2.2L Engine

➧ SEE FIG. 80

1. Disconnect the negative battery cable.
2. Drain the crankcase. Raise and support the front of the vehicle.
3. Remove the air conditioning brace if so equipped.
4. Remove the exhaust shield and disconnect the exhaust pipe at the manifold.
5. Remove the starter motor and position it out of the way.
6. Remove the flywheel cover.
7. On 1988–90 models, remove the four right support bolts. Lower the support slightly to gain clearance for oil pan removal.
8. On 1988–90 models, if equipped with automatic transaxle, remove the oil filter and extension.
9. Remove the oil pan bolts and remove the oil pan.

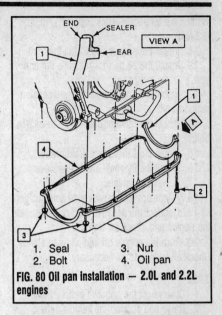

1. Seal
2. Bolt
3. Nut
4. Oil pan

FIG. 80 Oil pan installation — 2.0L and 2.2L engines

➥ Prior to oil pan installation, check that the sealing surfaces on the pan, cylinder block and front cover are clean and free of oil. If installing the old pan, be sure that all old RTV has been removed.

10. Apply a 1/8 in. (3mm) wide bead of RTV sealant to the oil pan sealing surface. Use a new oil pan rear seal, apply a thin coat of RTV sealer on the ends down to the ears, install the pan against the case and install bolts. Tighten the bolts to 71 inch lbs. (8 Nm) (minimum).
11. On cars equipped with automatic transmission, replace the oil filter adapter seal and replace the oil filter adapter.
12. Install the remaining components is in the reverse order of removal.

2.3L Engine

➧ SEE FIG. 81

1990–91

1. Disconnect the negative battery cable.
2. Raise and support the vehicle safely.
3. Remove the flywheel inspection cover.
4. Remove the splash shield-to-suspension support bolt.
5. Remove the exhaust manifold brace.
6. Remove the radiator outlet pipe-to-oil pan bolt.
7. Remove the transaxle-to-oil pan nut and stud using a 7mm socket.
8. Gently pry the spacer out from between oil pan and transaxle.
9. Remove the oil pan bolts. Remove the oil pan from the engine.

To install:

10. Install the oil pan to the engine. Install the oil pan bolts. Tighten the chain housing and carrier seal bolts to 106 inch lbs. (12 Nm).

Tighten the oil pan-to-block bolts to 17 ft. lbs. (23 Nm).

11. Install the spacer and install the stud.

12. Install the oil pan-to-transaxle nut and bolt.

13. Install the splash shield-to-suspension support bolt.

14. Install the radiator outlet pipe-to-oil pan bolt.

15. Install the exhaust manifold brace.

16. Install the flywheel inspection cover.

17. Lower the vehicle.

18. Fill the crankcase with oil to specification.

19. Connect the negative battery cable. Start the engine and check for leaks.

20. Turn the engine off and allow to stand. Check oil level, add as necessary.

1992

1. Disconnect the negative battery cable.

2. Raise and support the vehicle safely.

3. Drain the crankcase.

4. Drain the cooling system.

5. Remove the flywheel cover.

6. Remove the right front wheel and tire assembly.

7. Remove the right splash shield.

8. Remove the serpentine drive belt tension.

9. Disconnect the engine mount strut from the engine mount strut bracket.

10. Disconnect the A/C compressor from the bracket and suitably support.

11. Remove the engine mount strut bracket bolts and move the bracket aside.

12. Remove the radiator outlet pipe bolts.

13. Disconnect the air conditioner and radiator outlet pipes from the suspension supports.

14. Remove the exhaust manifold brace.

15. Remove the oil pan to flywheel cover bolt and nut.

16. Remove the flywheel cover stud for clearance.

17. Disconnect the radiator outlet pipe from the lower hose and oil pan.

17. Disconnect the oil level sensor wire.

18. Remove the oil pan bolts and remove the oil pan.

To install

19. Install the oil pan and new gasket (no sealer needed).

20. Loosely install the pan bolts.

21. Place the spacer in its approximate installed location but allow clearance to tighten the pan bolt directly above the spacer.

22. Tighten the chain housing and carrier seal bolts to 106 inch lbs. (12 Nm). Tighten the oil pan-to-block bolts to 17 ft. lbs. (23 Nm).

23. Place the spacer into its proper location and install the stud.

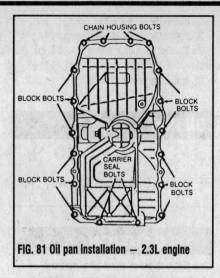

FIG. 81 Oil pan installation — 2.3L engine

24. Install the oil pan to transaxle nut and tighten to 41 ft. lbs. (56 Nm).

25. Connect the oil level sensor wire.

26. Connect the radiator outlet pipe to the lower hose and oil pan.

27. Install the exhaust manifold brace.

28. Connect the air conditioner and radiator outlet pipes to the suspension supports.

29. Install the radiator outlet pipe bolts.

30. Install the engine mount strut bracket bolts.

31. Install the air conditioner compressor.

32. Connect the engine mount strut to the engine mount strut bracket.

33. Install the serpentine drive belt tension.

34. Install the right splash shield.

36. Install the right front wheel and tire assembly.

37. Install the flywheel cover.

38. Fill the cooling system.

39. Fill the crankcase.

40. Connect the negative battery cable.

2.8L and 3.1L Engine

▶ SEE FIG. 82

1. Disconnect the battery ground.

2. Raise and support the car on jackstands.

3. Drain the oil.

4. Remove the bellhousing cover.

5. Remove the starter.

6. Remove the oil pan bolts and remove the oil pan.

7. Installation is the reverse of removal. The pan is installed using a gasket. Torque the 2 rear oil pan bolts to 18 ft. lbs. (25 Nm), the oil pan stud to cylinder block to 71 inch lbs. (8 Nm) and the remainder of the oil pan bolts and nuts to 71 inch lbs. (8 Nm).

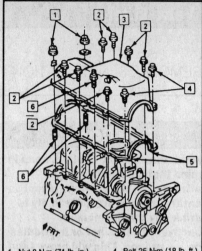

1. Nut 8 N·m (71 lb. in.)
2. Bolt 8 N·m (71 lb. in.)
3. Oil pan
4. Bolt 25 N·m (18 lb. ft.)
5. Apply sealer
6. Stud 8 N·m (71 lb. in.)

FIG. 82 Oil pan installation — 2.8L and 3.1L engines

Oil Pump

REMOVAL & INSTALLATION

2.0L and 2.2L Engines

▶ SEE FIG. 83

1. Remove the engine oil pan.

2. Remove the pump to rear bearing cap bolt.

3. Remove the extension shaft and retainer.

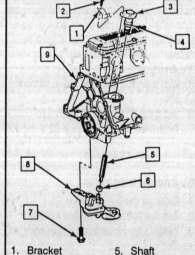

1. Bracket
2. Bolt
3. Oil pump drive assembly
4. O-ring
5. Shaft
6. Retainer
7. Bolt
8. Oil pump
9. Cylinder block

FIG. 83 Oil pump and drive assembly — 2.0L and 2.2L engines

To install

4. Heat the retainer in hot water prior to assembly and install in the extension to the oil pump.

➡ **Be sure the retainer does not crack upon installation.**

5. Install the pump to rear bearing cap bolt and torque to 32 ft. lbs. (43 Nm).

6. Install the oil pan.

2.3L Engine

♦ SEE FIG. 84

1. Disconnect the negative battery cable.
2. Raise and support the vehicle safely.
3. Remove the attaching bolts and the oil pan.
4. Remove the oil pump assembly retainers, bolts and nut.
5. Remove the oil pump assembly and shims if equipped.

➡ **Oil pump drive gear backlash must be checked when any of the following components are replaced: oil pump assembly, oil pump drive gear, crankshaft and cylinder block.**

To install:

6. Check and adjust oil pump drive gear backlash as follows:

   a. With oil pump assembly off engine, remove 3 attaching bolts and separate the driven gear cover and screen assembly from the oil pump.

   b. Install the oil pump on the block using the original shims. Tighten the bolts to 33 ft. lbs. (45 Nm) for 1990 and 40 ft. lbs. (54 Nm) for 1991–92.

   c. Install the dial indicator assembly to measure backlash between oil pump to drive gear.

   d. Record oil pump drive to driven gear backlash correct backlash clearance is 0.0091–0.0201 in. (0.23–0.51mm). When taking measurement crankshaft cannot move.

   e. Remove oil pump from block reinstall driven gear cover and screen assembly to pump and tighten to 106 inch lbs. (12 Nm).

   f. Reinstall the pump assembly on block. Tighten oil pump-to-block bolts 33 ft. lbs. (45 Nm).

7. Install the oil pump assembly, including shims if removed.

8. Tighten oil pump to block bolts to to 33 ft. lbs. (45 Nm) for 1990 and 40 ft. lbs. (54 Nm) for 1991–92.

9. Install the oil pan and attaching bolts.

10. Lower the vehicle.

11. Fill the crankcase with oil to specification.

12. Connect the negative battery cable. Start the engine and check oil pressure and check for leaks.

13. Turn the engine off and allow to stand. Check oil level, add as necessary.

2.8L and 3.1L Engine

♦ SEE FIG. 85

1. Remove the oil pan as described earlier.
2. Unbolt and remove the oil pump and pickup.
3. Installation is the reverse of removal. Torque to 20–31 ft. lbs.

Crankshaft Pulley and Timing Chain Front Cover

REMOVAL & INSTALLATION

✳✳ CAUTION

When draining the coolant, keep in mind that cats and dogs are attracted by the ethylene glycol antifreeze, and are quite likely to drink any that is left in an uncovered container or in puddles on the ground. This will prove fatal in sufficient quantity. Always drain the coolant into a sealable container. Coolant should be reused unless it is contaminated or several years old.

✳✳ WARNING

The EPA warns that prolonged contact with used engine oil may cause a number of skin disorders, including cancer! You should make every effort to minimize your exposure to used engine oil. Protective gloves should be worn when changing the oil. Wash your hands and any other exposed skin areas as soon as possible after exposure to used engine oil. Soap and water, or waterless hand cleaner should be used.

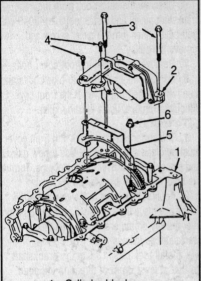

1. Cylinder block
2. Oil pump assembly
3. Oil pump to block bolt
4. Oil pump screen to brace bolt
5. Brace
6. Nut

FIG. 84 Oil pump assembly to block installation — 2.3L engine

2.0L and 2.2L Engines

♦ SEE FIG. 86

➡ **The following procedure requires the use of a special tool.**

1. Disconnect the negative battery cable.
2. Remove the serpentine belt and tensioner.
3. Raise the vehicle and support it safely.
4. Remove the wheel and tire assembly.
5. Remove the right front inner fender splash.

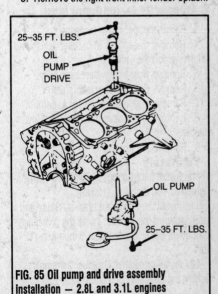

25–35 FT. LBS.

OIL PUMP DRIVE

OIL PUMP

25–35 FT. LBS.

FIG. 85 Oil pump and drive assembly installation — 2.8L and 3.1L engines

6. Unscrew the center bolt from the crankshaft pulley and install tool J 24420–B on their pulley, then turn the puller screw and remove the pulley.

7. Remove the oil pan-to-front cover bolts.

8. Remove the front cover-to-block bolts and then remove the front cover. If the front cover is difficult to remove, use a plastic mallet.

To Install

1. The surfaces of the block and front cover must be clean and free of oil. Use a new gasket and place the cover over the dowel pins. Torque the bolts to 6–9 ft. lbs. (4–7 Nm).

2. Apply RTV sealant to the keyway in the pulley and place the crankshaft pulley in position over the key on the crankshaft. Pull the crankshaft as follows

• Install tool J 29113 into the crankshaft so that at least 6mm of thread is engaged.

• Pull the pulley into position and remove the tool from the pulley.

3. Torque the pulley retaining bolt to 66–88 ft. lbs. (89–119 Nm)

4. Install the belt.

5. Install the oil pan.

6. Install the inner fender splash shield.

7. Install the wheel and tire assembly.

8. Lower the vehicle.

9. Connect the battery.

2.3L Engine

1990–91
▶ SEE FIG. 32

1. Disconnect the negative battery cable from the battery. Remove coolant recovery reservoir.

2. Remove the serpentine drive belt.

➡ **To avoid personal injury when rotating the serpentine belt tensioner, use a 13mm wrench that is at least 24 in. (610mm) long.**

3. Remove upper cover fasteners.

4. Remove the engine lift bracket. Raise and safely support the vehicle.

5. Remove right front wheel assembly.

6. Remove right lower splash shield.

7. Remove crankshaft balancer assembly.

8. Remove lower cover fasteners and lower vehicle.

9. Remove the front cover.

To install:

10. Install the front cover using new gaskets. Tighten to 106 inch lbs. (12 Nm).

11. Install the engine lift bracket. Raise and safely support the vehicle. Install the remaining front cover bolts. Tighten to 106 inch lbs. (12 Nm).

12. Install crankshaft balancer assembly. Tighten the attaching bolt and washer for

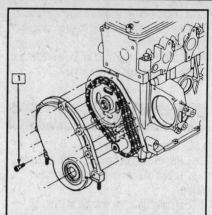

FIG. 86 Front cover installation — 2.0L and 2.2L engines

balancer assembly to 74 ft. lbs. (100 Nm). plus additional 90° turn.

➡ **The automatic transaxle crankshaft balancer must not be installed on a manual transaxle engine.**

13. Install right lower splash shield.

14. Install right front wheel assembly.

15. Lower the vehicle.

16. Install upper cover fasteners.

17. Install the serpentine drive belt.

➡ **To avoid personal injury when rotating the serpentine belt tensioner, use a 13mm wrench that is at least 24 in. (610mm) long.**

18. Install coolant recovery reservoir.

19. Connect the negative battery cable.

1992
▶ SEE FIG. 32

1. Disconnect the negative battery cable from the battery. Remove coolant recovery reservoir.

2. Remove the serpentine drive belt.

➡ **To avoid personal injury when rotating the serpentine belt tensioner, use a 13mm wrench that is at least 24 in. (610mm) long.**

3. Remove the alternator and lay to one side.

4. Reinstall the alternator through bolt and attach engine support fixture J28467 or equivalent.

3. Remove upper cover fasteners.

4. Remove the right engine mount and lift bracket. Raise and safely support the vehicle.

5. Remove right front wheel assembly.

6. Remove right lower splash shield.

7. Remove crankshaft balancer assembly.

8. Remove lower cover fasteners and lower vehicle.

9. Remove the front cover.

To install:

10. Install the front cover using new gaskets.

11. Place the nuts on the studs to retain the cover and tighten to 106 inch lbs. (12 Nm).

12. Raise and support the vehicle safely.

13. Install the remaining cover fasteners and tighten to 106 inch lbs. (12 Nm).

14. Lubricate the front oil seal and sealing surface of the crankshaft balancer with chassis grease.

15. Install crankshaft balancer assembly. Tighten the attaching bolt and washer for balancer assembly to 74 ft. lbs. (100 Nm). plus additional 90° turn.

16. Install right lower splash shield.

17. Install right front wheel assembly.

18. Lower the vehicle.

19. Install the alternator.

20. Install the engine mount and lift bracket.

21. Install the serpentine drive belt.

➡ **To avoid personal injury when rotating the serpentine belt tensioner, use a 13mm wrench that is at least 24 in. (610mm) long.**

22. Install coolant recovery reservoir.

23. Connect the negative battery cable.

2.8L and 3.1L Engines
▶ SEE FIG. 87

1. Disconnect the battery ground cable.

2. Drain the cooling system.

3. Remove the serpentine belt.

4. Remove the alternator and lay aside.

5. Remove the power steering pump and lay aside.

6. Jack up the car and support it safely.

7. Remove the inner splash shield.

8. Remove the flywheel cover at the transaxle.

9. Remove the harmonic balancer with tool J 24420.

❋❋❋ WARNING

The outer ring (weight) of the harmonic balancer is bonded to the hub with rubber. Breakage may occur if the balancer is hammered back onto the crankshaft. A press or special installation tool is necessary.

10. Remove the serpentine belt idler pulley.

11. Remove the starter.

12. Remove the pan to front cover bolts.

13. Remove the lower cover bolts.

14. Lower the vehicle.

15. Disconnect the radiator hose at the water pump.

16. Remove the heater coolant hose at cooling system fill pipe.

17. Disconnect the bypass and overflow hoses.

18. Disconnect the canister purge hose.

19. Remove the upper front cover bolts and remove the front cover.

To Install

20. Clean all the gasket mounting surfaces on the front cover and block and place a new gasket to the front cover sealing surface. Apply a sealer (1052080 or equivalent) as shown to the ends of the gasket.

22. Place the front cover on the engine and install the upper front cover bolts. Torque to the specifications shown in the illustration.

23. Raise the vehicle and support it safely.

24. Install the lower cover bolts. Torque to the specifications shown in the illustration.

25. Install the oil pan to cover screws.

26. Install the serpentine belt idler pulley.

27. Install the harmonic balancer as follows:

• Apply RTV sealant to the keyway in the pulley and place the crankshaft pulley in position over the key on the crankshaft.

• Install tool J–29113 into the crankshaft so that at least 6mm of thread is engaged.

• Pull the pulley into position and remove the tool from the pulley.

• Torque the pulley retaining bolt to 67–85 ft. lbs.

28. Install the flywheel cover on the transaxle.

29. Install the starter.

30. Install the inner splash shield.

31. Lower the vehicle.

32. Install the radiator hose at the water pump.

33. Install the heater hose at the cooling system fill pipe.

34. Connect the bypass and overflow hoses.

35. Connect the canister purge hose.

36. Install the power steering pump.

37. Tighten the alternator bracket.

38. Install the alternator.

39. Install the serpentine belt tensioner and belt.

40. Fill the cooling system.

41. Connect the battery cable.

Timing Cover Oil Seal

REPLACEMENT

All Except 2.3L Engine

♦ SEE FIGS. 25-35

The oil seal can be replaced with the cover either on or off the engine. If the cover is on the engine, remove the crankshaft pulley and hub first. Pry out the seal using a large screwdriver, being careful not to distort the seal mating surface. Install the new seal so that the open side or helical side is towards the engine. Press it into place with a seal driver made for the purpose. Chevrolet recommends a tool, J–35468 Seal Centering Tool. Install the hub if removed.

2.3L Engine

♦ SEE FIG. 32

1. Remove the front cover.

2. Support the front cover and drive the oil seal out the back (timing chain side) of the cover.

To Install

3. Using tool, Front Cover Crankshaft Seal Installer No. J 36010 or equivalent, install the seal in the cover. The tool will properly position the seal in the cover.

4. Install the front cover and check for leaks.

Timing Chain and Sprockets

REMOVAL & INSTALLATION

2.0L and 2.2L Engines

♦ SEE FIG. 88

1. Remove the front cover as previously detailed.

2. Place the No. 1 piston at TDC of the compression stroke so that the marks on the camshaft and crankshaft sprockets are in alignment (see illustration).

3. Loosen the timing chain tensioner nut as far as possible without actually removing it.

4. Remove the camshaft sprocket bolts and remove the sprocket and chain together. If the sprocket does not slide from the camshaft easily, a light blow with a soft mallet at the lower edge of the sprocket will dislodge it.

5. Use a gear puller (J–22888) and remove the crankshaft sprocket.

6. Install crankshaft sprocket back onto the crankshaft using tool J 5590.

7. Install the timing chain over the camshaft sprocket and then around the crankshaft

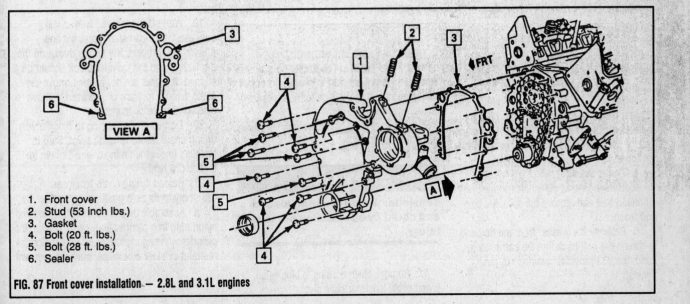

VIEW A

1. Front cover
2. Stud (53 inch lbs.)
3. Gasket
4. Bolt (20 ft. lbs.)
5. Bolt (28 ft. lbs.)
6. Sealer

FIG. 87 Front cover installation — 2.8L and 3.1L engines

sprocket. Make sure that the marks on the two sprockets are in alignment (see illustration). Lubricate the thrust surface with Molykote® or its equivalent.

8. Align the dowel in the camshaft with the dowel hole in the sprocket and then install the sprocket onto the camshaft. Use the mounting bolts to draw the sprocket onto the camshaft and then tighten to 66–88 ft. lbs.

9. Lubricate the timing chain with clean engine oil. Tighten the chain tensioner.

10. Installation of the remaining components is in the reverse order of removal.

2.3L Engine

◆ SEE FIG. 32 AND 90-92

☞ **Prior to removing the timing chain, review the entire procedure.**

1. Disconnect the negative battery cable.
2. Remove front engine cover and crankshaft oil slinger.
3. Rotate the crankshaft clockwise, as viewed from front of engine/normal rotation until the camshaft sprockets' timing dowel pin holes line up with the holes in the timing chain housing. The mark on the crankshaft sprocket should line up with the mark on the cylinder block. The crankshaft sprocket keyway should point upwards and line up with the centerline of the cylinder bores. This is the timed position.
4. Remove 3 timing chain guides.
5. Raise vehicle and support in safely.
6. Gently pry off timing chain tensioner spring retainer and remove spring.

☞ **Two styles of tensioner are used. One with a spring post, early production and 1 without a spring post, late production. Both styles are identical in operation and are interchangeable.**

7. Remove timing chain tensioner shoe retainer.
8. Make sure all the slack in the timing chain is above the tensioner assembly; remove the chain tensioner shoe. The timing chain must be disengaged from the wear grooves in the tensioner shoe in order to remove the shoe. Slide a prybar under the timing chain while pulling shoe outward.
9. If difficulty is encountered removing chain tensioner shoe, proceed as follows:
   a. Lower the vehicle.
   b. Hold the intake camshaft sprocket with a holding tool and remove the sprocket bolt and washer.
   c. Remove the washer from the bolt and re-thread the bolt back into the camshaft by hand, the bolt provides a surface to push against.

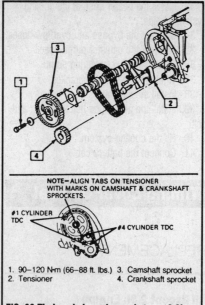

NOTE—ALIGN TABS ON TENSIONER WITH MARKS ON CAMSHAFT & CRANKSHAFT SPROCKETS.

#1 CYLINDER TDC   #4 CYLINDER TDC

1. 90–120 N·m (66–88 ft. lbs.)   3. Camshaft sprocket
2. Tensioner   4. Crankshaft sprocket

FIG. 88 Timing chain and sprockets — 2.0L and 2.2L engines

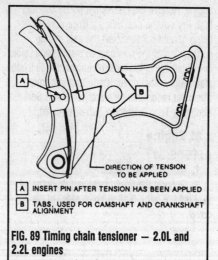

DIRECTION OF TENSION TO BE APPLIED

Ⓐ INSERT PIN AFTER TENSION HAS BEEN APPLIED
Ⓑ TABS, USED FOR CAMSHAFT AND CRANKSHAFT ALIGNMENT

FIG. 89 Timing chain tensioner — 2.0L and 2.2L engines

d. Remove intake camshaft sprocket using a 3-jaw puller in the 3 relief holes in the sprocket. Do not attempt to pry the sprocket off the camshaft or damage to the sprocket or chain housing could occur.

10. Remove tensioner assembly attaching bolts and tensioner.

✳✳ CAUTION

Tensioner piston is spring loaded and could fly out causing personal injury.

11. Remove chain housing to block stud, timing chain tensioner shoe pivot.

12. Remove timing chain.

☞ **Failure to follow this procedure could result in severe engine damage.**

To install:

13. Tighten intake camshaft sprocket attaching bolt and washer, to specification while holding sprocket in place.

14. Install a special tool through holes in camshaft sprockets into holes in timing chain housing, this positions the camshafts for correct timing.

15. If the camshafts are out of position and must be rotated more than 1/8 turn in order to install the alignment dowel pins, perform the following:
   a. The crankshaft must be rotated 90° clockwise off of TDC in order to give the valves adequate clearance to open.
   b. Once the camshafts are in position and the dowels installed, rotate the crankshaft counterclockwise back to top dead center. Do not rotate the crankshaft clockwise to TDC, valve or piston damage could occur.

16. Install timing chain over exhaust camshaft sprocket, around idler sprocket and around crankshaft sprocket.

17. Remove the alignment dowel pin from the intake camshaft. Using a dowel pin remover tool rotate the intake camshaft sprocket counterclockwise enough to slide the timing chain over the intake camshaft sprocket. Release the camshaft sprocket wrench. The length of chain between the 2 camshaft sprockets will tighten. If properly timed, the intake camshaft alignment dowel pin should slide in easily. If the dowel pin does not fully index, the camshafts are not timed correctly and the procedure must be repeated.

18. Leave the alignment dowel pins installed.

19. With slack removed from chain between intake camshaft sprocket and crankshaft sprocket, the timing marks on the crankshaft and the cylinder block should be aligned. If marks are not aligned, move the chain 1 tooth forward or rearward, remove slack and recheck marks.

20. Tighten chain housing to block stud, timing chain tensioner shoe pivot. Stud is installed under the timing chain. Tighten to 19 ft. lbs. (26 Nm).

21. Reload timing chain tensioner assembly to its zero position as follows:
   a. Assemble restraint cylinder, spring and nylon plug into plunger. Index slot in restraint cylinder with peg in plunger. While rotating the restraint cylinder clockwise, push the restraint

cylinder into the plunger until it bottoms. Keep rotating the restraint cylinder clockwise but allow the spring to push it out of the plunger. The pin in the plunger will lock the restraint in the loaded position.

   b. Install a special plunger installer tool into plunger assembly.

   c. Install plunger assembly into tensioner body with the long end toward the crankshaft when installed.

22. Install tensioner assembly to chain housing. Recheck plunger assembly installation. It is correctly installed when the long end is toward the crankshaft.

23. Install and tighten timing chain tensioner bolts and tighten to 10 ft. lbs. (14 Nm).

24. Install tensioner shoe and tensioner shoe retainer.

25. Remove the special tool from the plunger and squeeze plunger assembly into tensioner body to unload the plunger assembly.

26. Lower vehicle enough to reach and remove the alignment dowel pins. Rotate crankshaft clockwise 2 full rotations. Align crankshaft timing mark with mark on cylinder block and reinstall alignment dowel pins. Alignment dowel pins will slide in easily if engine is timed correctly.

➡ **If the engine is not correctly timed, severe engine damage could occur.**

27. Install 3 timing chain guides and crankshaft oil slinger.

28. Install engine front cover.

29. Connect the negative battery cable. Start engine and check for oil leaks.

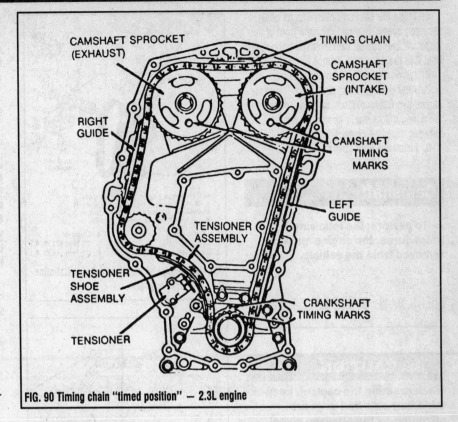

FIG. 90 Timing chain "timed position" — 2.3L engine

2.8L and 3.1L Engine

♦ SEE FIG. 93-94

1. Remove the front cover.

2. Place the No. 1 piston at TDC and the stamped timing marks on both sprockets are closest to one another and in line between the shaft centers (No. 4 firing position).

3. Take out the three bolts that hold the camshaft sprocket to the camshaft. This sprocket is a light press fit on the camshaft and will come off readily. If the sprocket does not come off easily, a light blow on the lower edge of the sprocket with a plastic mallet should dislodge the sprocket. The chain comes off with the camshaft sprocket. A gear puller will be required to remove the crankshaft sprocket.

4. Without disturbing the position of the engine, mount the new crank sprocket on the shaft, then mount the chain over the camshaft sprocket. Arrange the camshaft sprocket in such a way that the timing marks will line up between the shaft centers and the camshaft locating dowel will enter the dowel hole in the cam sprocket.

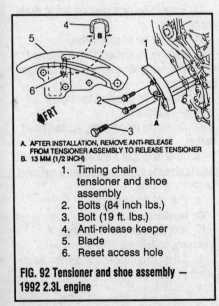

A. AFTER INSTALLATION, REMOVE ANTI-RELEASE FROM TENSIONER ASSEMBLY TO RELEASE TENSIONER
B. 13 MM (1/2 INCH)
1. Timing chain tensioner and shoe assembly
2. Bolts (84 inch lbs.)
3. Bolt (19 ft. lbs.)
4. Anti-release keeper
5. Blade
6. Reset access hole

FIG. 92 Tensioner and shoe assembly — 1992 2.3L engine

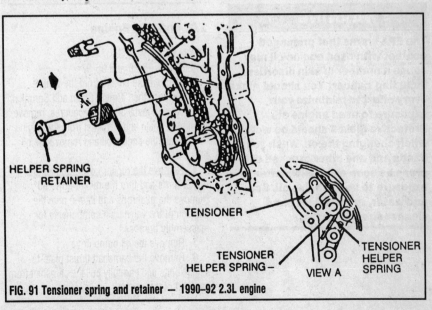

FIG. 91 Tensioner spring and retainer — 1990–92 2.3L engine

5. Place the cam sprocket, with its chain mounted over it, in position on the front of the camshaft and pull up with the three bolts that hold it to the camshaft. Torque to 15–20 ft. lbs.

6. Lubricate the timing chain with oil.

7. After the sprockets are in place, turn the engine two full revolutions to make certain that the timing marks are in correct alignment between the shaft centers.

8. Install the front cover.

Camshaft

➡ To perform the following procedures, the engine must be removed from the vehicle.

REMOVAL & INSTALLATION

❋❋ CAUTION

When draining the coolant, keep in mind that cats and dogs are attracted by the ethylene glycol antifreeze, and are quite likely to drink any that is left in an uncovered container or in puddles on the ground. This will prove fatal in sufficient quantity. Always drain the coolant into a sealable container. Coolant should be reused unless it is contaminated or several years old.

❋❋ WARNING

The EPA warns that prolonged contact with used engine oil may cause a number of skin disorders, including cancer! You should make every effort to minimize your exposure to used engine oil. Protective gloves should be worn when changing the oil. Wash your hands and any other exposed skin areas as soon as possible after exposure to used engine oil. Soap and water, or waterless hand cleaner should be used.

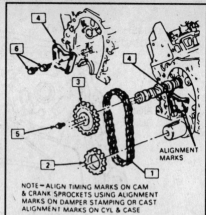

NOTE—ALIGN TIMING MARKS ON CAM & CRANK SPROCKETS USING ALIGNMENT MARKS ON DAMPER STAMPING OR CAST ALIGNMENT MARKS ON CYL & CASE

1. Timing chain
2. Crank sprocket
3. Camshaft sprocket
4. Damper
5. 28 N·m (21 lb. ft.)
6. 21 N·m (15 lb. ft.)

FIG. 93 Timing chain and sprocket installation 2.8L and 3.1L engines

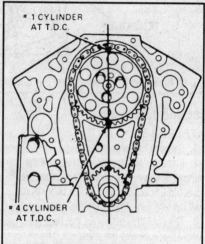

FIG. 94 Timing sprocket alignment — 2.8L and 3.1L engines

2.0L and 2.2L Engine

1988–90

▶ SEE FIGS. 25-26 and 95-97

1. Remove the engine from the vehicle.

2. Refer to the "Timing Chain and Sprocket, Removal and Installation" procedures, remove the timing chain and sprocket from the engine.

3. Drain the engine oil and remove the oil filter.

4. Remove the rocker cover. Loosen the rocker arms and turn the rocker arms 90°. Remove the pushrods and lifters; note the position of the valve train components for reassembly purposes.

5. Remove the oil pump drive.

6. Remove the camshaft thrust plate-to-engine bolts and carefully pull the camshaft from the front of the engine.

➡ Use care when removing and installing the camshaft; DO NOT damage the camshaft bearings or the bearing surfaces on the camshaft.

7. Using a gasket scraper, clean gasket mounting surfaces.

8. To install, lubricate the lobes of the new camshaft with GM E.O.S. 1051396 or equivalent and insert the camshaft into the engine.

➡ If a new camshaft is being used replace all of the lifters. Used lifters can only be used on the camshaft that they were originally installed with; provided they are installed in the exact same position they were removed.

9. Align the marks on the camshaft and crankshaft sprockets Install the timing chain and sprocket.

10. To complete the installation, use new gaskets and reverse the removal procedures. Torque the rocker arm nuts to 11–18 ft. lbs.

1991–92

1. Remove the engine and transaxle assembly and mount on an engine stand.

2. Remove the serpentine drive belt.

3. Remove the alternator and brackets.

4. Remove the power steering pump.

5. Remove the serpentine drive belt tensioner.

6. Remove the coolant pump pulley.

7. Drain the engine oil and remove the oil filter.

8. Remove the crankshaft pulley and hub.

9. Remove the rocker cover.

10. Remove the rocker arms and pushrods.

11. Remove the valve lifters.

12. Remove the crankshaft front cover.

13. Remove the cam sprocket, timing chain and tensioner.

14. Remove the oil pump drive.

15. Remove the camshaft thrust plate and remove the camshaft carefully without damaging the bearings.

16. Remove the camshaft bearings, if necessary, as follows:

a. Select the proper pilot, nut and thrust washer.

b. Assemble tool J 33049 or equivalent, making sure the puller nut engages a sufficient number of threads.

c. Pull out the bearings.

To install:

17. Install the camshaft bearings, if necessary, as follows:

a. Select new front rear and intermediate camshaft bearings.

b. Select the proper pilot, nut and thrust washer.

c. Assemble tool J 33049 or equivalent, place the bearing onto the tool and index the oil hole(s) of the bearing with the oil passage(s) in the cylinder block.

d. Pull the bearing into place.

e. Use a ⁹⁄₃₂ in. (2.4mm) brass rod with a 90° bend and probe the bearing holes to verify that they are properly aligned.

18. Coat the camshaft lobes with and bearings with GM Engine Oil Supplement (E.O.S.) 1051396 or equivalent and insert the camshaft and thrust plate in the engine.

19. Tighten the thrust plate bolts to 106 inch lbs. (12 Nm).

20. Install the timing chain and sprockets.

21. Install the crankcase front cover.

22. Install the valve lifters in the same bores from which they were removed.

➡ **If a new camshaft is installed, replace all the valve lifters.**

23. Install the oil pump drive.

24. Install the rocker arms and pushrods.

25. Install the rocker cover.

26. Install the crankshaft pulley hub and pulley.

27. Install the coolant pump pulley.

28. Install the serpentine drive belt tensioner.

29. Install the power steering pump.

30. Install the alternator and brackets.

31. Install the serpentine drive belt.

32. Install the engine and transaxle assembly.

33. Install the oil filter and refill with oil.

2.3L Engine

Intake Camshaft

◆ SEE FIGS: 33 AND 98-100

➡ **Any time the camshaft housing to cylinder head bolts are loosened or removed, the camshaft housing to cylinder head gasket must be replaced.**

1. Relieve the fuel system pressure. Disconnect the negative battery cable.

2. Remove ignition coil and module assembly electrical connections mark or tag, if necessary.

3. Remove 4 ignition coil and module assembly to camshaft housing bolts and remove assembly by pulling straight up. Use a special spark plug boot wire remover tool to remove connector assemblies if stuck to the spark plugs.

4. Remove the idle speed power steering pressure switch connector.

5. Loosen 3 power steering pump pivot bolts and remove drive belt.

6. Disconnect the 2 rear power steering pump bracket to transaxle bolts.

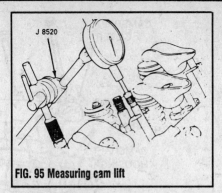

FIG. 95 Measuring cam lift

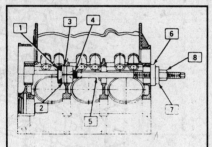

1. Back-up nut
2. Expanding collet
3. Bearing
4. Expanding mandrel
5. 2 piece puller screw
6. Pulling plate
7. Thrust bearing
8. Pulling nut

FIG. 96 Removing/installing camshaft bearings

7. Remove the front power steering pump bracket to cylinder block bolt.

8. Disconnect the power steering pump assembly and position aside.

9. Using special tools remove power steering pump drive pulley from intake camshaft.

10. Remove oil/air separator bolts and hoses. Leave the hoses attached to the separator, disconnect from the oil fill, chain housing and intake manifold. Remove as an assembly.

11. Remove vacuum line from fuel pressure regulator and fuel injector harness connector.

12. Disconnect fuel line retaining clamp from bracket on top of intake camshaft housing.

13. Remove fuel rail to camshaft housing attaching bolts.

14. Remove fuel rail from cylinder head. Cover injector openings in cylinder head and cover injector nozzles. Leave fuel lines attached and position fuel rail aside.

15. Disconnect timing chain and housing but do not remove from the engine.

16. Remove intake camshaft housing cover to camshaft housing attaching bolts.

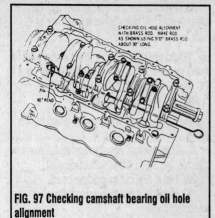

FIG. 97 Checking camshaft bearing oil hole alignment

17. Remove intake camshaft housing to cylinder head attaching bolts. Use the reverse of the tightening procedure when loosening camshaft housing to cylinder head attaching bolts. Leave 2 bolts loosely in place to hold the camshaft housing while separating camshaft cover from housing.

18. Push the cover off the housing by threading 4 of the housing to head attaching bolts into the tapped holes in the cam housing cover. Tighten the bolts in evenly so the cover does not bind on the dowel pins.

19. Remove the 2 loosely installed camshaft housing to head bolts and remove cover, discard gaskets.

20. Note the position of the chain sprocket dowel pin for reassembly. Remove camshaft being careful not to damage the camshaft oil seal from camshaft or journals.

21. Remove intake camshaft oil seal from camshaft and discard seal. This seal must be replaced any time the housing and cover are separated.

To Install:

➡ **If the camshaft is being replaced, the lifters must also be replaced. Lube camshaft lobes, journals and lifters with camshaft and lifter prelube. The camshaft lobes and journals must be adequately lubricated or engine damage could occur upon start up.**

22. Install camshaft in same position as when removed. The timing chain sprocket dowel pin should be straight up and line up with the centerline of the lifter bores.

23. Install new camshaft housing to camshaft housing cover seals into cover. Do not use sealer.

➡ **Cam housing to cover seals are all different.**

24. Apply locking type sealer to camshaft housing and cover attaching bolt threads.

25. Install bolts and tighten to 11 ft. lbs. (15 Nm). Rotate the bolts an additional 75° in sequence.

➡ **Tighten the 2 rear bolts that hold fuel pipe to camshaft housing to 11 ft. lbs. (15 Nm), then rotate the bolts an additional 25°.**

26. Install timing chain housing and timing chain.

27. Uncover fuel injectors and install new fuel injector ring seals lubed with engine oil.

28. Install fuel rail to cylinder head.

29. Install fuel rail to camshaft housing attaching bolts.

30. Connect fuel line retaining clamp to bracket on top of intake camshaft housing.

31. Install vacuum line to fuel pressure regulator and fuel injector harness connector.

32. Install oil/air separator bolts and hoses.

33. Install power steering pump drive pulley to intake camshaft.

34. Install the power steering pump assembly.

35. Install the front power steering pump bracket to cylinder block bolt.

36. Connect the 2 rear power steering pump bracket to transaxle bolts.

37. Tighten the 3 power steering pump pivot bolts and install serpentine belt.

38. Connect the idle speed power steering pressure switch connector.

39. Install ignition module assembly and the 4 ignition coil and module assembly to camshaft housing bolts.

➡ **Clean any loose lubricant that is present on the ignition coil and module assembly to camshaft housing bolts. Apply Loctite® 592 or equivalent onto the ignition coil and**

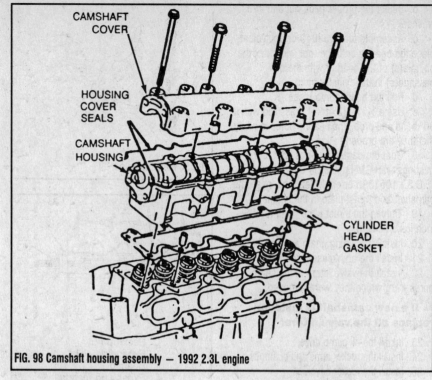

FIG. 98 Camshaft housing assembly — 1992 2.3L engine

module assembly to camshaft housing bolts. Install the bolts and tighten to 13 ft. lbs. (18 Nm).

40. Connect ignition coil and module assembly electrical connectors.

41. Connect the negative battery cable.

Exhaust Camshaft
♦ SEE FIGS. 98-100

➡ **Any time the camshaft housing to cylinder head bolts are loosened or removed the camshaft housing to cylinder head gasket must be replaced.**

1. Relieve the fuel system pressure. Disconnect the negative battery cable.

2. Remove electrical connection from ignition coil and module assembly.

3. Remove 4 ignition coil and module assembly to camshaft housing bolts and remove assembly by pulling straight up. Use a special tool to remove connector assembly if stuck to the spark plugs.

4. Remove electrical connection from oil pressure switch.

5. Remove transaxle fluid level indicator tube

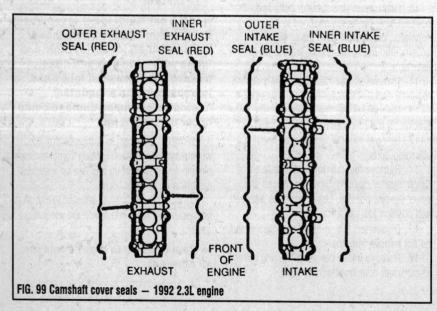

FIG. 99 Camshaft cover seals — 1992 2.3L engine

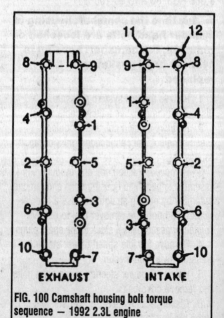

FIG. 100 Camshaft housing bolt torque sequence — 1992 2.3L engine

assembly from exhaust camshaft cover and position aside.

6. Remove exhaust camshaft cover and gasket.

7. Disconnect timing chain and housing but do not remove from the engine.

8. Remove exhaust camshaft housing to cylinder head bolts. Use the reverse of the tightening procedure when loosening camshaft housing while separating camshaft cover from housing.

9. Push the cover off the housing by threading 4 of the housing to head attaching bolts into the tapped holes in the camshaft cover. Tighten the bolts in evenly so the cover does not bind on the dowel pins.

10. Remove the 2 loosely installed camshaft housing to cylinder head bolts and remove cover, discard gaskets.

11. Loosely reinstall 1 camshaft housing to cylinder head bolt to hold the camshaft housing in place during camshaft and lifter removal.

12. Note the position of the chain sprocket dowel pin for reassembly. Remove camshaft being careful not to damage the camshaft or journals.

13. If removing the camshaft housing, remove the valve lifters. Keep the lifters in order so they can be reinstalled in the same location.

14. Remove the camshaft housing and gasket.

To install:

15. Install the camshaft housing and gasket.

16. Loosely install one camshaft housing-to-cylinder head bolt to hold the housing in place.

➡ **Used lifters must be returned to their original position in the camshaft. If the camshaft is being replaced, the lifters must also be replaced. Lube camshaft lobe, journals and lifters with camshaft and lifter prelube. The camshaft lobes and journals must be adequately lubricated or engine damage could occur upon start up.**

17. Install the lifters into the lifter bores.

18. Install camshaft in same position as when removed. The timing chain sprocket dowel pin should be straight up and line up with the centerline of the lifter bores.

19. Install new camshaft housing-to-camshaft housing cover seals into cover, no sealer is needed.

➡ **Cam housing to cover seals are all different.**

20. Remove the bolt holding the housing in place. Apply locking type sealer to camshaft housing and cover attaching bolt threads.

21. Install camshaft housing cover to camshaft housing.

22. Install bolts and tighten in sequence to 11 ft. lbs. (15 Nm), then rotate an additional 75° in sequence.

23. Install timing chain housing and timing chain.

24. Install exhaust camshaft housing cover and new gasket and tighten to 10 ft. lbs. (14 Nm).

25. Connect the oil pressure switch electrical connector.

26. Reinstall any spark plug boot connector that was stuck to a spark plug back onto the ignition coil assembly.

27. Locate the ignition coil and module assembly over the spark plugs and push straight down.

➡ **Clean any loose lubricant that is present on the ignition coil and module assembly to camshaft housing bolts.**

28. Apply Loctite® 592 or equivalent to the ignition coil and module assembly to camshaft housing bolts. Install and hand start the ignition coil and module assembly bolts. Tighten to 15 ft. lbs. (20 Nm).

29. Connect the ignition coil and module assembly electrical connectors.

30. Connect the negative battery cable.

2.8L and 3.1L Engine

▶ SEE FIGS. 34 AND 95-97

1. Remove the engine from the vehicle.

2. Refer to the "Intake Manifold, Removal and Installation" and the "Timing Chain and Sprocket, Removal and Installation" procedures in this section and remove the intake manifold, the timing chain and sprockets.

➡ **Be sure to the valve train components in order for reassembly purposes.**

3. Remove the valve lifters.

4. Carefully pull the camshaft from the front of the engine.

➡ **The camshaft journals are all the same size. Use extreme care when removing or installing the camshaft not to damage the camshaft bearings or the bearing journals of the camshaft.**

5. Using a gasket scraper, clean gasket mounting surfaces.

6. If installing a new camshaft, lubricate the camshaft lobes with GM E.O.S. 1051396 or equivalent and insert the camshaft in the engine.

➡ **If a new camshaft is being used replace all of the lifters. Used lifters can only be used on the camshaft that they were originally installed with; provided they are installed in the exact same position they were removed.**

7. Align the camshaft and crankshaft sprocket marks. Install the timing chain and sprocket.

8. Install the front cover and valve train components. Torque the rocker arm nuts to 14–20 ft. lbs.

9. To complete the installation, reverse the removal procedures. Start the engine, allow it to reach normal operating temperatures and check for leaks.

Pistons and Connecting Rod

REMOVAL

▶ SEE FIG. 105

1. Remove the engine assembly from the car, see Engine Removal and Installation.

2. Remove the intake manifold, cylinder head or heads.

3. Remove the oil pan.

4. Remove the oil pump assembly.

5. Stamp the cylinder number on the machined surfaces of the bolt bosses of the connecting rod and cap for identification when reinstalling. If the pistons are to be removed from the connecting rod, mark the cylinder number on the piston with a silver pencil or quick drying paint for proper cylinder identification and cap to rod location. The 2.8L and 3.1L V6 engine is numbered 1–3–5 on the right bank, 2–4–6 on the left bank.

6. Examine the cylinder bore above the ring travel. If a ridge exists, remove the ridge with a ridge reamer before attempting to remove the piston and rod assembly.

7. Remove the rod bearing cap and bearing.

8. Install a guide hose over threads of rod bolts. This is to prevent damage to bearing journal and rod bolt threads.

9. Remove the rod and piston assembly through the top of the cylinder bore.

10. Remove any other rod and piston assemblies in the same manner.

CLEANING AND INSPECTION

Connecting Rods

Wash connecting rods in cleaning solvent and dry with compressed air. Check for twisted or bent rods and inspect for nicks or cracks. Replace connecting rods that are damaged.

Pistons

Clean varnish from piston skirts and pins with a cleaning solvent. DO NOT WIRE BRUSH ANY PART OF THE PISTON. Clean the ring grooves with a groove cleaner and make sure oil ring holes and slots are clean.

Inspect the piston for cracked ring lands, skirts or pin bosses, wavy or worn ring lands, scuffed or damaged skirts, eroded areas at top of the piston. Replace pistons that are damaged or show signs of excessive wear.

Inspect the grooves for nicks or burrs that might cause the rings to hang up.

Measure piston skirt (across center line of piston pin) and check piston clearance.

PISTON PIN REMOVAL AND INSTALLATION

Use care at all times when handling and servicing connecting rods and pistons. To prevent possible damage to these units, do not clamp rod or piston in vise since they may become distorted. Do not allow pistons to strike against one another, against hard objects or bench surfaces, since distortion of piston contour or nicks in the soft aluminum material may result.

1. Remove piston rings using suitable piston ring remover.
2. Install guide bushing of piston pin removing and installing tool.
3. Install piston and connecting rod assembly on support and place assembly in an arbor press. Press pin out of connecting rod, using the appropriate piston pin tool.

MEASURING THE OLD PISTONS

♦ SEE FIG. 106

Check used piston to cylinder bore clearance as follows:

1. Measure the cylinder bore diameter with a telescope gauge.

2. Measure the piston diameter. When measuring piston for size or taper, measurement must be made with the piston pin removed.

3. Subtract piston diameter from cylinder bore diameter to determine piston-to-bore clearance.

4. Compare piston-to-bore clearance obtained with those clearances recommended. Determine if piston-to-bore clearance is in acceptable range.

5. When measuring taper, the largest reading must be at the bottom of the skirt.

SELECTING NEW PISTONS

1. If the used piston is not acceptable, check service piston sizes and determine if a new piston can be selected. Service pistons are available in standard, high limit and standard 0.254mm oversize.

2. If the cylinder bore must be reconditioned, measure the new piston diameter, then hone cylinder bore to obtain preferable clearance.

3. Select new piston and mark piston to identify the cylinder for which it was fitted. On some cars oversize pistons may be found. These pistons will be 0.254mm oversize.

CYLINDER HONING

1. When cylinders are being honed, follow the manufacturer's recommendations for the use of the hone.

2. Occasionally during the honing operation, the cylinder bore should be thoroughly cleaned and the selected piston checked for correct fit.

3. When finish honing a cylinder bore, the hone should be moved up and down at a sufficient speed to obtain very fine uniform

surface finish marks in a cross hatch pattern of approximately 45° to 65° included angle. The finish marks should be clean but not sharp, free from imbedded particles and torn or folded metal.

4. Permanently mark the piston for the cylinder to which it has been fitted and proceed to hone the remaining cylinders.

✲✲ WARNING

Handle pistons with care. Do not attempt to force pistons through cylinders until the cylinders have been honed to correct size. Pistons can be distorted through careless handling.

5. Thoroughly clean the bores with hot water and detergent. Scrub well with a stiff bristle brush and rinse thoroughly with hot water. It is extremely essential that a good cleaning operation be performed. If any of the abrasive material is allowed to remain in the cylinder bores, it will rapidly wear the new rings and cylinder bores. The bores should be swabbed several times with light engine oil and a clean cloth and then wiped with a clean dry cloth. CYLINDERS SHOULD NOT BE CLEANED WITH KEROSENE OR GASOLINE. Clean the remainder of the cylinder block to remove the excess material spread during the honing operation.

CHECKING CYLINDER BORE

♦ SEE FIG. 106

Cylinder bore size can be measured with inside micrometers or a cylinder gauge. The most wear will occur at the top of the ring travel.

Reconditioned cylinder bores should be held to not more than 0.02mm (2.0L), 0.013 (2.8L) out-of-round or taper. If the cylinder bores are smooth, the cylinder walls should not be deglazed. If the cylinder walls are scored, the walls may have to be honed before installing new

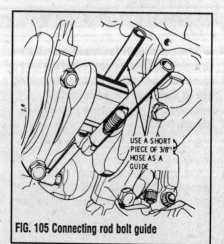

FIG. 105 Connecting rod bolt guide

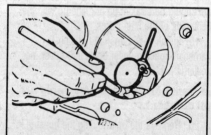

FIG. 106 Measuring the cylinder bore with a dial gauge

rings. It is important that reconditioned cylinder bores be thoroughly washed with a soap and water solution to remove all traces of abrasive material to eliminate premature wear.

Piston Rings

The pistons have 3 rings (2 compression rings and 1 oil ring). The oil ring consists of 2 rails and an expander. Pistons do not have oil drain holes behind the rings.

RING TOLERANCES

When installing new rings, ring gap and side clearance should be check as follows:

PISTON RING AND RAIL GAP

▶ SEE FIG. 101 AND 103-104

Each ring and rail gap must be measured with the ring or rail positioned squarely and at the bottom of the ring-travel area of the bore.

SIDE CLEARANCE

▶ SEE FIG. 102

Each ring must be checked for side clearance in its respective piston groove by inserting a feeler gauge between the ring and its upper land. The piston grooves must be cleaned before checking ring for side clearance. See PISTON RING CLEARANCE specifications at the end of this section for ring side clearance specifications. To check oil ring side clearance, the oil rings must be installed on the piston.

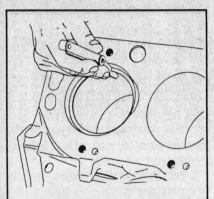

FIG. 101 Check the ring end gap with the ring installed in the cylinder

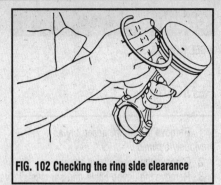

FIG. 102 Checking the ring side clearance

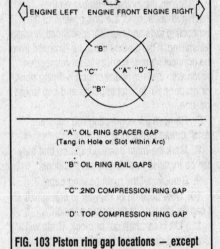

FIG. 103 Piston ring gap locations — except 1991–92 2.2L and 2.3L engine

RING INSTALLATION

For service ring specifications and detailed installation productions, refer to the instructions furnished with the parts package.

CONNECTING ROD BEARINGS

Removal, Inspection, Installation

▶ SEE FIG. 107

If you have already removed the connecting rod and piston assemblies from the engine, follow only steps 3-7 of the following procedure.

The connecting rod bearings are designed to have a slight projection above the rod and cap faces to insure a positive contact. The bearings can be replaced with removing the rod and piston assembly from the engine.

1. Remove the oil pan, see Oil Pan. It may be necessary to remove the oil pump to provide access to rear connecting rod bearings.

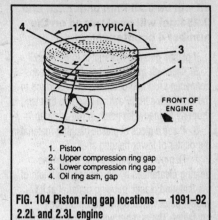

1. Piston
2. Upper compression ring gap
3. Lower compression ring gap
4. Oil ring asm, gap

FIG. 104 Piston ring gap locations — 1991–92 2.2L and 2.3L engine

2. With the connecting rod journal at the bottom, stamp the cylinder number on the machined surfaces of connecting rod and cap for identification when reinstalling, then remove caps.

3. Inspect journals for roughness and wear. Slight roughness may be removed with a fine grit polishing cloth saturated with engine oil. Burrs may be removed with a fine oil stone by moving the stone on the journal circumference.

❈ WARNING

Do not move the stone back and forth across the journal. If the journals are scored or ridged, the crankshaft must be replaced.

4. The connecting rod journals should be checked for out-of-round and correct size with a micrometer.

➡ **Crankshaft rod journals will normally be standard size. If any undersized crankshafts are used,**

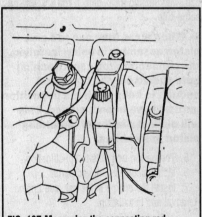

FIG. 107 Measuring the connecting rod side clearance

all will be 0.254mm undersize and 0.254mm will be stamped on the number 4 counterweight.

If plastic gauging material is to be used:

5. Clean oil from the journal bearing cap, connecting rod and outer and inner surface of the bearing inserts. Position insert so that tang is properly aligned with notch in rod and cap.

6. Place a piece of plastic gauging material in the center of lower bearing shell.

7. Remove bearing cap and determine bearing clearances by comparing the width of the flattened plastic gauging material at its widest point with the graduation on the container. The number within the graduation on the envelope indicates the clearance in thousandths of an inch or millimeters. If this clearance is excessive, replace the bearing and recheck clearance with plastic gauging material. Lubricate bearing with engine oil before installation. Repeat Steps 2 through 7 on remaining connecting rod bearings. All rods must be connected to their journals when rotating the crankshaft to prevent engine damage.

PISTON AND CONNECTING ROD

Assembly And Installation

1. Install connecting rod bolt guide hose over rod bolt threads.

2. Apply engine oil to the rings and piston, then install piston ring compressing tool on the piston.

3. Install the assembly in its respective cylinder bore (arrow of the piston towards the front of the engine).

4. Lubricate the crankshaft journal with engine oil and install connecting rod bearing and cap, with bearing index tang in rod and cap on same side.

➡ **When more than one rod and piston assembly is being installed, the connecting rod cap attaching nuts should only be tightened enough to keep each rod in position until all have been installed. This will aid installation of remaining piston assemblies.**

5. Torque rod bolt nuts to specification.

6. Install all other removed parts.

7. Install the engine in the car, see Engine Removal and Installation.

Crankshaft

◆ SEE FIGS. 25-35

REMOVAL

1. Remove the engine assembly as previously outlined.

2. Remove the engine front cover.

3. Remove the timing chain and sprockets.

4. Remove the oil pan.

5. Remove the oil pump.

6. Stamp the cylinder number on the machined surfaces of the bolt bosses of the connecting rods and caps for identification when reinstalling. If the pistons are to be removed from the connecting rod, mark cylinder number on piston with a silver pencil or quick-drying paint for proper cylinder identification and cap to rod location.

7. Remove the connecting rod caps and install thread protectors.

8. Mark the main bearing caps so that they can be installed in their original positions.

9. Remove all the main bearing caps.

10. Note position of keyway in crankshaft so it can be installed in the same position.

11. Lift crankshaft out of block. Rods will pivot to the center of the engine when the crankshaft is removed.

12. Remove both halves of the rear main oil seal.

INSTALLATION

1. Measure the crankshaft journals with a micrometer to determine the correct size rod and main bearings to be used. Whenever a new or reconditioned crankshaft is installed, new connecting rod bearings and main bearings should be installed. See Main Bearings and Rod Bearings.

2. Clean all oil passages in the block (and crankshaft if it is being reused).

➡ **A new rear main seal should be installed anytime the crankshaft is removed or replaced.**

3. Install sufficient oil pan bolts in the block to align with the connecting rod bolts. Use rubber bands between the bolts to position the connecting rods as required. Connecting rod position can be adjusted by increasing the tension on the rubber bands with additional turns around the pan bolts or thread protectors.

4. Position the upper half of main bearings in the block and lubricate with engine oil.

5. Position crankshaft keyway in the same position as removed and lower into block. The connecting rods will follow the crank pins into the correct position as the crankshaft is lowered.

6. Lubricate the thrust flanges with 1050169 Lubricant or equivalent. Install caps with lower half of bearings lubricated with engine oil. Lubricate cap bolts with engine oil and install, but do not tighten.

7. With a block of wood, bump shaft in each direction to align thrust flanges of main bearing. After bumping shaft in each direction, wedge the shaft to the front and hold it while torquing the thrust bearing cap bolts.

❊❊❊ WARNING

In order to prevent the possibility of cylinder block and/or main bearing cap damage, the main bearing caps are to be tapped into their cylinder block cavity using a brass or leather mallet before attaching bolts are installed. Do not use attaching bolts to pull main bearing caps into their seats. Failure to observe this information may damage the cylinder block or a bearing cap.

8. Torque all main bearing caps to specification.

9. Remove the connecting rod bolt thread protectors and lubricate the connecting rod bearings with engine oil.

10. Install the connecting rod bearing caps in their original position. Torque the nuts to specification.

11. Complete the installation by reversing the removal steps.

Main Bearings

CHECKING BEARING CLEARANCE

◆ SEE FIGS. 108-109

1. Remove bearing cap and wipe oil from crankshaft journal and outer and inner surfaces of bearing shell.

2. Place a piece of plastic gauging material in the center of bearing.

3. Use a floor jack or other means to hold crankshaft against upper bearing shell. This is necessary to obtain accurate clearance readings when using plastic gauging material.

4. Reinstall bearing cap and bearing. Place engine oil on cap bolts and install Torque bolts to specification.

5. Remove bearing cap and determine bearing clearance by comparing the width of the flattened plastic gauging material at its widest point with graduations on the gauging material container. The number within the graduation on the envelope indicates the clearance in millimeters or thousandths of an inch. If the clearance is greater than allowed, REPLACE BOTH BEARING SHELLS AS A SET. Recheck clearance after replacing shells. Refer to Main Bearing Replacement.

REPLACEMENT

Main bearing clearances must be corrected by the use of selective upper and lower shells. UNDER NO CIRCUMSTANCES should the use of shims behind the shells to compensate for wear be attempted. To install main bearing shells, proceed as follows:

1. Remove the oil pan as outlined elsewhere in this section. On some models, the oil pump may also have to be removed.

2. Loosen all main bearing caps.

3. Remove bearing cap and remove lower shell.

4. Insert a flattened cotter pin or roll out pin in the oil passage hole in the crankshaft, then rotate the crankshaft in the direction opposite to cranking rotation. The pin will contact the upper shell and roll it out.

5. The main bearing journals should be checked for roughness and wear. Slight roughness may be removed with a fine grit polishing cloth saturated with engine oil. Burrs may be removed with a fine oil stone. If the journals are scored or ridged, the crankshaft must be replaced.

The journals can be measured for out-of-round with the crankshaft installed by using a crankshaft caliper and inside micrometer or a main bearing micrometer. The upper bearing shell must be removed when measuring the crankshaft journals. Maximum out-of-round of the crankshaft journals must not exceed 0.037mm.

6. Clean crankshaft journals and bearing caps thoroughly before installing new main bearings.

7. Apply special lubricant, No. 1050169 or equivalent, to the thrust flanges of bearing shells.

8. Place new upper shell on crankshaft journal with locating tang in correct position and rotate shaft to turn it into place using cotter pin or roll out pin as during removal.

9. Place new bearing shell in bearing cap.

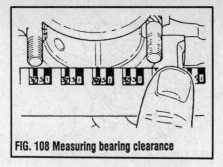

FIG. 108 Measuring bearing clearance

10. Install a new oil seal in the rear main bearing cap and block.

11. Lubricate the removed or replaced main bearings with engine oil. Lubricate the thrust surface with lubricant 1050169 or equivalent.

12. Lubricate the main bearing cap bolts with engine oil.

※※ WARNING

In order to prevent the possibility of cylinder block and/or main bearing cap damage, the main bearing caps are to be tapped into their cylinder block cavity using a brass or leather mallet before attaching bolts are installed. Do not use attaching bolts to pull main bearing caps into their seats. Failure to observe this information may damage the cylinder block or a bearing cap.

13. Torque the main bearing cap bolts to specifications.

Flywheel

REMOVAL & INSTALLATION

Manual Transaxles

※※ WARNING

The master cylinder pushrod must be disconnected from the clutch pedal or permanent damage to the slave cylinder will occur.

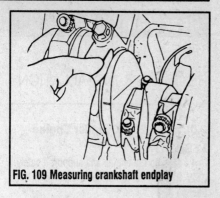

FIG. 109 Measuring crankshaft endplay

1. Disconnect the negative battery cable.

2. Remove the hush panel from inside the vehicle.

3. Disconnect the master cylinder pushrod from the clutch pedal.

4. Remove the transaxle assembly.

5. Remove the pressure plate and clutch disc assembly.

6. Remove the flywheel attaching bolts and remove the flywheel.

To Install

7. Install the flywheel and attaching bolts and torque the bolts to 50–55 ft. lbs. for all except the 2.3L engine. For the 2.3L engine torque the bolts to 22 ft. lbs. plus an additional 45° rotation.

8. Install the pressure plate and clutch disc assembly.

9. Install the transaxle assembly.

10. Connect the master cylinder pushrod to the clutch pedal.

11. Check cruise control switch adjustment at the clutch pedal bracket.

12. Install the hush panel.

13. Connect the negative battery cable.

Automatic Transaxles

1. Remove the transaxle assembly.

2. Remove the right splash shield.

3. Remove the flywheel attaching bolts.

4. Remove the retainer.

5. Remove the flywheel.

To Install

6. Remove all thread adhesive from the holes.

7. Apply thread adhesive to all the flywheel bolts.

8. Install the flywheel and retainer and tighten to 52–55 ft. lbs. (70–75 Nm).

9. Install the transaxle assembly.

Rear Main Oil Seal

REMOVAL & INSTALLATION

2.0L and 2.2L 4-Cylinder Engine

▶ SEE FIG. 110-112

1. Jack up the engine and support it safely.
2. Remove the transaxle as outlined in Section 7.
3. Remove the flywheel.

➡ **Now is the time to confirm that the rear seal is leaking.**

4. Insert a suitable pry tool in through the dust lip and pry out the seal by moving the tool around the seal until it is removed.

❄❄ **WARNING**

Use care not to damage the crankshaft seal surface with a pry tool.

To install

5. Before installing, lubricate the seal bore to seal surface with engine oil.
6. Install the new seal using tool J-34686.
7. Slide the new seal over the mandrel until the dust lip bottoms squarely against the tool collar.
8. Align the dowel pin of the tool with the dowel pin hole in the crankshaft and attach the tool to the crankshaft. Tighten the attaching screws to 2–5 ft. lbs.
9. Tighten the T-handle of the tool to push the seal into the bore. Continue until the tool collar is flush against the block.
10. Loosen the T-handle completely. Remove the attaching screws and the tool.

➡ **Check to see that the seal is squarely seated in the bore.**

11. Install the flywheel and transmission.
12. Start the engine and check for leaks.

2.3L Engine

▶ SEE FIG. 113

1. Remove the transaxle assembly.
2. Remove the clutch and pressure plate and clutch cover. Mark the relationship of the pressure plate and clutch cover assembly to the flywheel for reassembly in the same position for proper balance.
3. Remove the bolts attaching the flywheel to the crankshaft flange and flywheel.

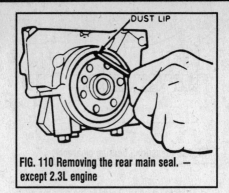

FIG. 110 Removing the rear main seal. — except 2.3L engine

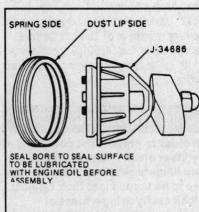

FIG. 111 Rear main seal installation tool — except 2.3L engine

4. Remove the oil pan to crankshaft seal housing bolts.
5. Support the seal housing for seal removal using 2 wood blocks of equal thickness. With the wood blocks on a flat surface, position the seal housing and blocks so the transaxle side of the seal housing is supported across the dowel pin and center bolt holes on both sides of the seal opening.

❄❄ **WARNING**

The seal housing could be damaged if not supported during seal removal.

6. Drive the crankshaft seal evenly out of the transaxle side of the seal housing using a small chisel in the 4 relief grooves on the crankshaft side of the seal housing.

❄❄ **WARNING**

Use care to avoid seal housing sealing surface damage or a leak will result.

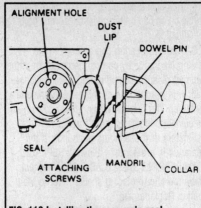

FIG. 112 Installing the rear main seal — except 2.3L engine

To install

7. Press the new seal into the crankshaft using J 36005 seal installer.
8. Position the new seal housing to the block gasket over the alignment dowel pins. The gasket is reversible and no sealant is necessary.
9. Lubricate the lip of the crankshaft seal with engine oil.
10. Install the seal housing assembly to the cylinder block bolts and tighten to 106 inch lbs. (12 Nm).
11. Tighten the oil pan to seal housing bolts to 106 inch lbs. (12 Nm).
12. Install the flywheel with new bolts and thread adhesive. Tighten the bolts to 22 ft. lbs. (30 Nm), plus an additional 45° rotation.
13. Install the clutch and pressure plate and clutch cover.
14. Install the transaxle assembly.
15. Start the engine and check for leaks.

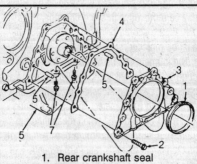

1. Rear crankshaft seal
2. Bolt
3. Rear crankshaft seal housing
4. Housing to block gasket
5. Dowel pin
6. Oil pan to seal housing bolt

FIG. 113 Rear crankshaft seal and housing to block — 2.3L engine

2.8L and 3.1L Engine

♦ SEE FIG. 110-112

1. Support the engine with J-28467 engine support or equivalent.
2. Remove the transaxle as outlined in Section 7.
3. Remove the flywheel.

➡ **Now is the time to confirm that the rear seal is leaking.**

4. Insert a suitable pry tool in through the dust lip and pry out the seal by moving the tool around the seal until it is removed.

❊❊❊ WARNING

Use care not to damage the crankshaft seal surface with a pry tool.

To install

5. Before installing, lubricate the seal bore to seal surface with engine oil.
6. Install the new seal using tool J-34686.
7. Slide the new seal over the mandrel until the dust lip bottoms squarely against the tool collar.

8. Align the dowel pin of the tool with the dowel pin hole in the crankshaft and attach the tool to the crankshaft. Tighten the attaching screws to 2–5 ft. lbs.
9. Tighten the T-handle of the tool to push the seal into the bore. Continue until the tool collar is flush against the block.
10. Loosen the T-handle completely. Remove the attaching screws and the tool.

➡ **Check to see that the seal is squarely seated in the bore.**

11. Install the flywheel and transmission.
12. Start the engine and check for leaks.

EXHAUST SYSTEM

Safety Precautions

For a number of reasons, exhaust system work can be the most dangerous type of work you can do on your car. Always observe the following precautions:

• Support the car extra securely. Not only will you often be working directly under it, but you'll frequently be using a lot of force, say, heavy hammer blows, to dislodge rusted parts. This can cause a car that's improperly supported to shift and possibly fall.

• Wear goggles. Exhaust system parts are always rusty. Metal chips can be dislodged, even when you're only turning rusted bolts. Attempting to pry pipes apart with a chisel makes the chips fly even more frequently.

• If you're using a cutting torch, keep it a great distance from either the fuel tank or lines. Stop what you're doing and feel the temperature of the fuel bearing pipes on the tank frequently. Even slight heat can expand and/or vaporize fuel, resulting in accumulated vapor, or even a liquid leak, near your torch.

• Watch where your hammer blows fall and make sure you hit squarely. You could easily tap a brake or fuel line when you hit an exhaust system part with a glancing blow. Inspect all lines and hoses in the area where you've been working.

❊❊❊ CAUTION

Be very careful when working on or near the catalytic converter. External temperatures can reach 1,500°F (816°C) and more, causing severe burns. Removal or installation should be performed only on a cold exhaust system.

Special Tools

A number of special exhaust system tools can be rented from auto supply houses or local stores that rent special equipment. A common one is a tail pipe expander, designed to enable you to join pipes of identical diameter.

It may also be quite helpful to use solvents designed to loosen rusted bolts or flanges. Soaking rusted parts the night before you do the job can speed the work of freeing rusted parts considerably. Remember that these solvents are often flammable. Apply only to parts after they are cool!

COMPONENT REPLACEMENT

♦ SEE FIGS. 114-122

System components may be welded or clamped together. The system consists of a head pipe, catalytic converter, intermediate pipe, muffler and tail pipe, in that order from the engine to the back of the car.

The head pipe is bolted to the exhaust manifold. Various hangers suspend the system from the floor pan. When assembling exhaust system parts, the relative clearances around all system parts is extremely critical. See the accompanying illustration and observe all clearances during assembly. In the event that the system is welded, the various parts will have to be cut apart for removal. In these cases, the cut parts may not be reused. To cut the parts, a hacksaw is the best choice. An oxy-acetylene cutting torch may be faster but the sparks are DANGEROUS near the fuel tank, and, at the very least, accidents could happen, resulting in damage to other under-car parts, not to mention yourself!

The following replacement steps relate to clamped parts:

1. Raise and support the car on jackstands. It's much easier on you if you can get the car up on 4 stands. Some pipes need lots of clearance for removal and installation. If the system has been in the car for a long time, spray the clamped joints with a rust dissolving solutions such as WD-40® or Liquid Wrench®, and let it set according to the instructions on the can.

2. Remove the nuts from the U-bolts; don't be surprised if the U-bolts break while removing the nuts. Age and rust account for this. Besides, you shouldn't reuse old U-bolts. When unbolting the headpipe from the exhaust manifold, make sure that the bolts are free before trying to remove them. If you snap a stud in the exhaust manifold, the stud will have to be removed with a bolt extractor, which often necessitates the removal of the manifold itself. The headpipe uses a necked collar for sealing purposes at the manifold, eliminating the need for a gasket.

3. After the clamps are removed from the joints, first twist the parts at the joints to break loose rust and scale, then pull the components apart with a twisting motion. If the parts twist freely but won't pull apart, check the joint. The clamp may have been installed so tightly that it has caused a slight crushing of the joint. In this event, the best thing to do is secure a chisel designed for the purpose and, using the chisel and a hammer, peel back the female pipe end until the parts are freed.

4. Once the parts are freed, check the condition of the pipes which you had intended keeping. If their condition is at all in doubt, replace them too. You went to a lot of work to get one or more components out. You don't want to have to go through that again in the near future. If you are retaining a pipe, check the pipe end. If it was crushed by a clamp, it can be restored to its original diameter using a pipe expander, which can be rented at most good auto parts stores. Check, also, the condition of the exhaust system hangers. If ANY deterioration is noted, replace them. Oh, and one note about parts: use only parts designed for your car. Don't use fits-all parts or flex pipes. The fits-all parts never fit and the flex pipes don't last very long.

5. When installing the new parts, coat the pipe ends with exhaust system lubricant. It makes fitting the parts much easier. It's also a good idea to assemble all the parts in position before clamping them. This will ensure a good fit, detect any problems and allow you to check all clearances between the parts and surrounding frame and floor members. See the accompanying illustrations for the proper clearances.

6. When you are satisfied with all fits and clearances, install the clamps. The headpipe-to-manifold nuts should be torqued to 20 ft. lbs. If the studs were rusty, wire-brush them clean and spray them with WD-40® or Liquid Wrench®. This will ensure a proper torque reading. Position the clamps on the slip points as illustrated. The slits in the female pipe ends should be under the U-bolts, not under the clamp end. Tighten the U-bolt nuts securely, without crushing the pipe. The pipe fit should be tight, so that you can't swivel the pipe by hand. Don't forget: always use new

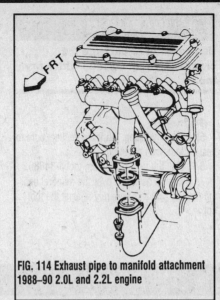

FIG. 114 Exhaust pipe to manifold attachment 1988–90 2.0L and 2.2L engine

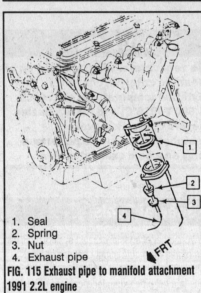

1. Seal
2. Spring
3. Nut
4. Exhaust pipe

FIG. 115 Exhaust pipe to manifold attachment 1991 2.2L engine

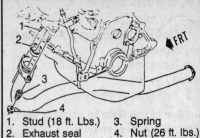

1. Stud (18 ft. Lbs.)   3. Spring
2. Exhaust seal   4. Nut (26 ft. lbs.)

FIG. 116 Exhaust pipe to manifold attachment 1992 2.2L engine

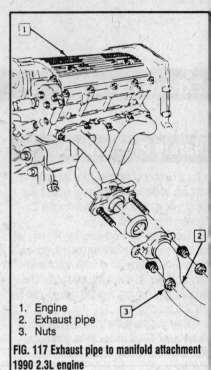

1. Engine
2. Exhaust pipe
3. Nuts

FIG. 117 Exhaust pipe to manifold attachment 1990 2.3L engine

clamps. When the system is tight, recheck all clearances. Start the engine and check the joints for leaks. A leak can be felt by hand. MAKE CERTAIN THAT THE CAR IS SECURE ON THE JACKSTANDS BEFORE GETTING UNDER IT WITH THE ENGINE RUNNING!! If any leaks are detected, tighten the clamp until the leak stops. If the pipe starts to deform before the leak stops, reposition the clamp and tighten it. If that still

doesn't stop the leak, it may be that you don't have enough overlap on the pipe fit. Shut off the engine and try pushing the pipe together further. Be careful; the pipe gets hot quickly.

7. When everything is tight and secure, lower the car and take it for a road test. Make sure there are no unusual sounds or vibration. Most new pipes are coated with a preservative, so the system will be pretty smelly for a day or two while the coating burns off.

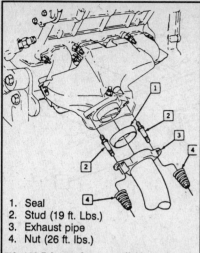

1. Seal
2. Stud (19 ft. Lbs.)
3. Exhaust pipe
4. Nut (26 ft. Lbs.)

FIG. 118 Exhaust pipe to manifold attachment 1991–92 2.3L engine

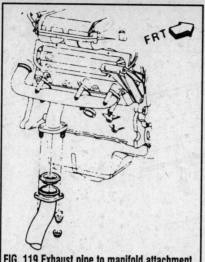

FIG. 119 Exhaust pipe to manifold attachment 2.8L and 3.1L engine

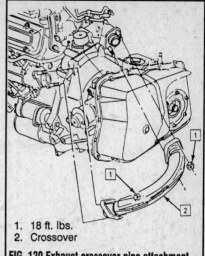

1. 18 ft. lbs.
2. Crossover

FIG. 120 Exhaust crossover pipe attachment — 2.8L and 3.1L engine

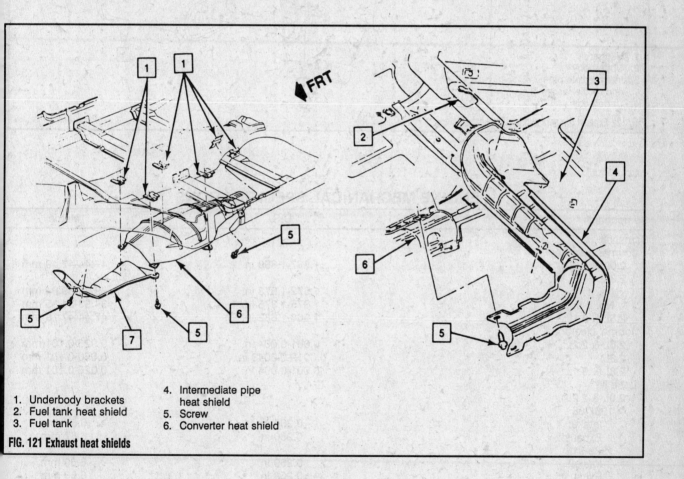

1. Underbody brackets
2. Fuel tank heat shield
3. Fuel tank
4. Intermediate pipe heat shield
5. Screw
6. Converter heat shield

FIG. 121 Exhaust heat shields

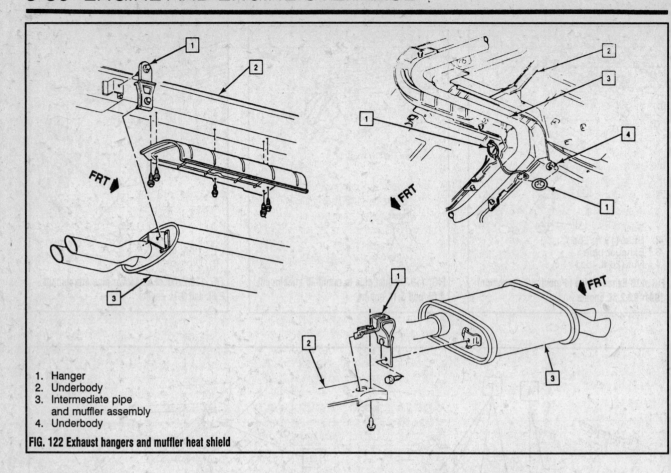

1. Hanger
2. Underbody
3. Intermediate pipe
   and muffler assembly
4. Underbody

FIG. 122 Exhaust hangers and muffler heat shield

ENGINE MECHANICAL SPECIFICATIONS

Component	U.S.	Metric
Camshaft		
Journal diameter		
2.0L & 2.2L:	1.867-1.869 in.	47.44-47.49 mm
2.3L:		
No. 1:	1.572-1.573 in.	39.93-39.94 mm
No. 2-5:	1.375-1.376 in.	34.93-34.95 mm
2.8L & 3.1L:	1.868-1.882 in.	47.44-47.79 mm
Journal clearance		
2.0L & 2.2L:	0.001-0.004 in.	0.026-0.101 mm
2.3L:	0.0019-0.0043 in.	0.050-0.101 mm
2.8L & 3.1L:	0.001-0.004 in.	0.026-0.101 mm
Lobe lift		
2.0L & 2.2L		
1987-88		
Intake:	0.260 in.	6.67 mm
Exhaust:	0.260 in.	6.67 mm
1989-91		
Intake:	0.259 in.	6.60 mm
Exhaust:	0.259 in.	6.60 mm
1992		
Intake:	0.259 in 6.60 mm	
Exhaust:	0.250 in.	6.35 mm
2.3L		
Intake:	0.410 in.	10.414 mm
Exhaust:	0.410 in.	10.414 mm
End play clearance		
2.3L:	0.009-0.0088 in.	0.025-0.225 mm

ENGINE MECHANICAL SPECIFICATIONS

Component	U.S.	Metric
Camshaft housing		
Camshaft bore I.D.		
2.3L:	1.378-1.379 in.	34.99-35.02 mm
Lifter O.D.		
2.3L:	1.376-1.377 in.	34.96-34.98 mm
Lifter to bore clearance		
2.3L:	0.0006-0.0024 in.	0.014-0.060 mm
Cam carrier flatness		
2.3L:	0.002 in.	0.025 mm
Connecting rod		
Rod bearing journal diameter		
2.0L & 2.2L:	1.9983-1.9994 in.	50.758-50.784 mm
2.3L:	1.8887-1.8897 in.	47.975-48.00 mm
2.8L & 3.1L:	1.9983-1.9994 in.	50.758-50.784 mm
Rod bearing clearance		
2.0L & 2.2L:	0.001-0.0031 in.	0.025-0.079 mm
2.3L:	0.0005-0.0020 in.	0.013-0.053 mm
2.8L		
1987-88:	0.0013-0.0026 in.	0.03-0.066 mm
1989:	0.0014-0.0036 in.	0.038-0.093 mm
3.1L		
1990-92:	0.0011-0.0037 in.	0.028-0.086 mm
Rod side clearance		
2.0L & 2.2L:	0.004-0.015 in.	0.10-0.38 mm
2.3L:	0.0059-0.0177 in.	0.150-0.450 mm
2.8L:	0.0063-0.0173 in.	0.16-0.44 mm
3.1L:	0.014-0.027 in.	0.36-0.68 mm
Crankshaft		
Main bearing journal diameter		
2.0L & 2.2L:	2.4945-2.4954 in.	63.360-63.384 mm
2.3L:	2.0470-2.0480 in.	51.996-52.020 mm
2.8L & 3.1L:	2.6473-2.6483 in.	67.241-67.265 mm
Main bearing oil clearance		
2.0L & 2.2L:	0.0006-0.0019 in.	0.15-0.047 mm
2.3L:	0.0005-0.0023 in.	0.013-0.053 mm
2.8L:	0.0016-0.0032 in.	0.041-0.081 mm
3.1L:	0.0012-0.0030 in.	0.032-0.077 mm
Crankshaft endplay		
2.0L:	0.002-0.008 in.	0.050-0.210 mm
2.2L:	0.002-0.007 in.	0.051-0.178 mm
2.3L:	0.0034-0.0095 in.	0.087-0.243 mm
2.8L & 3.1L:	0.0024-0.0083 in.	0.060-0.210 mm
Cylinder block		
Cylinder bore diameter		
2.0L & 2.2L:	3.5036-3.50367 in.	88.991-89.009 mm
2.3L:	3.6217-3.6223 in.	91.992-92.008 mm
2.8L		
1987-88:	3.503-3.506 in.	88.992-89.070 mm
1989:	3.5036-3.5043 in.	88.991-89.009 mm
3.1L:	3.5046-3.5053 in.	89.016-89.034 mm
Cylinder bore out-of-round (max.)		
2.0L & 2.2L:	0.0005 in.	0.013 mm
2.3L:	0.0004 in.	0.010 mm
2.8L & 3.1L:	0.0005 in.	0.013 mm
Cylinder bore taper (max.)		
2.0L & 2.2L:	0.0005 in.	0.013 mm
2.3L:	0.0003 in.	0.008 mm
Cylinder bore taper production thrust side (max.)		
2.3L:	0.001 in.	0.020 mm
2.8L:	0.0005 in.	0.013 mm
3.1L:	0.0006 in.	0.014 mm

ENGINE MECHANICAL SPECIFICATIONS

Component	U.S.	Metric
Cylinder Head		
Flatness (max.)		
2.0L, 2.2L, 2.8L & 3.1L	0.010 in.	0.250 mm
2.3L	0.008 in.	0.203 mm
Runout		
2.3L 0.00196 in.	0.050 mm	
Diameter		
2.3L		
Intake:	1.3018 in.	33.066 mm
Exhaust:	1.0850 in.	27.558 mm
Valve guide inside diameter		
2.3L:	0.2762-0.2772 in.	7.015-7.041 mm
Hydraulic lifters		
Leak down rate		
2.3L:	6-24 sec @ 50 lbs.	6-24 sec @ 222 Nm
Clearance in bore		
2.3L:	0.0006-0.0024 in.	0.014-0.060 mm
Oil pump		
2.0L & 2.8L		
Gear lash:	0.009-0.015 in.	0.230-0.380 mm
Gear pocket depth:	1.195-1.198 in.	30.35-30.43 mm
Drive gear length:	1.199-1.200 in.	30.45-30.48 mm
Idler gear length:	1.199-1.200 in.	30.45-30.48 mm
Drive gear diameter:	1.498-1.500 in.	38.05-38.10 mm
Idler gear diameter:	1.498-1.500 in.	38.05-38.10 mm
Drive gear side clearance:	0.003-0.004 in.	0.080-0.100 mm
Idler gear side clearance:	0.003-0.004 in.	0.080-0.100 mm
End clearance:	0.002-0.005 in.	0.050-0.130 mm
Valve-to-bore clearance:	0.0015-0.0035 in.	0.0380.0890 mm
2.2L		
Gear lash:	0.004-0.008 in.	0.094-0.095 mm
Gear pocket depth:	1.195-1.198 in.	30.35-30.43 mm
Gear pocket diameter:	1.503-1.506 in.	38.18-38.25 mm
Drive gear length:	1.199-1.200 in.	30.45-30.48 mm
Idler gear length:	1.199-1.200 in.	30.45-30.48 mm
Drive gear diameter:	1.498-1.500 in.	38.05-38.10 mm
Idler gear diameter:	1.498-1.500 in.	38.05-38.10 mm
Drive gear side clearance:	0.0015-0.004 in.	0.038-0.102 mm
Idler gear side clearance:	0.0015-0.004 in.	0.038-0.102 mm
End clearance:	0.002-0.006 in.	0.080-0.100 mm
Valve-to-bore clearance:	0.0015-0.0035 in.	0.038-0.089 mm
2.3L		
Gerotor pocket depth:	0.6736-0.6756 in.	17.11-17.16 mm
Gerotor pocket diameter:	2.1273-2.1292 in.	54.033-54.083 mm
Inner gerotor-to cover tip:	0.0059 in.	0.150 mm
Outer gerotor diameter clearance:	2.1240-2.1260 in.	53.95-54.00 mm
Outer gerotor thickness:	0.6727-0.6731 in.	17.087-17.099 mm
Oil pump to driven gear backlash:	0.0091-0.0201 in.	0.230-0.510 mm
3.1L (Aluminum body)		
Gear lash:	0.004-0.008 in.	0.094-0.095 mm
Gear pocket depth:	1.195-1.198 in.	30.35-30.43 mm
Gear pocket diameter:	1.503-1.506 in.	38.18-38.25 mm
Drive gear length:	1.199-1.200 in.	30.45-30.48 mm
Idler gear length:	1.199-1.200 in.	30.45-30.48 mm
Drive gear diameter:	1.498-1.500 in.	38.05-38.10 mm
Idler gear diameter:	1.498-1.500 in.	38.05-38.10 mm
Drive gear side clearance:	0.003-0.004 in.	0.080-0.10 mm
Idler gear side clearance:	0.003-0.004 in.	0.080-0.10 mm
End clearance:	0.0016-0.0067 in.	0.040-0.17 mm
Valve-to-bore clearance:	0.0015-0.0035 in.	0.0380.089 mm

ENGINE MECHANICAL SPECIFICATIONS

Component	U.S.	Metric
3.1L (Cast iron body)		
Gear lash:	0.004-0.008 in.	0.094-0.095 mm
Gear pocket depth:	1.195-1.198 in.	30.35-30.43 mm
Gear pocket diameter:	1.503-1.506 in.	38.18-38.25 mm
Drive gear length:	1.199-1.200 in.	30.45-30.48 mm
Idler gear length:	1.199-1.200 in.	30.45-30.48 mm
Drive gear diameter:	1.498-1.500 in.	38.05-38.10 mm
Idler gear diameter:	1.498-1.500 in.	38.05-38.10 mm
Drive gear side clearance:	0.003-0.004 in.	0.080-0.10 mm
Idler gear side clearance:	0.003-0.004 in.	0.080-0.10 mm
End clearance:	0.002-0.006 in.	0.050-0.152 mm
Valve-to-bore clearance:	0.0015-0.0035 in.	0.0380.089 mm
Pistons		
Ring end gap		
2.0L & 2.2L		
Compression No. 1	0.010-0.020 in.	0.250-0.500 mm
Compression No. 2	0.010-0.020 in.	0.250-0.500 mm
Oil:	0.010-0.050 in.	0.250-1.300 mm
2.3L		
Compression No. 1:	0.0138-0.0236 in.	0.350-0.600 mm
Compression No. 2:	0.0157-0.0256 in.	0.400-0.650 mm
Oil:	0.0157-0.0551 in.	0.400-1.400 mm
2.8L		
Compression No. 1	0.010-0.020 in.	0.250-0.500 mm
Compression No. 2	0.010-0.020 in.	0.250-0.500 mm
Oil:	0.020-0.055 in.	0.510-1.400 mm
3.1L		
Compression No. 1	0.010-0.020 in.	0.250-0.500 mm
Compression No. 2	0.0020-0.028 in.	0.500-0.710 mm
Oil:	0.010-0.030 in.	0.250-0.750 mm
Ring side clearance		
2.0L		
Compression No. 1	0.001-0.003 in.	0.030.0.070 mm
Compression No. 2	0.001-0.003 in.	0.030.0.070 mm
Oil:	0.006-0.009 in.	0.015-0.227 mm
2.2L		
Compression No. 1	0.0019-0.0027 in.	0.050-0.210 mm
Compression No. 2	0.0019-0.0027 in.	0.050-0.210 mm
Oil:	0.0019-0.0082 in.	0.050-0.210 mm
2.3L		
Compression No. 1	0.0027-0.0047 in.	0.070-0.120 mm
Compression No. 2	0.00157-0.00315 in.	0.040-0.080 mm
Oil:	0.01957-0.02060 in.	0.497-0.523 mm
2.8L		
Compression No. 1	0.001-0.003 in.	0.030.0.080 mm
Compression No. 2	0.001-0.003 in.	0.030.0.080 mm
Oil (max):	0.200 in.	0.008 mm
3.1L		
Compression No. 1	0.002-0.0035 in.	0.050-0.090 mm
Compression No. 2	0.002-0.0035 in.	0.050-0.090 mm
Oil (max):	0.200 in.	0.008 mm
Piston-to-bore clearance		
2.0L:	0.0010-0.0022 in.	0.025-0.055 mm
2.2L:	0.0007-0.0017 in.	0.015-0.045 mm
2.3L:	0.0007-0.0020 in.	0.019-0.051 mm
2.8L:	0.0020-0.0028 in.	0.051-0.073 mm
3.1L:	0.00093-0.00222 in.	0.0235-0.0565mm
Pin diameter		
2.0L & 2.2L:	0.8000-0.8002 in.	20.32-20.33 mm
2.3L:	0.8659-0.8661 in.	21.99-22.00 mm
2.8L:	0.9052-0.9056 in.	22.93-23.00 mm
3.1L:	0.9052-0.9054 in.	22.93-22.99 mm

ENGINE MECHANICAL SPECIFICATIONS

Component	U.S.	Metric
Pin-to piston clearance		
2.0L & 2.2L:	0.0004-0.0009 in.	0.010-0.022 mm
2.3L:	0.00031-0.00066 in.	0.008-0.017 mm
2.8L:	0.00025-0.00036 in.	0.0065-0.0091 mm
3.1L:	0.0004-0.0008 in.	0.0096-0.0215 mm
Pin press fit in rod		
2.0L & 2.2L:	0.00098-0.0017 in.	0.025-0.045 mm
2.3L:	0.00027-0.00122 in.	0.007-0.031 mm
2.8L:	0.00078-0.0021 in.	0.020-0.0515 mm
3.1L:	0.00065-0.0018 in.	0.0165-0.0464 mm
Valves		
Face angle		
2.0L, 2.2L, 2.8L & 3.1L:	45°	
2.3L		
Intake:	44°	
Exhaust:	44.5°	
Seat angle		
2.0L, 2.2L, 2.8L & 3.1L:	46°	
2.3L:	45°	
Seat runout		
2.0L & 2.2L:	0.002 in.	0.050 mm
2.8L & 3.1L:	0.001 in.	0.025 mm
Face runout		
2.3L:	0.0015 in.	0.038 mm
Seat width		
2.0L & 2.2L		
Intake:	0.049-0.059 in.	1.25-1.50 mm
Exhaust:	0.063-0.075 in.	1.60-1.90 mm
2.3L:	0.0037-0.0748 in.	0.09-1.90 mm
2.8L & 3.1L		
Intake:	0.061-0.073 in.	1.55-1.85 mm
Exhaust:	0.067-0.079 in.	1.70-2.00 mm
Stem Clearance		
2.0L & 2.2L		
Intake:	0.0011-0.0026 in.	0.028-0.066 mm
Exhaust:	0.0014-0.003 in.	0.035-0.078 mm
2.3L:		
Intake:	0.0098-0.0027 in.	0.025-0.069 mm
Exhaust:	0.00149-0.0031 in.	0.038-0.081 mm
2.8L & 3.1L		
Intake:	0.001-0.0027 in.	0.026-0.068 mm
Exhaust:	0.001-0.0027 in.	0.026-0.068 mm
Spring free length		
2.0L & 2.2L:	2.06 in.	52.3 mm
2.8L & 3.1L:	1.91 in.	48.5 mm
Spring Load		
2.0L		
Closed:	100-110 lbs. @ 1.61 in.	446-448 N @ 40.9 mm
Open:	208-222 lbs. @ 1.22 in.	925-987 N @ 30.9 mm
2.2L		
1990-91		
Closed:	100-110 lbs. @ 1.61 in.	446-448 N @ 40.9 mm
Open:	208-222 lbs. @ 1.22 in.	925-987 N @ 30.9 mm
1992		
Closed:	79-85 lbs. @ 1.63 in.	350-380 N @ 41.5 mm
Open:	225-233 lbs. @ 1.24 in.	956-1036 N @ 31.6 mm
2.3L		
Closed:	71-79 lbs. @ 1.43 in.	314-353 N @ 36.5 mm
Open:	193-207 lbs. @ 1.04 in.	857-922 N @ 26.0 mm
2.8L & 3.1L		
Closed:	90 lbs. @ 1.71 in.	400 N @ 43.0 mm
Open:	215 lbs. @ 1.29 in.	956 N @ 33.0 mm

TORQUE SPECIFICATIONS

Component	U.S.	Metric
Alternator		
2.0L and 2.2L		
Upper bracket bolt and nut:	22 ft. lbs.	30 Nm
Upper alternator mounting bolts:	22 ft. lbs.	30 Nm
Lower alternator mounting bolt:	33 ft. lbs.	45 Nm
2.3L		
Upper mounting bolt:	37 ft. lbs.	50 Nm
Lower mounting bolt:	19 ft. lbs.	26 Nm
2.8L and 3.1L		
Rear stud and bolt:	18 ft. lbs.	25 Nm
Front bolt:	18 ft. lbs.	25 Nm
Rear bolt to support:	37 ft. lbs.	50 Nm
Battery		
Holdown clamps:	6 ft. lbs.	8 Nm
Battery cables:	19 ft. lbs.	25 Nm
Starter		
2.0L and 2.2L		
1988		
Mounting bolts:	26-27 ft lbs.	30-50 Nm
1989-92		
Mounting bolts:	32 ft. lbs.	43 Nm
Support bracket:	9 ft. lbs.	12 Nm
2.3L		
1990		
Mounting bolts:	32 ft. lbs.	43 Nm
1991		
Lower mounting bolt:	46 ft. lbs.	63 Nm
Upper transaxle-to-starter bolt:	71 ft. lbs.	96 Nm
1992		
Mounting bolts:	74 ft lbs.	100 Nm
2.8L and 3.1L		
Mounting bolts:	32 ft. lbs.	43 Nm
Starter solenoid attching screws		
SD200:	60 inch lbs.	6.5 Nm
SD210:	95 inch lbs.	11 Nm
Starter thru bolts		
SD200:	75 inch lbs.	8.5 Nm
SD210:		
Bolts:	75 inch lbs.	8.5 Nm
Nuts:	70 inch lbs.	8.0 Nm
Rocker cover bolts		
All except 2.3L:	89 inch lbs.	10 Nm
Rocker arm nuts		
2.0L and 2.2L		
1988:	7-11 ft. lbs.	10-15 Nm
1989-92:	14 ft. lbs.	20 Nm
2.8L and 3.1L:	18 ft. lbs.	25 Nm
Thermostat housing		
2.0L and 2.2L:	6-9 ft. lbs.	8-10 Nm
2.3L:	19 ft. lbs.	26 Nm
2.8L and 3.1L:	18 ft. lbs.	25 Nm

TORQUE SPECIFICATIONS

Component	U.S.	Metric
Intake manifold to head bolts		
2.0L and 2.2L		
1988-91:	15-22 ft. lbs.	20-30 Nm
1992:	22 ft. lbs.	30 Nm
2.3L		
Bolts and nuts in sequence:	18 ft. lbs.	25 Nm
Intake manifold brace and retainers		
Nut to stud bolt:	18 ft. lbs.	25 Nm
Bolt to intake manifold:	40 ft. lbs.	55 Nm
Bolt to cylinder block:	40 ft. lbs.	55 Nm
2.8L and 3.1L		
Intake manifold to head bolts:	15 ft. lbs.	20 Nm
Retighten:	24 ft. lbs.	33 Nm
Exhaust manifold		
2.0L and 2.3L		
Manifold-to-cylinder head nuts		
1988-90:	3-11 ft. lbs.	5-15 Nm
1991-92:	115 inch lbs.	13 Nm
Manifold-to-cylinder head bolts		
1988-90:	6-13 ft. lbs.	8-18 Nm
Manifold-to-cylinder head studs		
1991-92:	89 inch lbs.	10 Nm
2.3L		
Manifold to head nuts:	27 ft. lbs.	37 Nm
Manifold to head Studs:	106 inch lbs.	12 Nm
2.8L and 3.1L		
Manifold to head bolts		
1988:	14-22 ft. lbs.	20-30 Nm
1989-92:	89 inch lbs.	10 Nm
Water pump attaching bolts		
2.0L and 2.2L:	14-22 ft. lbs.	19-30 Nm
2.3L		
Pump-to-timing chain housing nuts:	19 ft. lbs.	26 Nm
Water pump-to-pump cover assembly:	106 inch lbs.	12 Nm
Water Pump cover-to-engine:	19 ft. lbs.	26 Nm
Radiator outlet pipe-to-pump cover	125 ft. lbs.	14 Nm
2.8L and 3.1L:	6-9 ft. lbs.	8-12 Nm
Electric cooling fan		
Radiator support bolts to fan assembly:	7 ft. lbs.	10 Nm
Cylinder head bolts		
2.0L and 2.2L		
1988-89		
Long bolts:	73-83 ft. lbs.	99-113 Nm
Short bolts:	62-70 ft. lbs.	84-95 Nm
1990		
Tighten in sequence in 4 steps as follows:		
Step 1		
All bolts:	41 ft. lbs.	55 Nm
Step 2		
All bolts:	Additional 45 degrees turn	
Step 3		
All bolts:	Additional 45 degrees turn	
Step 4		
Long bolts-8, 4, 1, 1, 5 and 9	Additional 20 degrees turn	
Short bolts-7, 3, 2, 6 and 10	Additional 10 degrees turn	

TORQUE SPECIFICATIONS

Component	U.S.	Metric
1991-92		
Tighten in in sequence in 3 steps as follows:		
Step 1		
Long bolts:	46 ft. lbs.	63 Nm
Short bolts:	43 ft. lbs.	58 Nm
Step 3		
All bolts:	Additional 90 degree turn	
2.3L		
Tighten in sequence in 2 steps as follows:		
Step 1		
long and short bolts:	26 ft. lbs.	35 Nm
Step 2		
Two short bolts:	Additional 100 degree turn	
Eight long bolts:	Additional 110 degree turn	
2.8L and 3.1L		
Tighten in sequence in 2 steps as follows:		
Step 1		
All bolts:	33 ft. lbs.	45 Nm
Step 2		
All bolts:	Additional 90 degree turn	
Oil pan		
2.0L and 2.2L		
All bolts:	71 inch lbs.	8 Nm
2.3L		
Chain housing & carrier seal bolts:	106 inch lbs.	12 Nm
Oil pan-to-block bolts:	17 ft. lbs.	23 Nm
Oil pan to transaxle nut (1992):	41 ft. lbs.	56 Nm
2.8L and 3.1L		
Two rear oil pan bolts:	18 ft. lbs.	25 Nm
Oil pan stud to cylinder block:	71 inch lbs.	8 Nm
Remainder oil pan bolts and nuts:	71 inch lbs.	8 Nm
Oil pump		
2.0L and 2.2L:	32 ft. lbs.	43 Nm
2.3L		
1990:	33 ft. lbs.	45 Nm
1991-92:	40 ft. lbs.	54 Nm
2.8L and 3.1L:	20-31 ft. lbs.	25-40 Nm
Front timing cover		
2.0L and 2.2L		
1988-89:	6-9 ft. lbs.	4-7 Nm
1990-92:	106 inch lbs.	12 Nm
2.3L		
Front cover to chain housing:	106 inch lbs.	12 Nm
2.8L and 3.1L:	Refer to illustration	
Camshaft		
2.0L and 2.2L		
Thrust plate bolts:	106 inch lbs.	12 Nm
2.3L		
Camshaft housing bolts:	11 ft. lbs.	15 Nm
Plus rotate an additional 75 degrees in sequence		
Main bearing cap bolts		
2.0L and 2.2L:	70 ft. lbs.	95 Nm
2.3L:	15 ft. lbs	20 Nm
Plus an additional:	90 degree turn	
2.8L and 3.1L:	73 ft. lbs.	99 Nm

TORQUE SPECIFICATIONS

Component	U.S.	Metric
Connecting rod		
2.0L and 2.2L:	38 ft. lbs.	52 Nm
2.3L:	18 ft. lbs.	25 Nm
Plus an additional:	90 degree turn	
2.8L and 3.1L:	39 ft. lbs.	53 Nm
Flywheel		
2.0L and 2.2L		
Manual transaxle:	55 ft. lbs.	75 Nm
Automatic transaxle:	52 ft. lbs.	70 Nm
2.3L:	22 ft. lbs.	30 Nm
Plus an additional:	45 degree turn	
2.8L		
Manual transaxle:	55 ft. lbs.	75 Nm
Automatic transaxle:	52 ft. lbs.	70 Nm
3.1L:	52 ft. lbs.	70 Nm

4

EMISSION CONTROLS

AIR POLLUTION

The earth's atmosphere, at or near sea level, consists of 78% nitrogen, 21% oxygen and 1% other gases, approximately. If it were possible to remain in this state, 100% clean air would result. However, many varied causes allow other gases and particulates to mix with the clean air, causing the air to become unclean or polluted.

Certain of these pollutants are visible while others are invisible, with each having the capability of causing distress to the eyes, ears, throat, skin and respiratory system. Should these pollutants be concentrated in a specific area and under the right conditions, death could result due to the displacement or chemical change of the oxygen content in the air. These pollutants can cause much damage to the environment and to the many man made objects that are exposed to the elements.

To better understand the causes of air pollution, the pollutants can be categorized into 3 separate types, natural, industrial and automotive.

Natural Pollutants

Natural pollution has been present on earth before man appeared and is still a factor to be considered when discussing air pollution, although it causes only a small percentage of the present overall pollution problem existing in our country. It is the direct result of decaying organic matter, wind born smoke and particulates from such natural events as plains and forest fires (ignited by heat or lightning), volcanic ash, sand and dust which can spread over a large area of the countryside.

Such a phenomenon of natural pollution has been recent volcanic eruptions, with the resulting plume of smoke, steam and volcanic ash blotting out the sun's rays as it spreads and rises higher into the atmosphere, where the upper air currents catch and carry the smoke and ash, while condensing the steam back into water vapor. As the water vapor, smoke and ash traveled on their journey, the smoke dissipates into the atmosphere while the ash and moisture settle back to earth in a trail hundred of miles long. In many cases, lives are lost and millions of dollars of property damage result, and ironically, man can only stand by and watch it happen.

Industrial Pollution

Industrial pollution is caused primarily by industrial processes, the burning of coal, oil and natural gas, which in turn produces smoke and fumes. Because the burning fuels contain much sulfur, the principal ingredients of smoke and fumes are sulfur dioxide (SO_2) and particulate matter. This type of pollutant occurs most severely during still, damp and cool weather, such as at night. Even in its less severe form, this pollutant is not confined to just cities. Because of air movements, the pollutants move for miles over the surrounding countryside, leaving in its path a barren and unhealthy environment for all living things.

Working with Federal, State and Local mandated rules, regulations and by carefully monitoring the emissions, industries have greatly reduced the amount of pollutant emitted from their industrial sources, striving to obtain an acceptable level. Because of the mandated industrial emission clean up, many land areas and streams in and around the cities that were formerly barren of vegetation and life, have now begun to move back in the direction of nature's intended balance.

Automotive Pollutants

The third major source of air pollution is the automotive emissions. The emissions from the internal combustion engine were not an appreciable problem years ago because of the small number of registered vehicles and the nation's small highway system. However, during the early 1950's, the trend of the American people was to move from the cities to the surrounding suburbs. This caused an immediate problem in the transportation areas because the majority of the suburbs were not afforded mass transit conveniences. This lack of transportation created an attractive market for the automobile manufacturers, which resulted in a dramatic increase in the number of vehicles produced and sold, along with a marked increase in highway construction between cities and the suburbs. Multi-vehicle families emerged with much emphasis placed on the individual vehicle per family member. As the increase in vehicle ownership and usage occurred, so did the pollutant levels in and around the cities, as the suburbanites drove daily to their businesses and employment in the city and its fringe area,

returning at the end of the day to their homes in the suburbs.

It was noted that a fog and smoke type haze was being formed and at times, remained in suspension over the cities and did not quickly dissipate. At first this "smog", derived from the words "smoke" and "fog", was thought to result from industrial pollution but it was determined that the automobile emissions were largely to blame. It was discovered that as normal automobile emissions were exposed to sunlight for a period of time, complex chemical reactions would take place.

It was found the smog was a photo chemical layer and was developed when certain oxides of nitrogen (NOx) and unburned hydrocarbons (HC) from the automobile emissions were exposed to sunlight and was more severe when the smog would remain stagnant over an area in which a warm layer of air would settle over the top of a cooler air mass at ground level, trapping and holding the automobile emissions, instead of the emissions being dispersed and diluted through normal air flows. This type of air stagnation was given the name "Temperature Inversion".

Temperature Inversion

In normal weather situations, the surface air is warmed by the heat radiating from the earth's surface and the sun's rays and will rise upward, into the atmosphere, to be cooled through a convection type heat expands with the cooler upper air. As the warm air rises, the surface pollutants are carried upward and dissipated into the atmosphere.

When a temperature inversion occurs, we find the higher air is no longer cooler but warmer than the surface air, causing the cooler surface air to become trapped and unable to move. This warm air blanket can extend from above ground level to a few hundred or even a few thousand feet into the air. As the surface air is trapped, so are the pollutants, causing a severe smog condition. Should this stagnant air mass extend to a few thousand feet high, enough air movement with the inversion takes place to allow the smog layer to rise above ground level but the pollutants still cannot dissipate. This inversion can remain for days over an area, with only the smog level rising or lowering from ground level to a few hundred feet high. Meanwhile, the pollutant levels increases, causing eye irritation, respirator problems, reduced visibility, plant damage and in some cases, cancer type diseases.

This inversion phenomenon was first noted in the Los Angeles, California area. The city lies in a basin type of terrain and during certain weather conditions, a cold air mass is held in the basin while a warmer air mass covers it like a lid.

Because this type of condition was first documented as prevalent in the Los Angeles area, this type of smog was named Los Angeles Smog, although it occurs in other areas where a large concentration of automobiles are used and the air remains stagnant for any length of time.

Internal Combustion Engine Pollutants

Consider the internal combustion engine as a machine in which raw materials must be placed so a finished product comes out. As in any machine operation, a certain amount of wasted material is formed. When we relate this to the internal combustion engine, we find that by putting in air and fuel, we obtain power from this mixture during the combustion process to drive the vehicle. The by-product or waste of this power is, in part, heat and exhaust gases with which we must concern ourselves.

HEAT TRANSFER

The heat from the combustion process can rise to over 4000°F (2204°C). The dissipation of this heat is controlled by a ram air effect, the use of cooling fans to cause air flow and having a liquid coolant solution surrounding the combustion area and transferring the heat of combustion through the cylinder walls and into the coolant. The coolant is then directed to a thin-finned, multi-tubed radiator, from which the excess heat is transferred to the outside air by 1 or all of the 3 heat transfer methods, conduction, convection or radiation.

The cooling of the combustion area is an important part in the control of exhaust emissions. To understand the behavior of the combustion and transfer of its heat, consider the air/fuel charge. It is ignited and the flame front burns progressively across the combustion chamber until the burning charge reaches the cylinder walls. Some of the fuel in contact with the walls is not hot enough to burn, thereby snuffing out or Quenching the combustion process. This leaves unburned fuel in the combustion chamber. This unburned fuel is then forced out of the cylinder along with the exhaust gases and into the exhaust system.

Many attempts have been made to minimize the amount of unburned fuel in the combustion chambers due to the snuffing out or "Quenching", by increasing the coolant temperature and lessening the contact area of the coolant around the combustion area. Design limitations within the combustion chambers prevent the complete burning of the air/fuel charge, so a certain amount of the unburned fuel is still expelled into the exhaust system, regardless of modifications to the engine.

EXHAUST EMISSIONS

Composition Of The Exhaust Gases

The exhaust gases emitted into the atmosphere are a combination of burned and unburned fuel. To understand the exhaust emission and its composition review some basic chemistry.

When the air/fuel mixture is introduced into the engine, we are mixing air, composed of nitrogen (78%), oxygen (21%) and other gases (1%) with the fuel, which is 100% hydrocarbons (HC), in a semi-controlled ratio. As the combustion process is accomplished, power is produced to move the vehicle while the heat of combustion is transferred to the cooling system. The exhaust gases are then composed of nitrogen, a diatomic gas (N_2), the same as was introduced in the engine, carbon dioxide (CO2), the same gas that is used in beverage carbonation and water vapor (H_2O). The nitrogen (N_2), for the most part passes through the engine unchanged, while the oxygen (O_2) reacts (burns) with the hydrocarbons (HC) and produces the carbon dioxide (CO_2) and the water vapors (H_2O). If this chemical process would be the only process to take place, the exhaust emissions would be harmless. However, during the combustion process, other pollutants are formed and are considered dangerous. These pollutants are carbon monoxide (CO), hydrocarbons (HC), oxides of nitrogen (NOx) oxides of sulfur (SOx) and engine particulates.

Lead (Pb), is considered 1 of the particulates and is present in the exhaust gases whenever leaded fuels are used. Lead (Pb) does not dissipate easily. Levels can be high along roadways when it is emitted from vehicles and can pose a health threat. Since the increased usage of unleaded gasoline and the phasing out of leaded gasoline for fuel, this pollutant is gradually diminishing. While not considered a major threat lead is still considered a dangerous pollutant.

HYDROCARBONS

Hydrocarbons (HC) are essentially unburned fuel that have not been successfully burned during the combustion process or have escaped into the atmosphere through fuel evaporation. The main sources of incomplete combustion are rich air/fuel mixtures, low engine temperatures and improper spark timing. The main sources of hydrocarbon emission through fuel evaporation come from the vehicle's fuel tank and carburetor bowl.

To reduce combustion hydrocarbon emission, engine modifications were made to minimize dead space and surface area in the combustion chamber. In addition the air/fuel mixture was made more lean through improved carburetion, fuel injection and by the addition of external controls to aid in further combustion of the hydrocarbons outside the engine. Two such methods were the addition of an air injection system, to inject fresh air into the exhaust manifolds and the installation of a catalytic converter, a unit that is able to burn traces of hydrocarbons without affecting the internal combustion process or fuel economy.

To control hydrocarbon emissions through fuel evaporation, modifications were made to the fuel tank and carburetor bowl to allow storage of the fuel vapors during periods of engine shut-down, and at specific times during engine operation, to purge and burn these same vapors by blending them with the air/fuel mixture.

CARBON MONOXIDE

Carbon monoxide is formed when not enough oxygen is present during the combustion process to convert carbon (C) to carbon dioxide (CO_2). An increase in the carbon monoxide (CO) emission is normally accompanied by an increase in the hydrocarbon (HC) emission because of the lack of oxygen to completely burn all of the fuel mixture.

Carbon monoxide (CO) also increases the rate at which the photo chemical smog is formed by speeding up the conversion of nitric oxide (NO) to nitrogen dioxide (NO_2). To accomplish this, carbon monoxide (CO) combines with oxygen (O_2) and nitrogen dioxide (NO_2) to produce carbon dioxide (CO_2) and nitrogen dioxide (NO_2). $(CO + O_2 + NO = CO_2 + NO_2)$.

The dangers of carbon monoxide, which is an odorless, colorless toxic gas are many. When carbon monoxide is inhaled into the lungs and passed into the blood stream, oxygen is replaced by the carbon monoxide in the red blood cells, causing a reduction in the amount of oxygen being supplied to the many parts of the body. This lack of oxygen causes headaches, lack of coordination, reduced mental alertness and should the carbon monoxide concentration be high enough, death could result.

NITROGEN

Normally, nitrogen is an inert gas. When heated to approximately 2500°F (1371°C) through the combustion process, this gas becomes active and causes an increase in the nitric oxide (NOx) emission.

Oxides of nitrogen (NOx) are composed of approximately 97–98% nitric oxide (NO2). Nitric oxide is a colorless gas but when it is passed into the atmosphere, it combines with oxygen and forms nitrogen dioxide (NO2). The nitrogen dioxide then combines with chemically active hydrocarbons (HC) and when in the presence of sunlight, causes the formation of photo chemical smog.

OZONE

To further complicate matters, some of the nitrogen dioxide (NO_2) is broken apart by the sunlight to form nitric oxide and oxygen. $(NO_2 +$ sunlight $= NO + O)$. This single atom of oxygen then combines with diatomic (meaning 2 atoms) oxygen (O_2) to form ozone (O_3). Ozone is 1 of the smells associated with smog. It has a pungent and offensive odor, irritates the eyes and lung tissues, affects the growth of plant life and causes rapid deterioration of rubber products. Ozone can be formed by sunlight as well as electrical discharge into the air.

The most common discharge area on the automobile engine is the secondary ignition electrical system, especially when inferior quality spark plug cables are used. As the surge of high voltage is routed through the secondary cable, the circuit builds up an electrical field around the wire, acting upon the oxygen in the surrounding air to form the ozone. The faint glow along the cable with the engine running that may be visible on a dark night, is called the "corona discharge." It is the result of the electrical field passing from a high along the cable, to a low in the surrounding air, which forms the ozone gas. The combination of corona and ozone has been a major cause of cable deterioration. Recently, different types and better quality insulating materials have lengthened the life of the electrical cables.

Although ozone at ground level can be harmful, ozone is beneficial to the earth's inhabitants. By having a concentrated ozone layer called the 'ozonosphere', between 10 and 20 miles (16–32km) up in the atmosphere much of the ultra violet radiation from the sun's rays are absorbed and screened. If this ozone layer were not present, much of the earth's surface would be burned, dried and unfit for human life.

There is much discussion concerning the ozone layer and its density. A feeling exists that this protective layer of ozone is slowly diminishing and corrective action must be directed to this problem. Much experimenting is presently being conducted to determine if a problem exists and if so, the short and long term effects of the problem and how it can be remedied.

OXIDES OF SULFUR

Oxides of sulfur (SOx) were initially ignored in the exhaust system emissions, since the sulfur content of gasoline as a fuel is less than $\frac{1}{10}$ of 1%. Because of this small amount, it was felt that it contributed very little to the overall pollution problem. However, because of the difficulty in solving the sulfur emissions in industrial pollutions and the introduction of catalytic converter to the automobile exhaust systems, a change was mandated. The automobile exhaust system, when equipped with a catalytic converter, changes the sulfur dioxide (SO_2) into the sulfur trioxide (SO_3).

When this combines with water vapors (H_2O), a sulfuric acid mist (H_2SO_4) is formed and is a very difficult pollutant to handle and is extremely corrosive. This sulfuric acid mist that is formed, is the same mist that rises from the vents of an automobile storage battery when an active chemical reaction takes place within the battery cells.

When a large concentration of vehicles equipped with catalytic converters are operating in an area, this acid mist will rise and be distributed over a large ground area causing land, plant, crop, paints and building damage.

PARTICULATE MATTER

A certain amount of particulate matter is present in the burning of any fuel, with carbon constituting the largest percentage of the particulates. In gasoline, the remaining percentage of particulates is the burned remains of the various other compounds used in its manufacture. When a gasoline engine is in good internal condition, the particulate emissions are low but as the engine wears internally, the particulate emissions increase. By visually inspecting the tail pipe emissions, a determination can be made as to where an engine defect may exist. An engine with light gray smoke emitting from the tail pipe normally indicates an increase in the oil consumption through burning due to internal engine wear. Black smoke would indicate a defective fuel delivery system, causing the engine to operate in a rich mode. Regardless of the color of the smoke, the internal part of the engine or the fuel delivery system should be repaired to a "like new" condition to prevent excess particulate emissions.

Diesel and turbine engines emit a darkened plume of smoke from the exhaust system because of the type of fuel used. Emission control regulations are mandated for this type of emission and more stringent measures are being used to prevent excess emission of the particulate matter. Electronic components are being introduced to control the injection of the fuel at precisely the proper time of piston travel, to achieve the optimum in fuel ignition and fuel usage. Other particulate after-burning components are being tested to achieve a cleaner particular emission.

Good grades of engine lubricating oils should be used, meeting the manufacturers specification. "Cut-rate" oils can contribute to the particulate emission problem because of their low "flash" or ignition temperature point. Such oils burn prematurely during the combustion process causing emissions of particulate matter.

The cooling system is an important factor in the reduction of particulate matter. With the cooling system operating at a temperature specified by the manufacturer, the optimum of combustion will occur. The cooling system must be maintained in the same manner as the engine oiling system, as each system is required to perform properly in order for the engine to operate efficiently for a long time.

Other Automobile Emission Sources

Before emission controls were mandated on the internal combustion engines, other sources of engine pollutants were discovered, along with the exhaust emission. It was determined the engine combustion exhaust produced 60% of the total emission pollutants, fuel evaporation from the fuel tank and carburetor vents produced 20%, with the another 20% being produced through the crankcase as a by-product of the combustion process.

CRANKCASE EMISSIONS

Crankcase emissions are made up of water, acids, unburned fuel, oil fumes and particulates. The emissions are classified as hydrocarbons (HC) and are formed by the small amount of unburned, compressed air/fuel mixture entering the crankcase from the combustion area during the compression and power strokes, between the cylinder walls and piston rings. The head of the compression and combustion help to form the remaining crankcase emissions.

Since the first engines, crankcase emissions were allowed to go into the air through a road draft tube, mounted on the lower side of the engine block. Fresh air came in through an open oil filler cap or breather. The air passed through the crankcase mixing with blow-by gases. The motion of the vehicle and the air blowing past the open end of the road draft tube caused a low

To control the crankcase emission, the road draft tube was deleted. A hose and/or tubing was routed from the crankcase to the intake manifold so the blow-by emission could be burned with the air/fuel mixture. However, it was found that intake manifold vacuum, used to draw the crankcase emissions into the manifold, would vary in strength at the wrong time and not allow the proper emission flow. A regulating type valve pressure area at the end of the tube. Crankcase emissions were simply drawn out of the road draft tube into the air.
was needed to control the flow of air through the crankcase.

Testing, showed the removal of the blow-by gases from the crankcase as quickly as possible, was most important to the longevity of the engine. Should large accumulations of blow-by gases remain and condense, dilution of the engine oil would occur to form water, soots, resins, acids and lead salts, resulting in the formation of sludge and varnishes. This condensation of the blow-by gases occur more frequently on vehicles used in numerous starting and stopping conditions, excessive idling and when the engine is not allowed to attain normal operating temperature through short runs. The crankcase purge control or PCV system will be described in detail later in this section.

FUEL EVAPORATIVE EMISSIONS

Gasoline fuel is a major source of pollution, before and after it is burned in the automobile engine. From the time the fuel is refined, stored, pumped and transported, again stored until it is pumped into the fuel tank of the vehicle, the gasoline gives off unburned hydrocarbons (HC) into the atmosphere. Through redesigning of the storage areas and venting systems, the pollution factor has been diminished but not eliminated, from the refinery standpoint. However, the

automobile still remained the primary source of vaporized, unburned hydrocarbon (HC) emissions.

Fuel pumped form an underground storage tank is cool but when exposed to a warner ambient temperature, will expand. Before controls were mandated, an owner would fill the fuel tank with fuel from an underground storage tank and park the vehicle for some time in warm area, such as a parking lot. As the fuel would warm, it would expand and should no provisions or area be provided for the expansion, the fuel would spill out the filler neck and onto the ground, causing hydrocarbon (HC) pollution and creating a severe fire hazard. To correct this condition, the vehicle manufacturers added overflow plumbing and/or gasoline tanks with built in expansion areas or domes.

However, this did not control the fuel vapor emission from the fuel tank and the carburetor bowl. It was determined that most of the fuel evaporation occurred when the vehicle was stationary and the engine not operating. Most vehicles carry 5–25 gallons (19–95 liters) of gasoline. Should a large concentration of vehicles be parked in one area, such as a large parking lot, excessive fuel vapor emissions would take place, increasing as the temperature increases.

To prevent the vapor emission from escaping into the atmosphere, the fuel system is designed to trap the fuel vapors while the vehicle is stationary, by sealing the fuel system from the atmosphere. A storage system is used to collect and hold the fuel vapors from the carburetor and the fuel tank when the engine is not operating. When the engine is started, the storage system is then purged of the fuel vapors, which are drawn into the engine and burned with the air/fuel mixture.

The components of the fuel evaporative system will be described in detail later in this section.

EMISSION CONTROLS

There are three sources of automotive pollutants: crankcase fumes, exhaust gases, and gasoline evaporation. The pollutants formed from these substances fall into three categories: unburnt hydrocarbons (HC), carbon monoxide (CO), and oxides of nitrogen (NOx). The equipment that is used to limit these pollutants is commonly called emission control equipment.

Positive Crankcase Ventilation System

♦ SEE FIG. 1A

All Corsica/Beretta cars are equipped with a positive crankcase ventilation (PCV) system to control crankcase blow-by vapors. The system functions as follows:

When the engine is running, a small portion of the gases which are formed in the combustion chamber leak by the piston rings and enter the crankcase. Since these gases are under pressure, they tend to escape from the crankcase and enter the atmosphere. If these gases are allowed to remain in the crankcase for any period of time, they contaminate the engine oil and cause sludge to build up in the crankcase. If the gases are allowed to escape into the atmosphere, they pollute the air with unburned hydrocarbons. The job of the crankcase emission control equipment is to recycle these gases back into the engine combustion chamber where they are reburned.

The crankcase (blow-by gases are recycled in the following way: as the engine is running, clean, filtered air is drawn through the air filter and into the crankcase. As the air passes through the crankcase, it picks up the combustion gases and carries them out of the crankcase, through the oil separator, through the PCV valve, and into the induction system. As they enter the intake manifold, they are drawn into the combustion chamber where they are reburned.

The most critical component in the system is the PCV valve. This valve controls the amount of gases which are recycled into the combustion chamber. At low engine speeds, the valve is partially closed, limiting the flow of gases into the intake manifold. As engine speed increases, the valve opens to admit greater quantities of gases into the intake manifold. If the valve should become blocked or plugged, the gases will be

prevented from escaping from the crankcase by the normal route. Since these gases are under pressure, they will find their own way out of the crankcase. This alternate route is usually a weak oil seal or gasket in the engine. As the gas escapes by the gasket, it also creates an oil leak. Besides causing oil leaks, a clogged PCV valve also allows these gases to remain in the crankcase for an extended period of time, promoting the formation of sludge in the engine.

SERVICE

Inspect the PCV system hose and connections at each tune-up and replace any deteriorated hoses. Check the PCV valve at every tune-up and replace it at 30,000 mile intervals. Replacement procedures are in Section 1.

Evaporative Emission Control System

The basic Evaporative Emission Control System (EEC) used on all vehicles is the carbon canister storage method. The system is used to reduce emissions of fuel vapors from the car's fuel system. Evaporated fuel vapors are stored for burning during combustion rather than being vented into the atmosphere when the engine is not running. When the engine is running above idle speed the canister is purged when ambient air is allowed into the canister through the air tube in the top. The air mixes with the vapor and the mixture is drawn into the intake manifold and consumed in the normal combustion process.

2.0L and 2.2L Engines

1988
♦ SEE FIG. 1

On vehicles the canister control valve is located in the canister purge line, which connects with the tank line between the fuel tank and canister. This valve is opened by manifold vacuum to allow purge of both the canister and the fuel tank simultaneously.

The purge line is connected to a ported vacuum source on the throttle body. Purge occurs only when the throttle is above a certain opening, thus preventing purge operation under conditions of low ported vacuum, such as deceleration.

1989–92
♦ SEE FIG. 2-3

The system on these engines uses a 2 tube canister. The fuel vapors vent from the fuel tank to the tank tube of the canister. The canister purge is controlled by a ported vacuum source. The vapors are purged when the engine is running above idle speed.

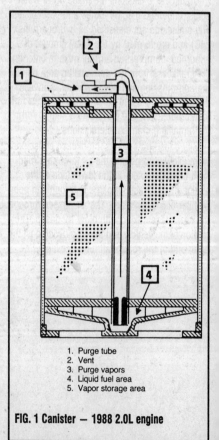

1. Purge tube
2. Vent
3. Purge vapors
4. Liquid fuel area
5. Vapor storage area

FIG. 1 Canister — 1988 2.0L engine

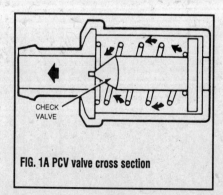

CHECK VALVE

FIG. 1A PCV valve cross section

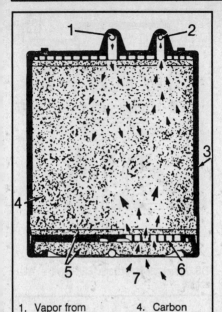

1. Vapor from fuel tank
2. Canister purge vacuum
3. Canister body
4. Carbon
5. Filter
6. Grid
7. Air flow during purge

FIG. 2 Canister — 1989–91 2.0L and 2.2L engine

1. Canister purge
2. Vapor from fuel tank
3. Carbon
4. Air

FIG. 3 Canister — 1990–92 2.3L and 1992 2.2L engine

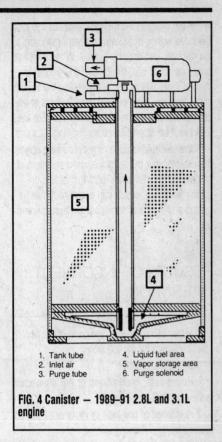

1. Tank tube
2. Inlet air
3. Purge tube
4. Liquid fuel area
5. Vapor storage area
6. Purge solenoid

FIG. 4 Canister — 1989–91 2.8L and 3.1L engine

2.3L Engine

▶ SEE FIG. 3

On these engines, the canister is purged by a solenoid which uses Pulse Width Modulation (PWM) to control purge. This means that the Electronic Control Module (ECM) opens and closes the solenoid many times a second.

Under cold engine or idle conditions, the solenoid is not energized by the ECM, which blocks vacuum to purge the canister.

2.8L and 3.1L Engines

1988–91

▶ SEE FIG. 4

On these engines equipped with (Port Fuel Injection), the Electronic Control Module (ECM) controls the vacuum to the canister purge valve by using an electrically operated solenoid valve. When the system is in the Open Loop mode, the solenoid valve is energized and blocks all vacuum to the canister purge valve. When the system is in the Closed Loop mode, the solenoid valve is de-energized and vacuum is then supplied to operate the purge valve. This releases the fuel vapors, collected in the canister, into the induction system.

The fuel tank pressure control valve located in the engine compartment, is a spring biased diaphragm valve, which is normally closed. When the vapor in the fuel tank exceeds 6.0 kPa, the valve will open allowing the vapors to vent to the canister and then be purged. When the tank

pressure drops sufficiently the tank pressure control valve will close, thus keeping the vapors in the fuel tank. The control vacuum tube of the control valve is connected into the canister line to prevent contamination from entering the valve.

If the solenoid is open or not receiving power, the canister can purge to the intake manifold at all times. This can allow extra fuel at idle or during warm-up, which can cause rough or unstable idle, or too rich operation during warm-up.

1992

▶ SEE FIG. 5

On these engines equipped with Port Fuel Injection, the Electronic Control Module (ECM) opens a normally opened pulse width modulated solenoid valve which controls vacuum to the purge valve in the charcoal canister. Under cold engine or idle conditions the solenoid is turned **ON** by the ECM, which closes the solenoid and blocks vacuum to the canister purge valve. The ECM turns **OFF** the solenoid valve and allows purge during the following:

- Engine is warm
- After the engine has been running a specified time
- Above a specified road speed
- Above a specified throttle opening

The fuel tank pressure control valve located in the top of the fuel tank, is a spring biased diaphragm valve, which is normally closed.

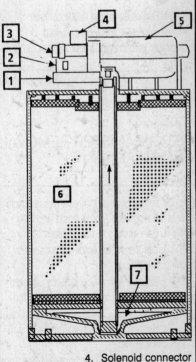

1. Tank tube
2. Inlet air
3. Purge tube
4. Solenoid connector
5. Purge solenoid
6. Vapor storage area
7. Liquid fuel area

FIG. 5 Canister — 1992 3.1L engine

When the vapor in the fuel tank exceeds 6.0 kPa, the valve will open allowing the vapors to vent to the canister and then be purged. When the tank pressure drops sufficiently the tank pressure control valve will close, thus keeping the vapors in the fuel tank. The control vacuum tube of the control valve is connected into the canister line to prevent contamination from entering the valve.

If the solenoid is open or not receiving power, the canister can purge to the intake manifold at all times. This can allow extra fuel at idle or during warm-up, which can cause rough or unstable idle, or too rich operation during warm-up.

RESULTS OF INCORRECT OPERATION

1. Poor idling, stalling and poor drivability can be caused by the following:
   • Damaged canister
   • Hoses split, cracked and/or not connected to the proper tubes
2. Evidence of fuel loss or vapor odor can be caused by the following:
   • Liquid fuel leaking from the fuel lines or TBI unit
   • Cracked or damaged vapor canister
   • Disconnected, misrouted, kinked, deteriorated or damaged vapor pipe or canister hoses
   • Air cleaner or air cleaner gasket improperly seated

VAPOR CANISTER REMOVAL & INSTALLATION

1. On some models it may be necessary to remove the right side fender fascia and filler panels to gain access to the canister.
2. Loosen the screw holding the canister retaining bracket.
3. If equipped with air conditioning, loosen the attachments holding the accumulator and pipe assembly.
4. Rotate the canister retaining bracket and remove the canister.
5. Tag and disconnect the hoses leading from the canister.
6. Installation is in the reverse order of removal.

Exhaust Gas Recirculation System (EGR)

▶ SEE FIGS. 6-8

All except the 2.3L engines are equipped with this system, which is used to lower the NOx (oxides of nitrogen) emission levels caused by high combustion temperature.

It does this by introducing exhaust gas, which contains very little oxygen, into the intake manifold. The exhaust gas will not support combustion, but does occupy volume, reducing the total amount of air/fuel mixture which burns in the cylinder. This reduces combustion temperatures.

There are 3 types of EGR valves used; The negative backpressure EGR valve (2.0L and 2.2L engines), Integrated Electronic EGR valve (2.8L engine) and the Digital EGR valve (3.1L engine). The principle of all systems is the same; the only difference is in the method used to control how far the EGR valve opens.

In addition, on 1992 2.2L engines, an ECM controlled solenoid is used in the vacuum line to help regulate air flow.

RESULTS OF INCORRECT OPERATION

1. Too much EGR flow (at idle, cruise, or cold operation) may result in any of the following conditions:
   • Engine stops after cold start

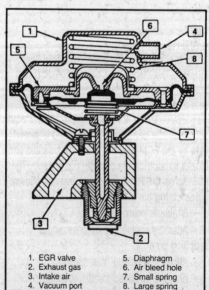

1. EGR valve
2. Exhaust gas
3. Intake air
4. Vacuum port
5. Diaphragm
6. Air bleed hole
7. Small spring
8. Large spring

FIG. 6 Negative back pressure EGR valve — 1989–92 2.0L and 2.2L engine

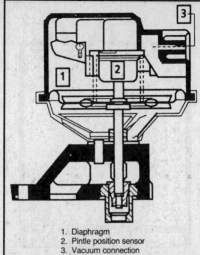

1. Diaphragm
2. Pintle position sensor
3. Vacuum connection

FIG. 7 Integrated electronic EGR valve — 2.8L engine

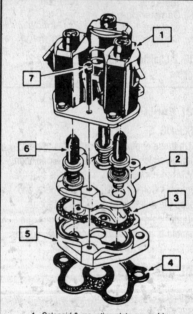

1. Solenoid & mounting plate assembly
2. EGR base plate
3. EGR base gasket
4. Insulator gasket
5. EGR base
6. Armature assembly
7. Screw assembly

FIG. 8 Digital EGR valve — 3.1L engine

• Engine stops at idle after deceleration
• Car surges during cruise
• Rough idle
2. Too little or no EGR flow allows combustion temperatures to get too high during acceleration and load conditions. This could cause the following:
   • Spark knock (detonation)
   • Engine overheating
   • Emission test failure

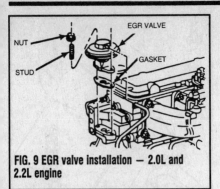

FIG. 9 EGR valve installation — 2.0L and 2.2L engine

REMOVAL & INSTALLATION

2.0L and 2.2L Engine

♦ SEE FIG. 9

1. Disconnect the EGR vacuum hose at the valve.

2. Remove the EGR retaining bolts.

3. Remove the EGR valve from the manifold.

4. Inspect the EGR manifold passage and clean any excessive build-up of deposits. Make sure all loose particles are completely removed.

5. With a wire brush or wheel, clean the exhaust deposits from the mounting surface and around the valve.

6. Look for exhaust deposits in the valve outlet remove with a suitable tool.

7. Clean the mounting surfaces of the intake manifold and valve assembly.

8. Install the EGR valve on the intake manifold using a new gasket.

9. Tighten the bolts to 11–18 ft. lbs. (15–25 Nm).

10. Install the vacuum hose to the valve.

2.8L Engine

♦ SEE FIG. 10

1. Disconnect the EGR vacuum hose at the valve.

2. Disconnect the electrical connector.

3. Disconnect the EGR tube from the exhaust manifold.

4. Remove the three EGR mounting nuts from the plenum studs.

5. Remove the EGR tube from the valve by removing the two bolts.

6. Inspect the EGR manifold passage and clean any excessive build-up of deposits. Make sure all loose particles are completely removed.

7. With a wire brush or wheel, clean the exhaust deposits from the mounting surface and around the valve.

8. Look for exhaust deposits in the valve outlet remove with a suitable tool.

9. Clean the mounting surfaces of the intake manifold and valve assembly.

10. Install the EGR tube to the EGR valve using a new gasket and tighten to 19 ft. lbs.

11. Install the EGR valve and tube assembly to the plenum using a new gasket.

12. Tighten the bolts to 19 ft. lbs.

13. Install the EGR tube to the exhaust manifold and tighten to 19 ft. lbs.

14. Connect the electrical connector.

15. Install the vacuum hose to the valve.

3.1L Engine

♦ SEE FIG. 8

1. Disconnect the electrical connector at the solenoid.

2. Remove the 2 base to flange bolts and remove the digital EGR valve.

To install:

3. Install the 2 base to flange bolts finger tight.

4. Tighten the bolts in the following sequence:

   a. Torque the long bolt to 11 ft. lbs. (15 Nm).

   b. Torque the short bolt to 11 ft. lbs. (15 Nm).

   c. Torque the long bolt to 30 ft. lbs. (22 Nm).

   d. Torque the short bolt to 30 ft. lbs. (22 Nm).

EGR Control Solenoid

REMOVAL & INSTALLATION

2.2L Engine

1992

♦ SEE FIG. 11

1. Disconnect the negative battery cable.

2. Remove the MAP sensor.

3. Disconnect the electrical connector at the solenoid.

4. Disconnect the vacuum hoses.

5. Remove the screw and remove the EGR solenoid.

To install:

6. Install the solenoid and bracket and tighten the screw to 17 ft. lbs. (24 Nm).

7. Connect the vacuum hoses.

8. Connect the electrical connector at the solenoid.

9. Install the seal on the MAP sensor.

10. Install the MAP sensor and tighten the screws to 17 ft. lbs. (24 Nm).

11. Connect the negative battery cable.

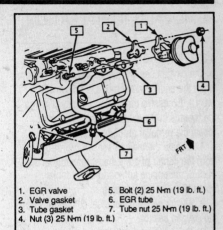

1. EGR valve
2. Valve gasket
3. Tube gasket
4. Nut (3) 25 N·m (19 lb. ft.)
5. Bolt (2) 25 N·m (19 lb. ft.)
6. EGR tube
7. Tube nut 25 N·m (19 lb. ft.)

FIG. 10 EGR valve installation — 2.8L engine

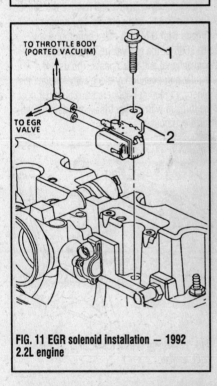

FIG. 11 EGR solenoid installation — 1992 2.2L engine

Oxygen Sensor

An oxygen sensor is used on all models. The sensor protrudes into the exhaust stream and monitors the oxygen content of the exhaust gases. The difference between the oxygen content of the exhaust gases and that of the outside air generates a voltage signal to the ECM. The ECM monitors this voltage and, depending upon the value of the signal received, issues a command to adjust for a rich or a lean condition.

REMOVAL & INSTALLATION

♦ SEE FIG. 12-16

The oxygen sensor may be difficult to remove when the engine temperature is below 120°F (49°C). Excessive removal force may damage the threads in the exhaust manifold or pipe; follow the removal procedure carefully.

1. Locate the oxygen sensor. It protrudes from the center of the exhaust manifold at the front of the engine compartment (it looks somewhat like a spark plug).

2. Disconnect the electrical connector from the oxygen sensor.

3. Spray a commercial heat riser solvent onto the sensor threads and allow it to soak in for at least five minutes.

4. Carefully unscrew and remove the sensor.

5. To install, first coat the new sensor's threads with G.M. anti-seize compound No. 5613695 or the equivalent. This is not a conventional anti-seize paste. The use of a regular compound may electrically insulate the sensor, rendering it inoperative. You must coat the threads with an electrically conductive anti-seize compound.

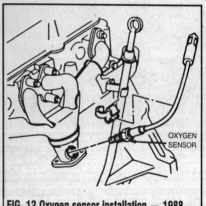

FIG. 12 Oxygen sensor installation — 1988 2.0L engine

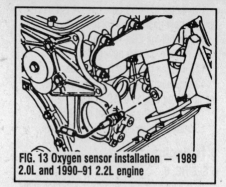

FIG. 13 Oxygen sensor installation — 1989 2.0L and 1990–91 2.2L engine

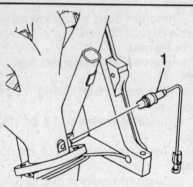

FIG. 14 Oxygen sensor installation — 1992 2.2L engine

➡ New or service sensors will already have the compound applied to the threads. If a sensor is removed from the engine, and for any reason it is to be reinstalled, the threads must have anti-seize compound applied before reinstallation.

6. Installation torque is 30 ft. lbs. (42 Nm.). Do not overtighten.

7. Reconnect the electrical connector. Be careful not to damage the electrical pigtail. Check the sensor boot for proper fit and installation.

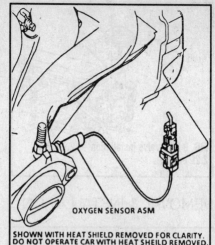

OXYGEN SENSOR ASM

SHOWN WITH HEAT SHIELD REMOVED FOR CLARITY. DO NOT OPERATE CAR WITH HEAT SHEILD REMOVED.

FIG. 15 Oxygen sensor installation — 2.3L engine

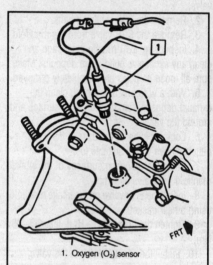

1. Oxygen (O₂) sensor

FIG. 16 Oxygen sensor installation — 2.8L and 3.1L engine

ELECTRONIC ENGINE CONTROLS

The Electronic Control Module (ECM) is designed to maintain and monitor a large number of interrelated emission control systems. It can monitor up to 15 various engine/vehicle operating conditions and then use this information to control as many as 9 engine related systems. The system is thereby making constant adjustments to maintain good vehicle performance under all normal driving conditions while at the same time allowing the catalytic converter to effectively control the emissions of HC, CO and NOx.

In addition, the system has a built in diagnostic system that recognizes and identifies possible operational problems and alerts the driver through a "Check Engine" light in the instrument panel. The light will remain on until the problem is corrected. The system also has built in back-up systems that in most cases of an operational problem will allow for the continued operation of the vehicle in a near normal manner until the repairs can be made.

INFORMATION SENSORS

Engine Coolant Temperature Sensor

The coolant sensor is a thermister (a resistor) which changes value based on temperature) mounted in the engine coolant stream. Low coolant temperature produces a high resistance (100,000Ω at −40°C/−40°F) while high temperature causes low resistance (70Ω at 130°C/266°F).

The ECM supplies a 5 volt signal to the coolant sensor thru a resistor in the ECM and measures the voltage. The voltage will be high when the engine is cold, and low when the engine is hot. By measuring the voltage, the ECM knows the engine coolant temperature. Engine coolant temperature affects most systems the ECM controls.

A failure in the coolant sensor circuit should set either a Code 14 or Code 15. Remember, these codes indicate a failure in the coolant temperature circuit, so proper use of the chart will lead to either repairing a wiring problem or replacing the sensor, to properly repair a problem.

MAP Sensor

The Manifold Absolute Pressure (MAP) Sensor measures the changes in the intake manifold pressure which result from engine load and speed changes, and converts this to a voltage output.

A closed throttle on engine coastdown would produce a relatively low MAP output, while a wide-open throttle would produce a high output. This high output is produced because the pressure inside the manifold is the same as outside the manifold, so you measure 100% of outside air pressure. Manifold Absolute Pressure (MAP) is the OPPOSITE of what you would measure on a vacuum gage. When manifold pressure is high, vacuum is low. The MAP sensor is also used to measure barometric pressure under certain conditions, which allows the ECM to automatically adjust for different altitudes.

The ECM sends a 5 volts reference signal to the MAP sensor. As the manifold pressure changes, the electrical resistance of the sensor also changes. By monitoring the sensor output voltage, the ECM knows the manifold pressure. A higher pressure, low vacuum (high voltage) requires more fuel, while a lower pressure, higher vacuum (low voltage) requires less fuel.

The ECM uses the MAP sensor to control fuel delivery and ignition timing.

A failure in the MAP sensor circuit should set a Code 33 or Code 34.

Oxygen (O₂) Sensor

The exhaust Oxygen (O_2) sensor is mounted in the exhaust system where it can monitor the oxygen content of the exhaust gas stream. The oxygen content in the exhaust reacts with the oxygen sensor to produce a voltage output. This voltage ranges from approximately 0.010 volt (high O_2 — lean mixture) to 0.9 volt (low O_2 — rich mixture).

By monitoring the voltage output of the O_2 sensor, the ECM will know what fuel mixture command to give to the injector (lean mixture — low voltage; rich command, rich mixture — high voltage, lean command). This voltage can be measured with a digital voltmeter having at least 10 megohms input impedance. Use of standard shop type voltmeters will result in very inaccurate readings.

An open O_2 sensor circuit, should set a Code 13. A shorted sensor circuit should set a Code 44. A high voltage in the circuit should set a Code 45. When any of these codes are set, the car will run in the "Open Loop" mode.

Throttle Position Sensor (TPS)

The Throttle Position Sensor (TPS) is connected to the throttle shaft on the TBI unit. It is a potentiometer with one end connected to 5 volts from the ECM and the other to ground. A third wire is connected to the ECM to measure the voltage from the TPS. As the throttle valve angle is changed (accelerator pedal moved), the output of the TPS also changes. At a closed throttle position, the output of the TPS is low (approximately 0.5 volt). As the throttle valve opens, the output increases so that, at wide-open throttle, the output voltage should be approximately 5 volts.

By monitoring the output voltage from the TPS, the ECM can determine fuel delivery based on throttle valve angle (driver demand). If the sensor CKT is open, the ECM will set a Trouble Code 22. If the circuit is shorted, the ECM will think the vehicle is at WOT, and a Trouble Code 21 will be set. A broken or loose TPS can cause intermittent bursts of fuel from the injector, and an unstable idle, because the ECM thinks the throttle is moving. Once a Trouble Code is set, the ECM will use an artificial value for TPS, and some vehicle performance will return.

On all engines, the TPS is not adjustable. The ECM uses the reading at idle for the zero reading, so no adjustment is necessary.

Knock Sensor

The knock sensor is mounted in the engine block. When abnormal engine vibrations (spark knock) are present, the sensor produces a voltage signal, which is sent to the ESC module.

Park/Neutral Switch

The Park/Neutral (P/N) switch indicates to the ECM when the transmission is in park or neutral. This information is used for the TCC, and the IAC valve operation.

➡ **Vehicle should not be driven with Park/Neutral (P/N) switch disconnected as idle quality will be affected and a possible false Code 24 VSS.**

Crank Signal

The ECM looks at the starter solenoid to tell when the engine is cranking. It uses this to tell when the car is in the Starting Mode.

If this signal is not available, the car may be hard to start in extremely cold weather.

Air Conditioner Request Signal

This signal tells the ECM that the A/C selector switch is turned "ON" and that the high side low pressure switch is closed. The ECM uses this to adjust the idle speed when the air conditioning is working.

Vehicle Speed Sensor (VSS)

The Vehicle Speed Sensor (VSS) sends a pulsing voltage signal the the ECM, which the ECM converts to miles per hour. This sensor mainly controls the operation the TCC system.

Distributor Reference Signal

The distributor sends a signal to the ECM to tell it both engine rpm and crankshaft position.

DIAGNOSIS

Since the ECM can have a failure which may effect only one circuit, following the diagnostic procedures in this section can reliably tell when a failure has occurred in the ECM. Also, a Code 55 indicates a failure of the ECM.

If a diagnostic chart indicates that the ECM connections or ECM is the cause of a problem, and the ECM is replaced, but does not correct the problem, one of the following may be the reason:

• There is a problem with the ECM terminal connections — the diagnostic chart will say ECM connections or ECM. The terminals may have to be removed from the connector in order to check them properly.

• The ECM or PROM is not correct for the application — The incorrect ECM or PROM may cause a malfunction and may or may not set a code.

• The problem is intermittent — This means that the problem is not present at the time the system is being checked. In this case, refer to the "Symptoms" portion of the manual and make a careful physical inspection of all portions of the system involved.

• Shorted solenoid, relay coil or harness — Solenoids and relays are turned "ON" and "OFF" by the ECM using internal electronic switches called "drivers." Each driver is part of a group of four called "Quad-Drivers."

A shorted solenoid, relay coil or harness may cause an ECM to fail, and a replacement ECM to fail when it is installed. Use a short tester, J 34696, BT 8405, or equivalent, as a fast, accurate means of checking for a short circuit.

• The PROM may be faulty — Although the PROM rarely fails, it operates as part of the ECM. Therefore, it could be the cause of the problem. Substitute a known good PROM.

• The replacement ECM may be faulty — After the ECM is replaced, the system should be rechecked for proper operation. If the diagnostic chart again indicates the ECM is the problem, substitute a known good ECM. Although this is a rare condition, it could happen.

The components or circuits and the codes or charts, related to them are:

• Code 55 indicates a failure of the ECM.
• PROM — CHART 51.
• Coolant Temperature Sensor — CHARTS 14–15.
• MAP Sensor — CHART 33 or 34. To check the sensor with no code set, use CHART C-1D.
• TPS — CHARTS 21 or 22.
• P/N switch — CHART C–1A.
• Crank Signal — CHART C–1B
• O$_2$ Sensor — CHARTS 13, 44, 45.
• P/N Switch, — CHART C–1A.
• A/C Request signal — If the A/C request signal is not reaching the ECM, it can cause rough idle, with A/C "ON."
• VSS — CHART 24 and in TCC System.
• Distributor — CHART 42 and in EST system.
• Distributor — Chart and in the EST system.

ECM

A faulty ECM will be determined in the diagnostic charts, or by a Code 55.

PROM

An incorrect or faulty PROM, which is part of the ECM, may set a Code 51.

ECM Inputs

All of the sensors and input switches can be diagnosed by the use of a "Scan" tool. Following is a short description of how the sensors and switches can be diagnosed by the use of "Scan." The "Scan" can also be used to compare the values for a normal running engine with the engine you're diagnosing.

Coolant Temperature Sensor (CTS)

A "Scan" tool displays engine temperature in degrees centigrade and farenheit. After the engine is started, the temperature should rise steadily between 88–106°C (190–222°F), then stabilize when thermostat opens. A fault in the coolant sensor circuit should set a Code 14 or 15. The code charts also contain a chart to check for sensor resistance values relative to temperature.

MAP Sensor

A "Scan" tool reads manifold pressure and will display volts and kPa of pressure.

Key "ON," engine stopped, (no vacuum), MAP will read high voltage or pressure, while at idle (high vacuum), MAP will read low voltage or pressure. Likewise, on acceleration, MAP will read high and on deceleration, will read low.

A failure in the MAP sensor, or circuit, should result in a Code 33 or 34.

Oxygen (O$_2$) Sensor

The "Scan" has several positions that will indicate the state of the exhaust gases, O$_2$ voltage, integrator, and block lear.

A problem in the O$_2$ sensor circuit should set a Code 13 (open circuit), Code 44 (lean O$_2$ indication), Code 45 (rich O$_2$ indication). Refer to applicable chart, if any of these codes were stored in memory

Throttle Position Sensor (TPS)

A "Scan" tool displays throttle position in volts. For example, the 3.1L should read under 1.25 volts, with throttle closed and ignition on, or at idle. Voltage should increase at a steady rate as throttle is moved toward WOT.

The ECM has the ability to auto-zero the TPS voltage, if it is below about 1.25 volts. This means that any voltage less than 1.25 volts will be determined by the ECM to be 0% throttle. Some "Scan" tools have the ability to read the percentage of throttle angle and should read 0%, when the throttle is closed. A failure in the TPS, or circuit, should set a Code 21 or 22.

Vehicle Speed Sensor (VSS)

A "Scan" tool reading should closely match with speedometer reading, with drive wheels turning. A failure in the VSS circuit should set a Code 24.

P/N Switch

A "Scan" tool should read "P–N–," when in park or neutral and "R–D–L," when in drive. This reading may vary with different makes of tools. Refer to CHART C–1A for P/N switch diagnosis, if so equipped.

A/C Request Signal

If the low pressure switch is closed and A/C is "ON," the A/C clutch should indicate "ON". See "ECM Controlled Air Conditioning".

Distributor Reference Signal

A "Scan" tool will read this signal and is displayed in rpm. See "Ignition System/(EST)".

Knock Signal

A "Scan" tool will indicate when the ESC module signals the ECM that knock is present. See "Electronic Spark Control (ESC), System".

BASIC KNOWLEDGE AND TOOLS REQUIRED

To use this manual most effectively, a general understanding of basic electrical circuits and circuit testing tools is required. You should be familiar with wiring diagrams, the meaning of voltage, ohms, amps, the basic theories of electricity, and understand what happens in an open or shorted wire.

To perform system diagnosis, the use of a TECH 1 Diagnostic Computer or equivalent "Scan" tool is required. A tachometer, test light, ohmmeter, digital voltmeter with 10 megohms impedance, vacuum gauge, and jumper wires are also required. Please become acquainted with the tools and their use before attempting to diagnose a vehicle. Special tools which are required for system service and the ones described above are illustrated at the end of this section.

DIAGNOSTIC INFORMATION

The diagnostic "tree" charts and functional checks in this manual are designed to locate a faulty circuit or component through logic based on the process of elimination.

"Service Engine Soon" Light

This light is on the instrument panel and has the following functions.

• It informs the driver that a problem has occurred and that the vehicle should be taken for service as soon as reasonably possible.

• It displays "Codes" stored by the ECM which help the technician diagnose system problems.

• It indicates "Open Loop" or "Closed Loop" operation.

As a bulb and system check, the light will come "ON" with the key "ON" and the engine not running. When the engine is started, the light will turn "OFF". If the light remains "ON", the self-diagnostic system has detected a problem. If the problem goes away, the light will go out in most cases after 10 seconds, but a Code will remain stored in the ECM.

When the light remains "ON" while the engine is running, or when a malfunction is suspected due to a driveability or emissions problem, a "Diagnostic Circuit Check" must be performed.

These checks will expose malfunctions which may not be detected if other diagnostics are performed prematurely.

Intermittent "Service Engine Soon" Light

In the case of an "intermittent" problem, the "Service Engine Soon" light will light for ten (10) seconds and then will go out. However, the corresponding code will be stored in the memory of the ECM until the battery voltage to the ECM has been removed. When unexpected codes appear during the code reading process, one can assume that these codes were set by an intermittent malfunction and could be helpful in diagnosing the system.

An intermittent code may or may not re-set. If it is an intermittent failure, a Diagnostic Code Chart is not used. A physical inspection of the applicable sub-system most often will resolve the problem.

Reading Codes

▶ SEE FIG. 17

The provision for communicating with the ECM is the Assembly Line Diagnostic Link (ALDL) connector. It is usually located under the instrument panel and is sometimes covered by a plastic cover labeled "DIAGNOSTIC CONNECTOR." It is used in the assembly plant to receive information in checking that the engine is operating properly before it leaves the plant. The code(s) stored in the ECM's memory can be read either through TECH 1 Diagnostic Computer, a hand-held diagnostic scanner plugged into the ALDL connector or by counting the number of flashes of the "Service Engine Soon" light when the diagnostic terminal of the ALDL connector is grounded. The ALDL connector terminal "B" (diagnostic terminal) is the second terminal from the right of the ALDL connector's top row. The terminal is most easily grounded by connecting it to terminal "A" (internal ECM ground), the terminal to the right of terminal "B" on top row of the ALDL connector.

Once terminals "A" and "B" have been connected, the ignition switch must be moved to the "ON" position, with the engine not running. At this point, the "Service Engine Soon" light should flash Code 12 three times consecutively. This would be the following flash sequence: "flash, pause, flash-flash, long pause, flash, pause, flash-flash, long pause, flash, pause, flash-flash." Code 12 indicates that the ECM's diagnostic system is operating. If Code 12 is not indicated, a problem is present within the diagnostic system itself, and should be addressed by consulting the appropriate diagnostic chart.

Following the output of Code 12, the "Service Engine Soon" light will indicate a diagnostic code three times if a code is present, or it will simply continue to output Code 12. If more than one diagnostic code has been stored in the ECM's memory, the codes will be output from the lowest to the highest, with each code being displayed three times.

Clearing Codes

To clear the codes from the memory of the ECM, either to determine if the malfunction will occur again or because repair has been completed, the ECM power feed must be disconnected for at least thirty (30) seconds. Depending on how the vehicle is equipped, the ECM power feed can be disconnected at the positive battery terminal "pigtail," the inline fuseholder that originates at the positive connection at the battery, or the ECM fuse in the fuse block. (The negative battery terminal may be disconnected, but other on-board memory data, such as preset radio tuning, will also be lost.)

☀☀ WARNING

To prevent ECM damage, the key must be "OFF when disconnecting or reconnecting ECM power.

➡ When using a hand-held TECH 1 Diagnostic Computer, or "Scan" tool to read the codes, clearing the diagnostic codes is done in the same manner as in the above procedure.

Diagnostic Mode

When the Diagnostic terminal is grounded with the ignition "ON" and the engine "OFF," the system will enter what is called the Diagnostic Mode. In this mode the ECM will:

1. Display a Code 12 by flashing the "Service Engine Soon" light (indicating the system is operating correctly).
2. Display any stored codes by flashing the "Service Engine Soon" light. Each code will be flashed three times, then Code 12 will be flashed again.
3. Energize all ECM controlled relays and solenoids except fuel pump relay. This allows checking circuits which may be difficult to energize without driving the vehicle and being under particular operating conditions.
4. The IAC valve moves to its fully extended position on most models, blocking the idle air passage. This is useful in checking the minimum idle speed.

TERMINAL IDENTIFICATION

A	GROUND	E	SERIAL DATA
B	DIAGNOSTIC TERMINAL	F	TCC (IF USED)
C	A.I.R. (IF USED)	G	FUEL PUMP (IF USED)
D	SERVICE ENGINE SOON LIGHT (IF USED)	M	SERIAL DATA (IF USED)

FIG. 17 ALDL connector

Field Service Mode

If the diagnostic terminal is grounded with the engine running, the system will enter the Field Service mode. In this mode, the "Service Engine Soon" light will indicate whether the system is in "Open Loop" or "Closed Loop."

In "Open Loop" the "Service Engine Soon" light flashes two and one-half times per second.

In "Closed Loop," the light flashes once per second. Also, in "Closed Loop," the light will stay "OFF" most of the time if the system is running lean. It will stay "ON" most of the time if the system is running rich.

While the system is in Field Service Mode, new codes cannot be stored in the ECM and the "Closed Loop" timer is bypassed.

ECM Learning Ability

The ECM has a "learning" ability which allows it to make corrections for minor variations in the fuel system to improve driveability. If the battery is disconnected, to clear diagnostic codes or for other repair, the "learning" process resets and begins again. A change may be noted in the vehicle's performance. To "teach" the vehicle, ensure that the engine is at operating temperature. The vehicle should be driven at part throttle, with moderate acceleration and idle conditions until normal performance returns.

VACUUM DIAGRAMS

The following selection of vacuum diagrams are supplied by the manufacturer and are as complete as possible, at the time of publication. The underhood sticker in your vehicle, often reflects the latest changes made during the production of the vehicle, and should always take preference over those shown in this manual.

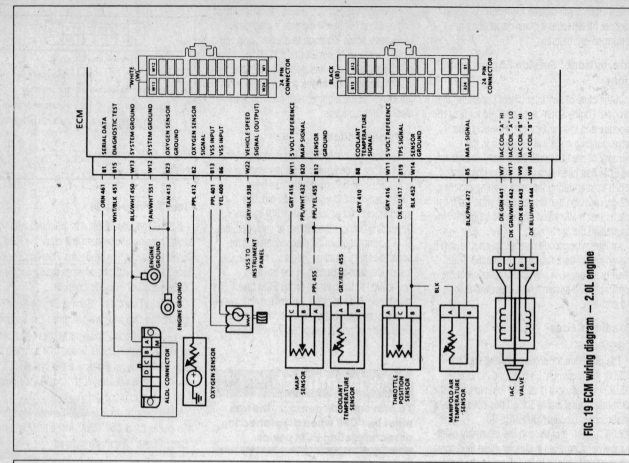

FIG. 19 ECM wiring diagram — 2.0L engine

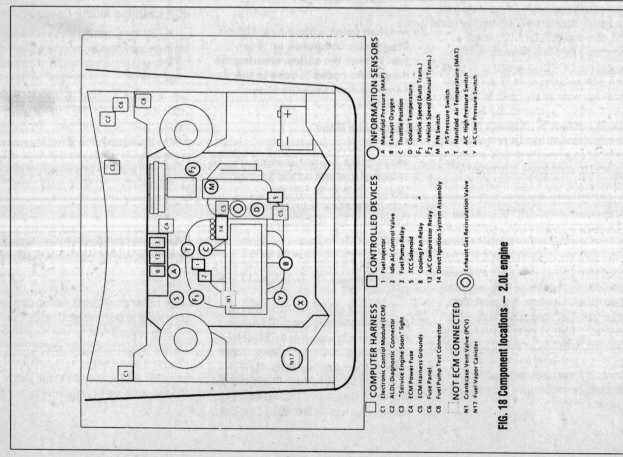

COMPUTER HARNESS
C1 Electronic Control Module (ECM)
C2 ALDL Diagnostic Connector
C3 "Service Engine Soon" light
C4 ECM Power Fuse
C5 ECM Harness Grounds
C6 Fuse Panel
C8 Fuel Pump Test Connector

NOT ECM CONNECTED
N1 Crankcase Vent Valve (PCV)
N17 Fuel Vapor Canister

CONTROLLED DEVICES
1 Fuel Injector
2 Idle Air Control Valve
3 Fuel Pump Relay
5 TCC Solenoid
8 Cooling Fan Relay
9 A/C Compressor Relay
14 Direct Ignition System Assembly
◎ Exhaust Gas Recirculation Valve

INFORMATION SENSORS
A Manifold Pressure (MAP)
B Exhaust Oxygen
C Throttle Position
D Coolant Temperature
F₁ Vehicle Speed (Auto Trans.)
F₂ Vehicle Speed (Manual Trans.)
M P/N Switch
T P/S Pressure Switch
X A/C High Pressure Switch
Y A/C Low Pressure Switch

FIG. 18 Component locations — 2.0L engine

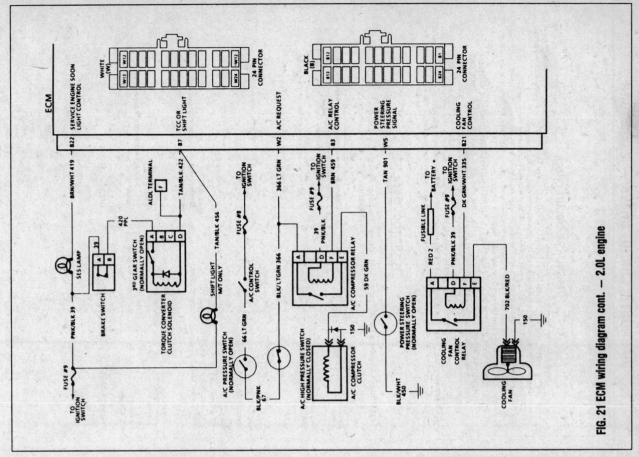

FIG. 21 ECM wiring diagram cont. — 2.0L engine

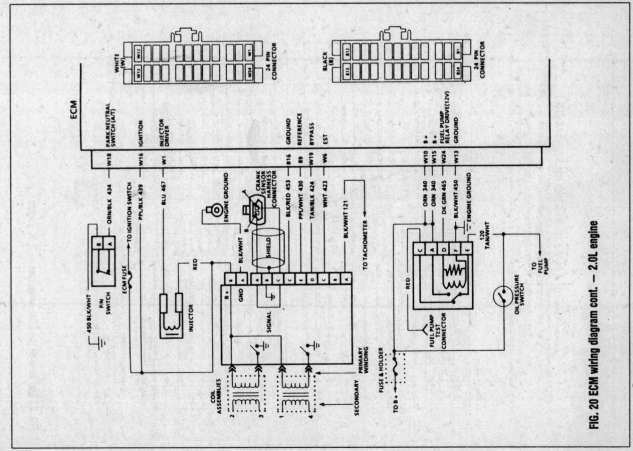

FIG. 20 ECM wiring diagram cont. — 2.0L engine

DIAGNOSTIC CIRCUIT CHECK — 2.0L ENGINE

DIAGNOSTIC CIRCUIT CHECK

The Diagnostic Circuit Check is an organized approach to identifying a problem created by an electronic engine control system malfunction. It must be the starting point for any driveability complaint diagnosis because it directs the service technician to the next logical step in diagnosing the complaint.

The "Scan" data listed in the table may be used for comparison after completing the diagnostic circuit check and finding the on-board diagnostics functioning properly with no trouble codes displayed. The "Typical Data Values" are an average of display values recorded from normally operating vehicles and are intended to represent what a normally functioning system would typically display

A "SCAN" TOOL THAT DISPLAYS FAULTY DATA SHOULD NOT BE USED, AND THE PROBLEM SHOULD BE REPORTED TO THE MANUFACTURER. THE USE OF A FAULTY "SCAN" TOOL CAN RESULT IN MISDIAGNOSIS AND UNNECESSARY PARTS REPLACEMENT.

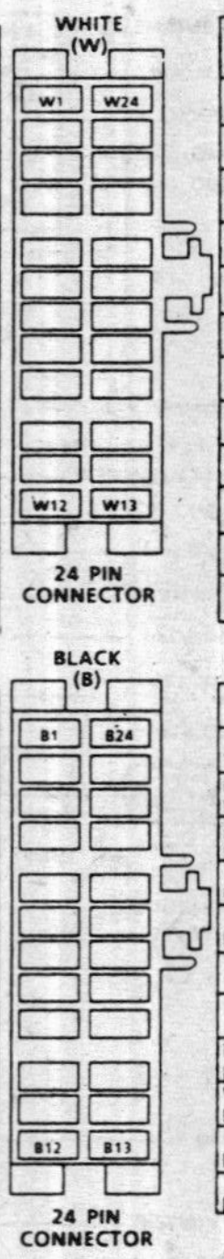

Only the parameters listed below are used in this manual for diagnosis. If a "Scan" tool reads other parameters, the values are not recommended by General Motors for use in diagnosis. For more description on the values and use of the "Scan" tool to diagnosis ECM inputs, refer to the applicable component diagnosis section in Section "C". If all values are within the range illustrated, refer to symptoms in Section "B"

"SCAN" TOOL DATA

Test Under Following Conditions: Idle, Upper Radiator Hose Hot, Closed Throttle, Park or Neutral, "Closed Loop", All Accessories "OFF"

"SCAN" Position	Units Displayed	Typical Data Value
Desired RPM	RPM	ECM idle command (varies with temperature)
RPM	RPM	± 50 RPM from desired rpm in drive (AUTO) ± 100 RPM from desired rpm in neutral (MANUAL)
Coolant Temperature	Degrees Celsius	85 - 105
MAT Temperature	Degrees Celsius	10 - 90 (varies with underhood temperature and sensor location)
MAP	Volts	1 - 2 (varies with manifold and barometric pressures)
E (base pulse width)	Milliseconds	8 - 3 0
C₁₂	Volts	1 - 1 (varies continuously)
TPS	Volts	4 - 1 25
Throttle Angle	0 - 100%	0
IAC	Counts (steps)	1 - 50
P/N Switch	P-N and R-D-L	Park/Neutral (P/N)
INT (Integrator)	Counts	110 - 145
BLM (Block Learn Memory)	Counts	118 - 138
Open/Closed Loop	Open/Closed	"Closed Loop" (may enter "Open Loop" with extended idle)
SS	MPH	0
°C	Degrees	"OFF"
Battery	Volts	Varies
Spark Advance	Degrees	13 5 - 14 5
Fan	ON/OFF	"OFF" (coolant temperature below 102°C)
P/S Switch	Normal/Hi Pressure	Normal
A/C Request	Yes/No	No
A/C Clutch	ON/OFF	"OFF"
Shift Light (M/T)	ON/OFF	"OFF"

FUEL INJECTION ECM CONNECTOR IDENTIFICATION

This ECM voltage chart is for use with a digital voltmeter to further aid in diagnosis. The voltages you get may vary due to low battery charge or other reasons, but they should be very close.

THE FOLLOWING CONDITIONS MUST BE MET BEFORE TESTING:

- Engine at operating temperature • Engine idling in "Closed Loop" (for "Engine Run" column)
- Test terminal not grounded • "Scan" tool not installed • All voltages shown "B + " indicates battery or charging voltage

VOLTAGE

	CIRCUIT	PIN	WIRE COLOR	KEY "ON" RUN	ENG. RUN
②	INJECTOR DRIVE	W1	BLU	B+	B+
	A/C REQUEST	W2	LT GRN	0*	0*
	NOT USED				
	CRUISE	W4	GRY/BLK		
	POWER STEERING SIGNAL	W5	TAN	B+	B+
	EST.	W6	WHT	0	1 1
⑤	IAC "B" HI	W7	DK GRN	⑤	⑤
⑤	IAC "B" LOW	W8	DK BLU/WHT	⑤	⑤
⑤	IAC "B" HI	W9	DK BLU	⑤	⑤
	12V BATTERY	W10	ORN	B+	B+
	5 VOLT REFERENCE	W11	GRY	5.0	5.0
	ECM GROUND	W12	TAN/WHT	0*	0*

	CIRCUIT	PIN	WIRE COLOR	KEY "ON" RUN	ENG. RUN
	FUEL PUMP	W24	DK GRN	B+	B+
	VSS OUTPUT 4000 PPM (IF USED)	W22	GRY/BLK	0*	
	NOT USED	W23	LT		
	CRUISE	W21	DK BLU	0*	
	CRUISE	W20	GRY/TAN/ORN	0*	
	BYPASS	W19	BLK	0*	4.5
	P/N SWITCH	W18	DK GRN	0*	0*
	IAC "A" LOW	W17	PPL/WHT	⑤	⑤
	12V IGNITION	W16	BLK	B+	B+
	12V BATTERY	W15	ORN	B+	B+
①	TPS MAT GROUND	W14	BLK/WHT	0*	0*
	ECM GROUND	W13	BLK/WHT	0*	0*

VOLTAGE

	CIRCUIT	PIN	WIRE COLOR	KEY "ON" RUN	ENG. RUN
	SERIAL DATA	B1	ORN	4.5	4.5
②	OXYGEN SENSOR SIGNAL	B2	PPL	.33-.55	1-.9
	A/C CLUTCH RELAY	B3	BRN	B+	B+
	NOT USED	B4			
④	MAT	B5	BLK/PNK	1 3	1 3
	MAGNETIC VSS (IF USED)	B6	YEL	1 3	1 3
	TCC OR SHIFT LIGHT	B7	TAN/BLK ~	0*	0*
④	COOLANT REFERENCE HI	B8	GRY	1 9	1 9
④	COOLANT REFERENCE HI	B9	PPL/WHT	A 6	3 0 5
	CRUISE	B10	LT GRN		
	CRUISE	B11	DK BLU/WHT		
	COOLANT AND MAP GROUND	B12	PPL/YEL	0*	0*

	CIRCUIT	PIN	WIRE COLOR	KEY "ON" RUN	ENG. RUN
	NOT USED	B24			
	OXYGEN SENSOR GROUND	B23	TAN	0*	0*
	SERVICE ENGINE SOON LIGHT	B22	BRN/WHT	0*	0*
	ENGINE COOLING FAN	B21	DK GRN/WHT	B+	B+
	MAP SIGNAL	B20	PPL/WHT	4.75	1.1
	TPS SIGNAL	B19	DK BLU	.6	.6
	NOT USED	B18			
	NOT USED	B17			
	IGNITION GROUND	B16	BLK/RED	0*	0*
	ALDL DIAG.	B15	WHT/BLK	5.0	5.0
	CRUISE	B14	DK BRN	0*	0*
	MAGNETIC VSS	B13	PPL		②

ENGINE 2.0L

* All voltages shown "0" should read less than .5 volt.
① This wire may also have a tracer color.
② A/C, Fan "OFF"
③ Reads battery voltage for 2 seconds after ignition "ON" then should read 0 volts
④ Varies depending on temperature
⑤ Not useable

FIG. 22 End view of the ECM connector — 2.0L engine

1988–89 2.0L ENGINE

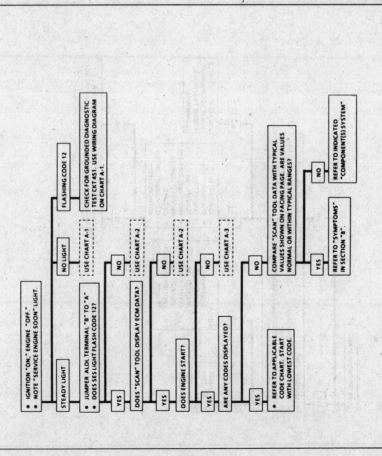

CHART A-1
NO "SERVICE ENGINE SOON" LIGHT
2.0L (VIN 1) "L" CARLINE (TBI)

Circuit Description:

There should always be a steady "Service Engine Soon" light, when the ignition is "ON" and engine "OFF." Battery voltage is supplied directly to the light bulb. The electronic control module (ECM) will control the light and turn it "ON" by providing a ground path through CKT 419 to the ECM.

Test Description: Numbers below refer to circled numbers on the diagnostic chart.

1. Battery feed CKT 340 is protected by a fusible link, at the battery.
2. Using a test light connected to B+, probe each of the system ground circuits to be sure a good ground is present. See ECM terminal end view in front of this section for ECM pin locations of ground circuits.

Diagnostic Aids:

If engine runs correctly, check for the following:
- Faulty light bulb.
- CKT 419 open.
- Gages fuse blown. This will result in no oil or generator lights, seat belt reminder, etc.

If engine cranks but will not run, use CHART A-3.

DIAGNOSTIC CIRCUIT CHECK — 2.0L ENGINE

DIAGNOSTIC CIRCUIT CHECK
2.0L (VIN 1) "L" CARLINE (TBI)

- IGNITION "ON," ENGINE "OFF."
- NOTE "SERVICE ENGINE SOON" LIGHT.

↓

STEADY LIGHT

- NO LIGHT → USE CHART A-1
- FLASHING CODE 12 → CHECK FOR GROUNDED DIAGNOSTIC TEST CKT 451. USE WIRING DIAGRAM ON CHART A-1.

↓

- JUMPER ALDL TERMINAL "B" TO "A"
- DOES SES LIGHT FLASH CODE 12?

- NO → USE CHART A-2
- YES ↓

DOES "SCAN" TOOL DISPLAY ECM DATA?

- NO → USE CHART A-2
- YES ↓

DOES ENGINE START?

- NO → USE CHART A-3
- YES ↓

ARE ANY CODES DISPLAYED?

- YES →
  - REFER TO APPLICABLE CODE CHART. START WITH LOWEST CODE.
- NO ↓

COMPARE "SCAN" TOOL DATA WITH TYPICAL VALUES SHOWN ON FACING PAGE. ARE VALUES NORMAL OR WITHIN TYPICAL RANGES?

- NO → REFER TO INDICATED "COMPONENT(S) SYSTEM"
- YES → REFER TO "SYMPTOMS" IN SECTION "B".

1988-89 2.0L ENGINE

CHART A-1
NO "SERVICE ENGINE SOON" LIGHT
2.0L (VIN 1) "L" CARLINE (TBI)

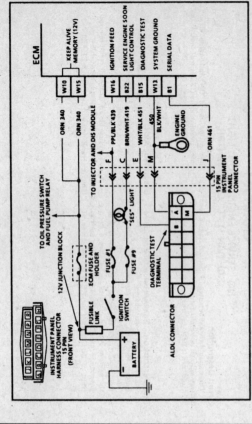

DOES THE ENGINE START?

- **NO** →
  - **(1) IS ECM BATTERY FEED CKT 340 AND ECM FUSE OK?**
    - **YES** →
      - **IGNITION "OFF". DISCONNECT ECM CONNECTORS. IGNITION "ON". PROBE CKTS 340 & 439 WITH TEST LIGHT TO GROUND. IS THE LIGHT "ON" ON BOTH CIRCUITS?**
        - **YES** → **(2) FAULTY ECM GROUNDS OR ECM.**
        - **NO** → **REPAIR OPEN IN CIRCUIT THAT DID NOT LIGHT THE TEST LIGHT.**
    - **NO** → **LOCATE AND CORRECT SHORT TO GROUND IN CIRCUIT THAT HAD A BLOWN FUSE.**
- **YES** →
  - **IGNITION "OFF". DISCONNECT ECM CONNECTORS. IGNITION "ON". PROBE CKT 419, WITH TEST LIGHT TO GROUND. IS THE "SES" LIGHT "ON"?**
    - **YES** → **FAULTY ECM CONNECTION OR ECM.**
    - **NO** → **CHECK:**
      - GAGE FUSE.
      - FAULTY BULB.
      - OPEN CKT 419.
      - CKT 419 SHORTED TO VOLTAGE.
      - OPEN IGNITION FEED TO BULB.

CLEAR CODES AND CONFIRM "CLOSED LOOP" OPERATION AND NO "SERVICE ENGINE SOON" LIGHT.

CHART A-2
NO ALDL DATA OR WON'T FLASH CODE 12
NO "SERVICE ENGINE SOON" LIGHT
2.0L (VIN 1) "L" CARLINE (TBI)

Circuit Description:

There should always be a steady "Service Engine Soon" light when the ignition is "ON" and the engine is "OFF." Battery voltage is supplied directly to the light bulb. The electronic control module (ECM) will control the light and turn it "ON" by providing a ground path through CKT 419 to the ECM.

With the diagnostic terminal grounded, the light should flash a Code 12, followed by any trouble code(s) stored in memory. A steady light suggests a short to ground in the light control CKT 419, or an open in diagnostic CKT 451.

Test Description: Numbers below refer to circled numbers on the diagnostic chart.

1. If there is a problem with the ECM that causes a "Scan" tool to not read data from the ECM, then the ECM should not flash a Code 12. If Code 12 does flash, be sure that the "Scan" tool is working properly on another vehicle. If the "Scan" is functioning properly and CKT 461 is OK, the PROM or ECM may be at fault for the "NO ALDL" symptom.

2. If the light turns "OFF" when the ECM connector is disconnected, then CKT 419 is not shorted to ground.

3. This step will check for an open diagnostic CKT 451.

4. At this point, the "Service Engine Soon" light wiring is OK. The problem is a faulty ECM or PROM. If Code 12 does not flash, the ECM should be replaced using the original PROM. Replace the PROM only after trying an ECM, as a defective PROM is an unlikely cause of the problem.

1988–89 2.0L ENGINE

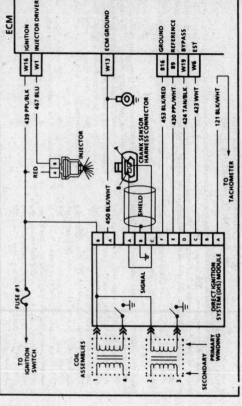

CHART A-3
(Page 1 of 3)
ENGINE CRANKS BUT WON'T RUN
2.0L (VIN 1) "L" CARLINE (TBI)

Circuit Description:

Before using this chart, battery condition, engine cranking speed, and fuel quantity should be checked and verified as being OK.

Test Description: Numbers below refer to circled numbers on the diagnostic chart.

1. A "Service Engine Soon" light "ON" is a basic test to determine if there is battery and ignition voltage at the ECM. No ALDL data may be due to an ECM problem, and CHART A-2 will diagnose the ECM. If TPS is over 2.5 volts, the engine may be in the clear flood mode, which will cause starting problems. The engine will not start without crank sensor reference pulses. The "Scan" tool should display rpm during cranking if pulses are received at the ECM.

2. Because the direct ignition system uses two plugs and wires to complete the circuit of each coil, the opposite spark plug wire should be left connected. If rpm was indicated during crank, the ignition module is receiving a crank signal, but "No Spark" at this test indicates the ignition module is not triggering the coil.

3. While cranking the engine, there should be no fuel spray with the injector electrical connector disconnected. Replace the injector if it sprays fuel or drips.

4. The test light should flash, indicating the ECM is controlling the injector. How bright the light flashes is not important. However, the test light should be a BT 8329 or equivalent.

5. Fuel spray from the injector indicates that fuel is available. However, the engine could be severely flooded due to too much fuel. No fuel spray from injector indicates a faulty fuel system or no ECM control of injector.

Diagnostic Aids:

Water or foreign material can cause a no start condition during freezing weather. The engine may start after approximately 5 minutes in a heated shop. The problem may not re-occur until an overnight park in freezing temperatures.

An EGR valve sticking open can cause a low air/fuel ratio during cranking. Unless engine enters "Clear Flood" at the first indication of a flooding condition, it can result in a no start.

Fuel Pressure: Low fuel pressure can result in a very lean air/fuel ratio. See CHART A-7.

CHART A-2

NO ALDL DATA OR WON'T FLASH CODE 12
"SERVICE ENGINE SOON" LIGHT "ON" STEADY
2.0L (VIN 1) "L" CARLINE (TBI)

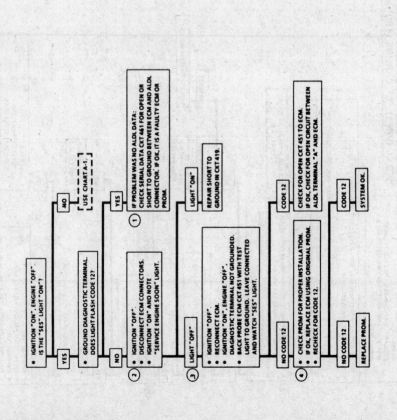

1988—89 2.0L ENGINE

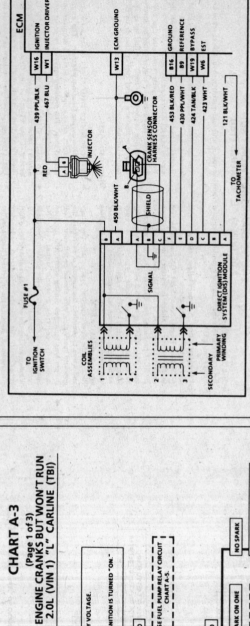

ECM
W16 IGNITION
W1 INJECTOR DRIVER
W13 ECM GROUND
B16 GROUND
B9 REFERENCE
W19 BYPASS
W6 EST

439 PPL/BLK
467 BLU
453 BLK/RED
430 PPL/WHT
424 TAN/BLK
423 WHT
121 BLK/WHT

RED — INJECTOR
450 BLK/WHT
SHIELD
CRANK SENSOR HARNESS CONNECTOR
SIGNAL
DIRECT IGNITION SYSTEM (DIS) MODULE
COIL ASSEMBLIES
PRIMARY WINDING
SECONDARY
TO TACHOMETER
FUSE #1
TO IGNITION SWITCH

CHART A-3
(Page 2 of 3)
ENGINE CRANKS BUT WON'T RUN
2.0L (VIN 1) "L" CARLINE (TBI)

Circuit Description:

A magnetic crank sensor is used to determine engine crankshaft position, much the same way as the pick-up coil did in HEI type systems. The sensor is mounted in the block, near a slotted wheel on the crankshaft. The rotation of the wheel creates a flux change in the sensor, which produces a voltage signal. The DIS ignition module processes this signal and creates the reference pulses needed by the ECM to trigger the correct coil at the correct time.

If the "Scan" tool did not indicate cranking rpm, and there is no spark present at the plugs, the problem lies in the direct ignition system or the power and ground supplies to the module.

Test Description: Numbers below refer to circled numbers on the diagnostic chart.

1. The direct ignition system uses two plugs and wires to complete the circuit of each coil. The other spark plug wire in the circuit must be left connected to create a spark.
2. This test will determine if the 12 volt supply and a good ground is available at the DIS ignition module.
3. This test will determine if the ignition module is not generating the reference pulse, or if the wiring or ECM are at fault. By touching and removing a test light to 12 volts on CKT 430, a reference pulse should be generated. If rpm is indicated, the ECM and wiring are OK.
4. This test will determine if the ignition module is not triggering the problem coil, or if the tested coil is at fault. This test could also be performed by substituting a known good coil. The secondary coil winding can be checked with a DVM. There should be 5,000 to 10,000 ohms across the coil towers. There should not be any continuity from either coil tower to ground.
5. Checks for continuity of the crank sensor and connections. Also checks sensor magnetism.

CHART A-3
(Page 1 of 3)
ENGINE CRANKS BUT WON'T RUN
2.0L (VIN 1) "L" CARLINE (TBI)

1. • IGNITION "ON" - IF "SES" LIGHT IS "OFF", USE CHART A-1.
   • INSTALL "SCAN" TOOL - IF NO DATA, USE CHART A-2.
   • CHECK THE FOLLOWING:
     TPS - IF OVER 2.5V AT CLOSED THROTTLE, USE CODE 22 CHART.
     COOLANT - IF BELOW -30°C, USE CODE 15 CHART.
     RPM - IF NO RPM WHILE CRANKING, USE CHART A-3 (Page 2 of 3).

   • PROBE FUEL PUMP TEST TERMINAL WITH A TEST LIGHT TO BATTERY VOLTAGE.
   • IGNITION "OFF" FOR 10 SECONDS.
   • IGNITION "ON."
   • TEST LIGHT SHOULD TURN "OFF" FOR ABOUT 2 SECONDS AFTER IGNITION IS TURNED "ON." DOES IT?

   NO → USE FUEL PUMP RELAY CIRCUIT CHART A-5.

   YES

2. • CRANK ENGINE AND CHECK FOR SPARK WITH ST-125 ON SPARK PLUG WIRES 1&2 OR 3&4.
   • CHECK ONE WIRE AT A TIME. LEAVE THE OTHER WIRES CONNECTED TO THE SPARK PLUGS DURING CRANKING.
   IS THERE SPARK ON BOTH WIRES?

   NO → SPARK ON ONE → USE CHART A-3 (Page 2 of 3).
       → NO SPARK → REPLACE IGNITION MODULE.

   YES

3. • DISCONNECT INJECTOR CONNECTOR.
   • CRANK ENGINE. IS THERE FUEL SPRAY FROM INJECTOR?

   YES → FAULTY INJECTOR OR O-RING.

   NO

4. • CONNECT INJECTOR TEST LIGHT TO HARNESS CONNECTOR.
   • CRANK ENGINE. DOES TEST LIGHT FLASH?

   NO → USE CHART A-3 (Page 3 of 3).

   YES

5. • RECONNECT INJECTOR CONNECTOR.
   • CRANK ENGINE. IS THERE FUEL SPRAY FROM INJECTOR?

   YES → CHECK FOR:
     • FOULED SPARK PLUGS.
     • EGR VALVE STUCK OPEN.
     • LOW FUEL PRESSURE USE CHART A-7.
     REFER TO "DIAGNOSTIC AIDS" ON FACING PAGE.

   NO

   • IGNITION "OFF."
   • INSTALL FUEL PRESSURE GAGE.
   • IGNITION "ON."
   • FUEL PRESSURE SHOULD BE 62-90 kPa (9-13 psi). IS IT?

   YES → USE FUEL SYSTEM DIAGNOSIS CHART A-7.

   NO → REPLACE INJECTOR.

1988–89 2.0L ENGINE

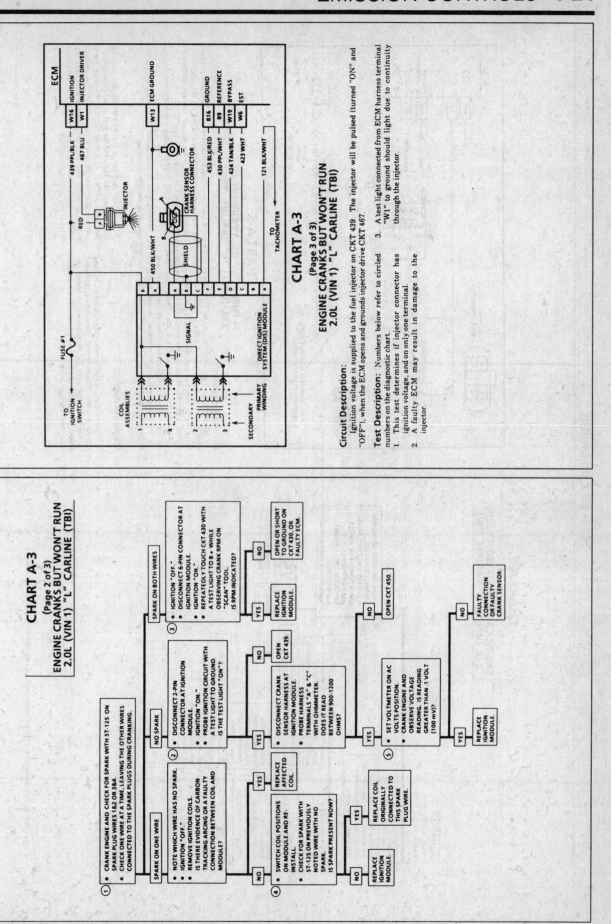

1988–89 2.0L ENGINE

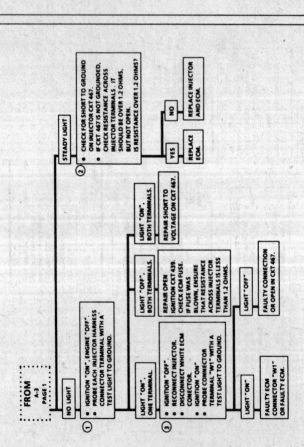

CHART A-5
FUEL PUMP RELAY CIRCUIT
2.0L (VIN 1) "L" CARLINE (TBI)

ECM

W10 W15 W24 W13

12 VOLT RELAY DRIVE

150

340 ORN

465 DK GRN

450 BLK/WHT

FUEL PUMP (IN TANK)

120

15 PIN BODY CONNECTOR

FUEL PUMP RELAY CONNECTOR

C A F
D E F

ENGINE GROUND

FUEL PUMP RELAY

BULKHEAD CONNECTOR

OIL PRESSURE SWITCH

RED

UNDERHOOD FUSE & HOLDER

RED

BATTERY JUNCTION BLOCK (12 VOLT)

FUEL PUMP TEST TERMINAL (LOCATED BEHIND LEFT SHOCK TOWER)

Circuit Description:

When the ignition switch is turned "ON," the engine control module (ECM) will activate the fuel pump relay with a 12 volt signal and run the in-tank fuel pump. The fuel pump will operate as long as the engine is cranking or running and the ECM is receiving ignition reference pulses. If there are no ignition reference pulses, the ECM will no longer supply the fuel pump relay signal within 2 seconds after key "ON."

Should the fuel pump relay or the 12 volt relay drive from the ECM fail, the fuel pump will receive electrical current through the oil pressure switch back-up circuit.

The fuel pump test terminal is located in the left side of the engine compartment. When the engine is stopped, the pump can be turned "ON" by applying battery voltage to the test terminal.

Diagnostic Aids:

An inoperative fuel pump relay can result in long cranking times. The extended crank period is caused by the time necessary for oil pressure to reach the pressure required to close the oil pressure switch and turn "ON" the fuel pump.

A "Scan" tool set in the PPSW position may be used to check the status of the fuel pump relay circuit. Normally, PPSW will read battery voltage for 2 seconds after the ignition is turned "ON." A reading of zero volts for the first two seconds after ignition "ON" would indicate a problem with the fuel pump relay or the relay drive circuit.

CHART A-3
(Page 3 of 3)
ENGINE CRANKS BUT WON'T RUN
2.0L (VIN 1) "L" CARLINE (TBI)

FROM A-3 PAGE 1

① IGNITION "ON", ENGINE "OFF". PROBE EACH INJECTOR HARNESS CONNECTOR TERMINAL WITH A TEST LIGHT TO GROUND.

NO LIGHT

LIGHT "ON", ONE TERMINAL.

③ IGNITION "OFF". RECONNECT INJECTOR. DISCONNECT WHITE ECM CONNECTOR. IGNITION "ON". PROBE CONNECTOR TERMINAL "W1" WITH A TEST LIGHT TO GROUND.

LIGHT "ON"

FAULTY ECM CONNECTOR "W1" OR FAULTY ECM.

LIGHT "OFF".

FAULTY CONNECTION OR OPEN IN CKT 467.

LIGHT "OFF", BOTH TERMINALS.

REPAIR OPEN IGNITION CKT 439. CHECK ECM FUSE. IF FUSE WAS BLOWN, ENSURE THAT RESISTANCE ACROSS INJECTOR TERMINALS IS LESS THAN 1.2 OHMS.

LIGHT "ON", BOTH TERMINALS.

REPAIR SHORT TO VOLTAGE ON CKT 467.

STEADY LIGHT

② CHECK FOR SHORT TO GROUND ON INJECTOR CKT 467. IF CKT 467 IS NOT GROUNDED, CHECK RESISTANCE ACROSS INJECTOR TERMINALS. IT SHOULD BE OVER 1.2 OHMS, BUT NOT OPEN.

IS RESISTANCE OVER 1.2 OHMS?

YES — REPLACE ECM.

NO — REPLACE INJECTOR AND ECM.

• CLEAR CODES AND CONFIRM "CLOSED LOOP" OPERATION AND NO "SERVICE ENGINE SOON" LIGHT.

1988–89 2.0L ENGINE

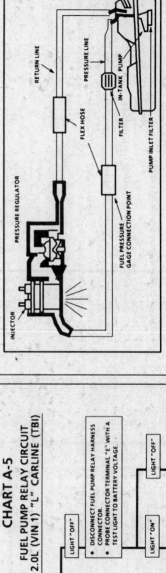

CHART A-7
FUEL SYSTEM DIAGNOSIS
2.0L (VIN 1) "L" CARLINE (TBI)

Circuit Description:

The fuel pump test terminal delivers fuel to the TBI unit where the system pressure is controlled to 62 to 90 kPa (9 to 13 psi). Excess fuel is returned to the fuel tank.

When the ignition switch is turned "ON," the electronic control module (ECM) will activate the fuel pump relay with a 12 volt signal and run the in-tank fuel pump. The fuel pump will operate as long as the engine is cranking or running and the ECM is receiving ignition reference pulses. If there are no ignition reference pulses, the ECM will no longer supply the fuel pump relay signal within 2 seconds after key "ON."

Should the fuel pump relay or the 12 volt relay drive from the ECM fail, the fuel pump will receive electrical current through the oil pressure switch back-up circuit.

Test Description: Numbers below refer to circled numbers on the diagnostic chart.

1. If fuse in jumper wire blows, check CKT 120, between relay and fuel pump, for a short to ground.

2. Fuel flow at less than 62 kPa (9 psi) can cause the following:
   System will run lean and may set Code 44. Also, hard starting and poor overall performance will result.
   Engine surging and possible stalling during driving with satisfactory idle quality. This would be caused by a restriction in the fuel flow. As the fuel flow increases, the pressure drop across the restriction becomes great enough to starve the engine of fuel. At idle, the pressure may still be adequate. Normally, an engine with a fuel pressure less than 62 kPa (9 psi) at idle will not be driveable.

3. Gradually restricting the fuel return line allows the fuel pump to develop its maximum pressure (dead head pressure). When battery voltage is applied to the pump test terminal, pressure should be between 90 and 124 kPa (13 to 18 psi).

4. This test determines if the high fuel pressure is due to a restricted fuel return line or a throttle body pressure regulator problem.

Diagnostic Aids:

Improper fuel system pressure can result in one of the following symptoms:
- Cranks, but won't run.
- Code 44.
- Code 45.
- Cuts out, may feel like ignition problem.
- Poor fuel economy, loss of power.
- Hesitation.

CHART A-5
FUEL PUMP RELAY CIRCUIT
2.0L (VIN 1) "L" CARLINE (TBI)

- ENGINE "OFF", IGNITION "OFF".
- PROBE FUEL PUMP TEST TERMINAL WITH TEST LIGHT TO BATTERY VOLTAGE.

- IGNITION MUST BE "OFF" FOR TEN SECONDS.
- TURN IGNITION "ON".
- TEST LIGHT SHOULD GO "OFF" FOR ABOUT TWO SECONDS. DOES IT?

LIGHT "ON" → DISCONNECT FUEL PUMP RELAY HARNESS CONNECTOR. PROBE CONNECTOR TERMINAL "A" WITH A TEST LIGHT TO GROUND.

YES → REPLACE FUEL PUMP RELAY.

LIGHT "ON" → REPLACE FUEL RELAY.

LIGHT "OFF" → OPEN CKT 340 (CHECK FUEL PUMP FUSE, WIRING, AND CONNECTIONS).

NO → DISCONNECT FUEL PUMP RELAY HARNESS CONNECTOR. PROBE HARNESS CONNECTOR TERMINAL "F" WITH A TEST LIGHT TO BATTERY VOLTAGE.

LIGHT "ON" → OPEN CKT 450.

LIGHT "OFF" → OPEN CIRCUIT BETWEEN FUEL PUMP TEST TERMINAL AND FAULTY RELAY.

DISCONNECT FUEL PUMP RELAY HARNESS CONNECTOR. PROBE CONNECTOR TERMINAL "E" WITH A TEST LIGHT TO BATTERY VOLTAGE.

LIGHT "OFF" → OPEN CKT 120, OPEN CKT 150, FAULTY CONNECTIONS, OR FAULTY IN-TANK FUEL PUMP.

LIGHT "ON" → PROBE FUEL PUMP RELAY HARNESS CONNECTOR TERMINAL "D" WITH A TEST LIGHT TO GROUND. IGNITION MUST BE "ON" FOR TEN SECONDS. TURN IGNITION "ON". TEST LIGHT SHOULD LIGHT FOR ABOUT TWO SECONDS. DOES IT?

LIGHT "OFF" (connects to above)

YES → REPLACE FUEL PUMP RELAY.

NO → OPEN OR GROUNDED CKT 465 OR FAULTY ECM.

IF ORIGINAL SYMPTOM WAS "ENGINE CRANKS BUT WON'T RUN", TEST OIL PRESSURE SWITCH AS FOLLOWS:
- ALLOW ENGINE TO RUN AT NORMAL TEMPERATURE AND OIL PRESSURE.
- DISCONNECT FUEL PUMP RELAY HARNESS CONNECTOR.
- ENGINE SHOULD CONTINUE TO RUN. DOES IT?

YES → NO TROUBLE FOUND.

NO → REPLACE OIL PRESSURE SWITCH.

1988-89 2.0L ENGINE

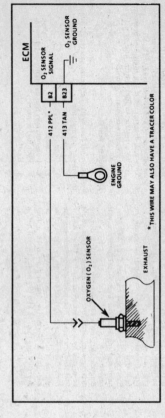

ECM

O₂ SENSOR SIGNAL — B2 — 412 PPL*

O₂ SENSOR GROUND — B23 — 413 TAN

ENGINE GROUND

OXYGEN (O₂) SENSOR

EXHAUST

* THIS WIRE MAY ALSO HAVE A TRACER COLOR

CODE 13
OXYGEN SENSOR CIRCUIT
(OPEN CIRCUIT)
2.0L (VIN 1) "L" CARLINE (TBI)

Circuit Description:

The ECM supplies a voltage of about .45 volt between terminals "B2" and "B23". (If measured with a 10 megohm digital voltmeter, this may read as low as .32 volt).

When the O₂ sensor reaches operating temperature, it varies this voltage from about .1 volt (exhaust is lean) to about .9 volt (exhaust is rich).

The sensor is like an open circuit and produces no voltage when it is below 360°C (600°F). An open sensor circuit, or cold sensor, causes "Open Loop" operation.

Test Description: Numbers below refer to circled numbers on the diagnostic chart.

1. Code 13 will set under the following conditions:
   - Engine at normal operating temperature
   - At least 1 minutes have elapsed since engine start-up
   - O₂ signal voltage is steady between .35 and .55 volt
   - Throttle angle is above 7%
   - All above conditions are met for about 20 seconds.

   If the conditions for a Code 13 exist, the system will not operate in "Closed Loop."

2. This test determines if the O₂ sensor is the problem or if the ECM and wiring are at fault.

3. In doing this test, use only a 10 megohm digital voltmeter. This test checks the continuity of CKTs 412 and 413. If CKT 413 is open, the ECM voltage on CKT 412 will be over .6 volt (600 mV).

Diagnostic Aids:

Normal "Scan" tool O₂ sensor voltage varies between 100mV to 999 mV (.1 and 1.0 volt) while in "Closed Loop." Code 13 sets in one minute if sensor signal voltage remains between .35 and .55 volt, but the system will go to "Open Loop" in about 15 seconds.

Verify a clean, tight ground connection for CKT 413. Open CKT(s) 412 or 413 will result in a Code 13. If Code 13 is intermittent, refer to Section "B".

CHART A-7
FUEL SYSTEM DIAGNOSIS
2.0L (VIN 1) "L" CARLINE (TBI)

NOTICE: FUEL SYSTEM IS UNDER PRESSURE. TO AVOID FUEL SPILLAGE, REFER TO FIELD SERVICE PROCEDURE FOR TESTING OR MAKING REPAIRS REQUIRING DISASSEMBLY OF FUEL LINES OR FITTINGS.

(1)
- CHECK FUEL TANK QUANTITY.
- IGNITION "OFF".
- INSTALL PRESSURE GAGE.
- JUMPER THE FUEL PUMP TEST TERMINAL TO BATTERY VOLTAGE USING A FUSED JUMPER WIRE.
- NOTE PRESSURE, IT SHOULD BE 62-90 kPa (9-13 psi).

(2)
PRESSURE IS LESS THAN 62 kPa (9 psi).

LISTEN FOR PUMP RUNNING AT FUEL TANK. IS IT RUNNING?

NO

YES

(3)
- RESTRICT FUEL FLOW BY GRADUALLY PINCHING HOSE ON GAGE ASSEMBLY BETWEEN GAGE AND TBI UNIT.
- NOTE PRESSURE.

CHECK FOR THE FOLLOWING:
- OPEN WIRE IN FUEL PUMP POWER CKT 120.
- OPEN PUMP GROUND WIRE CKT 150.
IF OK, REPLACE FUEL PUMP.

NO PRESSURE

PRESSURE IS ABOVE 62 kPa (9 psi).

CHECK FOR THE FOLLOWING:
- PLUGGED IN-LINE FILTER.
- PLUGGED PUMP INLET FILTER.
- RESTRICTED FUEL LINE.
- LEAKING RUBBER PUMP COUPLING.
IF OK, REPLACE FUEL PUMP.

REPLACE PRESSURE REGULATOR.

(4)
PRESSURE IS ABOVE 90 kPa (13 psi).

- DISCONNECT INJECTOR CONNECTOR.
- DISCONNECT FUEL RETURN LINE AT ENGINE/BODY FUEL LINE CONNECTION.
- ATTACH 5/16" ID FLEX HOSE TO ENGINE SIDE OF RETURN LINE. INSERT THE OTHER END IN AN APPROVED GASOLINE CONTAINER.
- NOTE FUEL PRESSURE WITHIN 2 SECONDS AFTER IGNITION IS TURNED "ON."

PRESSURE IS BETWEEN 62 kPa AND 89 kPa (9 psi - 13 psi).

LOCATE AND CORRECT RESTRICTED FUEL RETURN LINE TO FUEL TANK.

PRESSURE IS ABOVE 89.63 kPa (13 psi).

CHECK FOR RESTRICTED FUEL RETURN LINE FROM THROTTLE BODY TO WHERE LINE WAS DISCONNECTED. IF LINE IS OK, REPLACE PRESSURE REGULATOR.

CLEAR CODES AND CONFIRM "CLOSED LOOP" OPERATION AND NO "SERVICE ENGINE SOON" LIGHT.

1988–89 2.0L ENGINE

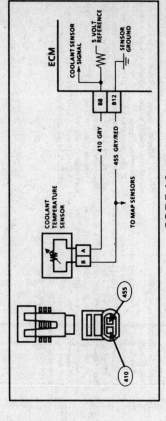

CODE 14
COOLANT TEMPERATURE SENSOR CIRCUIT
(HIGH TEMPERATURE INDICATED)
2.0L (VIN 1) "L" CARLINE (TBI)

Circuit Description:

The coolant temperature sensor uses a thermistor to control the signal voltage to the ECM. The ECM applies a voltage on CKT 410 to the sensor. When the engine is cold, the sensor (thermistor) resistance is high. The ECM will then sense a high signal voltage.

As the engine warms up, the sensor resistance decreases and the voltage drops. At normal engine operating temperature, the voltage will measure about 1.5 to 2.0 volts at ECM terminal "B8".

Coolant temperature is one of the inputs used to control the following:

- Fuel delivery
- Electronic spark timing (EST)
- Cooling fan
- Torque converter clutch (TCC)
- Idle air control (IAC)

Test Description: Numbers below refer to circled numbers on the diagnostic chart.

1. Checks to see if code was set as result of hard failure or intermittent condition. Code 14 will set if:
   - Engine has been running for more than 10 seconds
   - Signal voltage indicates a coolant temperature above 135°C (275°F) for 3 seconds

2. This test simulates conditions for a Code 15. If the ECM recognizes the open circuit (high voltage), and displays a low temperature, the ECM and wiring are OK.

Diagnostic Aids:

A "Scan" tool reads engine temperature in degrees Celsius. After the engine is started, the temperature should rise steadily to about 90°, then stabilize when the thermostat opens.

If the engine has been allowed to cool to an ambient temperature (overnight), coolant and MAT temperature may be checked with a "Scan" tool and should read close to each other.

When a Code 14 is set, the ECM will turn "ON" the engine cooling fan.

A Code 14 will result if CKT 410 is shorted to ground.

If Code 14 is intermittent refer to Section "B".

CODE 13
OXYGEN SENSOR CIRCUIT
(OPEN CIRCUIT)
2.0L (VIN 1) "L" CARLINE (TBI)

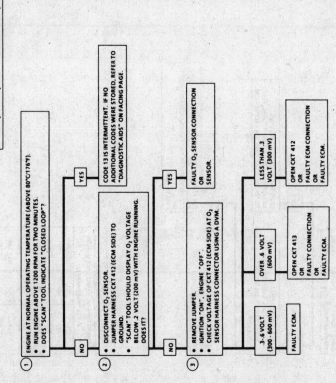

① ENGINE AT NORMAL OPERATING TEMPERATURE (ABOVE 80°C/176°F).
- RUN ENGINE ABOVE 1200 RPM FOR TWO MINUTES.
- DOES "SCAN" TOOL INDICATE "CLOSED LOOP"?

YES → CODE 13 IS INTERMITTENT. IF NO ADDITIONAL CODES WERE STORED, REFER TO "DIAGNOSTIC AIDS" ON FACING PAGE.

NO →

② DISCONNECT O₂ SENSOR.
- JUMPER HARNESS CKT 412 (ECM SIDE) TO GROUND.
- "SCAN" TOOL SHOULD DISPLAY O₂ VOLTAGE BELOW .2 VOLT (200 mV) WITH ENGINE RUNNING. DOES IT?

YES → FAULTY O₂ SENSOR CONNECTION OR SENSOR.

NO →

③ REMOVE JUMPER.
- IGNITION "ON", ENGINE "OFF".
- CHECK VOLTAGE OF CKT 412 (ECM SIDE) AT O₂ SENSOR HARNESS CONNECTOR USING A DVM.

- **LESS THAN 3 VOLT (300 mV)** → OPEN CKT 412 OR FAULTY ECM CONNECTION OR FAULTY ECM.
- **.3 - .6 VOLT (300 - 600 mV)** → FAULTY ECM.
- **OVER .6 VOLT (600 mV)** → OPEN CKT 413 OR FAULTY CONNECTION OR FAULTY ECM.

CLEAR CODES AND CONFIRM "CLOSED LOOP" OPERATION AND NO "SERVICE ENGINE SOON" LIGHT.

1988-89 2.0L ENGINE

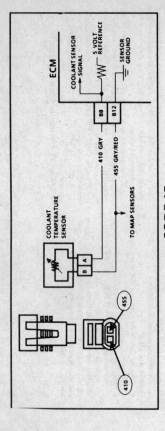

CODE 15

COOLANT TEMPERATURE SENSOR CIRCUIT
(LOW TEMPERATURE INDICATED)
2.0L (VIN 1) "L" CARLINE (TBI)

Circuit Description:

The coolant temperature sensor uses a thermistor to control the signal voltage to the ECM. The ECM applies a voltage on CKT 410 to the sensor. When the engine is cold, the sensor (thermistor) resistance is high. The ECM will then sense a high signal voltage.

As the engine warms up, the sensor resistance decreases and the voltage drops. At normal engine operating temperature, the voltage will measure about 1.5 to 2.0 volts at ECM terminal "B8".

Coolant temperature is one of the inputs used to control the following:

- Fuel delivery
- Electronic spark timing (EST)
- Cooling fan
- Torque converter clutch (TCC)
- Idle air control (IAC)

Test Description: Numbers below refer to circled numbers on the diagnostic chart.

1. Check to see if code was set as result of hard failure or intermittent condition. Code 15 will set if:
   - Engine has been running for more than 50 seconds
   - Signal voltage indicates a coolant temperature below -30°C (-22°F).
2. This test simulates conditions for a Code 14. If the ECM recognizes the grounded circuit (low voltage), and displays a high temperature, the ECM and wiring are OK.
3. This test will determine if there is a wiring problem or a faulty ECM. If CKT 452 is open, there may also abe a Code 33 stored

Diagnostic Aids:

A "Scan" tool reads engine temperature in degrees Celsius. After the engine is started, the temperature should rise steadily to about 90°, then stabilize, when the thermostat opens.

If the engine has been allowed to cool to an ambient temperature (overnight), coolant and MAT temperature may be checked with a "Scan" tool and should read close to each other.

When a Code 15 is set, the ECM will turn "ON" the engine cooling fan.

A Code 15 will result if CKTs 410 or 455 are open

If Code 15 is intermittent, refer to Section "B"

CODE 14

COOLANT TEMPERATURE SENSOR CIRCUIT
(HIGH TEMPERATURE INDICATED)
2.0L (VIN 1) "L" CARLINE (TBI)

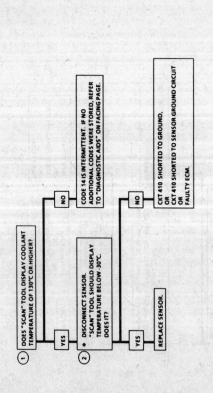

① DOES "SCAN" TOOL DISPLAY COOLANT TEMPERATURE OF 130°C OR HIGHER?

NO → CODE 14 IS INTERMITTENT. IF NO ADDITIONAL CODES WERE STORED, REFER TO "DIAGNOSTIC AIDS" ON FACING PAGE.

YES ↓

② DISCONNECT SENSOR. "SCAN" TOOL SHOULD DISPLAY TEMPERATURE BELOW -30°C. DOES IT?

NO → CKT 410 SHORTED TO GROUND, OR CKT 410 SHORTED TO SENSOR GROUND CIRCUIT OR FAULTY ECM.

YES ↓

REPLACE SENSOR.

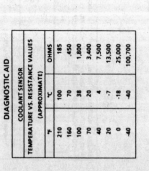

DIAGNOSTIC AID

COOLANT SENSOR		
TEMPERATURE VS. RESISTANCE VALUES (APPROXIMATE)		
°F	°C	OHMS
210	100	185
160	70	450
100	38	1,800
70	20	3,400
40	4	7,500
20	-7	13,500
0	-18	25,000
-40	-40	100,700

CLEAR CODES AND CONFIRM "CLOSED LOOP" OPERATION AND NO "SERVICE ENGINE SOON" LIGHT.

1988–89 2.0L ENGINE

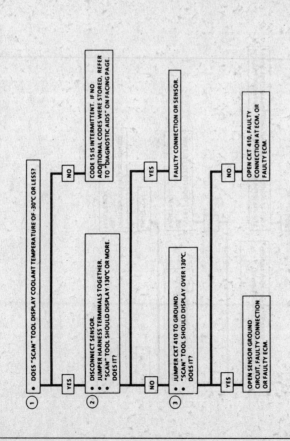

CODE 21
THROTTLE POSITION SENSOR (TPS) CIRCUIT
(SIGNAL VOLTAGE HIGH)
2.0L (VIN 1) "L" CARLINE (TBI)

Circuit Description:

The throttle position sensor (TPS) provides a voltage signal that changes relative to the throttle valve. Signal voltage will vary from less than 1.25 volts at idle to about 5 volts at wide open throttle (WOT). The TPS signal is one of the most important inputs used by the ECM for fuel control and for many of the ECM controlled outputs.

Test Description: Numbers below refer to circled numbers on the diagnostic chart.

1. This step checks to see if Code 21 is the result of a hard failure or an intermittent condition. A Code 21 will set under the following conditions:
   - TPS reading above 2.5 volts.
   - MAP reading below 55 kPa.
   - All of the above conditions present for 5 seconds.
2. This step simulates conditions for a Code 22. If the ECM recognizes the change of state, the ECM and CKTs 416 and 417 are OK.
3. This step isolates a faulty sensor, ECM, or an open CKT 452. If CKT 452 is open, there may also be a Code 23 stored.

Diagnostic Aids:

A "Scan" tool displays throttle position in volts. Closed throttle voltage should be less than 1.25 volts. TPS voltage should increase at a steady rate as throttle is moved to WOT.

A Code 21 will result if CKT 452 is open or CKT 417 is shorted to voltage. If Code 21 is intermittent, refer to Section "B".

CODE 15
COOLANT TEMPERATURE SENSOR CIRCUIT
(LOW TEMPERATURE INDICATED)
2.0L (VIN 1) "L" CARLINE (TBI)

1. DOES "SCAN" TOOL DISPLAY COOLANT TEMPERATURE OF -30°C OR LESS?

   NO → CODE 15 IS INTERMITTENT. IF NO ADDITIONAL CODES WERE STORED, REFER TO "DIAGNOSTIC AIDS" ON FACING PAGE.

   YES ↓

2. - DISCONNECT SENSOR.
   - JUMPER HARNESS TERMINALS TOGETHER.
   - "SCAN" TOOL SHOULD DISPLAY 130°C OR MORE. DOES IT?

   YES → FAULTY CONNECTION OR SENSOR.

   NO ↓

3. - JUMPER CKT 410 TO GROUND.
   - "SCAN" TOOL SHOULD DISPLAY OVER 130°C. DOES IT?

   YES → OPEN SENSOR GROUND CIRCUIT, FAULTY CONNECTION OR FAULTY ECM.

   NO → OPEN CKT 410, FAULTY CONNECTION AT ECM, OR FAULTY ECM.

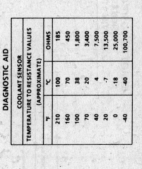

DIAGNOSTIC AID

COOLANT SENSOR

TEMPERATURE TO RESISTANCE VALUES (APPROXIMATE)

°F	°C	OHMS
210	100	185
160	70	450
100	38	1,800
70	20	3,400
40	4	7,500
20	-7	13,500
0	-18	25,000
-40	-40	100,700

CLEAR CODES AND CONFIRM "CLOSED LOOP" OPERATION AND NO "SERVICE ENGINE SOON" LIGHT.

1988–89 2.0L ENGINE

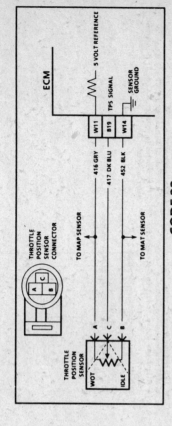

THROTTLE POSITION SENSOR CONNECTOR

THROTTLE POSITION SENSOR

WOT

IDLE

A C B

TO MAP SENSOR

TO MAT SENSOR

ECM

5 VOLT REFERENCE

W11 — 416 GRY

B19 — 417 DK BLU — TPS SIGNAL

W14 — 452 BLK — SENSOR GROUND

CODE 22

THROTTLE POSITION SENSOR (TPS) CIRCUIT
(SIGNAL VOLTAGE LOW)
2.0L (VIN 1) "L" CARLINE (TBI)

Circuit Description:

The throttle position sensor (TPS) provides a voltage signal that changes relative to the throttle valve. Signal voltage will vary from less than 1.25 volts at idle to about 5 volts at wide open throttle (WOT).

The TPS signal is one of the most important inputs used by the ECM for fuel control and for many of the ECM controlled outputs.

Test Description: Numbers below refer to circled numbers on the diagnostic chart.

1. This step checks to see if Code 22 is the result of a hard failure or an intermittent condition.

   A Code 22 will set under the following conditions:
   - The engine is running.
   - TPS voltage is below 2 volt (200 mV).

2. This step simulates conditions for a Code 21. If a Code 21 is set or the "Scan" tool displays over 4 volts, the ECM and wiring are OK.

3. The "Scan" tool may not display 12 volts. What is important is that the ECM recognizes the voltage as over 4 volts, indicating that CKT 417 and the ECM are OK.

4. If CKT 416 is shorted to ground, there may also be a stored Code 34.

   If CKT 416 is NOT shorted to ground and a Code 34 is stored, check CKT 432 for a short to ground.

Diagnostic Aids:

A "Scan" tool displays throttle position in volts. Closed throttle voltage should be less than 1.25 volts. TPS voltage should increase at a steady rate as throttle is moved to WOT.

An open or grounded 416 or 417 will result in a Code 22.

If Code 22 is intermittent, refer to Section "B".

CODE 21

THROTTLE POSITION SENSOR (TPS) CIRCUIT
(SIGNAL VOLTAGE HIGH)
2.0L (VIN 1) "L" CARLINE (TBI)

1. THROTTLE CLOSED. DOES "SCAN" TOOL DISPLAY TPS OVER 2.5 VOLTS?

   - NO → CODE 21 IS INTERMITTENT. IF NO ADDITIONAL CODES WERE STORED, REFER TO "DIAGNOSTIC AIDS" ON FACING PAGE.

   - YES → 2. DISCONNECT SENSOR. "SCAN" TOOL SHOULD DISPLAY TPS BELOW .2 VOLT (200mV). DOES IT?

     - NO → CKT 417 SHORTED TO VOLTAGE OR FAULTY ECM.

     - YES → 3. PROBE SENSOR GROUND CIRCUIT WITH A TEST LIGHT CONNECTED TO BATTERY VOLTAGE.

       - LIGHT "OFF" → OPEN SENSOR GROUND CIRCUIT OR FAULTY ECM.

       - LIGHT "ON" → FAULTY CONNECTION OR SENSOR.

CLEAR CODES AND CONFIRM "CLOSED LOOP" OPERATION AND NO "SERVICE ENGINE SOON" LIGHT.

1988-89 2.0L ENGINE

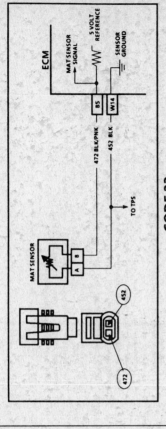

CODE 23

MANIFOLD AIR TEMPERATURE (MAT) SENSOR CIRCUIT
(LOW TEMPERATURE INDICATED)
2.0L (VIN 1) "L" CARLINE (TBI)

Circuit Description:

The manifold air temperature sensor uses a thermistor to control the signal voltage to the ECM. The ECM applies a reference voltage (4-6 volts) on CKT 472 to the sensor. When manifold air is cold, the sensor (thermistor) resistance is high. The ECM will then sense a high signal voltage. As the air warms, the sensor resistance becomes less and the voltage drops.

Test Description: Numbers below refer to circled numbers on the diagnostic chart.

1. This step checks to see if Code 23 is the result of a hard failure or an intermittent condition.
   Code 23 will set under the following conditions:
   - Engine is running for longer than 8.5 minutes.
   - Signal voltage indicates a MAT temperature less than -30°C.
   - There is no VSS signal.
2. This test simulates conditions for a Code 25. If the "Scan" tool displays a high temperature, the ECM and wiring are OK.
3. This step checks continuity of CKTs 472 and 452. If CKT 452 is open, there may also be a Code 21.

Diagnostic Aids:

If the engine has been allowed to cool to an ambient temperature (overnight), coolant and MAT temperatures may be checked with a "Scan" tool and should read close to each other.

A Code 23 will result if CKTs 472 or 452 become open.

If Code 23 is intermittent, refer to Section "B".

CODE 22

THROTTLE POSITION SENSOR (TPS) CIRCUIT
(SIGNAL VOLTAGE LOW)
2.0L (VIN 1) "L" CARLINE (TBI)

1. • THROTTLE CLOSED.
   DOES "SCAN" DISPLAY TPS .2V (200 mV) OR BELOW?

   YES →

   2. • DISCONNECT TPS SENSOR.
      • JUMPER CKTS 416 & 417 TOGETHER.
      • "SCAN" SHOULD DISPLAY TPS OVER 4.0 V (4000 mV).
      DOES IT?

      NO →

      4. • PROBE CKT 417 WITH A TEST LIGHT CONNECTED TO BATTERY VOLTAGE.
         • "SCAN" TOOL SHOULD DISPLAY TPS OVER 4.0V (4000 mV).
         DOES IT?

         YES →

         CKT 416 OPEN OR SHORTED TO GROUND
         OR
         FAULTY CONNECTION
         OR
         FAULTY ECM.

         NO →

         CKT 417 OPEN OR SHORTED TO GROUND, OR SHORTED TO SENSOR GROUND CIRCUIT
         OR
         FAULTY ECM CONNECTION
         OR
         FAULTY ECM.

   NO →

   • CODE 22 IS INTERMITTENT.
   IF NO ADDITIONAL CODES WERE STORED, REFER TO "DIAGNOSTIC AIDS" ON FACING PAGE.

   YES →

   3. • REFER TO FACING PAGE FOR SPECIFIC INSTRUCTIONS.

CLEAR CODES AND CONFIRM "CLOSED LOOP" OPERATION AND NO "SERVICE ENGINE SOON" LIGHT.

1988–89 2.0L ENGINE

CODE 23
MANIFOLD AIR TEMPERATURE (MAT) SENSOR CIRCUIT
(LOW TEMPERATURE INDICATED)
2.0L (VIN 1) "L" CARLINE (TBI)

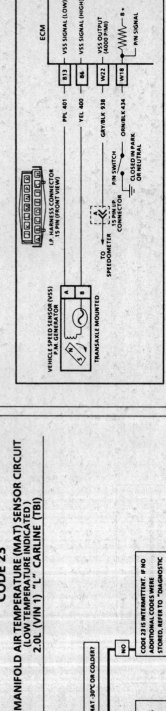

1. DOES "SCAN" TOOL DISPLAY MAT -30°C OR COLDER?

NO → CODE 23 IS INTERMITTENT. IF NO ADDITIONAL CODES WERE STORED, REFER TO "DIAGNOSTIC AIDS" ON FACING PAGE.

YES →

2. • DISCONNECT SENSOR.
   • JUMPER HARNESS TERMINALS TOGETHER.
   • "SCAN" TOOL SHOULD DISPLAY TEMPERATURE OVER 130°C. DOES IT?

YES → FAULTY CONNECTION OR SENSOR.

NO →

3. • JUMPER CKT 472 TO GROUND.
   • "SCAN" TOOL SHOULD DISPLAY TEMPERATURE OVER 130°C. DOES IT?

YES → OPEN SENSOR GROUND CIRCUIT, FAULTY CONNECTION OR FAULTY ECM.

NO → OPEN CKT 472, FAULTY CONNECTION OR FAULTY ECM.

DIAGNOSTIC AID

MAT SENSOR
TEMPERATURE VS. RESISTANCE VALUES (APPROXIMATE)

°F	°C	OHMS
210	100	185
160	70	450
100	38	1,800
70	20	3,400
40	4	7,500
20	-7	13,500
0	-18	25,000
-40	-40	100,700

CLEAR CODES AND CONFIRM "CLOSED LOOP" OPERATION AND NO "SERVICE ENGINE SOON" LIGHT.

ECM
VSS SIGNAL (LOW) — B13 — PPL 401
VSS SIGNAL (HIGH) — B6 — YEL 400
VSS OUTPUT (4000 PPM) — W22 — GRY/BLK 938
P/N SIGNAL — W18 — B+ — ORN/BLK 434

P/N SWITCH
CLOSED IN PARK OR NEUTRAL

I.P. HARNESS CONNECTOR 15 PIN (FRONT VIEW)
15 PIN I/P CONNECTOR
TO SPEEDOMETER
VEHICLE SPEED SENSOR (VSS) P.M. GENERATOR
TRANSAXLE MOUNTED

CODE 24
VEHICLE SPEED SENSOR (VSS) CIRCUIT
2.0L (VIN 1) "L" CARLINE (TBI)

Circuit Description:

Vehicle speed information is provided to the ECM by the vehicle speed sensor, which is a permanent magnet (PM) generator and it is mounted in the transaxle. The PM generator produces a pulsing voltage, whenever vehicle speed is over about 3 mph. The AC voltage level and the number of pulses increases with vehicle speed. The ECM, then, converts the pulsing voltage to mph, which is used for calculations, and the mph can be displayed with a "Scan" tool.

The function of VSS buffer used in past model years has been incorporated into the ECM. The ECM then supplies the necessary signal for the instrument panel (4000 pulses per mile) for operating the speedometer and the odometer. If the vehicle is equipped with cruise control, the ECM also provides a signal (2000 pulses per mile) to the cruise control module.

Test Description:

1. Code 24 will set if vehicle speed equals 0 mph when:
   • Engine speed is between 1400 and 3600 rpm
   • TPS is less than 2%
   • Low load condition (low MAP voltage, high manifold vacuum)
   • Transmission not in park or neutral
   All above conditions are met for 5 seconds
   These conditions are met during a road load deceleration.
   Disregard a Code 24 that sets when the the drive wheels are not turning. This can be caused by a faulty park/neutral switch circuit.
   The PM generator only produces a signal if the drive wheels are turning greater than 3 mph.
2. Before replacing ECM, make sure that the correct PROM is installed for the application.

Diagnostic Aids:

"Scan" tool should indicate a vehicle speed whenever the drive wheels are turning greater than 3 mph.

A problem in CKT 938 will not affect the VSS input or the readings on a "Scan" tool.

Check CKTs 400 and 401 for proper connections to be sure they are clean and tight and the harness is routed correctly. Refer to intermittents in Section "B".

(A/T) - A faulty or misadjusted park/neutral switch can result in a false Code 24. Use a "Scan" tool and check for the proper signal while in a drive range. Refer to CHART C-1A for the P/N switch check.

1988-89 2.0L ENGINE

CODE 25

MANIFOLD AIR TEMPERATURE (MAT) SENSOR CIRCUIT
(HIGH TEMPERATURE INDICATED)
2.0L (VIN 1) "L" CARLINE (TBI)

Circuit Description:

The manifold air temperature sensor uses a thermistor to control the signal voltage to the ECM. The ECM applies a reference voltage (4-6 volts) on CKT 472 to the sensor. When manifold air is cold, the sensor (thermistor) resistance is high. The ECM will then sense a high signal voltage. As the air warms, the sensor resistance becomes less and the voltage drops.

Test Description: Numbers below refer to circled numbers on the diagnostic chart.

1. This check determines if the Code 25 is the result of a hard failure or an intermittent condition. A Code 25 will be set under the following conditions:
   - Engine has been running longer than 8.5 minutes.
   - A MAT temperature greater than 135°C is detected for a time longer than 2 seconds.
   - VSS signal present.

Diagnostic Aids:

If the engine has been allowed to cool to an ambient temperature (overnight), coolant and MAT temperatures may be checked with a "Scan" tool and should read close to each other.

A Code 25 will result if CKT 472 is shorted to ground.

If Code 25 is intermittent, refer to Section "B".

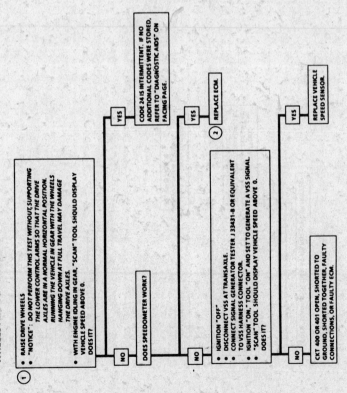

CODE 24

VEHICLE SPEED SENSOR (VSS) CIRCUIT
2.0L (VIN 1) "L" CARLINE (TBI)

1. • RAISE DRIVE WHEELS
   • "NOTICE": DO NOT PERFORM THIS TEST WITHOUT SUPPORTING THE LOWER CONTROL ARMS SO THAT THE DRIVE AXLES ARE IN A NORMAL HORIZONTAL POSITION. RUNNING THE VEHICLE IN GEAR WITH THE WHEELS HANGING DOWN AT FULL TRAVEL MAY DAMAGE THE DRIVE AXLES.
   • WITH ENGINE IDLING IN GEAR, "SCAN" TOOL SHOULD DISPLAY VEHICLE SPEED ABOVE 0.

DISREGARD CODE 24 IF SET WHILE DRIVE WHEELS ARE NOT TURNING.

DOES IT?

— NO —

DOES SPEEDOMETER WORK?

— YES — CODE 24 IS INTERMITTENT. IF NO ADDITIONAL CODES WERE STORED, REFER TO "DIAGNOSTIC AIDS" ON FACING PAGE.

— NO —

• IGNITION "OFF"
• DISCONNECT VSS AT TRANSAXLE.
• CONNECT SIGNAL GENERATOR TESTER J 33431-B OR EQUIVALENT TO VSS HARNESS CONNECTOR.
• IGNITION "ON", TOOL "ON" AND SET TO GENERATE A VSS SIGNAL.
• "SCAN" TOOL SHOULD DISPLAY VEHICLE SPEED ABOVE 0.

DOES IT?

— YES — 2 REPLACE ECM.

— NO —

CKT 400 OR 401 OPEN, SHORTED TO GROUND, SHORTED TOGETHER, FAULTY CONNECTIONS, OR FAULTY ECM.

— YES — REPLACE VEHICLE SPEED SENSOR.

CLEAR CODES AND CONFIRM "CLOSED LOOP" OPERATION AND NO "SERVICE ENGINE SOON" LIGHT.

1988–89 2.0L ENGINE

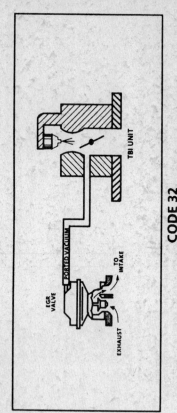

CODE 32
EXHAUST GAS RECIRCULATION (EGR) SYSTEM FAILURE
2.0L (VIN 1) "L" CARLINE (TBI)

Code Description:

A properly operating EGR system will directly affect the air/fuel mixture requirements of the engine. Since the exhaust gas introduced into the air/fuel mixture cannot be used in combustion (contains very little oxygen), less fuel is required to maintain a correct air/fuel ratio. If the EGR system were to fail in a closed position, the exhaust gas would be replaced with air, and the air/fuel mixture would be leaner. The ECM would compensate for the lean condition by adding fuel, resulting in higher block learn values.

The fuel control on this engine is conducted within 16 block learn cells. Since EGR is not used at idle, the closed throttle cell would not be affected by EGR system operation. The other block learn cells are affected by EGR operation, and, when the EGR system is operating properly, the block learn values in all cells should be close to the same. If the EGR system becomes inoperative, the block learn values in the open throttle cells would change to compensate for the resulting lean mixtures, but the block learn value in the closed throttle cell would not change.

The difference in block learn values between the idle (closed throttle) cell and cell 10 is used to monitor EGR system performance. When the difference between the two block learn values is greater than 12 and the block learn value in cell 10 is greater than 140, Code 32 is set. The system operates in block learn cell 10 during a cruise condition at approximately 55 mph.

Diagnostic Aids:

The Code 32 chart is a functional check of the EGR system. If the EGR system works properly but a Code 32 has been set, check other items that could result in high block learn values in block learn cell 10, but not in the closed throttle cell.

Check for restricted or blocked EGR passages. Perform a MAP output check. Follow the procedure in CHART C-10.

CODE 25
MANIFOLD AIR TEMPERATURE (MAT) SENSOR CIRCUIT
(HIGH TEMPERATURE INDICATED)
2.0L (VIN 1) "L" CARLINE (TBI)

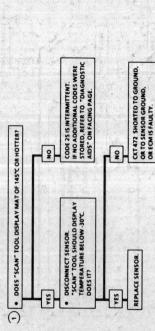

1. DOES "SCAN" TOOL DISPLAY MAT AT 145°C OR HOTTER?

- NO → CODE 25 IS INTERMITTENT. IF NO ADDITIONAL CODES WERE STORED, REFER TO "DIAGNOSTIC AIDS" ON FACING PAGE.
- YES → DISCONNECT SENSOR. "SCAN" TOOL SHOULD DISPLAY TEMPERATURE BELOW -30°C. DOES IT?
  - NO → REPLACE SENSOR.
  - YES → CKT 472 SHORTED TO GROUND, OR TO SENSOR GROUND, OR ECM IS FAULTY.

DIAGNOSTIC AID

MAT SENSOR
TEMPERATURE VS. RESISTANCE VALUES (APPROXIMATE)

°F	°C	OHMS
210	100	185
160	70	450
100	38	1,800
70	20	3,400
40	4	7,500
20	-7	13,500
0	-18	25,000
-40	-40	100,700

CLEAR CODES AND CONFIRM "CLOSED LOOP" OPERATION AND NO "SERVICE ENGINE SOON" LIGHT.

1988-89 2.0L ENGINE

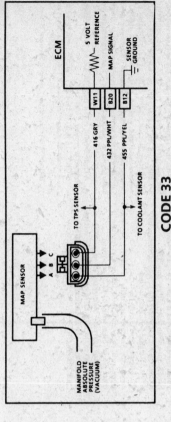

CODE 33

MANIFOLD ABSOLUTE PRESSURE (MAP) SENSOR CIRCUIT
(SIGNAL VOLTAGE HIGH - LOW VACUUM)
2.0L (VIN 1) "L" CARLINE (TBI)

Circuit Description:

The manifold absolute pressure (MAP) sensor responds to changes in manifold pressure (vacuum). The ECM receives this information as a signal voltage that will vary from about 1 to 1.5 volts at closed throttle idle, to 4-4.5 volts at wide open throttle (low vacuum).

If the MAP sensor fails, the ECM will substitute a fixed MAP value and use the throttle position sensor (TPS) to control fuel delivery.

Test Description: Numbers below refer to circled numbers on the diagnostic chart.

1. This step will determine if Code 33 is the result of a hard failure or an intermittent condition.
   A Code 33 will set if:
   - MAP signal voltage is too high (low manifold vacuum)
   - TPS less than 12%
   - No VSS signal
   - These conditions for a time longer than 5 seconds.

2. This step simulates conditions for a Code 34. If the ECM recognizes the change, the ECM and CKTs 416 and 432 are OK.

Diagnostic Aids:

With the ignition "ON" and the engine stopped, the manifold pressure is equal to atmospheric pressure and the signal voltage will be high. This information is used by the ECM as an indication of vehicle altitude and is referred to as BARO. Comparison of this BARO reading with a known good vehicle with the same sensor is a good way to check accuracy of a "suspect" sensor. Reading should be within .4 volt.

A Code 33 will result if CKT 455 is open, or if CKT 432 is shorted to voltage or to CKT 416.

If Code 33 is intermittent, refer to Section "B".

CODE 32

EXHAUST GAS RECIRCULATION (EGR) SYSTEM FAILURE
2.0L (VIN 1) "L" CARLINE (TBI)

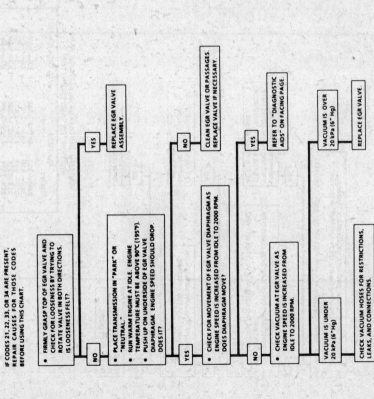

IF CODES 21, 22, 33, OR 34 ARE PRESENT, REPAIR CAUSES FOR THOSE CODES BEFORE USING THIS CHART.

- FIRMLY GRASP TOP OF EGR VALVE AND CHECK FOR LOOSENESS BY TRYING TO ROTATE VALVE IN BOTH DIRECTIONS. IS LOOSENESS FELT?

YES → REPLACE EGR VALVE ASSEMBLY.

NO →

- PLACE TRANSMISSION IN "PARK" OR "NEUTRAL".
- RUN WARM ENGINE AT IDLE. ENGINE TEMPERATURE MUST BE ABOVE 90°C (195°F).
- PUSH UP ON UNDERSIDE OF EGR VALVE DIAPHRAGM. ENGINE SPEED SHOULD DROP. DOES IT?

YES →

- CHECK FOR MOVEMENT OF EGR VALVE DIAPHRAGM AS ENGINE SPEED IS INCREASED FROM IDLE TO 2000 RPM. DOES DIAPHRAGM MOVE?

NO → CLEAN EGR VALVE OR PASSAGES. REPLACE VALVE IF NECESSARY.

NO →

- CHECK VACUUM AT EGR VALVE AS ENGINE SPEED IS INCREASED FROM IDLE TO 2000 RPM.

VACUUM IS UNDER 20 kPa (6" Hg)

YES → REFER TO "DIAGNOSTIC AIDS" ON FACING PAGE.

VACUUM IS OVER 20 kPa (6" Hg) → REPLACE EGR VALVE.

CHECK VACUUM HOSES FOR RESTRICTIONS, LEAKS, AND CONNECTIONS.

CLEAR CODES AND CONFIRM "CLOSED LOOP" OPERATION AND NO "SERVICE ENGINE SOON" LIGHT.

1988–89 2.0L ENGINE

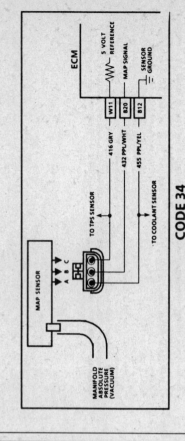

CODE 34

MANIFOLD ABSOLUTE PRESSURE (MAP) SENSOR CIRCUIT
(SIGNAL VOLTAGE LOW - HIGH VACUUM)
2.0L (VIN 1) "L" CARLINE (TBI)

Circuit Description:

The manifold absolute pressure (MAP) sensor responds to changes in manifold pressure (vacuum). The ECM receives this information as a signal voltage that will vary from about 1 to 1.5 volts at closed throttle (idle), to 4-4.5 volts at wide open throttle (low vacuum).

If the MAP sensor fails, the ECM will substitute a fixed MAP value and use the throttle position sensor (TPS) to control fuel delivery.

Test Description: Numbers below refer to circled numbers on the diagnostic chart.

1. This step determines if Code 34 is the result of a hard failure or an intermittent condition.
   A Code 34 will set under the following conditions:
   - MAP signal voltage is too low
   - Engine speed is over 1200 rpm

2. Jumpering harness terminals "B" to "C", 5 volt to signal, will determine if the sensor is at fault, or if there is a problem with the ECM or wiring.

3. The "Scan" tool may not display 12 volts. What is important is that the ECM recognizes the voltage as more than 4 volts, indicating that the ECM and CKT 432 are OK.

Diagnostic Aids:

With the ignition "ON" and the engine stopped, the manifold pressure is equal to atmospheric pressure and the signal voltage will be high. This information is used by the ECM as an indication of vehicle altitude and is referred to as BARO. Comparison of this BARO reading with a known good vehicle with the same sensor is a good way to check accuracy of a "suspect" sensor. Reading should be within .4 volt.

A Code 34 will result if CKTs 416 or 432 are open or shorted to ground.

If CKT 416 is NOT shorted to ground and there is also a Code 22 stored, check CKT 432 for a short to ground.

If Code 34 is intermittent, refer to Section "B".

CODE 33

MANIFOLD ABSOLUTE PRESSURE (MAP) SENSOR CIRCUIT
(SIGNAL VOLTAGE HIGH - LOW VACUUM)
2.0L (VIN 1) "L" CARLINE (TBI)

1.
   - IF ENGINE IDLE IS ROUGH, UNSTABLE, OR INCORRECT, CORRECT CONDITION BEFORE USING CHART. SEE "SYMPTOMS" IN SECTION "B".
   - ENGINE IDLING.
   - DOES "SCAN" TOOL DISPLAY A MAP VOLTAGE OF 4.0 VOLTS OR OVER?

   YES →
   - IGNITION "OFF".
   - DISCONNECT MAP SENSOR ELECTRICAL CONNECTOR.
   - IGNITION "ON".
   - "SCAN" TOOL SHOULD READ A VOLTAGE OF 1 VOLT OR LESS.
   - DOES IT?

   NO → CODE 33 IS INTERMITTENT. IF NO ADDITIONAL CODES WERE STORED, REFER TO "DIAGNOSTIC AIDS" ON FACING PAGE.

2.
   YES →
   - PROBE SENSOR GROUND CIRCUIT WITH A TEST LIGHT TO BATTERY VOLTAGE.
   - TEST LIGHT SHOULD LIGHT.
   - DOES IT?

   NO → CKT 432 SHORTED TO VOLTAGE, SHORTED TO CKT 416, OR FAULTY ECM.

   YES → PLUGGED OR LEAKING SENSOR VACUUM HOSE OR FAULTY MAP SENSOR.

   NO → OPEN SENSOR GROUND CIRCUIT.

MAP SENSOR VOLTAGE VS. ALTITUDE WITH IGNITION "ON" AND ENGINE "OFF"

ALTITUDE		VOLTAGE RANGE
Meters	Feet	
Below 305	Below 1,000	3.8—5.5V
305—610	1,000—2,000	3.6—5.3V
610—914	2,000—3,000	3.5—5.1V
914—1219	3,000—4,000	3.3—5.0V
1219—1524	4,000—5,000	3.2—4.8V
1524—1829	5,000—6,000	3.0—4.6V
1829—2133	6,000—7,000	2.9—4.5V
2133—2438	7,000—8,000	2.8—4.3V
2438—2743	8,000—9,000	2.6—4.2V
2743—3048	9,000—10,000	2.5—4.0V

LOW ALTITUDE = HIGH PRESSURE = HIGH VOLTAGE

1988–89 2.0L ENGINE

CODE 34
MANIFOLD ABSOLUTE PRESSURE (MAP) SENSOR CIRCUIT
(SIGNAL VOLTAGE LOW - HIGH VACUUM)
2.0L (VIN 1) "L" CARLINE (TBI)

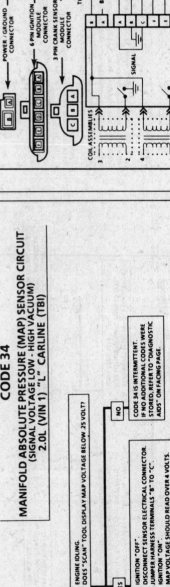

① ENGINE IDLING.
DOES "SCAN" TOOL DISPLAY MAP VOLTAGE BELOW .25 VOLT?

- NO → CODE 34 IS INTERMITTENT. IF NO ADDITIONAL CODES WERE STORED, REFER TO "DIAGNOSTIC AIDS" ON FACING PAGE.

② IGNITION "OFF".
DISCONNECT SENSOR ELECTRICAL CONNECTOR.
JUMPER HARNESS TERMINALS "B" TO "C".
IGNITION "ON".
MAP VOLTAGE SHOULD READ OVER 4 VOLTS.
DOES IT?

- YES → FAULTY CONNECTION OR SENSOR.

③ IGNITION "OFF".
REMOVE JUMPER WIRE.
PROBE TERMINAL "B" (CKT 432) WITH A TEST LIGHT TO BATTERY VOLTAGE.
IGNITION "ON".
"SCAN" TOOL SHOULD READ OVER 4 VOLTS.
DOES IT?

- YES → CKT 432 OPEN OR CKT 432 SHORTED TO GROUND OR CKT 432 SHORTED TO SENSOR GROUND OR FAULTY ECM.
- NO → 5V REFERENCE CIRCUIT OPEN OR SHORTED TO GROUND OR FAULTY ECM.

MAP SENSOR VOLTAGE VS. ALTITUDE WITH IGNITION "ON" AND ENGINE "OFF"

ALTITUDE Meters	Feet	VOLTAGE RANGE
Below 305	Below 1,000	3.8—5.5V
305— 610	1,000—2,000	3.6—5.3V
610—1219	2,000—3,000	3.5—5.1V
910—1219	3,000—4,000	3.3—5.0V
1219—1524	4,000—5,000	3.2—4.8V
1524—1829	5,000—6,000	3.0—4.6V
1829—2133	6,000—7,000	2.9—4.3V
2133—2438	7,000—8,000	2.8—4.3V
2438—2743	8,000—9,000	2.5—4.2V
2743—3048	9,000—10,000	2.5—4.0V

LOW ALTITUDE = HIGH PRESSURE = HIGH VOLTAGE

CODE 42
ELECTRONIC SPARK TIMING (EST) CIRCUIT
2.0L (VIN 1) "L" CARLINE (TBI)

Circuit Description:
The DIS module sends a reference signal to the ECM when the engine is cranking. While the engine speed is under 400 rpm, the DIS module controls the ignition timing. When the system is running on the ignition module (no voltage on the bypass line), the ignition module grounds the EST signal. The ECM expects to sense no voltage on the EST line during this condition. If it senses a voltage, it sets Code 42 and will not enter the EST mode.

When the engine speed exceeds 400 rpm, the ECM applies 5 volts to the bypass line to switch the timing to ECM control (EST). If the bypass line is open or grounded, once the rpm for EST control is reached, the ignition module will not switch to EST mode. This results in a Code 42. If the EST voltage and the setting of Code 42. If the EST line is grounded, the ignition module will switch to EST, but because the line is grounded, there will be no EST signal. A Code 42 will be set.

Test Description: Numbers below refer to circled numbers on the diagnostic chart.
1. Code 42 means the ECM has sensed an open or short to ground in the EST or bypass circuits. This test confirms Code 42 and that the fault causing the code is present.
2. Checks for a normal EST ground path through the ignition module. An EST CKT 423, shorted to ground, will also read less than 500 ohms, but this will be checked later.
3. As the test light voltage contacts CKT 424, the module should switch, causing the ohmmeter to "overrange" if the meter is in the 1000-2000 ohms position. Selecting the 10 - 20,000 ohms position will indicate a reading above 5000 ohms.

The important thing is that the module "switched."
4. The module did not switch and this step checks for:
   - EST CKT 423 shorted to ground
   - Bypass CKT 424 open
   - Faulty ignition module connection or module
5. Confirms that Code 42 is a faulty ECM and not an intermittent in CKTs 423 or 424.

Diagnostic Aids:
The "Scan" tool does not have any ability to help diagnose a Code 42 problem.
If Code 42 is intermittent, refer to Section "B"

Diagram labels: ECM — W16 IGNITION, W13 ECM GROUND, B16 GROUND, B9 REFERENCE, W19 BYPASS, W6 EST; MODULE / COIL ASSEMBLY; POWER / GROUND CONNECTOR; 6 PIN IGNITION MODULE CONNECTOR; 3 PIN CRANK SENSOR MODULE CONNECTOR; FUSE #1 TO IGNITION SWITCH; PPL/BLK 439; CRANK SENSOR HARNESS CONNECTOR; BLK/WHT 450; BLK/RED 453; PPL/WHT 430; TAN/BLK 424; WHT 423; BLK/WHT 121; TO INJECTOR; SHIELD; SIGNAL; TO TACHOMETER; COIL ASSEMBLIES; PRIMARY WINDING; SECONDARY; DIRECT IGNITION SYSTEM (DIS) MODULE

1988–89 2.0L ENGINE

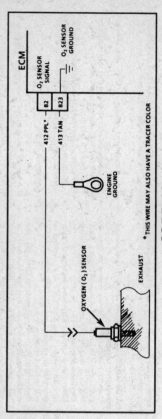

OXYGEN (O₂) SENSOR

EXHAUST

*THIS WIRE MAY ALSO HAVE A TRACER COLOR

ECM

O₂ SENSOR SIGNAL   B2   412 PPL*

O₂ SENSOR GROUND   B23   413 TAN

ENGINE GROUND

CODE 44

OXYGEN SENSOR CIRCUIT
(LEAN EXHAUST INDICATED)
2.0L (VIN 1) "L" CARLINE (TBI)

Circuit Description:

The ECM supplies a voltage of about .45 volt between terminals "B2" and "B23". (If measured with a 10 megohm digital voltmeter, this may read as low as .32 volt).

When the O₂ sensor reaches operating temperature, it varies this voltage from about .1 volt (exhaust is lean) to about .9 volt (exhaust is rich).

The sensor is like an open circuit and produces no voltage when it is below 360° C (600°F). An open sensor circuit, or cold sensor, causes "Open Loop" operation.

Test Description: Numbers below refer to circled numbers on the diagnostic chart.

1. Code 44 is set when the O₂ sensor signal voltage on CKT 412 remains below .3 volt for 50 seconds or more and the system is operating in "Closed Loop."

Diagnostic Aids:

Using the "Scan" tool, observe the block learn value at different engine speeds. The "Scan" tool also displays the block learn cells so the block learn values can be checked in each of the cells to determine when the Code 44 may have been set. If the conditions for Code 44 exists, the block learn values will be around 150 or higher.

Check the following possible causes:

- O₂ Sensor Wire. Sensor pigtail may be mispositioned and contacting the exhaust manifold.

Check for ground in wire between connector and sensor.

- Fuel Contamination. Water, even in small amounts, near the in-tank fuel pump inlet can be delivered to the injector. The water causes a lean exhaust and can set a Code 44.

- Fuel Pressure. System will be lean if fuel pressure is too low. It may be necessary to monitor fuel pressure while driving the car at various road speeds and/or loads to confirm. See "Fuel System Diagnosis," CHART A-7.

- Exhaust Leaks. If there is an exhaust leak, the engine can cause outside air to be pulled into the exhaust and past the sensor. Vacuum or crankcase leaks can cause a lean condition.

- If Code 44 is intermittent, refer to Section "B".

CODE 42

ELECTRONIC SPARK TIMING (EST) CIRCUIT
2.0L (VIN 1) "L" CARLINE (TBI)

1.
- CLEAR CODES.
- IDLE ENGINE FOR 1 MINUTE OR UNTIL CODE 42 SETS.
  DOES CODE 42 SET?

  NO → CODE 42 INTERMITTENT. REFER TO "DIAGNOSTIC AIDS" ON FACING PAGE.

  YES ↓

2.
- IGNITION "OFF".
- DISCONNECT ECM CONNECTORS.
- IGNITION "ON".
- SET OHMMETER SELECTOR SWITCH IN THE 1000 TO 2000 OHMS RANGE.
- PROBE ECM HARNESS CONNECTOR CKT 423 WITH AN OHMMETER TO GROUND.
  IT SHOULD READ LESS THAN 500 OHMS.
  DOES IT?

  NO → OPEN CKT 423, FAULTY CONNECTION, OR FAULTY IGNITION MODULE.

  YES ↓

3.
- PROBE ECM HARNESS CONNECTOR CKT 424 WITH A TEST LIGHT TO BATTERY VOLTAGE AND OBSERVE LIGHT.

  LIGHT "ON" → OPEN CKT 423, FAULTY CONNECTION, OR FAULTY IGNITION MODULE.

  LIGHT "OFF" ↓

- DISCONNECT IGNITION MODULE 6-WAY CONNECTOR.

  LIGHT "OFF" → REPLACE IGNITION MODULE.

  LIGHT "ON" ↓

- WITH OHMMETER STILL CONNECTED TO ECM HARNESS CKT 423 AND GROUND, AGAIN PROBE ECM HARNESS CKT 424 WITH THE TEST LIGHT CONNECTED TO BATTERY VOLTAGE. AS TEST LIGHT CONTACTS CKT 424, RESISTANCE SHOULD SWITCH FROM UNDER 500 TO OVER 5,000 OHMS.
  DOES IT?

  CKT 424 SHORTED TO GROUND.

4.
- DISCONNECT DIS 6-WAY CONNECTOR. NOTE OHMMETER THAT IS STILL CONNECTED TO CKT 423 AND GROUND. RESISTANCE SHOULD HAVE BECOME VERY HIGH (OPEN CIRCUIT).
  DOES IT?

  NO → CKT 423 SHORTED TO GROUND.

  YES ↓

  CKT 424 OPEN, FAULTY CONNECTIONS, OR FAULTY IGNITION MODULE.

5.
- RECONNECT ECM AND IDLE ENGINE FOR ONE MINUTE OR UNTIL CODE 42 SETS.
  DOES CODE SET?

  YES → REPLACE ECM.

  NO → CODE 42 INTERMITTENT. REFER TO "DIAGNOSTIC AIDS" ON FACING PAGE.

CLEAR CODES AND CONFIRM "CLOSED LOOP" OPERATION AND NO "SERVICE ENGINE SOON" LIGHT.

1988-89 2.0L ENGINE

CODE 44

OXYGEN SENSOR CIRCUIT
(LEAN EXHAUST INDICATED)
2.0L (VIN 1) "L" CARLINE (TBI)

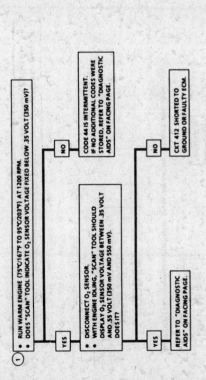

CODE 45

OXYGEN SENSOR CIRCUIT
(RICH EXHAUST INDICATED)
2.0L (VIN 1) "L" CARLINE (TBI)

Circuit Description:

The ECM supplies a voltage of about 45 volt between terminals "B2" and "B23". (If measured with a 10 megohm digital voltmeter, this may read as low as .32 volt).

When the O_2 sensor reaches operating temperature, it varies this voltage from about .1 volt (exhaust is lean) to about .9 volt (exhaust is rich).

The sensor is like an open circuit and produces no voltage when it is below 360° C (600°F). An open sensor circuit, or cold sensor, causes "Open Loop" operation.

Test Description: Numbers below refer to circled numbers on the diagnostic chart.

1. Code 45 is set when the O_2 sensor signal voltage on CKT 412 remains above .7 volt under the following conditions:
   - 30 seconds or more.
   - System is operating in "Closed Loop."
   - Engine run time after start is 1 minute or more.
   - Throttle angle is between 2% and 20%.

Diagnostic Aids:

Code 45, or rich exhaust, is most likely caused by one of the following:

- **Fuel Pressure.** System will go rich, if pressure is too high. The ECM can compensate for some increase. However, if it gets too high, a Code 45 will be set. See "Fuel System Diagnosis," CHART A-7.
- **Leaking Injector.** See CHART A-7.
- **HEI Shielding.** An open ground CKT 453 may result in EMI, or induced electrical "noise." The ECM looks at this "noise" as reference pulses. The additional pulses result in a higher than actual engine speed signal. The ECM then delivers too much fuel causing the system to go rich.

The engine tachometer will also show higher than actual engine speed, which can help in diagnosing this problem.

- **Canister Purge.** Check for fuel saturation. If full of fuel, check canister control and hoses. See "Canister Purge," Section "C3".
- **MAP Sensor.** An output that causes the ECM to sense a higher than normal manifold pressure (low vacuum) can cause the system to go rich. Disconnecting the MAP sensor will allow the ECM to set a fixed value for the MAP sensor. Substitute a different MAP sensor if the rich condition is gone, while the sensor is disconnected.
- **TPS.** An intermittent TPS output will cause the system to operate richly due to a false indication of the engine accelerating.
- **O_2 Sensor Contamination.** Inspect oxygen sensor for silicone contamination from fuel, or use of improper RTV sealant. The sensor may have a white, powdery coating and result in a high but false signal voltage (rich exhaust indication). The ECM will then reduce the amount of fuel delivered to the engine causing a severe surge driveability problem.
- **EGR Valve.** EGR sticking open at idle is usually accompanied by a rough idle and/or stall condition.

If Code 45 is intermittent, refer to Section "B".

SECTION B
SYMPTOMS
TABLE OF CONTENTS

PERFORMING SYMPTOM DIAGNOSIS

The DIAGNOSTIC CIRCUIT CHECK should be performed before using this section. The purpose of this section is to locate the source of a driveability or emissions problem when other diagnostic procedures cannot be used. This may be because of difficulties in locating a suspected sub-system or component.

Many driveability related problems can be eliminated by following the procedures found in Service Bulletins. These bulletins supersede this manual. Be sure to check all bulletins related to the complaint or suspected system.

If the engine cranks but will not run, use CHART A-3.

The sequence of the checks listed in this section is not intended to be followed as on a step-by-step procedure. The checks are listed such that the less difficult and time consuming operations are performed before more difficult ones.

Most of the symptom procedures call for a careful visual and physical check. *The importance of this step cannot be stressed too strongly.* It can lead to correcting a problem without further checks, and can save valuable time. This procedure includes checking the following:

- Vacuum hoses for splits, kinks, and proper connections, as shown on the underhood Emission Control Information label
- Throttle body and intake manifold for leaks
- Ignition wires for cracking, hardness, proper routing, and carbon tracking
- Wiring for proper connections, pinches, and cuts

1988-89 2.0L ENGINE

CODE 45
OXYGEN SENSOR CIRCUIT
(RICH EXHAUST INDICATED)
2.0L (VIN 1) "L" CARLINE (TBI)

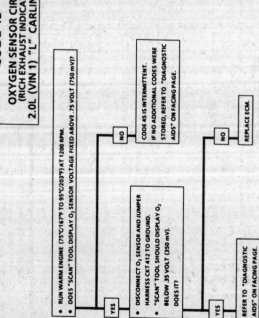

① • RUN WARM ENGINE (75°C/167°F TO 95°C/203°F) AT 1200 RPM.
• DOES "SCAN" TOOL DISPLAY O₂ SENSOR VOLTAGE FIXED ABOVE .75 VOLT (750 mV)?

NO → CODE 45 IS INTERMITTENT.
IF NO ADDITIONAL CODES WERE STORED, REFER TO "DIAGNOSTIC AIDS" ON FACING PAGE.

YES
• DISCONNECT O₂ SENSOR AND JUMPER HARNESS CKT 412 TO GROUND.
• "SCAN" TOOL SHOULD DISPLAY O₂ BELOW .35 VOLT (350 mV).
DOES IT?

NO → REPLACE ECM.

YES → REFER TO "DIAGNOSTIC AIDS" ON FACING PAGE.

CLEAR CODES AND CONFIRM "CLOSED LOOP" OPERATION AND NO "SERVICE ENGINE SOON" LIGHT.

CODE 51
PROM ERROR
(FAULTY OR INCORRECT PROM)
2.0L (VIN 1) "L" CARLINE (TBI)

CHECK THAT ALL PINS ARE FULLY INSERTED IN THE SOCKET AND THAT PROM IS PROPERLY SEATED. IF OK, REPLACE PROM, CLEAR MEMORY, AND RECHECK. IF CODE 51 REAPPEARS, REPLACE ECM.

CLEAR CODES AND CONFIRM "CLOSED LOOP" OPERATION AND NO "SERVICE ENGINE SOON" LIGHT.

1988-89 2.0L ENGINE

INTERMITTENTS

Definition: Problem may or may not activate the "Service Engine Soon" light or store a trouble code.

DO NOT use the trouble code charts in Section "A" for intermittent problems. The fault must be present to locate the problem. If a fault is intermittent, the use of trouble code charts may result in the replacement of good parts.

- Most intermittent problems are caused by faulty electrical connections or wiring. Perform careful checks of suspected circuits for
  - Poor mating of the connector halves and terminals not fully seated in the connector body (backed out)
  - Improperly formed or damaged terminals. All connector terminals in problem circuit should be carefully reformed to increase contact tension
  - Poor terminal to wire connection. This requires removing the terminal from the connector body to check

- If a visual and physical check does not locate the cause of the problem, the car can be driven with a voltmeter connected to a suspected circuit or a "Scan" tool may be used. An abnormal voltage reading while the problem occurs indicates that the problem may be in that circuit.

HARD START

Definition: Engine cranks well but does not start for a long time. Engine does eventually start, but may or may not continue to run.

Perform careful visual and physical check as described at the beginning of Section "B" Perform "Diagnostic Circuit Check."

• CHECK
- Fuel for poor quality, "stale" fuel, and water contamination
- Ignition wires for shorts or faulty insulation Ignition coil connections
- Fuel pump relay. Connect test light between pump test terminal and battery voltage. Light should be "OFF" for 2 seconds following ignition "ON." If not, use CHART A-5
- Secondary ignition voltage output with ST-125 tester
- Spark plugs. Look for wetness, cracks, improper gap, burned electrodes, and heavy deposits. Visually inspect ignition system for moisture, dust, cracks, burns, etc.
- For faulty ECM and ignition grounds
- PROM for correct application. Spray plug wires with fine water mist to check for shorts.
- For possibility of misfiring, crossfiring, or cutting out under load or at idle. If possible, refer to the "Misfire" Chart
- For improper crank sensor resistance or faulty connections
- EGR operation. Use CHART C-7.
- Idle Air Control system. Use Code 35 chart.
- Fuel system for restricted filter or improper pressure. Use CHART A-7.
- Injector and TBI assembly for leakage. Pressurize system by energizing fuel pump through the underhood fuel pump test connector.
- Coolant sensor for a shift in calibration. Use Code 14 or Code 15 chart.

TPS for sticking or binding. TPS voltage should read less than 1.25 V on a "Scan" tool. In-tank fuel pump check valve. A faulty valve would allow the fuel in the lines to drain back to the tank after the engine is stopped. To check for this condition, conduct the following test.
1. Ignition "OFF."
2. Disconnect fuel line at the filter.
3. Remove the tank filler cap.
4. Connect a radiator test pump to the line and apply 103 kPa (15 psi) pressure. If the pressure will hold for 60 seconds, the check valve is OK.

For the possibility of an exhaust restriction or improper valve timing by performing the following test.
1. With engine at normal operating temperature, connect a vacuum gauge to any convenient vacuum port on intake manifold.
2. Run engine at 1000 rpm and record vacuum reading
3. Increase engine speed slowly to 2500 rpm. Note vacuum reading at steady 2500 rpm.
4. If vacuum at 2500 rpm decreases more than 3" Hg from reading at 1000 rpm, the exhaust system should be inspected for restrictions
5. Disconnect exhaust pipe from engine and repeat Steps 3 & 4. If vacuum still drops more than 3" Hg with exhaust disconnected, check valve timing

- Engine valve timing and compression.

ROUGH, UNSTABLE, OR INCORRECT IDLE, STALLING

Definition: The engine runs unevenly at idle. If severe, the car may shake. Also, the idle speed may vary (called "hunting"). Either condition may be severe enough to cause stalling. Engine idles at incorrect speed.

Perform careful visual and physical check as described at the beginning of Section "B." Perform "Diagnostic Circuit Check."
• CHECK
- MAP sensor. Use CHART C1-D
- Throttle for sticking shaft or binding linkage. This will cause a high TPS voltage (open throttle indication) and the ECM will not control idle. TPS voltage should be less than 1.25 volts with throttle closed.
- Battery cables and ground straps for poor contact. Erratic voltage will cause the IAC valve to change its position, resulting in poor idle quality
- Ignition wires for shorts or faulty insulation. Ignition system for moisture, dust, cracks, burns, etc. Spray plug wires with fine water mist to check for shorts.
- For possibility of misfiring, crossfiring, or cutting out under load or at idle. If present, refer to the "Misfire" Chart
- Secondary ignition voltage output with ST-1 tester.
- Ignition coil connections.
- ECM and ignition system for faulty grounds.
- Proper operation of EST

- Spark plugs. Look for wetness, cracks, improper gap, burned electrodes, and heavy deposits.
- Fuel system for restricted filter or improper pressure. Use CHART A-7. Injector and TBI assembly for leakage. Pressurize system by energizing fuel pump through the underhood fuel pump test connector.
- EGR operation. Use CHART C-7.
- Idle Air Control system. Use Code 35 chart.
- Electrical system voltage. IAC valve will not move if voltage is below 9 volts or greater than 17.8 volts. Also check battery cables and ground straps for poor contact. Erratic voltage will cause the IAC valve to change its position, resulting in poor idle quality
- PCV valve for proper operation by placing finger over inlet hole in valve and several times. Valve should snap back. If not, replace valve. Ensure that valve is correct part. Also check PCV hose.

1988–89 2.0L ENGINE

- Canister purge system for proper operation. Use CHART C.3.
- PROM for correct application.

- Throttle shaft or TPS for sticking or binding. TPS voltage should read less than 1.25 V on a "Scan" tool with the throttle closed.
- MAP sensor output. Use CHART C1-D and/or check sensor by comparing it to the output on a similar vehicle if possible.
- Oxygen sensor for silicone contamination from contaminated fuel or use of improper RTV sealant. The sensor will have a white, powdery coating and will cause a high but false signal voltage (rich exhaust indication). The ECM will reduce the amount of fuel delivered to the engine, causing a severe driveability problem.
- Coolant sensor for a shift in calibration. Use Code 14 or Code 15 chart.
- A/C refrigerant pressure for high pressure. Check for overcharging or faulty pressure switch.
- P/N switch circuit on vehicle with automatic transmission. Use CHART C-1A.
- Generator output voltage. Repair if less than 9 V or more than 16 V
- Power steering. Use CHART C-1E. The ECM should compensate for power steering loads. Loss of this signal would be most noticeable when steering loads are high such as during parking.
- Engine valve timing and compression.

- For worn or incorrect basic engine parts such as cam, heads, pistons, etc. Also check for bent pushrods, worn rocker arms, and broken or weak valve springs.

POOR GAS MILEAGE

Definition: Gas mileage, as measured by an actual road test, is noticeably lower than expected. Gas mileage is noticeably lower than it was during a previous actual road test.

- **CHECK**

Perform careful visual and physical check as described at the beginning of Section "B".

Perform "Diagnostic Circuit Check".

- Proper operation of EST
- For possibility of misfiring, crossfiring, or cutting out under load or at idle. If present, refer to the "Misfire" Chart.
- Spark plugs. Look for wetness, cracks, improper gap, burned electrodes, and heavy deposits

- For the possibility of an exhaust restriction or improper valve, timing, perform the following test.
  1. With engine at normal operating temperature, connect a vacuum gauge to any convenient vacuum port on intake manifold.
  2. Run engine at 1000 rpm and record vacuum reading.
  3. Increase engine speed slowly to 2500 rpm. Note vacuum reading at steady 2500 rpm.
  4. If vacuum at 2500 rpm decreases more than 3" Hg from reading at 1000 rpm, the exhaust system should be inspected for restrictions
  5. Disconnect exhaust pipe from engine and repeat Steps 3 & 4. If vacuum still drops more than 3" Hg with exhaust disconnected, check valve timing

- For overheating and possible causes. Look for the following
  - Low or incorrect coolant solution. It should be a 50/50 mix of GM #1052753 anti-freeze coolant (or equivalent) and water
  - Loose water pump belt.
  - Restricted air flow to radiator, or restricted water flow through radiator
  - Faulty or incorrect thermostat
  - Inoperative electric cooling fan circuit
- If the system is running RICH, (block learn less than 118), refer to "Diagnostic Aids" on facing page of Code 45
- If the system is running LEAN, (block learn greater than 138), refer to "Diagnostic Aids" on facing page of Code 44

- Spark plugs for correct heat range
- Fuel for poor quality, "stale" fuel, and water contamination.
- Fuel system for restricted filter or improper pressure. Use CHART A-7.
- Injector and TBI assembly for leakage. Pressurize system by energizing fuel pump through the underhood fuel pump test connector
- EGR operation. Use CHART C-7.

- For vacuum leaks at intake manifold gasket, Air cleaner element (filter) for dirt or plugging
- Idle Air Control system. Use Code 35 chart.
- Canister purge system for proper operation. Use CHART C.3.
- PROM for correct application

- Throttle shaft or TPS for sticking or binding. TPS voltage should read less than 1.25 V on a "Scan" tool with the throttle closed
- MAP sensor output. Use CHART C1-D and/or check sensor by comparing it to the output on a similar vehicle if possible
- Oxygen sensor for silicone contamination from contaminated fuel or use of improper RTV sealant. The sensor will have a white, powdery coating and will cause a high but false signal voltage (rich exhaust indication). The ECM will reduce the amount of fuel delivered to the engine, causing a severe driveability problem
- Coolant sensor for a shift in calibration. Use Code 14 or Code 15 chart.
- Vehicle speed sensor (VSS) input with a "Scan" tool to make sure reading of VSS matches that of vehicle speedometer
- A/C relay operation. A/C should cut out at wide open throttle. Use CHART C-10
- A/C refrigerant pressure for high pressure. Check for overcharging or faulty pressure switch.
- Generator output voltage. Repair if less than 9 V or more than 16 V
- Cooling fan operation. Use CHART C-12.
- Power steering. Use CHART C-1E. The ECM should compensate for power steering loads. Loss of this signal would be most noticeable when steering loads are high such as during parking
- Transmission torque converter clutch

- Transmission for proper shift points

- Transmission torque converter clutch operation. Use CHART C-8.

- Engine valve timing and compression.

- For worn or incorrect basic engine parts such as cam, heads, pistons, etc. Also check for bent pushrods, worn rocker arms, and broken or weak valve springs.
- For the possibility of an exhaust restriction or improper valve timing by performing the following test.
  1. With engine at normal operating temperature, connect a vacuum gauge to any convenient vacuum port on intake manifold.
  2. Run engine at 1000 rpm and record vacuum reading.
  3. Increase engine speed slowly to 2500 rpm. Note vacuum reading at steady 2500 rpm.
  4. If vacuum at 2500 rpm decreases more than 3" Hg from reading at 1000 rpm, the exhaust system should be inspected for restrictions.
  5. Disconnect exhaust pipe from engine and repeat Steps 3 & 4. If vacuum still drops more than 3" Hg with exhaust disconnected, check valve timing
  Thermostat for incorrect heat range or being inoperative

- Check driver's driving habits and vehicle conditions which affect gas mileage.
  - Suggest driver read "Important Facts on Fuel Economy" in Owner's Manual
  - Is A/C "ON" full time (Defroster mode "ON")?
  - Are tires at correct pressure?
  - Are excessively heavy loads being carried?
  - Is acceleration often heavy?
  - Are the wheels aligned correctly?
  - Is the speedometer calibrated correctly?
  - Are the vehicle brakes dragging?
  - Is the brake switch applying excessive force on the brake pedal?

- If the system is running RICH, (block learn less than 118), refer to "Diagnostic Aids" on facing page of Code 45

1988–89 2.0L ENGINE

DETONATION/SPARK KNOCK

Definition: A mild to severe ping, usually worse under acceleration. The engine makes sharp metallic knocks that change with throttle opening.

Perform careful visual and physical check as described at the beginning of Section "B".
Perform "Diagnostic Circuit Check."

- **CHECK**
- Ignition wires for shorts or faulty insulation.
- For possibility of misfiring, crossfiring, or cutting out under load or at idle. If present, refer to the "Misfire" Chart.
- Spark plugs for correct heat range.
- Fuel for poor quality, "stale", fuel, and water contamination.
- Fuel system for restricted filter or improper pressure. Use CHART C-7.
- For excessive oil entering combustion chamber. Oil will reduce the effective octane of fuel.
- EGR operation. Use CHART C-7.
- For vacuum leaks at intake manifold gasket.
- PCV valve for proper operation by placing finger over inlet hole in valve end several times. Valve should snap back. If not, replace valve. Ensure that valve is correct part. Also check PCV hose.
- MAP sensor output. Use CHART C1-D and/or check sensor by comparing it to the output on a Similar vehicle if possible.
- Coolant sensor for a shift in calibration.
- Oxygen sensor for silicone contamination from contaminated fuel or use of improper RTV sealant. The sensor will have a white, powdery coating and will cause a high but false signal voltage (rich exhaust indication). The ECM will reduce the amount of fuel delivered to the engine, causing a severe driveability problem.
- Vehicle speed sensor (VSS) input with a "Scan" tool to make sure reading of VSS matches that of vehicle speedometer.
- Transmission for proper shift points.
- Transmission torque converter clutch operation. Use CHART C-8.
- Vehicle brakes for dragging

- PROM for correct application.
- For overheating and possible causes. Look for the following.
  - Low or incorrect coolant solution. It should be a 50/50 mix of GM #1052753 anti-freeze coolant (or equivalent) and water.
  - Loose water pump belt
  - Restricted air flow to radiator or restricted water flow through radiator
  - Faulty or incorrect thermostat
  - Inoperative electric cooling fan circuit.
  - Engine valve timing and compression.

- For worn or incorrect basic engine parts such as cam, heads, pistons, etc. Also check for bent pushrods, worn rocker arms, and broken or weak valve springs.

- For the possibility of an exhaust restriction or improper valve timing by performing the following test.
  1. With engine at normal operating temperature, connect a vacuum gauge to any convenient vacuum port on intake manifold
  2. Run engine at 1000 rpm and record vacuum reading.
  3. Increase engine speed slowly to 2500 rpm. Note vacuum reading at steady 2500 rpm.
  4. If vacuum at 2500 rpm decreases more than 3" Hg from reading at 1000 rpm, the exhaust system should be inspected for restrictions
  5. Disconnect exhaust pipe from engine and repeat Steps 3 & 4. If vacuum still drops more than 3" Hg with exhaust disconnected, check valve timing
- Remove internal engine carbon with top engine cleaner.
- If the system is running LEAN, (block learn greater than 138), refer to "Diagnostic Aids" on facing page of Code 44.

LACK OF POWER, SLUGGISH, OR SPONGY

Definition: Engine delivers less than expected power. There is little or no increase in speed when the accelerator pedal is depressed partially.

Perform careful visual and physical check as described at the beginning of Section "B".
Perform "Diagnostic Circuit Check."

- **CHECK**
- Ignition wires for shorts or faulty insulation
- Ignition system for moisture, dust, cracks, burns, etc. Spray plug wires with fine water mist to check for shorts.
- For possibility of misfiring, crossfiring, or cutting out under load or at idle. If present, refer to the "Misfire" Chart
- Secondary ignition voltage output with ST-125 tester.
- Ignition coil connections
- ECM and ignition system for faulty grounds
- Proper operation of EST.
- Spark plugs. Look for wetness, cracks, improper gap, burned electrodes, and heavy deposits.
- Spark plugs for correct heat range
- Fuel for poor quality, "stale" fuel, and water contamination
- Fuel system for restricted filter or improper pressure. Use CHART C-7.
- EGR operation. Use CHART C-7.
- For vacuum leaks at intake manifold gasket.
- Air cleaner element (filter) for dirt or plugging
- PROM for correct application.•

- Throttle shaft or TPS for sticking or binding. TPS voltage should read less than 1.25 V on a "Scan" tool with the throttle closed.
- MAP sensor output. Use CHART C1-D and/or check sensor by comparing it to the output on a similar vehicle if possible.
- Oxygen sensor for silicone contamination from contaminated fuel or use of improper RTV sealant. The sensor will have a white, powdery coating and will cause a high but false signal voltage (rich exhaust indication). The ECM will reduce the amount of fuel delivered to the engine, causing a severe driveability problem. Coolant sensor for a shift in calibration. Use Code 14 or Code 15 chart.

- Vehicle speed sensor (VSS) input with a "Scan" tool to make sure reading of VSS matches that of vehicle speedometer.
- Engine for improper or worn camshaft.

- A/C relay operation. A/C should cut out at wide open throttle. Use CHART C-10.
- A/C refrigerant pressure for high pressure. Check for overcharging or faulty pressure switch.
- Generator output voltage. Repair if less than 9 V or more than 16 V.
- Cooling fan operation. Use CHART C-12.
- Power steering. Use CHART C-1E. The ECM should compensate for power steering loads. Loss of this signal would be most noticeable when steering loads are high such as during parking.
- Transmission torque converter operation.

- Transmission for proper shift points.

- Transmission torque converter clutch operation. Use CHART C-8.
- Vehicle brakes for dragging
- Engine valve timing and compression.

- For worn or incorrect basic engine parts such as cam, heads, pistons, etc. Also check for bent pushrods, worn rocker arms, and broken or weak valve springs.

- For the possibility of an exhaust restriction or improper valve timing by performing the following test.
  1. With engine at normal operating temperature, connect a vacuum gauge to any convenient vacuum port on intake manifold.
  2. Run engine at 1000 rpm and record vacuum reading.
  3. Increase engine speed slowly to 2500 rpm. Note vacuum reading at steady 2500 rpm.
  4. If vacuum at 2500 rpm decreases more than 3" Hg from reading at 1000 rpm, the exhaust system should be inspected for restrictions.

1988–89 2.0L ENGINE

5. Disconnect exhaust pipe from engine and repeat Steps 3 & 4. If vacuum still drops more than 3" Hg with exhaust disconnected, check valve timing.

For overheating and possible causes. Look for the following:
- Low or incorrect coolant solution. It should be a 50/50 mix of GM #1052753 anti-freeze coolant (or equivalent) and water.
- Loose water pump belt.

SURGES AND/OR CHUGGLE

Definition: Engine power variation under steady throttle or cruise. Feels like the car speeds up and slows down with no change in the accelerator pedal.

Perform careful visual and physical check as described at the beginning of Section "B". Perform "Diagnostic Circuit Check."

- **CHECK**
  - Ignition wires for shorts or faulty insulation.
  - Ignition system for moisture, dust, cracks, burns, etc. Spray plug wires with fine water mist to check for shorts.
  - For possibility of misfiring, crossfiring, or cutting out under load or at idle. If present, refer to the "Misfire" Chart
  - Secondary ignition voltage output with ST-125 tester.
  - Ignition coil connections
  - ECM and ignition system for faulty grounds.
  - Proper operation of EST.
  - Spark plugs. Look for wetness, cracks, improper gap, burned electrodes, and heavy deposits.
  - Spark plugs for correct heat range.
  - Fuel for poor quality, "stale" fuel, and water contamination.
  - Fuel system for restricted filter or improper pressure Use CHART A-7
  - Injector and TBI assembly for leakage. Pressurize system by energizing fuel pump through the underhood fuel pump test connector.
  - EGR operation. Use CHART C-7.
  - For vacuum leaks at intake manifold gasket.
  - Idle Air Control system. Use CHART C-10 chart.
  - Electrical system voltage. IAC valve will not move if voltage is below 9 V or greater than 17.8 V. Also check battery cables and ground straps for poor contact.
  - Restricted air flow to radiator, or restricted water flow through radiator. Faulty or incorrect thermostat.
  - Inoperative electric cooling fan circuit. See CHART C-12.
- If the system is running RICH (block learn less than 118), refer to "Diagnostic Aids" on facing page of Code 45
- If the system is running LEAN (block learn greater than 138), refer to "Diagnostic Aids" on facing page of Code 44.

Erratic voltage will cause the IAC valve to change its position, resulting in poor idle quality.
PCV valve for proper operation by placing finger over inlet hole in valve end several times. Valve should snap back. If not, replace valve. Ensure that valve is correct part. Also check PCV hose.
Canister purge system for proper operation. Use CHART C-3.
PROM for correct application

Throttle shaft or TPS for sticking or binding. TPS voltage should read less than 1.25 volts on a "Scan" tool with the throttle closed
MAP sensor output. Use CHART C1-D and/or check sensor by comparing it to the output on a similar vehicle, if possible.
Oxygen sensor for silicone contamination from contaminated fuel or use of improper RTV sealant. The sensor will have a white, powdery coating and will cause a high but false signal voltage (rich exhaust indication). The ECM will reduce the amount of fuel delivered to the engine, causing a severe driveability problem.
Coolant sensor for a shift in calibration. Use Code 14 or Code 15 chart.
Vehicle speed sensor (VSS) input with a "Scan" tool to make sure reading of VSS matches that of vehicle speedometer.

A/C relay operation. A/C should cut out at wide open throttle. Use CHART C-10
P/N switch circuit on vehicle with automatic transmission. Use CHART C-1A
Transmission torque converter clutch operation. Use CHART C-8.

For the possibility of an exhaust restriction or improper valve timing by performing the following test.
1. With engine at normal operating temperature, connect a vacuum gauge to any convenient vacuum port on intake manifold
2. Run engine at 1000 rpm and record vacuum reading.
3. Increase engine speed slowly to 2500 rpm. Note vacuum reading at steady 2500 rpm.
4. If vacuum at 2500 rpm decreases more than 3" Hg from reading at 1000 rpm, the exhaust system should be inspected for restrictions.

CUTS OUT, MISSES

Definition: Steady pulsation or jerking that follows engine speed, usually more pronounced as engine load increases. The exhaust has a steady spitting sound at idle or low speed

Perform careful visual and physical check as described at the beginning of Section "B".
Perform "Diagnostic Circuit Check."

- **CHECK**
  - Ignition wires for shorts or faulty insulation
  - Ignition system for moisture, dust, cracks, burns, etc. Spray plug wires with fine water mist to check for shorts.
  - For possibility of misfiring, crossfiring, or cutting out under load or at idle. If present, refer to the "Misfire" Chart
  - Secondary ignition voltage output with ST-125 tester
  - Ignition coil connections
  - ECM and ignition system for faulty grounds

HESITATION, SAG, STUMBLE

Definition: Momentary lack of response as the accelerator is pushed down. Can occur at all vehicle speeds. Usually most severe when first trying to make the car move, as from a stop sign. May cause the engine to stall if severe enough.

Perform careful visual and physical check as described at the beginning of Section "B".
Perform "Diagnostic Circuit Check."

- **CHECK**
  - Ignition wires for shorts or faulty insulation
  - Ignition system for moisture, dust, cracks, burns, etc. Spray plug wires with fine water mist to check for shorts.
  - For possibility of misfiring, crossfiring, or cutting out under load or at idle. If present, refer to the "Misfire" Chart
  - Secondary ignition voltage output with ST-125 tester

---

5. Disconnect exhaust pipe from engine and repeat Steps 3 & 4. If vacuum still drops more than 3" Hg with exhaust disconnected, check valve timing. Engine valve timing and compression.
- For worn or incorrect basic engine parts such as cam, heads, pistons, etc. Also check for bent pushrods, worn rocker arms, and broken or weak valve springs.
- If the system is running RICH, (block learn less than 118), refer to "Diagnostic Aids" on facing page of Code 45.
- If the system is running LEAN, (block learn greater than 138), refer to "Diagnostic Aids" on facing page of Code 44.

- Proper operation of EST.
- Spark plugs. Look for wetness, cracks, improper gap, burned electrodes, and heavy deposits.
- Spark plugs for correct heat range
- For improper crank sensor resistance or faulty connections
- Fuel for poor quality, "stale" fuel, and water contamination
- Fuel system for restricted filter or improper pressure. Use CHART A-7.
- Throttle shaft or TPS for sticking or binding. TPS voltage should read less than 1.25 V on a "Scan" tool with the throttle closed

- Ignition coil connections
- ECM and ignition system for faulty grounds
- Proper operation of EST. See Section "C4"
- Spark plugs. Look for wetness, cracks, improper gap, burned electrodes, and heavy deposits.
- Spark plugs for correct heat range
- Fuel for poor quality, "stale" fuel, and water contamination
- Fuel system for restricted filter or improper pressure. Use CHART A-7.

1988-89 2.0L ENGINE

- EGR operation. Use CHART C-7.
- For vacuum leaks at intake manifold gasket
- Air cleaner element (filter) for dirt or plugging
- Idle Air Control system
  Check electrical system voltage. IAC valve will not move if voltage is below 8.7 volts. Also check battery cables and ground straps for poor contact. Erratic voltage will cause the IAC valve to change its position, resulting in poor idle quality.
- PCV valve for proper operation by placing finger over inlet hole in valve end several times. Valve should snap back. If not, replace valve. Ensure that valve is correct part. Also check PCV hose.
- Canister purge system for proper operation. Use CHART C-3.
- PROM for correct application

- Throttle shaft or TPS for sticking or binding. TPS voltage should read less than 1.25 volts on a "Scan" tool with the throttle closed
- MAP sensor output. Use CHART C1-D and/or check sensor by comparing it to the output on a similar vehicle, if possible
- Oxygen sensor for silicone contamination from contaminated fuel or use of improper RTV sealant. The sensor will have a white, powdery coating and will cause a high but false signal voltage (rich exhaust indication). The ECM will reduce the amount of fuel delivered to the engine, causing a severe driveability problem
- Coolant sensor for a shift in calibration. Use Code 14 or Code 15 chart.
- A/C relay operation. A/C should cut out at wide open throttle. Use CHART C-10.
- A/C refrigerant pressure for high pressure. Check for overcharging or faulty pressure switch.
- P/N switch circuit on vehicle with automatic transmission. Use CHART C-1A.
- Generator output voltage. Repair if less than 9 volts or more than 16 volts
- Transmission torque converter operation.

- Transmission for proper shift points.

- Transmission torque converter clutch operation. Use CHART C-8.
- Vehicle brakes for dragging
- Engine valve timing and compression.

- For the possibility of an exhaust restriction or improper valve timing by performing the following test.
  1. With engine at normal operating temperature, connect a vacuum gauge to any convenient vacuum port on intake manifold.
  2. Run engine at 1000 rpm and record vacuum reading.
  3. Increase engine speed slowly to 2500 rpm. Note vacuum reading at steady 200 rpm.
  4. If vacuum at 2500 rpm decreases more than 3" Hg from reading at 1000 rpm, the exhaust system should be inspected for restrictions.
  5. Disconnect exhaust pipe from engine and repeat steps 3 & 4. If vacuum still drops more than 3" Hg with exhaust disconnected, check valve timing.

- For worn or incorrect basic engine parts such as cam, heads, pistons, etc. Also check for bent pushrods, worn rocker arms, and broken or weak valve springs

- For overheating and possible causes. Look for the following.
- Low or incorrect coolant solution. It should be a 50/50 mix of GM #1052753 anti-freeze coolant (or equivalent) and water
- Loose water pump belt
- Restricted air flow to radiator, or restricted water flow through radiator
- Faulty or incorrect thermostat
- Inoperative electric cooling fan circuit. See CHART C-12.
- If the system is running RICH (block learn less than 118), refer to "Diagnostic Aids" on facing page of Code 45
- If the system is running LEAN (block learn greater than 145), refer to "Diagnostic Aids" on facing page of Code 44

EXCESSIVE EXHAUST EMISSIONS OR ODORS

Definition: Vehicle fails an emission test or vehicle has excessive "rotten egg" smell. (Excessive odors do not necessarily indicate excessive emissions).

Perform careful visual and physical check as described at the beginning of Section "B". Perform "Diagnostic Circuit Check."

- **CHECK**
  - EGR valve not opening. Use CHART C-7.
  - Vacuum leaks
  - Faulty coolant system and/or coolant fan operation. Use CHART C-12.
  - Remove carbon with top engine cleaner. Follow instructions on can.
- If the system is running RICH (block learn less than 118), refer to "Diagnostic Aids" on facing page of Code 45.
- If the system is running LEAN (block learn greater than 138), refer to "Diagnostic Aids" on facing page of Code 44.

- If emission test indicates excessive NO$_x$, check for items which cause car to run lean or too hot.
- If emission test indicates excessive HC and CO or exhaust has excessive odors, check for items which cause car to run RICH.
  - Incorrect fuel pressure. Use CHART A-7.
  - Fuel loading of evaporative vapor canister. Use CHART C-3.
  - PCV valve plugging, sticking, or blocked PCV hose. Check for fuel in crankcase.
  - Catalytic converter lead contamination (Look for removal of fuel filler neck restrictor.)
  - Improper fuel cap installation
  - Faulty spark plugs, plug wires, or ignition components.

DIESELING, RUN-ON

Definition: Engine continues to run after key is turned "OFF," but runs very roughly. (If engine runs smoothly, check ignition switch).

Perform careful visual and physical check as described at the beginning of Section "B". Perform "Diagnostic Circuit Check."

- **CHECK**
  - Injector and TBI assembly for leakage. Pressurize system by energizing fuel pump through the fuel pump test connector.

BACKFIRE

Definition: Fuel ignites in intake manifold or in exhaust system, making a loud popping sound.

Perform careful visual and physical check as described at the beginning of Section "B". Perform "Diagnostic Circuit Check."

- **CHECK**
  - EGR operation for valve being open all the time. Use CHART C-7.
  - Intake manifold gasket for leaks
  - For possibility of misfiring, crossfiring, or cutting out under load or at idle. If present, refer to the "Misfire" Chart
  - Spark plugs. Look for wetness, cracks, improper gap, burned electrodes, and heavy deposits.
  - Ignition coil connections

- Ignition system for moisture, dust, cracks, burns, etc. Spray plug wires with fine water mist to check for shorts.
- ECM and ignition system for faulty grounds
- Secondary ignition voltage output with ST-125 tester
- For vacuum leaks at intake manifold gasket
- Engine valve timing and compression.

- For worn or incorrect basic engine parts such as cam, heads, pistons, etc. Also check for bent pushrods, worn rocker arms, and broken or weak valve springs.

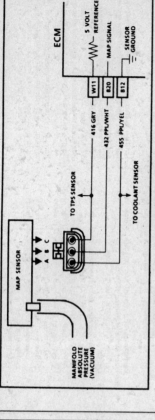

CHART C-1D
MAP OUTPUT CHECK
2.0L (VIN 1) "L" CARLINE (TBI)

Circuit Description:

The manifold absolute pressure sensor (MAP) measures manifold pressure (vacuum) and sends that signal to the ECM. The MAP sensor is mainly used to calculate engine load, which is fundamental input for spark and fuel calculations. The MAP sensor is also used to determine the barometric pressure.

Test Description: Numbers below refer to circled numbers on the diagnostic chart.

1. Checks MAP sensor output voltage to the ECM. This voltage, without engine running, represents a barometer reading to the ECM.

2. Applying 34 kPa (10" Hg) vacuum to the MAP sensor should cause the voltage to be 1.2 to 2.3 volts less than the voltage at Step 1. Upon applying vacuum to the sensor, the change in voltage should be instantaneous. A slow voltage change indicates a faulty sensor.

3. Check vacuum hose to sensor for leaking or restriction. Be sure no other vacuum devices are connected to the MAP hose.

RESTRICTED EXHAUST SYSTEM CHECK
ALL ENGINES

Proper diagnosis for a restricted exhaust system is essential before any components are replaced. Either of the following procedures may be used for diagnosis, depending upon engine or tool used:

CHECK AT A. I. R. PIPE:

1. Remove the rubber hose at the exhaust manifold A.I.R. pipe check valve. Remove check valve.
2. Connect a fuel pump pressure gauge to a hose and nipple from a Propane Enrichment Device (J26911) (see illustration).
3. Insert the nipple into the exhaust manifold A.I.R. pipe.

OR CHECK AT O₂ SENSOR:

1. Carefully remove O₂ sensor.
2. Install Borroughs Exhaust Backpressure Tester (BT 8515 or BT 8603) or equivalent in place of O₂ sensor (see illustration).
3. After completing test described below, be sure to coat threads of O₂ sensor with anti-seize compound P/N 5613695 or equivalent prior to re-installation.

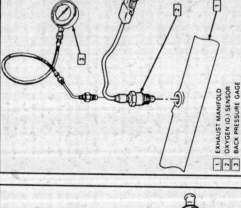

1. EXHAUST MANIFOLD
2. OXYGEN (O₂) SENSOR
3. BACK PRESSURE GAGE

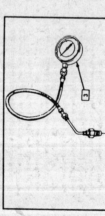

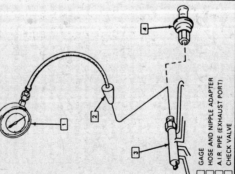

1. GAGE
2. HOSE AND NIPPLE ADAPTER
3. A.I.R PIPE (EXHAUST PORT)
4. CHECK VALVE

DIAGNOSIS:

1. With the engine idling at normal operating temperature, observe the exhaust system backpressure reading on the gauge. Reading should not exceed 1 psi (8.6 kPa).
2. Accelerate engine to 2000 RPM and observe gauge. Reading should not exceed 3 psi (20.7 kPa).
3. If the backpressure, at either RPM, exceeds specification, a restricted exhaust system is indicated.
4. Inspect the entire exhaust system for a collapsed pipe, heat distress, or possible internal muffler failure.
5. If there are no obvious reasons for the excessive backpressure, a restricted catalytic converter should be suspected and replaced using current recommended procedures.

1988—89 2.0L ENGINE

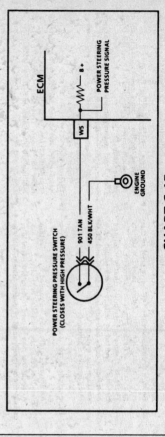

CHART C-1E
POWER STEERING PRESSURE SWITCH (PSPS) DIAGNOSIS
2.0L (VIN 1) "L" CARLINE (TBI)

Circuit Description:

The power steering pressure switch is normally open to ground, with CKT 901 supplying battery voltage to the switch.

Turning the steering wheel increases power steering oil pressure and its load on an idling engine. The pressure switch will close before the load can cause an idle problem.

Closing the switch causes CKT 901 to read less than 1 volt and the ECM will increase the idle air rate and de-energize the A/C relay.

- A pressure switch that will not close, or an open CKT 901 or 450, may cause the engine to stall when power steering loads are high.
- A switch that will not open, or a CKT 901 shorted to ground, may affect idle quality, and will cause the A/C relay to be de-energized.

Test Description: Numbers below refer to circled numbers on the diagnostic chart.

1. Different makes of "Scan" tools may display the state of this switch in different ways. Refer to "Scan" tool upgrading to determine how this input is indicated.

2. Checks to determine if CKT 901 is shorted to ground.

3. This should simulate a closed switch.

CHART C-1D
MAP OUTPUT CHECK
2.0L (VIN 1) "L" CARLINE (TBI)

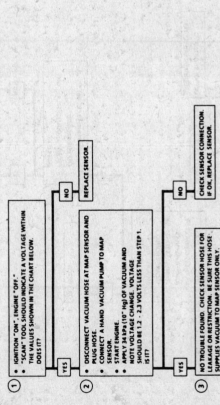

1. • IGNITION "ON", ENGINE "OFF."
   • "SCAN" TOOL SHOULD INDICATE A VOLTAGE WITHIN THE VALUES SHOWN IN THE CHART BELOW.
   DOES IT?

   NO → REPLACE SENSOR.

2. • DISCONNECT VACUUM HOSE AT MAP SENSOR AND PLUG HOSE.
   • CONNECT A HAND VACUUM PUMP TO MAP SENSOR.
   • START ENGINE.
   • APPLY 34 kPa (10" Hg) OF VACUUM AND NOTE VOLTAGE CHANGE. VOLTAGE SHOULD BE 1.2 - 2.3 VOLTS LESS THAN STEP 1.
   IS IT?

   NO → CHECK SENSOR CONNECTION. IF OK, REPLACE SENSOR.

3. • NO TROUBLE FOUND. CHECK SENSOR HOSE FOR LEAKAGE OR RESTRICTION. BE SURE THIS HOSE SUPPLIES VACUUM TO MAP SENSOR ONLY.

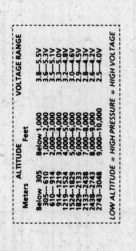

ALTITUDE		VOLTAGE RANGE
Meters	Feet	
Below 305	Below 1,000	3.8—5.5V
305— 610	1,000—2,000	3.6—5.3V
610— 914	2,000—3,000	3.5—5.1V
914—1219	3,000—4,000	3.3—5.0V
1219—1524	4,000—5,000	3.2—4.8V
1524—1829	5,000—6,000	3.0—4.6V
1829—2133	6,000—7,000	2.9—4.5V
2133—2438	7,000—8,000	2.8—4.3V
2438—2743	8,000—9,000	2.6—4.2V
2743—3048	9,000—10,000	2.5—4.0V

LOW ALTITUDE = HIGH PRESSURE = HIGH VOLTAGE

CLEAR CODES AND CONFIRM "CLOSED LOOP" OPERATION AND NO "SERVICE ENGINE SOON" LIGHT.

1988–89 2.0L ENGINE

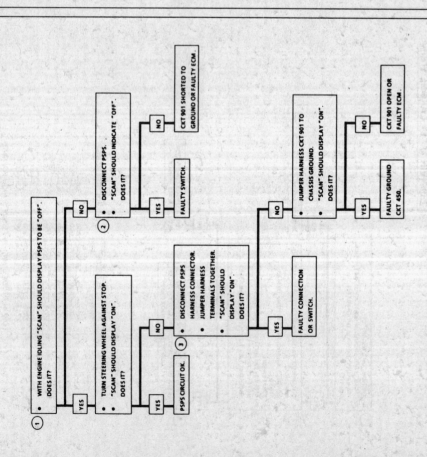

CHART C-2C
IDLE AIR CONTROL (IAC) SYSTEM CHECK
2.0L (VIN 1) "L" CARLINE (TBI)

Circuit Description:

The ECM controls idle rpm with the IAC valve. To increase idle rpm, the ECM moves the IAC valve out allowing more air to pass by the throttle plate. To decrease rpm, it moves the IAC valve in, reducing air flow by the throttle plate. A "Scan" tool will read the ECM commands to the IAC valve in counts. The higher the counts, the more air allowed (higher idle). The lower the counts, the less air allowed (lower idle).

Test Description: Numbers below refer to circled numbers on the diagnostic chart.

1. Continue with test, even if engine will not idle. If idle is to low, "Scan" will display 80 or more counts, or steps. If idle is high, it will display "0" counts. Occasionally an erratic or unstable idle may occur. Engine speed may vary 200 rpm or more up and down. Disconnect IAC. If the condition is unchanged, the IAC is not at fault.

2. When the engine was stopped, the IAC valve retracted (more air) to a fixed "Park" position for increased air flow and idle speed during the next engine start. A "Scan" will display 100 or more counts.

3. Be sure to disconnect the IAC valve prior to this test. The test light will confirm the ECM signals by a steady or flashing light on all circuits.

4. There is a remote possibility that one of the circuits is shorted to voltage which would have been indicated by a steady light. Disconnect ECM and turn the ignition "ON" and probe terminals to check for this condition.

Diagnostic Aids:

An incorrect idle may be caused by a system problem that cannot be controlled by the IAC.

A "Scan" tool may be used to monitor desired idle, actual engine speed, and IAC counts to help isolate a system problem.

For example, a vacuum leak may be indicated if the desired idle is 900 rpm, IAC counts are at 0, but the actual engine speed is 1500 rpm.

- **System too lean (High Air/Fuel Ratio)**
  Idle speed may be too high or too low. Engine speed may vary up and down, disconnecting IAC does not help. May set Code 44.
  "Scan" and/or voltmeter will read an oxygen sensor output less than 300 mV (.3 volt). Check for low regulated fuel pressure or water in fuel. A lean exhaust, with an oxygen sensor output fixed above 800 mV (.8 volt) will be a contaminated sensor, usually silicone. This may also set a Code 45.

- **System too rich (Low Air/Fuel Ratio)**
  Idle speed too low. "Scan" counts usually above 80. System obviously rich and may exhibit black smoke exhaust.
  "Scan" tool and/or voltmeter will read an oxygen sensor signal fixed above 800 mV (.8 volt).
  Check:
  - High fuel pressure
  - Injector leaking or sticking
  - Throttle Body

Remove IAC and inspect bore for foreign material or evidence of IAC valve dragging the bore. Refer to "Rough, Unstable, Incorrect Idle or Stalling" in "Symptoms" in Section "B".

CHART C-1E
POWER STEERING PRESSURE SWITCH (PSPS) DIAGNOSIS
2.0L (VIN 1) "L" CARLINE (TBI)

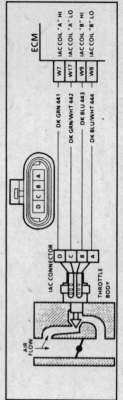

(1) • WITH ENGINE IDLING "SCAN" SHOULD DISPLAY PSPS TO BE "OFF". DOES IT?

→ NO →
(2) • DISCONNECT PSPS. "SCAN" SHOULD INDICATE "OFF". DOES IT?
  → NO → CKT 901 SHORTED TO GROUND OR FAULTY ECM.
  → YES → FAULTY SWITCH.

→ YES → • TURN STEERING WHEEL AGAINST STOP. "SCAN" SHOULD DISPLAY "ON". DOES IT?

  → NO → (3) • DISCONNECT PSPS HARNESS CONNECTOR. • JUMPER HARNESS TERMINALS TOGETHER. • "SCAN" SHOULD DISPLAY "ON". DOES IT?
    → NO → • JUMPER HARNESS CKT 901 TO CHASSIS GROUND. "SCAN" SHOULD DISPLAY "ON". DOES IT?
      → NO → CKT 901 OPEN OR FAULTY ECM.
      → YES → FAULTY GROUND CKT 450.
    → YES → FAULTY CONNECTION OR SWITCH.

  → YES → PSPS CIRCUIT OK.

CLEAR CODES AND CONFIRM "CLOSED LOOP" OPERATION AND NO "SERVICE ENGINE SOON" LIGHT.

1988—89 2.0L ENGINE

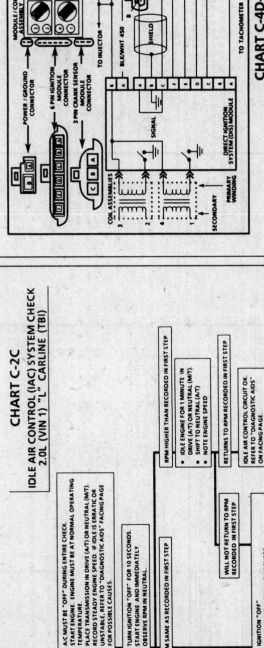

CHART C-2C
IDLE AIR CONTROL (IAC) SYSTEM CHECK
2.0L (VIN 1) "L" CARLINE (TBI)

1
- A/C MUST BE "OFF" DURING ENTIRE CHECK.
- START ENGINE. ENGINE MUST BE AT NORMAL OPERATING TEMPERATURE.
- PLACE TRANSMISSION IN DRIVE (A/T) OR NEUTRAL (M/T).
- RECORD STEADY ENGINE SPEED. IF IDLE IS ERRATIC OR UNSTABLE, REFER TO "DIAGNOSTIC AIDS" FACING PAGE FOR POSSIBLE CAUSES.

2
- TURN IGNITION "OFF" FOR 10 SECONDS. START ENGINE AND IMMEDIATELY OBSERVE RPM IN NEUTRAL.

RPM SAME AS RECORDED IN FIRST STEP

RPM HIGHER THAN RECORDED IN FIRST STEP
- IDLE ENGINE FOR 1 MINUTE IN DRIVE (A/T) OR NEUTRAL (M/T).
- SHIFT TO NEUTRAL (A/T)
- NOTE ENGINE SPEED

RETURNS TO RPM RECORDED IN FIRST STEP

IDLE AIR CONTROL CIRCUIT OK. REFER TO "DIAGNOSTIC AIDS" ON FACING PAGE.

WILL NOT RETURN TO RPM RECORDED IN FIRST STEP

3
- IGNITION "OFF".
- DISCONNECT IAC VALVE HARNESS.
- IGNITION "ON". ENGINE "OFF".
- GROUND DIAGNOSTIC TEST TERMINAL.
- CONNECT A TEST LIGHT BETWEEN EACH IAC VALVE HARNESS CONNECTOR TERMINAL AND GROUND.

4 LIGHT STEADY OR FLASHING ALL CIRCUITS

FAULTY IAC CONNECTION OR IAC VALVE, OR PLUGGED PASSAGE. IF LIGHT APPEARS TO BE STEADY, REFER TO STEP 4 ON FACING PAGE.

NO LIGHTS, ONE OR MORE CIRCUITS
- CHECK FOR OPEN OR SHORT TO GROUND IN CIRCUIT WITH NO LIGHT. ARE ALL CIRCUITS OK?

NO → REPAIR WIRING AND RECHECK.

YES
- CHECK RESISTANCE ACROSS IAC VALVE COILS. IT SHOULD BE MORE THAN 20 OHMS BETWEEN IAC VALVE TERMINALS "A" & "B" AND "C" & "D". IS IT?

NO → REPLACE IAC VALVE AND RETEST.

YES → FAULTY ECM CONNECTION OR ECM.

CLEAR CODES, CONFIRM "CLOSED LOOP" OPERATION, NO "SERVICE ENGINE SOON" LIGHT.

CHART C-4D-1
"DIS" MISFIRE AT IDLE
2.0L (VIN 1) "L" CARLINE (TBI)

Circuit Description:

The "direct ignition system" (DIS) uses a waste spark method of distribution. In this type of system, the ignition module triggers the #1/4 coil pair resulting in both #1 and #4 spark plugs firing at the same time. #1 cylinder is on the compression stroke at the same time #4 is on the exhaust stroke, resulting in a lower energy requirement to fire #4 spark plug. This leaves the remainder of the high voltage to be used to fire #1 spark plug. The crank sensor is remotely mounted beside the module/coil assembly and protrudes through the block to within approximately .050" of the crankshaft reluctor. Since the reluctor is a machined portion of the crankshaft and the crankshaft sensor is mounted in a fixed position on the block, timing adjustments are not possible or necessary.

Test Description: Numbers below refer to circled numbers on the diagnostic chart.

1. If the "Misfire" complaint exists under load only, the diagnostic chart on page 2 must be used. Engine rpm should drop approximately equally on all plug leads.
2. A spark tester, such as a ST-125, must be used because it is essential to verify adequate available secondary voltage at the spark plug (25,000 volts).
3. If the spark jumps the tester gap after grounding the opposite plug wire, it indicates excessive resistance in the plug which was bypassed. A faulty or poor connection at that plug could also result in the miss condition. Also, check for carbon deposits inside the spark plug boot.
4. If carbon tracking is evident, replace coil and be sure plug wires relating to that coil are clean and tight. Excessive wire resistance or faulty connections could have caused the coil to be damaged.
5. If the no spark condition follows the suspected coil, that coil is faulty. Otherwise, the ignition module is the cause of no spark. This test could also be performed by substituting a known good coil for the one causing the no spark condition.

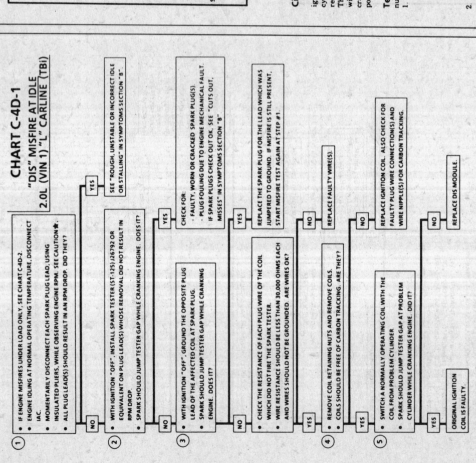

CHART C-4D-2
"DIS" MISFIRE UNDER LOAD
2.0L (VIN 1) "L" CARLINE (TBI)

Circuit Description:

The "direct ignition system" (DIS) uses a waste spark method of distribution. In this type of system, the ignition module triggers the #1/4 coil pair resulting in both #1 and #4 spark plugs firing at the same time. #1 cylinder is on the compression stroke at the same time #4 is on the exhaust stroke, resulting in a lower energy requirement to fire #4 spark plug. This leaves the remainder of the high voltage to be used to fire #1 spark plug. The crank sensor is remotely mounted beside the module/coil assembly and protrudes through the block to within approximately .050" of the crankshaft reluctor. Since the reluctor is a machined portion of the crankshaft, and the crankshaft sensor is mounted in a fixed position on the block, timing adjustments are not possible or necessary.

Test Description: Numbers below refer to circled numbers on the diagnostic chart.

1. If the "Misfire" complaint exists at idle only, the diagnostic chart on page 1 must be used. A spark tester such as a ST-125 must be used because it is essential to verify adequate available secondary voltage at the spark plug. (25,000 volts). Spark should jump the test gap on all 4 leads. This simulates a "load" condition.

2. If the spark jumps the tester gap after grounding the opposite plug wire, it indicates excessive resistance in the plug which was bypassed.

3. A faulty or poor connection at that plug could also result in the miss condition. Also, check for carbon deposits inside the spark plug boot. If carbon tracing is evident replace coil and be sure plug wires relating to that coil are clean and tight. Excessive wire resistance or faulty connections could have caused the coil to be damaged.

4. If the no spark condition follows the suspected coil, that coil is faulty. Otherwise, the ignition module is the cause of no spark. This test could also be performed by substituting a known good coil for the one causing the no spark condition.

1988-89 2.0L ENGINE

CHART C-4D-1
"DIS" MISFIRE AT IDLE
2.0L (VIN 1) "L" CARLINE (TBi)

1.
- IF ENGINE MISFIRES UNDER LOAD ONLY, SEE CHART C-4D-2.
- ENGINE IDLING AT NORMAL OPERATING TEMPERATURE, DISCONNECT IAC.
- MOMENTARILY DISCONNECT EACH SPARK PLUG LEAD, USING INSULATED PLIERS, WHILE OBSERVING ENGINE RPM. SEE CAUTION★.
- ALL PLUG LEAD(S) SHOULD RESULT IN AN RPM DROP. DID THEY?

YES → SEE "ROUGH, UNSTABLE OR INCORRECT IDLE OR STALLING" IN SYMPTOMS SECTION "b".

NO ↓

2.
- WITH IGNITION "OFF", INSTALL SPARK TESTER (ST-125) 26792 OR EQUIVALENT ON PLUG LEAD(S) WHOSE REMOVAL DID NOT RESULT IN RPM DROP.
- SPARK SHOULD JUMP TESTER GAP WHILE CRANKING ENGINE. DOES IT?

YES → CHECK FOR:
- FAULTY, WORN OR CRACKED SPARK PLUG(S).
- PLUG FOULING DUE TO ENGINE MECHANICAL FAULT.
IF SPARK PLUGS CHECK OUT OK, SEE "CUTS OUT, MISSES" IN SYMPTOMS SECTION "b".

NO ↓

3.
- WITH IGNITION "OFF", GROUND THE OPPOSITE PLUG LEAD OF THE AFFECTED COIL AT SPARK PLUG.
- SPARK SHOULD JUMP TESTER GAP WHILE CRANKING ENGINE. DOES IT?

YES → REPLACE THE SPARK PLUG FOR THE LEAD WHICH WAS JUMPERED TO GROUND. IF MISFIRE IS STILL PRESENT, START MISFIRE TEST AGAIN AT STEP #1.

NO ↓

4.
- CHECK THE RESISTANCE OF EACH PLUG WIRE OF THE COIL WHICH DID NOT FIRE THE SPARK TESTER.
- WIRE RESISTANCE SHOULD BE LESS THAN 30,000 OHMS EACH AND WIRES SHOULD NOT BE GROUNDED. ARE WIRES OK?

NO → REPLACE FAULTY WIRE(S).

YES ↓
- REMOVE COIL RETAINING NUTS AND REMOVE COILS.
- COILS SHOULD BE FREE OF CARBON TRACKING. ARE THEY?

NO → REPLACE IGNITION COIL. ALSO CHECK FOR FAULTY PLUG WIRE CONNECTION(S) AND WIRE NIPPLE(S) FOR CARBON TRACKING.

YES ↓

5.
- SWITCH A NORMALLY OPERATING COIL WITH THE COIL FROM PROBLEM CYLINDER.
- SPARK SHOULD JUMP TESTER GAP AT PROBLEM CYLINDER WHILE CRANKING ENGINE. DID IT?

YES → ORIGINAL IGNITION COIL IS FAULTY.

NO → REPLACE DIS MODULE.

★ CAUTION: When handling secondary spark plug leads with engine running, insulated pliers must be used and care exercised to prevent a possible electrical shock.

CLEAR CODES AND CONFIRM "CLOSED LOOP" OPERATION AND NO "SERVICE ENGINE SOON" LIGHT.

1988–89 2.0L ENGINE

CHART C-4D-2

"DIS" MISFIRE UNDER LOAD
2.0L (VIN 1) "L" CARLINE (TBI)

1.
   - IF ENGINE MISFIRES AT IDLE ONLY, SEE CHART C-4D-1.
   - IGNITION "OFF".
   - DISCONNECT ONE SPARK PLUG LEAD AT A TIME AND,
   - INSTALL SPARK TESTER (ST-125) J26792 OR EQUIVALENT.
   - OBSERVE SPARK TESTER WITH ENGINE IDLING. REPEAT THIS TEST FOR ALL PLUG LEADS. SEE CAUTION★
   - SPARK SHOULD JUMP TESTER GAP ON ALL LEADS WITH ENGINE IDLING. DID IT?

   NO → 2.
   - WITH IGNITION "OFF", GROUND THE OPPOSITE PLUG LEAD OF THE AFFECTED COIL AT SPARK PLUG.
   - SPARK SHOULD JUMP TESTER GAP WHILE CRANKING ENGINE. DOES IT?

   YES → CHECK FOR:
   - FAULTY, WORN OR CRACKED SPARK PLUG(S).
   - PLUG FOULING DUE TO ENGINE MECHANICAL FAULT.
   IF SPARK PLUGS CHECK OUT OK, SEE "CUTS OUT, MISSES" IN SYMPTOMS SECTION "B".

2.
   NO → 3.
   - CHECK THE RESISTANCE OF EACH PLUG WIRE OF THE COIL WHICH DID NOT FIRE THE SPARK TESTER.
   - WIRE RESISTANCE SHOULD BE LESS THAN 30,000 OHMS EACH AND WIRES SHOULD NOT BE GROUNDED. ARE WIRES OK?

   YES → REPLACE THE SPARK PLUG FOR THE LEAD WHICH WAS JUMPERED TO GROUND. IF MISFIRE IS STILL PRESENT, START MISFIRE TEST AGAIN AT STEP #1.

3.
   - REMOVE COIL RETAINING NUTS AND REMOVE COILS. COILS SHOULD BE FREE OF CARBON TRACKING. ARE THEY?

   NO → REPLACE FAULTY WIRE(S).

   YES → 4.

4.
   - SWITCH A NORMALLY OPERATING COIL WITH THE COIL FROM PROBLEM CYLINDER.
   - SPARK SHOULD JUMP TESTER GAP WITH ENGINE IDLING. DID IT?

   NO → REPLACE IGNITION COIL. ALSO CHECK FOR FAULTY PLUG WIRE CONNECTIONS AND WIRE NIPPLES FOR CARBON TRACKING.

   YES → ORIGINAL IGNITION COIL IS FAULTY.

   NO → REPLACE DIS MODULE.

★CAUTION: When handling secondary spark plug leads with engine running, insulated pliers must be used and care exercised to prevent a possible electrical shock.

CLEAR CODES AND CONFIRM "CLOSED LOOP" OPERATION AND NO "SERVICE ENGINE SOON" LIGHT.

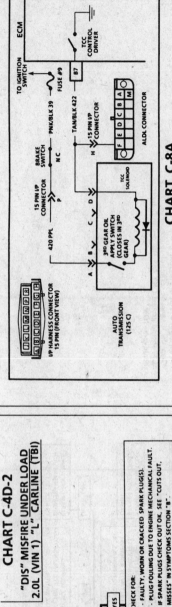

CHART C-8A

TORQUE CONVERTER CLUTCH (TCC)
(ELECTRICAL DIAGNOSIS)
2.0L (VIN 1) "L" CARLINE (TBI)

Circuit Description:

The purpose of the automatic transmission torque converter clutch is to eliminate the power loss of the torque converter when the vehicle is in a cruise condition. This allows the convenience of the automatic transmission and the fuel economy of a manual transmission.

Fused battery ignition is supplied to the TCC solenoid through the brake switch and transmission third gear apply switch. The ECM will engage TCC by grounding CKT 422 to energize the solenoid.

TCC will engage when:
- Vehicle speed above 30 mph (48 km/h).
- Engine at normal operating temperature (above 70°C, 156°F).
- Throttle position sensor output not changing, indicating a steady road speed.
- Transmission third gear switch closed.
- Brake switch closed.

Test Description: Numbers below refer to circled numbers on the diagnostic chart.

1. Light "OFF" confirms transmission third gear apply switch is open.
2. At 48 km/h (30 mph), the transmission third gear switch should close. Test light will come "ON" and confirm battery supply and closed brake switch.
3. Grounding the diagnostic terminal with engine "OFF" should energize the TCC solenoid. This test checks the capability of the ECM to control the solenoid.

Check TCC solenoid resistance as follows:
1. Disconnect TCC solenoid at transmission.
2. Connect ohmmeter between transmission connector opposite harness connector terminal "A" and "D".

3. Raise drive wheels.
4. Run engine in drive about 48 km/h (30 mph) to close third gear apply switch.
5. Replace the TCC solenoid and ECM if resistance measures less than 20 ohms when switch is closed.

Diagnostic Aids:

An engine coolant thermostat that is stuck open, or opens at too low a temperature may result in an inoperative TCC.

1988-89 2.0L ENGINE

CHART C-8A

TORQUE CONVERTER CLUTCH (TCC)
(ELECTRICAL DIAGNOSIS)
2.0L (VIN 1) "L" CARLINE (TBI)

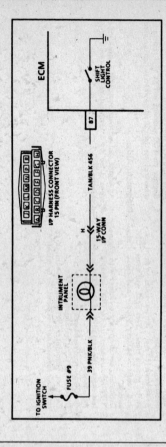

USING A "SCAN" TOOL, CHECK THE FOLLOWING AND CORRECT IF NECESSARY:
- COOLANT TEMPERATURE SHOULD BE ABOVE 65°C.
- TPS - BE SURE TPS SIGNAL IS NOT ERRATIC.
- VSS - SHOULD INDICATE VSS WITH WHEELS TURNING.
- CODES - IF 24 IS PRESENT, SEE CODE CHART 24.

① PERFORM MECHANICAL CHECKS ON LINKAGE, OIL LEVEL, ETC., BEFORE USING THIS CHART.
- CONNECT TEST LIGHT FROM TCC TEST POINT (ALDL TERMINAL "F") TO GROUND.
- RAISE DRIVE WHEELS.
- START ENGINE AND IDLE ENGINE IN DRIVE. DO NOT DEPRESS BRAKE PEDAL.
- DO NOT PERFORM THIS TEST WITHOUT SUPPORTING THE LOWER CONTROL ARMS SO THAT THE DRIVE AXLES ARE IN A NORMAL HORIZONTAL POSITION. RUNNING THE VEHICLE IN GEAR WITH THE WHEELS HANGING DOWN AT FULL TRAVEL MAY DAMAGE THE DRIVE AXLES.
- OBSERVE LIGHT.

LIGHT "OFF"	LIGHT "ON"
	FAULTY TRANSMISSION 3RD GEAR SWITCH OR CKT 422 SHORTED TO VOLTAGE.

② INCREASE SPEED SLOWLY UNTIL TRANSMISSION SHIFTS INTO 3RD GEAR.
- OBSERVE TEST LIGHT.

LIGHT "ON"	LIGHT "OFF"

TEST LIGHT SHOULD GO OUT AS BRAKE PEDAL IS DEPRESSED. DOES IT?

YES	NO
	FAULTY BRAKE SWITCH OR ADJUSTMENT.

③ IGNITION "ON", ENGINE "OFF".
- CONNECT TEST LIGHT TO BATTERY VOLTAGE AND PROBE ALDL TERMINAL "F".
- GROUND DIAGNOSTIC TERMINAL AND OBSERVE LIGHT.

LIGHT "ON"	LIGHT "OFF"
CHECK FOR CORRECT PROM. IF OK, TCC ELECTRICAL CONTROL IS OK.	CHECK FOR OPEN CKT 422 FROM ALDL TO ECM CONNECTOR TERMINAL. IF CKT 422 IS OK, ECM IS FAULTY.

- IGNITION "ON", ENGINE "OFF".
- CHECK FOR BLOWN FUSE. IF OK, DISCONNECT TCC SOLENOID HARNESS CONNECTOR AT TRANSMISSION.
- CONNECT TEST LIGHT BETWEEN HARNESS CONNECTOR TERMINALS "A" AND "D".

LIGHT "OFF"	LIGHT "ON"
CONNECT A TEST LIGHT FROM TERMINAL "A" TO GROUND.	CHECK FOR SHORT TO GROUND IN CKT 422. IF NOT GROUNDED, REPLACE ECM.

LIGHT "ON"	LIGHT "OFF"
GROUND TCC TEST POINT AND AGAIN CONNECT TEST LIGHT BETWEEN HARNESS CONNECTOR TERMINALS "A" AND "D".	REPAIR OPEN IN TCC BRAKE SWITCH CIRCUIT OR ADJUST SWITCH.

LIGHT "ON"	LIGHT "OFF"
FAULTY TCC SOLENOID CONNECTOR, TCC SOLENOID OR 3RD GEAR SWITCH.	REPAIR OPEN IN WIRE FROM TRANSMISSION TO ALDL TEST POINT TERMINAL "F".

CLEAR CODES AND CONFIRM "CLOSED LOOP" OPERATION AND NO "SERVICE ENGINE SOON" LIGHT.

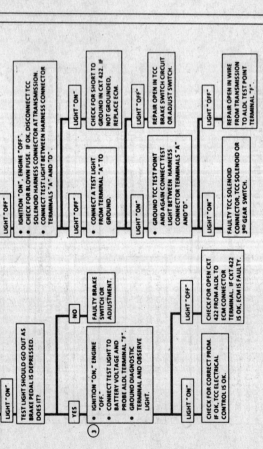

CHART C-8B

MANUAL TRANSMISSION (M/T) SHIFT LIGHT CHECK
2.0L (VIN 1) "L" CARLINE (TBI)

Circuit Description:
The shift light indicates the best transmission shift point for maximum fuel economy. The light is controlled by the ECM and is turned "ON" by grounding CKT 456. The ECM uses information from the following inputs to control the shift light:
- Coolant temperature
- TPS
- VSS
- rpm

The ECM uses the measured rpm and the vehicle speed to calculate what gear the vehicle is in. It's this calculation that determines when the shift light should be turned "ON."

Test Description: Numbers below refer to circled numbers on the diagnostic chart.

1. This should not turn "ON" the shift light. If the light is "ON," there is a short to ground in CKT 456 wiring or a fault in the ECM.

2. When the diagnostic terminal is grounded, the ECM should ground CKT 456 and the shift light should come "ON."

3. This checks the shift light circuit up to the ECM connector. If the shift light illuminates, then the ECM connector is faulty or the ECM does not have the ability to ground the circuit.

1988–89 2.0L ENGINE

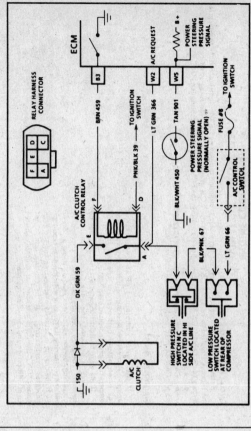

CHART C-10
A/C CLUTCH CONTROL
2.0L (VIN 1) "L" CARLINE (TBI)

Circuit Description:

When an A/C mode is selected on the A/C control switch, ignition voltage is supplied to the compressor low pressure switch. If there is sufficient charge, the low pressure switch will be closed and complete the circuit to the closed high pressure cut-off switch and to CKTs 67 and 366. The voltage on CKT 366 to the ECM is shown by the "Scan" tool as A/C request "ON" (voltage present). "OFF" (no voltage). When a request for A/C is seen by the ECM, the ECM will ground CKT 459 of the A/C clutch control relay, the relay contact will close, and current will flow from CKT 366 to CKT 59 and engage the A/C compressor clutch. A "Scan" tool will show the grounding or CKT 459 as A/C clutch "ON." Also, when voltage is seen by the ECM on CKT 366, the cooling fan will be turned "ON."

When power steering hydraulic pressure increases, the power steering pressure switch will close, grounding CKT 901. The ECM will then open CKT 459 which de-energizes the A/C clutch control relay, disengaging the A/C compressor clutch.

Diagnostic Aids:

The low pressure switch will be closed at 40-47 psi and allow A/C clutch operation. Below 37 psi, the low pressure switch will be open and the A/C clutch will not operate.

At about 430 psi, the high pressure switch will open on CKT 901 to disengage the A/C clutch and prevent system damage.

CHART C-8B
MANUAL TRANSMISSION (M/T) SHIFT LIGHT CHECK
2.0L (VIN 1) "L" CARLINE (TBI)

1.
   - IGNITION "ON", ENGINE "OFF".
   - OBSERVE SHIFT LIGHT.

   LIGHT "OFF"

   2.
   - GROUND ALDL DIAGNOSTIC TERMINAL AND OBSERVE SHIFT LIGHT.

   LIGHT "ON"

   LIGHT "OFF"

   3.
   - IGNITION "OFF".
   - DISCONNECT ECM CONNECTORS.
   - IGNITION "ON".
   - JUMPER CKT 456 TO GROUND AND OBSERVE SHIFT LIGHT.

   LIGHT "OFF"
   OPEN IGNITION CKT 39, OPEN CKT 456, OR FAULTY BULB.

   LIGHT "ON"
   POOR CONNECTION AT ECM OR FAULTY ECM.

   LIGHT "ON"
   CHECK FOR:
   - CODE 24. (NO VSS).
   - THERMOSTAT FAULTY OR HAS INCORRECT HEAT RANGE. IF OK, REVIEW SYMPTOMS IN SECTION "B".

   LIGHT "ON"
   - IGNITION "OFF".
   - DISCONNECT ECM CONNECTORS.
   - TURN IGNITION "ON" AND OBSERVE SHIFT LIGHT.

   LIGHT "OFF"
   REPLACE ECM.

   LIGHT "ON"
   REPAIR SHORT TO GROUND IN CKT 456.

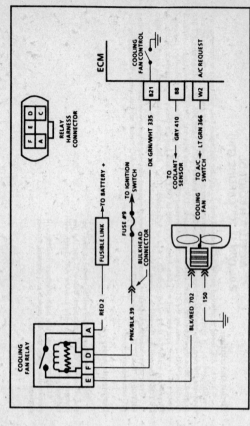

CHART C-12
ENGINE COOLING FAN
2.0L (VIN 1) "L" CARLINE (TBI)

Circuit Description:

Battery voltage to operate the cooling fan motor is supplied to relay by CKT 2. Ignition voltage to energize the relay is supplied to relay by CKT 39. When the engine is running, the ECM grounds CKT 335, the relay is energized and the cooling fan is turned "ON." When the engine is running, the ECM will turn the cooling fan "ON" if:

- A/C is "ON."
- Coolant temperature greater than 108°C (230°F).
- Code 14 or 15, coolant sensor failure.

Diagnostic Aids:

If the owner complained of an overheating problem, it must be determined if the complaint was due to an actual boil over, or the hot light, or temperature gage indicated over heating.

If the gage or light indicates overheating, but no boil over is detected, the gage circuit should be checked. The gage accuracy can also be checked by comparing the coolant sensor reading using a "Scan" tool and comparing its reading with the gage reading.

If the engine is actually overheating and the gage indicates overheating, but the cooling fan is not coming "ON," the coolant sensor has probably shifted out of calibration and should be replaced.

1988-89 2.0L ENGINE

CHART C-10
A/C CLUTCH CONTROL
2.0L (VIN 1) "L" CARLINE (TBI)

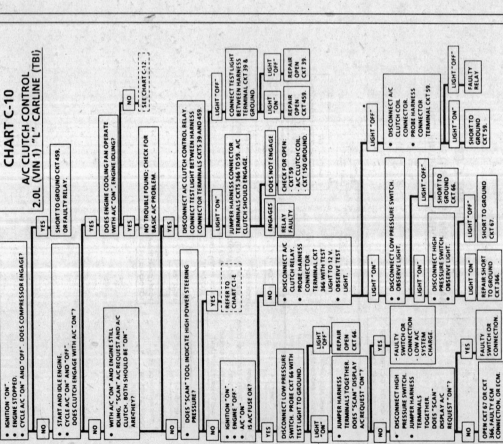

COMPONENT LOCATIONS — 2.8L ENGINE

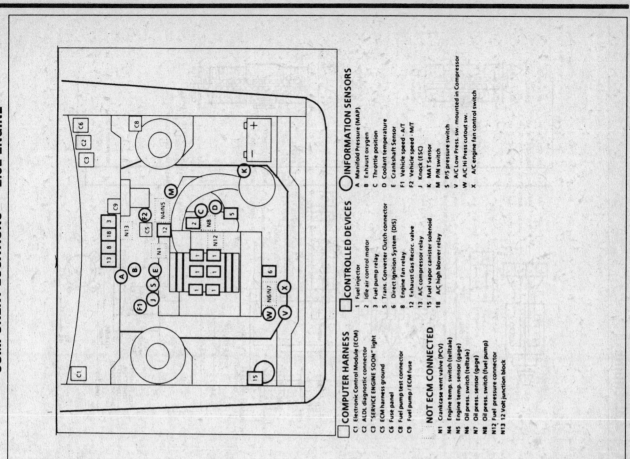

COMPUTER HARNESS

- C1 Electronic Control Module (ECM)
- C2 ALDL diagnostic connector
- C3 "SERVICE ENGINE SOON" light
- C5 ECM harness ground
- C6 Fuse panel
- C8 Fuel pump test connector
- C9 Fuel pump / ECM fuse

NOT ECM CONNECTED

- N1 Crankcase vent valve (PCV)
- N4 Engine temp. switch (telltale)
- N5 Engine temp. sensor (gage)
- N6 Oil press. switch (telltale)
- N7 Oil press. switch (gage)
- N8 Oil press. sensor (gage)
- N12 Oil press. switch (fuel pump)
- N13 12 Volt junction block

CONTROLLED DEVICES

- 1 Fuel injector
- 2 Idle air control motor
- 3 Fuel pump relay
- 5 Trans. Converter Clutch connector
- 6 Direct Ignition System (DIS)
- 8 Engine fan relay
- 12 Exhaust Gas Recirc. valve
- 13 A/C compressor relay
- 15 Fuel vapor canister solenoid
- 18 A/C high blower relay

INFORMATION SENSORS

- A Manifold Pressure (MAP)
- B Exhaust oxygen
- C Throttle position
- D Coolant temperature
- E Crankshaft Sensor
- F1 Vehicle speed - A/T
- F2 Vehicle speed - M/T
- J Knock (ESC)
- K MAT Sensor
- M P/N switch
- S P/S pressure switch
- V A/C Low Press. sw. mounted in Compressor
- W A/C Hi Press cutout sw.
- X A/C engine fan control switch

1988-89 2.0L ENGINE

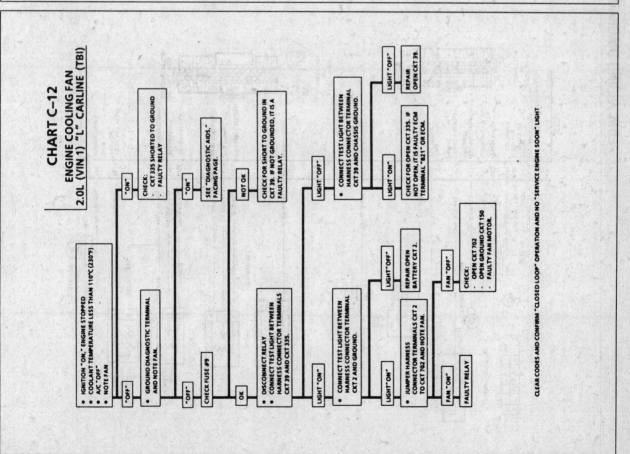

CHART C-12

ENGINE COOLING FAN

2.0L (VIN 1) "L" CARLINE (TBI)

ECM WIRING DIAGRAM — 2.8L ENGINE

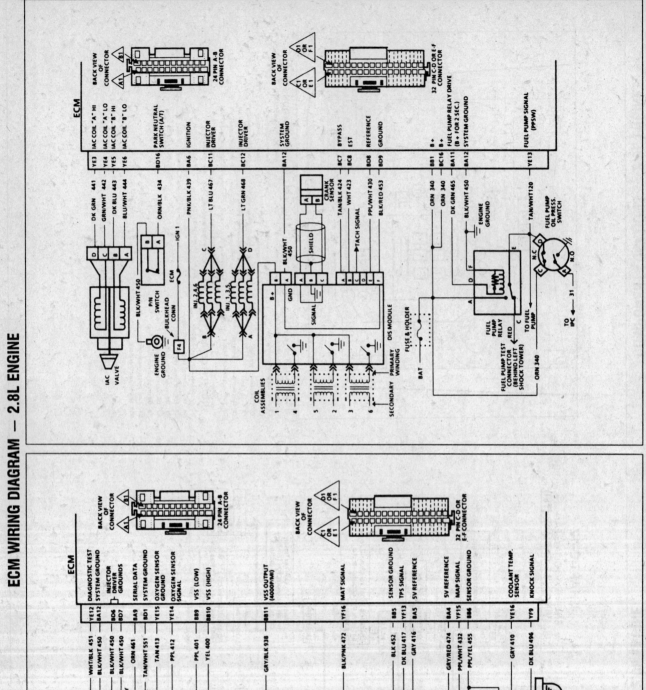

END VIEW OF THE ECM CONNECTOR — 2.8L ENGINE

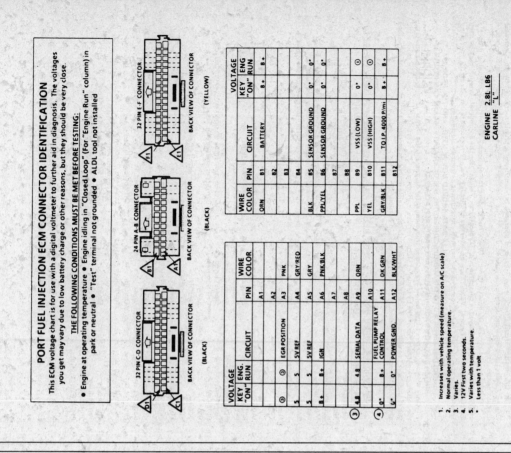

PORT FUEL INJECTION ECM CONNECTOR IDENTIFICATION

This ECM voltage chart is for use with a digital voltmeter to further aid in diagnosis. The voltages you get may vary due to low battery charge or other reasons, but they should be very close.

THE FOLLOWING CONDITIONS MUST BE MET BEFORE TESTING:

- Engine at operating temperature • Engine idling in "Closed Loop" (For "Engine Run" column) in park or neutral • "Test" terminal not grounded • ALDL tool not installed

VOLTAGE				
WIRE COLOR	PIN	CIRCUIT	KEY "ON"	ENG. RUN
	A1			
	A2			
PNK	A3	EGR POSITION	②	②
GRY/RED	A4	5V REF	5	5
GRY	A5	5V REF	5	5
PNK/BLK	A6	IGN	B+	B+
	A7			
	A8			
ORN	A9	SERIAL DATA	4.8	4.8
A10	FUEL PUMP RELAY CONTROL		B+	②*
DK GRN	A11			
BLK/WHT	A12	POWER GND.	①*	①*

32 PIN C-D CONNECTOR (BLACK)
BACK VIEW OF CONNECTOR

24 PIN A-B CONNECTOR (BLACK)
BACK VIEW OF CONNECTOR

32 PIN E-F CONNECTOR (YELLOW)
BACK VIEW OF CONNECTOR

VOLTAGE				
WIRE COLOR	PIN	CIRCUIT	KEY "ON"	ENG RUN
ORN	B1	BATTERY	B+	B+
	B2			
	B3			
	B4			
BLK	B5	SENSOR GROUND	0*	0*
PPL/YEL	B6	SENSOR GROUND	0*	0*
	B7			
	B8			
PPL	B9	VSS (LOW)	①	①
YEL	B10	VSS (HIGH)	①	①
GRY/BLK	B11	TO I.P. 4000 P/mi	B+	B+
	B12			

Engine 2.8L LB6
Carline "L"

1. Increases with vehicle speed (measure on A/C scale)
2. Normal operating temperature.
3. Varies.
4. 12V first two seconds.
5. Varies with temperature.
*. Less than 1 volt

ECM WIRING DIAGRAM CONT. — 2.8L ENGINE

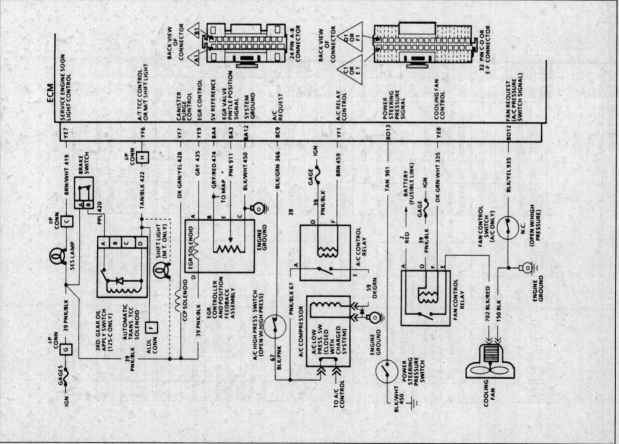

DIAGNOSTIC CIRCUIT CHECK — 2.8L ENGINE

DIAGNOSTIC CIRCUIT CHECK

The Diagnostic Circuit Check must be the starting point for any driveability complaint diagnosis. The Diagnostic Circuit Check is an organized approach to identifying a problem created by an Electronic Engine Control System malfunction because it directs the Service Technician to the next logical step in diagnosing the complaint.

If after completing the Diagnostic Circuit Check and finding the on-board diagnostics functioning properly and no trouble codes displayed, a comparison of "Typical Scan Values", for the appropriate engine, may be used for comparison. The "Typical Values" are an average of display values recorded from normally operating vehicles and are intended to represent what a normally functioning system would display.

A "SCAN" TOOL THAT DISPLAYS FAULTY DATA SHOULD NOT BE USED, AND THE PROBLEM SHOULD BE REPORTED TO THE MANUFACTURER. THE USE OF A FAULTY "SCAN" CAN RESULT IN MISDIAGNOSIS AND UNNECESSARY PARTS REPLACEMENT.

Only the parameters listed below are used in this manual for diagnosis. If a "Scan" reads other parameters, the values are not recommended by General Motors for use in diagnosis. For more description on the values and use of the "Scan" to diagnose ECM inputs, refer to the applicable diagnosis section. If all values are within the range illustrated, refer to "Symptoms" in Section "B".

"SCAN" DATA

Idle / Upper Radiator Hose Hot / Closed Throttle / Park or Neutral / Closed Loop / Acc. off

"SCAN" Position	Units Displayed	Typical Data Value
Desired RPM	RPM	ECM idle command (varies with temp.)
RPM	RPM	± 100 RPM from desired RPM (± 50 in drive)
Coolant Temp.	C°	85° - 105°
MAT Temp.	C°	10° - 80° (depends on underhood temp.)
MAP	Volts	1 - 2 (depends on Vac. & Baro pressure)
BARO	Volts	2.5 - 5.5 (depends on altitude & Baro pressure)
BPW (base pulse width)	M/Sec	1 - 4, and varying
O2	Volts	.1-1.0, and varying
TPS	Volts	.65
Throttle Angle	0 - 100%	0
IAC	Counts (steps)	5 - 50
P/N Switch	P/N and RDL	Park/Neutral (P/N)
INT (Integrator)	Counts	Varies
BLM (Block Learn)	Counts	118 - 138
Open/Closed Loop	Open/Closed	Closed Loop (may go open with extended idle)
BLM Cell	Cell Number	0 or 1 (depends on Air Flow & RPM)
VSS	MPH	0
TCC	On/Off	Off (on with TCC commanded)
EGRDC	Volts	0 at idle
Spark Advance	# of Degrees	Varies
Knock Retard	Degrees of Retard	0°
Knock Signal	Yes/No	No
Battery	Volts	13.5 - 14.5
Fan	On/Off	Off (below 106°C)
P/S Switch	Normal/Hi Press.	Normal
A/C Request	Yes/No	No (yes, with A/C requested)
A/C Clutch	On/Off	Off (on, with A/C commanded on)
Fan Request	Yes/No	No (yes, with A/C high pressure)
Shift Light (M/T)	On/Off	Off
PPSW (Fuel Pump)	Volts	13.5 - 14.5

NOTE: If maximum retard is indicated, go to CHART C-5.

WIRE COLOR	PIN	CIRCUIT	VOLTAGE KEY "ON" RUN	VOLTAGE ENG. RUN
	C1		0°	0°
	C2			
	C3			
	C4			
	C5			
	C6			
TAN/BLK (BLACK)	C7	BYPASS	0°	4.7
WHT	C8	EST	0°	1.3
BLK/PNK	C9	WITH A/C "ON"	B+	B+
BLK/GRN		A/C REQUEST	0°	0°
	C10			
LT BLU	C11	INJECTOR 2,4,6	B+	B+
LT GRN	C12	INJECTOR 1,3,5	B+	B+
	C13			
	C14			
	C15			
ORN	C16	BATTERY	B+	B+

WIRE COLOR	PIN	CIRCUIT	VOLTAGE KEY "ON"	VOLTAGE ENG. RUN
TAN/WHT	D1	POWER GROUND	0°	0°
	D2			
	D3			
	D4			
	D5			
BLK/WHT	D6	IN) DRIVE LOW	0°	0°
BLK/WHT	D7	IN) DRIVE LOW	0°	0°
PPL/WHT	D8	REFERENCE	0°	2.3
BLK/RED	D9	REFERENCE LOW	0°	0°
	D10			
	D11			
BLK/YEL	D12	A/C PRESS FAN SW.	B+	B+
TAN	D13	P/S	0°	0°
	D14			
	D15			
ORN/BLK	D16	P/N SWITCH	0°	0°

WIRE COLOR	PIN	CIRCUIT	VOLTAGE KEY "ON" RUN	VOLTAGE ENG. RUN
DK GRN	E1	IAC "A" HI	NOT USEABLE	
GRN/WHT	E2	IAC "A" LO	NOT USEABLE	
DK BLU	E3	IAC "B" HI	NOT USEABLE	
BLU/WHT	E4	IAC "B" LO	NOT USEABLE	
BRN/WHT (YELLOW)	E5	"SERVICE ENGINE SOON" LIGHT	0°	B+
DK GRN/WHT	E6	FAN RELAY CONTROL	B+	B+
GRY	E7	EGR CONTROL	0°	B+
	E8			
	E9			
	E10			
	E11			
WHT/BLK	E12	DIAG. TERMINAL	5	5
TAN/WHT	E13	FUEL PUMP SIGNAL	35-55	B+ (3)
PPL	E14	O2 SIGNAL	0°	(3)
TAN	E15	O2 GROUND	0°	0°
GRY	E16	COOLANT TEMP.	(5)	(5)

WIRE COLOR	PIN	CIRCUIT	VOLTAGE KEY "ON"	VOLTAGE ENG. RUN
BRN	F1	A/C RELAY CONTROL	B+	B+
	F2			
	F3			
	F4			
TAN/BLK	F5 / F6	TCC CONTROL A/T SHIFT LIGHT M/T	0°	0°
DK GRN/YEL	F7	PURGE CONTROL	B+	B+
	F8			
DK BLU	F9	ESC SIGNAL	2.5	2.5
	F10			
	F11			
	F12			
DK BLU	F13	TPS SIGNAL	.65	.65
	F14			
PPL/WHT	F15	MAP SIGNAL	4.57	1.7 (3)
BLK/PNK	F16	MAT SIGNAL	3.1	3.2 (5)

1. Increases with vehicle speed (measure on A/C scale).
2. Normal operating temperature.
3. Varies.
4. .12 volts first two seconds.
5. Varies with temperature.
6. Less than 1 volt.

1988–89 2.8L ENGINE

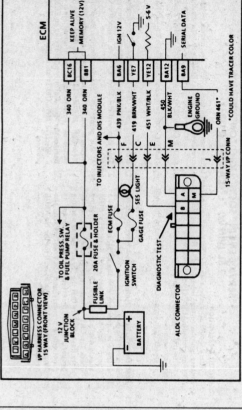

CHART A-1
NO "SERVICE ENGINE SOON" LIGHT
2.8L (VIN W) "L" CARLINE (PORT)

Circuit Description:
There should always be a steady "Service Engine Soon" light when the ignition is "ON" and engine stopped. Battery is supplied directly to the light bulb. The electronic control module (ECM) will control the light and turn it "ON" by providing a ground path through CKT 419 to the ECM.

Test Description: Numbers below refer to circled numbers on the diagnostic chart.
1. If the fuse in holder is blown refer to facing page of Code 54 for complete circuit.
2. Using a test light connected to 12 volts probe each of the system ground circuits to be sure a good ground is present. See ECM terminal end view in front of this section for ECM pin locations of ground circuits.

Diagnostic Aids:
Engine runs OK, check
- Faulty light bulb
- CKT 419 open.
- Gage fuse blown. This will result in no oil or generator lights, seat belt reminder, etc.
Engine cranks but will not run.
- Continuous battery · fuse or fusible link open.
- ECM ignition fuse open.
- Battery CKT 340 to ECM open.
- Ignition CKT 439 to ECM open.
- Poor connection to ECM

DIAGNOSTIC CIRCUIT CHECK — 2.8L ENGINE

DIAGNOSTIC CIRCUIT CHECK
2.8L (VIN W) "L" CARLINE (PORT)

- IGNITION "ON", ENGINE "OFF".
- NOTE "SERVICE ENGINE SOON" LIGHT.

STEADY LIGHT → NO LIGHT → USE CHART A-1.

- JUMPER ALDL TERMINAL "B" TO "A"
- DOES SES LIGHT FLASH CODE 12?

FLASHING CODE 12

CHECK FOR GROUNDED DIAGNOSTIC TEST CKT 451. USE WIRING DIAGRAM ON CHART A-1.

DOES "SCAN" TOOL DISPLAY ECM DATA? — NO → USE CHART A-2.

DOES ENGINE START? — NO → USE CHART A-2.

ARE ANY CODES DISPLAYED? — NO → USE CHART A-3.

- REFER TO APPLICABLE CODE CHART. START WITH LOWEST CODE.

COMPARE "SCAN" TOOL DATA WITH TYPICAL VALUES SHOWN ON FACING PAGE. ARE VALUES NORMAL OR WITHIN TYPICAL RANGES? — NO → REFER TO INDICATED COMPONENT(S) SYSTEM CHECKS

YES → REFER TO SYMPTOMS IN SECTION "B".

1988–89 2.8L ENGINE

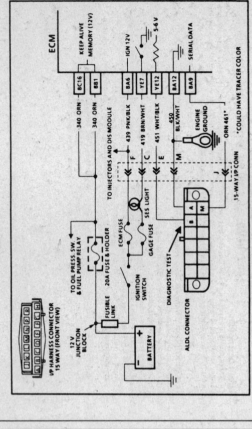

ECM

KEEP ALIVE MEMORY (12V) — BC16 / BB1

BA6 — IGM 12V — YE7

YE12 — 5-6 V

BA12 — SERIAL DATA — BA9

340 ORN — 340 ORN — *COULD HAVE TRACER COLOR

TO INJECTORS AND DIS MODULE

439 PNK/BLK — F

419 BRN/WHT — C

451 WHT/BLK — E

450 BLK/WHT — M

ENGINE GROUND

ORN 461*

TO OIL PRESS. SW & FUEL PUMP RELAY

ECM FUSE

SES LIGHT

GAGE FUSE

20A FUSE & HOLDER

IGNITION SWITCH

FUSIBLE LINK

12 V JUNCTION BLOCK

BATTERY + −

DIAGNOSTIC TEST

ALDL CONNECTOR — B / A / M

15-WAY I/P CONN

I/P HARNESS CONNECTOR 15 WAY (FRONT VIEW)

CHART A-2

NO ALDL DATA OR WON'T FLASH CODE 12 "SERVICE ENGINE SOON" LIGHT "ON" STEADY 2.8L (VIN W) "L" CARLINE (PORT)

Circuit Description:

There should always be a steady "Service Engine Soon" light when the ignition is "ON" and engine stopped. Battery ignition voltage is supplied to the light bulb. The electronic control module (ECM) will turn the light "ON" by grounding CKT 419 at the ECM.

With the diagnostic terminal grounded, the light should flash a Code 12, followed by any trouble code(s) stored in memory.

A steady light suggests a short to ground in the light control CKT 419, or an open in diagnostic CKT 451.

Test Description: Numbers below refer to circled numbers on the diagnostic chart.

1. If there is a problem with the ECM that causes a "Scan" tool to not read serial data, the ECM should not flash a Code 12. If Code 12 is flashing check for CKT 451 short to ground. If Code 12 does flash, be sure that the "Scan" tool is working properly on another vehicle. If the "Scan" is functioning properly and CKT 461 is OK, the Mem-Cal or ECM may be at fault for the No ALDL symptom.

2. If the light goes "OFF" when the ECM connector is disconnected, CKT 419 is not shorted to ground.

3. This step will check for an open diagnostic CKT 451.

4. At this point, the "Service Engine Soon" light wiring is OK. The problem is a faulty ECM or Mem-Cal. If Code 12 does not flash, the ECM should be replaced using the original Mem-Cal. Replace the Mem-Cal only after trying an ECM, as a defective Mem-Cal is an unlikely cause of the problem.

CHART A-1

NO "SERVICE ENGINE SOON" LIGHT 2.8L (VIN W) "L" CARLINE (PORT)

DOES THE ENGINE START?

NO →
- IGNITION "OFF".
- DISCONNECT ECM CONNECTORS.
- IGNITION "ON".
- PROBE CKT 419, WITH TEST LIGHT TO GROUND.
- IS THE "SES" LIGHT "ON"?

  - YES → FAULTY ECM CONNECTION OR ECM.
  - NO → CHECK:
    - GAGE FUSE.
    - FAULTY BULB.
    - OPEN CKT 419.
    - CKT 419 SHORTED TO VOLTAGE.
    - OPEN IGNITION FEED TO BULB.

YES → IS THE 20A CONTINUOUS BATTERY FUSE (IN HOLDER) AND ECM FUSE OK?

  - NO → ① LOCATE AND CORRECT SHORT TO GROUND IN CIRCUIT THAT HAD A BLOWN FUSE.

  - YES →
    - IGNITION "OFF".
    - IGNITION "ON".
    - PROBE CKT 340 & 439 WITH TEST LIGHT TO GROUND.
    - IS THE LIGHT "ON" ON BOTH CIRCUITS?

      - YES → ② FAULTY ECM GROUNDS OR ECM.
      - NO → REPAIR OPEN IN CIRCUIT THAT DID NOT LIGHT THE TEST LIGHT.

CLEAR CODES AND CONFIRM "CLOSED LOOP" OPERATION AND NO "SERVICE ENGINE SOON" LIGHT.

1988–89 2.8L ENGINE

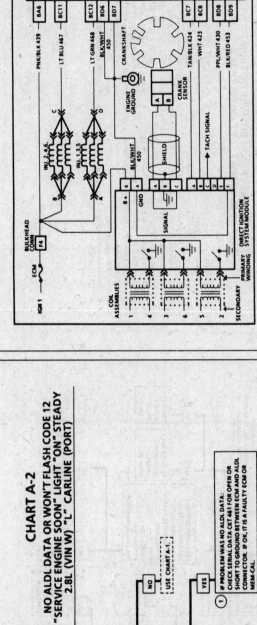

ECM

INJECTOR DRIVER
INJECTOR DRIVER GROUNDS

IGNITION — BA6
— BC11
— BC12
BD6
BD7

PNK/BLK 439
LT BLU 467
LT GRN 468
BLK/WHT 450

CRANKSHAFT

BYPASS — BC7
EST — BC8
REFERENCE — BD8
GROUND — BD9

TAN/BLK 424
WHT 423
PPL/WHT 430
BLK/RED 453

→ TACH SIGNAL

ENGINE GROUND

CRANK SENSOR
A
B

SHIELD

BULKHEAD CONN
F4

ECM
KGM 1

INJ. 2,4,6
INJ. 1,3,5

C
D
B
A

BLK/WHT 450

B+
GND
SIGNAL

COIL ASSEMBLIES
1 4 3 6 5 2

SECONDARY
PRIMARY WINDING
DIRECT IGNITION SYSTEM MODULE

CHART A-3
(Page 1 of 3)
ENGINE CRANKS BUT WILL NOT RUN
2.8L (VIN W) "L" CARLINE (PORT)

Circuit Description:
This chart assumes that battery condition and engine cranking speed are OK, and there is adequate fuel in the tank.

Test Description: Numbers below refer to circled numbers on the diagnostic chart.

1. A "Service Engine Soon" light "ON" is a basic test to determine if there is a 12 volt supply and ignition 12 volts to ECM. No ALDL may be due to an ECM problem and CHART A-2 will diagnose the ECM. If TPS is over 2.5 volts the engine may be in the clear flood mode which will cause starting problems. The engine will not start without reference pulses and therefore the "Scan" should read rpm (reference) during crank.

2. For the first two seconds with ignition "ON" or whenever reference pulses are being received, PPSW should indicate fuel pump circuit voltage (8 to 12 volts).

3. Because the direct ignition system uses two plugs and wires to complete the circuit of each coil, the opposite spark should be left connected. If rpm was indicated during crank, the ignition module is receiving a crank signal, but no spark at this test

indicates the ignition module is not triggering the coils.

4. The test light should blink indicating the ECM is controlling the injectors OK. How bright the light blinks is not important. However, the test light should be a J-34730-3 or equivalent.

5. Use fuel pressure gage J-34730-1 or equivalent. Wrap a shop towel around the fuel pressure tap to absorb any small amount of fuel leakage that may occur when installing the gage.

6. This test will determine if the ignition module is not generating the reference pulse or if the wiring or ECM are at fault. By touching and removing a test light to 12 volts on CKT 430, a reference pulse should be generated. If rpm is indicated, the ECM and wiring are OK.

7. This test will determine if the ignition module is not triggering the problem coil or if the tested coil is at fault. This test could also be performed by using another known good coil.

CHART A-2
NO ALDL DATA OR WON'T FLASH CODE 12
"SERVICE ENGINE SOON" LIGHT "ON" STEADY
2.8L (VIN W) "L" CARLINE (PORT)

- IGNITION "ON," ENGINE "OFF." IS THE "SES" LIGHT "ON"?

  - YES
    - GROUND DIAGNOSTIC TERMINAL. DOES LIGHT FLASH CODE 12?
      - NO
        - ② IGNITION "OFF." DISCONNECT ECM CONNECTORS. IGNITION "ON" AND NOTE "SERVICE ENGINE SOON" LIGHT.
          - LIGHT "ON"
            - REPAIR SHORT TO GROUND IN CKT 419.
          - LIGHT "OFF"
            - ③ IGNITION "OFF." RECONNECT ECM. IGNITION "ON," ENGINE "OFF." DIAGNOSTIC TERMINAL NOT GROUNDED. BACK PROBE ECM CKT 451 WITH TEST LIGHT TO GROUND. LEAVE CONNECTED AND WATCH "SES" LIGHT.
      - YES
        - ① IF PROBLEM WAS NO ALDL DATA: CHECK SERIAL DATA CKT 461 FOR OPEN OR SHORT TO GROUND BETWEEN ECM AND ALDL CONNECTOR. IF OK, IT IS A FAULTY ECM OR MEM-CAL.
  - NO
    - USE CHART A-1.

- NO CODE 12
  - ④ CHECK MEM-CAL FOR PROPER INSTALLATION. IF OK, REPLACE ECM USING ORIGINAL MEM-CAL. RECHECK FOR CODE 12.
    - NO CODE 12
      - REPLACE MEM-CAL.
    - CODE 12
      - SYSTEM OK.
- CODE 12
  - CHECK FOR OPEN CKT 451 TO ECM. IF OK, CHECK FOR OPEN CIRCUIT BETWEEN ALDL TERMINAL "A" AND ECM.

CLEAR CODES AND CONFIRM "CLOSED LOOP" OPERATION AND NO "SERVICE ENGINE SOON" LIGHT.

1988-89 2.8L ENGINE

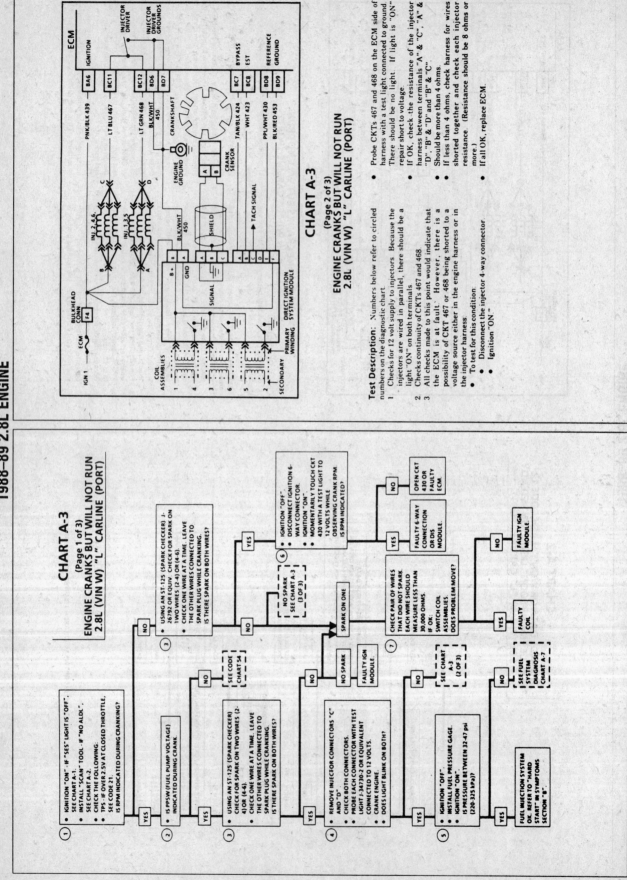

CHART A-3

(Page 2 of 3)

ENGINE CRANKS BUT WILL NOT RUN
2.8L (VIN W) "L" CARLINE (PORT)

Test Description: Numbers below refer to circled numbers on the diagnostic chart.

1. Checks for 12 volt supply to injectors. Because the injectors are wired in parallel, there should be a light "ON" on both terminals

2. Checks continuity of CKTs 467 and 468

3. All checks made to this point would indicate that the ECM is at fault. However, there is a possibility of CKT 467 or 468 being shorted to a voltage source either in the engine harness or in the injector harness.

To test for this condition:
- Disconnect the injector 4-way connector.
- Ignition "ON."

- Probe CKTs 467 and 468 on the ECM side of harness with a test light connected to ground There should be no light. If light is "ON" repair short to voltage.
- If OK, check the resistance of the injector harness between terminals "A" & "C", "A" & "D", "B" & "D" and "B" & "C". Should be more than 4 ohms.
- If less than 4 ohms, check harness for wires shorted together and check each injector resistance. (Resistance should be 8 ohms or more.)
- If all OK, replace ECM.

CHART A-3

(Page 1 of 3)

ENGINE CRANKS BUT WILL NOT RUN
2.8L (VIN W) "L" CARLINE (PORT)

1988-89 2.8L ENGINE

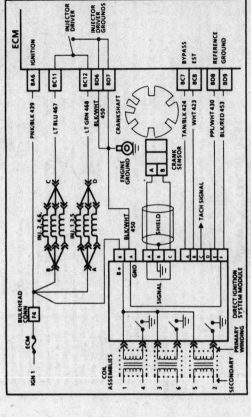

ECM

IGNITION — BA6 — PNK/BLK 439

INJECTOR DRIVER — BC11 — LT BLU 467

— BC12 — LT GRN 468
INJECTOR DRIVER GROUNDS — BD6 — BLK/WHT 450
— BD7

BYPASS — BC7 — TAN/BLK 424
EST — BC9 — WHT 423
REFERENCE — BD8 — PPL/WHT 430
GROUND — BD9 — BLK/RED 453

INJ. 2,4,6. — C
INJ. 1,3,5. — D

ENGINE GROUND

CRANKSHAFT

CRANK SENSOR

SHIELD

TACH SIGNAL

COIL ASSEMBLIES — 1 4 3 6 5 2

SECONDARY WINDING

PRIMARY WINDING

DIRECT IGNITION SYSTEM MODULE

B+ GND SIGNAL

BULKHEAD CONN F4

ECM IGM 1

CHART A-3
(Page 3 of 3)
ENGINE CRANKS BUT WILL NOT RUN
2.8L (VIN W) "L" CARLINE (PORT)

Circuit Description:

If the "Scan" tool did not indicate a cranking rpm and there is no spark present at the plugs, the problem lies in the direct ignition system or the power and ground supplies to the module.

The magnetic crank sensor is used to determine engine crankshaft position much the same way as the pick-up coil did in distributor type systems. The sensor is mounted in the block near a seven slot wheel on the crankshaft. The rotation of the wheel creates a flux change in the sensor which produces a voltage signal. The ignition module then processes this signal and creates the reference pulses needed by the ECM and the signal triggers the correct coil at the correct time.

Test Description: Numbers below refer to circled numbers on the diagnostic chart.

1. This test will determine if the 12 volt supply and a good ground is available at the ignition module.

2. Tests for continuity of CKT 439 to the ignition module. If test light does not light but the "Service Engine Soon" light is "ON" with ignition repair open in CKT 439 between DIS ignition module and splice.

3. Checks for continuity of the crank sensor and connections.

4. Voltage will vary in this test depending on cranking speed of engine. The voltage will vary from about 500 mV, at very slow cranking speeds to about 100 mV at high speeds.

CHART A-3
(Page 2 of 3)
ENGINE CRANKS BUT WILL NOT RUN
2.8L (VIN W) "L" CARLINE (PORT)

FROM A-3 (1 OF 3)

→ NO BLINKING LIGHT AT INJECTOR(S).

NO LIGHT

(1)
• IGNITION "ON".
• PROBE INJECTOR HARNESS TERMINALS WITH A TEST LIGHT TO GROUND.
• LIGHT SHOULD BE "ON" AT BOTH TERMINALS.

STEADY LIGHT →
• CHECK INJECTOR DRIVER CKT WITH STEADY LIGHT FOR SHORT TO GROUND.
• IF CKT IS NOT SHORTED, CHECK RESISTANCE ACROSS EACH INJECTOR IN THE CIRCUIT.
• RESISTANCE SHOULD BE GREATER THAN 8 OHMS.

OK → FAULTY ECM

NOT OK → REPLACE ANY INJECTOR THAT MEASURES UNDER 8 OHMS.

LIGHT "ON" BOTH

(2)
• RECONNECT INJECTOR(S).
• IGNITION "OFF".
• DISCONNECT ECM.
• IGNITION "ON".
• PROBE TERMINALS C11 AND C12 WITH A TEST LIGHT TO GROUND.

LIGHT "ON" ONE →
DUE TO INJECTORS WIRED IN PARALLEL, THERE SHOULD BE A LIGHT ON BOTH TERMINALS. IF NOT, THE PROBLEM IS IN THE HARNESS TO THE TESTED INJECTOR.

LIGHT "OFF" → REPAIR OPEN IN INJECTOR FEED CKT.

LIGHT "OFF"

(3)
REFER TO FACING PAGE

LIGHT "OFF" → OPEN CKT 467 OR 468

1988-89 2.8L ENGINE

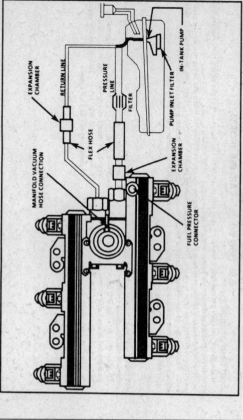

CHART A-7
(Page 1 of 2)
FUEL SYSTEM DIAGNOSIS
2.8L (VIN W) "L" CARLINE (PORT)

Circuit Description:

When the ignition switch is turned "ON," the electronic control module (ECM) will turn "ON" the in-tank fuel pump. It will remain "ON" as long as the engine is cranking or running, and the ECM is receiving reference pulses. If there are no reference pulses, the ECM will shut "OFF" the fuel pump within 2 seconds after ignition "ON" or engine stops.

The pump will deliver fuel to the fuel rail and injectors, then to the pressure regulator, where the system pressure is controlled to about 234 to 325 kPa (34 to 47 psi). Excess fuel is then returned to the fuel tank.

Test Description: Numbers below refer to circled numbers on the diagnostic chart.

1. Wrap a shop towel around the fuel pressure connector to absorb any small amount of fuel leakage that may occur when installing the gage. Ignition "ON" pump pressure should be 280-325 kPa (40.5-47 psi). This pressure is controlled by spring pressure within the regulator assembly.

2. When the engine is idling, the manifold pressure is low (high vacuum) and is applied to the fuel regulator diaphragm. This will offset the spring and result in a lower fuel pressure. This idle pressure will vary somewhat depending on barometric pressure, however, the pressure idling should be less indicating pressure regulator control.

3. Pressure that continues to fall is caused by one of the following:

• In-tank fuel pump check valve not holding

• Pump coupling hose or pulsator leaking
• Fuel pressure regulator valve leaking
• Injector(s) sticking open.

4. An injector sticking open can best be determined by checking for a fouled or saturated spark plug(s). If a leaking injector can not be determined by a fouled or saturated spark plug the following procedure should be used

• Remove plenum and fuel rail bolts. Follow the procedures in the Fuel Control Section of this manual but leave fuel lines connected
• Lift fuel rail out just enough to leave injector nozzles in the ports

CAUTION: Be sure injector(s) are not allowed to spray on engine and that injector retaining clips are intact. This should be carefully followed to prevent fuel spray on engine which would cause a fire hazard
• Pressurize the fuel system and observe injector nozzles

CHART A-3
(Page 3 of 3)
ENGINE CRANKS BUT WILL NOT RUN
2.8L (VIN W) "L" CARLINE (PORT)

1988–89 2.8L ENGINE

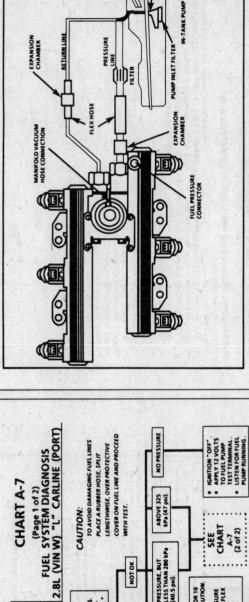

Diagram labels: EXPANSION CHAMBER, RETURN LINE, PRESSURE LINE, IN-TANK PUMP, FILTER, PUMP INLET FILTER, FLEX HOSE, MANIFOLD VACUUM HOSE CONNECTION, EXPANSION CHAMBER, FUEL PRESSURE CONNECTOR

CHART A-7
(Page 2 of 2)
FUEL SYSTEM DIAGNOSIS
2.8L (VIN W) "L" CARLINE (PORT)

Test Description: Numbers below refer to circled numbers on the diagnostic chart.

1. Pressure but less than 280 kPa (40.5 psi) falls into two areas:
   - Regulated pressure but less than 280 kPa (40.5 psi). Amount of fuel to injectors OK, but pressure is too low. System will be lean running and may set Code 44. Also, hard starting cold and overall poor performance.
   - Restricted flow causing pressure drop. Normally, a vehicle with a fuel pressure of less than 165 kPa (24 psi) at idle will not be driveable. However, if the pressure drop occurs only while driving, the engine will normally surge then stop running as pressure begins to drop rapidly. This is most likely caused by a restricted fuel line or plugged filter.

2. Restricting the the fuel return line allows fuel prssure to build above regulated pressure. With battery applied to the pump "test" terminal, pressure should rise above 325 kPa (47 psi) as the fuel return hose is gradually pinched. NOTICE: Do not allow pressure to exceed 414 kPa (60 psi), as damage to the regulator may result.

3. This test determines if the high fuel pressure is due to a restricted fuel return line or a pressure regulator problem.

CHART A-7
(Page 1 of 2)
FUEL SYSTEM DIAGNOSIS
2.8L (VIN W) "L" CARLINE (PORT)

CAUTION: TO AVOID DAMAGING FUEL LINES PLACE A RUBBER HOSE, SPLIT LENGTHWISE, OVER PROTECTIVE COVER ON FUEL LINE AND PROCEED WITH TEST.

FROM CHART A-3 — THIS CHART ASSUMES THERE IS NO CODE 54.

1.
- INSTALL FUEL PRESSURE GAGE, J-34730-1 OR EQUIVALENT.
- IGNITION "OFF" FOR 10 SECONDS. A/C "OFF".
- IGNITION "ON". FUEL PUMP WILL RUN FOR ABOUT 2 SECONDS.
- NOTE FUEL PRESSURE. WITH PUMP RUNNING SHOULD BE 280-325 kPa (40.5-47 psi) AND HOLD STEADY WHEN PUMP STOPS.*

NO PRESSURE → IGNITION "OFF". APPLY 12 VOLTS TO FUEL PUMP TEST TERMINAL. LISTEN FOR FUEL PUMP RUNNING.

ABOVE 325 kPa (47 psi) → SEE CHART A-7 (2 of 2)

PRESSURE, BUT LESS THAN 280 kPa (40.5 psi) →
3. IGNITION "OFF" FOR 10 SECONDS. SEE CAUTION. IGNITION "ON". BLOCK FUEL PRESSURE LINE BY PINCHING FLEX HOSE. PRESSURE SHOULD HOLD.

PRESSURE, BUT NOT HOLDING → IGNITION "OFF" FOR 10 SECONDS. IGNITION "ON". BLOCK FUEL RETURN LINE BY PINCHING HOSE. RECHECK PRESSURE.

HOLDS → CHECK: LEAKING PUMP COUPLING HOSE OR PULSATOR. FAULTY IN-TANK PUMP.

NOT HOLDING → 4. LOCATE AND CORRECT LEAKING INJECTOR(S).

HOLDS → FAULTY FUEL PRESSURE REGULATOR

PUMP NOT RUNNING → CHECK FOR: OPEN WIRE IN CKT 120. OPEN PUMP. GROUND CIRCUIT.

PUMP RUNS → CHECK FOR: PLUGGED IN-LINE FILTER. PLUGGED PUMP INLET FILTER. RESTRICTED FUEL LINE. DISCONNECTED COUPLING HOSE OR PULSATOR.

IF OK → REPLACE IN-TANK FUEL PUMP

2.
- START AND IDLE ENGINE AT NORMAL OPERATING TEMPERATURE. PRESSURE SHOULD BE LOWER BY 21-69 kPa (3-10 psi).

OK → NO TROUBLE FOUND. REVIEW SYMPTOMS SECTION "B".

NOT OK → APPLY 10 INCHES OF VACUUM TO PRESSURE REGULATOR. FUEL PRESSURE SHOULD DROP 21-69 kPa (3-10 psi).

NOT OK → REPLACE REGULATOR ASSEMBLY
OK → REPAIR VACUUM SOURCE TO REGULATOR

* THE IGNITION MAY HAVE TO BE CYCLED "ON" MORE THAN ONCE TO OBTAIN MAXIMUM PRESSURE. ALSO, IT IS NORMAL FOR THE PRESSURE TO DROP SLIGHTLY WHEN THE PUMP STOPS.

1988-89 2.8L ENGINE

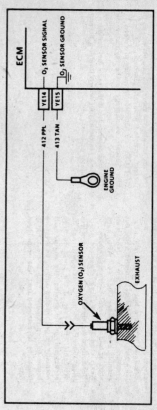

CODE 13
OXYGEN SENSOR CIRCUIT
(OPEN CIRCUIT)
2.8L (VIN W) "L" CARLINE (PORT)

Circuit Description:

The ECM supplies a voltage of about .45 volt between terminals "YE14" and "YE15". (If measured with a 10 megohm digital voltmeter, this may read as low as .32 volt.) The O₂ sensor varies the voltage within a range of about 1 volt if the exhaust is rich, down through about .10 volt if exhaust is lean.

The sensor is like an open circuit and produces no voltage when it is below 315°C (600°F). An open sensor circuit or cold sensor causes "Open Loop" operation.

Test Description: Numbers below refer to circled numbers on the diagnostic chart.

1. Code 13 will set
   - Engine at normal operating temperature
   - At least 2 minutes engine time after start
   - O₂ signal voltage steady between .35 and .55 volt.
   - Throttle position sensor signal above 4%
   - All conditions must be met for about 60 seconds

   If the conditions for a Code 13 exist, the system will not go "Closed Loop."

2. This will determine if the sensor is at fault, or the wiring, or ECM is the cause of the Code 13.

3. In doing this test use only a high impedance digital volt ohm meter. This test checks the continuity of CKTs 412 and 413 because if CKT 413 is open the ECM voltage on CKT 412 will be over .6 volt (600 mV).

Diagnostic Aids:

Normal "Scan" voltage varies between 100 mV to 999 mV (.1 and 1.0 volt) while in "Closed Loop". Code 13 sets in one minute if voltage remains between .35 and .55 volt, but the system will go "Open Loop" in about 15 seconds. Refer to "Intermittents" in Section "B".

CHART A-7
(Page 2 of 2)
FUEL SYSTEM DIAGNOSIS
2.8L (VIN W) "L" CARLINE (PORT)

NOTICE: FUEL SYSTEM UNDER PRESSURE. TO AVOID FUEL SPILLAGE, REFER TO FIELD SERVICE PROCEDURES FOR TESTING OR MAKING REPAIRS REQUIRING DISASSEMBLY OF FUEL LINES OR FITTINGS.

FROM CHART A-7 (1 of 2)

(1) HAS PRESSURE BUT LESS THAN 280 kPa (40.5 psi).

CHECK FOR RESTRICTED FUEL LINES OR IN-LINE FILTER.

- NOT OK → REPLACE FILTER OR REPAIR FUEL LINE AND RECHECK.
- OK

(2)
- IGNITION "OFF".
- APPLY 12 VOLTS TO FUEL PUMP RELAY HARNESS TERMINAL "A" OR FUEL PUMP TEST CONNECTOR.
- SLOWLY PINCH FUEL RETURN HOSE. PRESSURE SHOULD RISE ABOVE 325 kPa (47 psi). DO NOT ALLOW PRESSURE TO EXCEED 414 kPa (60 psi).

ABOVE 325 kPa (47 psi). → FAULTY PRESSURE REGULATOR.

PRESSURE BUT LESS THAN 280 kPa (40.5 psi). → FAULTY IN-TANK
- FUEL PUMP
- COUPLING HOSE OR PULSATOR
- INLET FILTER
- WRONG FUEL PUMP

ABOVE 325 kPa (47 psi).

(3)
- DISCONNECT FUEL RETURN LINE FLEXIBLE HOSE. ATTACH 5/16 I.D. FLEX HOSE TO PRESSURE REGULATOR SIDE OF OF RETURN LINE. INSERT THE OTHER END IN AN APPROVED GASOLINE CONTAINER.
- NOTE FUEL PRESSURE WITHIN 2 SECONDS AFTER IGNITION "ON."

ABOVE 325 kPa (47 psi) → CHECK FOR RESTRICTED FUEL RETURN LINE FROM FUEL PRESSURE REGULATOR TO POINT WHERE FUEL LINE WAS DISCONNECTED.

280-325 kPa (40.5-47 psi) → LOCATE AND CORRECT RESTRICTED FUEL RETURN LINE TO FUEL TANK.

IF LINE OK REPLACE FUEL PRESSURE REGULATOR.

CLEAR CODES AND CONFIRM "CLOSED LOOP" OPERATION AND NO "SERVICE ENGINE SOON" LIGHT.

1988-89 2.8L ENGINE

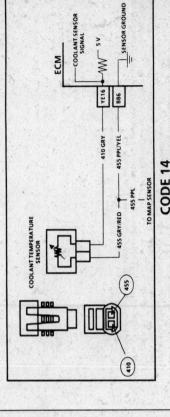

CODE 14
COOLANT TEMPERATURE SENSOR CIRCUIT
(HIGH TEMPERATURE INDICATED)
2.8L (VIN W) "L" CARLINE (PORT)

Circuit Description:

The coolant temperature sensor uses a thermistor to control the signal voltage to the ECM. The ECM applies a voltage on CKT 410 to the sensor. When the engine is cold, the sensor (thermistor) resistance is high, therefore, the ECM will see high signal voltage.

As the engine warms, the sensor resistance becomes less and the voltage drops. At normal engine operating temperature (85°C to 95°C), the voltage will measure about 1.5 to 2.0 volts.

Test Description: Numbers below refer to circled numbers on the diagnostic chart.

1. Code 14 will set if:
   - Signal voltage indicates a coolant temperature above 135°C (275°F) for 3 seconds
2. This test will determine if CKT 410 is shorted to ground which will cause the conditions for Code 14.

Diagnostic Aids:

Check harness routing for a potential short to ground in CKT 410. "Scan" tool displays engine temperature in degrees centigrade. After engine is started, the temperature should rise steadily to about 90°C then stabilize when thermostat opens. Refer to "Intermittents" in Section "B".

CODE 13
OXYGEN SENSOR CIRCUIT
(OPEN CIRCUIT)
2.8L (VIN W) "L" CARLINE (PORT)

1. - ENGINE AT NORMAL OPERATING TEMPERATURE (ABOVE 80°C).
   - RUN ENGINE ABOVE 1200 RPM FOR TWO MINUTES.
   - DOES "SCAN" TOOL INDICATE "CLOSED LOOP"?

   NO → 2
   YES → CODE 13 IS INTERMITTENT. IF NO ADDITIONAL CODES WERE STORED, REFER TO "DIAGNOSTIC AIDS" ON FACING PAGE.

2. - DISCONNECT O₂ SENSOR.
   - JUMPER HARNESS CKT 412 (ECM SIDE) TO GROUND.
   - "SCAN" TOOL SHOULD DISPLAY O₂ VOLTAGE BELOW .2 VOLT (200 mV) WITH ENGINE RUNNING. DOES IT?

   NO → 3
   YES → FAULTY O₂ SENSOR CONNECTION OR SENSOR.

3. - REMOVE JUMPER.
   - IGNITION "ON", ENGINE "OFF".
   - CHECK VOLTAGE OF CKT 412 (ECM SIDE) AT O₂ SENSOR HARNESS CONNECTOR USING A DVM.

   3-.6 VOLT (300-600 mV) → FAULTY ECM.
   OVER .6 VOLT (600 mV) → OPEN CKT 413 OR FAULTY CONNECTION OR FAULTY ECM.
   LESS THAN .3 VOLT (300 mV) → OPEN CKT 412 OR FAULTY ECM CONNECTION OR FAULTY ECM.

CLEAR CODES AND CONFIRM "CLOSED LOOP" OPERATION AND NO "SERVICE ENGINE SOON" LIGHT.

1988–89 2.8L ENGINE

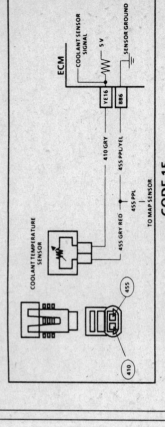

CODE 15

COOLANT TEMPERATURE SENSOR CIRCUIT
(LOW TEMPERATURE INDICATED)
2.8L (VIN W) "L" CARLINE (PORT)

Circuit Description:

The coolant temperature sensor uses a thermistor to control the signal voltage to the ECM. The ECM applies a voltage on CKT 410 to the sensor. When the engine is cold, the sensor (thermistor) resistance is high, therefore, the ECM will see high signal voltage.

As the engine warms, the sensor resistance becomes less and the voltage drops. At normal engine operating temperature (85°C to 95°C), the voltage will measure about 1.5 to 2.0 volts at the ECM.

Test Description: Numbers below refer to circled numbers on the diagnostic chart.

1. Code 15 will set if:
   • Signal voltage indicates a coolant temperature less than –44°C (–47°F) for 3 seconds
2. This test simulates a Code 14. If the ECM recognizes the low signal voltage (high temperature) and the "Scan" reads 130°C, the ECM and wiring are OK.
3. This test will determine if CKT 410 is open. There should be 5 volts present at sensor connector if measured with a DVM.

Diagnostic Aids:

A "Scan" tool reads engine temperature in degrees centigrade. After engine is started, the temperature should rise steadily to about 90°C then stabilize when thermostat opens.

A faulty connection or an open in CKT 410 or 455 will result in a Code 15.

If Code 21 or 23 is also set, check CKT 455 for faulty wiring or connections. Check terminals at sensor for good contact. Refer to "Intermittents" in Section "B".

CODE 14

COOLANT TEMPERATURE SENSOR CIRCUIT
(HIGH TEMPERATURE INDICATED)
2.8L (VIN W) "L" CARLINE (PORT)

1. DOES "SCAN" TOOL DISPLAY COOLANT TEMPERATURE OF 130°C OR HIGHER?
   - YES
   - NO → CODE 14 IS INTERMITTENT. IF NO ADDITIONAL CODES WERE STORED, REFER TO "DIAGNOSTIC AIDS" ON FACING PAGE.

2. • DISCONNECT SENSOR. "SCAN" TOOL SHOULD DISPLAY TEMPERATURE BELOW -30°C. DOES IT?
   - YES → REPLACE SENSOR
   - NO → CKT 410 SHORTED TO GROUND. OR CKT 410 SHORTED TO SENSOR GROUND CIRCUIT. OR FAULTY ECM.

DIAGNOSTIC AID

COOLANT SENSOR
TEMPERATURE VS. RESISTANCE VALUES (APPROXIMATE)

°F	°C	OHMS
210	100	185
160	70	450
100	38	1,800
70	20	3,400
40	4	7,500
20	-7	13,500
0	-18	25,000
-40	-40	100,700

CLEAR CODES AND CONFIRM "CLOSED LOOP" OPERATION AND NO "SERVICE ENGINE SOON" LIGHT.

1988–89 2.8L ENGINE

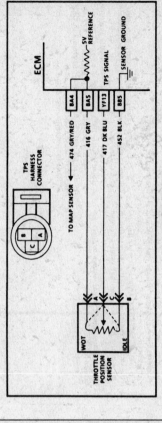

ECM

474 GRY/RED → TO MAP SENSOR

BA4

416 GRY — BA5 — 5V REFERENCE

417 DK BLU — VF13 — TPS SIGNAL

452 BLK — BB5 — SENSOR GROUND

TPS HARNESS CONNECTOR

WOT

IDLE

THROTTLE POSITION SENSOR

CODE 21
THROTTLE POSITION SENSOR (TPS) CIRCUIT
(SIGNAL VOLTAGE HIGH)
2.8L (VIN W) "L" CARLINE (PORT)

Circuit Description:

The throttle position sensor (TPS) provides a voltage signal that changes relative to the throttle blade. Signal voltage will vary from about .5 at idle to about 5 volts at wide open throttle, and is nonadjustable.

The TPS signal is one of the most important inputs used by the ECM for fuel control and for most of the ECM control outputs.

Test Description: Numbers below refer to circled numbers on the diagnostic chart.

1. Code 21 will set if
   - Engine is running
   - TPS signal voltage is greater than 4.3 volts
   - Air flow is less than 17 GM/sec
   - All conditions met for 10 seconds

   OR

   - TPS signal voltage over 4.5 volts with ignition "ON."
   - TPS check: The TPS has an auto zeroing feature. If the voltage reading is within the range of 0.45 to 0.85 volt, the ECM will use that value as closed throttle. If TPS is out of range, make sure cruise control and throttle cables are not being held open.

2. With the TPS sensor disconnected, the TPS voltage should go low if the ECM and wiring are OK.

3. Probing CKT 452 with a test light checks the 5 volt return circuit because a faulty 5 volt return will cause a Code 21.

Diagnostic Aids:

A "Scan" tool reads throttle position in volts. Voltage should increase at a steady rate as throttle is moved toward WOT.

Also some "Scan" tools will read throttle angle. 0% = closed throttle 100% = WOT.

An open on CKT 452 will result in a Code 21 and may also set Codes 15 and 23. Refer to "Intermittents" in Section "B".

CODE 15
COOLANT TEMPERATURE SENSOR CIRCUIT
(LOW TEMPERATURE INDICATED)
2.8L (VIN W) "L" CARLINE (PORT)

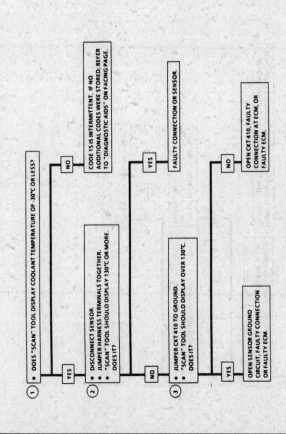

① • DOES "SCAN" TOOL DISPLAY COOLANT TEMPERATURE OF -30°C OR LESS?

YES → ②

NO → CODE 15 IS INTERMITTENT. IF NO ADDITIONAL CODES WERE STORED, REFER TO "DIAGNOSTIC AIDS" ON FACING PAGE.

② • DISCONNECT SENSOR.
• JUMPER HARNESS TERMINALS TOGETHER.
• "SCAN" TOOL SHOULD DISPLAY 130°C OR MORE.
  DOES IT?

NO → ③

YES → FAULTY CONNECTION OR SENSOR.

③ • JUMPER CKT 410 TO GROUND.
• "SCAN" TOOL SHOULD DISPLAY OVER 130°C.
  DOES IT?

YES → OPEN SENSOR GROUND CIRCUIT, FAULTY CONNECTION OR FAULTY ECM.

NO → OPEN CKT 410, FAULTY CONNECTION AT ECM, OR FAULTY ECM.

DIAGNOSTIC AID

COOLANT SENSOR
TEMPERATURE TO RESISTANCE VALUES
(APPROXIMATE)

°F	°C	OHMS
210	100	185
160	70	450
100	38	1,800
70	20	3,400
40	4	7,500
20	-7	13,500
0	-18	25,000
-40	-40	100,700

CLEAR CODES AND CONFIRM "CLOSED LOOP" OPERATION AND NO "SERVICE ENGINE SOON" LIGHT.

1988–89 2.8L ENGINE

CODE 22

THROTTLE POSITION SENSOR (TPS) CIRCUIT
(SIGNAL VOLTAGE LOW)
2.8L (VIN W) "L" CARLINE (PORT)

Circuit Description:

The throttle position sensor (TPS) provides a voltage signal that changes relative to the throttle blade. Signal voltage will vary from about .5 at idle to about 5 volts at wide open throttle, and is nonadjustable.

The TPS signal is one of the most important inputs used by the ECM for fuel control and for most of the ECM control outputs.

Test Description: Numbers below refer to circled numbers on the diagnostic chart.

1. Code 22 will set if
   - Engine running
   - TPS signal voltage is less than about 2 volt for 3 seconds

2. Simulates Code 21: (high voltage) if the ECM recognizes the high signal voltage, the ECM and wiring are OK.

3. TPS check. The TPS has an auto zeroing feature. If the voltage reading is within the range of 0.45 to 0.85 volt, the ECM will use that value as closed throttle.

4. This simulates a high signal voltage to check for an open in CKT 417.

5. CKTs 416 and 474 share a common 5 volts buffered reference signal. If either circuit is shorted to ground, Code 22 will set. To determine if the MAP sensor is causing the 22 problem, disconnect it to see if the conditions for Code 22 still exist.

Diagnostic Aids:

A "Scan" tool reads throttle position in volts. Voltage should increase at a steady rate as throttle is moved toward WOT.

Also some "Scan" tools will read throttle angle 0% = closed throttle 100% = WOT.

An open or short to ground in CKT 416 or 417 will result in a Code 22. Also, a short to ground in CKT 474 will result in a Code 22.

Refer to "Intermittents" in Section "B".

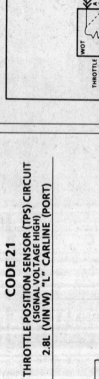

CODE 21

THROTTLE POSITION SENSOR (TPS) CIRCUIT
(SIGNAL VOLTAGE HIGH)
2.8L (VIN W) "L" CARLINE (PORT)

1. THROTTLE CLOSED. DOES "SCAN" TOOL DISPLAY TPS OVER 2.5 VOLTS?

   - YES →
   - NO → CODE 21 IS INTERMITTENT. IF NO ADDITIONAL CODES WERE STORED, REFER TO "DIAGNOSTIC AIDS" ON FACING PAGE.

2. DISCONNECT SENSOR. "SCAN" TOOL SHOULD DISPLAY TPS BELOW .2 VOLT (200mV). DOES IT?

   - YES →
   - NO → CKT 417 SHORTED TO VOLTAGE OR FAULTY ECM.

3. PROBE SENSOR GROUND CIRCUIT WITH A TEST LIGHT CONNECTED TO BATTERY VOLTAGE.

   - LIGHT "ON" → FAULTY CONNECTION OR SENSOR.
   - LIGHT "OFF" → OPEN SENSOR GROUND CIRCUIT OR FAULTY ECM.

CLEAR CODES AND CONFIRM "CLOSED LOOP" OPERATION AND NO "SERVICE ENGINE SOON" LIGHT.

1988-89 2.8L ENGINE

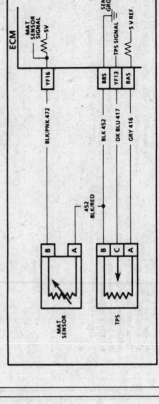

MAT SENSOR

TPS

CODE 23
MANIFOLD AIR TEMPERATURE (MAT) SENSOR CIRCUIT
(LOW TEMPERATURE INDICATED)
2.8L (VIN W) "L" CARLINE (PORT)

Circuit Description:

The MAT sensor uses a thermistor to control the signal voltage to the ECM. The ECM applies a voltage (about 5 volts) on CKT 472 to the sensor. When the air is cold, the sensor (thermistor) resistance is high, therefore, the ECM will see a high signal voltage. If the air is warm the sensor resistance is low, the ECM will see a low voltage.

Test Description: Numbers below refer to circled numbers on the diagnostic chart.

1. Code 23 will set if:
   - A signal voltage indicates a manifold air temperature below -35°C (-31°F) for 3 seconds
   - Time since engine start is 4 minutes or longer
   - No VSS
2. A Code 23 will set due to an open sensor, wire, or connection. This test will determine if the wiring and ECM are OK.
3. This will determine if the signal CKT 472 or the sensor ground CKT 452 is open.

Diagnostic Aids:

A "Scan" tool reads temperature of the air entering the engine and should read close to ambient air temperature when engine is cold, and rises as underhood temperature increases.

A faulty connection or an open in CKT 472 or 452 will result in a Code 23

Refer to "Intermittents" in Section "B".

CODE 22
THROTTLE POSITION SENSOR (TPS) CIRCUIT
(SIGNAL VOLTAGE LOW)
2.8L (VIN W) "L" CARLINE (PORT)

1. • THROTTLE CLOSED.
   • DOES "SCAN" DISPLAY TPS .2V (200 mV) OR BELOW?

YES | **NO**

2. • DISCONNECT TPS SENSOR.
   • JUMPER CKTS 416 & 417 TOGETHER.
   • "SCAN" SHOULD DISPLAY TPS OVER 4.0 V (4000 mV).
   DOES IT?

(NO path) → • CODE 22 IS INTERMITTENT.
IF NO ADDITIONAL CODES WERE STORED, REFER TO "DIAGNOSTIC AIDS" ON FACING PAGE.

NO | **YES**

4. • PROBE CKT 417 WITH A TEST LIGHT CONNECTED TO 12 VOLTS.
   • "SCAN" TOOL SHOULD DISPLAY TPS OVER 4.0 V (4000 mV).
   DOES IT?

3. → REFER TO FACING PAGE FOR SPECIFIC INSTRUCTIONS.

YES | **NO**

CKT 416 OPEN OR SHORTED TO GROUND
OR
FAULTY CONNECTION
OR
FAULTY ECM.

CKT 417 OPEN OR SHORTED TO GROUND, OR SHORTED TO SENSOR GROUND CIRCUIT
OR
FAULTY ECM CONNECTION
OR
FAULTY ECM.

CLEAR CODES AND CONFIRM "CLOSED LOOP" OPERATION AND NO "SERVICE ENGINE SOON" LIGHT.

ECM

MAT SENSOR SIGNAL —5V

SENSOR GROUND

TPS SIGNAL

5 V REF.

YF16

BB5

YF13

BA5

BLK/PNK 472

BLK 452

DK BLU 417

GRY 416

452 BLK/RED

1988–89 2.8L ENGINE

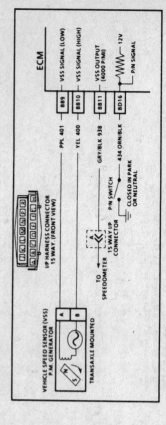

ECM

BB9	PPL 401 — VSS SIGNAL (LOW)
BB10	YEL 400 — VSS SIGNAL (HIGH)
BB11	GRY/BLK 938 — VSS OUTPUT (4000 P/MI)
BD16	434 ORN/BLK — P/N SIGNAL — 12V

I/P HARNESS CONNECTOR 15 WAY. (FRONT VIEW)

A — 15 WAY I/P CONNECTOR

P/N SWITCH — CLOSED IN PARK OR NEUTRAL

TO SPEEDOMETER

VEHICLE SPEED SENSOR (VSS) P.M. GENERATOR

A — B

TRANSAXLE MOUNTED

CODE 24

VEHICLE SPEED SENSOR (VSS) CIRCUIT
2.8L (VIN W) "L" CARLINE (PORT)

Circuit Description:

Vehicle speed information is provided to the ECM by the vehicle speed sensor which is a permanent magnet (PM) generator and it is mounted in the transaxle. The PM generator produces a pulsing voltage whenever vehicle speed is over about 3 mph. The voltage level and the number of pulses increases with vehicle speed. The ECM then converts the pulsing voltage to mph which is used for calculations, and the mph can be displayed with a "Scan" tool.

The function of VSS buffer used in past model years has been incorporated into the ECM. The ECM then supplies the necessary signal for the instrument panel (4000 pulses per mile) for operating the speedometer and the odometer.

Test Description: Numbers below refer to circled numbers on the diagnostic chart.

1. Code 24 will set if vehicle speed equals 0 mph when:
   - Engine speed is between 1400 and 3600 rpm
   - TPS is less than 2%
   - Low load condition (low air flow)
   - Not in park or neutral
   - All conditions met for 5 seconds

   These conditions are met during a road load deceleration. Disregard Code 24 that sets when drive wheels are not turning.
   - The PM generator only produces a signal if drive wheels are turning greater than 3 mph.

Diagnostic Aids:

"Scan" should indicate a vehicle speed whenever the drive wheels are turning greater than 3 mph.

A problem in CKT 938 will not affect the VSS input or the readings on a "Scan."

Check CKTs 400 and 401 for proper connections to be sure they're clean and tight and the harness is routed correctly. Refer to "Intermittents" in Section "B".

(A/T) A faulty or misadjusted Park/Neutral switch can result in a false Code 24. Use a "Scan" and check for proper signal while in drive (125C). Refer to CHART C-1A for P/N switch diagnosis check.

CODE 23

MANIFOLD AIR TEMPERATURE (MAT) SENSOR CIRCUIT
(LOW TEMPERATURE INDICATED)
2.8L (VIN W) "L" CARLINE (PORT)

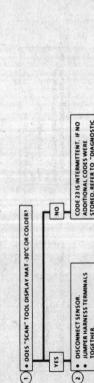

1. DOES "SCAN" TOOL DISPLAY MAT -30°C OR COLDER?

   NO → CODE 23 IS INTERMITTENT. IF NO ADDITIONAL CODES WERE STORED, REFER TO "DIAGNOSTIC AIDS" ON FACING PAGE.

   YES ↓

2. DISCONNECT SENSOR. JUMPER HARNESS TERMINALS TOGETHER. "SCAN" TOOL SHOULD DISPLAY TEMPERATURE OVER 130°C DOES IT?

   YES → FAULTY CONNECTION OR SENSOR.

   NO ↓

3. JUMPER CKT 472 TO GROUND. "SCAN" TOOL SHOULD DISPLAY TEMPERATURE OVER 130°C DOES IT?

   YES → OPEN SENSOR GROUND CIRCUIT, FAULTY CONNECTION OR FAULTY ECM.

   NO → OPEN CKT 472, FAULTY CONNECTION OR FAULTY ECM.

DIAGNOSTIC AID

MAT SENSOR
TEMPERATURE VS. RESISTANCE VALUES
(APPROXIMATE)

°F	°C	OHMS
210	100	185
-160	70	450
100	38	1,800
70	20	3,400
40	4	7,500
20	-7	13,500
0	-18	25,000
-40	-40	100,700

CLEAR CODES AND CONFIRM "CLOSED LOOP" OPERATION AND NO "SERVICE ENGINE SOON" LIGHT.

1988–89 2.8L ENGINE

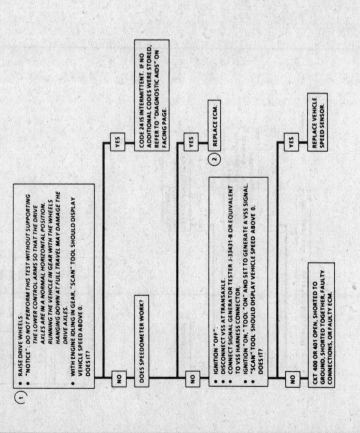

CODE 25

MANIFOLD AIR TEMPERATURE (MAT) SENSOR CIRCUIT
(HIGH TEMPERATURE INDICATED)
2.8L (VIN W) "L" CARLINE (PORT)

Circuit Description:

The manifold air temperature sensor uses a thermistor to control the signal voltage of the ECM. The ECM applies a voltage (about 5 volts) on CKT 472 to the sensor. When manifold air resistance is high, the ECM will see a high signal voltage. As the air warms, the sensor resistance becomes less and the voltage drops.

Test Description: Numbers below refer to circled numbers on the diagnostic chart.

1. Code 25 will set if
   - Signal voltage indicates a manifold air temperature greater than 145°C (293°F) for 3 seconds.
   - Time since engine start is 4 minutes or longer.
   - A vehicle speed is present.

Diagnostic Aids:

A "Scan" tool reads temperature of the air entering the engine and should read close to ambient air temperature when engine is cold, and rises as underhood temperature increases.

A short to ground in CKT 472 will result in a Code 25.

Refer to "Intermittents" in Section "B".

Circuit labels: ECM, MAT SENSOR SIGNAL, 5V, SENSOR GROUND, TPS SIGNAL, 5 V REF., YF16, BB5, YF13, BA5, BLK/PNK 472, BLK 452, DK BLU 417, GRY 416, 452 BLK/RED, MAT SENSOR (B, A), TPS (B, C, A)

CODE 24

VEHICLE SPEED SENSOR (VSS) CIRCUIT
2.8L (VIN W) "L" CARLINE (PORT)

DISREGARD CODE 24 IF SET WHILE DRIVE WHEELS ARE NOT TURNING.

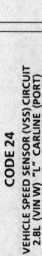

1. • RAISE DRIVE WHEELS
   • "NOTICE": DO NOT PERFORM THIS TEST WITHOUT SUPPORTING THE LOWER CONTROL ARMS SO THAT THE DRIVE AXLES ARE IN A NORMAL HORIZONTAL POSITION. RUNNING THE VEHICLE IN GEAR WITH THE WHEELS HANGING DOWN AT FULL TRAVEL MAY DAMAGE THE DRIVE AXLES.
   • WITH ENGINE IDLING IN GEAR, "SCAN" TOOL SHOULD DISPLAY VEHICLE SPEED ABOVE 0.
   DOES IT?

DOES SPEEDOMETER WORK?

YES → CODE 24 IS INTERMITTENT. IF NO ADDITIONAL CODES WERE STORED, REFER TO "DIAGNOSTIC AIDS" ON FACING PAGE.

NO → IGNITION "OFF".
• DISCONNECT VSS AT TRANSAXLE.
• CONNECT SIGNAL GENERATOR TESTER J-33431-B OR EQUIVALENT TO VSS HARNESS CONNECTOR.
• IGNITION "ON". TOOL "ON". AND SET TO GENERATE A VSS SIGNAL. "SCAN" TOOL SHOULD DISPLAY VEHICLE SPEED ABOVE 0.
   DOES IT?

YES → ② REPLACE ECM.

NO → CKT 400 OR 401 OPEN, SHORTED TO GROUND, SHORTED TOGETHER, FAULTY CONNECTIONS, OR FAULTY ECM.

YES → REPLACE VEHICLE SPEED SENSOR.

CLEAR CODES AND CONFIRM "CLOSED LOOP" OPERATION AND NO "SERVICE ENGINE SOON" LIGHT.

1988–89 2.8L ENGINE

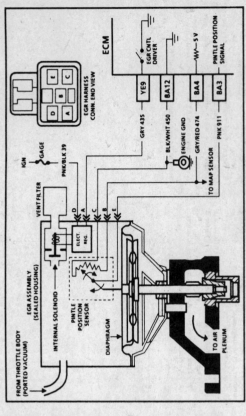

CODE 32

EXHAUST GAS RECIRCULATION (EGR) CIRCUIT
2.8L (VIN W) "L" CARLINE (PORT)

Circuit Description:

The Integrated Electronic EGR Valve functions similiar to a port valve with a remote vacuum regulator. The internal solenoid is normally open, which causes the vacuum signal to be vented off to the atmosphere when EGR is not being commanded by the ECM. This EGR valve has a sealed cap and the solenoid valve opens and closes the vacuum signal, which controls the amount of vacuum vented to atmosphere, which controls the amount of vacuum applied to the diaphragm. The electronic EGR valve contains a voltage regulator, which converts the ECM signal, to provide different amounts of EGR flow by regulating the current to the solenoid. The ECM controls EGR flow with a pulse width modulated signal (turns "ON" and "OFF" many times a second) based on AirFlow, TPS, and RPM.

This system, also, contains a pintle position sensor, which works similar to a TPS sensor, and as EGR flow is increased, the sensor output also increases.

If the ECM does not see the 12 volt signal on circuit 435, when the solenoid is not being energized, a code 26 may be set. Also, if the ECM is not able to ground CKT 435, due to a shorted solenoid or CKT 435 shorted to voltage, a Code 26 may also be set.

Test Description: Step numbers refer to step numbers on diagnostic chart.

1. With the engine running and the transmission in gear, with brakes applied, increasing engine rpm will put a load on the engine. Engine vacuum will be applied to the EGR diaphragm and cause the EGR pintle to open increasing pintle position voltage.

2. This test will determine if the EGR filter is plugged, or if the EGR itself is faulty. Use care, when removing the filter, to avoid damaging the EGR assembly. See ON-CAR Service for procedure.

3. If the valve moves in this test, it's probably due to CKT 435 being shorted to ground.

4. Grounding the diagnostic terminal should energize the solenoid which closes "OFF" the vent and allows the vacuum to move the diaphragm.

5. The EGR assembly is designed to have some leak and, therefore, 7" of vacuum is all that should be able to be held on the assembly. However, if too much of a leak exists (less than 4"), the EGR assembly is leaking and must be replaced.

Diagnostic Aids:

The EGR position voltage can be used to determine that the pintle is moving. When no EGR is commanded (0% duty cycle), the position sensor should read between .5 volt and 1.5 volts, and increase with the commanded EGR duty cycle.

CODE 25

MANIFOLD AIR TEMPERATURE (MAT) SENSOR CIRCUIT
(HIGH TEMPERATURE INDICATED)
2.8L (VIN W) "L" CARLINE (PORT)

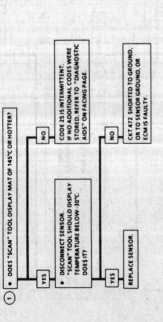

① • DOES "SCAN" TOOL DISPLAY MAT OF 145°C OR HOTTER?

NO → CODE 25 IS INTERMITTENT. IF NO ADDITIONAL CODES WERE STORED, REFER TO "DIAGNOSTIC AIDS" ON FACING PAGE.

YES ↓

• DISCONNECT SENSOR.
"SCAN" TOOL SHOULD DISPLAY TEMPERATURE BELOW -30°C. DOES IT?

NO → CKT 472 SHORTED TO GROUND, OR TO SENSOR GROUND, OR ECM IS FAULTY.

YES ↓

REPLACE SENSOR.

DIAGNOSTIC AID

MAT SENSOR

TEMPERATURE VS. RESISTANCE VALUES (APPROXIMATE)		
°F	°C	OHMS
210	100	185
160	70	450
100	38	1,800
70	20	3,400
40	4	7,500
20	-7	13,500
0	-18	25,000
-40	-40	100,700

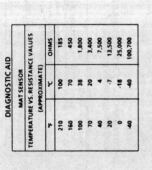

CLEAR CODES AND CONFIRM "CLOSED LOOP" OPERATION AND NO "SERVICE ENGINE SOON" LIGHT.

1988–89 2.8L ENGINE

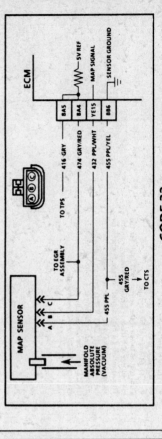

CODE 33

MANIFOLD ABSOLUTE PRESSURE (MAP) SENSOR CIRCUIT
(SIGNAL VOLTAGE HIGH - LOW VACUUM)
2.8L (VIN W) "L" CARLINE (PORT)

Circuit Description:
The manifold absolute pressure sensor (MAP) responds to changes in manifold pressure (vacuum). The ECM receives this information as a signal voltage that will vary from about 1 to 1.5 volts at idle (high vacuum) to 4-4.5 volts at wide open throttle (low vacuum).

Test Description: Numbers below refer to circled numbers on the diagnostic chart.
1. Code 33 will set when
   - Engine Running
   - Manifold pressure greater than 75.3 kPa (A/C "OFF") 81.2 kPa (A/C "ON")
   - Throttle angle less than 2%
   - Conditions met for 2 seconds
   Engine misfire or a low unstable idle may set Code 33.
2. With the MAP sensor disconnected, the ECM should see a low voltage if the ECM and wiring are OK.

Diagnostic Aids:
If idle is rough or unstable refer to "Symptoms" in Section "B" for items which can cause an unstable idle.
An open in CKT 455 or the connection will result in a Code 33.
Ignition "ON" engine "OFF," voltage should be within the values shown in the table on the chart. Also, CHART C-1D can be used to test the MAP sensor.
Refer to "Intermittents" in Section "B".

CODE 32

EXHAUST GAS RECIRCULATION (EGR) CIRCUIT
2.8L (VIN W) "L" CARLINE (PORT)

1988-89 2.8L ENGINE

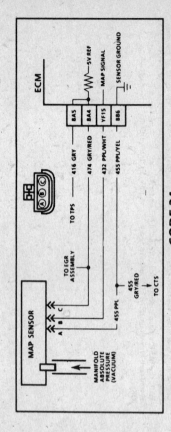

CODE 34

MANIFOLD ABSOLUTE PRESSURE (MAP) SENSOR CIRCUIT
(SIGNAL VOLTAGE LOW - HIGH VACUUM)
2.8L (VIN W) "L" CARLINE (PORT)

Circuit Description:

The manifold absolute pressure sensor (MAP) responds to changes in manifold pressure (vacuum). The ECM receives this information as a signal voltage that will vary from about 1 to 1.5 volts at idle (high vacuum) to 4-4.5 volts at wide open throttle (low vacuum).

Test Description: Numbers below refer to circled numbers on the diagnostic chart.

1. Code 34 will set if
   - Engine rpm less than 600
   - Manifold pressure reading less than 13 kPa.
   - Conditions met for 1 second

   or

   - Engine rpm greater than 600
   - Throttle angle over 20%
   - Manifold pressure less than 13 kPa
   - Conditions met for 1 second
2. This test is to see if the sensor is at fault for the low voltage or if there is a ECM or wiring problem.
3. This simulates a high signal voltage to check for an open in CKT 432. If the test light is bright during this test, CKT 432 is probably shorted to ground. If "Scan" reads over 4 volts at this test, CKT 474 can be checked by measuring the voltage at terminal "C" (should be 5 volts).

Diagnostic Aids:

An intermittent open in CKT 432 or 474 will result in a Code 34.

Ignition "ON" engine "OFF", voltages should be within the values shown in the table on the chart. Also CHART C-1D can be used to test MAP sensor.

Refer to "Intermittents" in Section "B".

CODE 33

MANIFOLD ABSOLUTE PRESSURE (MAP) SENSOR CIRCUIT
(SIGNAL VOLTAGE HIGH - LOW VACUUM)
2.8L (VIN W) "L" CARLINE (PORT)

① IF ENGINE IDLE IS ROUGH, UNSTABLE OR INCORRECT, CORRECT BEFORE USING CHART. SEE SYMPTOMS IN SECTION B.
- ENGINE IDLING.
- DOES "SCAN" DISPLAY A MAP OF 3.75 VOLTS OR OVER?

YES →

② IGNITION "OFF".
- DISCONNECT MAP SENSOR ELECTRICAL CONNECTOR.
- IGNITION "ON".
- "SCAN" SHOULD READ A VOLTAGE OF 1 VOLT OR LESS.
- DOES IT?

YES →

- PROBE CKT 455 WITH A TEST LIGHT TO 12 VOLTS.
- TEST LIGHT SHOULD LIGHT.
- DOES IT?

YES →

PLUGGED OR LEAKING SENSOR VACUUM HOSE OR FAULTY MAP SENSOR.

NO (from ①) →

CODE 33 IS INTERMITTENT. IF NO ADDITIONAL CODES WERE STORED, REFER TO "DIAGNOSTIC AIDS" ON FACING PAGE.

NO (from ②) →

CKT 432 SHORTED TO VOLTAGE, SHORTED TO CKT 474, OR FAULTY ECM.

NO →

OPEN CKT 455.

IGNITION "ON" ENGINE STOPPED VOLTAGES

ALTITUDE		VOLTAGE RANGE
Meters	Feet	
Below 305	Below 1,000	3.8—5.5V
305—610	1,000—2,000	3.6—5.3V
610—914	2,000—3,000	3.5—5.1V
914—1219	3,000—4,000	3.3—5.0V
1219—1524	4,000—5,000	3.2—4.8V
1524—1829	5,000—6,000	3.0—4.6V
1829—2133	6,000—7,000	2.9—4.5V
2133—2438	7,000—8,000	2.8—4.3V
2438—2743	8,000—9,000	2.6—4.2V
2743—3048	9,000—10,000	2.5—4.0V

LOW ALTITUDE = HIGH PRESSURE = HIGH VOLTAGE

1988–89 2.8L ENGINE

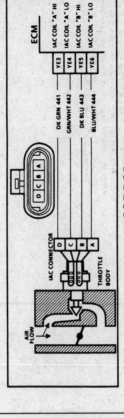

ECM

IAC COIL "A" HI	YE3	DK GRN 441
IAC COIL "A" LO	YE4	GRN/WHT 442
IAC COIL "B" HI	YE5	DK BLU 443
IAC COIL "B" LO	YE6	BLU/WHT 444

IAC CONNECTOR — THROTTLE BODY — AIR FLOW

CODE 35
IDLE SPEED ERROR
2.8L (VIN W) "L" CARLINE (PORT)

Circuit Description:

Code 35 will set when the closed throttle engine speed is 300 rpm above or below the desired (commanded) idle speed for 50 seconds.

Test Description: Numbers below refer to circled numbers on the diagnostic chart.

1. Continue with test even if engine will not idle. If idle is too low, "Scan" will display 80 or more counts or steps. If idle is high, it will display "0" counts. Occasionally an erratic or unstable idle may occur. Engine speed may vary 200 rpm or more up and down. Disconnect IAC. If the condition is unchanged, the IAC is not at fault. There is a system problem. Proceed to diagnostic aids below.
2. When the engine was stopped, the IAC Valve retracted (more air) to a fixed "Park" position for increased air flow and idle speed during the next engine start. A "Scan" will display 80 or more counts. Observe idle immediately as on a warm engine, the idle speed should decrease rapidly.
3. Be sure to disconnect the IAC valve prior to this test. The test light will confirm the ECM signals by a steady or flashing light on all circuits.
4. There is a remote possibility that one of the circuits is shorted to voltage which would have been indicated by a steady light. Disconnect ECM and turn the ignition "ON" and probe terminals to check for this condition.

Diagnostic Aids:

A slow unstable idle may be caused by a system problem that cannot be controlled by the IAC. "Scan" counts will be above 80 counts if idle is too low, and "0" counts if it is too high.

If idle is too high, stop engine. Ignition "ON." Ground diagnostic terminal. Wait a few seconds for IAC to seat, then disconnect IAC. Start engine. If idle speed is above 600-700 rpm in drive with an A/T or 800-900 in neutral with a M/T, locate and correct vacuum leak. If rpm is below spec., check for foreign material around throttle plates and if OK.

- **System too lean (High Air/fuel ratio)**
  Idle speed may be too high or too low. Engine speed may vary up and down, disconnecting IAC does not help. This may set Code 44.
  "Scan" and/or Voltmeter will read an oxygen sensor output less than 300 mV (.3 volt). Check for low regulated fuel pressure or water in fuel. A lean exhaust with an oxygen sensor output fixed above 800 mV (.8 volt) will be a contaminated sensor, usually silicone. This may also set a Code 45 or 61.
- **System too rich (Low Air/fuel ratio)**
  Idle speed too low. "Scan" counts usually above 80. System obviously rich and may exhibit black smoke exhaust.
  "Scan" tool and/or Voltmeter will read an oxygen sensor signal fixed above 800 mV (.8 volt).
  Check
  - For fuel in pressure regulator hose
  - High fuel pressure
  - Injector leaking or sticking
- **Throttle body.** Remove IAC and inspect bore for foreign material or evidence of IAC valve dragging the bore.
- **A/C Compressor or Relay failure.** See CHART C-10 if the A/C control relay drive circuit is shorted to ground or if the relay is faulty, an idle problem may exist.

If above are all OK, refer to "Rough, Unstable, Incorrect Idle or Stalling" in "Symptoms" in Section "B"

CODE 34
MANIFOLD ABSOLUTE PRESSURE (MAP) SENSOR CIRCUIT
(SIGNAL VOLTAGE LOW - HIGH VACUUM)
2.8L (VIN W) "L" CARLINE (PORT)

① IGNITION "OFF" FOR 10 SECONDS. START ENGINE AND IMMEDIATELY NOTE MAP VALUE ON "SCAN". DOES "SCAN" DISPLAY MAP BELOW .25 VOLTS?

→ YES

② IGNITION "OFF". DISCONNECT SENSOR ELECTRICAL CONNECTOR. JUMPER HARNESS TERMINALS "B" TO "C". IGNITION "ON". MAP VOLTAGE SHOULD READ OVER 4 VOLTS. DOES IT?

→ NO

CODE 34 IS INTERMITTENT. IF NO ADDITIONAL CODES WERE STORED, REFER TO "DIAGNOSTIC AIDS" ON FACING PAGE.

③ IGNITION "OFF". REMOVE JUMPER WIRE. PROBE TERMINAL "B" (CKT 432) WITH A LIGHT TO 12 VOLTS. IGNITION "ON". "SCAN" SHOULD READ OVER 4 VOLTS. DOES IT?

→ YES: FAULTY CONNECTION OR SENSOR.

→ NO: CKT 432 OPEN OR SHORTED TO GROUND OR FAULTY ECM.

→ YES: CKT 474 OPEN OR SHORTED TO GROUND OR FAULTY ECM.

IGNITION "ON" ENGINE STOPPED VOLTAGES

ALTITUDE Meters	Feet	VOLTAGE RANGE
Below 305	Below 1,000	3.8—5.5V
305—610	1,000—2,000	3.6—5.3V
610—914	2,000—3,000	3.5—5.1V
914—1219	3,000—4,000	3.3—5.0V
1219—1524	4,000—5,000	3.2—4.8V
1524—1829	5,000—6,000	3.0—4.6V
1829—2133	6,000—7,000	2.9—4.5V
2133—2438	7,000—8,000	2.8—4.3V
2438—2743	8,000—9,000	2.6—4.2V
2743—3048	9,000—10,000	2.5—4.0V

LOW ALTITUDE = HIGH PRESSURE = HIGH VOLTAGE

1988—89 2.8L ENGINE

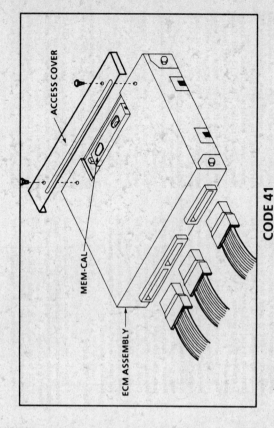

CODE 41
CYLINDER SELECT ERROR
(FAULTY OR INCORRECT MEM-CAL)
2.8L (VIN W) "L" CARLINE (PORT)

ACCESS COVER

MEM-CAL

ECM ASSEMBLY

Test Description: Numbers below refer to circled numbers on the diagnostic chart.

1. The ECM used for this engine can also be used for other engines, and the difference is in the Mem-Cal. If a Code 41 sets, the incorrect Mem-Cal has been installed or it is faulty, and it must be replaced

Diagnostic Aids:

Check Mem-Cal to be sure locking tabs are secure. Also check the pins on both the Mem-Cal and ECM to assure they are making proper contact. Check the Mem-Cal part number to assure it is the correct part. If the Mem-Cal is faulty, it must be replaced. It is also possible that the ECM is faulty. However, it should not be replaced until all of the above have been checked. For additional information, refer to "Intermittents" on page 6E3-B-2.

CODE 35
IDLE SPEED ERROR
2.8L (VIN W) "L" CARLINE (PORT)

NOTE: ECM WILL NOT CYCLE IAC IF THE COOLANT FAN IS ON.

① ENGINE IDLING AT NORMAL OPERATING TEMPERATURE. NOTE RPM IN PARK OR NEUTRAL.

② IGNITION "OFF" FOR 10 SECONDS. START ENGINE AND IMMEDIATELY NOTE RPM.

IDLE RPM, INCREASE
- IDLE ENGINE FOR 1 MINUTE AND NOTE RPM.

RETURNS TO IDLE RPM RECORDED ABOVE.

IDLE AIR CONTROL CIRCUIT OK. SEE FACING PAGE "DIAGNOSTIC AIDS"

WILL NOT RETURN TO IDLE RPM RECORDED ABOVE.

IDLE RPM, NO INCREASE

③ ENGINE STILL RUNNING.
- DISCONNECT IAC VALVE HARNESS.
- GROUND DIAGNOSTIC TEST TERMINAL.
- CONNECT A TEST LIGHT TO GROUND AND PROBE TERMINALS "A" AND "D" AND "B" AND "C" OR USE IAC CIRCUIT TESTER J-37101.
- LIGHT SHOULD CYCLE "ON" AND "OFF" ON ALL. DOES IT?

④ YES → FAULTY IAC CONNECTION OR IAC VALVE

NO → CHECK FOR OPEN OR SHORT TO GROUND IN CIRCUIT THAT DOES NOT CYCLE.

ARE ALL CIRCUITS OK?

NO → REPAIR WIRING AND RECHECK.

YES → ENGINE STOPPED.

CHECK RESISTANCE ACROSS IAC COILS. SHOULD BE MORE THAN 20 OHMS BETWEEN IAC TERMINALS OPPOSITE HARNESS CONNECTOR TERMS. "A" TO "B" AND "C" TO "D"

OK → FAULTY ECM CONNECTION OR ECM.

NOT OK → REPLACE IAC VALVE AND RETEST.

CLEAR CODES AND CONFIRM "CLOSED LOOP" OPERATION AND NO "SERVICE ENGINE SOON" LIGHT.

1988-89 2.8L ENGINE

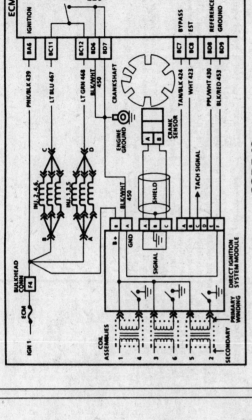

CODE 42
ELECTRONIC SPARK TIMING (EST) CIRCUIT
2.8L (VIN W) "L" CARLINE (PORT)

Circuit Description:

When the system is running on the ignition module, that is no voltage on the Bypass line, the ignition module grounds the EST signal. The ECM expects to see no voltage on the EST line during this condition. If it sees a voltage, it sets Code 42 and will not go into the EST mode.

When the rpm for EST is reached (about 400 rpm) and Bypass voltage applied, the EST should no longer be grounded in the ignition module so the EST voltage should be varying.

If the Bypass line is open or grounded, the ignition module will not switch to EST mode so the EST voltage will be low and Code 42 will be set.

If the EST line is grounded, the ignition module will switch to EST, but because the line is grounded there will be no EST signal. A Code 42 will be set.

Test Description: Numbers below refer to circled numbers on the diagnostic chart.

1. Code 42 means the ECM has seen an open or short to ground in the EST or Bypass circuits. This test confirms Code 42 and that the fault causing the code is present.

2. Checks for a normal EST ground path through the ignition module. An EST CKT 423 shorted to ground will also read less than 500 ohms, however, this will be checked later.

3. As the test light voltage touches CKT 424, the module should switch causing the ohmmeter to "overrange" if the meter is in the 1000-2000 ohms position. Selecting the 10-20,000 ohms position will indicate above 5000 ohms. The important thing is that the module "switched."

4. The module did not switch and this step checks for
   - EST CKT 423 shorted to ground
   - Bypass CKT 424 open
   - Faulty ignition module connection or module

5. Confirms that Code 42 is a faulty ECM and not an intermittent in CKT 423 or 424.

Diagnostic Aids:

The "Scan" tool does not have any ability to help diagnose a Code 42 problem.

A Mem-Cal not fully seated in the ECM can result in a Code 42.

If Code 42 is intermittent, there is a possibility of an open EST line. To check for an open EST line, crank engine while in a "Clear Flood Mode" for five seconds, then start engine and check for Code 42. If Code 42 is set, repair open in CKT 423 (EST line). Refer to "Intermittents" in Section "B".

CODE 41
CYLINDER SELECT ERROR
(FAULTY OR INCORRECT MEM-CAL)
2.8L (VIN W) "L" CARLINE (PORT)

(1)
- IGNITION "OFF". CLEAR CODES.
- START ENGINE AND RUN FOR 1 MINUTE OR UNTIL CODE 41 SETS.

DOES CODE 41 SET?

YES → FAULTY CONNECTIONS DUE TO MEM-CAL NOT LOCKED IN PLACE, OR INCORRECT MEM-CAL INSTALLED.

NO → CODE 41 IS INTERMITTENT. REVIEW "DIAGNOSTIC AIDS" ON FACING PAGE.

1988–89 2.8L ENGINE

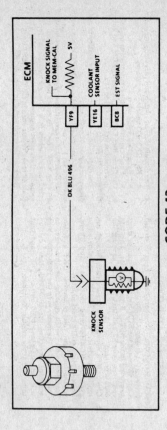

CODE 43
ELECTRONIC SPARK CONTROL (ESC) CIRCUIT
2.8L (VIN W) "L" CARLINE (PORT)

Circuit Description:

The knock sensor is used to detect engine detonation and the ECM will retard the electronic spark timing based on the signal being received. The circuitry within the knock sensor causes the ECM 5 volts to be pulled down so that under a no knock condition, CKT 496 would measure about 2.5 volts. The knock sensor produces an A/C signal which rides on the 2.5 volts DC voltage. The amplitude and signal frequency is dependent upon the knock level.

If CKT 496 becomes open or shorted to ground, the voltage will either go above 3.5 volts or below 1.5 volts. If either of these conditions are met for about ½ second, a Code 43 will be stored.

Test Description: Numbers below refer to circled numbers on the diagnostic chart.

1. This step determines if conditions for Code 43 still exist (voltage on CKT 496 above 3.5 volts or below 1.5 volts). The system is designed to retard the spark 6°, if either condition exists.

2. The ECM has a 5 volt pull-up resistor, which applies 5 volts to CKT 496. The five volt signal should be present at the knock sensor terminal during these test conditions.

3. This step determines if the knock sensor resistance is 3900 ohms ± 15%. If the resistance is between 3300 to 4500 ohms, the sensor is OK.

4. If CKT 496 is not open or shorted to ground and the voltage reading is below 4 volts, the most likely cause is an open circuit in the ECM. It is possible that a faulty Mem-Cal could be drawing the 5 volt signal down and it should be replaced, if a replacement ECM did not correct the problem.

Diagnostic Aids:

Check CKT 496 for a potential open or short to ground. Also, check for proper installation of Mem-Cal.

Refer to "Intermittents" in Section "B".

CODE 42
ELECTRONIC SPARK TIMING (EST) CIRCUIT
2.8L (VIN W) "L" CARLINE (PORT)

1. CLEAR CODES. IDLE ENGINE FOR 1 MINUTE OR UNTIL CODE 42 SETS. DOES CODE 42 SET?
   - NO → CODE 42 INTERMITTENT. REFER TO "DIAGNOSTIC AIDS" ON FACING PAGE.
   - YES →

2. IGNITION "OFF". DISCONNECT ECM CONNECTORS. IGNITION "ON". SET OHMMETER SELECTOR SWITCH IN THE 1000 TO 2000 OHMS RANGE. PROBE ECM HARNESS CONNECTOR CKT 423 WITH AN OHMMETER TO GROUND. IT SHOULD READ LESS THAN 500 OHMS. DOES IT?
   - NO → PROBE ECM HARNESS CONNECTOR CKT 424 WITH A TEST LIGHT TO 12 VOLTS AND OBSERVE LIGHT.
     - LIGHT "ON" → OPEN CKT 423, FAULTY CONNECTION, OR FAULTY IGNITION MODULE.
     - LIGHT "OFF" → DISCONNECT IGNITION MODULE 6-WAY CONNECTOR.
       - LIGHT "OFF" → REPLACE IGNITION MODULE.
       - LIGHT "ON" → CKT 424 SHORTED TO GROUND.
   - YES →

3. WITH OHMMETER STILL CONNECTED TO ECM HARNESS CKT 423 AND GROUND, AGAIN PROBE ECM HARNESS CKT 424 WITH THE TEST LIGHT CONNECTED TO 12 VOLTS. AS TEST LIGHT CONTACTS CKT 424, RESISTANCE SHOULD SWITCH FROM UNDER 500 TO OVER 5,000 OHMS. DOES IT?
   - NO →

4. DISCONNECT DIS 6-WAY CONNECTOR. NOTE OHMMETER THAT IS STILL CONNECTED TO CKT 423 AND GROUND RESISTANCE SHOULD HAVE BECOME VERY HIGH (OPEN CIRCUIT) DOES IT?
   - YES → CKT 424 OPEN, FAULTY CONNECTIONS, OR FAULTY IGNITION MODULE.
   - NO → CKT 423 SHORTED TO GROUND.
   - (from step 3 YES) →

5. RECONNECT ECM AND IDLE ENGINE FOR ONE MINUTE OR UNTIL CODE 42 SETS. DOES CODE SET?
   - YES → REPLACE ECM.
   - NO → CODE 42 INTERMITTENT. REFER TO "DIAGNOSTIC AIDS" ON FACING PAGE.

CLEAR CODES AND CONFIRM "CLOSED LOOP" OPERATION AND NO "SERVICE ENGINE SOON" LIGHT.

1988–89 2.8L ENGINE

CODE 43

ELECTRONIC SPARK CONTROL (ESC) CIRCUIT
2.8L (VIN W) "L" CARLINE (PORT)

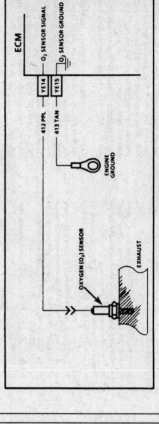

(1)
- ENGINE IDLING COOLANT TEMP ABOVE 67°C.
- DOES "SCAN" INDICATE 13-17 DEGREES OF KNOCK RETARD?

YES →

(2)
- DISCONNECT KNOCK SENSOR.
- IGNITION "ON"
- USING A DVOM, CHECK VOLTAGE BETWEEN HARNESS CKT 496 AND GROUND.
- VOLTAGE SHOULD READ BETWEEN 4-6 VOLTS.
  DOES IT?

NO → CODE 43 IS INTERMITTENT. SEE "DIAGNOSTIC AIDS" ON FACING PAGE.

YES →

(3)
- CHECK RESISTANCE OF KNOCK SENSOR BY CONNECTING OHMMETER BETWEEN SENSOR TERMINAL AND ENGINE BLOCK.
- SHOULD BE BETWEEN 3300 & 4500 OHMS. IS IT?

NO → OVER 6 VOLTS → CKT 496 SHORTED TO VOLTAGE OR FAULTY ECM.

LESS THAN 4 VOLTS →

(4) CKT 496 OPEN, SHORTED TO GROUND, OR FAULTY ECM.

YES →

- CHECK HARNESS AND SENSOR CONNECTOR. IF OK:
- REMOVE ECM AND BE SURE MEM-CAL IS PROPERLY SEATED INTO ECM. IF OK:
- REPLACE MEM-CAL.

NO → FAULTY KNOCK SENSOR

CODE 44

OXYGEN SENSOR CIRCUIT
(LEAN EXHAUST INDICATED)
2.8L (VIN W) "L" CARLINE (PORT)

ECM

YE14 — O₂ SENSOR SIGNAL
YE15 — O₂ SENSOR GROUND

412 PPL
413 TAN

OXYGEN (O₂) SENSOR
EXHAUST
ENGINE GROUND

Circuit Description:

The ECM supplies a voltage of about .45 volt between terminals "YE14" and "YE15". (If measured with a 10 megohm digital voltmeter, this may read as low as .32 volt.) The O₂ sensor varies the voltage within a range of about 1 volt if the exhaust is rich, down through about .10 volt if exhaust is lean.

The sensor is like an open circuit and produces no voltage when it is below about 315°C (600°F). An open sensor circuit or cold sensor causes "Open Loop" operation.

Test Description: Numbers below refer to circled numbers on the diagnostic chart.

1. Code 44 is set when the O₂ sensor signal voltage on CKT 412
   - Remains below .2 volt for 60 seconds or more
   - And the system is operating in "Closed Loop"

Diagnostic Aids:

Using the "Scan," observe the block learn values at different rpm and air flow conditions. The "Scan" also displays the block learn cells, so the block learn values can be checked in each of the cells to determine when the Code 44 may have been set. If the conditions for Code 44 exist, the block learn values will be around 150.

- O₂ Sensor Wire. Sensor pigtail may be mispositioned and contacting the exhaust manifold.

- Check for intermittent ground in wire between connector and sensor.

- Lean Injector(s). Perform injector balance test CHART C-2A.

- Fuel Contamination. Water, even in small amounts near the in-tank fuel pump inlet can be delivered to the injectors. The water causes a lean exhaust and can set a Code 44

- Fuel Pressure. System will be lean if pressure is too low. It may be necessary to monitor fuel pressure while driving the car at various road speeds and/or loads to confirm. See Fuel System diagnosis CHART A-7.

- Exhaust Leaks. If there is an exhaust leak, the engine can cause outside air to be pulled into the exhaust and past the sensor. Vacuum or crankcase leaks can cause a lean condition.

- If the above are OK, it is a faulty oxygen sensor.

1988-89 2.8L ENGINE

CODE 44

OXYGEN SENSOR CIRCUIT
(LEAN EXHAUST INDICATED)
2.8L (VIN W) "L" CARLINE (PORT)

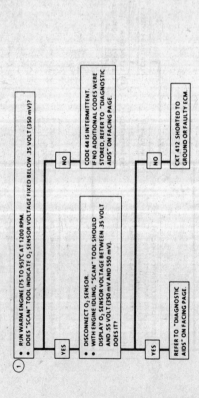

① • RUN WARM ENGINE (75 TO 95)°C AT 1200 RPM.
• DOES "SCAN" TOOL INDICATE O₂ SENSOR VOLTAGE FIXED BELOW .35 VOLT (350 mV)?

YES	NO

NO → CODE 44 IS INTERMITTENT. IF NO ADDITIONAL CODES WERE STORED, REFER TO "DIAGNOSTIC AIDS" ON FACING PAGE.

YES →
• DISCONNECT O₂ SENSOR.
• WITH ENGINE IDLING, "SCAN" TOOL SHOULD DISPLAY O₂ SENSOR VOLTAGE BETWEEN .35 VOLT AND .55 VOLT (350 mV AND 550 mV).
• DOES IT?

YES → CKT 412 SHORTED TO GROUND OR FAULTY ECM.

NO → REFER TO "DIAGNOSTIC AIDS" ON FACING PAGE.

CLEAR CODES AND CONFIRM "CLOSED LOOP" OPERATION AND NO "SERVICE ENGINE SOON" LIGHT.

CODE 45

OXYGEN SENSOR CIRCUIT
(RICH EXHAUST INDICATED)
2.8L (VIN W) "L" CARLINE (PORT)

Circuit Description:

The ECM supplies a voltage of about .45 volt between terminals "YE14" and "YE15". (If measured with a 10 megohm digital voltmeter, this may read as low as .32 volt.) The O₂ sensor varies the voltage within a range of about 1 volt if the exhaust is rich, down through about .10 volt if exhaust is lean.

The sensor is like an open circuit and produces no voltage when it is below about 315°C (600°F). An open sensor circuit or cold sensor causes "Open Loop" operation.

Test Description: Numbers below refer to circled numbers on the diagnostic chart.

1. Code 45 is set when the O₂ sensor signal voltage or CKT 412

• Remains above .7 volt for 30 seconds, and in "Closed Loop"
• Engine time after start is 1 minute or more
• Throttle angle between 3% and 45%

Diagnostic Aids:

Using the "Scan", observe the block learn values at different rpm and air flow conditions. The "Scan" also displays the block cells, so the block learn values can be checked in each of the cells to determine when the Code 45 may have been set. If the conditions for Code 45 exists, the block learn values will be around 115.

• **Fuel Pressure.** System will go rich if pressure is too high. The ECM can compensate for some increase. However, if it gets too high, a Code 45 may be set. See Fuel System diagnosis CHART A-7.
• **Rich injector.** Perform injector balance test CHART C-2A.

• Leaking injector, see CHART A-7.
• Check for fuel contaminated oil
• Check for short to voltage on CKT 412
• **HEI Shielding.** An open ground CKT 453 (ignition system reflow) may result in EMI, or induced electrical "noise." The ECM looks at this "noise" as reference pulses. The additional pulses result in a higher than actual engine speed signal. The ECM then delivers too much fuel, causing system to go rich. Engine tachometer will also show higher than actual engine speed, which can help in diagnosing this problem.
• **Canister purge.** Check for fuel saturation. If full of fuel, check canister control and hoses.
• Check for leaking fuel pressure regulator diaphragm by checking vacuum line to regulator for fuel.
• **TPS.** An intermittent TPS output will cause the system to go rich, due to a false indication of the engine accelerating.
• **EGR.** An EGR staying open (especially at idle) will cause the O₂ sensor to indicate a rich exhaust.

(Diagram: ECM terminals O₂ SENSOR SIGNAL, YE14, 412 PPL; O₂ SENSOR GROUND, YE15, 413 TAN; ENGINE GROUND; OXYGEN (O₂) SENSOR; EXHAUST)

1988-89 2.8L ENGINE

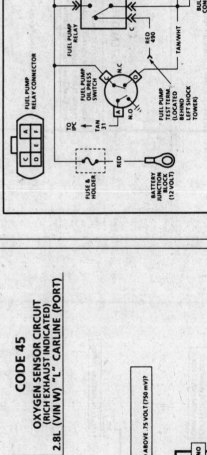

ECM

BB1 B+
BC16 B+
BA11 12 VOLT RELAY DRIVE
BA12
YE13 VOLTAGE MONITOR (PPSW)

340 ORN
465 DK GRN
450 BLK/WHT
120 TAN/WHT

FUEL PUMP (IN TANK)

150

120
15 WAY BODY CONNECTOR

FUEL PUMP RELAY CONNECTOR

A B C D E F

FUEL PUMP RELAY

ENGINE GROUND

120

BULKHEAD CONNECTOR

TAN/WHT

FUEL PUMP OIL PRESS SWITCH

RED 490

N.C.

FUEL PUMP TEST TERM. (LOCATED BEHIND LEFT SHOCK TOWER)

TO IPC

TAN 31

N.O.

FUSE & HOLDER

RED

BATTERY JUNCTION BLOCK (12 VOLT)

CODE 54
FUEL PUMP CIRCUIT
(LOW VOLTAGE)
2.8L (VIN W) "L" CARLINE (PORT)

Circuit Description:

The status of the fuel pump CKT 120 is monitored by the ECM at terminal "YE13" and is used to compensate fuel delivery based on system voltage. This signal is also used to store a trouble code if the fuel pump relay is defective or fuel pump voltage is lost while the engine is running. There should be about 12 volts on CKT 120 for 2 seconds after the ignition is turned, or any time references pulses are being received by the ECM.

Code 54 will set if the voltage at terminal "YE13" is less than 2 volts for 1.5 seconds since the last reference pulse was received. This code is designed to detect a faulty relay, causing extended crank time, and the code will help the diagnosis of an engine that "CRANKS BUT WILL NOT RUN."

If a fault is detected during start-up the "Service Engine Soon" light will stay "ON" until the ignition is cycled "OFF." However, if the voltage is detected below 2 volts with the engine running, the light will only remain "ON" while the condition exists.

CODE 45
OXYGEN SENSOR CIRCUIT
(RICH EXHAUST INDICATED)
2.8L (VIN W) "L" CARLINE (PORT)

① • RUN WARM ENGINE (75°C TO 95°C) AT 1200 RPM.
   • DOES "SCAN" TOOL DISPLAY O₂ SENSOR VOLTAGE FIXED ABOVE .75 VOLT (750 mV)?

YES

NO

• DISCONNECT O₂ SENSOR AND JUMPER HARNESS CKT 412 TO GROUND.
• "SCAN" TOOL SHOULD DISPLAY O₂ BELOW .35 VOLT (350 mV).
  DOES IT?

CODE 45 IS INTERMITTENT. IF NO ADDITIONAL CODES WERE STORED, REFER TO "DIAGNOSTIC AIDS" ON FACING PAGE.

YES

NO

REFER TO "DIAGNOSTIC AIDS" ON FACING PAGE.

REPLACE ECM.

CLEAR CODES AND CONFIRM "CLOSED LOOP" OPERATION AND NO "SERVICE ENGINE SOON" LIGHT.

1988–89 2.8L ENGINE

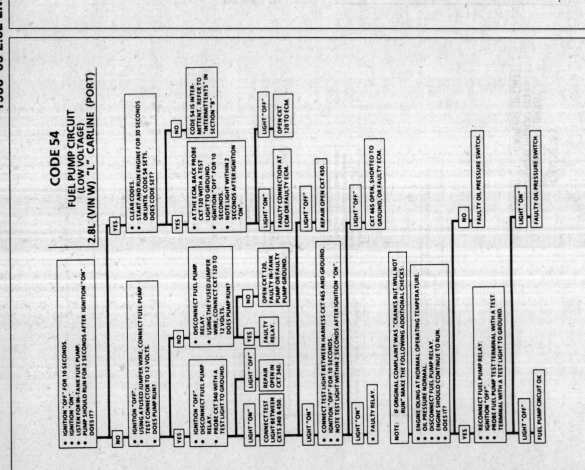

CODE 51
CODE 52
CODE 53
2.8L (VIN W) "L" CARLINE (PORT)

CODE 51
MEM-CAL ERROR
(FAULTY OR INCORRECT MEM-CAL)

CHECK THAT ALL PINS ARE FULLY INSERTED IN THE SOCKET AND THAT MEM-CAL IS PROPERLY LATCHED. IF OK, REPLACE MEM-CAL, CLEAR MEMORY, AND RECHECK. IF CODE 51 REAPPEARS, REPLACE ECM.

CLEAR CODES AND CONFIRM "CLOSED LOOP" OPERATION AND NO "SERVICE ENGINE SOON" LIGHT.

CODE 52
CALPAK ERROR
(FAULTY OR INCORRECT CALPAK)

CHECK THAT THE MEM-CAL IS FULLY SEATED AND LATCHED INTO THE MEM-CAL SOCKET. IF OK, REPLACE MEM-CAL, CLEAR MEMORY, AND RECHECK. IF CODE 52 REAPPEARS, REPLACE ECM.

CLEAR CODES AND CONFIRM "CLOSED LOOP" OPERATION AND NO "SERVICE ENGINE SOON" LIGHT.

CODE 53
SYSTEM OVER VOLTAGE

THIS CODE INDICATES THERE IS A BASIC GENERATOR PROBLEM.
- CODE 53 WILL SET, IF VOLTAGE AT ECM IGNITION INPUT PIN IS GREATER THAN 17.1 VOLTS FOR 2 SECONDS.
- CHECK AND REPAIR CHARGING SYSTEM. REFER TO SECTION "6D".

CLEAR CODES AND CONFIRM "CLOSED LOOP" OPERATION AND NO "SERVICE ENGINE SOON" LIGHT.

CODE 54
FUEL PUMP CIRCUIT
(LOW VOLTAGE)
2.8L (VIN W) "L" CARLINE (PORT)

- IGNITION "OFF" FOR 10 SECONDS.
- IGNITION "ON".
- LISTEN FOR IN-TANK FUEL PUMP.
- PUMP SHOULD RUN FOR 2 SECONDS AFTER IGNITION "ON".
- DOES IT?

YES → • CLEAR CODES. • START AND RUN ENGINE FOR 30 SECONDS OR UNTIL CODE 54 SETS. DOES CODE SET?
- **NO** → CODE 54 IS INTERMITTENT. REFER TO "INTERMITTENTS" IN SECTION "B".
- **YES** → • AT THE ECM, BACK PROBE CKT 120 WITH A TEST LIGHT TO GROUND. • IGNITION "OFF" FOR 10 SECONDS. • NOTE LIGHT WITHIN 2 SECONDS AFTER IGNITION "ON".
  - LIGHT "OFF" → OPEN CKT 120 TO ECM.
  - LIGHT "ON" → FAULTY CONNECTION AT ECM OR FAULTY ECM.

NO → • IGNITION "OFF". • USING A FUSED JUMPER WIRE, CONNECT FUEL PUMP TEST CONNECTOR TO 12 VOLTS. • DOES PUMP RUN?
- **NO** → • IGNITION "OFF". • DISCONNECT FUEL PUMP RELAY. • PROBE CKT 340 WITH A TEST LIGHT TO GROUND.
  - LIGHT "OFF" → CONNECT TEST LIGHT BETWEEN CKTS 340 & 650.
    - LIGHT "ON" → REPAIR OPEN IN CKT 340.
    - LIGHT "OFF" → FAULTY RELAY.
- **YES** → • DISCONNECT FUEL PUMP RELAY. • USING THE FUSED JUMPER WIRE, CONNECT CKT 120 TO 12 VOLTS. • DOES PUMP RUN?
  - **YES** → FAULTY RELAY.
  - **NO** → OPEN CKT 120, FAULTY IN-TANK PUMP OR FAULTY PUMP GROUND.

- LIGHT "OFF" → REPAIR OPEN CKT 450.
- LIGHT "ON" → • CONNECT TEST LIGHT BETWEEN HARNESS CKT 465 AND GROUND. • IGNITION "OFF" FOR 10 SECONDS. • NOTE TEST LIGHT WITHIN 2 SECONDS AFTER IGNITION "ON".
  - LIGHT "ON" → FAULTY RELAY.
  - LIGHT "OFF" → CKT 465 OPEN, SHORTED TO GROUND, OR FAULTY ECM.

OPEN CKT 120 TO ECM.

NOTE: IF ORIGINAL COMPLAINT WAS "CRANKS BUT WILL NOT RUN" MAKE THE FOLLOWING ADDITIONAL CHECKS:
- ENGINE IDLING AT NORMAL OPERATING TEMPERATURE.
- OIL PRESSURE NORMAL.
- DISCONNECT FUEL PUMP RELAY.
- ENGINE SHOULD CONTINUE TO RUN. DOES IT?
  - **YES** → • RECONNECT FUEL PUMP RELAY. • IGNITION "OFF". • PROBE FUEL PUMP TEST TERMINAL WITH A TEST TERMINAL WITH A TEST LIGHT TO GROUND.
    - LIGHT "ON" → FAULTY OIL PRESSURE SWITCH
    - LIGHT "OFF" → FUEL PUMP CIRCUIT OK
  - **NO** → FAULTY OIL PRESSURE SWITCH.

1988–89 2.8L ENGINE

CODE 61

DEGRADED OXYGEN SENSOR
2.8L (VIN W) "L" CARLINE (PORT)

IF A CODE 61 IS STORED IN MEMORY THE ECM HAS DETERMINED THE OXYGEN SENSOR IS CONTAMINATED OR DEGRADED, BECAUSE THE VOLTAGE CHANGE TIME IS SLOW OR SLUGGISH.

THE ECM PERFORMS THE OXYGEN SENSOR RESPONSE TIME TEST WHEN:

COOLANT TEMPERATURE IS GREATER THAN 85°C.

MAT TEMPERATURE IS GREATER THAN 10°C.

IN CLOSED LOOP.

IN DECEL FUEL CUT-OFF MODE.

IF A CODE 61 IS STORED THE OXYGEN SENSOR SHOULD BE REPLACED. A CONTAMINATED SENSOR CAN BE CAUSED BY FUEL ADDITIVES, SUCH AS SILICON, OR BY USE OF NON-GM APPROVED LUBRICANTS OR SEALANTS. SILICON CONTAMINATION IS USUALLY INDICATED BY A WHITE POWDERY SUBSTANCE ON THE SENSOR FINS.

CLEAR CODES AND CONFIRM "CLOSED LOOP" OPERATION AND NO "SERVICE ENGINE SOON" LIGHT.

SECTION B
SYMPTOMS

TABLE OF CONTENTS

BEFORE STARTING

Before using this section you should have performed the DIAGNOSTIC CIRCUIT CHECK and found out that:

1. The ECM and "Service Engine Soon" light are operating.

2. There are no trouble codes.

Verify the customer complaint, and locate the correct SYMPTOM below. Check the items indicated under that symptom.

If the ENGINE CRANKS BUT WILL NOT RUN, see CHART A-3.

Several of the symptom procedures below call for a Careful Visual Check. This check should include:

- ECM grounds for being clean and tight.

- Vacuum hoses for splits, kinks, and proper connections, as shown on Emission Control Information label.

- Air leaks at throttle body mounting and intake manifold.

- Ignition wires for cracking, hardness, proper routing, and carbon tracking.

- Wiring for proper connections, pinches, and cuts. The importance of this step cannot be stressed too strongly - it can lead to correcting a problem without further checks and can save valuable time.

1988–89 2.8L ENGINE

INTERMITTENTS

Problem may or may not turn "ON" the "Service Engine Soon" light, or store a code.

DO NOT use the Trouble Code Charts in Section "A" for intermittent problems. The fault must be present to locate the problem. If a fault is intermittent, use of trouble code charts may result in replacement of good parts.

- Most intermittent problems are caused by faulty electrical connections or wiring. Perform careful check as described at start of Section "B". Check for
  - Poor mating of the connector halves, or terminals not fully seated in the connector body (backed out).
  - Improperly formed or damaged terminals. All connector terminals in problem circuit should be carefully reformed to increase contact tension.
  - Poor terminal to wire connection. This requires removing the terminal from the connector body to check.

- If a visual check does not find the cause of the problem, the car can be driven with a voltmeter connected to a suspected circuit. A "Scan" tool can, also, be used for monitoring input signals to help detect intermittent conditions. An abnormal voltage, or "Scan" reading, when the problem occurs, indicates the problem may be in that circuit. If the wiring and connectors check OK and a trouble code was stored for a circuit having a sensor, except for Codes 43, 44, and 45, substitute a known good sensor and recheck.

An intermittent "Service Engine Soon" light with no stored code may be caused by

- Ignition coil shorted to ground and arcing at spark plug wires or plugs.
- "Service Engine Soon" light wire to ECM shorted to ground. (CKT 419)
- Diagnostic "Test" terminal wire to ECM, shorted to ground. (CKT 451)
- ECM power grounds. See ECM wiring diagrams.
- Loss of trouble code memory. To check, disconnect TPS and idle engine until "Service Engine Soon" light comes "ON." Code 22 should be stored, and kept in memory when ignition is turned "OFF." If not, the ECM is faulty.
- Check for an electrical system interference caused by a defective relay, ECM driven solenoid, or switch. They can cause a sharp electrical surge. Normally the problem will occur when the faulty component is operated.
- Check for improper installation of electrical options, such as lights, 2-way radios, etc.
- EST wires should be kept away from spark plug wires, coils and generator. Wire from ECM to ignition system (CKT 453) should be a good connection.
- Check for open diode across A/C compressor clutch, and for other open diodes (see wiring diagrams).

HARD START

Definition: Engine cranks OK, but does not start for a long time. Does eventually run, or may start but immediately dies.

- Perform careful check as described at start of Section "B".
- Make sure driver is using correct starting procedure.
- CHECK:
  - Ignition system - Check for:
    - Bare and shorted wires and proper output with spark tester J-26792 (ST-125) or equivalent.
    - IAC operation - See Code 35 chart.
  - A faulty in-tank fuel pump check valve will allow the fuel in the lines to drain back to the tank after the engine is stopped. To check for this condition:
    Perform Fuel System Diagnosis, CHART A-7.
  - TPS for sticking or binding or a high TPS voltage with the throttle closed.
  - High resistance in coolant sensor circuit or sensor itself. See Code 15 chart or with a "Scan" tool compare coolant temperature with ambient temperature on a cold engine. Fuel pressure CHART A-7.
  - Water contaminated fuel.
  - EGR operation. Be sure valve seats properly and is not staying open. See CHART C-7.
  - Remove spark plugs. Check for wet plugs, cracks, wear, improper gap, burned electrodes, or heavy deposits. Repair or replace as necessary.

HESITATION, SAG, STUMBLE

Definition: Momentary lack of response as the accelerator is pushed down. Can occur at all car speeds. Usually most severe when first trying to make the car move, as from a stop sign. May cause the engine to stall if severe enough.

- Perform careful visual check as described at start of Section "B".
- CHECK:
  - Fuel pressure See CHART A-7. Also Check for water contaminated fuel.
  - Spark plugs for being fouled or faulty wiring.
  - Mem-Cal number and Service Bulletins for latest Mem-Cal.
  - TPS for binding or sticking. Voltage should increase at a steady rate as throttle is moved toward WOT.
  - Generator output voltage. Repair, if less than 9 or more than 16 volts.
  - Ignition system ground, CKT 453.
  - Canister purge system for proper operation. See CHART C-3.
  - EGR - See CHART C-7.
  - Check for Codes 33 and 34. (MAP sensor circuit)
- Perform injector balance test, CHART C-2A.

SURGES AND/OR CHUGGLE

Definition: Engine power variation under steady throttle or cruise. Feels like the car speeds up and slows down with no change in the accelerator pedal.

- Be sure driver understands Torque Converter Clutch and A/C compressor operation in Owner's Manual.
- Perform careful visual inspection as described at start of Section "B".
- To help determine if the condition is caused by a rich or lean system, the car should be driven at the speed of the complaint. Monitoring block learn at the complaint speed will help identify the cause of the problem. If the system is running lean (block learn greater than 138), refer to diagnostic aids on facing page of Code 44. If the system is running rich (block learn less than 118), refer to diagnostic aids on facing page of Code 45.
- CHECK:
  - Generator output voltage. Repair if less than 9 or more than 16 volts.
  - EGR - There should be no EGR at idle. See CHART C-7.
  - EGR filter for being plugged, see CHART C-7.
  - Vacuum lines for kinks or leaks.
  - In-line fuel filter. Replace if dirty or plugged.
  - Fuel pressure while condition exists. See CHART A-7.
  - Remove spark plugs. Check for cracks, wear, improper gap, burned electrodes, or heavy deposits. Also check condition of spark plug wires and check for proper output voltage using spark tester J-26792 (ST-125) or equivalent.

1988–89 2.8L ENGINE

LACK OF POWER, SLUGGISH, OR SPONGY

Definition: Engine delivers less than expected power. Little or no increase in speed when accelerator pedal is pushed down part way.

- Perform careful visual check as described at start of Section "B".
- Compare customer's car to similar unit. Make sure the customer's car has an actual problem.
- Remove air filter and check for dirt, or for being plugged. Replace as necessary.
- CHECK:
  - Restricted fuel filter, contaminated fuel or improper fuel pressure. See CHART A-7.
  - ECM power grounds, see wiring diagrams.
  - EGR operation for being open or partly open all the time - See CHART C-7.
- Exhaust system for possible restriction: See CHART B-1.
  - Inspect exhaust system for damaged or collapsed pipes.
  - Inspect muffler for heat distress or possible internal failure.
- Generator output voltage. Repair if less than 9 or more than 16 volts.
- Engine valve timing and compression.
- Engine for proper or worn camshaft.
- Secondary voltage using a shop octilliscope or a spark tester J-26792 (ST-125) or equivalent. Check A/C operation. A/C clutch should cut out at WOT. See A/C CHART C-10.

DETONATION/SPARK KNOCK

Definition: A mild to severe ping, usually worse under acceleration. The engine makes sharp metallic knocks that change with throttle opening. Sounds like popcorn popping.

- Check for obvious overheating problems:
  - Low coolant.
  - Loose belt.
  - Restricted air flow to radiator, or restricted water flow through radiator.
  - Inoperative electric cooling fan circuit. See CHART C-12.
- To help determine if the conditions is caused by a rich or lean system, the car should be driven at the speed of the complaint. Monitoring block learn, at the complaint speed, will help identify the cause of the problem. If the system is running lean (block learn greater than 138), refer to diagnostic aids on facing page of Code 44. If the system is running rich (block learn less than 118), refer to facing page of Code 45.
- CHECK:
  - EGR system for not opening or plugged EGR passages - See CHART C-7.
  - ESC system for no retard - See CHART C-5.
  - Park/Neutral switch. Be sure "Scan" indicates drive with gear selector in drive or overdrive. - See CHART C-1A.
  - TCC operation, TCC applying too soon - see CHART C-8.
  - Fuel system pressure - See CHART A-7.
  - Engine for excessive carbon build-up. Remove carbon with top engine cleaner. Follow instructions on can.
  - Mem-Cal for correct part.
  - Combustion chamber for excessive oil.
  - Engine for incorrect basic parts such as cam, heads, pistons, etc.
  - Fuel for poor quality, proper octane rating.

CUTS OUT, MISSES

Definition: Steady pulsation or jerking that follows engine speed, usually more pronounced as engine load increases. The exhaust has a steady spitting sound at idle or under a load.

- Perform careful visual (physical) check as described at start of Section "B".
- If ignition system is suspected of causing a miss at idle or cutting out under load, refer to appropriate ignition "Misfire" chart.
- If the previous checks did not find the problem:
  - Visually inspect ignition system for moisture, dust, cracks, burns, etc. Spray plug wires with fine water mist to check for shorts.
- If above checks did not correct problem, check the following:
  - To determine if one injector or connector is faulty, disconnect injector 4-way connector. On the injector side of the harness, connect ohmmeter between the B+ circuit and the injector drive side of the harness for each bank of injectors. Because each bank of injectors is wired in parallel, an ohmmeter should measure about 4 ohms. If the reading is 6 ohms, or greater, an open circuit is likely the cause. If 2 ohms or less, a shorted circuit or injector is likely. Reconnect injector 4-way connector.
- If either ohm reading is out of range:
  - Disconnect all injector harness connectors. Connect J-34730-2 Injector Test Light or equivalent 6 volt test light between the harness terminals of each injector connector and note light while cranking. If test light fails to blink at any connector, it is a faulty injector drive circuit harness, connector, or terminal.
- CHECK:
  - Injector Balance. See CHART C-2A.
  - Fuel System - Plugged fuel filter, water, low pressure. See CHART A-7.
  - Valve Timing
  - Remove rocker covers. Check for bent pushrods, worn rocker arms, broken valve springs, worn camshaft lobes. Repair as necessary.
- Perform compression check.

BACKFIRE

Definition: Fuel ignites in intake manifold, or in exhaust system, making a loud popping noise.

- CHECK:
  - Compression - Look for sticking or leaking valves.
  - EGR operation for being open all the time. See CHART C-7.
  - EGR gasket for faulty or loose fit.
  - Output voltage of ignition coils, using a shop octilliscope or spark tester J-26792 (ST-125), or equivalent.
  - Valve timing.
  - Spark plugs, spark plug wires, and proper routing of plug wires.

1988–89 2.8L ENGINE

POOR FUEL ECONOMY

Definition: Fuel economy, as measured by an actual road test, is noticeably lower than expected. Also, economy is noticeably lower than it was on this car at one time, as previously shown by an actual road test.

- Check owner's driving habits.
  - Is A/C "ON" full time? (Defroster mode "ON"?)
  - Are tires at correct pressure?
  - Are excessively heavy loads being carried?
  - Is acceleration too much, too often?
  - Suggest owner fill fuel tank and recheck fuel economy.
  - Suggest driver read "Important Facts on Fuel Economy" in Owner's Manual.
- Check for proper calibration of speedometer.
- Visually (physically) Check:
  - Vacuum hoses for splits, kinks, and proper connections as shown on Vehicle Emission Control Information label.
  - Ignition wires for cracking, hardness, and proper connections.
  - Air cleaner element (filter) for dirt or being plugged.
- Remove spark plugs. Check for cracks, wear, improper gap, burned electrodes, or heavy deposits. Repair or replace as necessary.

- **CHECK:**
  - Engine thermostat for faulty part (always open) or for wrong heat range. Using a "Scan" tool, monitor engine temperature. A "Scan" displays engine temp. in degrees centigrade. After engine is started, the temperature should rise steadily to about 90°C, then stabilize, when thermostat opens.
  - Fuel Pressure. See CHART A-7.
  - Compression.
  - TCC for proper operation. See CHART C-8A. A "Scan" should indicate an rpm drop, when the TCC is commanded "ON."
  - Exhaust system restriction. See CHART B-1.
  - Using a "Scan" tool, crank engine for five seconds while in clear flood mode. Start engine and check for a Code 42. An open EST line will cause poor fuel economy. Refer to Code 42 diagnostic chart for repair procedure.

DIESELING, RUN-ON

Definition: Engine continues to run after key is turned "OFF" but runs very roughly.

- Check injectors for leaking. See CHART A-7.
- If engine runs smoothly, check ignition switch and adjustment.

ROUGH, UNSTABLE, OR INCORRECT IDLE, STALLING

Definition: The engine runs unevenly at idle. If bad enough, the car may shake. Also, the idle may vary in rpm (called "hunting"). Either condition may be bad enough to cause stalling. Engine idles at incorrect speed.

- Perform careful visual check as described at start of Section "B".
- **CHECK:**
  - Motor mounts for damage, grounding out on frame, or mispositioned, etc.
  - Throttle linkage for sticking or binding.
  - TPS for sticking or binding, be sure output is stable at idle and adjustment specification is correct.
  - IAC system. See Code 35 chart.
  - Generator output voltage. Repair if less than 9 or more than 16 volts.
  - P/N switch circuit. See CHART C-1A, or use "Scan" tool, and be sure tool indicates vehicle is in drive with gear selector in drive (125C).
  - Injector balance. See CHART C-2A.
  - PCV valve for proper operation by placing finger over inlet hole in valve end several times. Valve should snap back. If not, replace valve.
  - Evaporative Emission Control System. CHART C-3.

- Engine will run rough or stall if loss of battery power to the ECM (Electronic Control Module) has occurred. This ECM has an idle learn feature. (See Section "C2" for IDLE Learn Procedure.)
  - Power Steering Pressure switch input. The state of the switch should only change when wheels are turned up against the stops. See CHART C-1E.
  - ECM ground circuits.
  - EGR valve: There should be no EGR at idle.
- Monitoring block learn values may help identify the cause of the problem. If the system is running lean (block learn greater than 138) refer to Diagnostic Aids on facing page of Code 44. If the system is running rich (block learn values less than 118) refer to Diagnostic Aids on facing page of Code 45.
- Run a cylinder compression check.

- Check for fuel in pressure regulator hose. If present, replace regulator assembly.
- Check ignition system; wires and plugs.
- If problem exists with A/C "ON", check A/C system operation CHART C-10.

EXCESSIVE EXHAUST EMISSIONS OR ODORS

Definition: Vehicle fails an emission test. Vehicle has excessive "rotten egg" smell. Excessive odors do not necessarily indicate excessive emissions.

- Perform "Diagnostic Circuit Check."
- IF TEST SHOWS EXCESSIVE CO AND HC, (or also has excessive odors?)
  - Check items which cause car to run RICH.
  - Make sure engine is at normal operating temperature.
- **CHECK:**
  - Fuel pressure. See CHART A-7.
  - Canister for fuel loading. See CHART C-3.
  - Injector balance. See CHART C-2A.
  - PCV valve for being plugged, stuck, or blocked PCV hose, or fuel in the crankcase.
  - Spark plugs, plug wires, and ignition components.
  - Check for lead contamination of catalytic converter (look for removal of fuel filler neck restrictor).
  - Check for properly installed fuel cap.

- If the system is running rich, (block learn less than 118), refer to "Diagnostic Aids" on facing page of Code 45.
- IF TEST SHOWS EXCESSIVE NOx:
  - Check items which cause car to run LEAN, or to run too hot. See CHART C-7.
    - EGR valve for not opening. See CHART C-7.
    - Vacuum leaks.
    - Coolant system and coolant fan for proper operation. See CHART C-12.
    - Remove carbon with top engine cleaner. Follow instructions on can.
  - If the system is running lean, (block learn greater than 138), refer to "Diagnostic Aids" on facing page of Code 44.

1988–89 2.8L ENGINE

CHART B-1

RESTRICTED EXHAUST SYSTEM CHECK
ALL ENGINES

Proper diagnosis for a restricted exhaust system is essential before any components are replaced. Either of the following procedures may be used for diagnosis, depending upon engine or tool used:

CHECK AT A. I. R. PIPE:

1. Remove the rubber hose at the exhaust manifold A.I.R. pipe check valve. Remove check valve.
2. Connect a fuel pump pressure gauge to a hose and nipple from a Propane Enrichment Device (J26911) (see illustration).
3. Insert the nipple into the exhaust manifold A.I.R. pipe.

OR CHECK AT O₂ SENSOR:

1. Carefully remove O₂ sensor.
2. Install Borroughs exhaust backpressure tester (BT 8515 or BT 8603) or equivalent in place of O₂ sensor (see illustration).
3. After completing test described below, be sure to coat threads of O₂ sensor with anti-seize compound P/N 5613695 or equivalent prior to re-installation.

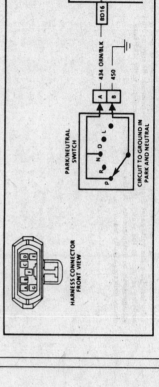

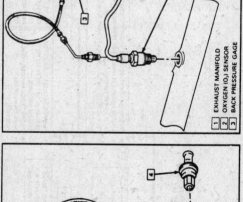

① EXHAUST MANIFOLD
② OXYGEN (O₂) SENSOR
③ BACK PRESSURE GAGE

① GAGE
② HOSE AND NIPPLE ADAPTER
③ A.I.R. PIPE (EXHAUST PORT)
④ CHECK VALVE

DIAGNOSIS:

1. With the engine idling at normal operating temperature, observe the exhaust system backpressure reading on the gauge. Reading should not exceed 8.6 kPa (1.25 psi).
2. Increase engine speed to 2000 rpm and observe gauge. Reading should not exceed 20.7 kPa (3 psi).
3. If the backpressure at either speed exceeds specification, a restricted exhaust system is indicated.
4. Inspect the entire exhaust system for a collapsed pipe, heat distress, or possible internal muffler failure.
5. If there are no obvious reasons for the excessive backpressure, the catalytic converter is suspected to be restricted and should be replaced using current recommended procedures.

CHART C-1A

PARK/NEUTRAL SWITCH DIAGNOSIS
(AUTO TRANSMISSION ONLY)
2.8L (VIN W) "L" CARLINE (PORT)

Circuit Description:

The park/neutral switch contacts are a part of the neutral start switch and are closed to ground in park or neutral, and open in drive ranges.

The ECM supplies ignition voltage through a current limiting resistor to CKT 434 and senses a closed switch when the voltage on CKT 434 drops to less than one volt.

The ECM uses the P/N signal as one of the inputs to control:
Idle Air Control
VSS Diagnostics
EGR

If CKT 434 indicates P/N (grounded) while in drive range, the EGR would be inoperative, resulting in possible detonation.

If CKT 434 indicates drive (open), a drop in the idle may occur when the gear selector is moved into drive range

Test Description: Numbers below refer to circled numbers on the diagnostic chart.

1. Checks for a closed switch to ground in park position. Different makes of "Scan" tools will read P/N differently. Refer to tool operator's manual for type of display used for a specific tool.

2. Checks for an open switch in drive range.
3. Be sure "Scan" indicates drive, even while wiggling shifter, to test for an intermittent or misadjusted switch in drive or overdrive range.

HARNESS CONNECTOR
FRONT VIEW

PARK/NEUTRAL SWITCH

CIRCUIT TO GROUND IN PARK AND NEUTRAL

ECM

1988–89 2.8L ENGINE

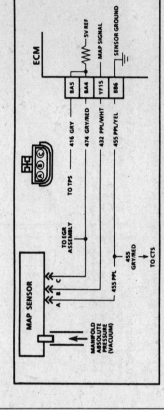

CHART C-1D

MANIFOLD ABSOLUTE PRESSURE (MAP) OUTPUT CHECK
2.8L (VIN W) "L" CARLINE (PORT)

Circuit Description:

The manifold absolute pressure sensor (MAP) measures manifold pressure (vacuum) and sends that signal to the ECM. The MAP sensor is mainly used for fuel calculation when the ECM is running in the throttle body backup mode. The MAP sensor is also used to determine the barometric pressure and to help calculate fuel delivery.

Test Description: Numbers below refer to circled numbers on the diagnostic chart.

1. Checks MAP sensor output voltage to the ECM. This voltage without engine running, represents a barometer reading to the ECM.
2. Applying 34 kPa (10 inches Hg) vacuum to the MAP sensor should cause the voltage to be 1.2 volts less than the voltage at Step 1. Upon applying vacuum to the sensor, the change in voltage should be instantaneous. A slow voltage change indicates a faulty sensor.

The engine must be running in this step or the "Scanner" will not indicate a change in voltage. It is normal for the "Service Engine Soon" light to come "ON" and for the system to set a Code 33 during this step. Make sure the code is cleared when this test is completed.

3. Check vacuum hose to sensor for leaking or restriction. Be sure no other vacuum devices are connected to the MAP hose.

CHART C-1A

PARK/NEUTRAL SWITCH DIAGNOSIS
(AUTO TRANSMISSION ONLY)
2.8L (VIN W) "L" CARLINE (PORT)

① WITH TRANSAXLE/TRANSMISSION IN PARK, "SCAN" TOOL SHOULD INDICATE PARK OR NEUTRAL.
• DOES IT?

YES

③ • SHIFT TRANSAXLE/TRANSMISSION INTO DRIVE.
• "SCAN" TOOL SHOULD DISPLAY A CHANGE TO INDICATE DRIVE.
• DOES IT?

NO

• DISCONNECT P/N SWITCH.
• THIS SHOULD CAUSE "SCAN" TOOL TO DISPLAY DRIVE RANGE.
• DOES IT?

YES

NO TROUBLE FOUND. P/N CIRCUIT OK.

NO

CKT 434 SHORTED TO GROUND OR FAULTY ECM.

YES

FAULTY P/N SWITCH CONNECTION OR P/N SWITCH MISADJUSTED OR FAULTY.

② • DISCONNECT PARK/NEUTRAL SWITCH CONNECTOR.
• JUMPER HARNESS CONNECTOR TERMINALS "A" AND "B" (CKT 434 TO 450).
• "SCAN" TOOL SHOULD INDICATE PARK OR NEUTRAL.
• DOES IT?

YES

FAULTY P/N SWITCH CONNECTION OR P/N SWITCH MISADJUSTED OR FAULTY.

NO

JUMPER HARNESS CONNECTOR TERMINAL "A" (CKT 434) TO ENGINE GROUND.
• "SCAN" TOOL SHOULD INDICATE PARK OR NEUTRAL.
• DOES IT?

YES

OPEN GROUND CKT 450.

NO

CKT 434 OPEN OR FAULTY ECM CONNECTION OR ECM.

1988—89 2.8L ENGINE

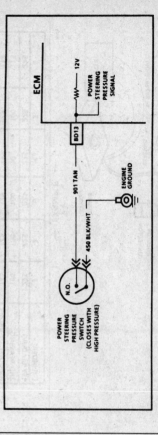

CHART C-1E

POWER STEERING PRESSURE SWITCH (PSPS) DIAGNOSIS
2.8L (VIN W) "L" CARLINE (PORT)

Circuit Description:

The power steering pressure switch is normally open to ground, and CKT 901 will be near the battery voltage.

Turning the steering wheel increases power steering oil pressure and its load on an idling engine. The pressure switch will close before the load can cause an idle problem.

Closing the switch causes CKT 901 to read less than 1 volt. The ECM will increase the idle air rate and disengage the A/C relay.

- A pressure switch that will not close, or an open CKT 901 or 450, may cause the engine to stop when power steering loads are high.
- A switch that will not open, or a CKT 901 shorted to ground, may affect idle quality and will cause the A/C relay to be de-energized.

Test Description: Numbers below refer to circled numbers on the diagnostic chart.

1. Different makes of "Scan" tools may display the state of this switch in different ways. Refer to "Scan" tool operator's manual to determine how this input is indicated.

2. Checks to determine if CKT 901 is shorted to ground.

3. This should simulate a closed switch.

CHART C-1D

MANIFOLD ABSOLUTE PRESSURE (MAP) OUTPUT CHECK
2.8L (VIN W) "L" CARLINE (PORT)

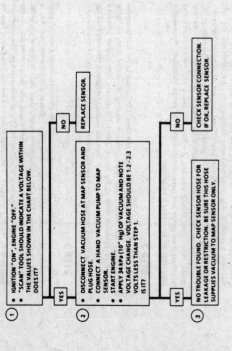

① • IGNITION "ON", ENGINE "OFF."
• "SCAN" TOOL SHOULD INDICATE A VOLTAGE WITHIN THE VALUES SHOWN IN THE CHART BELOW.
DOES IT?

YES → NO → REPLACE SENSOR.

② • DISCONNECT VACUUM HOSE AT MAP SENSOR AND PLUG HOSE.
• CONNECT A HAND VACUUM PUMP TO MAP SENSOR.
• START ENGINE.
• APPLY 34 kPa (10" Hg) OF VACUUM AND NOTE VOLTAGE CHANGE. VOLTAGE SHOULD BE 1.2 - 2.3 VOLTS LESS THAN STEP 1.
IS IT?

YES → NO → CHECK SENSOR CONNECTION. IF OK, REPLACE SENSOR.

③ NO TROUBLE FOUND. CHECK SENSOR HOSE FOR LEAKAGE OR RESTRICTION. BE SURE THIS HOSE SUPPLIES VACUUM TO MAP SENSOR ONLY.

ALTITUDE		VOLTAGE RANGE
Meters	Feet	
Below 305	Below 1,000	3.8—5.5V
305—610	1,000—2,000	3.6—5.3V
610—914	2,000—3,000	3.5—5.1V
914—1219	3,000—4,000	3.3—5.0V
1219—1524	4,000—5,000	3.2—4.8V
1524—1829	5,000—6,000	3.0—4.6V
1829—2133	6,000—7,000	2.9—4.5V
2133—2438	7,000—8,000	2.8—4.3V
2438—2743	8,000—9,000	2.6—4.2V
2743—3048	9,000—10,000	2.5—4.0V

LOW ALTITUDE = HIGH PRESSURE = HIGH VOLTAGE

CLEAR CODES AND CONFIRM "CLOSED LOOP" OPERATION AND NO "SERVICE ENGINE SOON" LIGHT.

CHART C-2A
INJECTOR BALANCE TEST

The injector balance tester is a tool used to turn the injector on for a precise amount of time, thus spraying a measured amount of fuel into the manifold. This causes a drop in fuel rail pressure that we can record and compare between each injector. All injectors should have the same amount of pressure drop (± 10 kPa). Any injector with a pressure drop that is 10 kPa (or more) greater or less than the average drop of the other injectors should be considered faulty and replaced.

STEP 1

Engine "cool down" period (10 minutes) is necessary to avoid irregular readings due to "Hot Soak" fuel boiling. With ignition "OFF" connect fuel gauge J347301 or equivalent to fuel pressure tap. Wrap a shop towel around fitting while connecting gage to avoid fuel spillage.

Disconnect harness connectors at all injectors, and connect injector tester J-34730-3, or equivalent, to one injector. On Turbo equipped engines, use adaptor harness furnished with injector tester to energize injectors that are not accessible. Follow manufacturers instructions for use of adaptor harness. Ignition must be "OFF" at least 10 seconds to complete ECM shutdown cycle. Fuel pump should run about 2 seconds after ignition is turned "ON". At this point, insert clear tubing attached to vent valve into a suitable container and bleed air from gauge and hose to insure accurate gauge operation. Repeat this step until all air is bled from gauge.

STEP 2

Turn ignition "OFF" for 10 seconds and then "ON" again to get fuel pressure to its maximum. Record this initial pressure reading. Energize tester one time and note pressure drop at its lowest point. (Disregard any slight pressure increase after drop hits low point.). By subtracting this second pressure reading from the initial pressure, we have the actual amount of injector pressure drop.

STEP 3

Repeat step 2 on each injector and compare the amount of drop. Usually, good injectors will have virtually the same drop. Retest any injector that has a pressure difference of 10 kPa, either more or less than the average of the other injectors on the engine. Replace any injector that also fails the retest. If the pressure drop of all injectors is within 10 kPa of this average, the injectors appear to be flowing properly. Reconnect them and review Symptoms, Section "B".

NOTE: The entire test should not be repeated more than once without running the engine to prevent flooding. (This includes any retest on faulty injectors).

CHART C-2A
INJECTOR BALANCE TEST
2.8L (VIN W) "L" CARLINE (PORT)

NOTE: The fuel pressure test in Section "A", CHART A-7, should be completed prior to this test.

Step 1. If engine is at operating temperature, allow a 10 minute "cool down" period then connect fuel pressure gauge and injector tester.
1. Ignition "OFF".
2. Connect fuel pressure gauge and injector tester.
3. Ignition "ON".
4. Bleed off air in gauge. Repeat until all air is bled from gauge.

Step 2. Run test:
1. Ignition "OFF" for 10 seconds.
2. Ignition "ON". Record gauge pressure. (Pressure must hold steady, if not see the Fuel System diagnosis, Chart A-7, in Section "A").
3. Turn injector on, by depressing button on injector tester, and note pressure at the instant the gauge needle stops.

Step 3.
1. Repeat step 2 on all injectors and record pressure drop on each. Retest injectors that appear faulty (Any injectors that have a 10 kPa difference, either more or less, in pressure from the average). If no problem is found, review "Symptoms" Section "B".

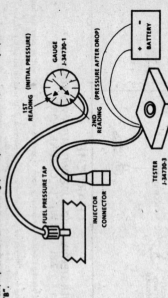

— EXAMPLE —

CYLINDER	1	2	3	4	5	6
1ST READING	225	225	225	225	225	225
2ND READING	100	100	100	90	100	115
AMOUNT OF DROP	125	125	125	135	125	110
	OK	OK	OK	FAULTY, RICH (TOO MUCH) (FUEL DROP)	OK	FAULTY, LEAN (TOO LITTLE) (FUEL DROP)

1988–89 2.8L ENGINE

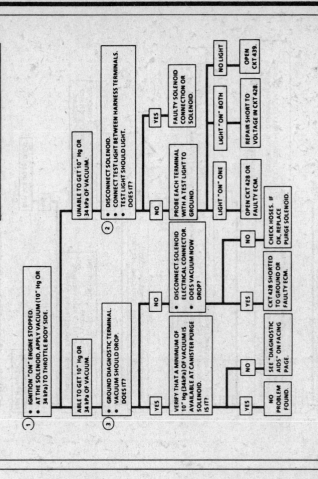

CHART C-3
CANISTER PURGE VALVE CHECK
2.8L (VIN W) "L" CARLINE (PORT)

① • IGNITION "ON" ENGINE STOPPED.
• AT THE SOLENOID, APPLY VACUUM (10" Hg OR 34 kPa) TO THROTTLE BODY SIDE.

ABLE TO GET 10" Hg OR 34 kPa OF VACUUM.

UNABLE TO GET 10" Hg OR 34 kPa OF VACUUM.

② • DISCONNECT SOLENOID.
• CONNECT TEST LIGHT BETWEEN HARNESS TERMINALS.
• TEST LIGHT SHOULD LIGHT.
DOES IT?

③ • GROUND DIAGNOSTIC TERMINAL.
• VACUUM SHOULD DROP.
DOES IT?

YES → FAULTY SOLENOID CONNECTION OR SOLENOID.

NO → PROBE EACH TERMINAL WITH A TEST LIGHT TO GROUND.

• DISCONNECT SOLENOID ELECTRICAL CONNECTOR.
• DOES VACUUM NOW DROP?

LIGHT "ON" BOTH → REPAIR SHORT TO VOLTAGE IN CKT 428.

LIGHT "ON" ONE → OPEN CKT 428 OR FAULTY ECM.

NO LIGHT → OPEN CKT 439.

VERIFY THAT A MINIMUM OF 10" Hg (34 kPa) OF VACUUM IS AVAILABLE AT CANISTER PURGE SOLENOID.
IS IT?

NO → CKT 428 SHORTED TO GROUND OR FAULTY ECM.

YES → CHECK HOSES. IF OK, REPLACE PURGE SOLENOID.

YES → NO PROBLEM FOUND.

NO → SEE "DIAGNOSTIC AIDS" ON FACING PAGE.

CLEAR CODES AND CONFIRM "CLOSED LOOP" OPERATION AND NO "SERVICE ENGINE SOON" LIGHT.

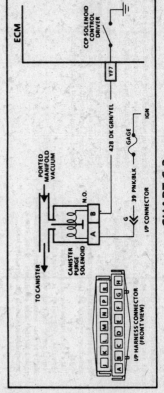

CHART C-3
CANISTER PURGE VALVE CHECK
2.8L (VIN W) "L" CARLINE (PORT)

Circuit Description:

Canister purge is controlled by a solenoid that allows manifold vacuum to purge the canister when de-energized. The ECM supplies a ground to energize the solenoid (purge "OFF"). The purge solenoid control by the ECM is pulse width modulated (turned "ON" and "OFF" several times a second). The duty cycle (pulse width) is determined by the amount of air flow, and the engine vacuum as determined by the MAP sensor input. The duty cycle is calculated by the ECM and the output commanded when the following conditions have been met.

• Engine run time after start more than 3 minutes
• Coolant temperature above 80°C
• Vehicle speed above 5 mph
• Throttle off idle (about 3%)

Also, if the diagnostic "test" terminal is grounded with the engine stopped, the purge solenoid is de-energized (purge "ON.")

Test Description: Numbers below refer to circled numbers on the diagnostic chart.

1. Checks to see if the solenoid is opened or closed. The solenoid is normally energized in this step; so it should be closed.

2. Checks for a complete circuit. Normally there is ignition voltage on CKT 39 and the ECM provides a ground on CKT 428

3. Completes functional check by grounding "test" terminal. This should normally de-energize the solenoid opening the valve which should allow the vacuum to drop (purge "ON.")

1988-89 2.8L ENGINE

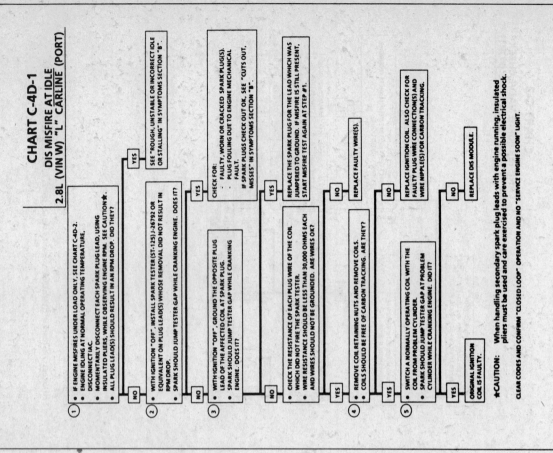

CHART C-4D-1
DIS MISFIRE AT IDLE
2.8L (VIN W) "L" CARLINE (PORT)

1. IF ENGINE MISFIRES UNDER LOAD ONLY, SEE CHART C-4D-2.
   ENGINE IDLING AT NORMAL OPERATING TEMPERATURE,
   DISCONNECT IAC.
   MOMENTARILY DISCONNECT EACH SPARK PLUG LEAD, USING
   INSULATED PLIERS, WHILE OBSERVING ENGINE RPM. SEE CAUTION★.
   ALL PLUG LEAD(S) SHOULD RESULT IN AN RPM DROP. DID THEY?

   - **YES** → SEE "ROUGH, UNSTABLE OR INCORRECT IDLE OR STALLING" IN SYMPTOMS SECTION "B".
   - **NO** ↓

2. WITH IGNITION "OFF", INSTALL SPARK TESTER (ST-125) J-26792 OR
   EQUIVALENT ON PLUG LEAD(S) WHOSE REMOVAL DID NOT RESULT IN
   RPM DROP.
   SPARK SHOULD JUMP TESTER GAP WHILE CRANKING ENGINE. DOES IT?

   - **YES** → CHECK FOR:
     - FAULTY, WORN OR CRACKED SPARK PLUG(S).
     - PLUG FOULING DUE TO ENGINE MECHANICAL FAULT.
     - IF SPARK PLUGS CHECK OUT OK, SEE "CUTS OUT, MISSES" IN SYMPTOMS SECTION "B".
   - **NO** ↓

3. WITH IGNITION "OFF", GROUND THE OPPOSITE PLUG LEAD OF THE AFFECTED COIL AT SPARK PLUG.
   SPARK SHOULD JUMP TESTER GAP WHILE CRANKING ENGINE. DOES IT?

   - **YES** → REPLACE THE SPARK PLUG FOR THE LEAD WHICH WAS JUMPERED TO GROUND. IF MISFIRE IS STILL PRESENT, START MISFIRE TEST AGAIN AT STEP #1.
   - **NO** ↓

4. CHECK THE RESISTANCE OF EACH PLUG WIRE OF THE COIL WHICH DID NOT FIRE THE SPARK TESTER.
   WIRE RESISTANCE SHOULD BE LESS THAN 30,000 OHMS EACH AND WIRES SHOULD NOT BE GROUNDED. ARE WIRES OK?

   - **NO** → REPLACE FAULTY WIRE(S).
   - **YES** ↓

   REMOVE COIL RETAINING NUTS AND REMOVE COILS.
   COILS SHOULD BE FREE OF CARBON TRACKING. ARE THEY?

   - **NO** → REPLACE IGNITION COIL. ALSO CHECK FOR FAULTY PLUG WIRE CONNECTION(S) AND WIRE NIPPLE(S) FOR CARBON TRACKING.
   - **YES** ↓

5. SWITCH A NORMALLY OPERATING COIL WITH THE COIL FROM PROBLEM CYLINDER.
   SPARK SHOULD JUMP TESTER GAP AT PROBLEM CYLINDER WHILE CRANKING ENGINE. DID IT?

   - **YES** → ORIGINAL IGNITION COIL IS FAULTY.
   - **NO** → REPLACE DIS MODULE.

★CAUTION: When handling secondary spark plug leads with engine running, insulated pliers must be used and care exercised to prevent a possible electrical shock.

CLEAR CODES AND CONFIRM "CLOSED LOOP" OPERATION AND NO "SERVICE ENGINE SOON" LIGHT.

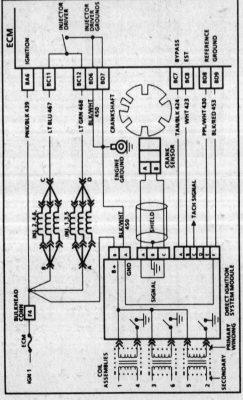

CHART C-4D-1
DIS MISFIRE AT IDLE
2.8L (VIN W) "L" CARLINE (PORT)

Circuit Description:

The direct ignition system (DIS) uses a waste spark method of distribution. For example, in this type of system the ignition module triggers the #1/4 coil pair resulting in both #1 and #4 spark plugs firing at the same time. #1 cylinder is on the compression stroke at the same time #4 is on the exhaust stroke, resulting in a lower energy requirement to fire #4 spark plug. This leaves the remainder of the high voltage to be used to fire #1 spark plug. On this application, the crank sensor is mounted to the engine block and protrudes through the block to within approximately .050" of the crankshaft reluctor. Since the reluctor is a machined portion of the crankshaft and the crank sensor is mounted in a fixed position on the block, timing adjustments are not possible or necessary.

Test Description: Numbers below refer to circled numbers on the diagnostic chart.

1. If the "Misfire" complaint exists under load only, the diagnostic chart on page 2 must be used. Engine rpm should drop approximately equally on all plug leads.

2. A spark test such as a ST-125 must be used because it is essential to verify adequate available secondary voltage at the spark plug. (25,000 volts).

3. If the spark jumps the test gap after grounding the opposite plug wire, it indicates excessive resistance in the plug which was Bypassed. A faulty or poor connection at that plug could also result in the miss condition. Also, check for carbon deposits inside the spark plug boot.

4. If carbon tracking is evident, replace coil and be sure plug wires relating to that coil are clean and tight. Excessive wire resistance or faulty connections could have caused the coil to be damaged.

5. If the no spark condition follows the suspected coil, that coil is faulty, otherwise, the ignition module is the cause of no spark. This test could also be performed by substituting a known good coil for the one causing the no spark condition.

1988–89 2.8L ENGINE

CHART C-4D-2
DIS MISFIRE UNDER LOAD
2.8L (VIN W) "L" CARLINE (PORT)

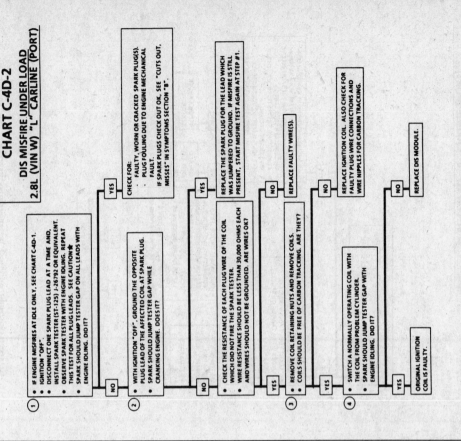

① IF ENGINE MISFIRES AT IDLE ONLY, SEE CHART C-4D-1.
IGNITION "OFF".
• DISCONNECT ONE SPARK PLUG LEAD AT A TIME AND, INSTALL SPARK TESTER (ST-125) J-26792 OR EQUIVALENT.
• OBSERVE SPARK TESTER WITH ENGINE IDLING. REPEAT THIS TEST FOR ALL PLUG LEADS. SEE CAUTION★
• SPARK SHOULD JUMP TESTER GAP ON ALL LEADS WITH ENGINE IDLING. DID IT?

NO →

② • WITH IGNITION "OFF" GROUND THE OPPOSITE PLUG LEAD OF THE AFFECTED COIL AT SPARK PLUG.
• SPARK SHOULD JUMP TESTER GAP WHILE CRANKING ENGINE. DOES IT?

YES →

CHECK FOR:
• FAULTY, WORN OR CRACKED SPARK PLUG(S).
• PLUG FOULING DUE TO ENGINE MECHANICAL FAULT.
IF SPARK PLUGS CHECK OUT OK, SEE "CUTS OUT, MISSES" IN SYMPTOMS SECTION ★.

YES →

REPLACE THE SPARK PLUG FOR THE LEAD WHICH WAS JUMPERED TO GROUND. IF MISFIRE IS STILL PRESENT, START MISFIRE TEST AGAIN AT STEP #1.

NO →

③ • CHECK THE RESISTANCE OF EACH PLUG WIRE OF THE COIL WHICH DID NOT FIRE THE SPARK TESTER.
• WIRE RESISTANCE SHOULD BE LESS THAN 30,000 OHMS EACH AND WIRES SHOULD NOT BE GROUNDED. ARE WIRES OK?

NO →

REPLACE FAULTY WIRE(S).

YES →

• REMOVE COIL RETAINING NUTS AND REMOVE COILS.
• COILS SHOULD BE FREE OF CARBON TRACKING. ARE THEY?

NO →

REPLACE IGNITION COIL. ALSO CHECK FOR FAULTY PLUG WIRE CONNECTIONS AND WIRE NIPPLES FOR CARBON TRACKING.

YES →

④ • SWITCH A NORMALLY OPERATING COIL WITH THE COIL FROM PROBLEM CYLINDER.
• SPARK SHOULD JUMP TESTER GAP WITH ENGINE IDLING. DID IT?

YES →

ORIGINAL IGNITION COIL IS FAULTY.

NO →

REPLACE DIS MODULE.

★CAUTION: When handling secondary spark plug leads with engine running, insulated pliers must be used and care exercised to prevent a possible electrical shock.

CLEAR CODES AND CONFIRM "CLOSED LOOP" OPERATION AND NO "SERVICE ENGINE SOON" LIGHT.

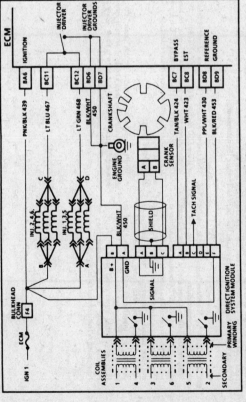

CHART C-4D-2
DIS MISFIRE UNDER LOAD
2.8L (VIN W) "L" CARLINE (PORT)

Circuit Description:

The direct ignition system (DIS) uses a waste spark method of distribution. For example, in this type of system, the ignition module triggers the #1/4 coil pair resulting in both #1 and #4 spark plugs firing at the same time. #1 cylinder is on the compression stroke at the same time #4 is on the exhaust stroke, resulting in a lower energy requirement to fire #4 spark plug. This leaves the remainder of the high voltage to be used to fire #1 spark plug. On this application, the crank sensor is mounted to the engine block and protrudes through the block to within approximately 050" of the crankshaft reluctor. Since the reluctor is a machined portion of the crankshaft and the crank sensor is mounted in a fixed position on the block, timing adjustments are not possible or necessary.

Test Description: Numbers below refer to circled numbers on the diagnostic chart.

1. If the "Misfire" complaint exists at idle only, the diagnostic chart on page 1 must be used. A spark tester such as a ST-125 must be used because it is essential to verify adequate available secondary voltage at the spark plug. (25,000 volts). Spark should jump the test gap on all 4 leads. This simulates a "load" condition.

2. If the spark jumps the tester gap after grounding the opposite plug wire, it indicates excessive resistance in the plug which was Bypassed. A faulty or poor connection at that plug could also result in the miss condition. Also, check for carbon deposits inside the spark plug boot.

3. If carbon tracing is evident replace coil and be sure plug wires relating to that coil are clean and tight. Excessive wire resistance or faulty connections could have caused the coil to be damaged.

4. If the no spark condition follows the suspected coil, that coil is faulty, otherwise, the ignition module is the cause of no spark. This test could also be performed by substituting a known good coil for the one causing the no spark condition.

1988-89 2.8L ENGINE

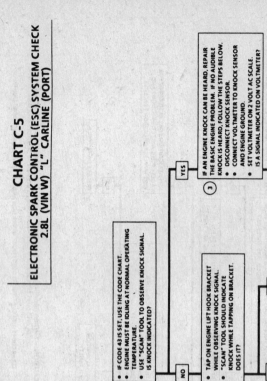

CHART C-5

ELECTRONIC SPARK CONTROL (ESC) SYSTEM CHECK
2.8L (VIN W) "L" CARLINE (PORT)

①
- IF CODE 43 IS SET, USE THE CODE CHART.
- ENGINE MUST BE IDLING AT NORMAL OPERATING TEMPERATURE.
- USE "SCAN" TOOL TO OBSERVE KNOCK SIGNAL.

IS KNOCK INDICATED?

NO →

② TAP ON ENGINE LIFT HOOK BRACKET WHILE OBSERVING KNOCK SIGNAL. "SCAN" TOOL SHOULD INDICATE KNOCK WHILE TAPPING ON BRACKET. DOES IT?

YES → SYSTEM IS OPERATING PROPERLY. REFER TO "DIAGNOSTIC AIDS" ON FACING PAGE.

NO →

④
- DISCONNECT KNOCK SENSOR.
- CONNECT VOLTMETER TO KNOCK SENSOR AND ENGINE GROUND.
- SET VOLTMETER ON 2 VOLT AC SCALE.
- TAP ON ENGINE BLOCK NEAR SENSOR.

IS A SIGNAL INDICATED ON VOLTMETER WHILE TAPPING ON ENGINE BLOCK?

- **YES →** REPLACE MEM-CAL OR ECM.
- **NO →** REPLACE KNOCK SENSOR.

YES → (from ①)

③ IF AN ENGINE KNOCK CAN BE HEARD, REPAIR THE BASIC ENGINE PROBLEM. IF NO AUDIBLE KNOCK IS HEARD, FOLLOW THE STEPS BELOW.
- DISCONNECT KNOCK SENSOR.
- CONNECT VOLTMETER TO KNOCK SENSOR AND ENGINE GROUND.
- SET VOLTMETER ON 2 VOLT AC SCALE.

IS A SIGNAL INDICATED ON VOLTMETER?

- **YES →** REPLACE KNOCK SENSOR.
- **NO →** REPLACE MEM-CAL OR ECM.

CLEAR CODES AND CONFIRM "CLOSED LOOP" OPERATION AND NO "SERVICE ENGINE SOON" LIGHT

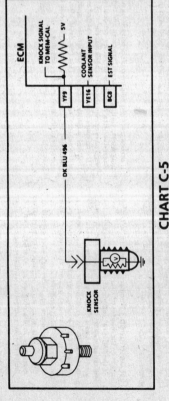

KNOCK SENSOR — DK BLU 496 — YF9 — KNOCK SIGNAL TO MEM-CAL — 5V — ECM
YE16 — COOLANT SENSOR INPUT
BC9 — EST SIGNAL

CHART C-5

ELECTRONIC SPARK CONTROL (ESC) SYSTEM CHECK
2.8L (VIN W) "L" CARLINE (PORT)

Circuit Description:
The knock sensor is used to detect engine detonation and the ECM will retard the electronic spark timing based on the signal being received. The circuitry within the knock sensor causes the ECM's 5 volts to be pulled down so that under a no knock condition, CKT 496 would measure about 2.5 volts. The knock sensor produces an A/C signal which rides on the 2.5 volts DC voltage. The amplitude and frequency are dependent upon the knock level.

The Mem-Cal used with this engine, contains the functions which were part of remotely mounted ESC modules used on other GM vehicles. The ESC portion of the Mem-Cal, then sends a signal to other parts of the ECM which adjusts the spark timing to retard the spark and reduce the detonation.

Test Description: Numbers below refer to circled numbers on the diagnostic chart.
1. With engine idling, there should not be a knock signal present at the ECM because detonation is not likely under a no load condition.
2. Tapping on the engine lift bracket should simulate a knock signal to determine if the sensor is capable of detecting detonation. If no knock is detected, try tapping on engine block closer to sensor before replacing sensor.
3. If the engine has an internal problem which is creating a knock, the knock sensor may be responding to the internal failure.
4. This test determines if the knock sensor is faulty or if the ESC portion of the Mem-Cal is faulty. If it is determined that the Mem-Cal is faulty, be sure that it is properly installed and latched into place. If not properly installed, repair and retest.

Diagnostic Aids:
While observing knock signal on the "Scan," there should be an indication that knock is present when detonation can be heard. Detonation is most likely to occur under high engine load conditions.

1988–89 2.8L ENGINE

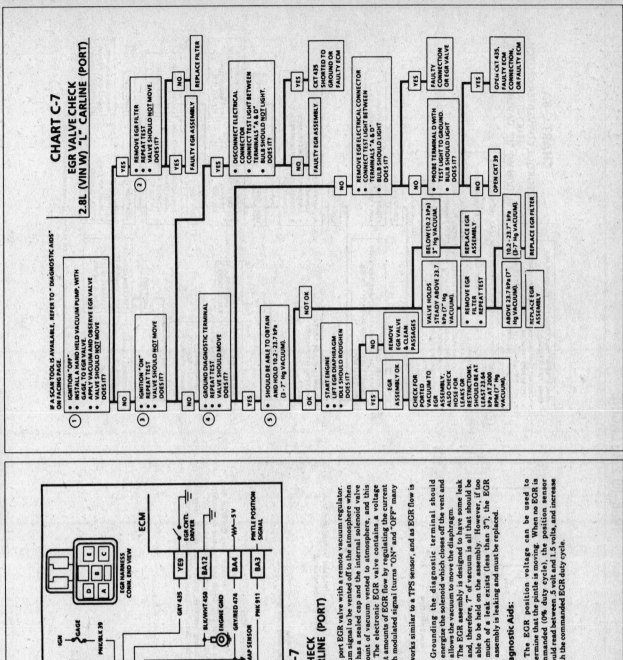

CHART C-7
EGR VALVE CHECK
2.8L (VIN W) "L" CARLINE (PORT)

IF A SCAN TOOL IS AVAILABLE, REFER TO "DIAGNOSTIC AIDS" ON FACING PAGE.

1
- IGNITION "OFF"
- INSTALL A HAND HELD VACUUM PUMP, WITH GAGE, TO EGR VALVE.
- APPLY VACUUM AND OBSERVE EGR VALVE.
- VALVE SHOULD **NOT** MOVE.
DOES IT?

2
- REMOVE EGR FILTER
- REPEAT TEST
- VALVE SHOULD **NOT** MOVE.
DOES IT?
- NO → REPLACE FILTER
- YES → FAULTY EGR ASSEMBLY

3
- IGNITION "ON"
- REPEAT TEST
- VALVE SHOULD **NOT** MOVE
DOES IT?

DISCONNECT ELECTRICAL CONNECTOR
- CONNECT TEST LIGHT BETWEEN TERMINALS "A" & "D"
- BULB SHOULD NOT LIGHT.
DOES IT?
- YES → CKT 435 SHORTED TO GROUND OR FAULTY ECM
- NO → FAULTY EGR ASSEMBLY

4
- GROUND DIAGNOSTIC TERMINAL
- REPEAT TEST
- VALVE SHOULD MOVE
DOES IT?

REMOVE EGR ELECTRICAL CONNECTOR
- CONNECT TEST LIGHT BETWEEN TERMINALS "A" & "D"
- BULB SHOULD LIGHT.
DOES IT?
- YES → FAULTY CONNECTION OR EGR VALVE
- NO → PROBE TERMINAL "D" WITH TEST LIGHT TO GROUND. BULB SHOULD LIGHT. DOES IT?
  - YES → OPEN CKT 435, FAULTY ECM CONNECTION, OR FAULTY ECM
  - NO → OPEN CKT 39

5
- SHOULD BE ABLE TO OBTAIN AND HOLD 10.2-23.7 kPa (3-7" Hg VACUUM).
- NOT OK / OK

- START ENGINE
- LIFT EGR DIAPHRAGM
- IDLE SHOULD ROUGHEN
DOES IT?
- YES → EGR ASSEMBLY OK
- NO → REMOVE EGR VALVE & CLEAN PASSAGES

CHECK FOR PORTED VACUUM TO EGR ASSEMBLY, ALSO CHECK HOSE FOR RESTRICTIONS. SHOULD BE AT LEAST 23.64 kPa AT 2000 RPM (7" Hg VACUUM).

VALVE HOLDS STEADY ABOVE 23.7 kPa (7" Hg VACUUM).
- BELOW (10.2 kPa) 3" Hg VACUUM. → REPLACE EGR ASSEMBLY
- ABOVE 23.7 kPa (7" Hg VACUUM). → REPLACE EGR ASSEMBLY
- REMOVE EGR FILTER
- REPEAT TEST
- 10.2 - 23.7 kPa (3-7" Hg VACUUM). → REPLACE EGR FILTER

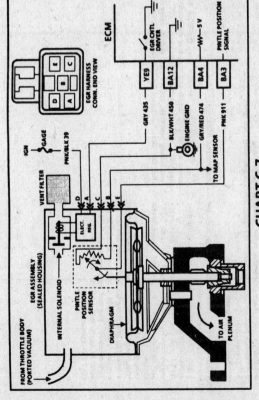

ECM

EGR CNTL DRIVER — 5V — PINTLE POSITION SIGNAL
YE9 — BA12 — BA4 — BA3
GRY 435 — BLK/WHT 450 — ENGINE GND — GRY/RED 474 — PNK 911 — TO MAP SENSOR

EGR HARNESS CONN. END VIEW

FROM THROTTLE BODY (PORTED VACUUM) — EGR ASSEMBLY (SEALED HOUSING) — VENT FILTER — ELECT. REG. — INTERNAL SOLENOID — PINTLE POSITION SENSOR — DIAPHRAGM — TO AIR PLENUM — GAGE — PNK/BLK 39

CHART C-7
EGR VALVE CHECK
2.8L (VIN W) "L" CARLINE (PORT)

Circuit Description:
The integrated electronic EGR valve functions similar to a port EGR valve with a remote vacuum regulator. The internal solenoid is normally open, which causes the vacuum signal to be vented off to the atmosphere when EGR is not being commanded by the ECM. This EGR valve has a sealed cap and the internal solenoid valve opens and closes the vacuum signal, which controls the amount of vacuum vented to atmosphere, and this controls the amount of vacuum applied to the diaphragm. The electronic EGR valve contains a voltage regulator, which converts the ECM signal, to provide different amounts of EGR flow by regulating the current to the solenoid. The ECM controls EGR flow with a pulse width modulated signal (turns "ON" and "OFF" many times a second) based on airflow, TPS, and rpm.
This system also contains a pintle position sensor, which works similar to a TPS sensor, and as EGR flow is increased, the sensor output also increases.

Test Description: Numbers below refer to circled numbers on the diagnostic chart.
1. Whenever the internal solenoid is de-energized, the solenoid valve should be open, which should not allow the vacuum to move the EGR diaphragm. However, if the filter is plugged, the vacuum applied with the hand held vacuum pump will cause the diaphragm to move because the vacuum will not be vented to the atmosphere.
2. This test will determine if the EGR filter is plugged or if the EGR itself is faulty. Use care, when removing the filter, to avoid damaging the EGR assembly.
3. If the valve moves in this test, it's probably due to CKT 435 being shorted to ground.
4. Grounding the diagnostic terminal should energize the solenoid which closes off the vent and allows the vacuum to move the diaphragm.
5. The EGR assembly is designed to have some leak and, therefore, 7" of vacuum is all that should be able to be held on the assembly. However, if too much of a leak exists (less than 3"), the EGR assembly is leaking and must be replaced.

Diagnostic Aids:
The EGR position voltage can be used to determine that the pintle is moving. When no EGR is commanded (0% duty cycle), the position sensor should read between .5 volt and 1.5 volts, and increase with the commanded EGR duty cycle.

1988–89 2.8L ENGINE

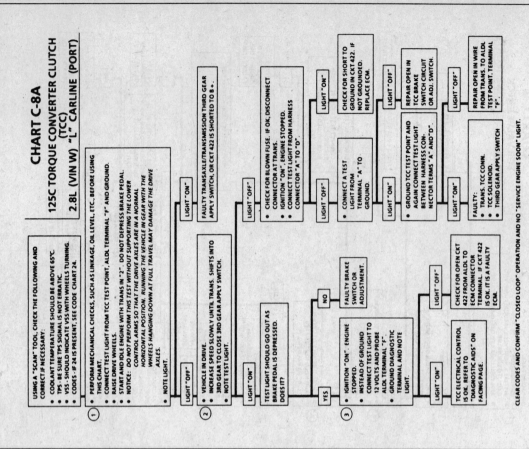

CHART C-8A

125C TORQUE CONVERTER CLUTCH (TCC)
2.8L (VIN W) "L" CARLINE (PORT)

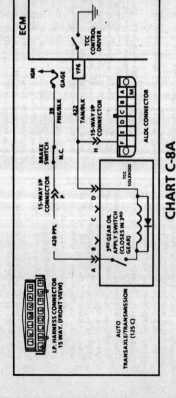

CHART C-8A

125C TORQUE CONVERTER CLUTCH (TCC)
2.8L (VIN W) "L" CARLINE (PORT)

Circuit Description:

The purpose of the torque converter clutch feature is to eliminate the power loss of the transmission converter stage when the vehicle is in a cruise condition. This allows the convenience of the automatic transmission and the fuel economy of a manual transmission.

Fused battery ignition is supplied to the TCC solenoid through the brake switch, and transmission third gear apply switch. The ECM will engage TCC by grounding CKT 422 to energize the solenoid. TCC will engage when:

- Engine warmed up
- Vehicle speed above a calibrated value. (about 32 mph 51 km/h)
- Throttle position sensor output not changing, indicating a steady road speed
- Transmission third gear switch closed
- Brake switch closed

Test Description: Numbers below refer to circled numbers on the diagnostic chart.

1. Light "OFF" confirms transmission third gear apply switch is open.

2. At 25 mph the transmission third gear apply switch should close. Test light will come "ON" and confirm battery supply and closed brake switch.

3. Grounding the diagnostic terminal with ignition "ON", engine "OFF", should energize the TCC solenoid by grounding CKT 422. This test checks the ability of the ECM to supply a ground to the TCC solenoid. The test light connected from 12 volts to ALDL terminal "F" will turn "ON" as CKT 422 is grounded.

Diagnostic Aids:

A "Scan" tool only indicates when the ECM has turned on the TCC driver and this does not confirm that the TCC has engaged. To determine if TCC is functioning properly, engine rpm should decrease when the "Scan" indicates the TCC driver has turned "ON."

USING A "SCAN" TOOL, CHECK THE FOLLOWING AND CORRECT IF NECESSARY:
- COOLANT TEMPERATURE SHOULD BE ABOVE 65°C.
- TPS - BE SURE TPS SIGNAL IS NOT ERRATIC.
- VSS - SHOULD INDICATE VSS WITH WHEELS TURNING.
- CODES - IF 24 IS PRESENT, SEE CODE CHART 24.

(1) PERFORM MECHANICAL CHECKS, SUCH AS LINKAGE, OIL LEVEL, ETC., BEFORE USING THIS CHART.
- CONNECT TEST LIGHT FROM TCC TEST POINT, ALDL TERMINAL "F" AND GROUND.
- RAISE DRIVE WHEELS.
- START AND IDLE ENGINE WITH TRANS IN "2". DO NOT DEPRESS BRAKE PEDAL.
- **NOTICE:** DO NOT PERFORM THIS TEST WITHOUT SUPPORTING THE LOWER CONTROL ARMS SO THAT THE DRIVE AXLES ARE IN A NORMAL HORIZONTAL POSITION. RUNNING THE VEHICLE IN GEAR WITH THE WHEELS HANGING DOWN AT FULL TRAVEL MAY DAMAGE THE DRIVE AXLES.
- NOTE LIGHT.

↓ LIGHT "OFF" → **(2)** VEHICLE IN DRIVE.
- INCREASE SPEED SLOWLY UNTIL TRANS. SHIFTS INTO 3RD GEAR TO CLOSE 3RD GEAR APPLY SWITCH.
- NOTE TEST LIGHT.

LIGHT "ON" → FAULTY TRANSAXLE/TRANSMISSION THIRD GEAR APPLY SWITCH, OR CKT 422 IS SHORTED TO B +.

LIGHT "OFF" → CHECK FOR BLOWN FUSE. IF OK, DISCONNECT CONNECTOR AT TRANS.
- IGNITION "ON", ENGINE STOPPED.
- CONNECT TEST LIGHT FROM HARNESS CONNECTOR "A" TO "D".

LIGHT "ON" → TEST LIGHT SHOULD GO OUT AS BRAKE PEDAL IS DEPRESSED. DOES IT?
- NO → FAULTY BRAKE SWITCH OR ADJUSTMENT.
- YES → **(3)** IGNITION "ON", ENGINE STOPPED.
  - INSTEAD OF GROUND CONNECT TEST LIGHT TO 12 VOLTS AND PROBE ALDL TERMINAL "F".
  - GROUND DIAGNOSTIC TERMINAL AND NOTE LIGHT.

LIGHT "OFF" → CONNECT A TEST LIGHT FROM TERMINAL "A" TO GROUND.

LIGHT "ON" → CHECK FOR SHORT TO GROUND IN CKT 422. IF NOT GROUNDED, REPLACE ECM.

LIGHT "OFF" → GROUND TCC TEST POINT AND AGAIN CONNECT TEST LIGHT BETWEEN HARNESS CONNECTOR TERMS "A" AND "D".

LIGHT "ON" → REPAIR OPEN IN TCC BRAKE SWITCH CIRCUIT OR ADJ. SWITCH.

LIGHT "OFF" → FAULTY:
- TRANS. TCC CONN.
- TCC SOLENOID.
- THIRD GEAR APPLY SWITCH

LIGHT "ON" → TCC ELECTRICAL CONTROL IS OK. REFER TO "DIAGNOSTIC AIDS" ON FACING PAGE.

LIGHT "OFF" → CHECK FOR OPEN CKT 422 FROM ALDL TO ECM CONNECTOR TERMINAL. IF CKT 422 IS OK, IT IS A FAULTY ECM.

REPAIR OPEN IN WIRE FROM TRANS. TO ALDL TEST POINT, TERMINAL "F".

CLEAR CODES AND CONFIRM "CLOSED LOOP" OPERATION AND NO "SERVICE ENGINE SOON" LIGHT.

1988–89 2.8L ENGINE

CHART C-8C
MANUAL TRANSMISSION (M/T) SHIFT LIGHT CHECK
2.8L (VIN W) "L" CARLINE (PORT)

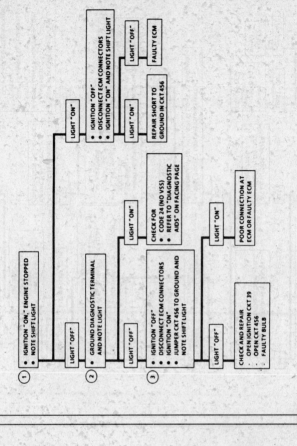

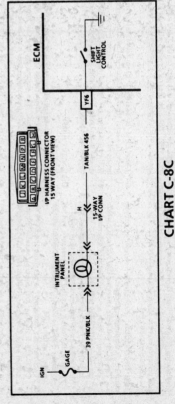

CHART C-8C
MANUAL TRANSMISSION (M/T) SHIFT LIGHT CHECK
2.8L (VIN W) "L" CARLINE (PORT)

Circuit Description:
The shift light indicates the best transmission shift point for maximum fuel economy. The light is controlled by the ECM and is turned "ON" by grounding CKT 456.
The ECM uses information from the following inputs to control the shift light:
- Coolant temperature must be above 16°C (61°F)
- TPS above 4%
- VSS
- RPM above about 1900
- Air Flow - The ECM uses rpm, airflow VSS to calculate what gear the vehicle is in.
It's this calculation that determines when the shift light should be turned "ON." The shift light will only stay "ON." 5 seconds after the conditions were met to turn it on.

Test Description: Numbers below refer to circled numbers on the diagnostic chart.
1. This should not turn "ON" the shift light. If the light is "ON," there is a short to ground in CKT 456 wiring or a fault in the ECM
2. When the diagnostic terminal is grounded, the ECM should ground CKT 456 and the shift light should come "ON."
3. This checks the shift light circuit up to the ECM connector. If the shift light illuminates, then the ECM connector is faulty or the ECM does not have the ability to ground the circuit.

1988–89 2.8L ENGINE

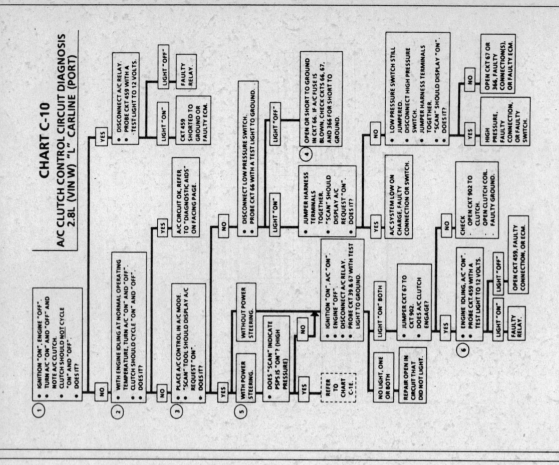

CHART C-10
A/C CLUTCH CONTROL CIRCUIT DIAGNOSIS 2.8L (VIN W) "L" CARLINE (PORT)

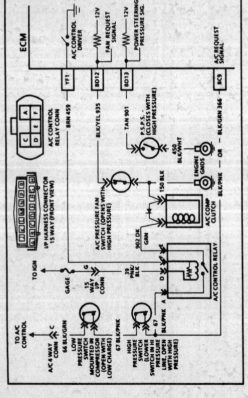

CHART C-10
A/C CLUTCH CONTROL CIRCUIT DIAGNOSIS 2.8L (VIN W) "L" CARLINE (PORT)

Circuit Description:

The A/C clutch control relay is ECM controlled to delay A/C clutch engagement about .4 second after A/C is turned "ON." This allows the IAC to adjust engine rpm before the A/C clutch engages. The ECM also causes the relay to disengage the A/C clutch during WOT when high power steering pressure is present, or if engine is overheating. The A/C clutch control relay is energized when the ECM provides a ground path for CKT 459. The low pressure switch will open if A/C pressure is less than 40 psi (276 kPa). The high pressure switch will open if A/C pressure exceeds about 440 psi (3034 kPa). The A/C pressure fan switch opens when A/C pressure exceeds about 200 psi (1380 kPa).

Test Description: Numbers below refer to circled numbers on the diagnostic chart.

1. The ECM will only energize the A/C relay when the engine is running. This test will determine if the relay or CKT 459 is faulty.

2. In order for the clutch to properly be engaged, the low pressure switch must be closed to provide 12 volts to the relay and the high pressure switch must be closed so the A/C request (12 volts) will be present at the ECM.

3. Determines if the signal is reaching the ECM on CKT 366 from the A/C control panel. Signal should only be present when the A/C mode or defrost mode has been selected.

4. A short to ground in any part of the A/C request circuit, CKT 67 to the relay, CKT 902 to the A/C clutch, or the A/C clutch, could be the cause of the blown fuse.

5. If the ECM is seeing a high power steering pressure signal the A/C clutch will be disengaged by the ECM.

6. With the engine idling and A/C "ON," the ECM should be grounding CKT 459, which should cause the test light to be "ON."

Diagnostic Aids:

If complaint was insufficient cooling, the problem may be caused by a inoperative cooling fan or A/C pressure fan switch. The engine cooling fan should turn "ON" when A/C pressure exceeds a value to open the switch which causes the ECM to energize the cooling fan relay. See CHART C-12 for cooling fan diagnosis.

1988–89 2.8L ENGINE

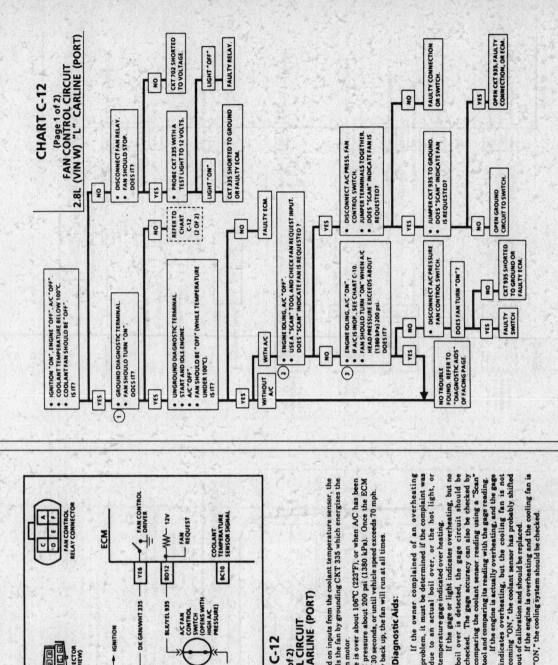

CHART C-12
(Page 1 of 2)
FAN CONTROL CIRCUIT
2.8L (VIN W) "L" CARLINE (PORT)

Flowchart boxes:

- IGNITION "ON", ENGINE "OFF", A/C "OFF". COOLANT TEMPERATURE BELOW 100°C. COOLANT FAN SHOULD BE "OFF". IS IT?
  - YES ①
  - NO
    - DISCONNECT FAN RELAY. FAN SHOULD STOP. DOES IT?
      - YES
        - PROBE CKT 335 WITH A TEST LIGHT TO 12 VOLTS.
          - LIGHT "ON" → CKT 335 SHORTED TO GROUND OR FAULTY ECM.
          - LIGHT "OFF" → FAULTY RELAY.
      - NO → CKT 702 SHORTED TO VOLTAGE.

① GROUND DIAGNOSTIC TERMINAL. FAN SHOULD TURN "ON". DOES IT?
  - YES
    - UNGROUND DIAGNOSTIC TERMINAL. FAN SHOULD BE "OFF" (WHILE TEMPERATURE UNDER 100°C). IS IT?
      - YES
        - WITH A/C
          - ② ENGINE IDLING, A/C "OFF". USE A "SCAN" TOOL AND CHECK FAN REQUEST INPUT. DOES "SCAN" INDICATE FAN IS REQUESTED?
            - NO
              - ③ ENGINE IDLING, A/C "ON". IF A/C IS INOP., SEE CHART C-10. FAN SHOULD TURN "ON" WHEN A/C HEAD PRESSURE EXCEEDS ABOUT (1380 kPa) 200 psi. DOES IT?
                - YES → DISCONNECT A/C PRESSURE FAN CONTROL SWITCH. DOES FAN TURN "ON"?
                  - YES → FAULTY SWITCH.
                  - NO → CKT 935 SHORTED TO GROUND OR FAULTY ECM.
                - NO → DISCONNECT A/C PRESSURE FAN CONTROL SWITCH. JUMPER TERMINALS TOGETHER. DOES "SCAN" INDICATE FAN IS REQUESTED?
                  - YES → JUMPER CKT 935 TO GROUND. DOES "SCAN" INDICATE FAN IS REQUESTED?
                    - YES → OPEN CKT 935, FAULTY CONNECTION, OR ECM.
                    - NO → OPEN GROUND CIRCUIT TO SWITCH.
                  - NO → FAULTY CONNECTION OR SWITCH.
            - YES → FAULTY ECM.
        - WITHOUT A/C → NO TROUBLE FOUND. REFER TO "DIAGNOSTIC AIDS" OF FACING PAGE.
      - NO → FAULTY ECM.
  - NO → REFER TO CHART C-12 (2 OF 2).

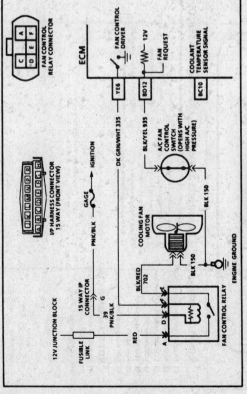

Wiring diagram labels:
- 12V JUNCTION BLOCK
- FUSIBLE LINK
- 15 WAY IP CONNECTOR
- I/P HARNESS CONNECTOR 15 WAY (FRONT VIEW)
- GAGE — IGNITION
- PNK/BLK
- 39 PNK/BLK
- RED
- FAN CONTROL RELAY
- FAN CONTROL RELAY CONNECTOR
- BLK/RED 702
- DK GRN/WHT 335
- COOLING FAN MOTOR
- BLK 150
- BLK 150
- ENGINE GROUND
- BLK/YEL 935
- A/C FAN CONTROL SWITCH (OPENS WITH HIGH A/C PRESSURE)
- ECM
- YE6 — FAN CONTROL DRIVER
- BD12 — 12V — FAN REQUEST
- BC10 — COOLANT TEMPERATURE SENSOR SIGNAL

CHART C-12
(Page 1 of 2)
FAN CONTROL CIRCUIT
2.8L (VIN W) "L" CARLINE (PORT)

Circuit Description:

The electric cooling fan is controlled by the ECM, based on inputs from the coolant temperature sensor, the A/C fan control switch and vehicle speed. The ECM controls the fan by grounding CKT 335 which energizes the fan control relay. Battery voltage is then supplied to the fan motor.

The ECM grounds CKT 335 when coolant temperature is over about 106°C (223°F), or when A/C has been requested and the fan control switch opens with high A/C pressure about 200 psi (1380 kPa). Once the ECM turns the relay "ON", it will keep it "ON" for a minimum of 30 seconds, or until vehicle speed exceeds 70 mph.

Also, if Code 14 or 15 sets or the ECM is in throttle body back up, the fan will run at all times.

Test Description: Numbers below refer to circled numbers on the diagnostic chart.

1. With the diagnostic terminal grounded, the cooling fan control driver will close, which should energize the fan control relay.

2. If the A/C fan control switch or circuit is open, the fan would run whenever A/C is requested.

3. With A/C clutch engaged, the A/C fan control switch should open when A/C high pressure exceeds about 200 psi (1380 kPa). This signal should cause the ECM to energize the fan control relay.

Diagnostic Aids:

If the owner complained of an overheating problem, it must be determined if the complaint was due to an actual boil over, or the hot light, or temperature gage indicated over heating.

If the gage or light indicates overheating, but no boil over is detected, the gage circuit should be checked. The gage accuracy can also be checked by comparing the coolant sensor reading with the gage reading using a "Scan" tool and comparing its reading with the gage reading.

If the engine is actually overheating, and the gage indicates overheating, but the cooling fan is not coming "ON," the coolant sensor has probably shifted out of calibration and should be replaced.

If the engine is overheating and the cooling fan is "ON," the cooling system should be checked.

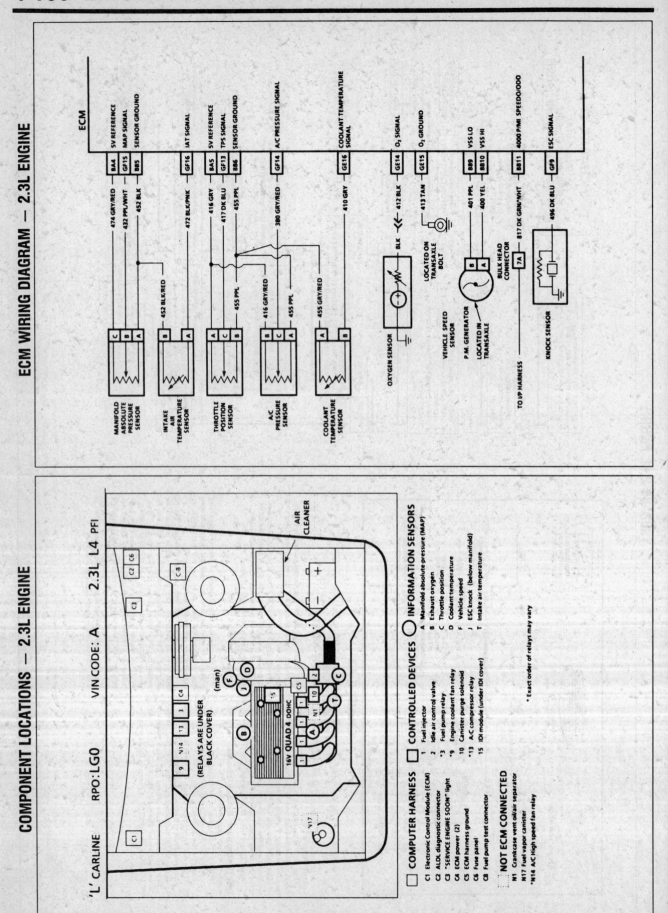

ECM WIRING DIAGRAM — 2.3L ENGINE

COMPONENT LOCATIONS — 2.3L ENGINE

'L' CARLINE   RPO: LG0   VIN CODE: A   2.3L L4 PFI

AIR CLEANER

16V QUAD 4 DOHC

(RELAYS ARE UNDER BLACK COVER)

COMPUTER HARNESS
- C1 Electronic Control Module (ECM)
- C2 ALDL diagnostic connector
- C3 "SERVICE ENGINE SOON" light
- C4 ECM power (2)
- C5 ECM harness ground
- C6 Fuse panel
- C8 Fuel pump test connector

NOT ECM CONNECTED
- N1 Crankcase vent oil/air separator
- N17 Fuel vapor canister
- *N14 A/C High speed fan relay

CONTROLLED DEVICES
- 1 Fuel injector
- 2 Idle air control valve
- *3 Fuel pump relay
- *9 Engine coolant fan relay
- 10 Canister purge solenoid
- *13 A/C compressor relay
- 15 IDI module (under IDI cover)

INFORMATION SENSORS
- A Manifold absolute pressure (MAP)
- B Exhaust oxygen
- C Throttle position
- D Coolant temperature
- F Vehicle speed
- J ESC knock (below manifold)
- T Intake air temperature

* Exact order of relays may vary

ECM WIRING DIAGRAM CONT. — 2.3L ENGINE

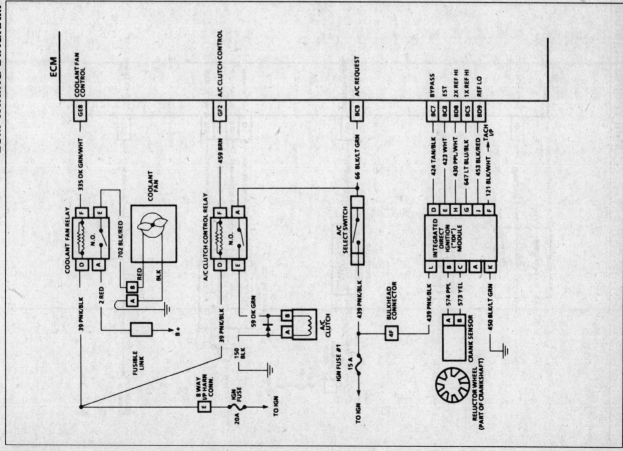

ECM WIRING DIAGRAM CONT. — 2.3L ENGINE

PORT FUEL INJECTION ECM CONNECTOR IDENTIFICATION

This ECM voltage chart is for use with a digital voltmeter to further aid in diagnosis. The voltages you get may vary due to low battery charge or other reasons, but they should be very close. The "B +" symbol indicates a nominal system voltage of 12-14 V.

THE FOLLOWING CONDITIONS MUST BE MET BEFORE TESTING:

- Engine at operating temperature (upper rad. hose hot) ● Engine idling in "Closed Loop" (For "Engine Run" column) in park or neutral ● Test terminal not grounded ● "SCAN" tool not installed

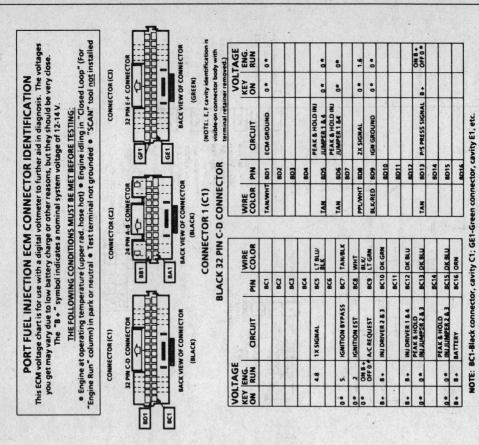

CONNECTOR (C1) — 32 PIN C-D CONNECTOR (BLACK) — BACK VIEW OF CONNECTOR

CONNECTOR (C2) — 24 PIN A-B CONNECTOR (BLACK) — BACK VIEW OF CONNECTOR

CONNECTOR (C3) — 32 PIN E-F CONNECTOR (GREEN) — BACK VIEW OF CONNECTOR

(NOTE: E, F cavity identification is visible on connector body with terminal retainer removed.)

CONNECTOR 1 (C1) — BLACK 32 PIN C-D CONNECTOR

VOLTAGE KEY ON	ENG. RUN	CIRCUIT	PIN	WIRE COLOR
			BC1	
			BC2	
			BC3	
			BC4	
0*	4.8	1 X SIGNAL	BC5	LT BLU/BLK
			BC6	
0*	5.	IGNITION BYPASS	BC7	TAN/BLK
0*	2	IGNITION EST	BC8	WHT
ON B+ OFF 0		A/C REQUEST	BC9	BLK/ LT GRN
B+		INJ DRIVER 2 & 3	BC10	DK GRN
			BC11	
B+		INJ DRIVER 1 & 4	BC12	DK BLU
B+	0*	PEAK & HOLD INJ JUMPER 2 & 3	BC13	DK BLU
			BC14	
0*	0*	PEAK & HOLD INJ JUMPER 2 & 3	BC15	DK BLU
B+		BATTERY	BC16	DK BLU

WIRE COLOR	PIN	CIRCUIT	VOLTAGE KEY ON	ENG. RUN
TAN/WHT	BD1	ECM GROUND	0*	0*
	BD2			
	BD3			
	BD4			
TAN	BD5	PEAK & HOLD INJ JUMPER 1 & 4	0*	0*
TAN	BD6	PEAK & HOLD INJ JUMPER 1 &4	0*	0*
	BD7			
PPL/WHT	BD8	2X SIGNAL	0*	1.6
BLK/RED	BD9	IGN GROUND	0*	0*
	BD10			
	BD11			
	BD12			
TAN	BD13	P/S PRESS SIGNAL	B+	ON B+ OFF 0*
	BD14			
	BD15			
	BD16			

NOTE: BC1-Black connector, cavity C1; GE1-Green connector, cavity E1, etc.

* Less than .5 volt.
1. Varies from .50 to battery voltage depending on position of drive wheels.
2. Varies.
3. 12V first two seconds.
4. Varies with temperature.
5. Non A/C cars 0* volt. A/C cars should not have a wire in term. "BC3".

ENGINE - 2.3L / LGO
CARLINE - "L" Series

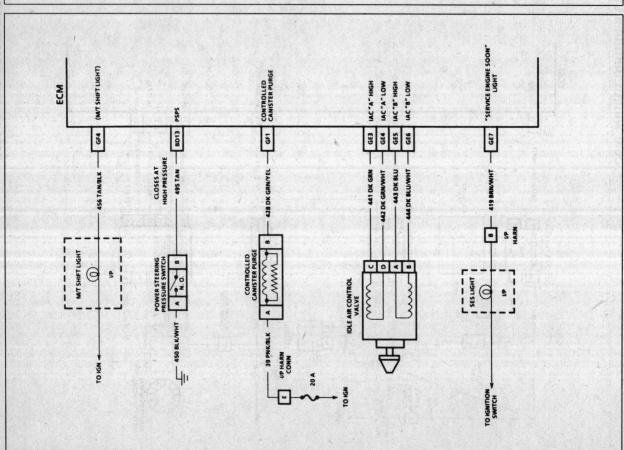

ECM

GF4 — (M/T SHIFT LIGHT) — 456 TAN/BLK — TO IGN — M/T SHIFT LIGHT — I/P

BD13 — PSPS — 495 TAN — CLOSES AT HIGH PRESSURE — POWER STEERING PRESSURE SWITCH — 450 BLK/WHT

GF1 — CONTROLLED CANISTER PURGE — 428 DK GRN/YEL — CONTROLLED CANISTER PURGE — 39 PNK/BLK — I/P HARN CONN — E — 20 A — TO IGN

GE3 — IAC "A" - HIGH — 441 DK GRN
GE4 — IAC "A" - LOW — 442 DK GRN/WHT
GE5 — IAC "B" - HIGH — 443 DK BLU
GE6 — IAC "B" - LOW — 446 DK BLU/WHT
IDLE AIR CONTROL VALVE

GE7 — "SERVICE ENGINE SOON" LIGHT — 419 BRN/WHT — I/P HARN — SES LIGHT — I/P — TO IGNITION SWITCH

DIAGNOSTIC CIRCUIT CHECK — 2.3L ENGINE

DIAGNOSTIC CIRCUIT CHECK

The Diagnostic Circuit Check is an organized approach to identifying a problem created by an electronic engine control system malfunction. It must be the starting point for any driveability complaint diagnosis, because it directs the service technician to the next logical step in diagnosing the complaint.

The Tech 1 data listed in the table may be used for comparison, after completing the diagnostic circuit check and finding the on-board diagnostics functioning properly and no trouble codes displayed. The "Typical Values" are an average of display values recorded from normally operating vehicles and are intended to represent what a normally functioning system would typically display.

A "SCAN" TOOL THAT DISPLAYS FAULTY DATA SHOULD NOT BE USED, AND THE PROBLEM SHOULD BE REPORTED TO THE MANUFACTURER. THE USE OF A FAULTY "SCAN" CAN RESULT IN MISDIAGNOSIS AND UNNECESSARY PARTS REPLACEMENT.

Only the parameters listed below are used in this manual for diagnosing. If a "Scan" reads other parameters, the values are not recommended by General Motors for use in diagnosing. For more description on the values and use of the "Scan" to diagnosis ECM inputs, refer to the applicable diagnosis section. If all values are within the range illustrated, refer to "Symptoms" Section.

TECH 1 DATA

Idle / Upper Radiator Hose Hot / Closed Throttle / Park or Neutral / "Closed Loop" / Acc. "OFF"

"SCAN" Position	Units Displayed	Typical Data Value
Engine Speed	RPM	± 100 RPM from desired RPM (± 50 in drive)
Desired Idle	RPM	ECM idle command (varies with calibration temp.)
Coolant Temp.	C° F°	85° – 115°C
IAT Temp.	C° F°	10° – 80°C (depends on underhood temp.)
MAP	kPa, V	1 – 3 Volts (depends on Vacuum & Baro pressure)
BARO	kPa, V	3 – 5 Volts (depends on altitude & Baro pressure)
Throttle Position	Volts	400 – 900 (up to 5.0 at wide open throttle)
Throttle Angle	0 – 100%	0% (up to 100% at wide open throttle)
Oxygen Sensor	mV	1 – 1000 and varying
Injector Pulse Width	m Sec.	1 – 4 and varying
Spark Advance	# of Degrees	Varies
Eng. Speed	RPM	Varies
Fuel Integrator	Counts	Varies
Block Learn	Counts	58 – 198
Open/Closed Loop	Open/Closed	Closed Loop (may go open with extended idle)
Block Learn Cell	Cell Number	18 to 21 at idle (depends on Air Flow, RPM, P/N & A/C)
Knock Retard	Degrees of Retard	0
Knock Signal	Yes/No	No
BYP Line Volts	LOW/HI	HI
EST Command	Yes/No	Yes
Idle Air Control	Counts (steps)	5 – 60
Park Neutral Switch	Park Neutral and RDL	P - N - (or - R-DL manual only)
VSS	MPH/KPH	0
Torque Conv. Cl (TCC)	On/Off	Off ("ON," with TCC commanded)
Battery Voltage	Volts	13.5 – 14.5
1X Ref Pulse	0 – 255 Counts	0 – 255 (Useable for Code 41)
2X Ref Pulse	Yes/No	Yes
A/C Request	Yes/No	No (yes, with A/C requested, ie: selector "ON")
A/C Clutch	On/Off	Off ("ON," with A/C commanded on)
A/C Clutch	On/Off	Off ("ON," with A/C commanded on)
A/C Pressure	psi/volts	0 – 450 psi (varying with high side pressure)
Power Steering	Normal/Hi Press.	Normal
Purge Duty Cycle	%	0 – 100%
Brake Switch (AT)	Yes/No	No or not avail.
Torque Conv Clutch	On/Off	Off
EGR 1 EGR 2	On/Off or N/A	Off
QDM A	LOW/HI	Low
QDM B	LOW/HI	Low
Fan LO Fan Hi	On/Off	Off ("ON," with A/C "ON" or hot eng)
2nd Gear	Yes/No	No (yes, when in 2nd or 3rd gear)
3rd Gear	Yes/No	No (yes, when in 3rd gear) or yes (Man. Trans. only)
PROM ID	#	Production ECM/PROM ID (not useable)
Time From Start	min/sec	Varies (engine run time since start)

DIAGNOSTIC CIRCUIT CHECK

CONNECTOR 2 (C-2) BLACK 24 PIN A-B CONNECTOR

VOLTAGE KEY ON	VOLTAGE ENG. RUN	CIRCUIT	PIN	WIRE COLOR
			BA1	
			BA2	
			BA3	
5.0	5.0	+5V REFERENCE	BA4	GRAY/RED
5.0	5.0	+5V REFERENCE	BA5	GRAY
B+	B+	IGNITION FEED	BA6	PNK/BLK
			BA7	
		SERIAL DATA/ALDL	BA9	ORN
			BA10	
0*	B+	FUEL PUMP	BA11	DK GRN
0*	0*	ECM GROUND	BA12	BLU/WHT

WIRE COLOR	PIN	CIRCUIT	VOLTAGE KEY ON	VOLTAGE ENG. RUN
ORN	BB1	BATTERY	B+	B+
	BB2			
	BB3			
	BB4			
BLK	BB5	IAT & MAP GND	0*	0*
PPL	BB6	A/C-CTS,TPS GND	0*	0*
	BB7			
	BB8			
PPL	BB9	MAG. VSS LOW	0*	0*
YEL	BB10	MAG. VSS HIGH	0*	0*
DK GRN/WHT	BB11	4000 P/MI SPEED	4.85	5.3

GREEN 32 PIN E-F CONNECTOR 3 (C-3)

VOLTAGE KEY ON	VOLTAGE ENG. RUN	CIRCUIT	PIN	WIRE COLOR
NOT USEABLE		IAC-A-HIGH	GE3	DK GRN
NOT USEABLE		IAC-A-LOW	GE4	DK GRN/WHT
NOT USEABLE		IAC-B-HIGH	GE5	DK BLU
NOT USEABLE		IAC-B-LOW	GE6	DK BLU/WHT
			GE7	BRN/WHT
5.0	5.0	ALDL/DIAG TERM	GE8	DK GRN/WHT
			GE9	
			GE10	
			GE11	
			GE12	WHT/BLK
			GE13	
ON 0* / OFF B+		SES LIGHT	GE14	BLK
0*	0*	O₂ SIGNAL	GE15	TAN
1.8	1.8	CLG FAN RLY	GE16	GRY

WIRE COLOR	PIN	CIRCUIT	VOLTAGE KEY ON	VOLTAGE ENG. RUN
GRN/YEL	GF1	CANISTER PURGE	B+	3
BRN	GF2	A/C CLUTCH RELAY	B+	OFF B+ / ON 0*
	GF3			
TAN/BLK	GF4	SHIFT LT	B+	OFF B+ / ON 0*
	GF5			
	GF6			
	GF7			
	GF8			
DK BLU	GF9	KNOCK SIGNAL	2.3	2.3
	GF10			
	GF11			
	GF12			
DK BLU	GF13	TPS SIGNAL	.54	.54
GRY/RED	GF14	A/C PRESS SIGNAL	1.0	1.0
PPL/WHT	GF15	MAP SIGNAL	4.7	1.4
BLK/PNK	GF16	IAT SIGNAL	2.33	1.5

Note: BA1 = Black Connector, cavity A1, etc. GE1 = Green Connector, cavity E1, etc.

ENGINE - 2.3L / LG0
CARLINE - "L" Series

* Less than .5 volt.
1. Varies from .60 to battery voltage depending on position of drive wheels.
2. Varies.
3. B+ first two seconds.

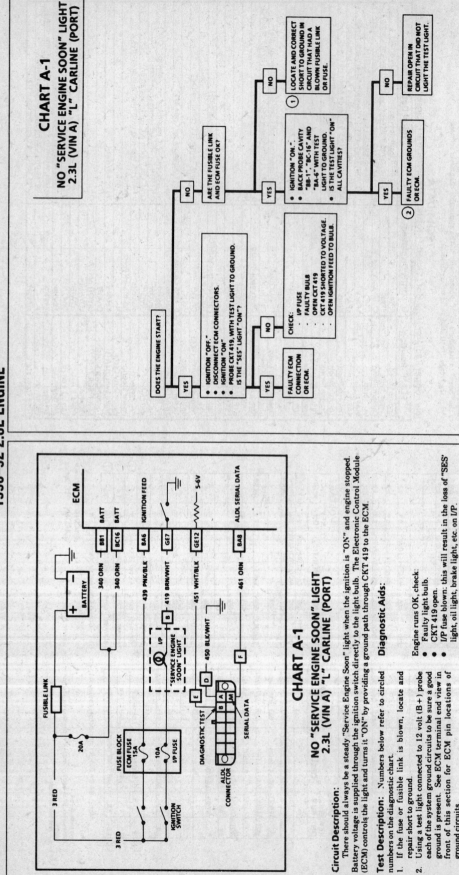

CHART A-1

NO "SERVICE ENGINE SOON" LIGHT 2.3L (VIN A) "L" CARLINE (PORT)

Circuit Description:

There should always be a steady "Service Engine Soon" light when the ignition is "ON" and engine stopped. Battery voltage is supplied through the ignition switch directly to the light bulb. The Electronic Control Module (ECM) controls the light and turns it "ON" by providing a ground path through CKT 419 to the ECM.

Test Description: Numbers below refer to circled numbers on the diagnostic chart.

1. If the fuse or fusible link is blown, locate and repair short to ground.
2. Using a test light connected to 12 volt (B+) probe each of the system ground circuits to be sure a good ground is present. See ECM terminal end view in front of this section for ECM pin locations of ground circuits.

Diagnostic Aids:

Engine runs OK, check:
- Faulty light bulb.
- CKT 419 open.
- I/P fuse blown: this will result in the loss of "SES" light, oil light, brake light, etc. on I/P.

Engine cranks but will not run.
- Continuous battery - fuse or fusible link open.
- ECM ignition fuse open.
- Battery CKT 340 to ECM open.
- Ignition CKT 439 to ECM open.
- Poor connection to ECM.
- Poor ECM ground.

"AFTER REPAIRS," CONFIRM "CLOSED LOOP" OPERATION AND NO "SERVICE ENGINE SOON" LIGHT.

1990-92 2.3L ENGINE

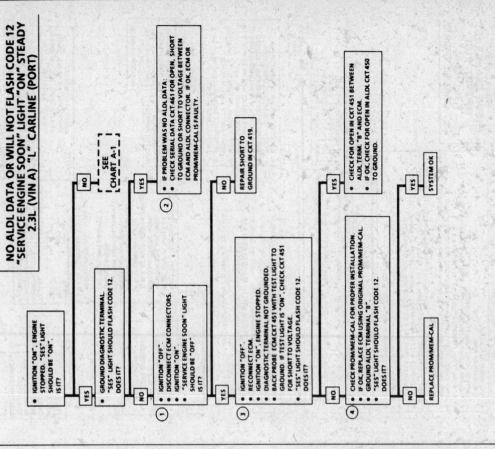

CHART A-2

**NO ALDL DATA OR WILL NOT FLASH CODE 12
"SERVICE ENGINE SOON" LIGHT "ON" STEADY
2.3L (VIN A) "L" CARLINE (PORT)**

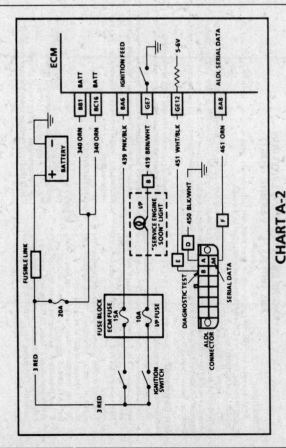

CHART A-2

**NO ALDL DATA OR WILL NOT FLASH CODE 12
"SERVICE ENGINE SOON" LIGHT "ON" STEADY
2.3L (VIN A) "L" CARLINE (PORT)**

Circuit Description:

There should always be a steady "Service Engine Soon" light when the ignition is "ON" and engine stopped. Battery ignition voltage is supplied to the light bulb. The Electronic Control Module (ECM) turns the light "ON" by grounding CKT 419 at the ECM.

With the diagnostic terminal grounded, the light should flash a Code 12, followed by any trouble code(s) stored in memory.

A steady light suggests a short to ground in the light control CKT 419, or an open in diagnostic CKT 451.

Test Description: Numbers below refer to circled numbers on the diagnostic chart.

1. Light "OFF" with CKT 419 disconnected from ECM indicates that ground circuit was completed through the ECM, not through external short to ground.

2. If there is a problem with the ECM that causes a Tech 1 "Scan" tool to not read serial data, the ECM should not flash a Code 12. If Code 12 is flashing, check for CKT 451 short to ground. If Code 12 does flash, be sure that the "Scan" tool is functioning properly, check CKT 461 for open or short to ground or voltage. If CKT 461 is OK, the ECM or MEM-CAL may be the fault for the "NO ALDL" symptom.

3. This step will check for an open diagnostic CKT 451.

4. At this point, the "Service Engine Soon" light wiring is OK. The problem is a faulty ECM or MEM-CAL. If Code 12 does not flash, the ECM should be replaced using the original MEM-CAL. Replace the MEM-CAL only after trying an ECM as a defective MEM-CAL is an unlikely cause the problem.

CHART A-3
(Page 1 of 3)
ENGINE CRANKS BUT WILL NOT RUN
2.3L (VIN A)
"L" CARLINE (PORT)

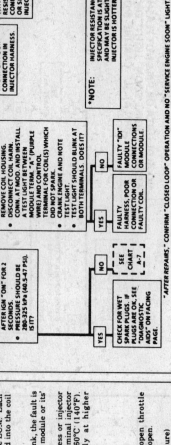

NOTICE: FUEL SYSTEM IS UNDER PRESSURE. TO AVOID FUEL SPILLAGE, REFER TO FIELD SERVICE PROCEDURES FOR TESTING OR REPAIRS REQUIRING DISASSEMBLY OF FUEL LINES OR FITTINGS

(1)
- FUEL PUMP/INJ FUSE OK.
- FUEL QUANTITY OK.
- IGNITION "ON." THROTTLE CLOSED.
- "SERVICE ENGINE SOON LIGHT" SHOULD BE "ON." (IF NOT SEE CHART A-1).
- IF "SCAN" TOOL INDICATES "NO ALDL," SEE CHART A-2.
- TPS SHOULD "SCAN" LESS THAN 2.5V. (IF NOT SEE CODE 21 CHART)
- COOLANT TEMP. "SCAN" BETWEEN -30°C & 130°C. (IF NOT SEE CODE 14 OR 15 CHART.
- "SCAN" 2X REFERENCE PULSES OR CRANK RPM WHILE CRANKING ENGINE. (IF "NO" 2X REFERENCE PULSES OR RPM IS "0", BEGIN AT STEP #11 ON PAGE 3)
- DISCONNECT 3 TERM. INJ HARNESS CONNECTOR AND CONNECT TEST LIGHT BETWEEN CAVITIES "A" AND "B" ON ECM SIDE OF HARNESS.
- CRANK ENGINE AND OBSERVE TEST LIGHT. (SHOULD BLINK).
- PERFORM TEST AGAIN WITH TEST LIGHT BETWEEN CAVITIES "A" AND "C".
- LIGHT SHOULD BLINK ON BOTH TESTS. DOES IT?

(2)
- WITH DVM ON 200 OHM SCALE, MEASURE RESISTANCE BETWEEN CAVITIES "A" AND "B" ON INJECTOR SIDE OF 3 TERMINAL INJECTOR HARNESS CONNECTOR.
- "PERFORM MEASUREMENT AGAIN BETWEEN CAVITIES "A" AND "C."
- RESISTANCE MEASUREMENT SHOULD BE BETWEEN ABOUT .9 TO 1.1 OHM* ON EACH TEST. IS IT?

(3)
- TEMPORARILY REMOVE "DI" ASSEMBLY AND INSTALL SPARK PLUG JUMPER WIRES (J 36012).
- REMOVE TEST LIGHT FROM INJ HARNESS.
- CHECK FOR SPARK WITH SPARK TESTER J 26792, (ST-125) OR EQUIV. ON 2 ADJACENT PLUG WIRES (1&2 OR 3&4 NOT 2 & 3) WHILE CRANKING WITH REMAINING PLUG WIRES STILL CONNECTED.
- SPARK SHOULD JUMP TESTER GAP ON BOTH WIRES. DOES IT?

(4)
- INSTALL FUEL PRESS. GAGE AND NOTE PRESS. AFTER IGN "ON" FOR 2 SECONDS.
- PRESSURE SHOULD BE 280-325 kPa (40.5-47 PSI). IS IT?

(5)
- IGN "OFF." DISCONNECT PLUG JUMPER WIRES AND REMOVE COIL HOUSING. DISCONNECT COIL HARN.
- CRANK AT MOD. AND INSTALL A TEST LIGHT BETWEEN MODULE TERM. "A" (PURPLE WIRE) AND CONTROL TERMINAL FOR COIL(S) WHICH DID NOT SPARK.
- CRANK ENGINE AND NOTE TEST LIGHT.
- TEST LIGHT SHOULD BLINK AT BOTH TERMINALS. DOES IT?

(6)
- REMOVE CV OIL/AIR SEPARATOR FOR ACCESS TO INJECTOR CONNECTORS
- DISCONNECT INJECTORS ON CIRCUIT(S) WITH INCORRECT RESISTANCE (CAVITY "B" - INJECTORS #1 AND #4, CAVITY "C" - INJECTORS #2 AND #3).
- WITH DVM ON 200 OHM SCALE, MEASURE RESISTANCE OF EACH INJECTOR. RESISTANCE SHOULD BE ABOUT 1.9 TO 2.1 OHMS* IS IT?

SEE CHART A-3, PAGE 2

NOTE WHETHER THERE WAS "NO LIGHT ON BOTH," "STEADY LIGHT ON ONE OR "STEADY LIGHT ON ONE OR BOTH" AND REFER TO CHART A-3, PAGE 2.

NO → REPLACE INJECTOR WITH INCORRECT RESISTANCE AND CONFIRM NO OPEN OR OHM IN INJECTOR HARNESS.

YES → REPAIR OPEN, SHORT OR POOR CONNECTION IN INJECTOR HARNESS.

NO → FAULTY "IDI" MODULE CONNECTIONS OR MODULE.

YES → FAULTY HARNESS, POOR CONNECTION OR FAULTY COIL.

SEE CHART A-7

YES → CHECK FOR WET SPARK PLUGS. IF PLUGS ARE OK, SEE "DIAGNOSTIC AIDS" ON FACING PAGE.

*AFTER REPAIRS," CONFIRM "CLOSED LOOP" OPERATION AND NO "SERVICE ENGINE SOON" LIGHT.

***NOTE:** INJECTOR RESISTANCE IS AT 60°C (140°F) AND MAY BE SLIGHTLY HIGHER IF INJECTOR IS HOTTER.

1990-92 2.3L ENGINE

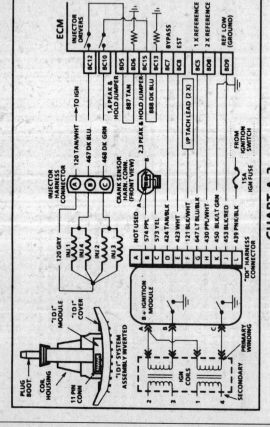

ECM — INJECTOR DRIVERS — BYPASS — EST — 1 X REFERENCE — 2 X REFERENCE — REF LOW (GROUND)

BC12 / BC10 / BD5 / BD6 / BC15 / BC13 / BC7 / BC5 / BD8 / BD9

CHART A-3
(Page 1 of 3)
ENGINE CRANKS BUT WILL NOT RUN
2.3L (VIN A) "L" CARLINE (PORT)

Condition:
Engine cranks but will not run, or engine may start, but immediately stops running. Battery condition and engine cranking speed are OK and there is adequate fuel in the tank.

Circuit Description:
This engine is equipped with a distributorless ignition system called the Integrated Direct Ignition (IDI) system. The primary circuit of the IDI consists of two separate ignition coils, an IDI module and crankshaft sensor as well as the related connecting wires and the Electronic Spark Timing (EST) portion of the ECM. Each secondary circuit consists of the secondary winding of the coil, two connecting metal strips molded into the coil housing, the spark plug boot/connector assemblies and spark plugs.

Test Description:
Numbers below refer to circled numbers on the diagnostic chart.

1. This step verifies that "SES" light operation, on-board diagnostics, cranking rpm, TPS and coolant sensor signals are normal. A blinking test light verifies that the ECM is receiving the IDI reference signal and is attempting to activate the injectors.

2. This step checks injector harness and injectors for opens or shorts. Resistance should measure half that of one injector due to parallel circuit.

3. By installing spark plug jumper leads and testing for spark on two adjacent plug leads (do not use 2 & 3 as they are on same coil), each ignition coil's ability to produce at least 25,000 volts is verified.

4. Checks to see if fuel pump and relay are operating correctly (fuel pump only "ON" 2-3 seconds) and fuel pressure is within proper range.

5. If module can make the test light blink, the fault is coil harness or connections. If not, module or its' connections are faulty.

6. This step determines whether harness or injector resistance is cause of incorrect resistance. Nominal injector resistance is 1.9 to 2.1 ohms at 60°C (140°F). Resistance will increase slightly at higher temperatures.

Diagnostic Aids:
Check For:
- TPS binding or sticking in wide open throttle position or intermittently shorted or open.
- Water or foreign material in fuel.
- Low Compression. (Timing chain failure)
- Verify that only resistor spark plugs are used.

CHART A-3

(Page 2 of 3)

ENGINE CRANKS BUT WILL NOT RUN
2.3L (VIN A) "L" CARLINE (PORT)

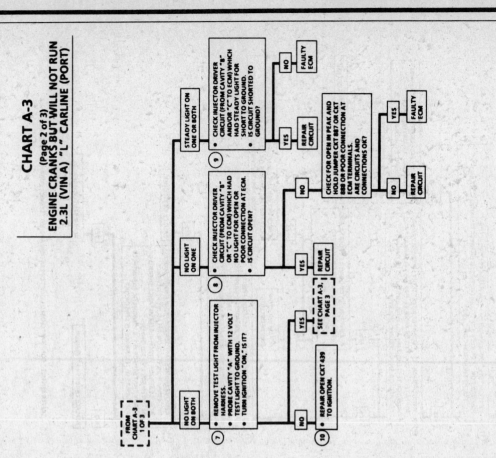

1990-92 2.3L ENGINE

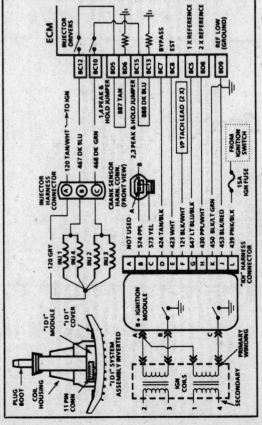

CHART A-3

(Page 2 of 3)

ENGINE CRANKS BUT WILL NOT RUN
2.3L (VIN A) "L" CARLINE (PORT)

Condition:

Engine cranks but will not run, or engine may start, but immediately stops running. Battery condition and engine cranking speed are OK and there is adequate fuel in the tank.

Circuit Description:

This engine is equipped with a distributorless ignition system called the Integrated Direct Ignition (IDI) system. The primary circuit of the IDI consists of two separate ignition coils, an IDI ignition module and crankshaft sensor as well as the related connecting wires and the Electronic Spark Timing (EST) portion of the ECM. Each secondary circuit consists of the secondary winding of the coil, two connecting metal strips molded into the coil housing, the spark plug boot/connector assemblies and spark plugs.

Test Description: Numbers below refer to circled numbers on the diagnostic chart.

7. Battery voltage should be available at cavity "A" whenever the fuel pump power feed circuit is switched "ON." The ECM should switch the fuel pump "ON" for 2-3 seconds after ignition is turned "ON" (and when ECM is receiving ignition reference pulses, as while cranking or running). The ignition must be turned "OFF" for at least 10 seconds to assure that the ECM powers down and will then switch the fuel pump back "ON" for 2-3 seconds when ignition is turned back "ON."

8. Light "ON" one circuit only indicates power is available at cavity "A", but grounded circuit is not being completed on the other circuit. This could be due to open circuit or ECM not switching the injector driver circuit to ground.

9. Steady light indicates ground circuit is always completed and is not being switched. This could be due to short to ground in circuit, or faulty ECM injector driver.

10. CKT 439 should have power whenever ignition is "ON."

1990–92 2.3L ENGINE

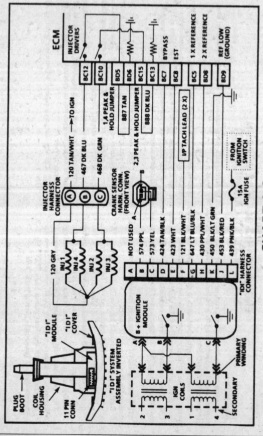

CHART A-3
(Page 3 of 3)
ENGINE CRANKS BUT WILL NOT RUN
2.3L (VIN A) "L" CARLINE (PORT)

Circuit Description:

The Integrated Direct Ignition (IDI) system uses a waste spark method of distribution. In this type of system the ignition module triggers the #1-4 coil pair resulting in both #1 and #4 spark plugs firing at the same time. #1 cylinder is on the compression stroke at the same time #4 is on the exhaust stroke, resulting in a lower energy requirement to fire # 4 spark plug. This leaves the remainder of the high voltage to be used to fire #1 spark plug. On this application, the crank sensor is mounted to, and protrudes through the block to within approximately 0.050" of the crankshaft reluctor. Since the reluctor is a machined portion of the crankshaft and the sensor is mounted in a fixed position on the block, timing adjustments are not possible or necessary.

Test Description: Numbers below refer to circled numbers on the diagnostic chart.

11. Battery voltage should be available at terminal "L" of the IDI 11 pin connector, and terminal "K" should be a good ground.

12. The test light to I2 volts simulates a reference signal to the ECM which will result in an injector test light blink for every other touch of the test light, if CKT 430, the ECM and the injector driver circuit are all functioning properly.

13. The crankshaft sensor should output a voltage as the crankshaft turns. If no voltage is produced, the indication is a poor sensor connection or faulty sensor.

14. The crank sensors core is a magnet, therefore, it should be magnetized and the resistance should be within a range of 500 to 900 ohms.

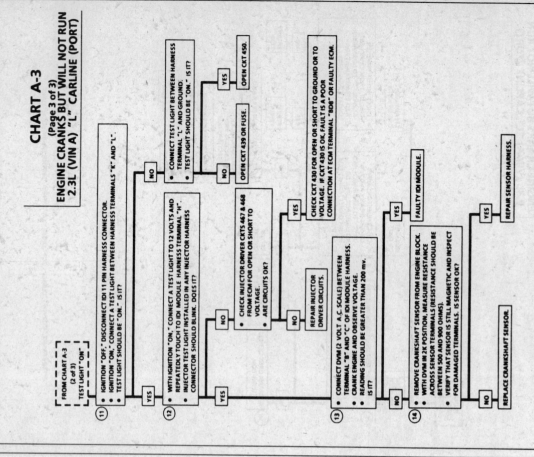

CHART A-3
(Page 3 of 3)
ENGINE CRANKS BUT WILL NOT RUN
2.3L (VIN A) "L" CARLINE (PORT)

FROM CHART A-3 (2 of 3)
TEST LIGHT "ON"

11.
- IGNITION "OFF." DISCONNECT IDI 11 PIN HARNESS CONNECTOR.
- IGNITION "ON." CONNECT A TEST LIGHT BETWEEN HARNESS TERMINALS "K" AND "L".
- TEST LIGHT SHOULD BE "ON." IS IT?

→ NO →
- CONNECT TEST LIGHT BETWEEN HARNESS TERMINAL "L" AND GROUND.
- TEST LIGHT SHOULD BE "ON." IS IT?

→ YES → OPEN CKT 450.

→ NO → OPEN CKT 439 OR FUSE.

(YES ↓)

12.
- WITH IGNITION "ON," CONNECT A TEST LIGHT TO 12 VOLTS AND REPEATEDLY TOUCH TO IDI MODULE HARNESS TERMINAL "H".
- INJECTOR TEST LIGHT INSTALLED IN ANY INJECTOR HARNESS CONNECTOR SHOULD BLINK. DOES IT?

→ NO →
- CHECK INJECTOR DRIVER CKTS 467 & 468 FROM ECM FOR OPEN OR SHORT TO VOLTAGE.
- ARE CIRCUITS OK?

→ YES → CHECK CKT 430 FOR OPEN OR SHORT TO GROUND OR TO VOLTAGE. IF CKT 430 IS OK, FAULT IS A POOR CONNECTION AT ECM TERMINAL "BD9" OR FAULTY ECM.

→ NO → REPAIR INJECTOR DRIVER CIRCUITS.

(YES ↓)

13.
- CONNECT DVM (2 VOLT A.C. SCALE) BETWEEN TERMINAL "B" AND "C" OF IDM MODULE HARNESS.
- CRANK ENGINE AND OBSERVE VOLTAGE.
- READING SHOULD BE GREATER THAN 200 mv. IS IT?

→ YES → FAULTY IDM MODULE.

(NO ↓)

14.
- REMOVE CRANKSHAFT SENSOR FROM ENGINE BLOCK.
- WITH DVM IN 2K POSITION, MEASURE RESISTANCE ACROSS SENSOR TERMINALS (RESISTANCE SHOULD BE BETWEEN 500 AND 900 OHMS).
- VERIFY THAT SENSOR IS STILL MAGNETIC AND INSPECT FOR DAMAGED TERMINALS. IS SENSOR OK?

→ YES → REPAIR SENSOR HARNESS.

→ NO → REPLACE CRANKSHAFT SENSOR.

*"AFTER REPAIRS," CONFIRM "CLOSED LOOP" OPERATION AND NO "SERVICE ENGINE SOON" LIGHT.

1990–92 2.3L ENGINE

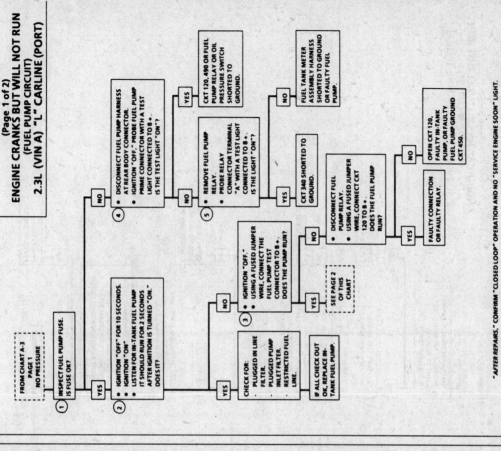

CHART A-5
(Page 1 of 2)
ENGINE CRANKS BUT WILL NOT RUN
(FUEL PUMP CIRCUIT)
2.3L (VIN A) "L" CARLINE (PORT)

FROM CHART A-3
PAGE 1
NO PRESSURE

1 INSPECT FUEL PUMP FUSE.
IS FUSE OK?

2 • IGNITION "OFF" FOR 10 SECONDS.
• IGNITION "ON"
• LISTEN FOR IN-TANK FUEL PUMP
IT SHOULD RUN FOR 2 SECONDS
AFTER IGNITION IS TURNED "ON."
DOES IT?

CHECK FOR:
- PLUGGED IN LINE
FILTER.
- PLUGGED PUMP
INLET FILTER.
- RESTRICTED FUEL
LINE.

IF ALL CHECK OUT
OK, REPLACE IN-
TANK FUEL PUMP.

3 IGNITION "OFF."
USING A FUSED JUMPER
WIRE, CONNECT THE
FUEL PUMP TEST
CONNECTOR TO B+.
DOES THE PUMP RUN?

SEE PAGE 2
OF THIS
CHART

4 • DISCONNECT FUEL PUMP HARNESS
AT REAR BODY CONNECTOR.
• IGNITION "OFF." PROBE FUEL PUMP
PRIME CONNECTOR WITH A TEST
LIGHT CONNECTED TO B+.
IS THE TEST LIGHT "ON"?

5 • REMOVE FUEL PUMP
RELAY.
• PROBE FUEL PUMP
CONNECTOR TERMINAL
"A" WITH A TEST LIGHT
CONNECTED TO B+.
IS THE TEST LIGHT "ON"?

CKT 340 SHORTED TO
GROUND.

CKT 120, 490 OR FUEL
PUMP RELAY OR OIL
PRESSURE SWITCH
SHORTED TO
GROUND.

FUEL TANK METER
ASSEMBLY HARNESS
SHORTED TO GROUND
OR FAULTY FUEL
PUMP.

• DISCONNECT FUEL
PUMP RELAY.
• USING A FUSED JUMPER
WIRE, CONNECT CKT
120 TO B+.
DOES THE FUEL PUMP
RUN?

FAULTY CONNECTION
OR FAULTY RELAY.

OPEN CKT 120,
FAULTY IN-TANK
PUMP, OR FAULTY
FUEL PUMP GROUND
CKT 450.

*AFTER REPAIRS," CONFIRM "CLOSED LOOP" OPERATION AND NO "SERVICE ENGINE SOON" LIGHT.

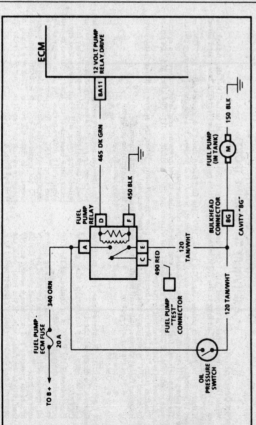

ECM

12 VOLT PUMP
RELAY DRIVE

BA11

465 DK GRN

450 BLK

FUEL PUMP
(IN TANK)

M 150 BLK

FUEL PUMP
RELAY

A D F
B C E

490 RED

FUEL PUMP
"TEST"
CONNECTOR

340 ORN

FUEL PUMP
ECM FUSE
20 A

TO B+

OIL
PRESSURE
SWITCH

120 TAN/WHT

BULKHEAD
CONNECTOR
"8G"

CAVITY "8G"

CHART A-5 (Page 1 of 2)
ENGINE CRANKS BUT WILL NOT RUN
(FUEL PUMP CIRCUIT)
2.3L (VIN A) "L" CARLINE (PORT)

Circuit Description:

When the ignition switch is turned "ON," the Electronic Control Module (ECM) turns "ON" the in-tank fuel pump. It will remain "ON" as long as the ECM is receiving ignition reference pulses from the Integrated Direct Ignition (IDI) module.

If there are no reference pulses, the ECM turns "OFF" the fuel pump about 2-3 seconds after key "ON," or about 10 seconds after reference pulses stop. If sufficient oil pressure is present to close the oil pressure switch, the fuel pump will remain "ON" during cranking without reference pulses.

The pump delivers fuel to the fuel rail and injectors, then to the pressure regulator, where the system pressure is controlled to 280 - 325 kPa (40.5 - 47 psi) with no manifold vacuum or 211 - 304 kPa (30.5 - 44 psi) at idle. Excess fuel is returned to the fuel tank.

The fuel pump "test" terminal is located in the engine compartment. When the engine is stopped, the pump can be turned "ON" by applying battery voltage to the test terminal.

Improper fuel system pressure will result in one or all of the following symptoms:
• Cranks but will not run.
• Cuts out, may feel like ignition problem.
• Poor fuel economy, loss of power.
• Code 44
• Code 45
• Hesitation.

Test Description: Numbers below refer to circled numbers on the diagnostic chart.

1. If the fuse is blown, a short to ground in CKTs 120, 340 or the fuel pump itself is the cause.

2. This step determines if the fuel pump circuit is being controlled by the ECM. The ECM should energize the fuel pump relay and turn the fuel pump "ON." If the engine is not cranking or running, the ECM should de-energize the relay and/or fuel pump within 2 seconds after the ignition is turned "ON."

3. Applying B+ to the pump test connector turns "ON" the fuel pump. This validates CKT 120 wiring, relay contacts and fuel pump.

4. This test will determine if a short to ground on CKT 120 caused the fuse to blow. To prevent a mis-diagnosis, be sure the fuel pump is disconnected before the test.

5. Checks for a short to ground in the fuel pump relay harness CKT 340.

CHART A-5
(Page 2 of 2)
ENGINE CRANKS BUT WILL NOT RUN
(FUEL PUMP CIRCUIT)
2.3L (VIN A) "L" CARLINE (PORT)

1990–92 2.3L ENGINE

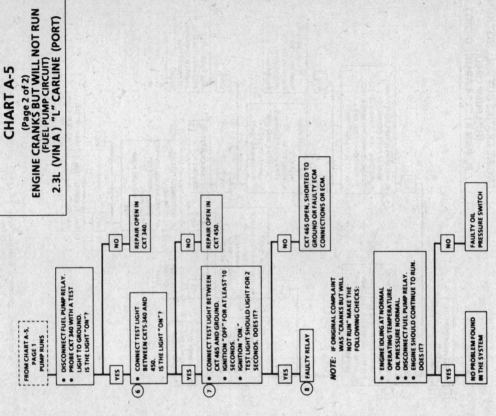

FROM CHART A-5, PAGE 1 PUMP RUNS

- DISCONNECT FUEL PUMP RELAY.
- PROBE CKT 340 WITH A TEST LIGHT TO GROUND.
- IS THE LIGHT "ON"?

YES → (6)

NO → REPAIR OPEN IN CKT 340.

(6)
- CONNECT TEST LIGHT BETWEEN CKTS 340 AND 450.
- IS THE LIGHT "ON"?

YES → (7)

NO → REPAIR OPEN IN CKT 450.

(7)
- CONNECT TEST LIGHT BETWEEN CKT 465 AND GROUND.
- IGNITION "OFF" FOR AT LEAST 10 SECONDS.
- IGNITION "ON."
- TEST LIGHT SHOULD LIGHT FOR 2 SECONDS. DOES IT?

YES → (8) FAULTY RELAY

NO → CKT 465 OPEN, SHORTED TO GROUND OR FAULTY ECM CONNECTIONS OR ECM.

NOTE: IF ORIGINAL COMPLAINT WAS "CRANKS BUT WILL NOT RUN" MAKE THE FOLLOWING CHECKS:

- ENGINE IDLING AT NORMAL OPERATING TEMPERATURE.
- OIL PRESSURE NORMAL.
- DISCONNECT FUEL PUMP RELAY.
- ENGINE SHOULD CONTINUE TO RUN. DOES IT?

YES → NO PROBLEM FOUND IN THE SYSTEM

NO → FAULTY OIL PRESSURE SWITCH

"AFTER REPAIRS," CONFIRM "CLOSED LOOP" OPERATION AND NO "SERVICE ENGINE SOON" LIGHT.

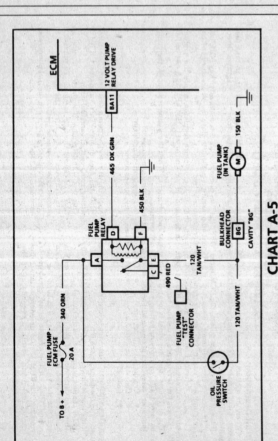

CHART A-5
(Page 2 of 2)
ENGINE CRANKS BUT WILL NOT RUN
(FUEL PUMP CIRCUIT)
2.3L (VIN A) "L" CARLINE (PORT)

Circuit Description:

When the ignition switch is turned "ON," the Electronic Control Module (ECM) turns "ON" the in-tank fuel pump. It will remain "ON" as long as the ECM is receiving ignition reference pulses from the Integrated Direct Ignition (IDI) module.

If there are no reference pulses, the ECM turns "OFF" the fuel pump about 2-3 seconds after key "ON," or about 10 seconds after reference pulses stop. If sufficient oil pressure is present to close the oil pressure switch, the fuel pump will remain "ON" during cranking without reference pulses.

The pump delivers fuel to the fuel rail and injectors, then to the pressure regulator, where the system pressure is controlled to 280 - 325 kPa (40.5 - 47 psi) with no manifold vacuum or 211 - 304 kPa (30.5 - 44 psi) at idle. Excess fuel is then returned to the fuel tank.

The fuel pump "test" terminal is located in the engine compartment. When the engine is stopped, the pump can be turned "ON" by applying battery voltage to the "test" terminal.

Improper fuel system pressure will result in one or all of the following symptoms:

- Cranks but will not run.
- Code 44
- Code 45
- Cuts out, may feel like ignition problem.
- Poor fuel economy, loss of power.
- Hesitation.

Test Description: Numbers below refer to circled numbers on the diagnostic chart.

6. Checks for open in the fuel pump relay ground CKT 150.
7. Determines if the ECM is in control of the fuel pump relay through CKT 465.
8. The fuel pump control circuit includes an engine oil pressure switch with a separate set of normally open contacts. The switch closes at about (4 lbs) 28 kPa of oil pressure and provides a second battery feed path to the fuel pump. If the relay fails, the pump will run due to the battery feed supplied by

the closed oil pressure switch. This step checks the oil pressure switch to be sure it provides battery feed to the fuel pump should the pump relay fail. A failed pump relay will result in extended engine crank time because of the time required to build enough oil pressure to close the oil pressure switch and turn "ON" the fuel pump. There may be instances when the relay has failed but the engine will not crank fast enough to build enough oil pressure to close the switch. This or a faulty oil pressure switch can result in "Engine Cranks But Will not Run."

(Wiring diagram labels: ECM, BA11, 12 VOLT PUMP RELAY DRIVE, 465 DK GRN, 450 BLK, FUEL PUMP RELAY, D, F, A, C, E, 490 RED, FUEL PUMP "TEST" CONNECTOR, 120 TAN/WHT, 120 TAN/WHT, BULKHEAD CONNECTOR, 8G, CAVITY "8G", FUEL PUMP (IN TANK), M, 150 BLK, OIL PRESSURE SWITCH, TO B+, 340 ORN, FUEL PUMP - ECM FUSE 20 A)

1990–92 2.3L ENGINE

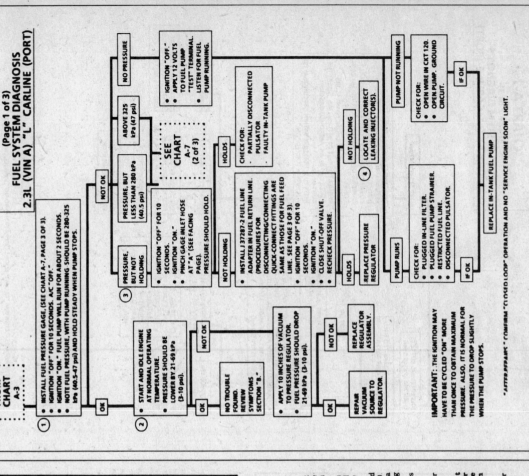

CHART A-7
(Page 1 of 3)
FUEL SYSTEM DIAGNOSIS
2.3L (VIN A) "L" CARLINE (PORT)

FROM CHART A-3

1. INSTALL FUEL PRESSURE GAGE. (SEE CHART A-7, PAGE 3 OF 3).
   • IGNITION "OFF" FOR 10 SECONDS. A/C "OFF."
   • IGNITION "ON." FUEL PUMP WILL RUN FOR ABOUT 2 SECONDS.
   • NOTE FUEL PRESSURE, WITH PUMP RUNNING SHOULD BE 280-325 kPa (40.5-47 psi) AND HOLD STEADY WHEN PUMP STOPS.

NOT OK / OK

Branches: PRESSURE, BUT NOT HOLDING — PRESSURE, BUT LESS THAN 280 kPa (40.5 psi) — ABOVE 325 kPa (47 psi) — NO PRESSURE

2. START AND IDLE ENGINE AT NORMAL OPERATING TEMPERATURE.
   • PRESSURE SHOULD BE LOWER BY 21-69 kPa (3-10 psi).

NOT OK / OK

NO TROUBLE FOUND, REVIEW SYMPTOMS SECTION "B".

• APPLY 10 INCHES OF VACUUM TO PRESSURE REGULATOR. FUEL PRESSURE SHOULD DROP 21-69 kPa (3-10 psi).

NOT OK / OK

REPAIR VACUUM SOURCE TO REGULATOR.

REPLACE REGULATOR ASSEMBLY.

3. (PRESSURE, BUT NOT HOLDING)
   • IGNITION "OFF" FOR 10 SECONDS.
   • IGNITION "ON."
   • PINCH GAGE INLET HOSE AT "A". (SEE FACING PAGE.) PRESSURE SHOULD HOLD.

HOLDS / NOT HOLDING

INSTALL J 37287-2 FUEL LINE ADAPTER IN FUEL RETURN LINE. (PROCEDURES FOR DISCONNECTING/CONNECTING QUICK-CONNECT FITTINGS ARE SAME AS THOSE FOR FUEL FEED LINE. SEE PAGE 3 OF 3).
   • IGNITION "OFF" FOR 10 SECONDS.
   • IGNITION "ON."
   • CLOSE SHUT-OFF VALVE.
   • RECHECK PRESSURE.

HOLDS / NOT HOLDING

REPLACE PRESSURE REGULATOR

4. LOCATE AND CORRECT LEAKING INJECTOR(S).

CHECK FOR:
   • PARTIALLY DISCONNECTED PULSATOR
   • FAULTY IN-TANK PUMP

SEE CHART A-7 (2 of 3)

(ABOVE 325 kPa (47 psi)) CHECK FOR:
   • PLUGGED IN-LINE FILTER.
   • PLUGGED FUEL PUMP STRAINER.
   • RESTRICTED FUEL LINE.
   • DISCONNECTED PULSATOR.

PUMP RUNS / IF OK

REPLACE IN-TANK FUEL PUMP

(NO PRESSURE)
   • IGNITION "OFF."
   • APPLY 12 VOLTS TO FUEL PUMP "TEST" TERMINAL. LISTEN FOR FUEL PUMP RUNNING.

PUMP NOT RUNNING / IF OK

CHECK FOR:
   • OPEN WIRE IN CKT 120.
   • OPEN PUMP. GROUND CIRCUIT.

IMPORTANT: THE IGNITION MAY HAVE TO BE CYCLED "ON" MORE THAN ONCE TO OBTAIN MAXIMUM PRESSURE. ALSO, IT IS NORMAL FOR THE PRESSURE TO DROP SLIGHTLY WHEN THE PUMP STOPS.

AFTER REPAIRS CONFIRM "CLOSED LOOP" OPERATION AND NO "SERVICE ENGINE SOON" LIGHT.

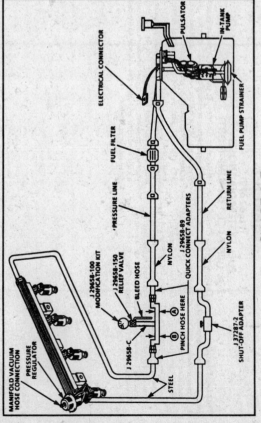

CHART A-7
(Page 1 of 3)
FUEL SYSTEM DIAGNOSIS
2.3L (VIN A) "L" CARLINE (PORT)

Circuit Description:
When the ignition switch is turned "ON," the Electronic Control Module (ECM) will turn "ON" the in-tank fuel pump. It will remain "ON" as long as the engine is cranking or running, and the ECM is receiving reference pulses. If there are no reference pulses, the ECM will shut "OFF" the fuel pump in about 2 seconds after ignition "ON" or 10 seconds after reference pulses stop.

An electric fuel pump, attached to the fuel sender assembly (inside the fuel tank) pumps fuel through an inline filter to the fuel rail assembly. The pump is designed to provide fuel at a pressure above the regulated pressure needed by the injectors. A pressure regulator, attached to the fuel rail, keeps fuel available to the injectors at a regulated pressure. Unused fuel is returned to the fuel tank by a separate line.

Test Description: Numbers below refer to circled numbers on the diagnostic chart.

1. Install fuel pressure gage per instructions on Page 3 of 3. Ignition "ON," pump pressure should be 280 to 325 kPa (40.5-47 psi). This pressure is controlled by spring pressure within the regulator assembly.
2. When the engine is idling, the manifold pressure is low (high vacuum) and is applied to the fuel regulator diaphragm. This will offset the spring and result in a lower fuel pressure. This idle pressure will vary somewhat depending on barometric pressure, however, the pressure idling should be less indicating pressure regulator control.
3. Pressure that continues to fall quickly is caused by one of the following:
   • In-tank fuel pump check valve not holding.
   • Partially disconnected pump pulsator.
   • Fuel pressure regulator valve leaking.
   • Injector(s) sticking open.
4. An injector sticking open can best be determined by checking for a fouled or saturated spark plug(s). If a leaking injector can not be determined by a fouled or saturated spark plug the following procedure should be used.
   • Remove fuel rail bolts, but leave fuel lines connected.
   • Lift fuel rail out just enough to leave injector nozzles in the ports.

CAUTION: Be sure injector(s) are not allowed to spray on engine and that injector retaining clips are intact. This should be carefully followed to prevent fuel spray on engine which would cause a fire hazard.
   • Pressurize the fuel system and observe for injector(s) leaking.

1990-92 2.3L ENGINE

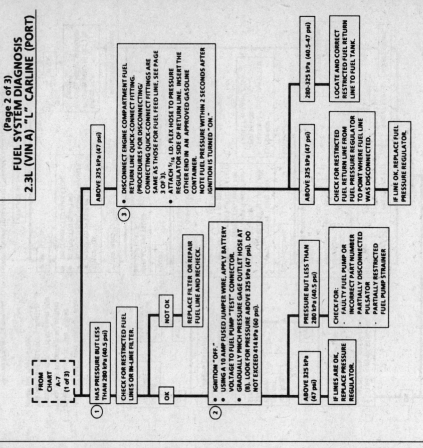

CHART A-7
(Page 2 of 3)
FUEL SYSTEM DIAGNOSIS
2.3L (VIN A) "L" CARLINE (PORT)

FROM CHART A-7 (1 of 3)

① HAS PRESSURE BUT LESS THAN 280 kPa (40.5 psi)

CHECK FOR RESTRICTED FUEL LINES OR IN-LINE FILTER.

NOT OK → REPLACE FILTER OR REPAIR FUEL LINE AND RECHECK.

OK

② • IGNITION "OFF."
• USING A 10 AMP FUSED JUMPER WIRE, APPLY BATTERY VOLTAGE TO FUEL PUMP "TEST" CONNECTOR.
• GRADUALLY PINCH PRESSURE GAGE OUTLET HOSE AT (B). LOOK FOR PRESSURE ABOVE 325 kPa (47 psi). DO NOT EXCEED 414 kPa (60 psi).

ABOVE 325 kPa (47 psi)

IF LINES ARE OK, REPLACE PRESSURE REGULATOR.

PRESSURE BUT LESS THAN 280 kPa (40.5 psi)

CHECK FOR:
- FAULTY FUEL PUMP OR INCORRECT PART NUMBER
- PARTIALLY DISCONNECTED PULSATOR
- PARTIALLY RESTRICTED FUEL PUMP STRAINER

ABOVE 325 kPa (47 psi)

③ • DISCONNECT ENGINE COMPARTMENT FUEL RETURN LINE QUICK-CONNECT FITTING. (PROCEDURES FOR DISCONNECTING/ CONNECTING QUICK-CONNECT FITTINGS ARE SAME AS THOSE FOR FUEL FEED LINE, SEE PAGE 3 OF 3.)
• ATTACH ¼₆ I.D. FLEX HOSE TO PRESSURE REGULATOR SIDE OF RETURN LINE. INSERT THE OTHER END IN AN APPROVED GASOLINE CONTAINER.
NOTE FUEL PRESSURE WITHIN 2 SECONDS AFTER IGNITION IS TURNED "ON."

280-325 kPa (40.5-47 psi) → LOCATE AND CORRECT RESTRICTED FUEL RETURN LINE TO FUEL TANK.

ABOVE 325 kPa (47 psi)

CHECK FOR RESTRICTED FUEL RETURN LINE FROM FUEL PRESSURE REGULATOR TO POINT WHERE FUEL LINE WAS DISCONNECTED.

IF LINE OK, REPLACE FUEL PRESSURE REGULATOR.

"AFTER REPAIRS," CONFIRM "CLOSED LOOP" OPERATION AND NO "SERVICE ENGINE SOON" LIGHT.

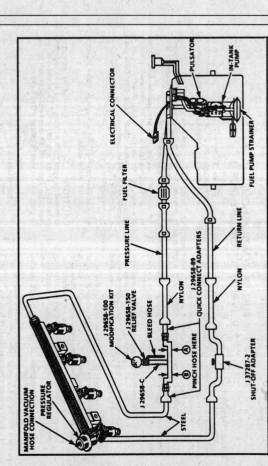

MANIFOLD VACUUM HOSE CONNECTION

PRESSURE REGULATOR

J 29658-100 MODIFICATION KIT

J 29658-150 RELIEF VALVE

BLEED HOSE

J 29658-C

PINCH HOSE HERE

J 37287-2 SHUT-OFF ADAPTER

STEEL

ELECTRICAL CONNECTOR

FUEL FILTER

PRESSURE LINE

NYLON

J 29658-89 QUICK CONNECT ADAPTERS

NYLON

RETURN LINE

PULSATOR

IN-TANK PUMP

FUEL PUMP STRAINER

CHART A-7
(Page 2 of 3)
FUEL SYSTEM DIAGNOSIS
2.3L (VIN A) "L" CARLINE (PORT)

Test Description: Numbers below refer to circled numbers on the diagnostic chart.

1. Pressure below 280 kPa (40.5 psi) may cause a lean condition and may set a Code 44. It could also cause hard starting cold and poor driveability. Low enough pressure will cause the engine not to run at all. Restricted flow may allow the engine to run at idle, or low speeds, but may cause a surge and stall when more fuel is required, as when accelerating or driving at high speeds.

2. Restricting fuel flow at the fuel pressure gage (at "B") causes fuel pressure to build above regulated pressure. With battery voltage applied to the pump "est" terminal, pressure should rise above 325 kPa (47 psi) as the gage outlet hose is restricted.

3. This test determines if the high fuel pressure is due to a restricted fuel return line or a pressure regulator problem. High fuel pressure may cause a rich condition and may set a Code 45 or cause driveability problems.

1990–92 2.3L ENGINE

CHART A-7
(Page 3 of 3)
FUEL SYSTEM DIAGNOSIS 2.3L (VIN A) "L" CARLINE (PORT)

FUEL PRESSURE CHECK

Tools Required:
J 29658-C - Fuel Pressure Gage
J 29658-150 - Fuel Pressure Gage Relief Valve
J 29658-100 - TBI Pressure Gage Modification Kit
J 29658-89 - Fuel Pressure Quick Connect Adapters
J 37088 - A - Fuel Line Quick-Connect Separators
J 37287-2 - Fuel Line Adapter (Shut-off Valve) (If Called for in Chart.)

CAUTION: To Reduce the Risk of Fire and Personal Injury:
- It is necessary to relieve fuel system pressure before connecting a fuel pressure gage.
- After relieving system pressure, a small amount of fuel may be released when disconnecting the fuel lines. Cover fuel line fittings with a shop towel before disconnecting, to catch any fuel that may leak out. Place towel in approved container when disconnect is completed.
- Do not pinch or restrict nylon fuel lines to avoid severing, which could cause a fuel leak.

NOTICE: ● If nylon fuel lines become kinked, and cannot be straightened, they must be replaced

1. Loosen fuel filler cap to relieve fuel tank pressure. (Do not tighten at this time.)
2. Raise vehicle.
3. Disconnect fuel pump electrical connector.
4. Lower vehicle.
5. Start and run engine until fuel supply remaining in fuel pipes is consumed. Engage starter for three seconds to assure relief of any remaining pressure.
6. Disconnect negative battery terminal.
7. Locate engine compartment fuel feed quick-connect fitting.
8. Grasp both ends of fitting, twist female end ¼ turn in each direction to loosen any dirt in fitting.

CAUTION: Safety glasses must be worn when using compressed air, as flying dirt particles may cause eye injury.

9. Using compressed air, blow dirt out of quick-connect fitting.
10. Choose correct tool from separator tool set J 37088-A for size of fitting. Insert tool into female end of connector, then push inward to release male connector.
11. If not previously installed, connect Fuel Pressure Gage Relief Valve J 29658-150, on Fuel Pressure Gage J 29658-C.
12. Connect 414 kPa (60 psi) gage from TBI Pressure Gage Modification kit J 29658-100 to fuel pressure gage J 29658-C.
13. Connect gage quick-connect adapters J 29658-89 to fuel pressure gage J 29658-C.

CAUTION: To Reduce the Risk of Fire and Personal Injury: Before connecting fuel line quick-connect fittings, always apply a few drops of clean engine oil to the male tube ends. This will ensure proper reconnection and prevent a possible fuel leak. (During normal operation, the O-rings located inside the female connector will swell and may prevent proper reconnection if not lubricated.)

14. Lubricate the male tube end of the fuel line and the gage adapter with engine oil.
15. Connect fuel pressure gage.
    - Push connectors together to cause the retaining tabs/fingers to snap into place.
    - Once installed, pull on both ends of each connection to make sure it is secure.

CHART A-7
(Page 3 of 3)
FUEL SYSTEM DIAGNOSIS
2.3L (VIN A) "L" CARLINE (PORT)

FUEL PRESSURE CHECK
-continued-

16. Raise vehicle.
17. Connect fuel pump electrical connector.
18. Lower vehicle.
19. Connect negative battery terminal.
20. Check fuel pressure.
21. Place bleed hose into an approved container and open valve to bleed system pressure.
22. Disconnect negative battery terminal.
23. Disconnect fuel pressure gage.
24. Lubricate the male tube end of the fuel line, and reconnect quick-connect fitting.
    - Push connector together to cause the retaining tabs/fingers to snap into place
    - Once installed, pull on both ends of connection to make sure it is secure
25. Tighten fuel filler cap.
26. Connect negative battery terminal.
27. Cycle ignition "ON" and "OFF" twice, waiting ten seconds between cycles, then check for fuel leaks.

1990–92 2.3L ENGINE

CODE 13
OXYGEN SENSOR CIRCUIT
(OPEN CIRCUIT)
2.3L (VIN A) "L" CARLINE (PORT)

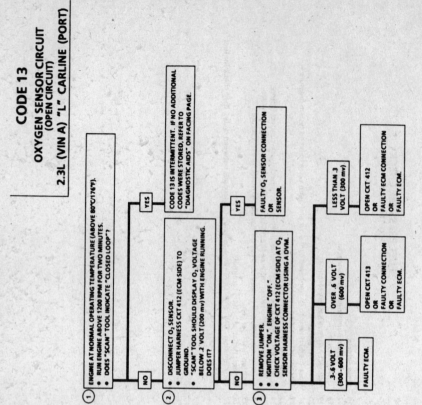

1
- ENGINE AT NORMAL OPERATING TEMPERATURE (ABOVE 80°C/176°F).
- RUN ENGINE ABOVE 1200 RPM FOR TWO MINUTES.
- DOES "SCAN" TOOL INDICATE "CLOSED LOOP"?

YES → CODE 13 IS INTERMITTENT. IF NO ADDITIONAL CODES WERE STORED, REFER TO "DIAGNOSTIC AIDS" ON FACING PAGE.

NO →

2
- DISCONNECT O₂ SENSOR.
- JUMPER HARNESS CKT 412 (ECM SIDE) TO GROUND.
- "SCAN" TOOL SHOULD DISPLAY O₂ VOLTAGE BELOW .2 VOLT (200 mv) WITH ENGINE RUNNING. DOES IT?

YES → FAULTY O₂ SENSOR CONNECTION OR SENSOR.

NO →

3
- REMOVE JUMPER.
- IGNITION "ON," ENGINE "OFF."
- CHECK VOLTAGE OF CKT 412 (ECM SIDE) AT O₂ SENSOR HARNESS CONNECTOR USING A DVM.

LESS THAN .3 VOLT (300 mv)	.3-.6 VOLT (300 - 600 mv)	OVER .6 VOLT (600 mv)
OPEN CKT 412 OR FAULTY ECM CONNECTION OR FAULTY ECM.	FAULTY ECM.	OPEN CKT 413 OR FAULTY CONNECTION OR FAULTY ECM.

"AFTER REPAIRS," REFER TO CODE CRITERIA ON FACING PAGE AND CONFIRM CODE DOES NOT RESET.

CODE 13
OXYGEN SENSOR CIRCUIT
(OPEN CIRCUIT)
2.3L (VIN A) "L" CARLINE (PORT)

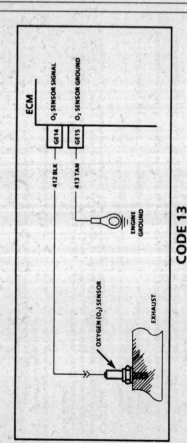

ECM
O₂ SENSOR SIGNAL — GE14 — 412 BLK
O₂ SENSOR GROUND — GE15 — 413 TAN
OXYGEN (O₂) SENSOR
EXHAUST
ENGINE GROUND

Circuit Description:

The ECM supplies a voltage of about .45 volt between terminals "GE14" and "GE15". (If measured with a 10 megaohm digital voltmeter, this may read as low as .32 volt.) The O₂ sensor varies the voltage within a range of about 1 volt if the exhaust is rich, down through about .10 volt if exhaust is lean.

The sensor is like an open circuit and produces no voltage when it is below 315°C (600° F). An open sensor circuit or cold sensor causes "Open Loop" operation.

Test Description: Numbers below refer to circled numbers on the diagnostic chart.

1. Code 13 WILL SET under the following conditions:
   - Engine running at least 40 seconds after start.
   - Coolant temperature at least 42.5°C (108.5°C).
   - No Code 21 or 22.
   - O₂ signal voltage steady between .34 and .55 volt.
   - Throttle position sensor signal above 6% for more time than TPS was below 6%. (About .3 volt above closed throttle voltage)
   - All conditions must be met and held for at least 20 seconds.

   If the conditions for a Code 13 exist, the system will not go "Closed Loop."

2. This will determine if the sensor is at fault or the wiring or ECM is the cause of the Code 13.

3. Use only a high impedance digital volt ohmmeter for this test. This test checks the continuity of CKTs 412 and 413; because if CKT 413 is open, the ECM voltage on CKT 412 will be over .6 volt (600 mv).

Diagnostic Aids:

Normal Tech 1 "Scan" voltage varies between 100 mv to 999 mv (.1 volt to 1.0 volt) while in "Closed Loop." Code 13 sets in 20 seconds if voltage remains between .35 volt and .55 volt, but the system will go "Open Loop" in about 15 seconds. Refer to "Intermittents" in "Symptoms," Section

1990–92 2.3L ENGINE

CODE 14
COOLANT TEMPERATURE SENSOR CIRCUIT
(HIGH TEMPERATURE INDICATED)
2.3L (VIN A) "L" CARLINE (PORT)

1. DOES "SCAN" TOOL DISPLAY COOLANT TEMPERATURE OF 130°C (266°F) OR HIGHER?
   - NO → CODE 14 IS INTERMITTENT. IF NO ADDITIONAL CODES WERE STORED, REFER TO "DIAGNOSTIC AIDS" ON FACING PAGE.
   - YES ↓

2. DISCONNECT COOLANT TEMPERATURE SENSOR. "SCAN" TOOL SHOULD DISPLAY COOLANT TEMPERATURE BELOW -30°C (-22°F). DOES IT?
   - NO → CKT 410 SHORTED TO GROUND OR CKT 410 SHORTED TO SENSOR GROUND CIRCUIT OR FAULTY ECM.
   - YES → REPLACE COOLANT TEMPERATURE SENSOR.

DIAGNOSTIC AID

COOLANT SENSOR
TEMPERATURE VS. RESISTANCE VALUES
(APPROXIMATE)

°C	°F	OHMS
100	212	177
90	194	241
80	176	332
70	158	467
60	140	667
50	122	973
45	113	1188
40	104	1459
35	95	1802
30	86	2238
25	77	2796
20	68	3520
15	59	4450
10	50	5670
5	41	7280
0	32	9420
-5	23	12300
-10	14	16180
-15	5	21450
-20	-4	28680
-30	-22	52700
-40	-40	100700

"AFTER REPAIRS," REFER TO CODE CRITERIA ON FACING PAGE AND CONFIRM CODE DOES NOT RESET.

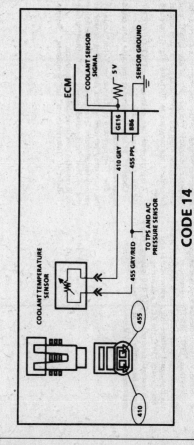

CODE 14
COOLANT TEMPERATURE SENSOR CIRCUIT
(HIGH TEMPERATURE INDICATED)
2.3L (VIN A) "L" CARLINE (PORT)

Circuit Description:
The coolant temperature sensor uses a thermistor to control the signal voltage at the ECM. The ECM applies a voltage on CKT 410 to the sensor. When the engine is cold the sensor (thermistor) resistance is high, therefore ECM terminal "GE16" voltage will be high.

As the engine warms, the sensor resistance becomes less, and the voltage drops. At normal engine operating temperature, the voltage will measure about 1.5 to 2.0 volts at ECM terminal "GE16".

Coolant temperature is one of the inputs used to control:
- Fuel delivery
- Engine Spark Timing (EST)
- Idle Air Control (IAC)
- Controlled Canister Purge (CCP)
- Cooling Fan

Test Description: Numbers below refer to circled numbers on the diagnostic chart.
1. Code 14 will set if:
   - Signal voltage indicates a coolant temperature above 140°C (285°F).
   - Engine running longer than 128 seconds
2. This test will determine if CKT 410 is shorted to ground which will cause the conditions for Code 14.

Diagnostic Aids:
Check harness routing for a potential short to ground on CKT 410.

Tech 1 "Scan" tool displays engine temperature in degrees celsius. After engine is started, the temperature should rise steadily to about 90°C, and then stabilize when thermostat opens. Refer to "Intermittents" in "Symptoms," Section

Verify that engine is not overheating and has not been subjected to conditions which could create an overheating condition (i.e., overload, trailer towing, hilly terrain, heavy stop and go traffic, etc.). The "Temperature To Resistance Value" scale at the right may be used to test the coolant sensor at various temperature levels to evaluate the possibility of a "shifted" (mis-scaled) sensor. A "shifted" sensor could result in poor driveability complaints.

1990–92 2.3L ENGINE

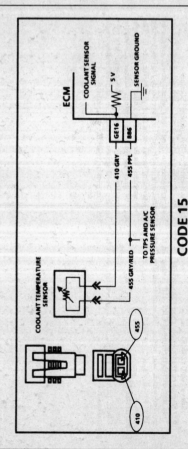

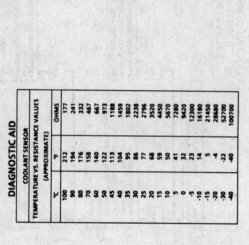

CODE 15

COOLANT TEMPERATURE SENSOR CIRCUIT
(LOW TEMPERATURE INDICATED)
2.3L (VIN A) "L" CARLINE (PORT)

1. • DOES "SCAN" TOOL DISPLAY COOLANT TEMPERATURE OF -30°C (-22°F) OR LESS?
   - **NO** → CODE 15 IS INTERMITTENT. IF NO ADDITIONAL CODES WERE STORED, REFER TO "DIAGNOSTIC AIDS" ON FACING PAGE.
   - **YES** ↓

2. • DISCONNECT COOLANT TEMPERATURE SENSOR. JUMPER HARNESS TERMINALS TOGETHER.
   • "SCAN" TOOL SHOULD DISPLAY 130°C (266°F) OR MORE. DOES IT?
   - **YES** → FAULTY CONNECTION OR COOLANT TEMPERATURE SENSOR.
   - **NO** ↓

3. • JUMPER CKT 410 TO GROUND.
   • "SCAN" TOOL SHOULD DISPLAY OVER 130°C (266°F). DOES IT?
   - **NO** → OPEN CKT 410, FAULTY CONNECTION AT ECM, OR FAULTY ECM.
   - **YES** → OPEN COOLANT TEMPERATURE SENSOR GROUND CIRCUIT, FAULTY CONNECTION OR FAULTY ECM.

DIAGNOSTIC AID

COOLANT SENSOR
TEMPERATURE VS. RESISTANCE VALUES
(APPROXIMATE)

°C	°F	OHMS
100	212	177
90	194	241
80	176	332
70	158	467
60	140	667
50	122	973
45	113	1188
40	104	1459
35	95	1802
30	86	2238
25	77	2796
20	68	3520
15	59	4450
10	50	5670
5	41	7280
0	32	9420
-5	23	12300
-10	14	16180
-15	5	21450
-20	-4	28680
-30	-22	52700
-40	-40	100700

"AFTER REPAIRS," REFER TO CODE CRITERIA ON FACING PAGE AND CONFIRM CODE DOES NOT RESET.

CODE 15

COOLANT TEMPERATURE SENSOR CIRCUIT
(LOW TEMPERATURE INDICATED)
2.3L (VIN A) "L" CARLINE (PORT)

Circuit Description:
The coolant temperature sensor uses a thermistor to control the signal voltage at the ECM. The ECM applies a voltage on CKT 410 to the sensor. When the engine is cold, the sensor (thermistor) resistance is high, therefore, ECM terminal "GE16" voltage will be high.

As the engine warms, the sensor resistance becomes less, and the voltage drops. At normal engine operating temperature the voltage will measure about 1.5 to 2.0 volts at ECM terminal "GE16."

Coolant temperature is one of the inputs used to control:
- Fuel delivery
- Engine Spark Timing (EST)
- Idle Air Control (IAC)
- Controlled Canister Purge (CCP)
- Cooling Fan

Test Description: Numbers below refer to circled numbers on the diagnostic chart.
1. Code 15 will set if:
   - Signal voltage indicates a coolant temperature less than -39°C (-38°F) for 60 seconds.
2. This test simulates a Code 14. If the ECM senses the low signal voltage (high temperature) and the "Scan" reads 130°C, the ECM and wiring are OK.
3. This test will determine if CKT 410 is open. There should be 5 volts present at sensor connector if measured with a DVM.

Diagnostic Aids:
A Tech 1 "Scan" tool displays engine temperature in degrees celsius. After the engine is started the temperature should rise steadily to about 95°C, and then stabilize when the thermostat opens. It is normal for coolant temperature to fluctuate slightly around 95°C.

A faulty connection, or an open in CKT 410 or CKT 455 can result in a Code 15.

Codes 15, 21 and 66 stored at the same time could be the result of an open CKT 455.

The "Temperature to Resistance Value" scale at the right may be used to test the coolant sensor at various temperature levels to evaluate the possibility of a "shifted" (mis-scaled) sensor. A "shifted" sensor could result in poor driveability complaints.

Refer to "Intermittents" in "Symptoms," Section

1990–92 2.3L ENGINE

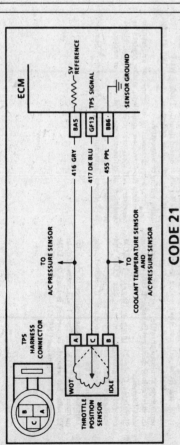

CODE 21

THROTTLE POSITION SENSOR (TPS) CIRCUIT
(SIGNAL VOLTAGE HIGH)
2.3L (VIN A) "L" CARLINE (PORT)

Circuit Description:

The Throttle Position Sensor (TPS) provides a voltage signal that changes relative to the throttle opening. Signal voltage will vary from about .5 volt at idle to about 4.9 volts at Wide Open Throttle (WOT).

The TPS signal is one of the most important inputs used by the ECM for fuel control and for most of the ECM control outputs.

Test Description: Numbers below refer to circled numbers on the diagnostic chart.

1. Code 21 will set if:
   - Engine is running
   - No Code 33 or 34
   - Manifold Absolute Pressure (MAP) less than 65 kPa
   - TPS signal voltage greater than approximately 4.0 volts (78%)
   - Above conditions exist for over 5 seconds.

   OR

   - TPS voltage greater than about 4.7 volts. With throttle closed the TPS should read less than .900 volt. If it doesn't, replace TPS.

2. With the TPS disconnected, the TPS voltage should go low if the ECM and wiring are OK.
3. Probing CKT 455 with a test light checks the TPS ground circuit because an open or very high resistance ground circuit will cause a Code 21.

Diagnostic Aids:

A Tech 1 "Scan" tool displays throttle position in volts. It should display .400 volt to .900 volt with throttle closed and ignition "ON" or at idle. Voltage should increase at a steady rate as throttle is moved toward Wide Open Throttle (WOT).

Also Tech 1 "Scan" tools will display throttle angle %, 0% = closed throttle 100% = WOT.

An open in CKT 455 will result in a Code 21.

Codes 15, 21 and 66 stored at the same time could be the result of an open CKT 455. "Scan" TPS while depressing accelerator pedal with engine stopped and ignition "ON." Display should vary from about .5 volt (500 mv) when throttle is closed, to over 4500 mv (4.5 volts) when throttle is held wide open.

Check condition of connector and sensor terminals for moisture or corrosion, and clean or replace as necessary. If corrosion found, check condition of connector seal, repair and/or replace if necessary.

Refer to "Intermittents" in "Symptoms," Section

CODE 21
THROTTLE POSITION SENSOR (TPS) CIRCUIT
(SIGNAL VOLTAGE HIGH)
2.3L (VIN A) "L" CARLINE (PORT)

1. THROTTLE CLOSED. DOES "SCAN" TOOL DISPLAY THROTTLE POSITION OVER 2.5 VOLTS?

   - **NO** → CODE 21 IS INTERMITTENT. IF NO ADDITIONAL CODES WERE STORED, REFER TO "DIAGNOSTIC AIDS" ON FACING PAGE.

   - **YES** ↓

2. DISCONNECT THROTTLE POSITION SENSOR. "SCAN" TOOL SHOULD DISPLAY THROTTLE POSITION BELOW 2 VOLT (200mv). DOES IT?

   - **NO** → TPS SIGNAL CIRCUIT SHORTED TO VOLTAGE OR FAULTY ECM.

   - **YES** ↓

3. PROBE SENSOR GROUND CIRCUIT WITH A TEST LIGHT CONNECTED TO BATTERY VOLTAGE.

   - **LIGHT "ON"** → FAULTY CONNECTION OR THROTTLE POSITION SENSOR.

   - **LIGHT "OFF"** → OPEN SENSOR GROUND CIRCUIT OR FAULTY ECM.

"AFTER REPAIRS," REFER TO CODE CRITERIA ON FACING PAGE AND CONFIRM CODE DOES NOT RESET.

1990–92 2.3L ENGINE

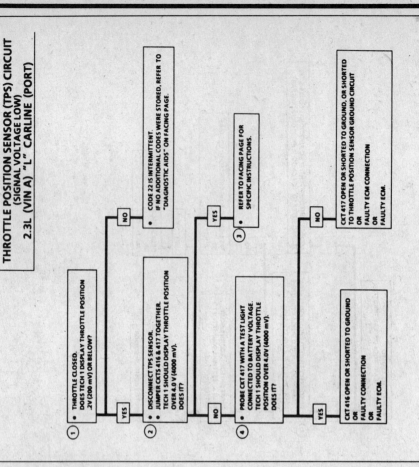

CODE 22
THROTTLE POSITION SENSOR (TPS) CIRCUIT
(SIGNAL VOLTAGE LOW)
2.3L (VIN A) "L" CARLINE (PORT)

1. THROTTLE CLOSED. DOES TECH 1 DISPLAY THROTTLE POSITION .2V (200 mV) OR BELOW?
   - YES
   - NO → CODE 22 IS INTERMITTENT. IF NO ADDITIONAL CODES WERE STORED, REFER TO "DIAGNOSTIC AIDS" ON FACING PAGE.

2. DISCONNECT TPS SENSOR. JUMPER CKTS 416 & 417 TOGETHER. TECH 1 SHOULD DISPLAY THROTTLE POSITION OVER 4.0 V (4000 mV). DOES IT?
   - NO
   - YES → (3) REFER TO FACING PAGE FOR SPECIFIC INSTRUCTIONS.

4. PROBE CKT 417 WITH A TEST LIGHT CONNECTED TO BATTERY VOLTAGE. TECH 1 SHOULD DISPLAY THROTTLE POSITION OVER 4.0V (4000 mV). DOES IT?
   - YES → CKT 416 OPEN OR SHORTED TO GROUND OR FAULTY CONNECTION OR FAULTY ECM.
   - NO → CKT 417 OPEN OR SHORTED TO GROUND, OR SHORTED TO THROTTLE POSITION SENSOR GROUND CIRCUIT OR FAULTY ECM CONNECTION OR FAULTY ECM.

"AFTER REPAIRS," REFER TO CODE CRITERIA ON FACING PAGE AND CONFIRM CODE DOES NOT RESET.

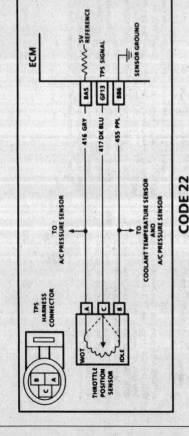

ECM
5V REFERENCE — BA5 — 416 GRY → TO A/C PRESSURE SENSOR
TPS SIGNAL — GF13 — 417 DK BLU
SENSOR GROUND — B86 — 455 PPL → TO COOLANT TEMPERATURE SENSOR AND A/C PRESSURE SENSOR

TPS HARNESS CONNECTOR
THROTTLE POSITION SENSOR
WOT — IDLE
A C B

CODE 22
THROTTLE POSITION SENSOR (TPS) CIRCUIT
(SIGNAL VOLTAGE LOW)
2.3L (VIN A) "L" CARLINE (PORT)

Circuit Description:

The Throttle Position Sensor (TPS) provides a voltage signal that changes relative to the throttle opening. Signal voltage will vary from about .5 volt at idle to about 4.9 volts at Wide Open Throttle (WOT).

The TPS signal is one of the most important inputs used by the ECM for fuel control and for most of the ECM control outputs.

Test Description: Numbers below refer to circled numbers on the diagnostic chart.

1. Code 22 will set if:
   - Engine is running
   - TPS signal voltage is less than about .2 volt for 5 seconds.

   The TPS has an auto zeroing feature. If the voltage reading is within the range of about .4 to .9 volts, the ECM will use that value as closed throttle. If the voltage reading is out of the auto zero range at closed throttle, check for a binding throttle cable or damaged linkage. If OK, continue with diagnosis.

2. Simulates Code 21 (high voltage). If ECM recognizes high signal voltage, the ECM and wiring are OK.

3. Check for good sensor connection. If connection is good, replace TPS.

4. This simulates a high signal voltage to check for an open in CKT 417. The Tech 1 will not read up to 12 volts, but what is important is that the ECM recognizes the signal on CKT 417.

Diagnostic Aids:

"Scan" TPS while depressing accelerator pedal with engine stopped and ignition "ON." Display should vary from about 500 mv (.5 volt) when throttle is closed, to over 4500 mv (4.5 volts) when throttle is held wide open.

Also, Tech 1 "Scan" tools will display throttle angle %. 0% = closed throttle. 100% = WOT.

If Code 22 and/or 66 are set, check CKT 416 for faulty wiring or connections.

Should check condition of connector and sensor terminals for corrosion, and clean and/or replace as necessary. If moisture or corrosion is found, check condition of connector seal and repair or replace if necessary.

Refer to "Intermittents" in "Symptoms," Section

1990–92 2.3L ENGINE

CODE 23

INTAKE AIR TEMPERATURE (IAT) SENSOR CIRCUIT
(LOW TEMPERATURE INDICATED)
2.3L (VIN A) "L" CARLINE (PORT)

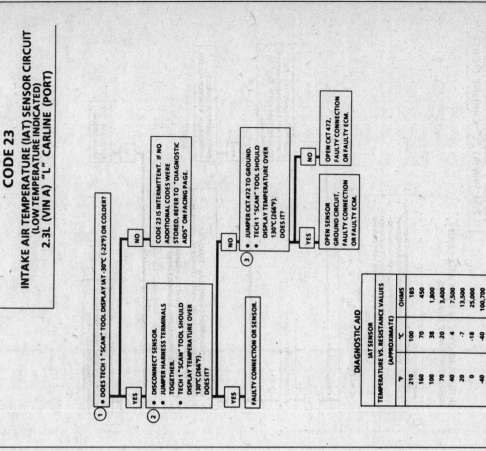

① • DOES TECH 1 "SCAN" TOOL DISPLAY IAT -30°C (-22°F) OR COLDER?

NO → CODE 23 IS INTERMITTENT. IF NO ADDITIONAL CODES WERE STORED, REFER TO "DIAGNOSTIC AIDS" ON FACING PAGE.

YES →

② • DISCONNECT SENSOR.
• JUMPER HARNESS TERMINALS TOGETHER.
• TECH 1 "SCAN" TOOL SHOULD DISPLAY TEMPERATURE OVER 130°C (266°F). DOES IT?

YES → FAULTY CONNECTION OR SENSOR.

NO →

③ • JUMPER CKT 472 TO GROUND.
• TECH 1 "SCAN" TOOL SHOULD DISPLAY TEMPERATURE OVER 130°C (266°F). DOES IT?

YES → OPEN SENSOR GROUND CIRCUIT, FAULTY CONNECTION OR FAULTY ECM.

NO → OPEN CKT 472, FAULTY CONNECTION OR FAULTY ECM.

DIAGNOSTIC AID

IAT SENSOR
TEMPERATURE VS. RESISTANCE VALUES
(APPROXIMATE)

°F	°C	OHMS
210	100	185
160	70	450
100	38	1,800
70	20	3,400
40	4	7,500
20	-7	13,500
0	-18	25,000
-40	-40	100,700

"AFTER REPAIRS," REFER TO CODE CRITERIA ON FACING PAGE AND CONFIRM CODE DOES NOT RESET.

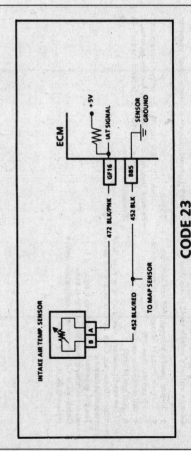

INTAKE AIR TEMP. SENSOR

472 BLK/PNK — IAT SIGNAL — GF16 — +5V

452 BLK — SENSOR GROUND — BB5

452 BLK/RED — TO MAP SENSOR

ECM

CODE 23

INTAKE AIR TEMPERATURE (IAT) SENSOR CIRCUIT
(LOW TEMPERATURE INDICATED)
2.3L (VIN A) "L" CARLINE (PORT)

Circuit Description:

The IAT sensor uses a thermistor to control the signal voltage at the ECM. The Electronic Control Module (ECM) applies a voltage (about 5 volts) on CKT 472 to the sensor. When the air is cold the sensor (thermistor) resistance is high, therefore the ECM terminal "GF16" voltage will be high. If the air is warm the sensor resistance is low, therefore the ECM terminal "GF16" voltage will be low.

Test Description: Numbers below refer to circled numbers on the diagnostic chart.

1. Code 23 will set if:
   • A signal voltage indicates a intake air temperature below about -34°C (-29°F).
   • Time since engine start is 320 seconds or longer.
   • Vehicle speed less than 15 mph.
2. A Code 23 will set due to an open sensor, wire, or connection. This test will determine if the wiring and ECM are OK.
3. This will determine if the signal CKT 472 or the 5 volts return CKT 452 is open.

Diagnostic Aids:

A Tech 1 "Scan" tool displays temperature of the air entering the engine, which should be close to ambient air temperature when engine is cold, and rise as underhood temperature increases.

A faulty connection, or an open in CKT 472 or CKT 452 can result in a Code 23.

Codes 23 and 34 stored at the same time, could be the result of an open CKT 452. The "Temperature to Resistance Values" scale at the right may be used to test the IAT sensor at various temperature levels to evaluate the possibility of a "slewed" (mis-scaled) sensor. A "slewed" sensor could result in poor driveability complaints.

Refer to "Intermittents" in "Symptoms," Section

1990-92 2.3L ENGINE

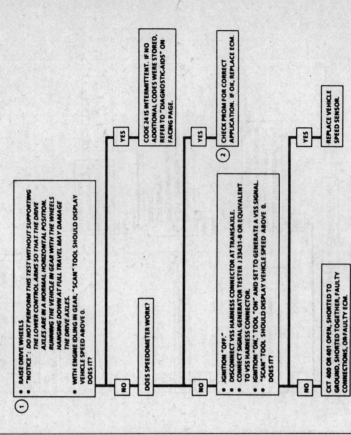

CODE 24
VEHICLE SPEED SENSOR (VSS) CIRCUIT
2.3L (VIN A) "L" CARLINE (PORT)

DISREGARD CODE 24 IF SET WHILE DRIVE WHEELS ARE NOT TURNING.

(1)
- RAISE DRIVE WHEELS
- "NOTICE": DO NOT PERFORM THIS TEST WITHOUT SUPPORTING THE LOWER CONTROL ARMS SO THAT THE DRIVE AXLES ARE IN A NORMAL HORIZONTAL POSITION. RUNNING THE VEHICLE IN GEAR WITH THE WHEELS HANGING DOWN AT FULL TRAVEL MAY DAMAGE THE DRIVE AXLES.
- WITH ENGINE IDLING IN GEAR, "SCAN" TOOL SHOULD DISPLAY VEHICLE SPEED ABOVE 0.

DOES IT?

NO → DOES SPEEDOMETER WORK?

  YES → CODE 24 IS INTERMITTENT. IF NO ADDITIONAL CODES WERE STORED, REFER TO "DIAGNOSTIC AIDS" ON FACING PAGE.

  NO →
- IGNITION "OFF."
- DISCONNECT VSS HARNESS CONNECTOR AT TRANSAXLE.
- CONNECT SIGNAL GENERATOR TESTER J 33431-B OR EQUIVALENT TO VSS HARNESS CONNECTOR.
- IGNITION "ON." TOOL "ON" AND SET TO GENERATE A VSS SIGNAL. "SCAN" TOOL SHOULD DISPLAY VEHICLE SPEED ABOVE 0.

DOES IT?

  YES → (2) CHECK PROM FOR CORRECT APPLICATION. IF OK, REPLACE ECM.

  NO → CKT 400 OR 401 OPEN, SHORTED TO GROUND, SHORTED TOGETHER, FAULTY CONNECTIONS, OR FAULTY ECM.

YES → REPLACE VEHICLE SPEED SENSOR.

"AFTER REPAIRS," REFER TO CODE CRITERIA ON FACING PAGE AND CONFIRM CODE DOES NOT RESET.

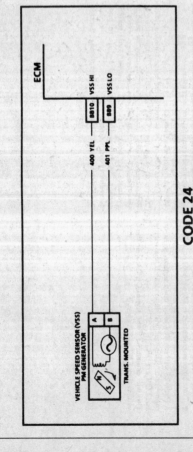

VEHICLE SPEED SENSOR (VSS) PM GENERATOR

A | B

TRANS. MOUNTED

400 YEL — BB10 VSS HI
401 PPL — BB9 VSS LO

ECM

CODE 24
VEHICLE SPEED SENSOR (VSS) CIRCUIT
2.3L (VIN A) "L" CARLINE (PORT)

Circuit Description:

Vehicle speed information is provided to the ECM by the Vehicle Speed Sensor (VSS) which is a Permanent Magnet (PM) generator that is mounted in the transmission. The PM generator produces a pulsing voltage whenever vehicle speed is over about 3 mph, (5 kph). The AC voltage level and the number of pulses increases with vehicle speed. The Electronic Control Module (ECM) then converts the pulsing voltage to mph which is used for calculations, and the mph can be displayed with a Tech 1 "Scan" tool. Output of the generator can also be seen by using a digital voltmeter on the AC scale while rotating the generator.

The function of VSS buffer used in past model years has been incorporated into the ECM. The ECM then supplies the necessary signal for operating the speedometer, the odometer, and for the cruise control module.

Test Description: Numbers below refer to circled numbers on the diagnostic chart.

1. Code 24 will set if vehicle speed is less than 2 mph when:
   - Engine speed is between 1600 and 3000 rpm.
   - Throttle Position Sensor (TPS) is greater than 7% and less than 20%.
   - All conditions met for 20 seconds.
   - No Code 21 or 22.

   These conditions are met during a road load operation. Disregard Code 24 that sets when drive wheels are not turning.

   The PM generator only produces a signal if drive wheels are turning greater than 3 mph (5 kph).

2. Check MEM-CAL for correct application before replacing ECM.

Diagnostic Aids:

Tech 1 should indicate a vehicle speed whenever the drive wheels are turning greater than 3 mph, (5 kph).

Check CKT 400 and 401 for proper connections. Be sure they are clean and tight and the harness is routed correctly. Refer to "Intermittents" in "Symptoms," Section

1990–92 2.3L ENGINE

CODE 25
INTAKE AIR TEMPERATURE (IAT) SENSOR CIRCUIT
(HIGH TEMPERATURE INDICATED)
2.3L (VIN A) "L" CARLINE (PORT)

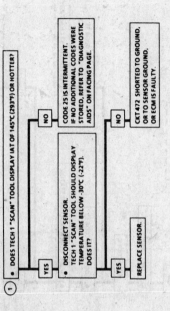

(1) • DOES TECH 1 "SCAN" TOOL DISPLAY IAT OF 145°C (293°F) OR HOTTER?

NO → CODE 25 IS INTERMITTENT. IF NO ADDITIONAL CODES WERE STORED, REFER TO "DIAGNOSTIC AIDS" ON FACING PAGE.

YES → • DISCONNECT SENSOR. TECH 1 "SCAN" TOOL SHOULD DISPLAY TEMPERATURE BELOW -30°C (-22°F). DOES IT?

NO → CKT 472 SHORTED TO GROUND, OR TO SENSOR GROUND, OR ECM IS FAULTY.

YES → REPLACE SENSOR.

DIAGNOSTIC AID

IAT SENSOR
TEMPERATURE VS. RESISTANCE VALUES
(APPROXIMATE)

°F	°C	OHMS
210	100	185
160	70	450
100	38	1,800
70	20	3,400
40	4	7,500
20	-7	13,500
0	-18	25,000
-40	-40	100,700

"AFTER REPAIRS," REFER TO CODE CRITERIA ON FACING PAGE AND CONFIRM CODE DOES NOT RESET.

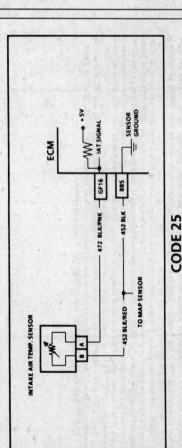

CODE 25
INTAKE AIR TEMPERATURE (IAT) SENSOR CIRCUIT
(HIGH TEMPERATURE INDICATED)
2.3L (VIN A) "L" CARLINE (PORT)

Circuit Description:

The Intake Air Temperature (IAT) sensor uses a thermistor to control the signal voltage to the Electronic Control Module (ECM). The ECM applies a voltage (about 5 volts) on CKT 472 to the sensor. When intake air is cold, the sensor (thermistor) resistance is high, therefore, the ECM terminal "GF16" voltage is high. As the air warms, the sensor resistance becomes less, and the voltage drops. As the incoming air gets warmer, the sensor resistance decreases, causing ECM terminal "GF16" voltage to decrease.

Test Description: Number below refers to circled number on the diagnostic chart.

1. Code 25 will set if:
   • Signal voltage indicates a intake air temperature greater than about 159°C (318°F).
   • Vehicle speed is greater than 15 mph.

Diagnostic Aids:

The "Temperature To Resistance Value" scale at the right may be used to test the Intake Air Temperature (IAT) sensor at various temperature levels to evaluate the possibility of a "slewed" (mis-scaled) sensor. A "slewed" sensor could result in poor driveability complaints.

Refer to "Intermittents" in "Symptoms," Section

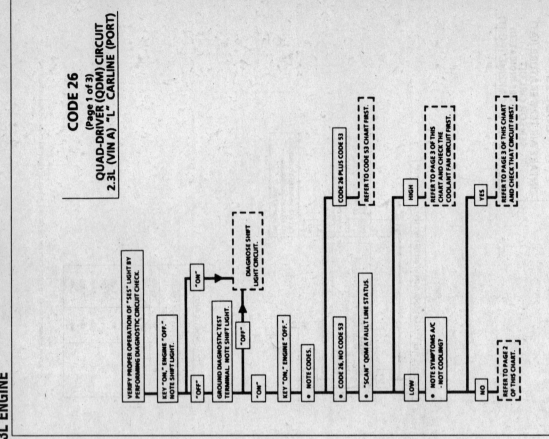

CODE 26
(Page 1 of 3)
QUAD-DRIVER (QDM) CIRCUIT
2.3L (VIN A) "L" CARLINE (PORT)

1990–92 2.3L ENGINE

Circuit Description:

The Electronic Control Module (ECM) controls most components with electronic switches which complete a ground circuit when turned "ON." These switches are arranged in groups of 4, called Quad-Driver Modules (QDM's) which can independently control up to 4 outputs (ECM terminals), although not all outputs are used. When an output is "ON," the terminal is grounded and its voltage normally will be low. When an output is "OFF," its terminal voltage normally will be high.

QDM's are fault protected. If a relay or solenoid coil is shorted, having very low or zero resistance, or if the control side of the circuit is shorted to voltage, it would allow too much current into the QDM. The QDM senses this and the output turns "OFF" or its internal resistance increases to limit current flow and protect the QDM. The result is high output terminal voltage when it should be low. If the circuit from B+ or the component is open, or the control side of the circuit is shorted to ground, terminal voltage will be low, even when output is commanded "OFF." Either of these conditions is considered to be a QDM fault.

Each QDM has a separate fault line to indicate the presence of a current fault to the ECM's central processor. A Tech 1 "Scan" tool displays the status of each of these fault lines as "Low" = OK, "High" = Fault. Code 26 is set if either QDM fault line is "High" for 20 seconds or more.

1990–92 2.3L ENGINE

CODE 26
(Page 3 of 3)
QUAD-DRIVER (QDM) CIRCUIT
2.3L (VIN A) "L" CARLINE (PORT)

CIRCUIT ISOLATED FROM PRIOR CHARTS

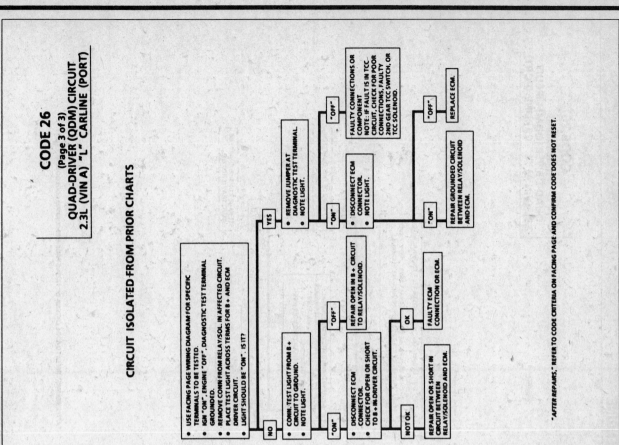

- USE FACING PAGE WIRING DIAGRAM FOR SPECIFIC TERMINALS TO BE TESTED.
- IGN "ON", ENGINE "OFF", DIAGNOSTIC TEST TERMINAL GROUNDED.
- REMOVE CONN FROM RELAY/SOL. IN AFFECTED CIRCUIT.
- PLACE TEST LIGHT ACROSS TERMS FOR B+ AND ECM DRIVER CIRCUIT.
- LIGHT SHOULD BE "ON". IS IT?

YES

- REMOVE JUMPER AT DIAGNOSTIC TEST TERMINAL.
- NOTE LIGHT.

"ON"
- DISCONNECT ECM CONNECTOR.
- NOTE LIGHT.

"OFF"
FAULTY CONNECTIONS OR COMPONENT
NOTE: IF FAULT IS IN TCC-CIRCUIT, CHECK FOR POOR CONNECTIONS, FAULTY 2ND GEAR TCC SWITCH, OR TCC SOLENOID.

"ON"
REPAIR GROUNDED CIRCUIT BETWEEN RELAY/SOLENOID AND ECM.

"OFF"
REPLACE ECM.

NO

- CONN. TEST LIGHT FROM B+ CIRCUIT TO GROUND.
- NOTE LIGHT.

"ON"
- DISCONNECT ECM CONNECTOR.
- CHECK FOR OPEN OR SHORT TO B+ IN DRIVER CIRCUIT.

"OFF"
REPAIR OPEN IN B+ CIRCUIT TO RELAY/SOLENOID.

NOT OK
REPAIR OPEN OR SHORT IN CIRCUIT BETWEEN RELAY/SOLENOID AND ECM.

OK
FAULTY ECM CONNECTION OR ECM.

"AFTER REPAIRS," REFER TO CODE CRITERIA ON FACING PAGE AND CONFIRM CODE DOES NOT RESET.

ECM

Terminal	Circuit	Wire
GF4	SHIFT LIGHT / SENSE LINE	456 TAN/BLK
GF1	CANISTER PURGE / SENSE LINE	428 DK GRN/YEL
GF2	A/C CLUTCH / SENSE LINE — QDM B	459 BRN
GE8	COOLANT FAN / SENSE LINE	335 DK GRN/WHT
GE7	SES LIGHT / SENSE LINE — QDM A	419 BRN/WHT

FAULT LINE

(B+) IGNITION — SHIFT LIGHT
(B+) IGNITION — CANISTER PURGE SOL
(B+) IGNITION — A/C CLUTCH RELAY
(B+) IGNITION — COOLANT FAN RELAY
(B+) IGNITION — SES LIGHT

NOTE: ONLY A PORTION OF EACH CIRCUIT IS SHOWN. REFER TO ECM WIRING DIAGRAMS IN THE BEGINNING OF THIS SECTION FOR MORE DETAIL.

CODE 26
(Page 3 of 3)
QUAD-DRIVER (QDM) CIRCUIT
2.3L (VIN A) "L" CARLINE (PORT)

Diagnostic Aids:

Intermittent faults must be continuously present for at least 20 seconds to cause Code 26 to set. QDM controlled circuits should be inspected for poor terminal contact or damaged harnesses. QDM faults can be detected as noted on page 1 of this chart and when outputs are "ON" or "OFF" as follows:

- Open circuit or control circuit short to ground - output commanded "OFF."
- Shorted device or control circuit short to voltage - output commanded "ON."

1990-92 2.3L ENGINE

CODE 26
(Page 2 of 3)
QUAD-DRIVER (QDM) CIRCUIT
2.3L (VIN A) "L" CARLINE (PORT)

ECM

- SHIFT LIGHT — SENSE LINE
- CANISTER PURGE — SENSE LINE
- A/C CLUTCH — SENSE LINE
- QDM B → FAULT LINE
- COOLANT FAN — SENSE LINE
- SES LIGHT — SENSE LINE
- QDM A → FAULT LINE

GF4 — 456 TAN/BLK
GF1 — 428 DK GRN/YEL
GF2 — 459 BRN
GE8 — 335 DK GRN/WHT
GE7 — 419 BRN/WHT

(B+) IGNITION — SHIFT LIGHT
(B+) IGNITION — CANISTER PURGE SOL
(B+) IGNITION — A/C CLUTCH RELAY
(B+) IGNITION — COOLANT FAN RELAY
(B+) IGNITION — SES LIGHT

NOTE: ONLY A PORTION OF EACH CIRCUIT IS SHOWN. REFER TO ECM WIRING DIAGRAMS IN THE BEGINNING OF THIS SECTION FOR MORE DETAIL.

Diagnostic Aids:

Intermittent faults must be continuously present for at least 20 seconds to cause Code 26 to set. QDM controlled circuits should be inspected for poor terminal contact or damaged harnesses. QDM faults can be detected by the ECM as noted on page 1 of this chart and when outputs are "ON" or "OFF" as follows:
- Open circuit or control circuit short to ground - output commanded "OFF."
- Shorted device or control circuit short to voltage - output commanded "ON."

CODE 26
(Page 2 of 3)
QUAD-DRIVER (QDM) CIRCUIT
2.3L (VIN A) "L" CARLINE (PORT)

• FROM PAGE 1 OF THIS CHART

↓

• KEY "ON", ENGINE "OFF". DIAGNOSTIC TEST TERMINAL NOT GROUNDED.
• WITH DVM, BACKPROBE ECM TERMINALS "GE8", "GF1", AND "GF2". MEASURE VOLTAGE TO GROUND. ALL TERMINALS SHOULD BE B+ (OVER 10 VOLTS).

OK ——→ • GROUND DIAGNOSTIC TEST TERMINAL.
• WITH DVM, BACKPROBE ECM TERMINALS "GE8", "GF1" AND "GF2". MEASURE VOLTAGE TO GROUND. ALL SHOULD BE NEAR ZERO VOLT (LESS THAN .5 VOLT.)

NOT OK ——→ SEE PAGE 3 OF THIS CHART FOR CIRCUIT THAT IS NOT OK.

OK ——→ • NO TROUBLE FOUND.
• CLEAR CODES AND RE-CHECK IF CODE 26 RE-SETS, REPLACE ECM.

NOT OK ——→ SEE PAGE 3 OF THIS CHART FOR CIRCUIT THAT IS NOT OK.

"AFTER REPAIRS," REFER TO CODE CRITERIA ON FACING PAGE AND CONFIRM CODE DOES NOT RESET.

CODE 33

MANIFOLD ABSOLUTE PRESSURE (MAP) SENSOR CIRCUIT
(SIGNAL VOLTAGE HIGH - LOW VACUUM)
2.3L (VIN A) "L" CARLINE (PORT)

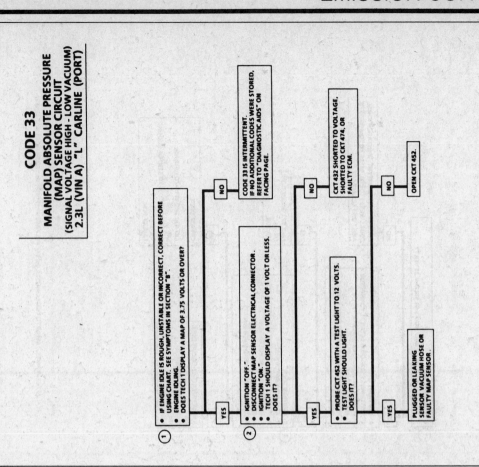

1
- IF ENGINE IDLE IS ROUGH, UNSTABLE OR INCORRECT, CORRECT BEFORE USING CHART. SEE SYMPTOMS IN SECTION "B".
- ENGINE IDLING.
- DOES TECH 1 DISPLAY A MAP OF 3.75 VOLTS OR OVER?

YES	NO

NO → CODE 33 IS INTERMITTENT. IF NO ADDITIONAL CODES WERE STORED, REFER TO "DIAGNOSTIC AIDS" ON FACING PAGE.

2
- IGNITION "OFF."
- DISCONNECT MAP SENSOR ELECTRICAL CONNECTOR.
- IGNITION "ON."
- TECH 1 SHOULD DISPLAY A VOLTAGE OF 1 VOLT OR LESS. DOES IT?

YES	NO

NO → CKT 432 SHORTED TO VOLTAGE, SHORTED TO CKT 474, OR FAULTY ECM.

- PROBE CKT 452 WITH A TEST LIGHT TO 12 VOLTS. TEST LIGHT SHOULD LIGHT.
- DOES IT?

YES	NO

NO → OPEN CKT 452.

YES → PLUGGED OR LEAKING SENSOR VACUUM HOSE OR FAULTY MAP SENSOR.

"AFTER REPAIRS," REFER TO CODE CRITERIA ON FACING PAGE AND CONFIRM CODE DOES NOT RESET.

1990-92 2.3L ENGINE

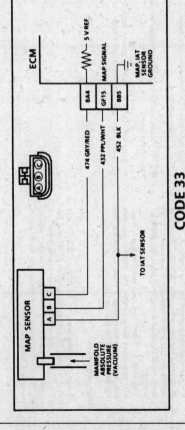

CODE 33

MANIFOLD ABSOLUTE PRESSURE (MAP) SENSOR CIRCUIT
(SIGNAL VOLTAGE HIGH - LOW VACUUM)
2.3L (VIN A) "L" CARLINE (PORT)

Circuit Description:

The Manifold Absolute Pressure (MAP) sensor responds to changes in manifold pressure (vacuum). The ECM receives this information as a signal voltage that will vary from about 1 to 1.5 volts at closed throttle (idle) to 4.5-4.8 volts at wide open throttle (low vacuum).

If the MAP sensor fails, the ECM will substitute a fixed MAP value and use the Throttle Position Sensor (TPS) to control fuel delivery.

Test Description: Numbers below refer to circled numbers on the diagnostic chart.

1. This step will determine if Code 33 is the result of a hard failure or an intermittent condition.

   A Code 33 will set under the following condition:
   - Engine running.
   - MAP signal greater than 80 kPa
   - No Codes 21 or 22.
   - TPS less than 12%.
   - VSS less than 1 mph.
   - Above conditions met for 5 seconds

2. This step simulates conditions for a Code 34. If the ECM recognizes the change, the ECM and CKT 474 and CKT 432 are OK. If CKT 452 is open, there may also be a stored Code 23.

A Code 33 will result if CKT 452 is open or if CKT 432 is shorted to voltage or to CKT 474.

If Code 33 is intermittent, refer to "Symptoms," Section

- Check all connections.
- Disconnect sensor from bracket and twist sensor by hand (only) to check for intermittent connections. Output changes greater than .1 volt indicates a bad connector or connection. If OK, replace sensor.

NOTE: Make sure electrical connector remains securely fastened.

- Refer to CHART C-1D, MAP sensor voltage vs. atmospheric pressure for further diagnosis.

Diagnostic Aids:

With the ignition "ON" and the engine stopped, the manifold pressure is equal to atmospheric pressure and the signal voltage will be high. This information is used by the ECM as an indication of vehicle altitude. Comparison of this reading with a known good vehicle with the same sensor is a good way to check accuracy of a "suspect" sensor. Readings should be the same ± .4 volt.

1990–92 2.3L ENGINE

CODE 34

MANIFOLD ABSOLUTE PRESSURE (MAP) SENSOR CIRCUIT
(SIGNAL VOLTAGE LOW - HIGH VACUUM)
2.3L (VIN A) "L" CARLINE (PORT)

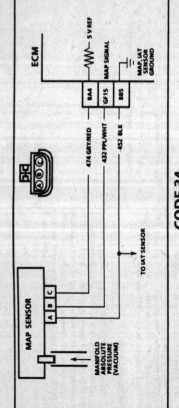

① ENGINE IDLING. DOES TECH 1 DISPLAY MAP VOLTAGE BELOW .25 VOLT?

YES → **② IGNITION "OFF." DISCONNECT SENSOR ELECTRICAL CONNECTOR. JUMPER HARNESS TERMINALS "B" TO "C". IGNITION "ON." MAP VOLTAGE SHOULD READ OVER 4 VOLTS. DOES IT?**

NO → CODE 34 IS INTERMITTENT. IF NO ADDITIONAL CODES WERE STORED, REFER TO "DIAGNOSTIC AIDS" ON FACING PAGE.

② YES → FAULTY CONNECTION OR SENSOR.

② NO → **③ IGNITION "OFF." REMOVE JUMPER WIRE. PROBE TERMINAL "B" (CKT 432) WITH A TEST LIGHT TO BATTERY VOLTAGE. IGNITION "ON." TECH 1 SHOULD READ OVER 4 VOLTS. DOES IT?**

③ YES → 5 VOLT REFERENCE CIRCUIT OPEN OR SHORTED TO GROUND OR FAULTY ECM.

③ NO → CKT 432 OPEN OR CKT 432 SHORTED TO GROUND OR CKT 432 SHORTED TO SENSOR GROUND OR FAULTY ECM.

"AFTER REPAIRS," REFER TO CODE CRITERIA ON FACING PAGE AND CONFIRM CODE DOES NOT RESET.

CODE 34

MANIFOLD ABSOLUTE PRESSURE (MAP) SENSOR CIRCUIT
(SIGNAL VOLTAGE LOW - HIGH VACUUM)
2.3L (VIN A) "L" CARLINE (PORT)

MAP SENSOR — MANIFOLD ABSOLUTE PRESSURE (VACUUM)

A B C

474 GRY/RED
432 PPL/WHT
452 BLK

ECM
5 V REF
BA4
GF15 MAP SIGNAL
BB5 MAP, IAT SENSOR GROUND

TO IAT SENSOR

Circuit Description:

The Manifold Absolute Pressure (MAP) sensor responds to changes in manifold pressure (vacuum). The Electronic Control Module (ECM) receives this information as a signal voltage that will vary from about 1 to 1.5 volts at closed throttle (idle), to 4.5 - 4.8 volts at wide open throttle (low vacuum).

If the MAP sensor fails, the ECM will substitute a fixed MAP value and use the Throttle Position Sensor (TPS) to control fuel delivery.

Test Description: Numbers below refer to circled numbers on the diagnostic chart.

1. This step determines if Code 34 is the result of a hard failure or an intermittent condition. Code 34 will set when:
   - Engine running
   - No Code 21
   - MAP less than 14 kPa
   - Engine rpm less than 1200 or TPS greater than 15.2%
   - Above conditions met for .2 seconds

2. Jumpering harness terminals "B" to "C" (5 volts to signal circuit) will determine if the sensor is at fault, or if there is a problem with the ECM or wiring.

3. The Tech 1 "Scan" tool may not display 5 volts. The important thing is that the ECM recognizes the voltage as more than 4 volts, indicating that the ECM and CKT 432 are OK.

Diagnostic Aids

An intermittent open in CKT 432 or CKT 474 will result in a Code 34. With the ignition "ON" and the engine "OFF," the manifold pressure is equal to atmospheric pressure and the signal voltage will be high. This information is used by the ECM as an indication of vehicle altitude.

Comparison of this reading with a known good vehicle with the same sensor is a good way to check accuracy of a "suspect" sensor. Readings should be the same ± .4 volts. Also CHART C-1D can be used to test the MAP sensor. Refer to "Intermittents" in "Symptoms," Section
   - Check all connections.
   - Disconnect sensor from bracket and twist sensor by hand (only) to check for intermittent connections. Output changes greater than .1 volt indicates a bad connector or connection. If OK, replace sensor.

NOTE: Make sure electrical connector remains securely fastened.
   - Refer to CHART C-1D, MAP sensor voltage vs. atmospheric pressure for further diagnosis.

1990–92 2.3L ENGINE

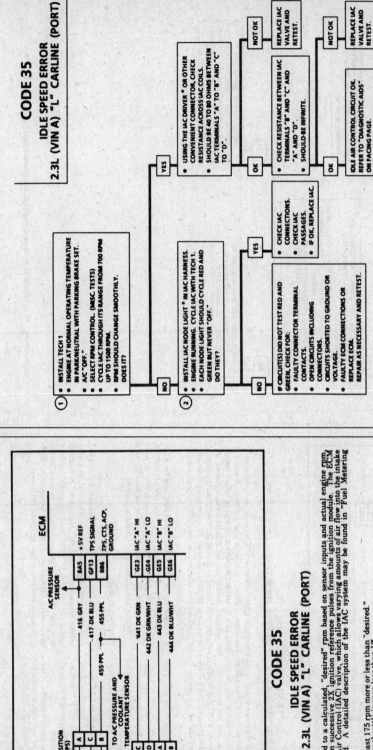

CODE 35
IDLE SPEED ERROR
2.3L (VIN A) "L" CARLINE (PORT)

Circuit Description:

The ECM controls idle speed to a calculated "desired" rpm based on sensor inputs and actual engine rpm, determined by the time between successive 2X ignition reference pulses from the ignition module. The ECM uses 4 circuits to move an Idle Air Control (IAC) valve, which allows varying amounts of air flow into the intake manifold, controlling idle speed. A detailed description of the IAC system may be found in "Fuel Metering System" Section.

Code 35 sets when:
- Engine speed is at least 175 rpm more or less than "desired."
- TPS voltage indicates throttle is open less than 1%.
- VSS indicates vehicle speed is less than 3 mph.
- All above conditions are continuously met for 5 seconds or more.
- IAC steps must be less than 10

Test Description: Numbers below refer to circled numbers on the diagnostic chart.

1. The IAC tester is used to extend and retract the IAC valve. Valve movement is verified by an engine speed change. If no change in engine speed occurs, the valve can be retested when removed from the throttle body.

2. This step checks the quality of the IAC movement in step 1. Between 700 rpm and about 1500 rpm, the engine speed should change smoothly with each flash of the tester light in both extend and retract. If the IAC valve is retracted beyond the control range (about 1500 rpm), it may take many flashes in the extend position before engine speed will begin to drop. This is normal on certain engines, fully extending IAC may cause engine stall. This may be normal.
   Step 1 verified proper IAC valve operation while this step checks the IAC circuits. Each lamp on the node light should flash red and green while the IAC valve is cycled. While the sequence of color is not important if either light is "OFF," or does not

flash red and green, check the circuits for faults, beginning with poor terminal contacts.

Diagnostic Aids:

Check for vacuum leaks, disconnected or brittle vacuum hoses, cuts, etc. Examine manifold and throttle body gaskets for proper seal. Check for cracked intake manifold. Check open, shorts, or poor connections to IAC valve in CKTs 441, 442, 443 and 444.
An open, short, or poor connection in CKTs 441, 442, 443 or 444 will result in improper idle control and may cause Code 35.
An IAC valve which is stopped and cannot respond to the ECM, a throttle stop screw which has been tampered with, or a damaged throttle body or linkage could cause Code 35. If no problem is found and Code 35 resets, replace ECM.

* IAC DRIVER AND NODE LIGHT REQUIRED KIT 222-L FROM: CONCEPT TECHNOLOGY, INC. J37027 FROM: KENT-MOORE, INC.

CLEAR CODES, CONFIRM "CLOSED LOOP" OPERATION, NO "SERVICE ENGINE SOON" LIGHT, PERFORM IAC RESET PROCEDURE PER APPLICABLE SERVICE MANUAL AND VERIFY CONTROLLED IDLE SPEED IS CORRECT.

CODE 41
1X REFERENCE CIRCUIT
2.3L (VIN A) "L" CARLINE (PORT)

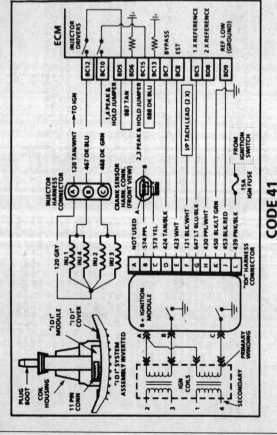

①
- CLEAR CODES.
- IDLE ENGINE FOR 2 MINUTES OR UNTIL "SERVICE ENGINE SOON" LIGHT TURNS "ON," IF SOONER.
- DOES TECH 1 DISPLAY CODE 41?

②
- IGNITION "OFF." DISCONNECT "IDI" CONNECTOR. IGNITION "ON." SET TECH 1 TO DISPLAY 1X REFERENCE PULSES.
- WITH TEST LIGHT CONNECTED TO B+, TOUCH ENGINE HARNESS CONNECTOR CAVITY "G" WITH LIGHT AND REMOVE. LIGHT ON = GROUND.
- TECH 1 DISPLAY SHOULD INDICATE 1X REFERENCE PULSE INCREMENT WHEN TEST LIGHT IS REMOVED. DOES IT?

③
- CHECK CKT 647 FOR OPEN OR SHORT TO GROUND OR VOLTAGE AND REPAIR AS NECESSARY. IF OK, REPLACE ECM.

④
- CHECK FOR POOR CONNECTION BETWEEN "IDI" CONNECTOR CAVITY "G" AND IGNITION MODULE AND REPAIR AS NECESSARY. IF OK, REPLACE IGNITION MODULE.

(① → NO) CODE 41 IS INTERMITTENT. IF NO ADDITIONAL CODES WERE DISPLAYED, REFER TO "DIAGNOSTIC AIDS."

* AFTER REPAIRS," REFER TO CODE CRITERIA ON FACING PAGE AND CONFIRM CODE DOES NOT RESET.

1990-92 2.3L ENGINE

CODE 41
1X REFERENCE CIRCUIT
2.3L (VIN A) "L" CARLINE (PORT)

Circuit Description:

The ignition module sends a reference signal to the Electronic Control Module (ECM) once per revolution to indicate crankshaft position so that the ECM can determine when to pulse the injectors for cylinders 2 and 3 in the ASDF fuel control mode. This signal may be described as a synchronization signal and is called the 1X reference because it occurs one time per revolution. The ignition module applies 5 volts from terminal "G" through CKT 647 to ECM terminal "BC5" and in effect, switches this circuit to ground for a very short period of time, 125 degrees before TDC of cylinders 2 and 3. Code 41 is set if the ECM receives (8) 2X reference pulses with no 1X reference pulses. When Code 41 is present, the ECM pulses the injectors in the SSDF (simultaneous) mode.

Test Description: Numbers below refer to circled numbers on the diagnostic chart.

1. This determines if the ECM recognizes a problem. If it doesn't set Code 41 at this point, the problem is intermittent and could be due to a loose connection. See "Diagnostic Aids."

2. This step simulates the 1X signal. The ECM should recognize the drop in voltage as the test light probe is removed, if the circuit and ECM are OK. This step will give accurate results only if the chart sequence is used - ignition "OFF," ignition "ON," "Scan" tool set to 1X reference and terminal "G" touched with test light probe.

3. If the ECM did not recognize the simulation of the 1X signal, CKT 647 may be open or shorted to ground or voltage. If CKT 647 is OK, the ECM is faulty.

4. Step 2 indicated that CKT 647 is OK and the ECM is capable of recognizing the simulated 1X reference pulse. This indicates either a poor connection at ignition module terminal "G" or a faulty ignition module caused the Code 41.

Diagnostic Aids:

An intermittent may be caused by a poor connection, rubbed through wire insulation, or a wire broken inside the insulation. Inspect ECM harness connector terminal "BC5" and ignition module terminal "G" for improper mating, broken locks, improperly formed or damaged terminals, poor terminal to wire connection and damaged harness.

1990–92 2.3L ENGINE

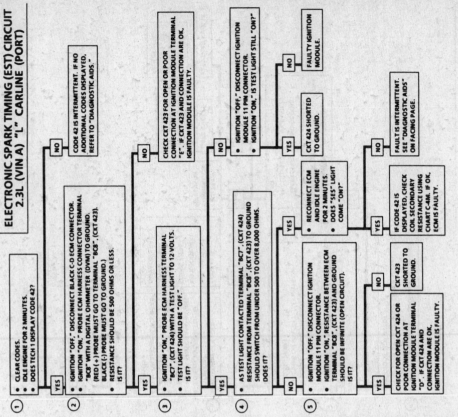

CODE 42

ELECTRONIC SPARK TIMING (EST) CIRCUIT 2.3L (VIN A) "L" CARLINE (PORT)

1.
- CLEAR CODES.
- IDLE ENGINE FOR 2 MINUTES.
- DOES TECH 1 DISPLAY CODE 42?

NO → CODE 42 IS INTERMITTENT. IF NO ADDITIONAL CODES DISPLAYED, REFER TO "DIAGNOSTIC AIDS."

YES ↓

2.
- IGNITION "OFF." DISCONNECT BLACK C-D ECM CONNECTOR.
- IGNITION "ON." PROBE ECM HARNESS CONNECTOR TERMINAL "BC8" WITH A DIGITAL OHMMETER (DVM) TO GROUND. (RED (+) PROBE MUST GO TO TERMINAL "BC8". (CKT 423). BLACK (–) PROBE MUST GO TO GROUND.)
- RESISTANCE SHOULD BE 500 OHMS OR LESS.
- IS IT?

NO → CHECK CKT 423 FOR OPEN OR POOR CONNECTION AT IGNITION MODULE TERMINAL "E". IF CKT 423 AND CONNECTION ARE OK, IGNITION MODULE IS FAULTY.

YES ↓

3.
- IGNITION "ON." PROBE ECM HARNESS TERMINAL "BC7" (CKT 424) WITH A TEST LIGHT TO 12 VOLTS.
- TEST LIGHT SHOULD BE "OFF."
- IS IT?

NO → IGNITION "OFF," DISCONNECT IGNITION MODULE 11 PIN CONNECTOR.
IGNITION "ON," IS TEST LIGHT STILL "ON"?

   NO → FAULTY IGNITION MODULE.

   YES → CKT 424 SHORTED TO GROUND.

YES ↓

4.
- AS TEST LIGHT CONTACTED TERMINAL "BC7" (CKT 424), RESISTANCE FROM TERMINAL "BC8" (CKT 423) TO GROUND SHOULD SWITCH FROM UNDER 500 TO OVER 8,000 OHMS.
- DOES IT?

YES →
- RECONNECT ECM AND IDLE ENGINE FOR 2 MINUTES.
- DOES "SES" LIGHT COME "ON"?

   NO → FAULT IS INTERMITTENT. SEE "DIAGNOSTIC AIDS" ON FACING PAGE.

   YES → IF CODE 42 IS DISPLAYED, CHECK COIL SECONDARY RESISTANCE USING CHART C-4M. IF OK, ECM IS FAULTY.

NO ↓

5.
- IGNITION "OFF." DISCONNECT IGNITION MODULE 11 PIN CONNECTOR.
- IGNITION "ON." RESISTANCE BETWEEN ECM TERMINAL "BC8" (CKT 423) AND GROUND SHOULD BE INFINITE (OPEN CIRCUIT).
- IS IT?

   NO → CKT 423 SHORTED TO GROUND.

   YES → CHECK FOR OPEN CKT 424 OR POOR CONNECTION AT IGNITION MODULE TERMINAL "D". IF CKT 424 AND CONNECTION ARE OK, IGNITION MODULE IS FAULTY.

"AFTER REPAIRS," REFER TO CODE CRITERIA ON FACING PAGE AND CONFIRM CODE DOES NOT RESET.

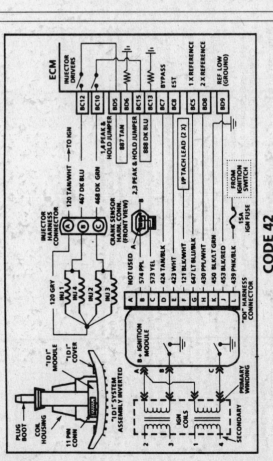

CODE 42

ELECTRONIC SPARK TIMING (EST) CIRCUIT 2.3L (VIN A) "L" CARLINE (PORT)

Circuit Description:

The ignition module sends a reference signal to the ECM when the engine is cranking or running. While the engine is under 700 rpm, the ignition module controls the ignition timing. When the engine speed exceeds 700 rpm, the ECM sends a 5 volts signal on the "Bypass" CKT 424 to switch the timing to ECM control through the EST CKT 423. Engine will remain under EST control until rpm drops below 150.

An open or ground in the EST or "Bypass" circuit will set a Code 42 and cause the engine to run on module or "Bypass" timing. This will result in poor performance and poor fuel economy.

Test Description: Numbers below refer to circled numbers on the diagnostic chart.

1. Checks to see if ECM recognizes a problem. If it doesn't set Code 42 at this point, it is an intermittent problem and could be due to a loose connection.

2. With the ECM disconnected, the ohmmeter should be reading less than 500 ohms, which is the normal resistance of the ignition module. A higher resistance would indicate a fault in CKT 423, a poor ignition module connection or a faulty ignition module.

3. If the test light was "ON" when connected from 12 volts to ECM harness terminal "BC7", either CKT 423 is shorted to ground or the ignition module is faulty.

4. Checks to see if ignition module switches when the bypass circuit is energized by 12 volts through the test light.

5. If the ignition module actually switches, the ohmmeter reading should shift to over 8000 ohms. Disconnecting the ignition module should make the ohmmeter read as if it were monitoring an open circuit (infinite reading). If the ohmmeter has a reading other than infinite, CKT 423 is shorted to ground.

Diagnostic Aids:

An intermittent may be caused by a poor connection, rubbed through wire insulation, or a wire broken inside the insulation. Inspect "BC7" or "BC8", connectors for backed out terminals "BC7" or "BC8", improper mating, broken locks, improperly formed or damaged terminals, poor terminal to wire connection, and damaged harness.

1990-92 2.3L ENGINE

CODE 43
ELECTRONIC SPARK CONTROL (ESC) CIRCUIT
2.3L (VIN A) "L" CARLINE (PORT)

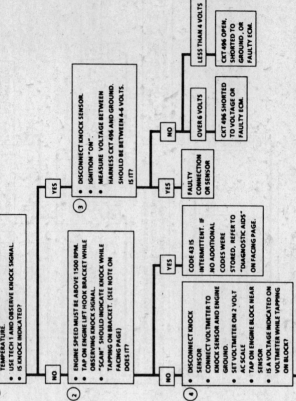

"AFTER REPAIRS," REFER TO CODE CRITERIA ON FACING PAGE AND CONFIRM CODE DOES NOT RESET.

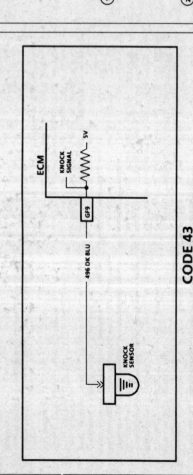

CODE 43
ELECTRONIC SPARK CONTROL (ESC) CIRCUIT
2.3L (VIN A) "L" CARLINE (PORT)

Circuit Description:

The knock sensor detects engine detonation and the ECM retards the electronic spark timing based on the signal being received. The circuitry within the knock sensor causes the ECM 5 volts to be pulled down so that, under a no knock condition, CKT 496 would measure about 2.5 volts. The knock sensor produces an AC signal which rides on the 2.5 volts DC voltage. The amplitude and signal frequency are dependent upon the knock level.

The ECM performs two tests on this circuit to determine if it is operating correctly. If either of the tests fail, a Code 43 will be set.

- If there is an indication of knock for 3.67 seconds over a 3.9 second interval with the engine running.
- If ECM terminal "GF9" voltage is either above about 3.75 volts (indicating open CKT 496), or below about 1.25 volts (indicating CKT 496 is shorted to ground) for 5 seconds or more.

Test Description: Numbers below refer to circled numbers on the diagnostic chart.

1. If the conditions for the test, as described above, are being met, the "Scan" tool will always indicate "Yes" when the knock signal position is selected. If an audible knock is heard from the engine, repair the internal engine problem, because normally, no knock should be detected at idle.
2. If tapping on the engine lift hook does not produce a knock signal, try tapping engine closer to sensor before proceeding.
3. The ECM has a 5 volts signal through a pull-up resistor which should be present at the knock sensor terminal.

4. This test determines if the knock sensor is faulty or if the ESC portion of the MEM-CAL is faulty.

Diagnostic Aids:

Check CKT 496 for a potential open or short to ground.

Also check for proper installation of MEM-CAL. Refer to "Intermittents" in "Symptoms," Section

Mechanical engine knock can cause a knock sensor signal. Abnormal engine noise must be corrected before using this chart.

1990–92 2.3L ENGINE

CODE 44

OXYGEN SENSOR CIRCUIT
(LEAN EXHAUST INDICATED)
2.3L (VIN A) "L" CARLINE (PORT)

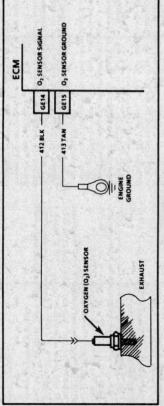

Circuit Description:

The ECM supplies a voltage of about .45 volt between terminals "GE14" and "GE15." (If measured with a 10 megaohm digital voltmeter, this may read as low as .32 volt.) The O_2 sensor varies the voltage within a range of about 1 volt if the exhaust is rich, down through about .10 volt if exhaust is lean.

The sensor is like an open circuit and produces no voltage when it is below 315°C (600°F). An open sensor circuit or cold sensor causes "Open Loop" operation.

Test Description: Number below refers to circled number on the diagnostic chart.

1. Code 44 is set when the O_2 sensor signal voltage on CKT 412:
   - Remains below .3 volt for 50 seconds or more.
   - The system is operating in "Closed Loop."
   - No Code 33 or 34.
   - "Closed Loop" integrator active.

Diagnostic Aids:

The Code 44 or lean exhaust is most likely caused by one of the following:

- CKT 413 If CKT 413 is open, the voltage at terminal "GE14" will be over one volt.
- **Fuel Pressure System** will be lean if pressure is too low. It may be necessary to monitor fuel pressure while driving the car at various road speeds and/or loads to confirm.

- **MAP Sensor** An output that causes the ECM to sense a lower than normal manifold pressure (high vacuum) can cause the system to go lean. Disconnecting the MAP sensor will allow the ECM to substitute a fixed (default) value for the MAP sensor. If the rich condition is gone when the sensor is disconnected, substitute a known good sensor and recheck.

- **Fuel Contamination** Water, even in small amounts, near the in-tank fuel pump inlet can be delivered to the injector. The water causes a lean exhaust and can set a Code 44.

- **Sensor Harness** Sensor pigtail may be mispositioned and contacting the MAP sensor manifold.

- **Engine Misfire** A cylinder misfire will result in unburned oxygen in the exhaust, which could cause Code 44. Refer to CHART C4-M and/or "Symptoms," Section

- **Cracked O_2 Sensor** A crack in the O_2 sensor ceramic or poor sensor ground could cause code 44.

- **Plugged Fuel Filter** A plugged fuel filter can cause a lean condition, and can cause a Code 44 to set.

CODE 44

OXYGEN SENSOR CIRCUIT
(LEAN EXHAUST INDICATED)
2.3L (VIN A) "L" CARLINE (PORT)

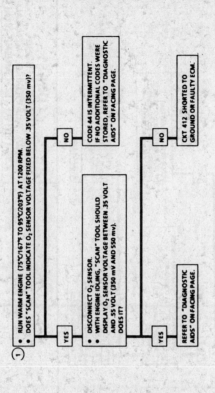

(1)
- RUN WARM ENGINE (75°C/167°F TO 95°C/203°F) AT 1200 RPM.
- DOES "SCAN" TOOL INDICATE O_2 SENSOR VOLTAGE FIXED BELOW .35 VOLT (350 mv)?

YES →
- DISCONNECT O_2 SENSOR.
- WITH ENGINE IDLING, "SCAN" TOOL SHOULD DISPLAY O_2 SENSOR VOLTAGE BETWEEN .35 VOLT AND .55 VOLT (350 mV AND 550 mv).
- DOES IT?

YES → REFER TO "DIAGNOSTIC AIDS" ON FACING PAGE.

NO → CODE 44 IS INTERMITTENT. IF NO ADDITIONAL CODES WERE STORED, REFER TO "DIAGNOSTIC AIDS" ON FACING PAGE.

NO → CKT 412 SHORTED TO GROUND OR FAULTY ECM.

"AFTER REPAIRS," REFER TO CODE CRITERIA ON FACING PAGE AND CONFIRM CODE DOES NOT RESET.

1990–92 2.3L ENGINE

CODE 45
OXYGEN SENSOR CIRCUIT
(RICH EXHAUST INDICATED)
2.3L (VIN A) "L" CARLINE (PORT)

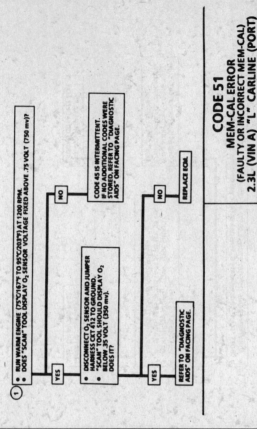

① • RUN WARM ENGINE (75°C/167°F TO 95°C/203°F) AT 1200 RPM.
  • DOES "SCAN" TOOL DISPLAY O₂ SENSOR VOLTAGE FIXED ABOVE .75 VOLT (750 mv)?

YES → • DISCONNECT O₂ SENSOR AND JUMPER HARNESS CKT 412 TO GROUND.
  • "SCAN" TOOL SHOULD DISPLAY O₂ BELOW .35 VOLT (350 mv).
  DOES IT?

  YES → REFER TO "DIAGNOSTIC AIDS" ON FACING PAGE.

  NO → REPLACE ECM.

NO → CODE 45 IS INTERMITTENT. IF NO ADDITIONAL CODES WERE STORED, REFER TO "DIAGNOSTIC AIDS" ON FACING PAGE.

CODE 51
MEM-CAL ERROR
(FAULTY OR INCORRECT MEM-CAL)
2.3L (VIN A) "L" CARLINE (PORT)

CHECK THAT ALL PINS ARE FULLY INSERTED IN THE SOCKET AND THAT MEM-CAL IS PROPERLY LATCHED. IF OK, REPLACE MEM-CAL, CLEAR MEMORY, AND RECHECK. IF CODE 51 REAPPEARS, REPLACE ECM.

NOTICE: TO PREVENT POSSIBLE ELECTROSTATIC DISCHARGE DAMAGE TO THE ECM OR MEM-CAL, DO NOT TOUCH THE COMPONENT LEADS, AND DO NOT REMOVE THE MEM CAL COVER OR THE INTEGRATED CIRCUIT FROM CARRIER.

"AFTER REPAIRS," REFER TO CODE CRITERIA ON FACING PAGE AND CONFIRM CODE DOES NOT RESET.

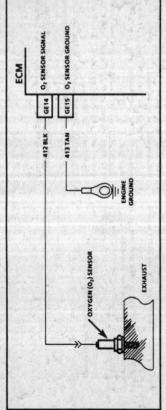

CODE 45
OXYGEN SENSOR CIRCUIT
(RICH EXHAUST INDICATED)
2.3L (VIN A) "L" CARLINE (PORT)

Circuit Description:

The ECM supplies a voltage of about .45 volt between terminals "GE14" and "GE15". (If measured with a 10 megohm digital voltmeter, this may read as low as .32 volt.) The O₂ sensor varies the voltage within a range of about 1 volt if the exhaust is rich, down through about .10 volt if exhaust is lean.

The sensor is like an open circuit and produces no voltage when it is below 315° C (600° F). An open sensor circuit or cold sensor causes "Open Loop" operation.

Test Description: Numbers below refer to circled numbers on the diagnostic chart.

1. Code 45 is set when:
   • O₂ voltage is above .75 volt
   • No Code 33 or 34
   • Fuel system in "Closed Loop"
   • TPS above 5%
   • Above conditions met for 30 seconds or O₂ voltage is above 1 volt for 5 seconds.

Diagnostic Aids:

The Code 45 or rich exhaust is most likely caused by one of the following:

• **Fuel Pressure** System will go rich if pressure is too high. The ECM can compensate for some increase. However, if it gets too high, a Code 45 will be set. See "Fuel System" diagnosis CHART A-7.

• **Leaking Injector** See CHART A-7.

• **HEI Shielding** An open ground CKT 453 may result in EMI or induced electrical noise. The ECM looks at this noise as reference pulses. The additional pulses result in a higher than actual engine speed signal. The ECM then delivers too much fuel causing system to go rich.

Engine tachometer will also show higher than actual engine speed which can help in diagnosing this problem.

• **Canister Purge** Check for fuel saturation. If full of fuel, check canister control and hoses. See "Canister Purge," "Evaporative Emission Control System (EECS)

• **MAP Sensor** An output that causes the ECM to sense a higher than normal manifold pressure (low vacuum) can cause the system to go rich. Disconnecting the MAP sensor will allow the ECM to set a fixed value for the MAP sensor. Substitute a different MAP sensor if the rich condition is gone while the sensor is disconnected.

• **Pressure Regulator** Check for leaking fuel pressure regulator diaphragm by checking for the presence of liquid fuel in the vacuum line to the regulator.

• **TPS** An intermittent TPS output will cause the system to go rich due to a false indication of the engine accelerating.

• **O₂ Sensor Contamination** Inspect oxygen sensor for silicone contamination from fuel or use of improper RTV sealant. The sensor may have a white powdery coating and result in a high but false signal (rich exhaust indication). The ECM will then reduce the amount of fuel delivered to the engine causing a severe surge driveability problem.

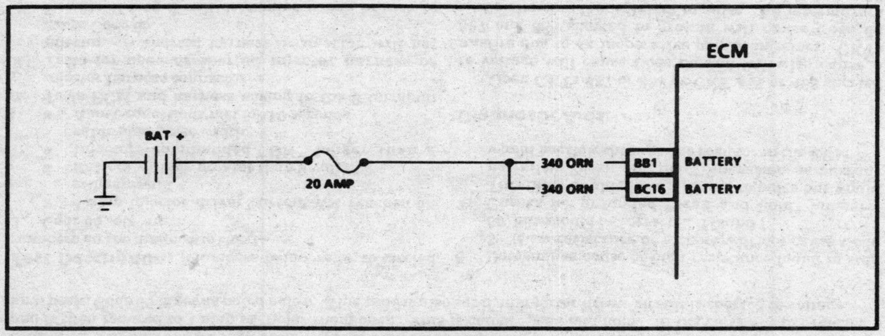

1990–92 2.3L ENGINE

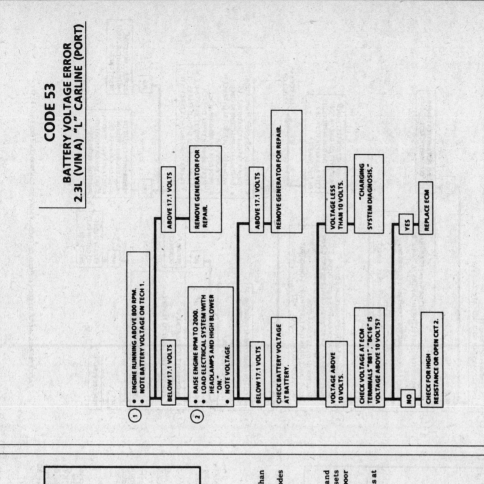

CODE 53
BATTERY VOLTAGE ERROR
2.3L (VIN A) "L" CARLINE (PORT)

Circuit Description:

Code 53 will set when the ignition is "ON" and ECM terminal "BB1" and "BC16" voltages are more than 17.1 volts for about 2 seconds, or under 10 volts for more than 240 seconds.

During the time the failure is present, all ECM outputs will be disengaged. (The setting of additional codes may result).

Test Description: Numbers below refer to circled numbers on the diagnostic chart.

1. Normal battery output is between 10 - 17.1 volts.
2. Checks to see if generator is faulty under load condition. If the voltage is above 17.1 volts or under 10 volts,

Note On Intermittents:

Charging battery with a battery charger and starting engine, may set Code 53. If code sets when an accessory is operated, check for poor connections or excessive current draw.

Also, check for poor connections at starter solenoid or fusible link junction box.

CODE 53
BATTERY VOLTAGE ERROR
2.3L (VIN A) "L" CARLINE (PORT)

Diagram text (flowchart):

① ENGINE RUNNING ABOVE 800 RPM.
• NOTE BATTERY VOLTAGE ON TECH 1.

BELOW 17.1 VOLTS | ABOVE 17.1 VOLTS

ABOVE 17.1 VOLTS → REMOVE GENERATOR FOR REPAIR.

② RAISE ENGINE RPM TO 2000.
• LOAD ELECTRICAL SYSTEM WITH HEADLAMPS AND HIGH BLOWER "ON."
• NOTE VOLTAGE.

BELOW 17.1 VOLTS | ABOVE 17.1 VOLTS

ABOVE 17.1 VOLTS → REMOVE GENERATOR FOR REPAIR.

CHECK BATTERY VOLTAGE AT BATTERY.

VOLTAGE ABOVE 10 VOLTS. | VOLTAGE LESS THAN 10 VOLTS.

VOLTAGE LESS THAN 10 VOLTS. → "CHARGING SYSTEM DIAGNOSIS."

CHECK VOLTAGE AT ECM TERMINALS "BB1", "BC16" IS VOLTAGE ABOVE 10 VOLTS?

NO | YES

YES → REPLACE ECM

NO → CHECK FOR HIGH RESISTANCE OR OPEN CKT 2.

Circuit diagram labels:

BAT +
20 AMP
340 OHM — BB1 — BATTERY
340 OHM — BC16 — BATTERY
ECM

"AFTER REPAIRS," REFER TO CODE CRITERIA ON FACING PAGE AND CONFIRM CODE DOES NOT RESET.

1990–92 2.3L ENGINE

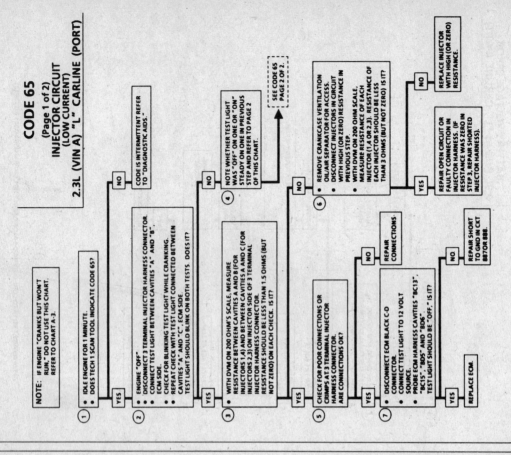

CODE 65
(Page 1 of 2)
INJECTOR CIRCUIT
(LOW CURRENT)
2.3L (VIN A) "L" CARLINE (PORT)

NOTE: IF ENGINE "CRANKS BUT WON'T RUN," DO NOT USE THIS CHART. REFER TO CHART A-3.

1.
- IDLE ENGINE FOR 1 MINUTE.
- DOES TECH 1 SCAN TOOL INDICATE CODE 65?

  NO → CODE IS INTERMITTENT. REFER TO "DIAGNOSTIC AIDS."

  YES ↓

2.
- ENGINE "OFF."
- DISCONNECT 3 TERMINAL INJECTOR HARNESS CONNECTOR.
- CONNECT TEST LIGHT BETWEEN CAVITIES "A" AND "B", ECM SIDE.
- CHECK FOR BLINKING TEST LIGHT WHILE CRANKING.
- REPEAT CHECK WITH TEST LIGHT CONNECTED BETWEEN CAVITIES "A" AND "C", ECM SIDE.
- TEST LIGHT SHOULD BLINK ON BOTH TESTS. DOES IT?

  NO ↓

3.
- WITH DVM ON 200 OHM'S SCALE, MEASURE RESISTANCE BETWEEN CAVITIES A AND B (FOR INJECTORS 1,4) AND BETWEEN CAVITIES A AND C (FOR INJECTORS 2,3) ON INJECTOR SIDE OF 3 TERMINAL INJECTOR HARNESS CONNECTOR.
- RESISTANCE SHOULD BE LESS THAN 1.5 OHMS (BUT NOT ZERO) ON EACH CHECK. IS IT?

  NO →

4. NOTE WHETHER TEST LIGHT WAS "OFF" ON ONE OR "ON" STEADY ON ONE IN PREVIOUS STEP AND REFER TO PAGE 2 OF THIS CHART.

  ↑ SEE CODE 65 PAGE 2 OF 2.

5. CHECK FOR POOR CONNECTIONS OR CRIMPS AT 3 TERMINAL INJECTOR HARNESS CONNECTOR. ARE CONNECTIONS OK?

  YES ↓
  NO → REPAIR CONNECTIONS.

6.
- REMOVE CRANKCASE VENTILATION OIL/AIR SEPARATOR FOR ACCESS.
- DISCONNECT INJECTORS IN CIRCUIT WITH HIGH (OR ZERO) RESISTANCE IN PREVIOUS STEP.
- WITH DVM ON 200 OHM SCALE, MEASURE RESISTANCE OF EACH INJECTOR (1,4 OR 2,3). RESISTANCE OF EACH INJECTOR SHOULD BE LESS THAN 3 OHMS (BUT NOT ZERO) IS IT?

  NO → REPLACE INJECTOR WITH HIGH (OR ZERO) RESISTANCE.

  YES → REPAIR OPEN CIRCUIT OR FAULTY CONNECTION IN INJECTOR HARNESS. (IF RESISTANCE WAS ZERO IN STEP 3, REPAIR SHORTED INJECTOR HARNESS).

7.
- DISCONNECT ECM BLACK C-D CONNECTOR.
- CONNECT TEST LIGHT TO 12 VOLT SOURCE.
- PROBE ECM HARNESS CAVITIES "BC13", "BC15", "BD5" AND "BD6".
- TEST LIGHT SHOULD BE "OFF." IS IT?

  NO → REPAIR SHORT TO GND IN CKT 887 OR 888.

  YES → REPLACE ECM.

"AFTER REPAIRS," REFER TO CODE CRITERIA ON FACING PAGE AND CONFIRM CODE DOES NOT RESET.

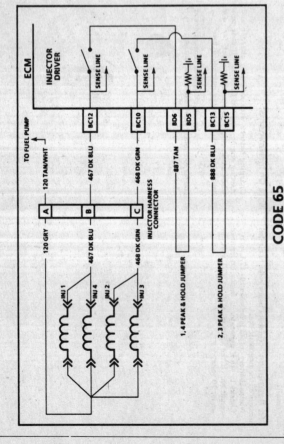

CODE 65
(Page 1 of 2)
FUEL INJECTOR CIRCUIT
(LOW CURRENT)
2.3L (VIN A) "L" CARLINE (PORT)

TO FUEL PUMP — 120 TAN/WHT
ECM
INJECTOR DRIVER
SENSE LINE
BC12 — 467 DK BLU
BC10 — 468 DK GRN
SENSE LINE
BD6 — 887 TAN
BD5
SENSE LINE
BC13 — 888 DK BLU
BC15
SENSE LINE

120 GRY
A
467 DK BLU
B
468 DK GRN
C
INJECTOR HARNESS CONNECTOR

INJ 1 / INJ 4 / INJ 2 / INJ 3

1,4 PEAK & HOLD JUMPER
2,3 PEAK & HOLD JUMPER

Circuit Description:

The ECM has two injector driver circuits, each of which controls a pair of injectors (1 and 4 or 2 and 3). The ECM monitors the current in each driver circuit by measuring voltage drop through a fixed resistor and is able to control it. The current through each driver is allowed to rise to a "peak" of 4 amps to quickly open the injectors and is then reduced to 1 amp to "hold" them open. This is called "peak and hold." If the current can't reach a 4 amp peak, Code 65 is set as noted below. This code is also set if an injector driver circuit is shorted to voltage.

Test Description: Numbers below refer to circled numbers on the diagnostic chart.

1. Code 65 sets when:
   - 4 amp injector driver current not reached on either circuit
   - Battery voltage greater than 9 volts.
   - Injectors commanded "ON" longer than a calibrated pulse width
   - Above conditions met for 10 seconds

2. Tests ECM and harness wiring to the 3 terminal injector harness connector.

3. Tests for open or shorted injector harness or injector. A shorted harness or injector will not cause Code 65.

4. Results of step 2 will determine which branch to follow on page 2.

5. Checks remainder of circuit from injectors to ECM as both harnesses were confirmed OK in steps 2 and 3.

6. Determines cause of high resistance found in step 3. (Low resistance or a short will not cause Code 65, but should be corrected if found.)

7. Checks for grounded "peak and hold" jumpers. This fault would allow injectors to pulse but would not allow "peak and hold" operation as current would not flow through the resistor in the ECM.

Diagnostic Aids:

Open CKTs 887 or 888 or CKT 467 or 468 shorted to voltage will cause Code 65 and will also cause a misfire due to an inoperative pair of injectors. CKTs 887 and 888 shorted to ground will cause Code 65 while allowing the injectors to pulse. An intermittent problem would have to be present for at least 20 seconds to set Code 65.

1990-92 2.3L ENGINE

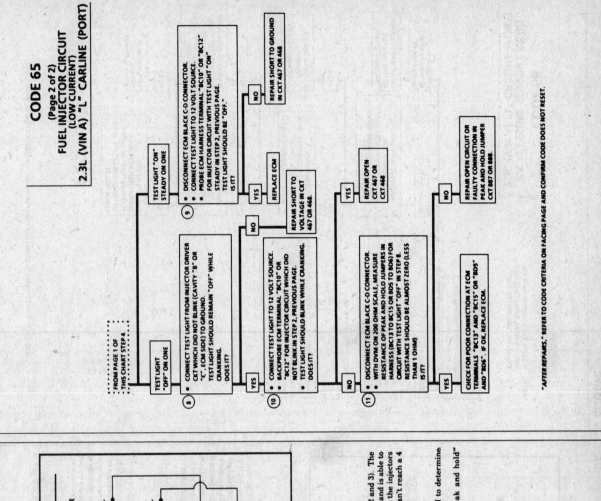

CODE 65

(Page 2 of 2)
FUEL INJECTOR CIRCUIT
(LOW CURRENT)
2.3L (VIN A) "L" CARLINE (PORT)

Circuit Description:

The ECM has two injector driver circuits, each of which controls a pair of injectors (1 and 4 or 2 and 3). The ECM monitors the current in each driver circuit by measuring voltage drop through a fixed resistor and is able to control it. The current through each driver is allowed to rise to a "peak" of 4 amps to quickly open the injectors and is then reduced to 1 amp to "hold" them open. This is called "peak and hold." If the current can't reach a 4 amp peak, Code 65 is set. This code is also set if an injector driver circuit is shorted to voltage.

Test Description: Numbers below refer to circled numbers on the diagnostic chart.

8. This checks for short to voltage in injector driver circuits. It is necessary to crank the engine to assure voltage to CKT 120.

9. Determines whether injector driver CKTs 467 and 468 are shorted to ground.

10. This checks the output at the ECM to determine if CKTs 467 and 468 are OK.

11. Checks for good continuity of "peak and hold" jumpers CKTs 887 and 888.

"AFTER REPAIRS," REFER TO CODE CRITERIA ON FACING PAGE AND CONFIRM CODE DOES NOT RESET.

1990–92 2.3L ENGINE

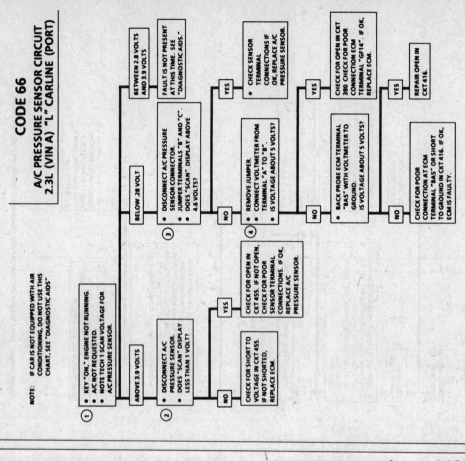

CODE 66
A/C PRESSURE SENSOR CIRCUIT
2.3L (VIN A) "L" CARLINE (PORT)

NOTE: IF CAR IS NOT EQUIPPED WITH AIR CONDITIONING, DO NOT USE THIS CHART, SEE "DIAGNOSTIC AIDS"

① • KEY "ON," ENGINE NOT RUNNING.
   • A/C NOT REQUESTED.
   • NOTE TECH 1 SCAN VOLTAGE FOR A/C PRESSURE SENSOR.

ABOVE 3.9 VOLTS

② • DISCONNECT A/C PRESSURE SENSOR.
   • DOES "SCAN" DISPLAY LESS THAN 1 VOLT?

- CHECK FOR SHORT TO VOLTAGE IN CKT 455. IF NOT SHORTED, REPLACE ECM.

NO → CHECK FOR OPEN IN CKT 455. IF NOT OPEN, CHECK FOR POOR SENSOR TERMINAL CONNECTIONS. IF OK, REPLACE A/C PRESSURE SENSOR.

YES

BELOW .28 VOLT

③ • DISCONNECT A/C PRESSURE SENSOR CONNECTOR.
   • JUMPER TERMINALS "B" AND "C".
   • DOES "SCAN" DISPLAY ABOVE 4.6 VOLTS?

BETWEEN 2.8 VOLTS AND 3.9 VOLTS

- FAULT IS NOT PRESENT AT THIS TIME. SEE "DIAGNOSTIC AIDS."

YES → • CHECK SENSOR TERMINAL CONNECTIONS IF OK, REPLACE A/C PRESSURE SENSOR.

NO

④ • REMOVE JUMPER.
   • CONNECT VOLTMETER FROM TERMINAL "A" TO "B".
   • IS VOLTAGE ABOUT 5 VOLTS?

YES → • CHECK FOR OPEN IN CKT 380 CHECK FOR POOR CONNECTION ECM TERMINAL "GF14". IF OK, REPLACE ECM.

NO → • BACK PROBE ECM TERMINAL "BA5" WITH VOLTMETER TO GROUND. IS VOLTAGE ABOUT 5 VOLTS?

YES → REPAIR OPEN IN CKT 416.

NO → CHECK FOR POOR CONNECTION AT ECM TERMINAL "BA5" OR SHORT TO GROUND IN CKT 416. IF OK, ECM IS FAULTY.

• CLEAR CODES AND CONFIRM "CLOSED LOOP" OPERATION AND NO "SERVICE ENGINE SOON" LIGHT.

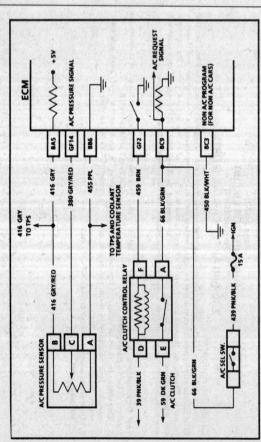

CODE 66
A/C PRESSURE SENSOR CIRCUIT
2.3L (VIN A) "L" CARLINE (PORT)

Circuit Description:

The A/C pressure sensor responds to changes in A/C refrigerant system high side pressure. This input indicates how much load the A/C compressor is putting on the engine and is one of the factors used by the ECM to determine IAC valve position for idle speed control. The circuit consists of a 5 volts reference and a ground, both provided by the ECM, and a signal line to the ECM. The signal is a voltage which is proportional to the pressure. The sensor's range of operation is 0 to 450 psi. At 0 psi, the signal will be about .1 volt, varying up to about 4.9 volts at 450 psi or above. Code 66 sets if the voltage is above 4.9 volts or below .28 volt 15 seconds or more. Code 66 will also set if A/C is not requested and voltage is greater than 3.9 volts. The A/C compressor is disabled by the ECM if Code 66 is present, or if pressure is above or below calibrated values described in "ECM Controlled Air Conditioning" Section.

Test Description: Numbers below refer to circled numbers on the diagnostic chart.

1. This step checks the voltage signal being received by the ECM from the A/C pressure sensor. The normal operating range is between .28 volt and 4.9 volts.

2. Checks to see if the high voltage signal is from a shorted sensor or a short to voltage in the circuit. Normally, disconnecting the sensor would make a normal circuit go to near zero volt.

3. Checks to see if low voltage signal is from the sensor or the circuit. Jumpering the sensor signal CKT 380 to 5 volts, checks the circuit, connections, and ECM.

4. This step checks to see if the low voltage signal was due to an open in the sensor circuit or the 5

volts reference circuit since the prior step eliminated the pressure sensor.

Diagnostic Aids:

Code 66 sets when signal voltage falls outside the normal possible range of the sensor and is not due to a refrigerant system problem. If problem is intermittent, check for opens or shorts in harness or poor connections. If OK, replace A/C pressure sensor. If Code 66 resets, replace ECM.

Non-A/C Program

Code 66 will set on a Non-A/C car if CKT 450 to terminal "BC3" is open or shorted to B + .

1990–92 2.3L ENGINE

ECM CONNECTOR "A"

	PIN FUNCTION	CKT #	WIRE COLOR	COMPONENT CONNECTOR CAVITY	NORMAL VOLTAGES KEY "ON"	NORMAL VOLTAGES ENG RUN	CODES AFFECT	POSSIBLE SYMPTOMS FROM FAULTY CIRCUIT
BA1								
BA2								
BA3								
BA4	MAP SENSOR 5 VOLT REFERENCE	474	GRY RED	MAP SENSOR "C"	5V	5V	34 (10)	LACK OF POWER ROUGH IDLE SURGE
BA5	TPS 5 VOLT REFERENCE	416	GRY	TPS "A"	5V	5V	22 (8)	HIGH IDLE
BA6	IGNITION FEED	439	PNK/BLK	ECM FUSE	B+	B+		NO SES LIGHT, ENGINE CRANKS BUT WILL NOT START (8)
9A7								
BA8	SERIAL DATA	461	ORN	ALDL CONNECTOR TERMINAL "M"				NO SERIAL DATA "SCAN" TOOL WILL NOT READ DATA (10)
9A9								
3A10	FUEL PUMP RELAY DRIVE	465	DK GRN	FUEL PUMP RELAY "D"	B + (4)	B + (4)		LONG CRANKING TIME BEFORE ENGINE STARTS (8)
3A11								
BA12	ECM GROUND	450	BLK/WHT	ENGINE BLOCK	0*	0*		

(1) VARIES FROM 60 TO BATTERY VOLTAGE, DEPENDING ON POSITION OF DRIVE WHEELS
(2) BATTERY VOLTAGE FOR FIRST TWO SECONDS
(3) VARIES
(4) BATTERY VOLTAGE WHEN FUEL PUMP'S RUNNING
(5) READS BATTERY VOLTAGE IN GEAR
(6) BATTERY VOLTAGE WHEN ENGINE'S CRANKING
(7) OPEN CIRCUIT
(8) GROUNDED CIRCUIT
(9) OPEN/GROUNDED CIRCUIT
(10) LESS THAN 1 VOLT
(11) LESS THAN 5 VOLT (500 MV)

ECM CONNECTOR "B"

	PIN FUNCTION	CKT #	WIRE COLOR	COMPONENT CONNECTOR CAVITY	NORMAL VOLTAGES KEY "ON"	NORMAL VOLTAGES ENG RUN	CODES AFFECT	POSSIBLE SYMPTOMS FROM FAULTY CIRCUIT
BB1	BATTERY FEED	340	ORN	FUEL PUMP RELAY TERMINAL "A" AND OIL PRESSURE TERM "C"	B +	B +		REDUNDANT B + FEED
BB2								
BB3								
BB4								
BB5	MAP AND IAT SENSOR GROUND	452	BLK	IAT TERM "B" MAP TERM "A"	0*	0*	23 (8) 33 (8)	STALLING AT IDLE AND RUNS ROUGH
BB6	TPS, CTS AND A/C SENSOR GROUND	455	PPL	TPS TERM "B" A/C TERM "A" CTS TERM "A"	0*	0*	15 (8) 21 (8) 66 (8)	ROUGH IDLE LACK OF PERFORMANCE EXHAUST ODOR
BB7								
BB8								
BB9	VEHICLE SPEED SENSOR (VSS) SIGNAL LOW	401	PPL	VEHICLE SPEED SENSOR (VSS) TERM "B"	0*	0*	24 (10)	NO VSS SIGNAL INOPERATIVE SPEEDOMETER INOPERATIVE CRUISE CONTROL
BB10	VEHICLE SPEED SENSOR (VSS) SIGNAL HIGH	400	YEL	VEHICLE SPEED SENSOR (VSS) TERM "A"	0*	0*	24 (10)	NO VSS SIGNAL INOPERATIVE SPEEDOMETER INOPERATIVE CRUISE CONTROL
BB11	ECM TO INSTRUMENT CLUSTER VSS	B17	DK GRN/WHT	P CLUSTER TERM "A"	(1) 4.85V	(1) 5.3V		INOPERATIVE SPEEDOMETER
BB12								

(1) VARIES FROM 60 TO BATTERY VOLTAGE, DEPENDING ON POSITION OF DRIVE WHEELS
(2) BATTERY VOLTAGE FOR FIRST TWO SECONDS
(3) VARIES
(4) BATTERY VOLTAGE WHEN FUEL PUMP IS RUNNING
(5) VARIES WITH TEMPERATURE
(6) READS BATTERY VOLTAGE IN GEAR
(7) BATTERY VOLTAGE WHEN ENGINE IS CRANKING
(8) OPEN CIRCUIT
(9) GROUNDED CIRCUIT
(10) OPEN/GROUNDED CIRCUIT
(11) LESS THAN 1 VOLT
* LESS THAN 5 VOLT (500 MV)

1990–92 2.3L ENGINE

ECM CONNECTOR "D"

PIN	FUNCTION	CKT #	WIRE COLOR	COMPONENT CONNECTOR CAVITY	NORMAL VOLTAGES KEY "ON"	NORMAL VOLTAGES ENG RUN	CODES AFFECT	POSSIBLE SYMPTOMS FROM FAULTY CIRCUIT
BD1	ECM GROUND	551	TAN/WHT	ENGINE BLOCK	0*	0*		
BD2								
BD3								
BD4								
BD5	PEAK & HOLD INJ JUMPER 1 & 4	887	TAN	ECM TERMINAL BD6	0*	0*	65 (10)	ROUGH IDLE, HARD TO START, LACK OF PERFORMANCE
BD6	PEAK & HOLD INJ JUMPER 1 & 4	887	TAN	ECM TERMINAL BD5	0*	0*	65 (10)	ROUGH IDLE, HARD TO START, LACK OF PERFORMANCE
BD7								
BD8	2X REF HI	430	PPL/WHT	IGNITION MODULE TERMINAL "H"	0*	1 6V		ENGINE CRANKS BUT WILL NOT START
BD9	REFERENCE GROUND	453	BLK-RED	IGNITION MODULE TERMINAL "J"	0*	0*		
BD10								
BD11								
BD12								
BD13	P/S PRESS SIGNAL	495	TAN	POWER STEERING PRESSURE SWITCH TERM "B"	8+	ON 0* OFF 8+		HIGH IDLE (9)
BD14								

(1) VARIES FROM 60 TO BATTERY VOLTAGE, DEPENDING ON POSITION OF DRIVE WHEELS
(2) BATTERY VOLTAGE FOR FIRST TWO SECONDS
(3) VARIES
(4) BATTERY VOLTAGE WHEN FUEL PUMP'S RUNNING
(5) VARIES WITH TEMPERATURE
(6) READS BATTERY VOLTAGE IN GEAR
(7) BATTERY VOLTAGE WHEN ENGINE'S CRANKING
(8) OPEN CIRCUIT
(9) GROUNDED CIRCUIT
(10) OPEN/GROUNDED CIRCUIT
(11) LESS THAN 1 VOLT
* LESS THAN 5 VOLT (500 MV)

ECM CONNECTOR "C"

PIN	FUNCTION	CKT #	WIRE COLOR	COMPONENT CONNECTOR CAVITY	NORMAL VOLTAGES KEY "ON"	NORMAL VOLTAGES ENG RUN	CODES AFFECT	POSSIBLE SYMPTOMS FROM FAULTY CIRCUIT
BC1								
BC2								
BC3								
BC4								
BC5	1X REF HI	647	LT BLU/BLK	IGNITION MODULE TERM G		4 8V	41 (10)	LACK OF PERFORMANCE
BC6								
BC7	IGNITION BYPASS	424	TAN/BLK	IGNITION MODULE TERM D	0*	5V	42 (10)	LACK OF POWER, HUNTING IDLE, STALLING
BC8	ELECTRONIC SPARK TIMING (EST)	423	WHT	IGNITION MODULE TERM E	0*	2 V	42 (10)	LACK OF POWER, STALLS, SURGES
BC9	A/C REQUEST SIGNAL	66	BLK/LT GRN	A/C SELECT SWITCH	0*	ON 8+ OFF 0*		INOPERATIVE A/C, INCORRECT IDLE
BC10	INJECTOR DRIVERS 2 & 3	468	DK GRN	INJECTOR CONNECTOR C	B+	B+	65 (10)	ROUGH IDLE, HARD TO START, LACK OF PERFORMANCE
BC11								
BC12	INJECTOR DRIVERS 1 & 4	467	DK BLU	INJECTOR CONNECTOR B	B+	B+	65 (10)	ROUGH IDLE, HARD TO START, LACK OF PERFORMANCE
BC13	PEAK & HOLD INJ JUMPER 2 & 3	888	DK BLU	ECM CONNECTOR BC15	0*	0*	55 (10)	ROUGH IDLE, HARD TO START, LACK OF PERFORMANCE
BC14								
BC15	PEAK & HOLD INJ JUMPER 2 & 3	888	DK BLU	ECM CONNECTOR BC13	0*	B+	65 (10)	ROUGH IDLE, HARD TO START, LACK OF PERFORMANCE
BC16	BATTERY FEED	340	ORN	FUEL PUMP ECM FUSE 20A	B+	B+		REDUNDANT B+ FEED

(1) VARIES FROM 60 TO BATTERY VOLTAGE, DEPENDING ON POSITION OF DRIVE WHEELS
(2) BATTERY VOLTAGE FOR FIRST TWO SECONDS
(3) VARIES
(4) BATTERY VOLTAGE WHEN FUEL PUMP'S RUNNING
(5) VARIES WITH TEMPERATURE
(6) READS BATTERY VOLTAGE IN GEAR
(7) BATTERY VOLTAGE WHEN ENGINE'S CRANKING
(8) OPEN CIRCUIT
(9) GROUNDED CIRCUIT
(10) OPEN/GROUNDED CIRCUIT
(11) LESS THAN 1 VOLT
* LESS THAN 5 VOLT (500 MV)

1990–92 2.3L ENGINE

ECM CONNECTOR "E"

PIN FUNCTION	CKT #	WIRE COLOR	COMPONENT CONNECTOR CAVITY	NORMAL VOLTAGES KEY "ON"	NORMAL VOLTAGES ENG RUN	CODES AFFECT	POSSIBLE SYMPTOMS FROM FAULTY CIRCUIT
GE1							
GE2							
GE3 IAC COIL "A" HIGH	441	DK GRN	IAC VALVE "C"	0 OR B+	0 OR B+	35	INCORRECT IDLE SURGES
GE4 IAC COIL "A" LOW	442	DK GRN/WHT	IAC VALVE "D"	0 OR B+	0 OR B+	35	INCORRECT IDLE SURGES
GE5 IAC COIL "B" HIGH	443	DK BLU	IAC VALVE "A"	0 OR B+	0 OR B+	35	INCORRECT IDLE SURGES
GE6 IAC COIL "B" LOW	444	DK BLU/WHT	IAC VALVE "B"	0 OR B+	0 OR B+	35	INCORRECT IDLE SURGES
GE7 SERVICE ENGINE SOON LIGHT	419	BRN/WHT	PRINTED CIRCUIT CONNECTOR 3	0*	B+		NO SES LIGHT (8) SES LIGHT ON CONSTANTLY (9)
GE8 PRIMARY COOLING FAN (FAN 1) CONTROL	335	DK GRN/WHT	PRIMARY FAN (FAN 1) RELAY TERM "F"	ON 0* OFF B+	ON 0* OFF B+		INOPERATIVE FAN 1 (8) FAN 1 RUNS ALL THE TIME (9)
GE9							
GE10							
GE11							
GE12 DIAGNOSTIC ENABLE TERMINAL	451	WHT/BLK	ALDL CONNECTOR "B"	5V (2)	5V (2)		SES LIGHT FLASHES ALL THE TIME (8) NO FIELD SERVICE MODE (9)
GE13							
GE14 OXYGEN (O2) SENSOR SIGNAL	412	BLK	OXYGEN (O2) SENSOR	35V–55V	1V–9V (3)	13 (10)	EXHAUST ODOR POOR PERFORMANCE
GE15 OXYGEN (O2) SENSOR GROUND	413	TAN	ON TRANSAXLE BOLT	0*	0*	13 (8)	EXHAUST ODOR POOR PERFORMANCE
GE16 COOLANT TEMP SENSOR	410	GRY	CTS "B"	1.8V (5)	1.8V (5)	14 (9) 15 (8)	LACK OF PERFORMANCE

(1) VARIES FROM 60 TO BATTERY VOLTAGE, DEPENDING ON POSITION OF DRIVE WHEELS
(2) BATTERY VOLTAGE FOR FIRST TWO SECONDS
(3) VARIES
(4) BATTERY VOLTAGE WHEN FUEL PUMP'S RUNNING
(5) VARIES WITH TEMPERATURE
(6) READS BATTERY VOLTAGE IN GEAR
(7) BATTERY VOLTAGE WHEN ENGINE IS CRANKING
(8) OPEN CIRCUIT
(9) GROUNDED CIRCUIT
(10) OPEN/GROUNDED CIRCUIT
(11) LESS THAN 1 VOLT
* LESS THAN 5 VOLT (500 MV)

ECM CONNECTOR "F"

PIN FUNCTION	CKT #	WIRE COLOR	COMPONENT CONNECTOR CAVITY	NORMAL VOLTAGES KEY "ON"	NORMAL VOLTAGES ENG RUN	CODES AFFECT	POSSIBLE SYMPTOMS FROM FAULTY CIRCUIT
GF1 CANISTER PURGE	428	DK GRY/YEL	CANISTER PURGE TERM "B"	B+	3V		
GF2 A/C CLUTCH CONTROL	459	BRN	A/C RELAY TERM "F"	B+	OFF B+ ON 0*		A/C CLUTCH INOPERATIVE (8)
GF3							
GF4 SHIFT LIGHT	456	TAN/BLK	M/T SHIFT LIGHT IN I/P	B+	OFF B+ ON 0*		SHIFT LIGHT INOPERATIVE (8) SHIFT LIGHT ON (9)
GF5							
GF6							
GF7							
GF8							
GF9 ESC KNOCK SENSOR SIGNAL	496	DK BLU	KNOCK SENSOR	2.3V	2.3V	43 (10)	SPARK KNOCK
GF10							
GF11							
GF12							
GF13 TPS SIGNAL	417	DK BLU	TPS "C"	54V	54V	22 (10)	LACK OF PERFORMANCE
GF14 A/C PRESS SIGNAL	380	GRY/RED	A/C SENSOR TERM "C"	1.0V (3)	1.0V (3)	66 (10)	A/C CLUTCH INOPERATIVE
GF15 MAP SIGNAL	432	PPL/WHT	MAP SENSOR "B"	4.7V	1.4V	34 (10)	LACK OF PERFORMANCE ROUGH IDLE SURGE
GF16 IAT SIGNAL	472	BLK/PNK	IAT SENSOR TERM "A"	2.33V	1.5V	23 (8) 25 (9)	

(1) VARIES FROM 60 TO BATTERY VOLTAGE, DEPENDING ON POSITION OF DRIVE WHEELS
(2) BATTERY VOLTAGE WHEN FUEL PUMP IS RUNNING
(3) VARIES
(4) VARIES WITH TEMPERATURE
(5) READS BATTERY VOLTAGE IN GEAR
(6) BATTERY VOLTAGE WHEN ENGINE IS CRANKING
(7) OPEN CIRCUIT
(8) GROUNDED CIRCUIT
(9) OPEN/GROUNDED CIRCUIT
(10) LESS THAN 1 VOLT
(11) LESS THAN .5 VOLT (500 MV)

1990–92 2.3L ENGINE

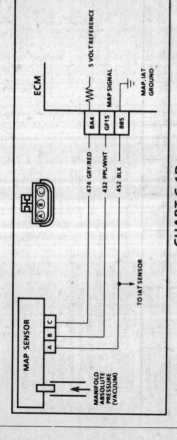

CHART C-1D
MANIFOLD ABSOLUTE PRESSURE (MAP) OUTPUT CHECK
2.3L (VIN A) "L" CARLINE (PORT)

MAP SENSOR — A B C

474 GRY/RED
432 PPL/WHT
452 BLK

TO IAT SENSOR

MANIFOLD ABSOLUTE PRESSURE (VACUUM)

ECM
BA4 — 5 VOLT REFERENCE
GF15 — MAP SIGNAL
BB5 — MAP, IAT GROUND

Circuit Description:
The Manifold Absolute Pressure (MAP) sensor measures the changes in the intake manifold pressure which result from engine load (intake manifold vacuum) and rpm changes, and converts these into a voltage output. The ECM sends a 5 volt reference voltage to the MAP sensor. As the manifold pressure changed, the output voltage of the sensor also changes. By monitoring the sensor output voltage, the ECM knows the manifold pressure. A lower pressure (low voltage) output voltage will be about 1-2 volts at idle. While higher pressure (high voltage) output voltage will be about 4 - 4.8 at Wide Open Throttle (WOT). The MAP sensor is also used, under certain conditions, to measure barometric pressure, allowing the ECM to make adjustments for different altitudes. The ECM uses the MAP sensor to control fuel delivery and ignition thing.

Test Description: Numbers below refer to circled numbers on the diagnostic chart.

Important
- Be sure to use the same Diagnostic Test Equipment for all measurements.

1. When comparing "Scan" readings to a known good vehicle, it is important to compare vehicles that use a MAP sensor having the same color insert or having the same "Hot Stamped" number. See figures on facing page.

2. Applying 34 kPa (10" Hg) vacuum to the MAP sensor should cause the voltage to change. Subtract second reading from the first. Voltage value should be greater than 1.5 volts. Upon applying vacuum to the sensor, the change in voltage should be instantaneous. A slow voltage change indicates a faulty sensor.

3. Check vacuum hose to sensor for leaking or restriction. Be sure that no other vacuum devices are connected to the MAP hose.

NOTE: Make sure electrical connector remains securely fastened.

4. Disconnect sensor from bracket and twist sensor by hand (only) to check for intermittent connection. Output changes greater than 1 volt indicate a bad connector or connection. If OK, replace sensor.

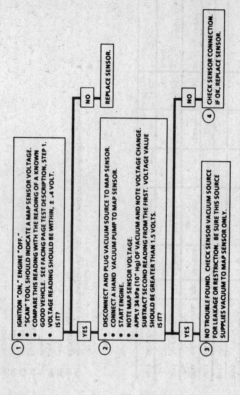

CHART C-1D
MANIFOLD ABSOLUTE PRESSURE (MAP) OUTPUT CHECK
2.3L (VIN A) "L" CARLINE (PORT)

NOTE: THIS CHART ONLY APPLIES TO MAP SENSORS HAVING GREEN OR BLACK COLOR KEY INSERT (SEE BELOW).

1. IGNITION "ON," ENGINE "OFF."
- "SCAN" TOOL SHOULD INDICATE A MAP SENSOR VOLTAGE.
- COMPARE THIS READING WITH THE READING OF A KNOWN GOOD VEHICLE. SEE FACING PAGE TEST DESCRIPTION, STEP 1.
- VOLTAGE READING SHOULD BE WITHIN, ± .4 VOLT.
IS IT?

→ NO → REPLACE SENSOR.

2. DISCONNECT AND PLUG VACUUM SOURCE TO MAP SENSOR.
- CONNECT A HAND VACUUM PUMP TO MAP SENSOR.
- START ENGINE.
- NOTE MAP SENSOR VOLTAGE.
- APPLY 34 kPa (10" Hg) OF VACUUM AND NOTE VOLTAGE CHANGE.
- SUBTRACT SECOND READING FROM THE FIRST. VOLTAGE VALUE SHOULD BE GREATER THAN 1.5 VOLTS.
IS IT?

→ NO → CHECK SENSOR CONNECTION. IF OK, REPLACE SENSOR.

3. NO TROUBLE FOUND. CHECK SENSOR VACUUM SOURCE FOR LEAKAGE OR RESTRICTION. BE SURE THIS SOURCE SUPPLIES VACUUM TO MAP SENSOR ONLY.

4. CHECK SENSOR CONNECTION. IF OK, REPLACE SENSOR.

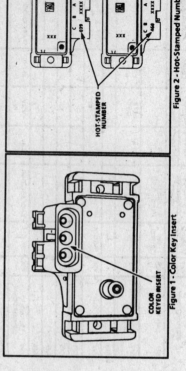

COLOR KEYED INSERT

Figure 1 - Color Key Insert

HOT-STAMPED NUMBER

Figure 2 - Hot-Stamped Number

"AFTER REPAIRS," CONFIRM "CLOSED LOOP" OPERATION AND NO "SERVICE ENGINE SOON" LIGHT.

1990-92 2.3L ENGINE

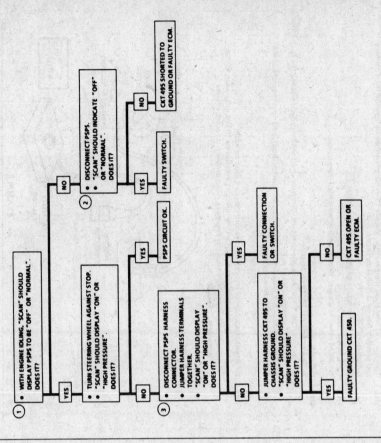

CHART C-1E

POWER STEERING PRESSURE SWITCH (PSPS) DIAGNOSIS
2.3L (VIN A) "L" CARLINE (PORT)

Circuit Description:

The Power Steering Pressure Switch (PSPS) is normally open to ground, and CKT 495 will be near battery voltage.

Turning the steering wheel increases power steering oil pressure and its load on an idling engine. The pressure switch will close before the load can cause an idle problem.

Closing the switch causes CKT 495 to read less than 1 volt. The Electronic Control Module (ECM) will increase the idle air rate and disengage the A/C relay.

- A pressure switch that will not close, or an open CKT 495 or 450, may cause the engine to stop when power steering loads are high.
- A switch that will not open, or a CKT 495 shorted to ground, may affect idle quality and will cause the A/C relay to be de-energized.

Test Description: Numbers below refer to circled numbers on the diagnostic chart.

1. Different makes of "Scan" tools may display the state of this switch in different ways. Refer to "Scan" tool operator's manual to determine how this input is indicated.

2. Checks to determine if CKT 495 is shorted to ground.

3. This should simulate a closed switch.

"AFTER REPAIRS," "CONFIRM "CLOSED LOOP" OPERATION AND NO "SERVICE ENGINE SOON" LIGHT.

1990-92 2.3L ENGINE

CHART C-2A
INJECTOR BALANCE TEST
2.3L (VIN A) "L" CARLINE (PORT)

The injector balance tester is a tool used to turn the injector on for a precise amount of time, thus spraying a measured amount of fuel into the manifold. This causes a drop in fuel rail pressure that we can record and compare between each injector. All injectors should have the same amount of pressure drop ($\pm$10 kPa). Any injector with a pressure drop that is 10 kPa (or more) greater or less than the average drop of the other injectors should be considered faulty and replaced.

STEP 1

Engine "cool down" period (10 minutes) is necessary to avoid irregular readings due to "Hot Soak" fuel boiling. Relieve fuel pressure in the fuel rail using the "fuel pressure relief procedure" described previously in this section. With ignition "OFF" connect fuel gauge J 34730-1 or equivalent to fuel pressure tap.

Disconnect harness connectors at all injectors, and connect injector tester J 34730-3, or equivalent, to one injector. On Turbo equipped engines, use adaptor harness furnished with injector tester to energize injectors that are not accessible. Follow manufacturers instructions for use of adaptor harness. Ignition must be "OFF" at least 10 seconds to complete ECM shutdown cycle. Fuel pump should run about 2 seconds after ignition is turned "ON." At this point, insert clear tubing attached to vent valve into a suitable container and bleed air from gauge and hose to insure accurate gauge operation. Repeat this step until all air is bled from gauge.

STEP 2

Turn ignition "OFF" for 10 seconds and then "ON" again to get fuel pressure to its maximum. Record this initial pressure reading. Energize tester one time and note pressure drop at its lowest point. (Disregard any slight pressure increase after drop hits low point.) By subtracting this second pressure reading from the initial pressure, we have the actual amount of injector pressure drop.

STEP 3

Repeat step 2 on each injector and compare the amount of drop. Usually, good injectors will have virtually the same drop. Retest any injector that has a pressure difference of 10 kPa, either more or less than the average of the other injectors on the engine. Replace any injector that also fails the retest. If the pressure drop of all injectors is within 10 kPa of this average, the injectors appear to be flowing properly. Reconnect them and review "Symptoms," Section

NOTE: *The entire test should not be repeated more than once without running the engine to prevent flooding. (This includes any retest on faulty injectors).*

CHART C-2A
INJECTOR BALANCE TEST
2.3L (VIN A) "L" CARLINE (PORT)

NOTE: If injectors are suspected of being dirty, they should be cleaned using an approved tool and procedure prior to performing this test. The fuel pressure test in CHART A-7, should be completed prior to this test.

Step 1. If engine is at operating temperature, allow a 10 minute "cool down" period then connect fuel pressure gauge and injector tester.
1. Ignition "OFF."
2. Connect fuel pressure gauge and injector tester.
3. Ignition "ON."
4. Bleed off air in gauge. Repeat until all air is bled from gauge.

Step 2. Run test:
1. Ignition "OFF" for 10 seconds.
2. Ignition "ON." Record gauge pressure. (Pressure must hold steady, if not see the Fuel System Diagnosis, CHART A-7.
3. Turn injector "ON," by depressing button on injector tester, and note pressure at the instant the gauge needle stops.

Step 3.
1. Repeat step 2 on all injectors and record pressure drop on each. Retest injectors that appear faulty (any injectors that have a 10 kPa difference, either more or less, in pressure from the average). If no problem is found, review "Symptoms," Section

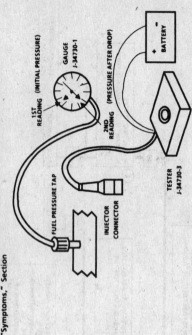

— EXAMPLE —

CYLINDER	1	2	3	4
1ST READING	225	225	225	225
2ND READING	100	115	100	85
AMOUNT OF DROP	125	110	125	140
	OK	FAULTY LEAN (TOO LITTLE) (FUEL DROP)	OK	FAULTY RICH (TOO MUCH) (FUEL DROP)

1990–92 2.3L ENGINE

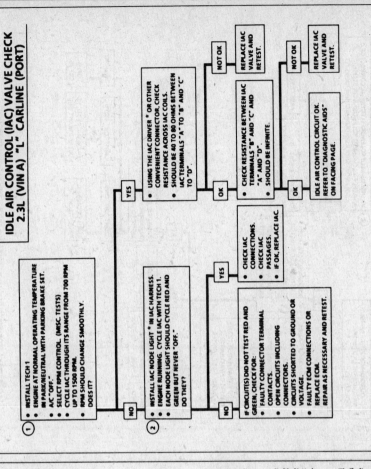

CHART C-2C

IDLE AIR CONTROL (IAC) VALVE CHECK
2.3L (VIN A) "L" CARLINE (PORT)

(1)
- INSTALL TECH 1.
- ENGINE AT NORMAL OPERATING TEMPERATURE IN PARK/NEUTRAL WITH PARKING BRAKE SET.
- A/C "OFF."
- SELECT RPM CONTROL (MISC. TESTS)
- CYCLE IAC THROUGH ITS RANGE FROM 700 RPM UP TO 1500 RPM.
- RPM SHOULD CHANGE SMOOTHLY.
  DOES IT?

NO →

(2)
- INSTALL IAC NODE LIGHT * IN IAC HARNESS.
- ENGINE RUNNING. CYCLE IAC WITH TECH 1.
- EACH NODE LIGHT SHOULD CYCLE RED AND GREEN BUT NEVER "OFF."
  DO THEY?

NO →

- IF CIRCUIT(S) DID NOT TEST RED AND GREEN, CHECK FOR:
  - FAULTY CONNECTOR TERMINAL CONTACTS.
  - OPEN CIRCUITS INCLUDING CONNECTORS.
  - CIRCUITS SHORTED TO GROUND OR VOLTAGE.
  - FAULTY ECM CONNECTIONS OR REPLACE ECM.
- REPAIR AS NECESSARY AND RETEST.

YES →

- CHECK IAC CONNECTIONS.
- CHECK IAC PASSAGES.
- IF OK, REPLACE IAC.

YES →

- USING THE IAC DRIVER * OR OTHER CONVENIENT CONNECTOR, CHECK RESISTANCE ACROSS IAC COILS.
- SHOULD BE 40 TO 80 OHMS BETWEEN IAC TERMINALS "A" TO "B" AND "C" TO "D".

NOT OK → REPLACE IAC VALVE AND RETEST.

OK →

- CHECK RESISTANCE BETWEEN IAC TERMINALS "B" AND "C" AND "A" AND "D".
- SHOULD BE INFINITE.

NOT OK → REPLACE IAC VALVE AND RETEST.

OK →

IDLE AIR CONTROL CIRCUIT OK. REFER TO "DIAGNOSTIC AIDS" ON FACING PAGE.

* IAC DRIVER AND NODE LIGHT REQUIRED KIT 222-L FROM: CONCEPT TECHNOLOGY, INC. J 37027 FROM: KENT-MOORE, INC.

CLEAR CODES, CONFIRM "CLOSED LOOP" OPERATION, NO "SERVICE ENGINE SOON" LIGHT, PERFORM IAC RESET PROCEDURE PER APPLICABLE SERVICE MANUAL AND VERIFY CONTROLLED IDLE SPEED IS CORRECT.

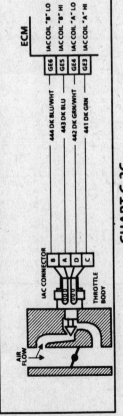

ECM

444 DK BLU/WHT	GE6	IAC COIL "B" LO
443 DK BLU	GE5	IAC COIL "B" HI
442 DK GRN/WHT	GE4	IAC COIL "A" LO
441 DK GRN	GE3	IAC COIL "A" HI

CHART C-2C

IDLE AIR CONTROL (IAC) VALVE CHECK
2.3L (VIN A) "L" CARLINE (PORT)

Circuit Description:

The ECM controls idle rpm with the IAC valve. To increase idle rpm, the ECM moves the IAC valve out, allowing more air to bypass the throttle plate. To decrease rpm, it moves the IAC valve in, reducing air flow by-passing the throttle plate. A Tech 1 "Scan" tool will read the ECM commands to the IAC valve in counts. The higher the counts, the more air is allowed (higher idle). The lower the counts, the less air is allowed (lower idle).

Test Description: Numbers below refer to circled numbers on the diagnostic chart.

1. The IAC tester is used to extend and retract the IAC valve. Valve movement is verified by an engine speed change. If no change in engine speed occurs, the valve can be retested when removed from the throttle body.
   This step checks the quality of the IAC movement in step 1. Between 700 rpm and about 1500 rpm, the engine speed should change smoothly with each flash of the tester light in both extend and retract. If the IAC valve is retracted beyond the control range (about 1500 rpm), it may take many flashes in the extend position before engine speed will begin to drop. This is normal on certain engines, fully extending IAC may cause engine stall. This may be normal.

2. Step 1 verified proper IAC valve operation while this step checks IAC circuits. Each lamp on the node light should flash red and green while the IAC valve is cycled. While the sequence of color is not important if either light is "OFF" or does not flash red and green, check the circuits for faults, beginning with poor terminal contacts.

Diagnostic Aids:

A slow, unstable, or fast idle may be caused by a non-IAC system problem that cannot be overcome by the IAC valve. Out of control range IAC Tech 1 counts will be above 60 if idle is too low, and zero counts if idle is too high. The following checks should be made to repair a non-IAC system problem.

- **Vacuum Leak (High Idle)**
  If idle is too high, stop the engine. Fully extend (low) IAC with tester. Start engine. If idle speed is above 800 rpm, locate and correct vacuum leak including CV system. Also check for binding of throttle plate or linkage.

- **System too lean (High Air/Fuel Ratio)**
  Idle speed may be too high or too low. Engine speed may vary up and down and disconnecting IAC does not help. Code 44 may be set. "Scan" O_2 voltage will be less than 300 mv (.3 volt). Check for low regulated fuel pressure, water in the fuel or a restricted injector.

- **System too rich (Low Air/Fuel Ratio)**
  The idle speed will be too low. Tech 1 "Scan" tool IAC counts will usually be above 80. System is obviously rich and may exhibit black smoke exhaust.
  "Scan" tool O_2 voltage will be fixed above 800 mv (.8 volt). Check for high fuel pressure, leaking or sticking injector. Silicone contaminated O_2 sensor will "Scan" an O_2 voltage slow to respond.

- **Throttle Body**
  Remove IAC and inspect bore for foreign material. Refer to "Rough, Unstable, Incorrect Idle or Stalling" in "Symptoms," Section ____.
  If intermittent poor driveability or idle symptoms are resolved by disconnecting the IAC, carefully recheck connections, valve terminal resistance, or replace IAC.

1990–92 2.3L ENGINE

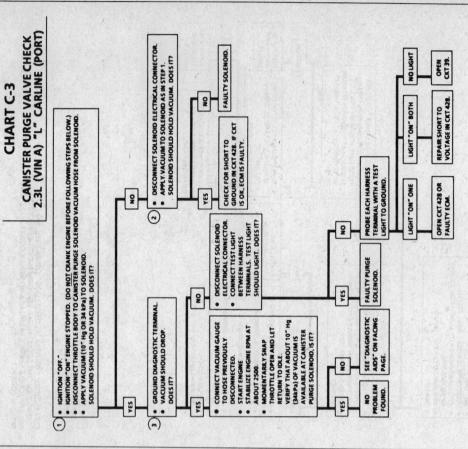

CHART C-3

CANISTER PURGE VALVE CHECK
2.3L (VIN A) "L" CARLINE (PORT)

① • IGNITION "OFF."
   • IGNITION "ON" ENGINE STOPPED. (DO NOT CRANK ENGINE BEFORE FOLLOWING STEPS BELOW.)
   • DISCONNECT THROTTLE BODY TO CANISTER PURGE SOLENOID VACUUM HOSE FROM SOLENOID.
   • APPLY VACUUM (10" Hg OR 34 kPa) TO SOLENOID.
   SOLENOID SHOULD HOLD VACUUM. DOES IT?

   YES → ③

   NO → ② • DISCONNECT SOLENOID ELECTRICAL CONNECTOR.
   • APPLY VACUUM TO SOLENOID AS IN STEP 1.
   SOLENOID SHOULD HOLD VACUUM. DOES IT?

   YES → CHECK FOR SHORT TO GROUND IN CKT 428. IF CKT IS OK, ECM IS FAULTY.

   NO → FAULTY SOLENOID.

③ • GROUND DIAGNOSTIC TERMINAL.
   VACUUM SHOULD DROP. DOES IT?

   YES → • CONNECT VACUUM GAUGE TO HOSE PREVIOUSLY DISCONNECTED.
   • START ENGINE.
   • STABILIZE ENGINE RPM AT ABOUT 2500.
   • MOMENTARILY SNAP THROTTLE OPEN AND LET RETURN TO IDLE.
   • VERIFY THAT ABOUT 10" Hg (34 kPa) OF VACUUM IS AVAILABLE AT CANISTER PURGE SOLENOID. IS IT?

   YES → NO PROBLEM FOUND.

   NO → SEE "DIAGNOSTIC AIDS" ON FACING PAGE.

   NO → • DISCONNECT SOLENOID ELECTRICAL CONNECTOR.
   • CONNECT TEST LIGHT BETWEEN HARNESS TERMINALS. TEST LIGHT SHOULD LIGHT. DOES IT?

   YES → FAULTY PURGE SOLENOID.

   NO → PROBE EACH HARNESS TERMINAL WITH A TEST LIGHT TO GROUND.

   LIGHT "ON" ONE → OPEN CKT 428 OR FAULTY ECM.

   LIGHT "ON" BOTH → REPAIR SHORT TO VOLTAGE IN CKT 428.

   NO LIGHT → OPEN CKT 39.

"AFTER REPAIRS," CONFIRM "CLOSED LOOP" OPERATION AND NO "SERVICE ENGINE SOON" LIGHT.

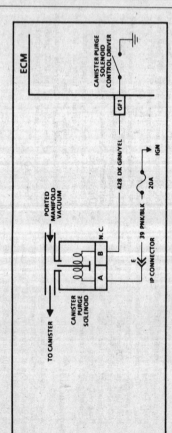

CHART C-3

CANISTER PURGE VALVE CHECK
2.3L (VIN A) "L" CARLINE (PORT)

Circuit Description:

Canister purge is controlled by a solenoid that allows manifold and/or ported vacuum to purge the canister when energized. The Electronic Control Module (ECM) supplies a ground to energize the solenoid (purge "ON"). The purge solenoid control by the ECM is pulse width modulated (turned "ON" and "OFF" several times a second). The duty cycle (pulse width) is determined by "Closed Loop" feed back from the O₂ sensor. The duty cycle is calculated by the ECM and the output commanded when the following conditions have been met:

 • Engine run time after start more than 65 seconds.
 • Coolant temperature above 56°C.

Also, if the diagnostic test terminal is grounded with the engine stopped, the purge solenoid is energized (purge "ON").

Test Description: Numbers below refer to circled numbers on the diagnostic chart.

1. Checks to see if the solenoid is opened or closed. The solenoid is normally de-energized in this step, so it should be closed.
2. Checks to determine if solenoid was open due to electrical circuit problem or defective solenoid.
3. Completes functional check by grounding test terminal. This should normally energize the solenoid opening the valve which should allow the vacuum to drop (purge "ON").

Diagnostic Aids:

Make a visual check of vacuum hose(s). Check throttle body for possible cracked, broken, or plugged vacuum block. Check engine for possible mechanical problem.

1990–92 2.3L ENGINE

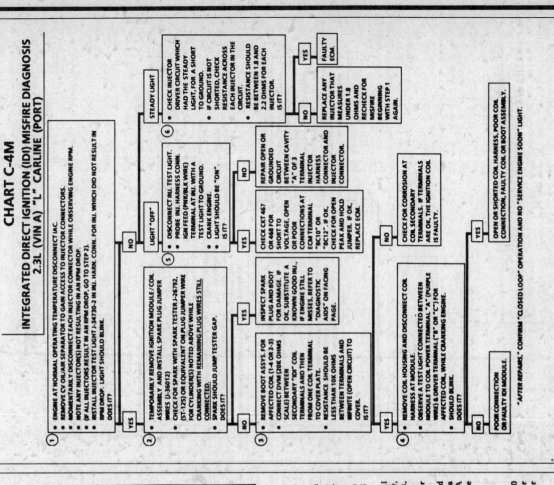

CHART C-4M

INTEGRATED DIRECT IGNITION (IDI) MISFIRE DIAGNOSIS
2.3L (VIN A) "L" CARLINE (PORT)

1. ① ENGINE AT NORMAL OPERATING TEMPERATURE DISCONNECT IAC.
   - REMOVE CV OIL/AIR SEPARATOR TO GAIN ACCESS TO INJECTOR CONNECTORS.
   - MOMENTARILY DISCONNECT EACH INJECTOR CONNECTOR WHILE OBSERVING ENGINE RPM.
   - NOTE ANY INJECTOR(S) NOT RESULTING IN AN RPM DROP.
   - (IF ALL INJECTORS RESULT IN AN RPM DROP, GO TO STEP 2).
   - INSTALL INJECTOR TEST LIGHT J-34730-2 IN INJ. HARN. CONN. FOR INJ. WHICH DID NOT RESULT IN RPM DROP. LIGHT SHOULD BLINK.
   - DOES IT?

2. ② TEMPORARILY REMOVE IGNITION MODULE/COIL ASSEMBLY AND INSTALL SPARK PLUG JUMPER WIRES (J-36012)
   - CHECK FOR SPARK WITH SPARK TESTER J-26792, (ST-125) OR EQUIVALENT ON PLUG JUMPER WIRE FOR CYLINDER(S) NOTED ABOVE WHILE CRANKING WITH REMAINING PLUG WIRES STILL CONNECTED.
   - SPARK SHOULD JUMP TESTER GAP.
   - DOES IT?

3. ③ REMOVE BOOT ASSY'S. FOR AFFECTED COIL (1-4 OR 2-3)
   - CONNECT DVM (20K OHMS SCALE) BETWEEN SECONDARY "IDI" COIL TERMINALS AND THEN FROM ONE COIL TERMINAL TO COVER PLATE.
   - RESISTANCE SHOULD BE LESS THAN 10K OHMS BETWEEN TERMINALS AND INFINITE (OPEN CIRCUIT) TO COVER.
   - IS IT?

4. ④ REMOVE COIL HOUSING AND DISCONNECT COIL HARNESS AT MODULE.
   - OBSERVE A TEST LIGHT CONNECTED BETWEEN MODULE TO COIL POWER TERMINAL ("B" OR "C") AND DRIVER TERMINAL ("B" OR "C") FOR AFFECTED COIL, WHILE CRANKING ENGINE.
   - SHOULD BLINK.
   - DOES IT?

5. ⑤ DISCONNECT INJ. TEST LIGHT.
   - PROBE INJ. HARNESS CONN.
   - IGN FEED (PNK/BLK WIRE) TERMINAL AT INJ. WITH A TEST LIGHT TO GROUND.
   - CRANK ENGINE.
   - LIGHT SHOULD BE "ON".
   - IS IT?

6. ⑥ CHECK INJECTOR DRIVER CIRCUIT WHICH HAD THE STEADY LIGHT, FOR A SHORT TO GROUND.
   - IF CIRCUIT IS NOT SHORTED, CHECK RESISTANCE ACROSS EACH INJECTOR IN THE CIRCUIT.
   - RESISTANCE SHOULD BE BETWEEN 1.8 AND 2.2 OHMS FOR EACH INJECTOR.
   - IS IT?

- STEADY LIGHT
- LIGHT "OFF"
- NO / YES

- CHECK CKT 467 OR 468 FOR SHORT TO VOLTAGE, OPEN OR POOR CONNECTIONS AT ECM TERMINAL "BC10" OR "BC12". IF OK, CHECK FOR OPEN PEAK AND HOLD JUMPER. IF OK, REPLACE ECM.

- REPAIR OPEN OR GROUNDED CIRCUIT BETWEEN CAVITY "A" OF TERMINAL HARNESS CONNECTOR AND INJECTOR CONNECTOR.

- INSPECT SPARK PLUG AND BOOT FOR DAMAGE. IF OK, SUBSTITUTE A KNOWN GOOD INJ., IF ENGINE STILL MISSES, REFER TO "DIAGNOSTIC AIDS" ON FACING PAGE.

- CHECK FOR CORROSION AT COIL SECONDARY TERMINALS. IF TERMINALS ARE OK, THE IGNITION COIL IS FAULTY.

- REPLACE ANY INJECTOR THAT MEASURES UNDER 1.8 OHMS AND RECHECK FOR MISFIRE BEGINNING WITH STEP 1 AGAIN.

- FAULTY ECM.

- OPEN OR SHORTED COIL HARNESS, POOR COIL CONNECTION, FAULTY COIL OR BOOT ASSEMBLY.

- POOR CONNECTION OR FAULTY "IDI" MODULE.

"AFTER REPAIRS," CONFIRM "CLOSED LOOP" OPERATION AND NO "SERVICE ENGINE SOON" LIGHT.

CHART C-4M

INTEGRATED DIRECT IGNITION (IDI) MISFIRE DIAGNOSIS
2.3L (VIN A) "L" CARLINE (PORT)

Circuit Description:

The Integrated Direct Ignition (IDI) system uses a waste spark method of distribution. In this type of system the ignition module triggers the #1-4 coil pair resulting in both #1 and #4 spark plugs firing at the same time. #1 cylinder is on the compression stroke at the same time #4 is on the exhaust stroke, resulting in a lower energy requirement to fire #4 spark plug. This leaves the remainder of the high voltage to be used to fire #1 spark plug. On this application, the crank sensor is mounted to, and protrudes through the block to within approximately 0.050" of the crankshaft reluctor. Since the reluctor is a machined portion of the crankshaft and the sensor is mounted in a fixed position on the block, timing adjustments are not possible or necessary.

Test Description: Numbers below refer to circled numbers on the diagnostic chart.

1. This checks for equal relative power output between the cylinders. Any injector which when disconnected did not result in an rpm drop approximately equal to the others, is located on the misfiring cylinder.
2. If a plug boot is burned, the other plug on that coil may still fire at idle. This step tests the system's ability to produce at least 25,000 volts at each spark plug.
3. No spark, on one coil, may be caused by an open secondary circuit. Therefore, the coil's secondary resistance should be checked. Resistance readings above 20,000 ohms, but not infinite, will probably not cause a no start but may cause an engine miss under certain conditions.
4. If the no spark condition is caused by coil connections, a coil or a secondary boot assembly, the test light will blink. If the light does not blink, the fault is module connections or the module.
5. Checks for ignition voltage feed to injector and for an open injector driver circuit.
6. An injector driver circuit shorted to ground would result in the test light "ON" steady, and possibly a flooded condition which could damage engine. A shorted injector (less than 2 ohms) could cause incorrect ECM operation.

Diagnostic Aid:

Verify IDI connector terminal "K", CKT 450 resistance to ground is less than .5 ohm. A shorted or low resistance injector may cause a miss in the other injector in that pair (1 & 4 or 2 & 3).

ECM
- INJECTOR DRIVERS
- BC12
- BC10
- BD5
- BD6
- BC13
- BYPASS
- BC7 EST
- BC1
- BC5 1 X REFERENCE
- BD8 2 X REFERENCE
- BD9 REF LOW (GROUND)

- INJECTOR HARNESS CONNECTOR (A) (B) (C)
- 120 TAN/WHT → TO IGN
- 467 DK BLU
- 468 DK GRN
- 1.4 PEAK & HOLD JUMPER
- 887 TAN
- 888 DK BLU
- 2.3 PEAK & HOLD JUMPER
- 1/P TACH LEAD (2 X)

- CRANK SENSOR HARN. CONN. (FRONT VIEW)

- 15A IGM FUSE
- FROM IGNITION SWITCH

- "IDI" MODULE
- "IDI" COVER
- 11 RPM CONN
- PLUG BOOT
- COIL HOUSING
- "IDI" SYSTEM ASSEMBLY INVERTED

- 120 GRY
- INJ1, INJ4, INJ2, INJ3
- B + IGNITION MODULE
- IGM COILS
- SECONDARY
- PRIMARY WINDING

- A NOT USED
- B 574 YEL
- C 573 YEL
- D 424 TAN/BLK
- E 423 WHT
- F 121 BLK/WHT
- G 647 LT BLU/BLK
- H 430 PPL/WHT
- K 450 BLK/LT GRN
- L 453 BLK/RED
- 439 PNK/BLK

- "IDI" HARNESS CONNECTOR

1990-92 2.3L ENGINE

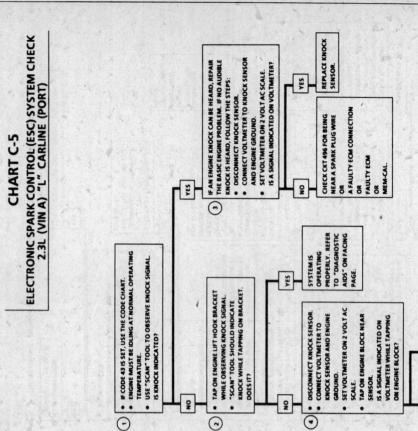

CHART C-5

ELECTRONIC SPARK CONTROL (ESC) SYSTEM CHECK
2.3L (VIN A) "L" CARLINE (PORT)

**① **
- IF CODE 43 IS SET, USE THE CODE CHART.
- ENGINE MUST BE IDLING AT NORMAL OPERATING TEMPERATURE.
- USE "SCAN" TOOL TO OBSERVE KNOCK SIGNAL.
  IS KNOCK INDICATED?

NO →

**② **
- TAP ON ENGINE LIFT HOOK BRACKET WHILE OBSERVING KNOCK SIGNAL. "SCAN" TOOL SHOULD INDICATE KNOCK WHILE TAPPING ON BRACKET. DOES IT?

NO →

**④ **
- DISCONNECT KNOCK SENSOR.
- CONNECT VOLTMETER TO KNOCK SENSOR AND ENGINE GROUND.
- SET VOLTMETER ON 2 VOLT AC SCALE.
- TAP ON ENGINE BLOCK NEAR SENSOR.
  IS A SIGNAL INDICATED ON VOLTMETER WHILE TAPPING ON ENGINE BLOCK?

YES → REPLACE MEM-CAL OR ECM.

NO → REPLACE KNOCK SENSOR.

YES (from ②) → SYSTEM IS OPERATING PROPERLY. REFER TO "DIAGNOSTIC AIDS" ON FACING PAGE.

YES (from ①) →

**③ **
IF AN ENGINE KNOCK CAN BE HEARD, REPAIR THE BASIC ENGINE PROBLEM. IF NO AUDIBLE KNOCK IS HEARD, FOLLOW THE STEPS:
- DISCONNECT KNOCK SENSOR.
- CONNECT VOLTMETER TO KNOCK SENSOR AND ENGINE GROUND.
- SET VOLTMETER ON 2 VOLT AC SCALE.
  IS A SIGNAL INDICATED ON VOLTMETER?

YES → REPLACE KNOCK SENSOR.

NO → CHECK CKT 496 FOR BEING NEAR A SPARK PLUG WIRE
OR
A FAULTY ECM CONNECTION
OR
FAULTY ECM
OR
MEM-CAL.

CLEAR CODES, DISCONNECT "SCAN" TOOL FROM ALDL, START ENGINE AND CONFIRM "CLOSED LOOP" OPERATION AND NO "SERVICE ENGINE SOON" LIGHT

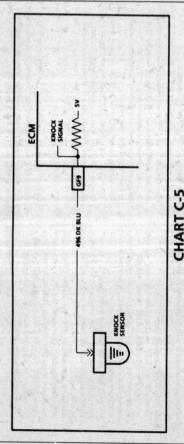

CHART C-5

ELECTRONIC SPARK CONTROL (ESC) SYSTEM CHECK
2.3L (VIN A) "L" CARLINE (PORT)

Circuit Description:

The knock sensor is used to detect engine detonation and the Electronic Control Module (ECM) will retard the Electronic Spark Timing (EST) based on the signal being received. The circuitry within the knock sensor causes the ECM's 5 volts to be pulled down so that CKT 496 would measure about 2.5 volts. The knock sensor produces an AC signal which rides on the 2.5 volts DC voltage. The amplitude and frequency are dependent upon the knock level.

The MEM-CAL used with this engine contains the functions which were part of remotely mounted ESC modules used on other GM vehicles. The ESC portion of the MEM-CAL then sends a signal to other parts of the ECM which adjusts the spark timing to retard the spark and reduce the detonation.

Test Description: Numbers below refer to circled numbers on the diagnostic chart.

1. With engine idling, there should not be a knock signal present at the ECM because detonation is not likely under a no load condition.
2. Tapping on the engine lift hood bracket should simulate a knock signal to determine if the sensor is capable of detecting detonation. If no knock is detected, try tapping on engine block closer to sensor before replacing sensor.
3. If the engine has an internal problem which is creating a knock, the knock sensor may be responding to the internal failure.
4. This test determines if the knock sensor is faulty or if the ESC portion of the MEM-CAL is faulty. If it is determined that the MEM-CAL is faulty, be sure that is is properly installed and latched into place. If not properly installed, repair and retest.

Diagnostic Aids:

While observing knock signal on the Tech 1, there should be an indication that knock is present when detonation can be heard. Detonation is most likely to occur under high engine load conditions.

1990–92 2.3L ENGINE

CHART C-8C

MANUAL TRANSAXLE (M/T) SHIFT LIGHT CHECK
2.3L (VIN A) "L" CARLINE (PORT)

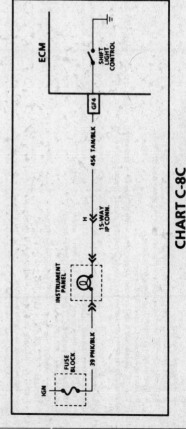

Circuit Description:

The shift light indicates the best transaxle shift point for maximum fuel economy. The light is controlled by the Electronic Control Module (ECM) and is turned "ON" by grounding CKT 456.

The ECM uses inputs from various sensors to calculate when the shift light should be turned "ON" as follows:

- Coolant temperature must be above -10°C (14°F).
- ECM can determine the transaxle has been in a gear for at least 1.2 seconds, by comparison of vehicle speed (from VSS) with engine rpm.
- Throttle Position Sensor (TPS) is between minimum and maximum calibrated values for each gear.
- Rpm is above a calibrated value for each gear (maximum 6500 rpm).

The light will be turned "ON" after a calibrated delay time which is dependent on last gear change or downshift, and will remain on for a minimum of 10 seconds.

Test Description: Numbers below refer to circled numbers on the diagnostic chart.

1. This should not turn "ON" the shift light. If the light is "ON," there is a short to ground in CKT 456 wiring or a fault in the ECM.

2. When the diagnostic terminal is grounded, the ECM should ground CKT 456 and the shift light should come "ON."

3. This checks the shift light circuit up to the ECM connector. If the shift light illuminates, then the ECM connector is faulty or the ECM does not have the ability to ground the circuit.

Diagnostic Aids:

Check for Code 24 (no VSS). Faulty thermostat or incorrect heat range. Incorrect or faulty MEM-CAL. A faulty or improper VSS may result in a shift light that does not operate.

CHART C-8C

MANUAL TRANSAXLE (M/T) SHIFT LIGHT CHECK
2.3L (VIN A) "L" CARLINE (PORT)

1.
- VERIFY PROPER "SERVICE ENGINE SOON" LIGHT OPERATION.
- IGNITION "ON", ENGINE STOPPED.
- NOTE SHIFT LIGHT.

→ **LIGHT "OFF"**

2.
- GROUND DIAGNOSTIC TERMINAL AND NOTE LIGHT.

→ **LIGHT "ON"**

→ **LIGHT "OFF"**

3.
- IGNITION "OFF".
- DISCONNECT ECM CONNECTORS.
- IGNITION "ON".
- JUMPER CKT 456 TO GROUND AND NOTE SHIFT LIGHT.

→ **LIGHT "ON"** — IF OK, SYSTEM IS OPERATING PROPERLY.

→ **LIGHT "OFF"**

CHECK AND REPAIR:
- OPEN IGNITION CKT 39.
- OPEN CKT 456.
- FAULTY BULB.

→ **LIGHT "ON"** — POOR CONNECTION AT ECM OR FAULTY ECM.

(from LIGHT "ON" at top)
- IGNITION "OFF".
- DISCONNECT ECM CONNECTORS.
- IGNITION "ON" AND NOTE SHIFT LIGHT.

→ **LIGHT "OFF"** — FAULTY ECM

→ **LIGHT "ON"** — REPAIR SHORT TO GROUND IN CKT 456.

"AFTER REPAIRS," CONFIRM "CLOSED LOOP" OPERATION AND NO "SERVICE ENGINE SOON" LIGHT.

1990-92 2.3L ENGINE

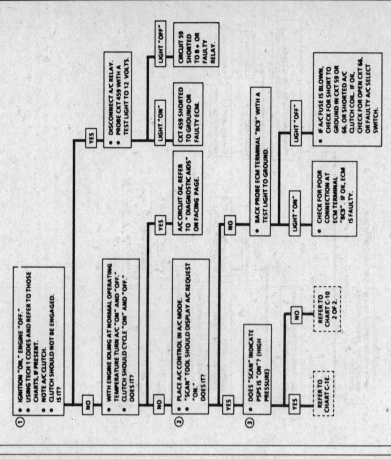

CHART C-10
(Page 1 of 2)
A/C CLUTCH CONTROL CIRCUIT DIAGNOSIS
2.3L (VIN A) "L" CARLINE (PORT)

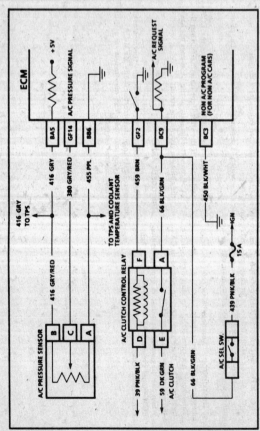

CHART C-10
(Page 1 of 2)
A/C CLUTCH CONTROL CIRCUIT DIAGNOSIS
2.3L (VIN A) "L" CARLINE (PORT)

Circuit Description:

The A/C clutch control relay is energized when the Electronic Control Module (ECM) provides a ground path through CKT 459 and A/C is requested. A/C clutch is delayed about .3 seconds after A/C is requested. This will allow the IAC to adjust engine rpm for the additional load.

The ECM will temporarily disengage the A/C clutch relay for calibrated times for one or more of the following:

• Hot engine restart.
• Wide Open Throttle (WOT) (TPS over 90%).
• Power steering pressure high (open power steering pressure switch).
• Engine rpm greater than about 6000 rpm.
• During Idle Air Control (IAC) reset.

The A/C clutch relay will remain disengaged when a Code 66 is present, if pressure is out of range described previously in this section, or there is no A/C request signal due to an open A/C select switch or circuit.

Test Description: Numbers below refer to circled numbers on the diagnostic chart.

1. The ECM will only energize the A/C relay when the engine is running. This test will determine if the relay or CKT 459 is faulty.

2. Determines if the signal is reaching the ECM through CKT 66 from the A/C control panel. Signal should only be present when an A/C mode or defrost mode has been selected.

3. If the ECM is receiving a high power steering pressure signal, the A/C clutch will be disengaged by the ECM.

1990-92 2.3L ENGINE

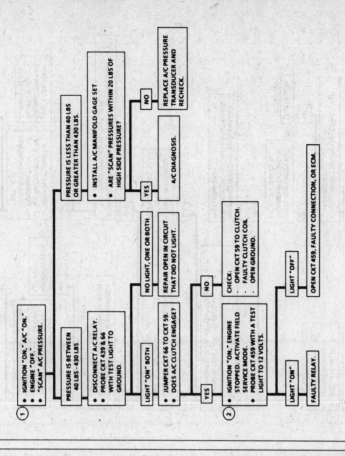

CHART C-10
(Page 2 of 2)
A/C CLUTCH CONTROL CIRCUIT DIAGNOSIS
2.3L (VIN A) "L" CARLINE (PORT)

① • IGNITION "ON," A/C "ON."
• ENGINE "OFF."
• "SCAN" A/C PRESSURE.

PRESSURE IS BETWEEN 40 LBS - 430 LBS.

PRESSURE IS LESS THAN 40 LBS OR GREATER THAN 430 LBS.

INSTALL A/C MANIFOLD GAGE SET
• ARE "SCAN" PRESSURES WITHIN 20 LBS OF HIGH SIDE PRESSURE?

YES → A/C DIAGNOSIS.

NO → REPLACE A/C PRESSURE TRANSDUCER AND RECHECK.

• DISCONNECT A/C RELAY.
• PROBE CKT 439 & 66 WITH TEST LIGHT TO GROUND.

LIGHT "ON" BOTH

NO LIGHT, ONE OR BOTH → REPAIR OPEN IN CIRCUIT THAT DID NOT LIGHT.

• JUMPER CKT 66 TO CKT 59.
• DOES A/C CLUTCH ENGAGE?

YES

NO → CHECK:
• OPEN CKT 59 TO CLUTCH.
• FAULTY CLUTCH COIL.
• OPEN GROUND.

② • IGNITION "ON," ENGINE STOPPED. ACTIVATE FIELD SERVICE MODE.
• PROBE CKT 459 WITH A TEST LIGHT TO 12 VOLTS.

LIGHT "ON" → FAULTY RELAY.

LIGHT "OFF" → OPEN CKT 459, FAULTY CONNECTION, OR ECM.

"AFTER REPAIRS," CONFIRM "CLOSED LOOP" OPERATION AND NO "SERVICE ENGINE SOON" LIGHT.

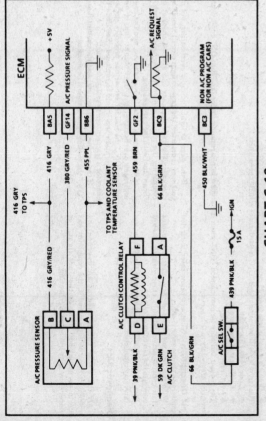

CHART C-10
(Page 2 of 2)
A/C CLUTCH CONTROL CIRCUIT DIAGNOSIS
2.3L (VIN A) "L" CARLINE (PORT)

Circuit Description:

The A/C clutch control relay is energized when the ECM provides a ground path through CKT 459 and A/C is requested. A/C clutch is delayed about .3 seconds after A/C is requested. This will allow the IAC to adjust engine rpm for the additional load.

The ECM will temporarily disengage the A/C clutch relay for calibrated times for one or more of the following:

• Hot engine restart.
• Wide open throttle (TPS over 90%).
• Power steering pressure high (open power steering pressure switch).
• Engine rpm greater than about 6000 rpm.
• During IAC reset.

The A/C clutch relay will remain disengaged when a Code 66 is present, if pressure is out of range described previously in this section, or there is no A/C request signal due to an open A/C select switch or circuit.

Test Description: Numbers below refer to circled numbers on the diagnostic chart.

1. Determines if the pressure transducer is out of range causing the compressor clutch to be disengaged.
2. With the engine stopped and field service mode activated, the ECM should be grounding CKT 459, which should cause the test light to be "ON."

Diagnostic Aids:

If complaint is insufficient cooling, the problem may be caused by an inoperative cooling fan. See

CHART C-12 for cooling fan diagnosis. If fan operates correctly.

A/C pressure outside of a range of 43 to 428 psi will cause the compressor to be disabled by the ECM. Observe Tech 1 A/C pressure for 2 minutes with engine idling and A/C "ON."

"Scan" pressure should be within 20 psi of actual. If not, check for a circuit problem using Code 66 chart or replace sensor.

1990-92 2.3L ENGINE

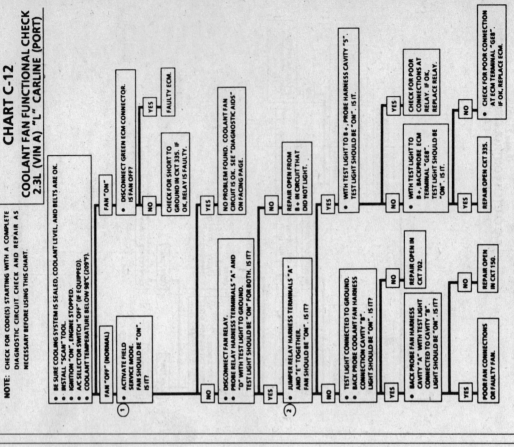

CHART C-12
COOLANT FAN FUNCTIONAL CHECK
2.3L (VIN A) "L" CARLINE (PORT)

NOTE: CHECK FOR CODE(S) STARTING WITH A COMPLETE DIAGNOSTIC CIRCUIT CHECK AND REPAIR AS NECESSARY BEFORE USING THIS CHART.

- BE SURE COOLING SYSTEM IS SEALED, COOLANT LEVEL, AND BELTS ARE OK.
- INSTALL "SCAN" TOOL.
- IGNITION "ON", ENGINE STOPPED.
- A/C SELECTOR SWITCH "OFF" (IF EQUIPPED).
- COOLANT TEMPERATURE BELOW 98°C (209°F).

FAN "OFF" (NORMAL)

①
- ACTIVATE FIELD SERVICE MODE. FAN SHOULD BE "ON". IS IT?

FAN "ON"
- DISCONNECT GREEN ECM CONNECTOR. IS FAN OFF?

YES → FAULTY ECM.

NO → CHECK FOR SHORT TO GROUND IN CKT 335. IF OK, RELAY IS FAULTY.

YES → NO PROBLEM FOUND. COOLANT FAN CIRCUIT IS OK. SEE "DIAGNOSTIC AIDS" ON FACING PAGE.

NO →
- DISCONNECT FAN RELAY.
- PROBE RELAY HARNESS TERMINALS "A" AND "D" WITH TEST LIGHT TO GROUND. TEST LIGHT SHOULD BE "ON" FOR BOTH. IS IT?

YES →
②
- JUMPER RELAY HARNESS TERMINALS "A" AND "E" TOGETHER. FAN SHOULD BE "ON". IS IT?

NO → REPAIR OPEN FROM B+ IN CIRCUIT THAT DID NOT LIGHT.

YES →
- TEST LIGHT CONNECTED TO GROUND.
- BACK PROBE COOLANT FAN HARNESS CONNECTION CAVITY "B".
LIGHT SHOULD BE "ON". IS IT?

- WITH TEST LIGHT TO B+, PROBE HARNESS CAVITY "5". TEST LIGHT SHOULD BE "ON". IS IT?

YES →
- WITH TEST LIGHT TO B+, BACKPROBE ECM TERMINAL "GEB". TEST LIGHT SHOULD BE "ON". IS IT?

NO → CHECK FOR POOR CONNECTIONS AT RELAY. IF OK, REPLACE RELAY.

YES →
- BACK PROBE FAN HARNESS CAVITY "A" WITH TEST LIGHT CONNECTED TO CAVITY "B". LIGHT SHOULD BE "ON". IS IT?

NO → REPAIR OPEN IN CKT 702.

YES → POOR FAN CONNECTIONS OR FAULTY FAN.

NO → REPAIR OPEN IN CKT 150.

NO → REPAIR OPEN CKT 335.

YES → CHECK FOR POOR CONNECTION AT ECM TERMINAL "GEB". IF OK, REPLACE ECM.

"AFTER REPAIRS," CONFIRM "CLOSED LOOP" OPERATION AND NO "SERVICE ENGINE SOON" LIGHT.

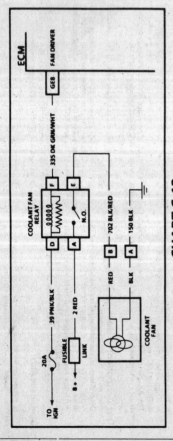

CHART C-12
COOLANT FAN FUNCTIONAL CHECK
2.3L (VIN A) "L" CARLINE (PORT)

Circuit Description:

The electric coolant fan is controlled by the Electronic Control Module (ECM) through the fan relay based on inputs from the coolant and manifold air temperature sensors, the A/C control switch, A/C pressure sensor and the vehicle speed sensor. The ECM controls the coolant fan by grounding CKT 335 which turns "ON" the fan relay.

The fan relay will be commanded "ON" when:

- Coolant temperature 103°C - 106°C or more.
- A/C clutch requested.
- Vehicle speed is less than 35 mph.

The fan relay will be commanded "ON" regardless of vehicle speed when:

- Code 14 or 15 are set.
- Coolant temperature 115°C - 118°C or more.
- A/C pressure is high.

The coolant fan may be commanded "ON" when the engine is not running under fan "Run-ON" conditions described previously in this section.

Test Description: Numbers below refer to circled numbers on the diagnostic chart.

1. With the field service mode activated, the coolant fan control driver should close, which should energize the fan control relay.
2. Test to see if fault is in wiring to the fan or the fan/relay connection.

Diagnostic Aids:

If the owner complained of an overheating problem, it must be determined if the complaint was due to an actual boil over, or the "hot light," or temperature gage indicated overheating.

If the gage, or light, indicates overheating, but no boil over is detected, the gage or light circuit should be checked. The gage accuracy can also be checked by comparing the coolant sensor reading using a Tech 1 "Scan" tool with the gage reading.

If the engine is actually overheating, and the gage indicates overheating, but the coolant fan is not coming "ON," the coolant sensor has probably shifted out of calibration and should be replaced. See Code 15 chart for a temperature to resistance chart.

If the engine is overheating, and the coolant fan is "ON," the cooling system should be checked.

ECM WIRING DIAGRAM — 1990-91 2.2L ENGINE

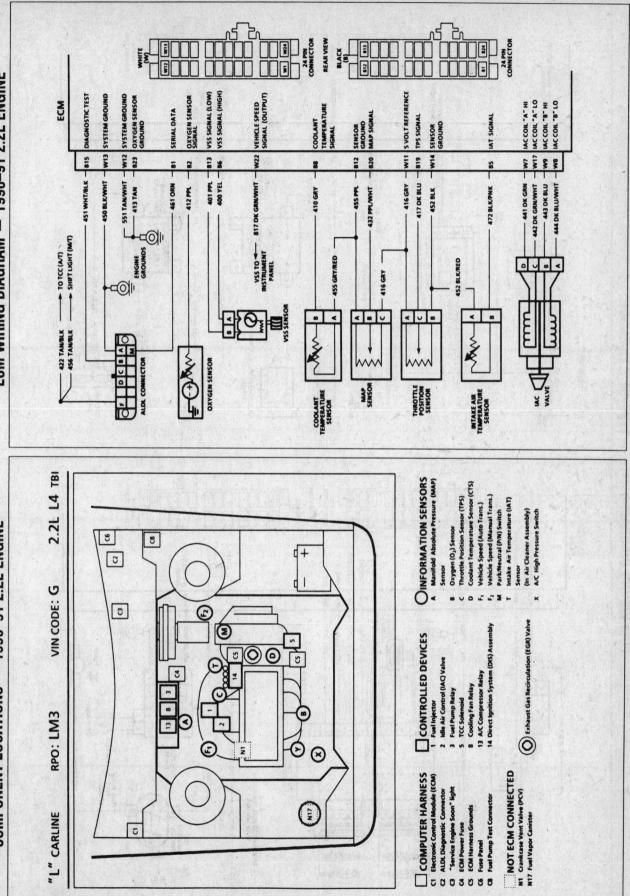

COMPONENT LOCATIONS — 1990-91 2.2L ENGINE

"L" CARLINE   RPO: LM3   VIN CODE: G   2.2L L4 TBI

COMPUTER HARNESS
- C1 Electronic Control Module (ECM)
- C2 ALDL Diagnostic Connector
- C3 "Service Engine Soon" light
- C4 ECM Power Fuse
- C5 ECM Harness Grounds
- C6 Fuse Panel
- C8 Fuel Pump Test Connector

NOT ECM CONNECTED
- N1 Crankcase Vent Valve (PCV)
- N17 Fuel Vapor Canister

CONTROLLED DEVICES
- 1 Fuel Injector
- 2 Idle Air Control (IAC) Valve
- 3 Fuel Pump Relay
- 5 TCC Solenoid
- 8 Cooling Fan Relay
- 13 A/C Compressor Relay
- 14 Direct Ignition System (DIS) Assembly
- ◎ Exhaust Gas Recirculation (EGR) Valve

INFORMATION SENSORS
- A Manifold Absolute Pressure (MAP) Sensor
- B Oxygen (O₂) Sensor
- C Throttle Position Sensor (TPS)
- D Coolant Temperature Sensor (CTS)
- F₁ Vehicle Speed (Auto Trans.)
- F₂ Vehicle Speed (Manual Trans.)
- M Park/Neutral (P/N) Switch
- T Intake Air Temperature (IAT) Sensor (In Air Cleaner Assembly)
- X A/C High Pressure Switch

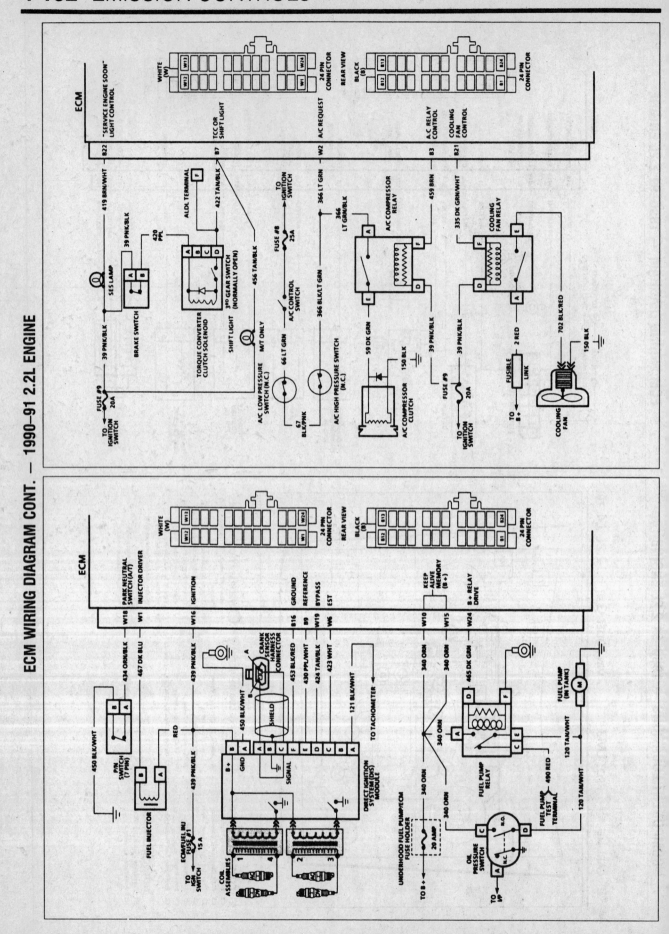

DIAGNOSTIC CIRCUIT CHECK — 1990–91 2.2L ENGINE

DIAGNOSTIC CIRCUIT CHECK

The Diagnostic Circuit Check is an organized approach to identifying a problem created by an electronic engine control system malfunction. It must be the starting point for any drivability complaint diagnosis because it directs the service technician to the next logical step in diagnosing the complaint.

The Tech 1 data listed in the table may be used for comparison after completing the diagnostic circuit check and finding the on-board diagnostics functioning properly with no trouble codes displayed. The "Typical Data Values" are an average of display values recorded from normally operating vehicles and are intended to represent what a normally functioning system would typically display.

A "SCAN" TOOL THAT DISPLAYS FAULTY DATA SHOULD NOT BE USED, AND THE PROBLEM SHOULD BE REPORTED TO THE MANUFACTURER. THE USE OF A FAULTY "SCAN" TOOL CAN RESULT IN MISDIAGNOSIS AND UNNECESSARY PARTS REPLACEMENT.

Only the parameters listed below are used in this manual for diagnosis. If a "Scan" tool reads other parameters, the values are not recommended by General Motors for use in diagnosis.

If all values are within the range illustrated, refer to "Symptoms"

TECH 1 TOOL DATA

Test Under Following Conditions: Idle, Upper Radiator Hose Hot, Closed Throttle, Park or Neutral, "Closed Loop", All Accessories "OFF."

"SCAN" Position	Units Displayed	Typical Data Value
Engine Speed	Rpm	± 50 RPM from desired rpm in drive (A/T); ± 100 RPM from desired rpm in neutral (M/T)
Desired Idle	Rpm	ECM idle command (varies with temp.)
Coolant Temperature	Degrees Celsius	85° - 105°
IAT/MAT	Degrees Celsius	10° - 90° (varies with underhood temp. and sensor location)
MAP	kPa/Volts	29-48 kPa/1 - 2 volts (varies with manifold and barometric pressures)
Open/Closed Loop	Open/Closed	"Closed Loop" (may enter "Open Loop" with extended idle)
Throt Position	Volts	.30 - 1.33
Throttle Angle	0 - 100%	0 - .....*
Oxygen Sensor	Millivolts	100 - 999 (varies continuously)
Inj. Pulse Width	Milliseconds	.8 - 3.0
Spark Advance	Degrees	Varies
Engine Speed	Rpm	± 50 RPM from desired rpm in drive (A/T); ± 100 RPM from desired rpm in neutral (M/T)
Fuel Integrator	Counts	110-145
Block Learn	Counts	118-138
Idle Air Control	Counts (steps)	1 - 50
P/N Switch	P-N and R-D-L	Park/Neutral (P/N)
MPH/KPH	0-255	0
TCC	"ON"/"OFF"	"OFF"
Crank Rpm	Rpm	>796
Ign/Batt Voltage	Volts	13.5 - 14.5
Cooling Fan Relay	"ON"/"OFF"	"OFF" (coolant temperature below 102°C)
A/C Request	"YES"/"NO"	No
A/C Clutch	"ON"/"OFF"	"OFF"
Power Steering	Normal/High Pressure	Normal
Shift Light (M/T)	"ON"/"OFF"	"OFF"

ECM WIRING DIAGRAM CONT. — 1990–91 2.2L ENGINE

FUEL INJECTION ECM CONNECTOR IDENTIFICATION

This ECM voltage chart is for use with a digital voltmeter to further aid in diagnosis. The voltages you get may vary due to low battery charge or other reasons, but they should be very close.

THE FOLLOWING CONDITIONS MUST BE MET BEFORE TESTING:
• Engine at operating temperature • Engine idling in "Closed Loop" (for "Engine Run" column) • Test terminal not grounded • "Scan" tool not installed • All voltages shown "B+" indicates battery or charging voltage.

VOLTAGE — White (W) Connector

KEY "ON" RUN	ENG. RUN	CIRCUIT	PIN	WIRE COLOR
① B+	0*	INJECTOR DRIVER	W1	DK BLU
0*		A/C REQUEST	W2	LT GRN
		NOT USED	W3	DK GRN
		CRUISE LIGHT	W4	GRY/BLK
		NOT USED	W5	DK BLU
0	1.1	EST	W6	WHT
④	④	IAC "A" HI	W7	DK GRN/WHT
④	④	IAC "B" LOW	W8	DK BLU/WHT
④	④	IAC "B" HI	W9	DK BLU
B+	B+	BATTERY	W10	ORN
5.0	5.0	5 VREF	W11	GRY
0*	0*	ECM GROUND	W12	TAN/WHT

WIRE COLOR	PIN	CIRCUIT	KEY "ON"	ENG. "RUN"
DK GRN	W24	FUEL PUMP	②	B+
	W23	NOT USED		
DK GRN/WHT	W22	VSS OUTPUT 4000 PPM (IF USED)	0*	0*
DK BLU	W21	CRUISE SET		
GRY	W20	CRUISE ENABLE		
TAN/BLK	W19	BYPASS	0*	4.5
ORN/BLK	W18	P/N SWITCH		
DK GRN/WHT	W17	IAC "A" LOW	④	④
PNK/BLK	W16	IGNITION	B+	B+
ORN	W15	BATTERY	B+	B+
BLK	W14	SENSOR GROUND	0*	0*
BLK/WHT	W13	ECM GROUND	0*	0*

WHITE (W) — 24 PIN CONNECTOR — REAR VIEW

VOLTAGE — Black (B) Connector

KEY "ON" RUN	ENG. RUN	CIRCUIT	PIN	WIRE COLOR
4.5	4.5	SERIAL DATA	B1	ORN
.01-.33	1-9	O₂ SIGNAL	B2	PPL
① B+	B+	A/C CLUTCH RELAY	B3	BRN
		NOT USED	B4	
1.3	1.3	IAT SIGNAL	B5	BLK/PNK
.13	.13	VSS SIGNAL (HIGH)	B6	YEL
③ 0*	0*	TCC OR SHIFT LIGHT	B7	TAN/BLK
1.9	1.9	CTS SIGNAL	B8	GRY
③ 4.6	3.05	REF HI	B9	PPL/WHT
		CRUISE SOLENOID	B10	LT GRN
		CRUISE SOLENOID	B11	DK BLU
0*	0*	SENSOR GROUNDS	B12	PPL

WIRE COLOR	PIN	CIRCUIT	KEY "ON"	ENG. "RUN"
TAN	B24	NOT USED		
BRN/WHT	B23	O₂ GROUND	0*	0*
DK GRN/WHT	B22	SES LIGHT	0*	B+
PPL/WHT	B21	COOLANT FAN	B+	B+
DK BLU	B20	MAP SIGNAL	4.75	1.1
	B19	NOT USED	.6	.6
	B18	NOT USED		
	B17	NOT USED		
BLK/RED	B16	REFLO		
WHT/BLK	B15	ALDL DIAG.	0*	0*
BRN	B14	BRAKE SIGNAL	5.0	5.0
PPL	B13	VSS SIGNAL (LOW)	0*	0*

BLACK (B) — 24 PIN CONNECTOR

ENGINE 2.2L

* Less than 5 volt.
① A/C, Fan "OFF"
② Reads battery voltage for 2 seconds after ignition "ON" then should read 0 volts
③ Varies depending on temperature
④ Not useable

1990-91 2.2L ENGINE

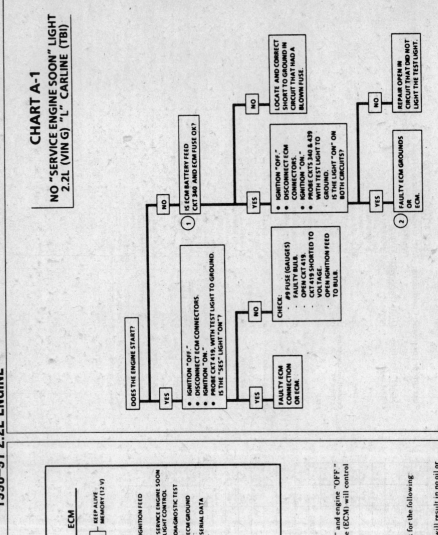

CHART A-1

NO "SERVICE ENGINE SOON" LIGHT
2.2L (VIN G) "L" CARLINE (TBI)

DOES THE ENGINE START?

YES
- IGNITION "OFF."
- DISCONNECT ECM CONNECTORS.
- IGNITION "ON."
- PROBE CKT 419, WITH TEST LIGHT TO GROUND.
- IS THE "SES" LIGHT "ON"?

NO → IS ECM BATTERY FEED CKT 340 AND ECM FUSE OK?

NO
- IGNITION "OFF."
- DISCONNECT ECM CONNECTORS.
- IGNITION "ON."
- PROBE CKTS 340 & 439 WITH TEST LIGHT TO GROUND.
- IS THE LIGHT "ON" ON BOTH CIRCUITS?

NO → LOCATE AND CORRECT SHORT TO GROUND IN CIRCUIT THAT HAD A BLOWN FUSE.

YES → (2) FAULTY ECM GROUNDS OR ECM.

(1)

YES → NO → YES

CHECK:
- #9 FUSE (GAUGES)
- FAULTY BULB.
- OPEN CKT 419.
- CKT 419 SHORTED TO VOLTAGE.
- OPEN IGNITION FEED TO BULB.

YES → FAULTY ECM CONNECTION OR ECM.

NO → REPAIR OPEN IN CIRCUIT THAT DID NOT LIGHT THE TEST LIGHT.

CHART A-1

NO "SERVICE ENGINE SOON" LIGHT
2.2L (VIN G) "L" CARLINE (TBI)

"AFTER REPAIRS," CONFIRM "CLOSED LOOP" OPERATION AND NO "SERVICE ENGINE SOON" LIGHT.

ECM

- KEEP ALIVE MEMORY (12 V) — W10
- W15
- IGNITION FEED — W16
- SERVICE ENGINE SOON LIGHT CONTROL — B22
- DIAGNOSTIC TEST — B15
- ECM GROUND — W13
- SERIAL DATA — B1

340 ORN
340 ORN
439 PNK/BLK
419 BRN/WHT
451 WHT/BLK
450 BLK/WHT
461 ORN

ECM FUSE AND HOLDER 20A

FUSE #1 15A

FUSE #9 20A

FUSIBLE LINK

IGNITION SWITCH

BATTERY

TO TCC ← 422 TAN/BLK

BULKHEAD CONNECTOR

"SES" LIGHT

ALDL CONNECTOR

TWIN 8-PIN J-P CONNECTORS

Circuit Description:

There should always be a steady "Service Engine Soon" light, when the ignition is "ON" and engine "OFF." Ignition battery voltage is supplied directly to the light bulb. The Electronic Control Module (ECM) will control the light and turn it "ON" by providing a ground path through CKT 419.

Test Description: Number(s) below refer to circled number(s) on the diagnostic chart.

1. Battery feed CKT 340 is protected by an underhood ECM fuse.

2. Using a test light connected to B+, probe each of the system ground circuits to be sure a good ground is present. See ECM terminal end view in front of this section for ECM pin locations of ground circuits.

Diagnostic Aids:

If engine runs correctly, check for the following:
- Faulty light bulb
- CKT 419 open
- Gauges fuse blown. This will result in no oil or generator lights, seat belt reminder, etc.

If "Engine Cranks But Will Not Run," use CHART A-3

1990-91 2.2L ENGINE

CHART A-2
NO ALDL DATA OR WON'T FLASH CODE 12
"SERVICE ENGINE SOON" LIGHT "ON" STEADY
2.2L (VIN G) "L" CARLINE (TBI)

- IGNITION "ON," ENGINE "OFF." IS THE "SES" LIGHT "ON"?
  - **NO** → USE CHART A-1.
  - **YES** → GROUND DIAGNOSTIC "TEST" TERMINAL. DOES LIGHT FLASH CODE 12?
    - **YES** → (1) IF PROBLEM WAS NO ALDL DATA: CHECK SERIAL DATA CKT 461 FOR OPEN OR SHORT TO GROUND BETWEEN ECM AND ALDL CONNECTOR. IF OK, IT IS A FAULTY ECM OR PROM.
    - **NO** → (2) IGNITION "OFF." DISCONNECT ECM CONNECTORS. IGNITION "ON" AND NOTE "SERVICE ENGINE SOON" LIGHT.
      - **LIGHT "ON"** → REPAIR SHORT TO GROUND IN CKT 419.
      - **LIGHT "OFF."** → (3) RECONNECT ECM. IGNITION "ON," ENGINE "OFF." DIAGNOSTIC "TEST" TERMINAL NOT GROUNDED. BACK PROBE ECM CKT 451 WITH TEST LIGHT TO GROUND. LEAVE CONNECTED AND WATCH "SES" LIGHT.
        - **CODE 12** → CHECK FOR OPEN CKT 451 FROM DIAGNOSTIC TEST TERMINAL TO ECM. IF OK, CHECK FOR OPEN CIRCUIT BETWEEN ALDL TERMINAL "A" AND ECM.
          - **CODE 12** → SYSTEM OK.
          - **NO CODE 12** → (4) CHECK PROM FOR PROPER INSTALLATION. IF OK, REPLACE ECM USING ORIGINAL PROM. RECHECK FOR CODE 12.
            - **NO CODE 12** → REPLACE PROM.

"AFTER REPAIRS," CONFIRM "CLOSED LOOP" OPERATION AND NO "SERVICE ENGINE SOON" LIGHT.

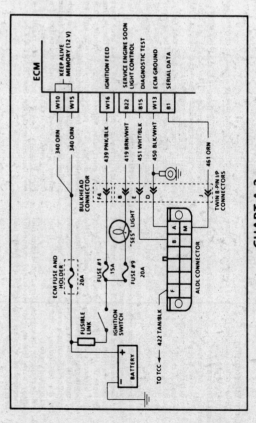

ECM

KEEP ALIVE MEMORY (12 V) — W10 — 340 ORN
W15 — 340 ORN
IGNITION FEED — W16 — 439 PNK/BLK
SERVICE ENGINE SOON LIGHT CONTROL — B22 — 419 BRN/WHT
DIAGNOSTIC TEST — B15 — 451 WHT/BLK
ECM GROUND — W13 — 450 BLK/WHT
SERIAL DATA — B1 — 461 ORN

ECM FUSE AND HOLDER 20A
FUSE #1 15A
FUSE #9 20A
FUSIBLE LINK
IGNITION SWITCH
BATTERY
TO TCC ← 422 TAN/BLK
BULKHEAD CONNECTOR
F4   B   E   D   J
"SES" LIGHT
ALDL CONNECTOR F B A M
TWIN 8-PIN I/P CONNECTORS

CHART A-2
NO ALDL DATA OR WON'T FLASH CODE 12
"SERVICE ENGINE SOON" LIGHT "ON" STEADY
2.2L (VIN G) "L" CARLINE (TBI)

Circuit Description:

There should always be a steady "Service Engine Soon" light when the ignition is "ON" and the engine is "OFF." Ignition battery voltage is supplied directly to the light bulb. The Electronic Control Module (ECM) will control the light and turn it "ON" by providing a ground path through CKT 419 to the ECM.

With the diagnostic terminal grounded, the light should flash a Code 12, followed by any trouble code(s) stored in memory. A steady light suggests a short to ground in the light control CKT 419, or an open in diagnostic CKT 451.

Test Description: Number(s) below refer to circled number(s) on the diagnostic chart.

1. If there is a problem with the ECM that causes a "Scan" tool to not read data from the ECM, then the ECM should not flash a Code 12. If Code 12 does flash, be sure the "Scan" tool is working properly on another vehicle. If the "Scan" tool is functioning properly and CKT 461 is OK, the PROM or ECM may be at fault for the "NO ALDL DATA" symptom.

2. The "Service Engine Soon" light should not be "ON" with ignition "ON," and the ECM disconnected

3. This step will check for an open diagnostic CKT 451

4. At this point, the "Service Engine Soon" light wiring is OK. The problem is a faulty ECM or PROM. If Code 12 does not flash, the ECM should be replaced using the original PROM. Replace the PROM only after trying an ECM, as a defective PROM is an unlikely cause of the problem

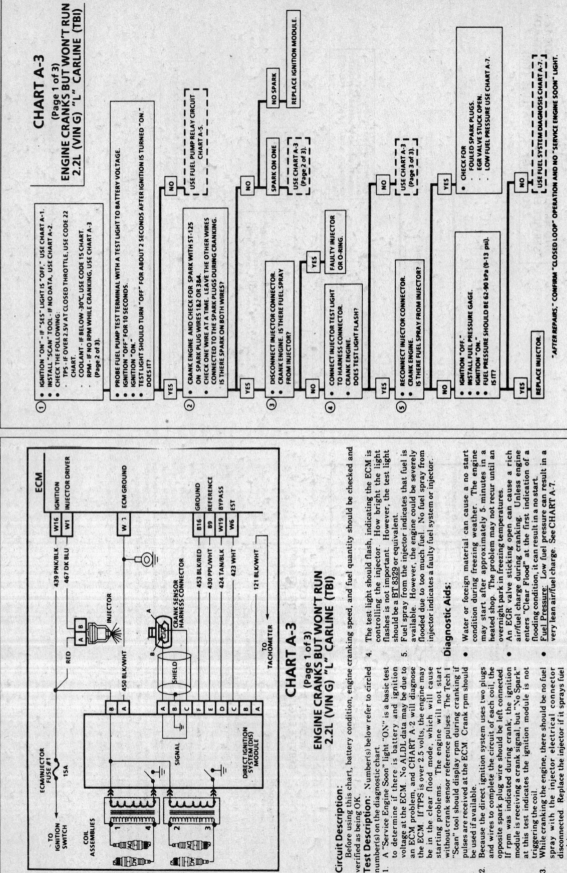

1990–91 2.2L ENGINE

CHART A-3 (Page 1 of 3) — ENGINE CRANKS BUT WON'T RUN — 2.2L (VIN G) "L" CARLINE (TBI)

(1)
- IGNITION "ON" - IF "SES" LIGHT IS "OFF," USE CHART A-1.
- INSTALL "SCAN" TOOL. - IF NO DATA, USE CHART A-2.
- CHECK THE FOLLOWING:
  - TPS - IF OVER 2.5V AT CLOSED THROTTLE, USE CODE 22 CHART.
  - COOLANT - IF BELOW -30°C, USE CODE 15 CHART.
  - RPM - IF NO RPM WHILE CRANKING, USE CHART A-3 (Page 2 of 3).

- PROBE FUEL PUMP TEST TERMINAL WITH A TEST LIGHT TO BATTERY VOLTAGE.
- IGNITION "OFF."
- IGNITION "ON."
- TEST LIGHT SHOULD TURN "OFF" FOR ABOUT 2 SECONDS AFTER IGNITION IS TURNED "ON." DOES IT?

NO → USE FUEL PUMP RELAY CIRCUIT CHART A-5.

(2)
- CRANK ENGINE AND CHECK FOR SPARK WITH ST-125 ON SPARK PLUG WIRES 1&2 OR 3&4.
- CHECK ONE WIRE AT A TIME. LEAVE THE OTHER WIRES CONNECTED TO THE SPARK PLUGS DURING CRANKING. IS THERE SPARK ON BOTH WIRES?

NO SPARK → REPLACE IGNITION MODULE.
SPARK ON ONE → USE CHART A-3 (Page 2 of 3).

(3)
- DISCONNECT INJECTOR CONNECTOR.
- CRANK ENGINE. IS THERE FUEL SPRAY FROM INJECTOR?

YES → FAULTY INJECTOR OR O-RING.

(4)
- CONNECT INJECTOR TEST LIGHT TO HARNESS CONNECTOR.
- CRANK ENGINE. DOES TEST LIGHT FLASH?

NO → USE CHART A-3 (Page 3 of 3).

(5)
- RECONNECT INJECTOR CONNECTOR.
- CRANK ENGINE. IS THERE FUEL SPRAY FROM INJECTOR?

YES → CHECK FOR
- FOULED SPARK PLUGS.
- EGR VALVE STUCK OPEN.
- LOW FUEL PRESSURE USE CHART A-7.

NO →
- IGNITION "OFF."
- INSTALL FUEL PRESSURE GAGE.
- IGNITION "ON."
- FUEL PRESSURE SHOULD BE 62-90 kPa (9-13 psi). IS IT?

YES → REPLACE INJECTOR.
NO → USE FUEL SYSTEM DIAGNOSIS CHART A-7.

"AFTER REPAIRS," CONFIRM "CLOSED LOOP" OPERATION AND NO "SERVICE ENGINE SOON" LIGHT.

CHART A-3 (Page 1 of 3) — ENGINE CRANKS BUT WON'T RUN — 2.2L (VIN G) "L" CARLINE (TBI)

Wiring diagram labels: ECM — IGNITION, INJECTOR DRIVER, ECM GROUND, GROUND, REFERENCE, BYPASS, EST; W16, W1, W 3, B16, B9, W19, W6; 439 PNK/BLK, 467 DK BLU, 453 BLK/RED, 430 PPL/WHT, 424 TAN/BLK, 423 WHT, 121 BLK/WHT, 450 BLK/WHT, RED; INJECTOR; CRANK SENSOR HARNESS CONNECTOR; SHIELD; SIGNAL; DIRECT IGNITION SYSTEM (DIS) MODULE; COIL ASSEMBLIES; ECM/INJECTOR FUSE #1 15A; TO IGNITION SWITCH; TO TACHOMETER.

Circuit Description:

Before using this chart, battery condition, engine cranking speed, and fuel quantity should be checked and verified as being OK.

Test Description: Number(s) below refer to circled number(s) on the diagnostic chart.

1. A "Service Engine Soon" light "ON" is a basic test to determine if there is battery and ignition voltage at the ECM. No ALDL data may be due to an ECM problem, and CHART A-2 will diagnose the ECM. If TPS is over 2.5 volts, the engine may be in the clear flood mode, which will cause starting problems. The engine will not start without crank sensor reference pulses. The Tech 1 "Scan" tool should display rpm during cranking if pulses are received at the ECM. Crank rpm should be used if available.
2. Because the direct ignition system uses two plugs and wires to complete the circuit of each coil, the opposite spark plug wire should be left connected. If rpm was indicated during crank, the ignition module is receiving a crank signal, but "No Spark" at this test indicates the ignition module is not triggering the coil.
3. While cranking the engine, there should be no fuel spray with the injector electrical connector disconnected. Replace the injector if it sprays fuel or drips.
4. The test light should flash, indicating the ECM is controlling the injector. How bright the light flashes is not important. However, the test light should be a BT 8329 or equivalent.
5. Fuel spray from the injector indicates that fuel is available. However, the engine could be severely flooded due to too much fuel. No fuel spray from injector indicates a faulty fuel system or injector.

Diagnostic Aids:

- Water or foreign material can cause a no start condition during freezing weather. The engine may start after approximately 5 minutes in a heated shop. The problem may not recur until an overnight park in freezing temperatures.
- An EGR valve sticking open can cause a rich air/fuel charge during cranking. Unless engine enters "Clear Flood" at the first indication of a flooding condition, it can result in a no start.
- Fuel Pressure: Low fuel pressure can result in a very lean air/fuel charge. See CHART A-7.

1990–91 2.2L ENGINE

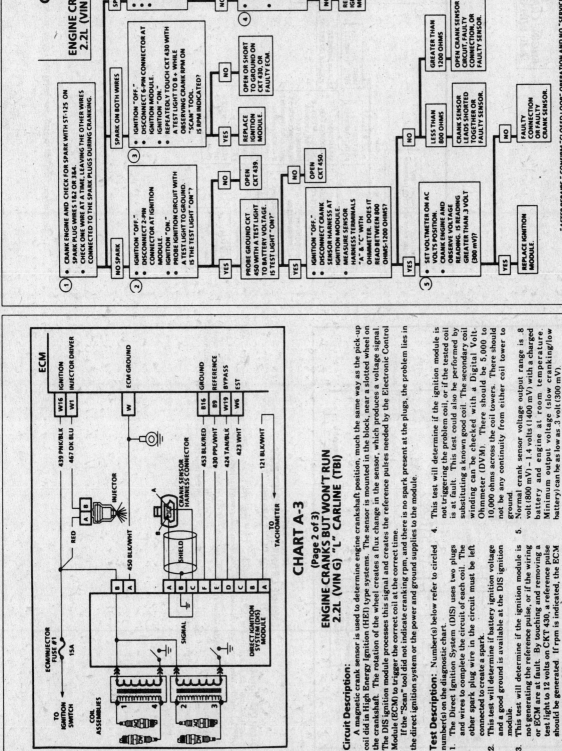

CHART A-3
(Page 2 of 3)
ENGINE CRANKS BUT WON'T RUN
2.2L (VIN G) "L" CARLINE (TBI)

Circuit Description:

A magnetic crank sensor is used to determine engine crankshaft position, much the same way as the pick-up coil did in High Energy Ignition (HEI) type systems. The sensor is mounted in the block, near a slotted wheel on the crankshaft. The rotation of the wheel creates a flux change in the sensor, which produces a voltage signal. The DIS ignition module processes this signal and creates the reference pulses needed by the Electronic Control Module (ECM) to trigger the correct coil at the correct time.

If the "Scan" tool did not indicate cranking rpm, and there is no spark present at the plugs, the problem lies in the direct ignition system or the power and ground supplies to the module.

Test Description: Number(s) below refer to circled number(s) on the diagnostic chart.

1. The Direct Ignition System (DIS) uses two plugs and wires to complete the circuit of each coil. The other spark plug wire in the circuit must be left connected to create a spark.

2. This test will determine if battery ignition voltage and a good ground is available at the DIS ignition module.

3. This test will determine if the ignition module is not generating the reference pulse, or if the wiring or ECM are at fault. By touching and removing a test light to 12 volts on CKT 430, a reference pulse should be generated. If rpm is indicated, the ECM and wiring are OK.

4. This test will determine if the ignition module is not triggering the problem coil, or if the tested coil is at fault. This test could also be performed by substituting a known good coil. The secondary coil winding can be checked with a Digital Volt-Ohmmeter (DVM). There should be 5,000 to 10,000 ohms across the coil towers. There should not be any continuity from either coil tower to ground.

5. Normal crank sensor voltage output range is .8 volt (800 mV) – 1.4 volts (1400 mV) with a charged battery and engine at room temperature. Minimum output voltage (slow cranking/low battery) can be as low as .3 volt (300 mV).

"AFTER REPAIRS," CONFIRM "CLOSED LOOP" OPERATION AND NO "SERVICE ENGINE SOON" LIGHT.

1990–91 2.2L ENGINE

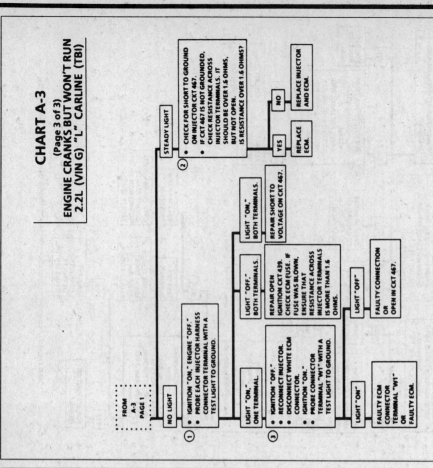

CHART A-3
(Page 3 of 3)
ENGINE CRANKS BUT WON'T RUN
2.2L (VIN G) "L" CARLINE (TBI)

STEADY LIGHT

② CHECK FOR SHORT TO GROUND ON INJECTOR CKT 467. IF CKT 467 IS NOT GROUNDED, CHECK RESISTANCE ACROSS INJECTOR TERMINALS. IT SHOULD BE OVER 1.6 OHMS, BUT NOT OPEN.
IS RESISTANCE OVER 1.6 OHMS?

YES	NO
REPLACE ECM.	REPLACE INJECTOR AND ECM.

LIGHT "ON," BOTH TERMINALS.

REPAIR SHORT TO VOLTAGE ON CKT 467.

LIGHT "OFF," BOTH TERMINALS.

REPAIR OPEN IGNITION CKT 439. CHECK ECM FUSE. IF FUSE WAS BLOWN, ENSURE THAT RESISTANCE ACROSS INJECTOR TERMINALS IS MORE THAN 1.6 OHMS.

LIGHT "OFF"

FAULTY CONNECTION OR OPEN IN CKT 467.

FROM A-3 PAGE 1

NO LIGHT

① IGNITION "ON," ENGINE "OFF."
• PROBE EACH INJECTOR HARNESS CONNECTOR TERMINAL WITH A TEST LIGHT TO GROUND.

LIGHT "ON," ONE TERMINAL

③ IGNITION "OFF."
• RECONNECT INJECTOR.
• DISCONNECT WHITE ECM CONNECTOR.
• IGNITION "ON."
• PROBE CONNECTOR TERMINAL "W1" WITH A TEST LIGHT TO GROUND.

LIGHT "ON"

FAULTY ECM CONNECTOR TERMINAL "W1" OR FAULTY ECM.

"AFTER REPAIRS," CONFIRM "CLOSED LOOP" OPERATION AND NO "SERVICE ENGINE SOON" LIGHT.

ECM

W16 IGNITION	W1 INJECTOR DRIVER	W ECM GROUND	B16 GROUND	B9 REFERENCE	W19 BYPASS	W6 EST

439 PNK/BLK
467 DK BLU

TO IGNITION SWITCH

ECM/INJECTOR FUSE #1
15A

RED

INJECTOR
A B

450 BLK/WHT

453 BLK/RED
430 PPL/WHT
424 TAN/BLK
423 WHT

121 BLK/WHT

TO TACHOMETER

CRANK SENSOR HARNESS CONNECTOR

SHIELD

SIGNAL

DIRECT IGNITION SYSTEM (DIS) MODULE

COIL ASSEMBLIES
1 4
2 3

CHART A-3
(Page 3 of 3)
ENGINE CRANKS BUT WON'T RUN
2.2L (VIN G) "L" CARLINE (TBI)

Circuit Description:
Ignition voltage is supplied to the fuel injector on CKT 439. The injector will be pulsed (turned "ON" and "OFF"), when the Electronic Control Module (ECM) opens and grounds injector drive CKT 467.

Test Description: Number(s) below refer to circled number(s) on the diagnostic chart.
1. This test determines if injector connector has ignition voltage, and on only one terminal.
2. A faulty ECM may result in damage to the injector.
3. A test light connected from ECM harness terminal "W1" to ground should light due to continuity through the injector.

1990–91 2.2L ENGINE

CHART A-5

**FUEL PUMP RELAY CIRCUIT
2.2L (VIN G) "L" CARLINE (TBI)**

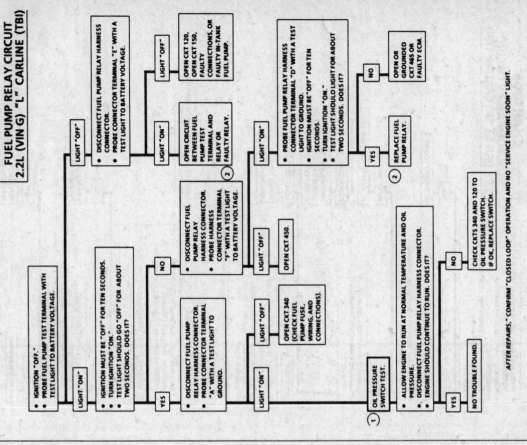

CHART A-5

**FUEL PUMP RELAY CIRCUIT
2.2L (VIN G) "L" CARLINE (TBI)**

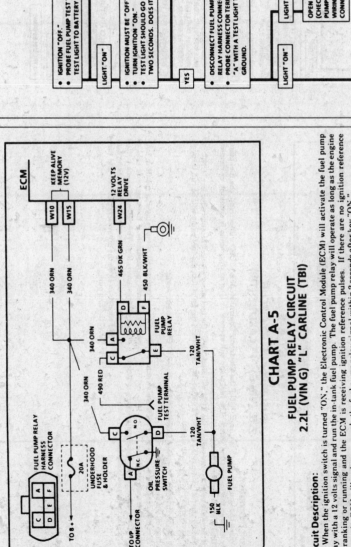

Circuit Description:

When the ignition switch is turned "ON," the Electronic Control Module (ECM) will activate the fuel pump relay with a 12 volts signal and run the in-tank fuel pump. The fuel pump relay will operate as long as the engine is cranking or running and the ECM is receiving ignition reference pulses. If there are no ignition reference pulses, the ECM will no longer supply the fuel pump relay signal within 2 seconds after key "ON."

Should the fuel pump relay or the 12 volts relay drive from the ECM fail, the fuel pump will receive electrical current through the oil pressure switch back-up circuit.

The fuel pump test terminal is located in the driver's side of the engine compartment. When the engine is stopped, the pump can be turned "ON" by applying battery voltage to the test terminal.

Test Description: Number(s) below refer to circled number(s) on the diagnostic chart.

1. At this point, the fuel pump relay is operating correctly. The back-up circuit through the oil pressure switch is now tested.
2. After the fuel pump relay is replaced, continue with "Oil Pressure Switch Test."

Diagnostic Aids:

An inoperative fuel pump relay can result in long cranking times. The extended crank period is caused by the time necessary for oil pressure to reach the pressure required to close the oil pressure switch and turn "ON" the fuel pump.

1990-91 2.2L ENGINE

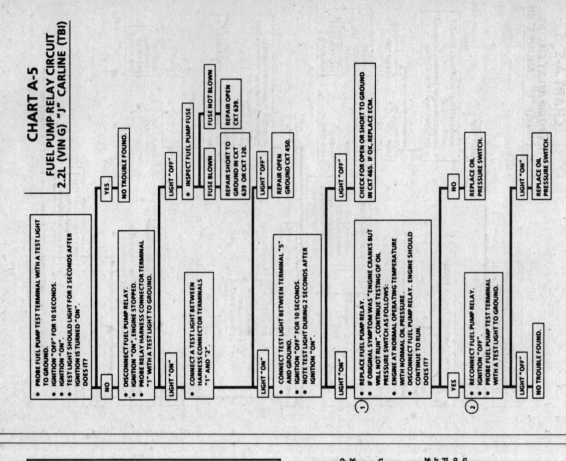

CHART A-5
FUEL PUMP RELAY CIRCUIT
2.2L (VIN G) "J" CARLINE (TBI)

Circuit Description:

When the ignition switch is turned "ON," the Electronic Control Module (ECM) will activate the fuel pump relay and run the in-tank fuel pump. The fuel pump will operate as long as the engine is cranking or running and the ECM is receiving ignition reference pulses.

If there are no reference pulses, the ECM will shut "OFF" the fuel pump within 2 seconds after key "ON."

Should the fuel pump relay or the 12 volts relay drive from the ECM fail, the fuel pump will be run through an oil pressure switch back-up circuit.

Test Description: Numbers below refer to circled numbers on the diagnostic chart.

1. This test determines if the oil pressure switch is stuck in the open position.
2. This test determines if the oil pressure switch is stuck in the closed position.

Diagnostic Aids:

An inoperative fuel pump relay can result in long cranking times, particularly if the engine is cold or engine oil pressure is low. The extended crank period is caused by the time necessary for oil pressure to build enough to close the oil pressure switch and turn "ON" the fuel pump.

1990–91 2.2L ENGINE

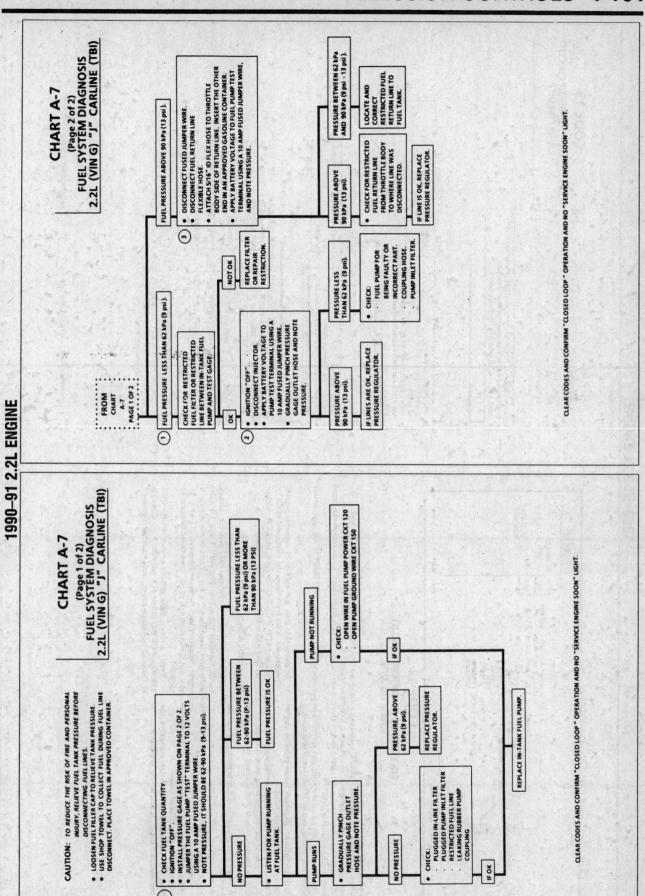

CHART A-7
(Page 1 of 2)
FUEL SYSTEM DIAGNOSIS
2.2L (VIN G) "J" CARLINE (TBI)

CHART A-7
(Page 2 of 2)
FUEL SYSTEM DIAGNOSIS
2.2L (VIN G) "J" CARLINE (TBI)

1990–91 2.2L ENGINE

CODE 13
OXYGEN (O₂) SENSOR CIRCUIT
(OPEN CIRCUIT)

Diagnostic flowchart:

① ENGINE AT NORMAL OPERATING TEMPERATURE (ABOVE 80°C/176°F).
• RUN ENGINE ABOVE 1200 RPM FOR TWO MINUTES.
• DOES TECH 1 TOOL INDICATE "CLOSED LOOP"?

  YES → CODE 13 IS INTERMITTENT.

② • DISCONNECT O₂ SENSOR.
• JUMPER HARNESS CKT 412 (ECM SIDE) TO GROUND.
• TECH 1 SHOULD DISPLAY O₂ VOLTAGE BELOW .2 VOLT (200 mv) WITH ENGINE RUNNING. DOES IT?

  YES → FAULTY O₂ SENSOR CONNECTION OR SENSOR.

③ • REMOVE JUMPER.
• IGNITION "ON," ENGINE "OFF."
• CHECK VOLTAGE OF CKT 412 (ECM SIDE) AT O₂ SENSOR HARNESS CONNECTOR USING A DVM.

  .3–.6 VOLT (300–600 mV) → FAULTY ECM.

  OVER .6 VOLT (600 mV) → OPEN CKT 413 OR FAULTY CONNECTION OR FAULTY ECM.

  LESS THAN .3 VOLT (300 mV) → OPEN CKT 412 OR FAULTY ECM CONNECTION OR FAULTY ECM.

"AFTER REPAIRS," REFER TO CODE CRITERIA AND CONFIRM CODE DOES NOT RESET.

CODE 13
OXYGEN (O₂) SENSOR CIRCUIT
(OPEN CIRCUIT)

ECM — O₂ SENSOR SIGNAL B2 — O₂ SENSOR GROUND B23 — 412 PPL — 413 TAN — ENGINE GROUND — OXYGEN (O₂) SENSOR — EXHAUST

Circuit Description:

The Electronic Control Module (ECM) supplies a voltage of about .45 volt between terminals "B2" and "B23". (If measured with a 10 megohm digital voltmeter, this may read as low as .32 volt).

When the O₂ sensor reaches operating temperature, it varies this voltage from about .1 volt (exhaust is lean) to about .9 volt (exhaust is rich).

The sensor is like an open circuit and produces no voltage when it is below 316°C (600°F). An open sensor circuit, or cold sensor, causes "Open Loop" operation.

Test Description: Numbers below refer to circled numbers on the diagnostic chart.

1. Code 13 will set under the following conditions:
   • Engine at normal operating temperature.
   • At least 1 minute has elapsed since engine start-up.
   • O₂ signal voltage is steady between .35 and .55 volt.
   • Throttle angle is above 7%.
   • All above conditions are met for about 20 seconds.

   If the conditions for a Code 13 exist, the system will not operate in "Closed Loop."

2. This test determines if the O₂ sensor is the problem or if the ECM and wiring are at fault.

3. In doing this test, use only a 10 megohm digital voltmeter. This test checks the continuity of CKTs 412 and 413. If CKT 413 is open, the ECM voltage on CKT 412 will be over .6 volt (600 mV).

Diagnostic Aids:

Normal Tech 1 "Scan" tool O₂ sensor voltage varies between 100 mV to 999 mV (.1 and 1.0 volt) while in "Closed Loop." Code 13 sets in one minute if sensor signal voltage remains between .35 and .55 volt, but the system will go to "Open Loop" in about 15 seconds.

Verify a clean, tight ground connection for CKT 413. Open CKT(s) 412 or 413 will result in a Code 13. If Code 13 is intermittent, refer to "Symptoms,"

1990–91 2.2L ENGINE

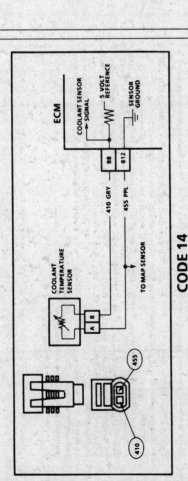

CODE 14
COOLANT TEMPERATURE SENSOR (CTS) CIRCUIT
(HIGH TEMPERATURE INDICATED)

Circuit Description:

The Coolant Temperature Sensor (CTS) uses a thermistor to control the signal voltage to the Electronic Control Module (ECM). The ECM applies a voltage on CKT 410 to the sensor. When the engine is cold, the sensor (thermistor) resistance is high. The ECM will then sense a high signal voltage.

As the engine warms up, the sensor resistance decreases and the voltage drops. At normal engine operating temperature, the voltage will measure about 1.5 to 2.0 volts at ECM terminal "B8".

Coolant temperature is one of the inputs used to control the following:

- Fuel delivery
- Electronic Spark Timing (EST)
- Cooling fan
- Torque Converter Clutch (TCC)
- Idle Air Control (IAC)

Test Description: Number(s) below refer to circled number(s) on the diagnostic chart.

1. Checks to see if code was set as result of hard failure or intermittent condition. Code 14 will set if:
   - Engine has been running for more than 10 seconds.
   - Signal voltage indicates a coolant temperature above 135°C (275°F) for 3 seconds.
2. This test simulates conditions for a Code 15. If the ECM recognizes the open circuit (high voltage), and displays a low temperature, the ECM and wiring are OK.

Diagnostic Aids:

A Tech 1 "Scan" tool reads engine temperature in degrees celsius. After the engine is started, the temperature should rise steadily to about 90°C (194°F), then stabilize when the thermostat opens.

If the engine has been allowed to cool to an ambient temperature (overnight), coolant and IAT temperature may be checked with a "Scan" tool and should read close to each other.

When a Code 14 is set, the ECM will turn "ON" the engine cooling fan.

A Code 14 will result if CKT 410 is shorted to ground.

If Code 14 is intermittent refer to "Symptoms,"

CODE 14
COOLANT TEMPERATURE SENSOR (CTS) CIRCUIT
(HIGH TEMPERATURE INDICATED)

1. DOES TECH 1 DISPLAY COOLANT TEMPERATURE OF 130°C (266°F) OR HIGHER?
   - NO → CODE 14 IS INTERMITTENT.
   - YES → 2. DISCONNECT COOLANT TEMPERATURE SENSOR. TECH 1 SHOULD DISPLAY COOLANT TEMPERATURE BELOW -30°C (-22°F). DOES IT?
     - NO → CKT 410 SHORTED TO GROUND OR CKT 410 SHORTED TO SENSOR GROUND CIRCUIT OR FAULTY ECM.
     - YES → REPLACE COOLANT TEMPERATURE SENSOR.

"AFTER REPAIRS," REFER TO CODE CRITERIA AND CONFIRM CODE DOES NOT RESET.

DIAGNOSTIC AID

COOLANT SENSOR
TEMPERATURE VS. RESISTANCE VALUES
(APPROXIMATE)

°C	°F	OHMS
100	212	177
90	194	241
80	176	332
70	158	467
60	140	667
50	122	973
45	113	1188
40	104	1459
35	95	1802
30	86	2238
25	77	2796
20	68	3520
15	59	4450
10	50	5670
5	41	7280
0	32	9420
-5	23	12300
-10	14	16180
-15	5	21450
-20	-4	28680
-30	-22	52700
-40	-40	100700

1990–91 2.2L ENGINE

CODE 15
COOLANT TEMPERATURE SENSOR (CTS) CIRCUIT
(LOW TEMPERATURE INDICATED)

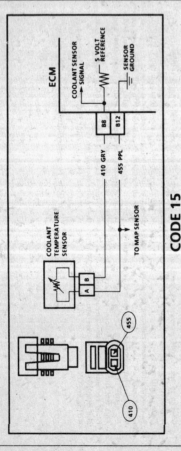

Circuit Description:

The Coolant Temperature Sensor (CTS) uses a thermistor to control the signal voltage to the Electronic Control Module (ECM). The ECM applies a voltage on CKT 410 to the sensor. When the engine is cold, the sensor (thermistor) resistance is high. The ECM will then sense a high signal voltage.

As the engine warms up, the sensor resistance decreases and the voltage drops. At normal engine operating temperature, the voltage will measure about 1.5 to 2.0 volts at ECM terminal "B8".

Coolant temperature is one of the inputs used to control the following:
- Fuel delivery
- Electronic Spark Timing (EST)
- Cooling fan
- Torque Converter Clutch (TCC)
- Idle Air Control (IAC)

Test Description: Number(s) below refer to circled number(s) on the diagnostic chart.

1. Check to see if code was set as result of hard failure or intermittent condition.
   Code 15 will set if:
   - Engine has been running for more than 120 seconds.
   - Signal voltage indicates a coolant temperature below -30°C (-22°F).

2. This test simulates conditions for a Code 14. If the ECM recognizes the grounded circuit (low voltage), and displays a high temperature, the ECM and wiring are OK.

3. This test will determine if there is a wiring problem or a faulty ECM. If CKT 452 is open, there may also be a Code 33 stored.

Diagnostic Aids:

A Tech 1 "Scan" tool reads engine temperature in degrees celsius. After the engine is started, the temperature should rise steadily to about 90°C (194°F), then stabilize, when the thermostat opens.

If the engine has been allowed to cool to an ambient temperature (overnight), coolant and Intake Air Temperature (IAT) temperature may be checked with a "Scan" tool and should read close to each other.

When a Code 15 is set, the ECM will turn "ON" the engine cooling fan.

A Code 15 will result if CKTs 410 or 455 are open.

If Code 15 is intermittent, refer to "Symptoms."

CODE 15
COOLANT TEMPERATURE SENSOR (CTS) CIRCUIT
(LOW TEMPERATURE INDICATED)

① • DOES TECH 1 DISPLAY COOLANT TEMPERATURE OF -30°C (-22°F) OR LESS?

   NO → CODE 15 IS INTERMITTENT.

   YES

② • DISCONNECT COOLANT TEMPERATURE SENSOR.
   • JUMPER HARNESS TERMINALS TOGETHER.
   • TECH 1 SHOULD DISPLAY 130°C (266°F) OR MORE. DOES IT?

   YES → FAULTY CONNECTION OR COOLANT TEMPERATURE SENSOR.

   NO

③ • JUMPER CKT 410 TO GROUND.
   • TECH 1 SHOULD DISPLAY OVER 130°C (266°F). DOES IT?

   NO → OPEN CKT 410, FAULTY CONNECTION AT ECM, OR FAULTY ECM.

   YES → OPEN COOLANT TEMPERATURE SENSOR GROUND CIRCUIT, FAULTY CONNECTION OR FAULTY ECM.

DIAGNOSTIC AID

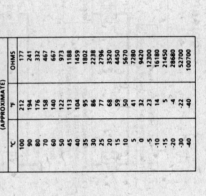

COOLANT SENSOR
TEMPERATURE VS. RESISTANCE VALUES
(APPROXIMATE)

°C	°F	OHMS
100	212	177
90	194	241
80	176	332
70	158	467
60	140	667
50	122	973
45	113	1188
40	104	1459
35	95	1802
30	86	2238
25	77	2796
20	68	3520
15	59	4450
10	50	5670
5	41	7280
0	32	9420
-5	23	12300
-10	14	16180
-15	5	21450
-20	-4	28680
-30	-22	52700
-40	-40	100700

"AFTER REPAIRS," REFER TO CODE CRITERIA AND CONFIRM CODE DOES NOT RESET.

1990–91 2.2L ENGINE

CODE 21
THROTTLE POSITION SENSOR (TPS) CIRCUIT
(SIGNAL VOLTAGE HIGH)

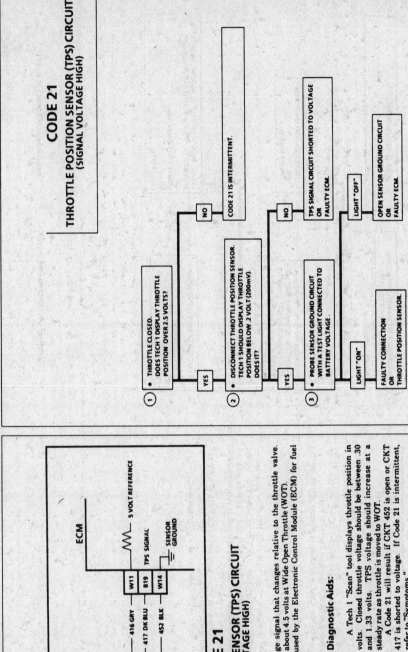

CODE 21
THROTTLE POSITION SENSOR (TPS) CIRCUIT
(SIGNAL VOLTAGE HIGH)

Circuit Description:
The Throttle Position Sensor (TPS) provides a voltage signal that changes relative to the throttle valve. Signal voltage will vary from less than 1.33 volts at idle to about 4.5 volts at Wide Open Throttle (WOT).
The TPS signal is one of the most important inputs used by the Electronic Control Module (ECM) for fuel control and for many of the ECM controlled outputs.

Test Description: Number(s) below refer to circled number(s) on the diagnostic chart.

1. This step checks to see if Code 21 is the result of a hard failure or an intermittent condition. A Code 21 will set under the following conditions:
   - TPS reading above 2.5 volts.
   - MAP reading below 55 kPa.
   - All of the above conditions present for 5 seconds.

2. This step simulates conditions for a Code 22. If the ECM recognizes the change of state, the ECM and CKTs 416 and 417 are OK.

3. This step isolates a faulty sensor, ECM, or an open CKT 452. If CKT 452 is open, there may also be a Code 23 stored.

Diagnostic Aids:
A Tech 1 "Scan" tool displays throttle position in volts. Closed throttle voltage should be between .30 and 1.33 volts. TPS voltage should increase at a steady rate as throttle is moved to WOT.
A Code 21 will result if CKT 452 is open or CKT 417 is shorted to voltage. If Code 21 is intermittent, refer to "Symptoms."

Flowchart:

① THROTTLE CLOSED. DOES TECH 1 DISPLAY THROTTLE POSITION OVER 2.5 VOLTS?
- NO → CODE 21 IS INTERMITTENT.
- YES →

② DISCONNECT THROTTLE POSITION SENSOR. TECH 1 SHOULD DISPLAY THROTTLE POSITION BELOW .2 VOLT (200mV). DOES IT?
- NO → TPS SIGNAL CIRCUIT SHORTED TO VOLTAGE OR FAULTY ECM.
- YES →

③ PROBE SENSOR GROUND CIRCUIT WITH A TEST LIGHT CONNECTED TO BATTERY VOLTAGE.
- LIGHT "OFF" → OPEN SENSOR GROUND CIRCUIT OR FAULTY ECM.
- LIGHT "ON" → FAULTY CONNECTION OR THROTTLE POSITION SENSOR.

"AFTER REPAIRS", REFER TO CODE CRITERIA AND CONFIRM CODE DOES NOT RESET.

1990–91 2.2L ENGINE

CODE 22
THROTTLE POSITION SENSOR (TPS) CIRCUIT
(SIGNAL VOLTAGE LOW)

THROTTLE POSITION SENSOR CONNECTOR

ECM

5 VOLT REFERENCE

TPS SIGNAL

SENSOR GROUND

W11
B19
W14

416 GRY
417 DK BLU
452 BLK

TO MAP SENSOR

TO IAT SENSOR

THROTTLE POSITION SENSOR

A C B

WOT
IDLE

CODE 22
THROTTLE POSITION SENSOR (TPS) CIRCUIT
(SIGNAL VOLTAGE LOW)

Circuit Description:

The Throttle Position Sensor (TPS) provides a voltage signal that changes relative to the throttle valve. Signal voltage will vary from less than 1.33 volts at idle to about 5 volts at Wide Open Throttle (WOT).

The TPS signal is one of the most important inputs used by the Electronic Control Module (ECM) for fuel control and many ECM controlled outputs.

Test Description: Number(s) below refer to circled number(s) on the diagnostic chart.

1 Code 22 will set if:
- Engine is running.
- TPS signal voltage is less than .20 volt.

The TPS has an auto zeroing feature. If the voltage reading is within the range of about .3 to 1.33 volts, the ECM will use that value as closed throttle. If the voltage reading is out of the auto zero range at closed throttle, check for a binding throttle cable or damaged linkage, if OK, continue with diagnosis.

2. Simulates Code 21: (high voltage). If the ECM recognizes the high signal voltage then the ECM and wiring are OK.

3. This simulates a high signal voltage to check for an open in CKT 417. The Tech 1 "Scan" tool will not read up to battery voltage, but what is important is that the ECM recognizes the signal on CKT 417.

Diagnostic Aids:

A Tech 1 "Scan" tool reads throttle position in volts. With ignition "ON" or at idle, TPS signal voltage should read from about .3 to 1.33 volts with the throttle closed and increase at a steady rate as throttle is moved toward WOT.

An open or short to ground in CKT 416 or CKT 417 will result in a Code 22.

Refer to "Intermittents" in "Symptoms."

CODE 22
THROTTLE POSITION SENSOR (TPS) CIRCUIT
(SIGNAL VOLTAGE LOW)

(1) THROTTLE CLOSED.
DOES TECH 1 DISPLAY THROTTLE POSITION .2V (200 mv) OR BELOW?

- YES
- NO → CODE 22 IS INTERMITTENT.

(2) DISCONNECT TPS SENSOR CONNECTOR. JUMPER CKTS 416 & 417 TOGETHER. TECH 1 SHOULD DISPLAY THROTTLE POSITION OVER 4.0V (4000 mv). DOES IT?

- YES → • FAULTY SENSOR CONNECTION OR FAULTY SENSOR.
- NO

(3) PROBE CKT 417 WITH A TEST LIGHT CONNECTED TO BATTERY VOLTAGE. TECH 1 SHOULD DISPLAY THROTTLE POSITION OVER 4.0V (4000 mv). DOES IT?

- YES → CKT 416 OPEN OR SHORTED TO GROUND OR FAULTY CONNECTION OR FAULTY ECM.
- NO → CKT 417 OPEN OR SHORTED TO GROUND, OR SHORTED TO THROTTLE POSITION SENSOR GROUND CIRCUIT OR FAULTY ECM CONNECTION OR FAULTY ECM.

*AFTER REPAIRS, "REFER TO CODE CRITERIA AND CONFIRM CODE DOES NOT RESET.

1990—91 2.2L ENGINE

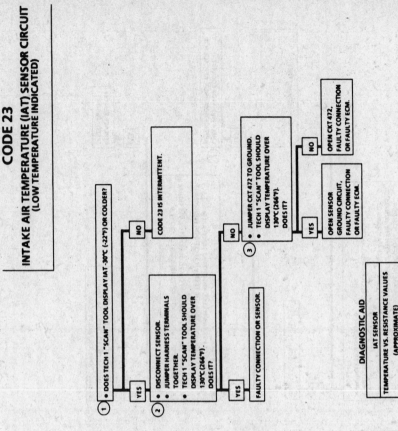

CODE 23

INTAKE AIR TEMPERATURE (IAT) SENSOR CIRCUIT
(LOW TEMPERATURE INDICATED)

1. • DOES TECH 1 "SCAN" TOOL DISPLAY IAT -30°C (-22°F) OR COLDER?

   YES →
   NO → CODE 23 IS INTERMITTENT.

2. • DISCONNECT SENSOR.
   • JUMPER HARNESS TERMINALS TOGETHER.
   • TECH 1 "SCAN" TOOL SHOULD DISPLAY TEMPERATURE OVER 130°C (266°F).
     DOES IT?

   YES → FAULTY CONNECTION OR SENSOR.
   NO →

3. • JUMPER CKT 472 TO GROUND.
   • TECH 1 "SCAN" TOOL SHOULD DISPLAY TEMPERATURE OVER 130°C (266°F).
     DOES IT?

   YES → OPEN SENSOR GROUND CIRCUIT, FAULTY CONNECTION OR FAULTY ECM.
   NO → OPEN CKT 472, FAULTY CONNECTION OR FAULTY ECM.

DIAGNOSTIC AID

IAT SENSOR
TEMPERATURE VS. RESISTANCE VALUES
(APPROXIMATE)

°F	°C	OHMS
210	100	185
160	70	450
100	38	1,800
70	20	3,400
40	4	7,500
20	-7	13,500
0	-18	25,000
-40	-40	100,700

"AFTER REPAIRS," REFER TO CODE CRITERIA AND CONFIRM CODE DOES NOT RESET.

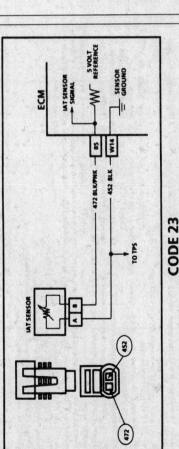

ECM

IAT SENSOR SIGNAL

5 VOLT REFERENCE

SENSOR GROUND

B5

W14

472 BLK/PNK

452 BLK

TO TPS

IAT SENSOR

A B

452

472

CODE 23

INTAKE AIR TEMPERATURE (IAT) SENSOR CIRCUIT
(LOW TEMPERATURE INDICATED)

Circuit Description:

The Intake Air Temperature (IAT) sensor uses a thermistor to control the signal voltage to the Electronic Control Module (ECM). The ECM applies a reference voltage (4-6 volts) on CKT 472 to the sensor. When manifold air is cold, the sensor (thermistor) resistance is high. The ECM will then sense a high signal voltage. As the air warms, the sensor resistance becomes less and the voltage drops.

Test Description: Number(s) below refer to circled number(s) on the diagnostic chart.

1. This step checks to see if Code 23 is the result of a hard failure or an intermittent condition. Code 23 will set under the following conditions:
   • Engine is running for longer than 2 minutes.
   • Signal voltage indicates an IAT temperature less than -30°C (-22°F).

2. This test simulates conditions for a Code 25. If the Tech 1 "Scan" tool displays a high temperature, the ECM and wiring are OK.

3. This step checks continuity of CKTs 472 and 452. If CKT 452 is open, there may also be a Code 21.

Diagnostic Aids:

If the engine has been allowed to cool to an ambient temperature (overnight), coolant and IAT temperatures may be checked with a "Scan" tool and should read close to each other.

A Code 23 will result if CKTs 472 or 452 become open.

If Code 23 is intermittent, refer to "Symptoms."

1990-91 2.2L ENGINE

CODE 24
VEHICLE SPEED SENSOR (VSS) CIRCUIT

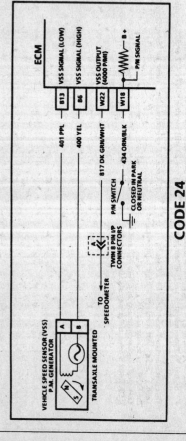

Circuit Description:

Vehicle speed information is provided to the Electronic Control Module (ECM) by the Vehicle Speed Sensor (VSS), which is a Permanent Magnet (PM) generator, and it is mounted in the transaxle. The PM generator produces a pulsing voltage, whenever vehicle speed is over about 3 mph. The AC voltage level and the number of pulses increases with vehicle speed. The ECM, then, converts the pulsing voltage to mph, which is used for calculations, and the mph can be displayed with a Tech 1 "Scan" tool.

The function of VSS buffer used in past model years has been incorporated into the ECM. The ECM then supplies the necessary signal for the instrument panel (4000 pulses per mile) for operating the speedometer and the odometer. If the vehicle is equipped with cruise control, the ECM also provides a signal (2000 pulses per mile) to the cruise control module.

Test Description: Number(s) below refer to circled number(s) on the diagnostic chart.

1. Code 24 will set if vehicle speed equals 0 mph when:
   - Engine speed is between 1200 and 4400 rpm.
   - MAP is less than 24 kPa.
   - Low load condition (low MAP voltage, high manifold vacuum).
   - Transmission not in park or neutral.
   - All above conditions are met for 5 seconds.

   These conditions are met during a road load deceleration.

   Disregard a Code 24 that sets when the drive wheels are not turning. This can be caused by a faulty park/neutral switch circuit.

   The PM generator only produces a signal if the drive wheels are turning greater than 3 mph.

2. Before replacing ECM, make sure that the correct PROM is installed for the application.

Diagnostic Aids:

Tech 1 "Scan" tool should indicate a vehicle speed whenever the drive wheels are turning greater than 3 mph.

A problem in CKT 938 will not affect the VSS input or the readings on a "Scan" tool.

Check CKTs 400 and 401 for proper connections to be sure they are clean and tight and the harness is routed correctly. Refer to "Intermittents" in "Symptoms."

(A/T) - A faulty or misadjusted park/neutral switch can result in a false Code 24. Use a "Scan" tool and check for the proper signal while in a drive range. P/N switch check.

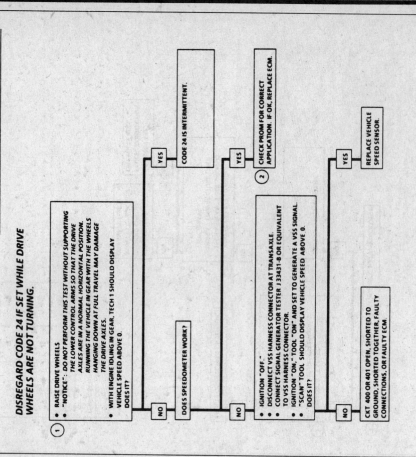

CODE 24
VEHICLE SPEED SENSOR (VSS) CIRCUIT

DISREGARD CODE 24 IF SET WHILE DRIVE WHEELS ARE NOT TURNING.

(1)
- RAISE DRIVE WHEELS
- "NOTICE": *DO NOT PERFORM THIS TEST WITHOUT SUPPORTING THE LOWER CONTROL ARMS SO THAT THE DRIVE AXLES ARE IN A NORMAL HORIZONTAL POSITION. RUNNING THE VEHICLE IN GEAR WITH THE WHEELS HANGING DOWN AT FULL TRAVEL MAY DAMAGE THE DRIVE AXLES.*
- WITH ENGINE IDLING IN GEAR, TECH 1 SHOULD DISPLAY VEHICLE SPEED ABOVE 0.

DOES IT? → **NO** → DOES SPEEDOMETER WORK? → **NO**
- IGNITION "OFF."
- DISCONNECT VSS HARNESS CONNECTOR AT TRANSAXLE.
- CONNECT SIGNAL GENERATOR TESTER J 33431-B OR EQUIVALENT TO VSS HARNESS CONNECTOR.
- IGNITION "ON." TOOL "ON" AND SET TO GENERATE A VSS SIGNAL.
- "SCAN" TOOL SHOULD DISPLAY VEHICLE SPEED ABOVE 0.

DOES IT? → **NO** → CKT 400 OR 401 OPEN, SHORTED TO GROUND, SHORTED TOGETHER, FAULTY CONNECTIONS, OR FAULTY ECM.

DOES IT? (first) → **YES** → CODE 24 IS INTERMITTENT.

DOES SPEEDOMETER WORK? → **YES** → (2) CHECK PROM FOR CORRECT APPLICATION. IF OK, REPLACE ECM.

DOES IT? (generator tester) → **YES** → REPLACE VEHICLE SPEED SENSOR.

"AFTER REPAIRS," REFER TO CODE CRITERIA

CONFIRM CODE DOES NOT RESET.

1990–91 2.2L ENGINE

CODE 25

INTAKE AIR TEMPERATURE (IAT) SENSOR CIRCUIT
(HIGH TEMPERATURE INDICATED)

Circuit Description:

The Intake Air Temperature (IAT) sensor uses a thermistor to control the signal voltage to the Electronic Control Module (ECM). The ECM applies a reference voltage (4-6 volts) on CKT 472 to the sensor. When intake air is cold, the sensor (thermistor) resistance is high. The ECM will then sense a high signal voltage. As the air warms, the sensor resistance becomes less and the voltage drops.

Test Description: Number(s) below refer to circled number(s) on the diagnostic chart.

1. This check determines if the Code 25 is the result of a hard failure or an intermittent condition. A Code 25 will set under the following conditions:
   - Engine has been running longer than 8.5 minutes.
   - An IAT temperature greater than 135°C (275°F) is detected for a time longer than 2 seconds.
   - VSS signal present.

Diagnostic Aids:

If the engine has been allowed to cool to an ambient temperature (overnight), coolant and IAT temperatures may be checked with a "Scan" tool and should read close to each other.

A Code 25 will result if CKT 472 is shorted to ground.

If Code 25 is intermittent, refer to "Symptoms."

CODE 25

INTAKE AIR TEMPERATURE (IAT) SENSOR CIRCUIT
(HIGH TEMPERATURE INDICATED)

1. • DOES TECH 1 "SCAN" TOOL DISPLAY IAT OF 145°C (293°F) OR HOTTER?

YES →
• DISCONNECT SENSOR.
  TECH 1 "SCAN" TOOL SHOULD DISPLAY TEMPERATURE BELOW -30°C (-22°F). DOES IT?

NO → CODE 25 IS INTERMITTENT.

YES → REPLACE SENSOR.

NO → CKT 472 SHORTED TO GROUND, OR TO SENSOR GROUND, OR ECM IS FAULTY.

DIAGNOSTIC AID

IAT SENSOR
TEMPERATURE VS. RESISTANCE VALUES
(APPROXIMATE)

°F	°C	OHMS
210	100	185
160	70	450
100	38	1,800
70	20	3,400
40	4	7,500
20	-7	13,500
0	-18	25,000
-40	-40	100,700

CONFIRM CODE DOES NOT RESET.

"AFTER REPAIRS," REFER TO CODE CRITERIA

1990–91 2.2L ENGINE

CODE 32

EXHAUST GAS RECIRCULATION (EGR) SYSTEM FAILURE

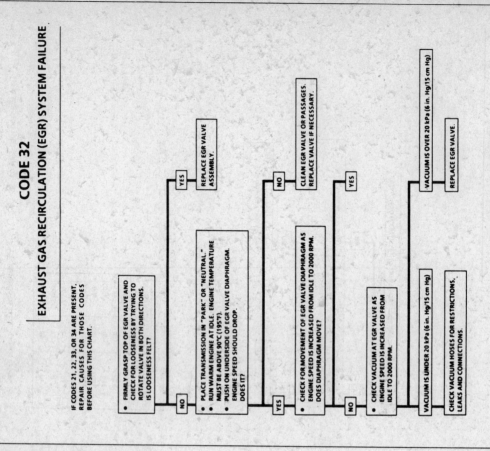

Flowchart — CODE 32 / EXHAUST GAS RECIRCULATION (EGR) SYSTEM FAILURE

- IF CODES 21, 22, 33, OR 34 ARE PRESENT, REPAIR CAUSES FOR THOSE CODES BEFORE USING THIS CHART.

- FIRMLY GRASP TOP OF EGR VALVE AND CHECK FOR LOOSENESS BY TRYING TO ROTATE VALVE IN BOTH DIRECTIONS. IS LOOSENESS FELT?
  - YES → REPLACE EGR VALVE ASSEMBLY.
  - NO →
    - PLACE TRANSMISSION IN "PARK" OR "NEUTRAL." RUN WARM ENGINE AT IDLE. ENGINE TEMPERATURE MUST BE ABOVE 90°C (195°F).
    - PUSH ON UNDERSIDE OF EGR VALVE DIAPHRAGM. ENGINE SPEED SHOULD DROP. DOES IT?
      - YES →
        - CHECK FOR MOVEMENT OF EGR VALVE DIAPHRAGM AS ENGINE SPEED IS INCREASED FROM IDLE TO 2000 RPM. DOES DIAPHRAGM MOVE?
          - NO → CLEAN EGR VALVE OR PASSAGES. REPLACE VALVE IF NECESSARY.
          - YES →
            - CHECK VACUUM AT EGR VALVE AS ENGINE SPEED IS INCREASED FROM IDLE TO 2000 RPM.
              - VACUUM IS UNDER 20 kPa (6 in. Hg/15 cm Hg) → CHECK VACUUM HOSES FOR RESTRICTIONS, LEAKS AND CONNECTIONS.
              - VACUUM IS OVER 20 kPa (6 in. Hg/15 cm Hg) → REPLACE EGR VALVE.

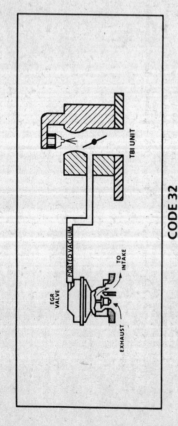

CODE 32

EXHAUST GAS RECIRCULATION (EGR) SYSTEM FAILURE

Code Description:

A properly operating Exhaust Gas Recirculation (EGR) system will directly affect the air/fuel mixture requirements of the engine. Since the exhaust gas introduced into the air/fuel mixture cannot be used in combustion (contains very little oxygen), less fuel is required to maintain a correct air/fuel ratio. If the EGR system were to fail in a closed position, the exhaust gas would be replaced with air, and the air/fuel mixture would be leaner. The Electronic Control Module (ECM) would compensate for the lean condition by adding fuel, resulting in higher block learn values.

The fuel control on this engine is conducted within 16 block learn cells. Since EGR is not used at idle, the closed throttle cell would not be affected by EGR system operation. The other block learn cells are affected by EGR operation, and, when the EGR system is operating properly, the block learn values in all cells should be close to the same. If the EGR system becomes inoperative, the block learn values in the open throttle cells would change to compensate for the resulting lean mixtures, but the block learn value in the closed throttle cell would not change.

The difference in block learn values between the idle (closed throttle) cell and cell 10 is used to monitor EGR system performance. When the difference between the two block learn values is greater than 12 and the block learn value in cell 10 is greater than 140, Code 32 is set. The system operates in block learn cell 10 during a cruise condition at approximately 55 mph.

Diagnostic Aids:

The Code 32 chart is a functional check of the EGR system. If the EGR system works properly but a Code 32 has been set, check other items that could result in high block learn values in block learn cell 10, but not in the closed throttle cell.

Check for restricted or blocked EGR passages.
Perform a MAP output check. Follow the procedure in CHART C-10.

1990-91 2.2L ENGINE

CODE 33

MANIFOLD ABSOLUTE PRESSURE (MAP) SENSOR CIRCUIT
(SIGNAL VOLTAGE HIGH - LOW VACUUM)

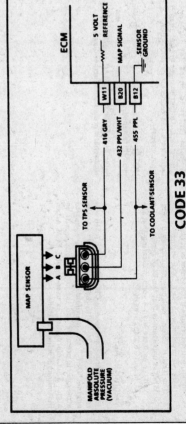

CODE 33

MANIFOLD ABSOLUTE PRESSURE (MAP) SENSOR CIRCUIT
(SIGNAL VOLTAGE HIGH - LOW VACUUM)

Circuit Description:

The Manifold Absolute Pressure (MAP) sensor responds to changes in manifold pressure (vacuum). The ECM receives this information as a signal voltage that will vary from about 1 to 1.5 volts at closed throttle idle, to 4.5-4.8 volts at wide open throttle (low vacuum).

If the MAP sensor fails, the Electronic Control Module (ECM) will substitute a fixed MAP value and use the Throttle Position Sensor (TPS) to control fuel delivery.

Test Description: Number(s) below refer to circled number(s) on the diagnostic chart.

1. This step will determine if Code 33 is the result of a hard failure or an intermittent condition. A Code 33 will set if:
   - MAP signal voltage is too high (low manifold vacuum).
   - TPS less than 12%.
   - No VSS signal (vehicle stopped).
   - These conditions for a time longer than 5 seconds.

2. This step simulates conditions for a Code 34. If the ECM recognizes the change, the ECM and CKTs 416 and 432 are OK.

Diagnostic Aids:

With the ignition "ON" and the engine stopped, the manifold pressure is equal to atmospheric pressure and the signal voltage will be high. This information is used by the ECM as an indication of vehicle altitude and is referred to as BARO. Comparison of this BARO reading with a known good vehicle with the same sensor is a good way to check accuracy of a "suspect" sensor. Readings should be equal ± .4 volt.

A Code 33 will result if CKT 455 is open, or if CKT 432 is shorted to voltage or to CKT 416. If Code 33 is intermittent, refer to "Symptoms,"

- Check all connections.
- Disconnect sensor from bracket and twist sensor by hand (only) to check for intermittent connections. Output changes greater than .1 volt indicates a faulty connection or connector. If OK, replace sensor.
- Refer to CHART C-1D, MAP sensor voltage vs. atmospheric pressure for further diagnosis.

1990–91 2.2L ENGINE

CODE 34
MANIFOLD ABSOLUTE PRESSURE (MAP) SENSOR CIRCUIT
(SIGNAL VOLTAGE LOW - HIGH VACUUM)

CODE 34

MANIFOLD ABSOLUTE PRESSURE (MAP) SENSOR CIRCUIT
(SIGNAL VOLTAGE LOW - HIGH VACUUM)

Circuit Description:

The Manifold Absolute Pressure (MAP) sensor responds to changes in manifold pressure (vacuum). The ECM receives this information as a signal voltage that will vary from about 1 to 1.5 volts at closed throttle (idle), to 4.5-4.8 volts at wide open throttle (low vacuum).

If the MAP sensor fails, the Electronic Control Module (ECM) will substitute a fixed MAP value and use the Throttle Position Sensor (TPS) to control fuel delivery.

Test Description: Number(s) below refer to circled number(s) on the diagnostic chart.

1. This step determines if Code 34 is the result of a hard failure or an intermittent condition.

   A Code 34 will set under the following conditions:
   - MAP signal voltage is too low
   - Engine speed is over 1200 rpm

2. Jumpering harness terminals "B" to "C", 5 volts to signal, will determine if the sensor is at fault, or if there is a problem with the ECM or wiring.

3. The Tech 1 "Scan" tool may not display 5 volts. What is important is that the ECM recognizes the voltage as more than 4 volts, indicating that the ECM and CKT 432 are OK.

Diagnostic Aids:

An intermittent open in CKT 432 or CKT 416 will result in a Code 34. With the ignition "ON" and the engine "OFF," the manifold pressure is equal to atmospheric pressure and the signal voltage will be high. This information is used by the ECM as an indication of vehicle altitude.

Comparison of this reading with a known good vehicle with same sensor is a good way to check accuracy of a "suspect" sensor. Reading should be the same ± .4 volt. Also CHART C-1D can be used to test the MAP sensor. Refer to "Intermittents" in "Symptoms."
- Check all connections.
- Disconnect sensor from bracket and twist sensor by hand (only) to check for intermittent connections. Output changes greater than .1 volt indicates a bad connector or connection. If OK, replace sensor.

NOTE: Make sure electrical connector remains securely fastened.

- Refer to CHART C-1D, MAP sensor voltage vs. atmospheric pressure for further diagnosis.

"AFTER REPAIRS," REFER TO CODE CRITERIA

CONFIRM CODE DOES NOT RESET.

1990–91 2.2L ENGINE

CODE 42
ELECTRONIC SPARK TIMING (EST) CIRCUIT

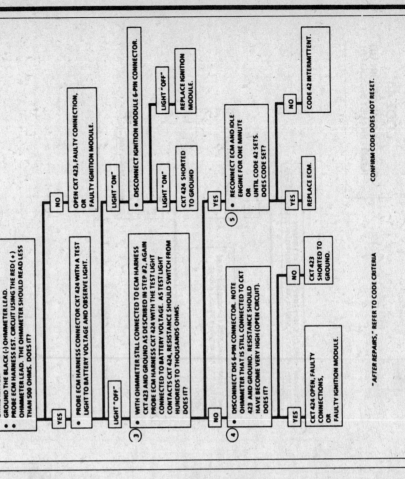

①
- CLEAR CODES.
- IDLE ENGINE FOR 1 MINUTE OR UNTIL CODE 42 SETS.
- DOES CODE 42 SET?

NO → CODE 42 INTERMITTENT.

YES

②
- IGNITION "OFF."
- DISCONNECT ECM CONNECTORS.
- IGNITION "ON."
- SET OHMMETER SELECTOR SWITCH IN THE 1000 TO 2000 OHMS RANGE.
- GROUND THE BLACK (–) OHMMETER LEAD.
- PROBE ECM HARNESS EST. CIRCUIT USING THE RED (+) OHMMETER LEAD. THE OHMMETER SHOULD READ LESS THAN 500 OHMS. DOES IT?

NO → OPEN CKT 423, FAULTY CONNECTION, OR FAULTY IGNITION MODULE.

YES
- PROBE ECM HARNESS CONNECTOR CKT 424 WITH A TEST LIGHT TO BATTERY VOLTAGE AND OBSERVE LIGHT.

LIGHT "OFF"

③
- WITH OHMMETER STILL CONNECTED TO ECM HARNESS CKT 423 AND GROUND AS DESCRIBED IN STEP #2. AGAIN PROBE ECM HARNESS CKT 424 WITH THE TEST LIGHT CONNECTED TO BATTERY VOLTAGE. AS TEST LIGHT CONTACTS CKT 424, RESISTANCE SHOULD SWITCH FROM HUNDREDS TO THOUSANDS OHMS. DOES IT?

NO

④
- DISCONNECT DIS 6-PIN CONNECTOR. NOTE OHMMETER THAT IS STILL CONNECTED TO CKT 423 AND GROUND. RESISTANCE SHOULD HAVE BECOME VERY HIGH (OPEN CIRCUIT). DOES IT?

YES → CKT 424 OPEN, FAULTY CONNECTIONS, OR FAULTY IGNITION MODULE.

NO → CKT 423 SHORTED TO GROUND.

LIGHT "ON"
- DISCONNECT IGNITION MODULE 6-PIN CONNECTOR.

LIGHT "OFF" → CKT 424 SHORTED TO GROUND

LIGHT "ON" → REPLACE IGNITION MODULE.

YES

⑤
- RECONNECT ECM AND IDLE ENGINE FOR ONE MINUTE OR UNTIL CODE 42 SETS. DOES CODE SET?

YES → REPLACE ECM.

NO → CODE 42 INTERMITTENT

"AFTER REPAIRS," REFER TO CODE CRITERIA

CONFIRM CODE DOES NOT RESET.

CODE 42
ELECTRONIC SPARK TIMING (EST) CIRCUIT

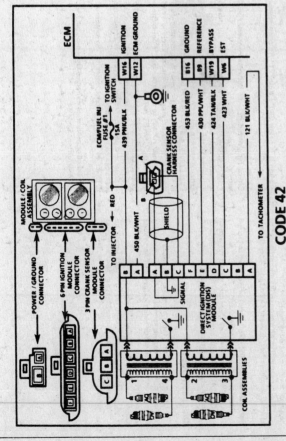

Circuit Description:

The Direct Ignition System (DIS) module sends a reference signal to the Electronic Control Module (ECM) when the engine is cranking. While the engine speed is under 400 rpm, the DIS module controls the ignition timing. When the system is running on the ignition module (no voltage on the bypass line), the ignition module grounds the EST signal. The ECM expects to sense no voltage on the Electronic Spark Timing (EST) line during this condition. If it senses a voltage, it sets Code 42 and will not enter the EST mode.

When the engine speed exceeds 400 rpm, the ECM applies 5 volts to the bypass line to switch the timing to ECM control (EST). If the bypass line is open or grounded, once the rpm for EST control is reached, the ignition module will not switch to EST. This results in low EST voltage and the setting of Code 42. If the EST line is grounded, the ignition module will switch to EST, but because the line is grounded, there will be no EST signal. A Code 42 will be set.

Test Description: Number(s) below refer to circled number(s) on the diagnostic chart.

1. Code 42 means the ECM has sensed an open or short to ground in the EST or bypass circuits. This test confirms Code 42 and that the fault causing the code is present.
2. Checks for a normal EST ground path through the ignition module. An EST CKT 423, shorted to ground, will also read less than 500 ohms, but this will be checked later.
3. As the test light voltage contacts CKT 424, the module should switch, causing the ohmmeter to "overrange" if the meter is in the 1000-2000 ohms position. Selecting the 10 - 20,000 ohms position will indicate a reading above 5000 ohms.

The important thing is that the module "switched."
4. The module did not switch and this step checks for:
   - EST CKT 423 shorted to ground
   - Bypass CKT 424 open
   - Faulty ignition module connection or module
5. Confirms that Code 42 is a faulty ECM and not an intermittent in CKTs 423 or 424.

Diagnostic Aids:

The "Scan" tool does not have any ability to help diagnose a Code 42 problem.

If Code 42 is intermittent, refer to "Symptoms,"

1990–91 2.2L ENGINE

CODE 44
OXYGEN SENSOR CIRCUIT
(LEAN EXHAUST INDICATED)

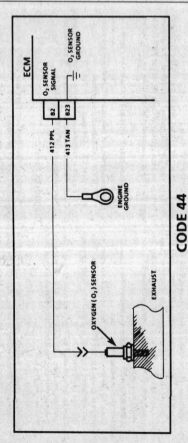

CODE 44

OXYGEN SENSOR CIRCUIT
(LEAN EXHAUST INDICATED)

Circuit Description:

The Electronic Control Module (ECM) supplies a voltage of about .45 volt between terminals "B2" and "B23".
(If measured with a 10 megohm digital voltmeter, this may read as low as .32 volt).

When the O_2 sensor reaches operating temperature, it varies this voltage from about .1 volt (exhaust is lean) to about .9 volt (exhaust is rich).

The sensor is like an open circuit and produces no voltage when it is below 360° C (600°F). An open sensor circuit, or cold sensor, causes "Open Loop" operation.

Test Description: Number(s) below refer to circled number(s) on the diagnostic chart.

1. Code 44 is set when the O_2 sensor signal voltage on CKT 412 remains below .3 volt for 50 seconds or more and the system is operating in "Closed Loop."

Diagnostic Aids:

Using the "Scan" tool, observe the block learn value at different engine speeds. If the conditions for Code 44 exists, the block learn values will be around 150 or higher.

Check the following possible causes:

- O_2 Sensor Wire. Sensor pigtail may be mispositioned and contacting the exhaust manifold.

Check for ground in wire between connector and sensor.

- Fuel Contamination. Water, even in small amounts, near the in-tank fuel pump inlet can be delivered to the injector. The water causes a lean exhaust and can set a Code 44.
- Fuel Pressure. System will be lean if fuel pressure is too low. It may be necessary to monitor fuel pressure while driving the car at various road speeds and/or loads to confirm. See "Fuel System Diagnosis," CHART A-7.
- Exhaust Leaks. If there is an exhaust leak, the engine can cause outside air to be pulled into the exhaust and past the sensor. Vacuum or crankcase leaks can cause a lean condition.
- If Code 44 is intermittent, refer to "Symptoms,"

- A cracked or otherwise damaged O_2 sensor may set an intermittent Code 44.

Diagnostic flowchart:

① • RUN WARM ENGINE (75°C/167°F TO 95°C/203°F) AT 1200 RPM.
• DOES TECH 1 INDICATE O_2 SENSOR VOLTAGE FIXED BELOW .35 VOLT (350 mV)?

YES
• DISCONNECT O_2 SENSOR.
• WITH ENGINE IDLING, TECH 1 SHOULD DISPLAY O_2 SENSOR VOLTAGE BETWEEN .35 VOLT AND .55 VOLT (350 mV AND 550 mV).
DOES IT?

NO → CODE 44 IS INTERMITTENT.

YES

NO → CKT 412 SHORTED TO GROUND OR FAULTY ECM.

"AFTER REPAIRS," REFER TO CODE CRITERIA

CONFIRM CODE DOES NOT RESET.

1990–91 2.2L ENGINE

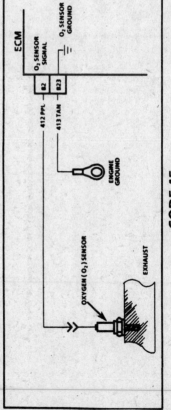

ECM

O₂ SENSOR SIGNAL — B2 — 412 PPL

O₂ SENSOR GROUND — B23 — 413 TAN

ENGINE GROUND

OXYGEN (O₂) SENSOR

EXHAUST

CODE 45
OXYGEN SENSOR CIRCUIT
(RICH EXHAUST INDICATED)

Circuit Description:

The Electronic Control Module (ECM) supplies a voltage of about .45 volt between terminals "B2" and "B23". (If measured with a 10 megohm digital voltmeter, this may read as low as .32 volt.)

When the O₂ sensor reaches operating temperature, it varies this voltage from about .1 volt (exhaust is lean) to about .9 volt (exhaust is rich).

The sensor is like an open circuit and produces no voltage when it is below 360°C (600°F). An open sensor circuit, or cold sensor, causes "Open Loop" operation.

Test Description: Number(s) below refer to circled number(s) on the diagnostic chart.

1. Code 45 is set when the O₂ sensor signal voltage on CKT 412 remains above .7 volt under the following conditions:

- 30 seconds or more.
- System is operating in "Closed Loop."
- Engine run time after start is 1 minute or more.
- Throttle angle less than 2% or greater than 20%.

Diagnostic Aids:

Code 45, or rich exhaust, is most likely caused by one of the following:

- **Fuel Pressure.** System will go rich, if pressure is too high. The ECM can compensate for some increase. However, if it gets too high, a Code 45 will be set. See "Fuel System Diagnosis," CHART A-7.

- **Leaking Injector.** See CHART A-7.

- **HEI Shielding.** An open ground CKT 453 may result in EMI, or induced electrical "noise." The ECM looks at this "noise" as reference pulses. The additional pulses result in a higher than actual engine speed signal. The ECM then delivers too much fuel causing the system to go rich. The engine tachometer will also show higher than actual engine speed, which can help in diagnosing this problem.

- **Canister Purge.** Check for fuel saturation. If full of fuel, check canister control and hoses.

- **MAP Sensor.** An output that causes the ECM to sense a higher than normal manifold pressure (low vacuum) can cause the system to go rich. Disconnecting the Manifold Absolute Pressure (MAP) sensor will allow the ECM to set a fixed value for the MAP sensor. Substitute a different MAP sensor if the rich condition is gone, while the sensor is disconnected.

- **TPS.** An intermittent Throttle Position Sensor (TPS) output will cause the system to operate richly due to a false indication of the engine accelerating.

- **O₂ Sensor Contamination.** Inspect oxygen sensor for silicone contamination from fuel, or use of improper RTV sealant. The sensor may have a white, powdery coating and result in a high but false signal voltage (rich exhaust indication). The ECM will then reduce the amount of fuel delivered to the engine causing a severe surge driveability problem.

- **EGR Valve.** Exhaust Gas Recirculation (EGR) sticking open at idle is usually accompanied by a rough idle and/or stall condition. If Code 45 is intermittent, refer to "Symptoms,"

1

- **RUN WARM ENGINE (75°C/167°F TO 95°C/203°F) AT 1200 RPM.**
- **DOES TECH 1 DISPLAY O₂ SENSOR VOLTAGE FIXED ABOVE .75 VOLT (750 mV)?**

YES

DISCONNECT O₂ SENSOR AND JUMPER HARNESS CKT 412 TO GROUND. TECH 1 SHOULD DISPLAY O₂ BELOW .35 VOLT (350 mV). DOES IT?

NO

CODE 45 IS INTERMITTENT.

YES

NO

REPLACE ECM.

"AFTER REPAIRS," REFER TO CODE CRITERIA

CONFIRM CODE DOES NOT RESET.

1990-91 2.2L ENGINE

CODE 51
PROM ERROR
(FAULTY OR INCORRECT PROM)
2.2L (VIN G) "L" CARLINE (TBI)

> CHECK THAT ALL PINS ARE FULLY INSERTED IN THE SOCKET AND THAT PROM IS PROPERLY SEATED. IF OK, REPLACE PROM, CLEAR MEMORY, AND RECHECK. IF CODE 51 REAPPEARS, REPLACE ECM.

2.2L (VIN G) "L" CARLINE (TBI) WHITE (W) 24 PIN ECM CONNECTOR

PIN FUNCTION	CKT #	WIRE COLOR	COMPONENT/ CONNECTOR CAVITY	NORMAL VOLTAGE KEY "ON"	NORMAL VOLTAGE ENG RUN**	CODES AFFECT.	POSSIBLE SYMPTOMS FROM FAULTY CIRCUIT
W1 INJECTOR DRIVER	467	DK BLU	FUEL INJECTOR "B"	B+	B+		(5) CRANKS, BUT WON'T RUN.
W2 A/C REQUEST	366	LT GRN	A/C RELAY "A"	0*	0*		(3) NO A/C COOLING, A/C CLUTCH INOPERATIVE
W4 CRUISE R/A	87	GRY/BLK					REFER TO ELECTRICAL DIAGNOSIS
W6 EST	423	WHT	"DIS" MODULE "C"	0*	1.1V	42	(5) STUMBLES, UNSTABLE IDLE.
W7 IAC "A" HI	441	DK GRN	IAC VALVE "D"	NOT USABLE	NOT USABLE	35	(5) UNSTABLE, INCORRECT IDLE.
W8 IAC "B" LO	444	DK BLU/ WHT	IAC VALVE "A"	NOT USABLE	NOT USABLE	35	(5) UNSTABLE, INCORRECT IDLE.
W9 IAC "B" HI	443	DK BLU	IAC VALVE "B"	NOT USABLE	NOT USABLE	35	(5) UNSTABLE, INCORRECT IDLE.
W10 ECM MEMORY (B+)	340	ORN	F/P ECM FUSE	B+	B+		(3) NO EFFECT. IF W15 IS ALSO OPEN, NO START. (4) BLOWN FUEL PUMP/ECM FUSE, NO START.
W11 5 VOLT REF. TPS & MAP	416	GRY	TPS "A" MAP "C"	5.0V	5.0V	22, 34	(5) STUMBLES, HESITATES; FUEL INTEGRATOR REMOVING FUEL (LOW COUNTS)
W12 ECM GROUND	551	TAN/WHT	ENGINE GROUND	0*	0*		(3) NO EFFECT. IF W13 IS ALSO OPEN, NO START.
W13 ECM GROUND	450	BLK/WHT	ENGINE GROUND	0*	0*		(3) NO EFFECT. IF W12 IS ALSO OPEN, NO START.
W14 MAP, IAT SENSOR GROUND	452	BLK	TPS "B" IAT "A"	0*	0*	33	(3) POOR PERFORMANCE, STRONG EXHAUST ODOR
W15 ECM MEMORY (B+)	340	ORN	F/P ECM FUSE	B+	B+		(3) NO EFFECT. IF W10 IS ALSO OPEN, NO START.
W16 IGNITION FEED	439	PNK/BLK	"DIS" MODULE "B"	B+	B+		(3) NO START
W17 IAC "A" LO	442	DK GRN/ WHT	IAC VALVE "C"	NOT USABLE	NOT USABLE	35	(5) UNSTABLE, INCORRECT IDLE.
W18 PARK/NEUTRAL SWITCH	434	ORN/BLK	P/N SWITCH "A"	0* P-N B+ R-D-L	0* P-N B+ R-D-L		(5) INCORRECT IDLE
W19 IGNITION BYPASS	424	TAN/BLK	"DIS" MODULE "D"	0*	0*		(5) POOR PERFORMANCE
W20 CRUISE ENABLE	397	GRY		0*	4.5V	42	REFER TO ELECTRICAL DIAGNOSIS
W21 CRUISE S/C	84	DK BLU					REFER TO ELECTRICAL DIAGNOSIS
W22 VSS OUTPUT	817	DK GRN/ WHT	BULK HEAD CONNECTOR "A7"	0*	0*		(5) SPEEDOMETER INOPERATIVE
W24 FUEL PUMP RELAY DRIVE	465	DK GRN	FUEL PUMP RELAY "D"	(6)	B+		(5) LONG CRANKING TIME WHEN COLD

NOTICE: The voltages may vary due to battery charge or other reasons, but they should be very close.

* All voltages shown 0* should read less than .5 volt.

** All voltages shown are typical with engine at idle, Closed Throttle, Normal Operating Temperature, Park or Neutral and "Closed Loop." All accessories "OFF."

(1) Changes with IAC valve activity (when moving throttle slightly up and down).
(2) Varies
(3) Open circuit
(4) Grounded circuit
(5) Open or grounded circuit
(6) Reads B+ for 2 seconds after ignition "ON," then should read 0 volts.

"AFTER REPAIRS," CONFIRM "CLOSED LOOP" OPERATION AND NO "SERVICE ENGINE SOON" LIGHT.

1990–91 2.2L ENGINE

2.2L (VIN G) "L" CARLINE (TBI) BLACK 24 PIN "B" ECM CONNECTOR

	PIN FUNCTION	CKT #	WIRE COLOR	COMPONENT/CONNECTOR CAVITY	NORMAL VOLTAGE KEY "ON"	NORMAL VOLTAGE ENG RUN**	CODES AFFECT.	POSSIBLE SYMPTOMS FROM FAULTY CIRCUIT
B13	VSS SIGNAL (HIGH)	401	PPL	PM GENERATOR "B"	0*	0*		(3) POOR FUEL ECONOMY, TCC INOPERATIVE.
B14	CRUISE/BRAKE SWITCH	86	BRN				24	REFER TO ELECTRICAL DIAGNOSIS
B15	DIAGNOSTIC TEST	451	WHT/BLK	ALDL "B"	5.0V	5.0V		(4) FIELD SERVICE MODE ACTIVE, "SES" LIGHT FLASHES RICH/LEAN.
B16	IGNITION REF LO	453	BLK/RED	DIS' MODULE "F"	0*	0*		(5) NO EFFECT
B19	TPS SIGNAL	417	DK BLU	TPS "C"	.6V	6V IDLE	21,22	(5) POOR PERFORMANCE, BACKFIRE, HESITATION.
B20	MAP SIGNAL	432	PPL/WHT	MAP SENSOR "B"	4.75V	1.1V	33,34	(5) INCORRECT IDLE, CHUGGLE, POOR PERFORMANCE.
B21	COOLING FAN RELAY	335	DK GRN/WHT	COOLING FAN RELAY "F"	B+	B+		(3) POSSIBLE OVERHEATING, SPARK KNOCK. (4) COOLING FAN RUNS AT ALL TIMES.
B22	"SERVICE ENGINE SOON" LIGHT	419	BRN/WHT	TWIN 8-PIN I/P CONNECTOR "B"	0*	B+		(4) "SES" LIGHT "ON" AT ALL TIMES
B23	OXYGEN (O2) SENSOR GROUND	413	TAN	ENGINE GROUND	0*	0*	13	(3) OPEN LOOP, TECH 1 READS (O2) SENSOR VOLTAGE FIXED AT 400-500 mV.

NOTICE: Voltages may vary due to low battery charge or other reasons, but should be very close.

* All voltages shown 0* should read less than .5 volt.
** All voltages shown are typical with engine at idle, Closed Throttle, Normal Operating Temperature, Park or Neutral and "Closed Loop." All accessories "OFF."
(A) A/C Select Switch "OFF"
(B) Varies depending on temperature
(1) Changes with IAC valve activity (when moving throttle slightly up and down).
(2) Varies
(3) Open circuit
(4) Grounded circuit
(5) Open or grounded circuit

2.2L (VIN G) "L" CARLINE (TBI) BLACK (B) 24 PIN ECM CONNECTOR

	PIN FUNCTION	CKT #	WIRE COLOR	COMPONENT/CONNECTOR CAVITY	NORMAL VOLTAGE KEY "ON"	NORMAL VOLTAGE ENG RUN**	CODES AFFECT.	POSSIBLE SYMPTOMS FROM FAULTY CIRCUIT
B1	SERIAL DATA	461	ORN	I/P CONNECTOR "F"	4.5V	4.5V		(5) NO TECH 1 DATA
B2	OXYGEN (O2) SENSOR SIGNAL	412	PPL	O2 SENSOR	33-55V	1-.9V	13,44,45	(5) OPEN LOOP, STRONG EXHAUST ODOR.
B3	A/C COMPRESSOR RELAY	459	BRN	A/C COMPRESSOR RELAY "F"	B+	B+		(3) A/C CLUTCH INOPERATIVE (4) BLOWN ENGINE CONTROL FUSE A/C CLUTCH INOPERATIVE
B5	IAT SIGNAL	472	BLK/PNK	IAT SENSOR "B"	1.3V	1.3V	23,25	(3) POSSIBLE STRONG EXHAUST, TECH 1 READS -38°C (-36°F) (4) TECH 1 READS 179°C (354°F)
B6	VSS SIGNAL (LOW)	400	YEL	PM GENERATOR "A"	0*	0*	24	(5) POOR FUEL ECONOMY, TCC DISENGAGED AT ALL TIMES, SPEEDOMETER INOPERATIVE.
B7	TCC CONTROL SHIFT LIGHT	422 456	TAN/BLK	TCC SOLENOID "D" ALDL "F"	0*	0*		(3) POOR FUEL ECONOMY, TCC DOES NOT ENGAGE, TECH 1 SHOWS TCC "ON". (4) TCC ENGAGES TOO SOON IN 3rd GEAR, LUGS ENGINE AT HIGHWAY SPEEDS
B8	COOLANT TEMPERATURE SIGNAL	410	GRY	CTS "B"	1.9V	1.9V	14,15	(3) INCORRECT IDLE, COOLING FAN RUNS AT ALL TIMES, TECH 1 READS 39°C (38°F) (4) SAME AS OPEN EXCEPT TECH 1 READS 151°C (304°F)
B9	IGNITION REFERENCE HI	430	PPL/WHT	"DIS" MODULE "E"	4.6V	3.05V		(5) NO START
B10	CRUISE (VAC)	402	LT GRN					REFER TO ELECTRICAL DIAGNOSIS
B11	CRUISE (VENT)	403	DK BLU					REFER TO ELECTRICAL DIAGNOSIS.
B12	CTS & TPS GROUND	455	PPL	CTS "A" MAP "A"	0*	0*	15,21	(3) INCORRECT IDLE, HESITATION, TECH 1 READS TPS - 5V, CTS 39°C (102°F)

NOTICE: The voltages may vary due to battery charge or other reasons, but should be very close.

* All voltages shown 0* should read less than .5 volt.
** All voltages shown are typical with engine at idle, Closed Throttle, Normal Operating Temperature, Park or Neutral and "Closed Loop." All accessories "OFF."
(A) A/C select switch "OFF"
(B) Varies depending on temperature
(1) Changes with IAC valve activity (when moving throttle slightly up and down).
(2) Varies
(3) Open circuit
(4) Grounded circuit
(5) Open or grounded circuit

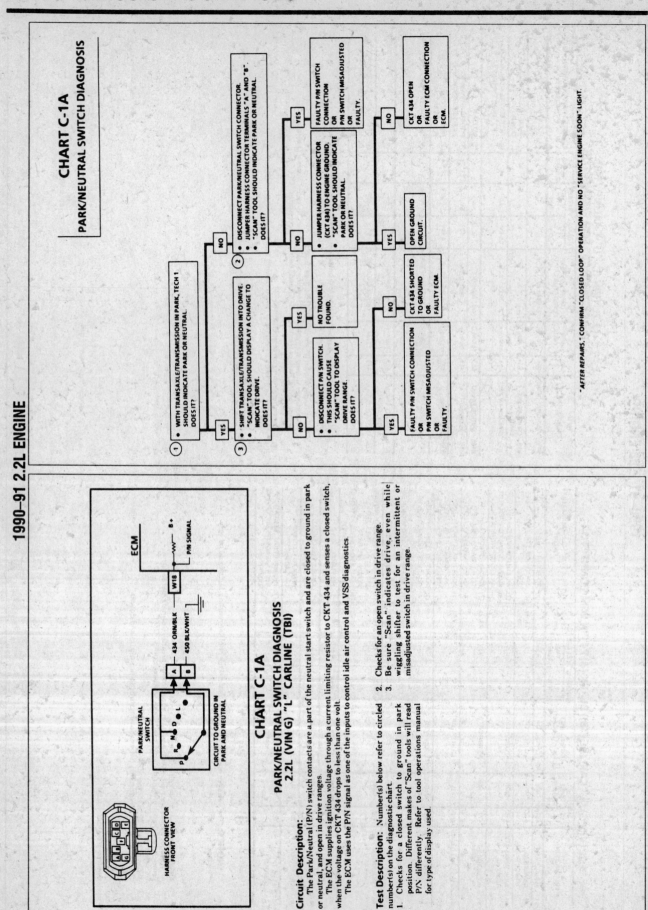

1990–91 2.2L ENGINE

CHART C-1A
PARK/NEUTRAL SWITCH DIAGNOSIS

CHART C-1A
PARK/NEUTRAL SWITCH DIAGNOSIS
2.2L (VIN G) "L" CARLINE (TBI)

Circuit Description:
The Park/Neutral (P/N) switch contacts are a part of the neutral start switch and are closed to ground in park or neutral, and open in drive ranges.
The ECM supplies ignition voltage through a current limiting resistor to CKT 434 and senses a closed switch, when the voltage on CKT 434 drops to less than one volt.
The ECM uses the P/N signal as one of the inputs to control idle air control and VSS diagnostics.

Test Description: Number(s) below refer to circled number(s) on the diagnostic chart.
1. Checks for a closed switch to ground in park position. Different makes of "Scan" tools will read P/N differently. Refer to tool operations manual for type of display used.

2. Checks for an open switch in drive range.
3. Be sure "Scan" indicates drive, even while wiggling shifter to test for an intermittent or misadjusted switch in drive range.

HARNESS CONNECTOR FRONT VIEW

PARK/NEUTRAL SWITCH

R   N   D   L
P   O

CIRCUIT TO GROUND IN PARK AND NEUTRAL

A   B

434 ORN/BLK
450 BLK/WHT

ECM
B+
P/N SIGNAL
W18

Chart boxes:

1 · WITH TRANSAXLE/TRANSMISSION IN PARK, TECH 1 "SCAN" TOOL SHOULD INDICATE PARK OR NEUTRAL. DOES IT?

3 · SHIFT TRANSAXLE/TRANSMISSION INTO DRIVE. "SCAN" TOOL SHOULD DISPLAY A CHANGE TO INDICATE DRIVE. DOES IT?

· DISCONNECT PARK/NEUTRAL SWITCH CONNECTOR. JUMPER HARNESS CONNECTOR TERMINALS "A" AND "B". "SCAN" TOOL SHOULD INDICATE PARK OR NEUTRAL. DOES IT?

NO TROUBLE FOUND.

· DISCONNECT P/N SWITCH. THIS SHOULD CAUSE "SCAN" TOOL TO DISPLAY DRIVE RANGE. DOES IT?

2 · JUMPER HARNESS CONNECTOR (CKT 434) TO ENGINE GROUND. "SCAN" TOOL SHOULD INDICATE PARK OR NEUTRAL. DOES IT?

FAULTY P/N SWITCH CONNECTION OR P/N SWITCH MISADJUSTED OR FAULTY.

OPEN GROUND CIRCUIT.

FAULTY P/N SWITCH CONNECTION OR P/N SWITCH MISADJUSTED OR FAULTY.

CKT 434 SHORTED TO GROUND OR FAULTY ECM.

CKT 434 OPEN OR FAULTY ECM CONNECTION OR ECM.

"AFTER REPAIRS." CONFIRM "CLOSED LOOP" OPERATION AND NO "SERVICE ENGINE SOON" LIGHT.

1990–91 2.2L ENGINE

CHART C-1D
MANIFOLD ABSOLUTE PRESSURE (MAP) SENSOR OUTPUT CHECK

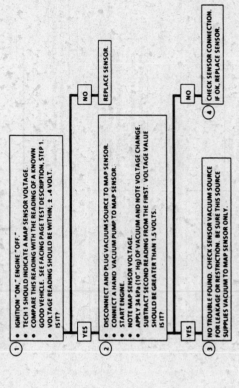

Circuit Description:

The Manifold Absolute Pressure (MAP) sensor measures the changes in the intake manifold pressure which result from engine load (intake manifold vacuum) and rpm changes; and converts these into a voltage output. The ECM sends a 5 volts reference voltage to the MAP sensor. As the manifold pressure changed, the output voltage of the sensor also changes. By monitoring the sensor signal voltage, the ECM determines the manifold pressure. a lower pressure (low voltage) output voltage will be about 1 - 2 volts at idle. While higher pressure (high voltage) output voltage will be about 4 - 4 8 at Wide Open Throttle (WOT). The MAP sensor is also used, under certain conditions, to measure barometric pressure, allowing the ECM to make adjustments for different altitudes. The ECM uses the MAP sensor to control fuel delivery and ignition timing.

Test Description: Number(s) below refer to circled number(s) on the diagnostic chart.

🛈 **Important**

- Be sure to use the same Diagnostic Test Equipment for all measurements

1. When comparing "Scan" readings to a known good vehicle, it is important to compare vehicles that use a MAP sensor having the same color insert or having the same "Hot Stamped" number. See figures on facing page.

2. Applying 34 kPa (10" Hg/25 cm Hg) vacuum to the MAP sensor second reading from the first. Voltage value should be greater than 1 5 volts. Upon applying vacuum to the sensor, the change in voltage should be instantaneous. A slow voltage change indicates a faulty sensor

3. Check vacuum hose to sensor for leaking or restriction. Be sure that no other vacuum devices are connected to the MAP hose.

NOTE: Make sure electrical connector remains securely fastened.

4. Disconnect sensor from bracket and twist sensor by hand (only) to check for intermittent connection. Output changes greater than 1 volt indicate a bad connector or connection. If OK, replace sensor

---

CHART C-1D
MANIFOLD ABSOLUTE PRESSURE (MAP) SENSOR OUTPUT CHECK

NOTE: THIS CHART ONLY APPLIES TO MAP SENSORS HAVING GREEN OR BLACK COLOR KEY INSERT (SEE BELOW).

1. • IGNITION "ON." ENGINE "OFF."
   • TECH 1 SHOULD INDICATE A MAP SENSOR VOLTAGE.
   • COMPARE THIS READING WITH THE READING OF A KNOWN GOOD VEHICLE. SEE FACING PAGE TEST DESCRIPTION, STEP 1.
   • VOLTAGE READING SHOULD BE WITHIN: ± .4 VOLT.
   IS IT?

   NO → REPLACE SENSOR.

   YES ↓

2. • DISCONNECT AND PLUG VACUUM SOURCE TO MAP SENSOR.
   • CONNECT A HAND VACUUM PUMP TO MAP SENSOR.
   • START ENGINE.
   • NOTE MAP SENSOR VOLTAGE.
   • APPLY 34 kPa (10" Hg) OF VACUUM AND NOTE VOLTAGE CHANGE. SUBTRACT SECOND READING FROM THE FIRST. VOLTAGE VALUE SHOULD BE GREATER THAN 1.5 VOLTS.
   IS IT?

   NO → CHECK SENSOR CONNECTION. IF OK, REPLACE SENSOR.

   YES ↓

3. NO TROUBLE FOUND. CHECK SENSOR VACUUM SOURCE FOR LEAKAGE OR RESTRICTION. BE SURE THIS SOURCE SUPPLIES VACUUM TO MAP SENSOR ONLY.

④ CHECK SENSOR CONNECTION. IF OK, REPLACE SENSOR.

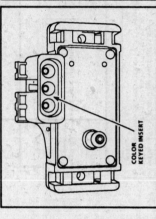

Figure 1 - Color Key Insert

Figure 2 - Hot-Stamped Number

"AFTER REPAIRS," CONFIRM "CLOSED LOOP" OPERATION AND NO "SERVICE ENGINE SOON" LIGHT.

1990–91 2.2L ENGINE

CHART C-2C
IDLE AIR CONTROL (IAC) SYSTEM CHECK

IAC CONNECTOR — D C B A — THROTTLE BODY — AIR FLOW

ECM:
W7	IAC COIL "A" HI	DK GRN 441
W17	IAC COIL "A" LO	DK GRN/WHT 442
W9	IAC COIL "B" HI	DK BLU 443
W8	IAC COIL "B" LO	DK BLU/WHT 446

Circuit Description:

The ECM controls engine idle speed with the IAC valve. To increase speed idle, the ECM retracts the IAC valve pintle away from its seat, allowing more air to bypass the throttle bore. To decrease idle speed, it extends the IAC valve pintle towards its seat, reducing bypass air flow. A Tech 1 "Scan" tool will read the ECM commands to the IAC valve in counts. Higher the counts indicate more air bypass (higher idle). The lower the counts indicate less air allowed to bypass (lower idle).

Test Description: Number(s) below refer to circled number(s) on the diagnostic chart.

1. The IAC tester is used to extend and retract the IAC valve. Valve movement is verified by an engine speed change. If no change in engine speed occurs, the valve can be retested when removed from the throttle body.

2. This step checks the quality of the IAC movement in Step 1. Between 700 rpm and about 1500 rpm, the engine speed should change smoothly with each flash of the tester light in both extend and retract. If the IAC valve is retracted beyond the control range (about 1500 rpm), it may take many flashes in the extend position before engine speed will begin to drop. This is normal on certain engines, fully extending IAC may cause engine stall. This may be normal

3. Steps 1 and 2 verified proper IAC valve operation while this step checks the IAC circuits. Each lamp on the node light should flash red and green while the IAC valve is cycled. While the sequence of color is not important if either light is "OFF" or does not flash red and green, check the circuits for faults, beginning with poor terminal contacts

Diagnostic Aids:

A slow, unstable, or fast idle may be caused by a non-IAC system problem that cannot be overcome by the IAC valve. Out of control range IAC "Scan" tool counts will be above 60 if idle is too low, and zero counts if idle is too high. The following checks should be made to repair a non-IAC system problem
- Vacuum Leak (High Idle)
If idle is too high, stop the engine. Fully extend (low) IAC with tester

Start engine. If idle speed is above 800 rpm, locate and correct vacuum leak including PCV system. Also check for binding of throttle valve or linkage
System too lean (High Air/Fuel Ratio)
The idle speed may be too high or too low. Engine speed may vary up and down and disconnecting the IAC valve does not help. Code 44 may be set. "Scan" O_2 voltage will be less than 300 mV (.3 volt). Check for low regulated fuel pressure, water in fuel or a restricted injector
System too rich (Low Air/Fuel Ratio)
The idle speed will be too low. "Scan" tool IAC counts will usually be above 80. System is obviously rich and may exhibit black smoke exhaust. "Scan" tool O_2 voltage will be fixed above 800 mV (.8 volt).
Check for high fuel pressure, leaking or sticking injector. Silicone contaminated O_2 sensor will "Scan" an O_2 voltage slow to respond
Throttle Body
Remove IAC valve and inspect bore for foreign material
IAC Valve Electrical Connections
IAC valve connections should be carefully checked for proper contact
- PCV Valve
An incorrect or faulty PCV valve may result in an incorrect idle speed
Refer to "Rough. Unstable. Incorrect Idle or Stalling" in "Symptoms."
If intermittent poor driveability or idle symptoms are resolved by disconnecting the IAC, carefully recheck connections, valve terminal resistance, or replace IAC

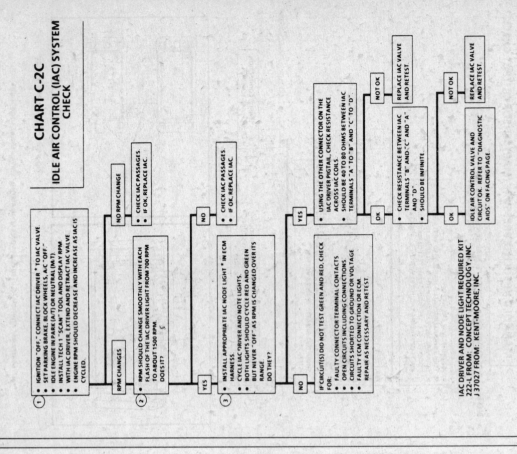

CHART C-2C
IDLE AIR CONTROL (IAC) SYSTEM CHECK

(1)
- IGNITION "OFF." CONNECT IAC DRIVER * TO IAC VALVE.
- SET PARKING BRAKE. BLOCK WHEELS. A/C "OFF."
- IDLE ENGINE IN PARK (A/T) OR NEUTRAL (M/T).
- INSTALL TECH 1 "SCAN" TOOL AND DISPLAY RPM
- WITH IAC DRIVER, EXTEND AND RETRACT IAC VALVE
- ENGINE RPM SHOULD DECREASE AND INCREASE AS IAC IS CYCLED.

→ NO RPM CHANGE → CHECK IAC PASSAGES. IF OK, REPLACE IAC.

→ RPM CHANGES

(2) RPM SHOULD CHANGE SMOOTHLY WITH EACH FLASH OF THE IAC DRIVER LIGHT FROM 700 RPM TO ABOUT 1500 RPM. DOES IT?

→ NO → CHECK IAC PASSAGES. IF OK, REPLACE IAC.

→ YES

(3) INSTALL APPROPRIATE IAC NODE LIGHT * IN ECM HARNESS.
CYCLE IAC DRIVER AND NOTE LIGHTS.
BOTH LIGHTS SHOULD CYCLE RED AND GREEN BUT NEVER "OFF" AS RPM IS CHANGED OVER ITS RANGE.
DO THEY?

→ YES → USING THE OTHER CONNECTOR ON THE IAC DRIVER PIGTAIL, CHECK RESISTANCE ACROSS IAC COILS.
SHOULD BE 40 TO 80 OHMS BETWEEN IAC TERMINALS "A" TO "B" AND "C" TO "D".

→ NOT OK → REPLACE IAC VALVE AND RETEST.

→ OK → CHECK RESISTANCE BETWEEN IAC TERMINALS "B" AND "C" AND "A" AND "D".
SHOULD BE INFINITE.

→ NOT OK → REPLACE IAC VALVE AND RETEST.

→ OK → IDLE AIR CONTROL VALVE AND CIRCUIT OK. REFER TO "DIAGNOSTIC AIDS" ON FACING PAGE.

→ NO → IF CIRCUIT(S) DID NOT TEST GREEN AND RED, CHECK FOR:
- FAULTY CONNECTOR TERMINAL CONTACTS
- OPEN CIRCUITS INCLUDING CONNECTIONS
- CIRCUITS SHORTED TO GROUND OR VOLTAGE
- FAULTY ECM CONNECTION OR ECM
REPAIR AS NECESSARY AND RETEST

IAC DRIVER AND NODE LIGHT REQUIRED KIT 222-L FROM: CONCEPT TECHNOLOGY, INC. J 37027 FROM: KENT-MOORE, INC.

* "AFTER REPAIRS." CONFIRM "CLOSED LOOP" OPERATION AND NO "SERVICE ENGINE SOON" LIGHT.

1990–91 2.2L ENGINE

CHART C-4D-1
"DIS" MISFIRE AT IDLE

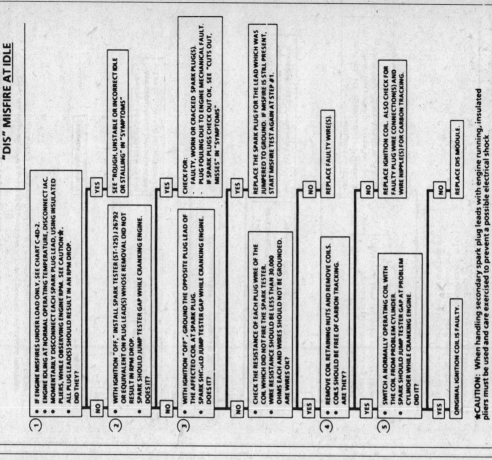

1
- IF ENGINE MISFIRES UNDER LOAD ONLY, SEE CHART C-4D-2.
- ENGINE IDLING AT NORMAL OPERATING TEMPERATURE, DISCONNECT IAC.
- MOMENTARILY DISCONNECT EACH SPARK PLUG LEAD, USING INSULATED PLIERS, WHILE OBSERVING ENGINE RPM. SEE CAUTION★.
- ALL PLUG LEAD(S) SHOULD RESULT IN AN RPM DROP.
DID THEY?

YES → SEE "ROUGH, UNSTABLE OR INCORRECT IDLE OR STALLING" IN "SYMPTOMS"

2
- WITH IGNITION "OFF", INSTALL SPARK TESTER (ST-125) J 26792 OR EQUIVALENT ON PLUG LEAD(S) WHOSE REMOVAL DID NOT RESULT IN RPM DROP.
- SPARK SHOULD JUMP TESTER GAP WHILE CRANKING ENGINE. DOES IT?

YES → CHECK FOR:
- FAULTY, WORN OR CRACKED SPARK PLUG(S).
- PLUG FOULING DUE TO ENGINE MECHANICAL FAULT.
IF SPARK PLUGS CHECK OUT OK, SEE "CUTS OUT, MISSES" IN "SYMPTOMS"

3
- WITH IGNITION "OFF", GROUND THE OPPOSITE PLUG LEAD OF THE AFFECTED COIL AT SPARK PLUG.
- SPARK SHOULD JUMP TESTER GAP WHILE CRANKING ENGINE. DOES IT?

YES → REPLACE THE SPARK PLUG FOR THE LEAD WHICH WAS JUMPED TO GROUND. IF MISFIRE IS STILL PRESENT, START MISFIRE TEST AGAIN AT STEP #1.

4
- CHECK THE RESISTANCE OF EACH PLUG WIRE OF THE COIL WHICH DID NOT FIRE THE SPARK TESTER. WIRE RESISTANCE SHOULD BE LESS THAN 30,000 OHMS EACH AND WIRES SHOULD NOT BE GROUNDED. ARE WIRES OK?

NO → REPLACE FAULTY WIRE(S).

5
- REMOVE COIL RETAINING NUTS AND REMOVE COILS. COILS SHOULD BE FREE OF CARBON TRACKING. ARE THEY?

YES → REPLACE IGNITION COIL. ALSO CHECK FOR FAULTY PLUG WIRE CONNECTION(S) AND WIRE NIPPLE(S) FOR CARBON TRACKING.

- SWITCH A NORMALLY OPERATING COIL WITH THE COIL FROM PROBLEM CYLINDER. SPARK SHOULD JUMP TESTER GAP AT PROBLEM CYLINDER WHILE CRANKING ENGINE. DID IT?

YES → ORIGINAL IGNITION COIL IS FAULTY.

NO → REPLACE DIS MODULE.

★CAUTION: When handling secondary spark plug leads with engine running, insulated pliers must be used and care exercised to prevent a possible electrical shock.

"AFTER REPAIRS," CONFIRM "CLOSED LOOP" OPERATION AND NO "SERVICE ENGINE SOON" LIGHT.

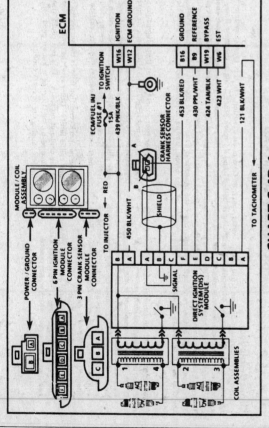

CHART C-4D-1
"DIS" MISFIRE AT IDLE

Circuit Description:

The Direct Ignition System (DIS) uses a waste spark method of distribution. In this type of system, the ignition module triggers the #1/4 coil pair resulting in both #1 and #4 spark plugs firing at the same time. #1 cylinder is on the compression stroke at the same time #4 is on the exhaust stroke, resulting in a lower energy requirement to fire #4 spark plug. This leaves the remainder of the high voltage to be used to fire #1 spark plug. The crank sensor is remotely mounted beside the module/coil assembly and protrudes through the block to within approximately .050" of the crankshaft reluctor. Since the reluctor is a machined portion of the crankshaft and the crankshaft sensor is mounted in a fixed position on the block, timing adjustments are not possible or necessary.

Test Description: Numbers(s) below refer to circled number(s) on the diagnostic chart.

1. If the "Misfire" complaint exists under load only, the diagnostic chart on page 2 must be used. Engine rpm should drop approximately equally on all plug leads.

2. A spark tester, such as a ST-125, must be used because it is essential to verify adequate available secondary voltage at the spark plug (25,000 volts).

3. If the spark jumps the tester gap after grounding the opposite plug wire, it indicates excessive resistance in the plug which was bypassed. A faulty or poor connection at that plug could also result in the miss condition. Also, check for carbon deposits inside the spark plug boot.

4. If carbon tracking is evident, replace coil and be sure plug wires relating to that coil are clean and tight. Excessive wire resistance or faulty connections could have caused the coil to be damaged.

5. If the no spark condition follows the suspected coil, that coil is faulty. Otherwise, the ignition module is the cause of no spark. This test could also be performed by substituting a known good coil for the one causing the no spark condition.

1990-91 2.2L ENGINE

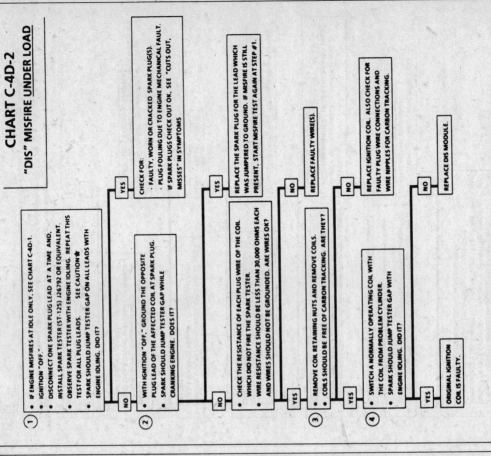

CHART C-4D-2
"DIS" MISFIRE UNDER LOAD

(1)
- IF ENGINE MISFIRES AT IDLE ONLY, SEE CHART C-4D-1.
- IGNITION "OFF."
- DISCONNECT ONE SPARK PLUG LEAD AT A TIME AND.
- INSTALL SPARK TESTER (ST-125) J26792 OR EQUIVALENT.
- OBSERVE SPARK TESTER WITH ENGINE IDLING. REPEAT THIS TEST FOR ALL PLUG LEADS. SEE CAUTION★
- SPARK SHOULD JUMP TESTER GAP ON ALL LEADS WITH ENGINE IDLING. DID IT?

YES → CHECK FOR:
- FAULTY, WORN OR CRACKED SPARK PLUG(S).
- PLUG FOULING DUE TO ENGINE MECHANICAL FAULT.
IF SPARK PLUGS CHECK OUT OK, SEE "CUTS OUT, MISSES" IN SYMPTOMS

NO ↓

(2)
- WITH IGNITION "OFF," GROUND THE OPPOSITE PLUG LEAD OF THE AFFECTED COIL AT SPARK PLUG.
- SPARK SHOULD JUMP TESTER GAP WHILE CRANKING ENGINE. DOES IT?

YES → REPLACE THE SPARK PLUG FOR THE LEAD WHICH WAS JUMPERED TO GROUND. IF MISFIRE IS STILL PRESENT, START MISFIRE TEST AGAIN AT STEP #1.

NO ↓

- CHECK THE RESISTANCE OF EACH PLUG WIRE OF THE COIL WHICH DID NOT FIRE THE SPARK TESTER.
- WIRE RESISTANCE SHOULD BE LESS THAN 30,000 OHMS EACH AND WIRES SHOULD NOT BE GROUNDED. ARE WIRES OK?

NO → REPLACE FAULTY WIRE(S).

(3)
- REMOVE COIL RETAINING NUTS AND REMOVE COILS.
- COILS SHOULD BE FREE OF CARBON TRACKING. ARE THEY?

NO → REPLACE IGNITION COIL. ALSO CHECK FOR FAULTY PLUG WIRE CONNECTIONS AND WIRE NIPPLES FOR CARBON TRACKING.

YES ↓

(4)
- SWITCH A NORMALLY OPERATING COIL WITH THE COIL FROM PROBLEM CYLINDER.
- SPARK SHOULD JUMP TESTER GAP WITH ENGINE IDLING. DID IT?

YES → ORIGINAL IGNITION COIL IS FAULTY.

NO → REPLACE DIS MODULE.

★CAUTION: When handling secondary spark plug leads with engine running, insulated pliers must be used and care exercised to prevent a possible electrical shock.

"AFTER REPAIRS," CONFIRM "CLOSED LOOP" OPERATION AND NO "SERVICE ENGINE SOON" LIGHT.

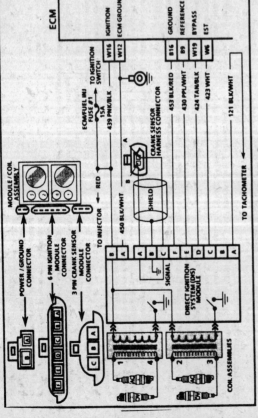

CHART C-4D-2
"DIS" MISFIRE UNDER LOAD

Circuit Description:

The Direct Ignition System (DIS) uses a waste spark method of distribution. In this type of system, the ignition module triggers the #1/4 coil pair resulting in both #1 and #4 spark plugs firing at the same time. #1 cylinder is on the compression stroke at the same time #4 is on the exhaust stroke, resulting in a lower energy requirement to fire #4 spark plug. This leaves the remainder of the high voltage to be used to fire #1 spark plug. The crank sensor is remotely mounted beside the module/coil assembly and protrudes through the block to within approximately .050" of the crankshaft reluctor. Since the reluctor is a machined portion of the crankshaft, and the crankshaft sensor is mounted in a fixed position on the block, timing adjustments are not possible or necessary.

Test Description: Number(s) below refer to circled number(s) on the diagnostic chart.

1. If the "Misfire" complaint exists at idle only, the diagnostic chart on page 1 must be used. A spark tester such as a ST-125 must be used because it is essential to verify adequate available secondary voltage at the spark plug (25,000 volts). Spark should jump the test gap on all 4 leads. This simulates a "load" condition.

2. If the spark jumps the tester gap after grounding the opposite plug wire, it indicates excessive resistance in the plug which was bypassed.

3. A faulty or poor connection at that plug could also result in the miss condition. Also, check for carbon deposits inside the spark plug boot. If carbon tracking is evident replace coil and be sure plug wires relating to that coil are clean and tight. Excessive wire resistance or faulty connections could have caused the coil to be damaged.

4. If the no spark condition follows the suspected coil, that coil is faulty. Otherwise, the ignition module is the cause of no spark. This test could also be performed by substituting a known good coil for the one causing the no spark condition.

1990–91 2.2L ENGINE

CHART C-8A
TORQUE CONVERTER CLUTCH (TCC)
(ELECTRICAL DIAGNOSIS)

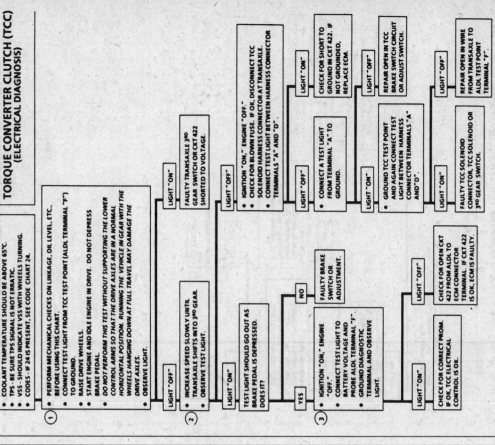

USING A TECH 1, CHECK THE FOLLOWING AND CORRECT IF NECESSARY:
- COOLANT TEMPERATURE SHOULD BE ABOVE 65°C.
- TPS - BE SURE TPS SIGNAL IS NOT ERRATIC.
- VSS - SHOULD INDICATE VSS WITH WHEELS TURNING.
- CODES - IF 24 IS PRESENT, SEE CODE CHART 24.

(1)
- PERFORM MECHANICAL CHECKS ON LINKAGE, OIL LEVEL, ETC., BEFORE USING THIS CHART.
- CONNECT TEST LIGHT FROM TCC TEST POINT (ALDL TERMINAL "F") TO GROUND.
- RAISE DRIVE WHEELS.
- START ENGINE AND IDLE ENGINE IN DRIVE. DO NOT DEPRESS BRAKE PEDAL.
- DO NOT PERFORM THIS TEST WITHOUT SUPPORTING THE LOWER CONTROL ARMS SO THAT THE DRIVE AXLES ARE IN A NORMAL HORIZONTAL POSITION. RUNNING THE VEHICLE IN GEAR WITH THE WHEELS HANGING DOWN AT FULL TRAVEL MAY DAMAGE THE DRIVE AXLES.
- OBSERVE LIGHT.

LIGHT "OFF"

LIGHT "ON" — FAULTY TRANSAXLE 3RD GEAR SWITCH OR CKT 422 SHORTED TO VOLTAGE.

(2)
- INCREASE SPEED SLOWLY UNTIL TRANSAXLE SHIFTS INTO 3RD GEAR.
- OBSERVE TEST LIGHT.

LIGHT "ON"

LIGHT "OFF"
- IGNITION "ON," ENGINE "OFF."
- CHECK FOR BLOWN FUSE. IF OK, DISCONNECT TCC SOLENOID HARNESS CONNECTOR AT TRANSAXLE.
- CONNECT TEST LIGHT BETWEEN HARNESS CONNECTOR TERMINALS "A" AND "D"

LIGHT "OFF"
- CONNECT A TEST LIGHT FROM TERMINAL "A" TO GROUND.

LIGHT "ON" — CHECK FOR SHORT TO GROUND IN CKT 422. IF NOT GROUNDED, REPLACE ECM.

LIGHT "OFF" — REPAIR OPEN IN TCC BRAKE SWITCH CIRCUIT OR ADJUST SWITCH.

LIGHT "ON"
- GROUND TCC TEST POINT AND AGAIN CONNECT TEST LIGHT BETWEEN HARNESS CONNECTOR TERMINALS "A" AND "D"

LIGHT "OFF" — FAULTY TCC SOLENOID CONNECTOR, TCC SOLENOID OR 3RD GEAR SWITCH.

LIGHT "ON" — REPAIR OPEN IN WIRE FROM TRANSAXLE TO ALDL TEST POINT TERMINAL "F."

(3)
- IGNITION "ON," ENGINE "OFF."
- CONNECT TEST LIGHT TO BATTERY VOLTAGE AND PROBE ALDL TERMINAL "F."
- GROUND DIAGNOSTIC TERMINAL AND OBSERVE LIGHT.

TEST LIGHT SHOULD GO OUT AS BRAKE PEDAL IS DEPRESSED. DOES IT?

NO — FAULTY BRAKE SWITCH OR ADJUSTMENT.

YES

LIGHT "OFF" — CHECK FOR CORRECT PROM. IF OK, TCC ELECTRICAL CONTROL IS OK.

LIGHT "ON" — CHECK FOR OPEN CKT 422 FROM ALDL TO ECM CONNECTOR TERMINAL. IF CKT 422 IS OK, ECM IS FAULTY.

"AFTER REPAIRS," CONFIRM "CLOSED LOOP" OPERATION AND NO "SERVICE ENGINE SOON" LIGHT.

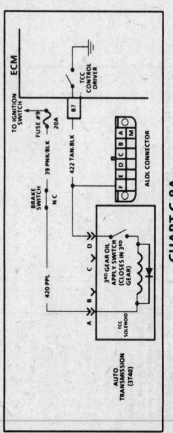

ECM
TCC CONTROL DRIVER
B7
TO IGNITION SWITCH
FUSE #9
20A
39 PNK/BLK
422 TAN/BLK
BRAKE SWITCH
N C
420 PPL
ALDL CONNECTOR
F E D C B A
M
A B C D
3RD GEAR OIL APPLY SWITCH (CLOSES IN 3RD GEAR)
TCC SOLENOID
AUTO TRANSMISSION (3T40)

CHART C-8A
TORQUE CONVERTER CLUTCH (TCC)
(ELECTRICAL DIAGNOSIS)

Circuit Description:

The purpose of the Torque Converter Clutch (TCC) is to eliminate the power loss of the torque converter when the vehicle is in a cruise condition. This allows the convenience of the automatic transaxle and the fuel economy of a manual transaxle.

Fused battery ignition voltage is supplied to the TCC solenoid through the brake switch and transaxle 3rd gear apply switch. The ECM will engage TCC by grounding CKT 422 to energize the solenoid.

TCC will engage when:
- Vehicle speed above 30 mph (48 km/h).
- Coolant temperature above 30°C (86°F).
- Throttle position sensor output not changing, indicating a steady road speed.
- Transaxle 3rd gear switch closed.
- Brake switch closed.

Test Description: Number(s) below refer to circled number(s) on the diagnostic chart.

1. Light "OFF" confirms transaxle 3rd gear apply switch is open.
2. When the transaxle 3rd gear switch closes, the test light should light.
3. Grounding the diagnostic terminal with engine "OFF" should energize the TCC solenoid. This test checks the capability of the ECM to control the solenoid.

   Check TCC solenoid resistance as follows:
   1. Disconnect TCC at transaxle.
   2. Connect ohmmeter between transaxle connector opposite harness connector terminal "A" and "D"

3. Raise drive wheels.
4. Run engine in drive about 48 km/h (30 mph) to close 3rd gear apply switch.
5. Replace the TCC solenoid and ECM if resistance measures less than 20 ohms when switch is closed.

Diagnostic Aids:

An engine coolant thermostat that is stuck open, or opens at too low a temperature may result in an inoperative TCC.

1990–91 2.2L ENGINE

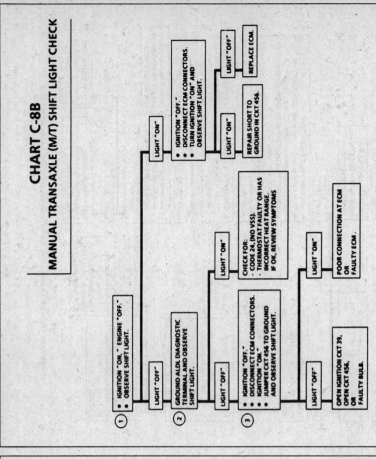

CHART C-8B

MANUAL TRANSAXLE (M/T) SHIFT LIGHT CHECK

Circuit Description:

The shift light indicates the best transaxle shift point for maximum fuel economy. The light is controlled by the ECM and is turned "ON" by grounding CKT 456.

The ECM uses information from the following inputs to control the shift light:
- CTS
- TPS
- VSS
- RPM

The ECM uses the measured rpm and the vehicle speed to calculate what gear the vehicle is in. It's this calculation that determines when the shift light should be turned "ON."

Test Description: Number(s) below refer to circled number(s) on the diagnostic chart.

1. This should not turn "ON" the shift light. If the light is "ON," there is a short to ground in CKT 456 wiring or a fault in the ECM.

2. When the diagnostic terminal is grounded, the ECM should ground CKT 456 and the shift light should come "ON."

3. This checks the shift light circuit up to the ECM connector. If the shift light illuminates, then the ECM connector is faulty or the ECM does not have the ability to ground the circuit.

1990-91 2.2L ENGINE

CHART C-10
A/C CLUTCH CONTROL

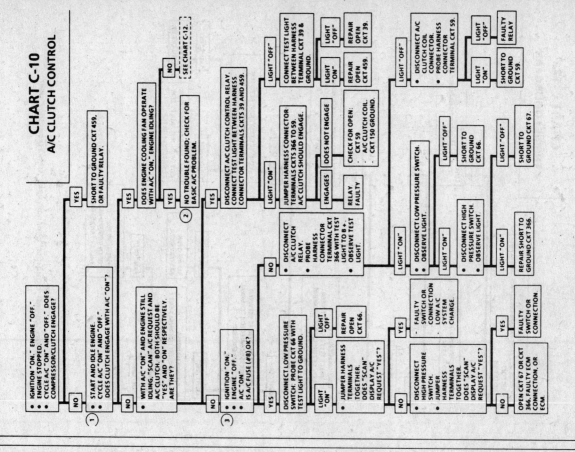

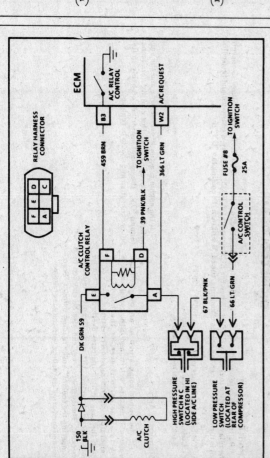

CHART C-10
A/C CLUTCH CONTROL

Circuit Description:

When an A/C mode is selected on the A/C control switch, ignition battery voltage is supplied through the A/C request circuit to the ECM. With sufficient A/C refrigerant charge, the low pressure switch will be closed and complete the circuit to the closed high pressure cut-off switch and to CKTs 67 and 366. When a request for A/C is sensed, the ECM will ground CKT 459 energizing the A/C clutch control relay and current will flow from CKT 366 to CKT 59 and engage the A/C compressor clutch. Also, when voltage is seen by the ECM on CKT 366, the cooling fan will be turned "ON."

The ECM will de-energize the A/C clutch control relay under the following conditions:
- Coolant temperature over 124°C (255°F)
- TPS at WOT
- Engine speed greater than 4800 rpm
- Ignition "OFF." (2 second delay on restart.)

Test Description: Number(s) below refer to circled number(s) on the diagnostic chart.
1. The A/C compressor clutch should not engage until 2 seconds after the engine is running.
2. Refer to AIR CONDITIONING DIAGNOSIS
3. A blown A/C fuse could be caused by a short to ground from the ignition switch to the compressor.

Diagnostic Aids:

The low pressure switch will be closed at 40-47 psi and allow A/C clutch operation. Below 37 psi, the low pressure switch will be open and the A/C clutch will not operate.

At about 430 psi, the high pressure switch will open, signaling the ECM to disengage the A/C clutch and prevent system damage.

CHART C-12
ENGINE COOLING FAN

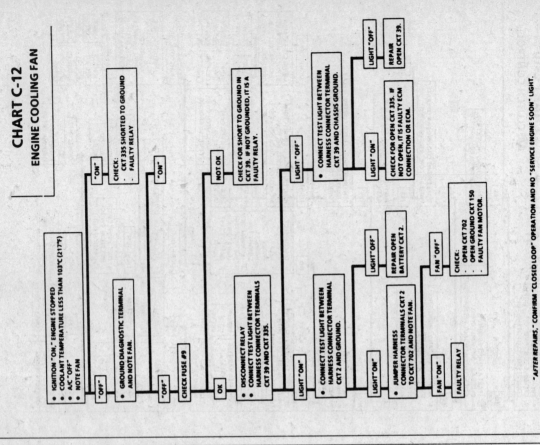

- IGNITION "ON," ENGINE STOPPED
- COOLANT TEMPERATURE LESS THAN 103°C (217°F)
- A/C "OFF"
- NOTE FAN

"ON" → CHECK:
- CKT 335 SHORTED TO GROUND
- FAULTY RELAY

"OFF" → GROUND DIAGNOSTIC TERMINAL AND NOTE FAN.

"ON" → CHECK FOR SHORT TO GROUND IN CKT 39. IF NOT GROUNDED, IT IS A FAULTY RELAY.

"OFF" → CHECK FUSE #9

OK → DISCONNECT RELAY
CONNECT TEST LIGHT BETWEEN HARNESS CONNECTOR TERMINALS CKT 39 AND CKT 335.

NOT OK → CHECK FOR SHORT TO GROUND IN CKT 39. IF NOT GROUNDED, IT IS A FAULTY RELAY.

LIGHT "ON" → CONNECT TEST LIGHT BETWEEN HARNESS CONNECTOR TERMINAL CKT 2 AND GROUND.

LIGHT "OFF" → CONNECT TEST LIGHT BETWEEN HARNESS CONNECTOR TERMINAL CKT 39 AND CHASSIS GROUND.

LIGHT "ON" → REPAIR OPEN BATTERY CKT 2.

LIGHT "OFF" → JUMPER HARNESS CONNECTOR TERMINALS CKT 2 TO CKT 702 AND NOTE FAN.

LIGHT "ON" → CHECK FOR OPEN CKT 335. IF NOT OPEN, IT IS FAULTY ECM CONNECTION OR ECM.

LIGHT "OFF" → REPAIR OPEN CKT 39.

FAN "ON" → FAULTY RELAY

FAN "OFF" → CHECK:
- OPEN CKT 702
- OPEN GROUND CKT 150
- FAULTY FAN MOTOR.

"AFTER REPAIRS," CONFIRM "CLOSED LOOP" OPERATION AND NO "SERVICE ENGINE SOON" LIGHT.

1990–91 2.2L ENGINE

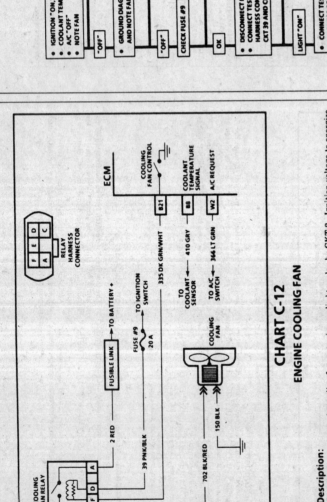

CHART C-12
ENGINE COOLING FAN

Circuit Description:

Battery voltage to operate the cooling fan motor is supplied to relay by CKT 2. Ignition voltage to energize the relay is supplied to relay by CKT 39. When the ECM grounds CKT 335, the relay is energized and the cooling fan is turned "ON." When the engine is running, the ECM will turn the cooling fan "ON" if:

- A/C is "ON."
- Coolant temperature greater than 108°C (230°F).
- Code 14 or 15, coolant sensor failure.
- Back-up fuel control mode is active.

Diagnostic Aids:

If the owner complained of an overheating problem, it must be determined if the complaint was due to an actual boil over, or the hot light, or temperature gage indicated over heating.

If the gage or light indicates overheating, but no boil over is detected, the gage circuit should be checked. The gage accuracy can also be checked by comparing the coolant sensor reading using a "Scan" tool and comparing its reading with the gage reading.

If the engine is actually overheating and the gage indicates overheating, but the cooling fan is not coming "ON," the coolant sensor has probably shifted out of calibration and should be replaced.

ECM WIRING DIAGRAM — 1992 2.2L ENGINE

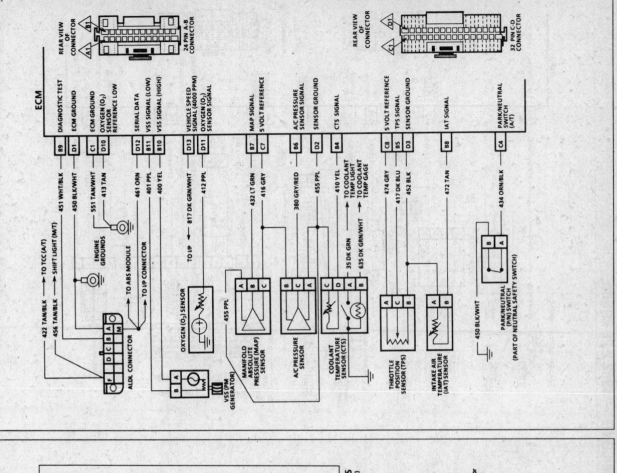

COMPONENT LOCATIONS — 1992 2.2L ENGINE

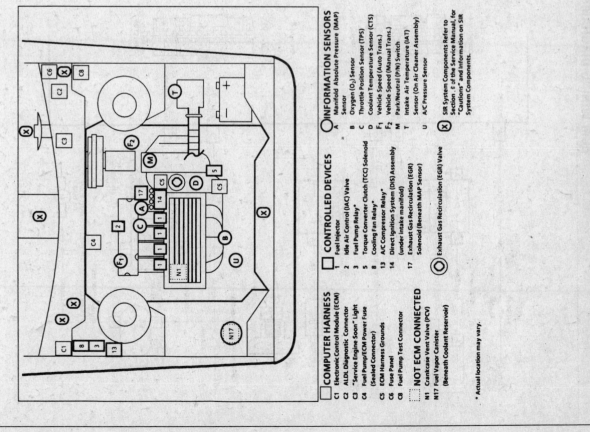

COMPUTER HARNESS
- C1 Electronic Control Module (ECM)
- C2 ALDL Diagnostic Connector
- C3 "Service Engine Soon" Light
- C4 Fuel Pump/ECM Power Fuse (Sealed Connector)
- C5 ECM Harness Grounds
- C6 Fuse Panel
- C8 Fuel Pump Test Connector

NOT ECM CONNECTED
- N1 Crankcase Vent Valve (PCV)
- N17 Fuel Vapor Canister (Beneath Coolant Reservoir)

☐ **CONTROLLED DEVICES**
- 1 Fuel Injector
- 2 Idle Air Control (IAC) Valve
- 3 Fuel Pump Relay*
- 5 Torque Converter Clutch (TCC) Solenoid
- 8 Cooling Fan Relay*
- 13 A/C Compressor Relay*
- 14 Direct Ignition System (DIS) Assembly
- 17 Exhaust Gas Recirculation (EGR) Solenoid (Beneath MAP Sensor)
- ◎ Exhaust Gas Recirculation (EGR) Valve

○ **INFORMATION SENSORS**
- A Manifold Absolute Pressure (MAP) Sensor
- B Oxygen (O_2) Sensor
- C Throttle Position Sensor (TPS)
- D Coolant Temperature Sensor (CTS)
- F_1 Vehicle Speed (Manual Trans.)
- F_2 Vehicle Speed (Auto Trans.)
- M Park/Neutral (P/N) Switch
- T Intake Air Temperature (IAT) Sensor (On Air Cleaner Assembly)
- U A/C Pressure Sensor

✕ **SIR System Components Refer to Section . 8 of the Service Manual, for "Cautions" and information on SIR System Components.**

*Actual location may vary.

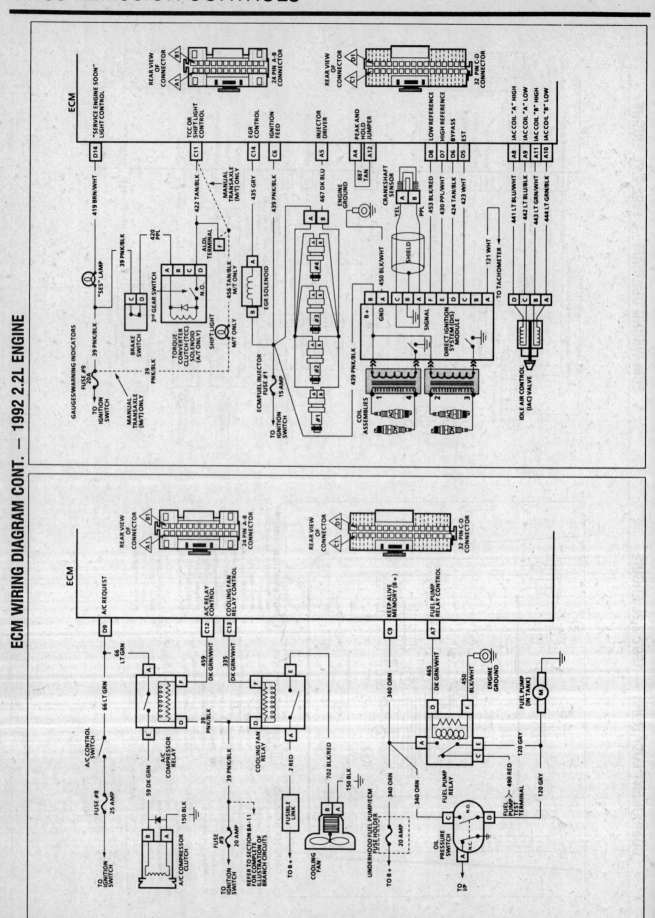

ECM WIRING DIAGRAM CONT. — 1992 2.2L ENGINE

END VIEW OF THE ECM CONNECTOR — 1992 2.2L ENGINE

PORT FUEL INJECTION ECM CONNECTOR IDENTIFICATION

This ECM voltage chart is for use with a digital voltmeter to further aid in diagnosis. The voltages you get may vary due to low battery charge or other reasons, but they should be very close.

THE FOLLOWING CONDITIONS MUST BE MET BEFORE TESTING:
- Engine at operating temperature • Engine idling in "Closed Loop" (For "Engine Run" column) in park or neutral • Test terminal not grounded • "Scan" tool not installed
- B + indicates battery or charging system voltage

24 PIN A-B CONNECTOR
REAR VIEW OF CONNECTOR (PINK)

PINK 24 PIN A-B CONNECTOR

VOLTAGE KEY "ON"	ENG. RUN	CIRCUIT	PIN	WIRE COLOR
		NOT USED	A1	
		NOT USED	A2	
		NOT USED	A3	
0*	0*	PEAK AND HOLD JUMPER	A4	887 TAN
B+	B+	INJECTOR DRIVER	A5	467 DK BLU
		NOT USED	A6	
B+	B+	FUEL PUMP RELAY CONTROL	A7	465 DK GRN/WHT
(1)	(1)	IAC COIL "A" HIGH	A8	441 LT BLU/WHT
(1)	(1)	IAC COIL "A" LOW	A9	442 LT BLU/BLK
(1)	(1)	IAC COIL "B" LOW	A10	444 LT GRN/BLK
(1)	(1)	IAC COIL "B" HIGH	A11	443 LT GRN/WHT
0*	0*	PEAK AND HOLD JUMPER	A12	887 TAN

CIRCUIT	PIN	WIRE COLOR	VOLTAGE KEY "ON"	ENG. RUN	
NOT USED	B1				
NOT USED	B2				
NOT USED	B3				
CTS SIGNAL	B4	410 YEL	2.0	2.0	
TPS SIGNAL	B5	417 DK BLU	.6	.6	
A/C PRESSURE SENSOR SIGNAL	B6	380 GRY/RED	VARIES	VARIES	(3)
MAP SIGNAL	B7	432 LT GRN	4.75	1.6	
IAT SIGNAL	B8	472 TAN	1.3	1.3	
ALDL DIAGNOSTIC TEST	B9	451 WHT/BLK	5.0	5.0	(3)
VSS SIGNAL (HIGH)	B10	400 YEL	VARIES	VARIES	(5)
VSS SIGNAL (LOW)	B11	401 PPL	VARIES	VARIES	(5)
NOT USED	B12				

ENGINE 2.2L LN2

* All voltages shown "0" should read less than .5 volt.
1. Not usable.
2. A/C select "OFF" and engine cooling fan "OFF."
3. Varies depending on temperature.
4. Reads B+ for 2 seconds after ignition "ON," then should read 0 volt.
5. Refer to Section 8A-33.

PORT FUEL INJECTION ECM CONNECTOR IDENTIFICATION

This ECM voltage chart is for use with a digital voltmeter to further aid in diagnosis. The voltages you get may vary due to low battery charge or other reasons, but they should be very close.

THE FOLLOWING CONDITIONS MUST BE MET BEFORE TESTING:
- Engine at operating temperature • Engine idling in "Closed Loop" (For "Engine Run" column) in park or neutral • Test terminal not grounded • "Scan" tool not installed
- B + indicates battery or charging system voltage

32 PIN C-D CONNECTOR
REAR VIEW OF CONNECTOR (PINK)

KEY "ON"	ENG. RUN	CIRCUIT	PIN	WIRE COLOR
0*	0*	ECM GROUND	C1	551 TAN/WHT
		NOT USED	C2	
		NOT USED	C3	
0*	0*	P/N SWITCH	C4	434 ORN/BLK
		NOT USED	C5	
B+	B+	IGNITION FEED	C6	439 PINK/BLK
5.0	5.0	5 V REFERENCE	C7	416 GRY
5.0	5.0	5 V REFERENCE	C8	474 GRY
B+	B+	KEEP ALIVE MEMORY (B.+)	C9	340 ORN
		NOT USED	C10	
0*	0*	TCC (A/T) OR SHIFT LIGHT (M/T)	C11	422 ~TAN/BLK 456
B+	B+	A/C RELAY CONTROL	C12	459 DK ORN/WHT
B+	B+	COOLING FAN RELAY CONTROL	C13	335 DK GRN/WHT
B+	B+	EGR SOLENOID CONTROL	C14	435 GRY
		NOT USED	C15	
		NOT USED	C16	

(2) TCC (A/T) or SHIFT LIGHT (M/T)
(2) A/C RELAY CONTROL

WIRE COLOR	PIN	CIRCUIT	KEY "ON"	ENG. RUN
450 BLK/WHT	D1	ECM GROUND	0*	0*
455 PPL	D2	SENSOR GROUND	0*	0*
452 BLK	D3	SENSOR GROUND	0*	0*
	D4	NOT USED		
423 WHT	D5	EST	0*	2.4
424 TAN/BLK	D6	BYPASS	0*	4.8
490 PPL/WHT	D7	REF HIGH	0*	3.2
453 BLK/RED	D8	REF LOW	0*	0*
66 LT GRN	D9	A/C REQUEST	0*	0*
413 TAN	D10	OXYGEN SENSOR GROUND	0*	0*
412 PPL	D11	OXYGEN SENSOR SIGNAL	.01-.55	.1-.9
461 DK ORN	D12	SERIAL DATA	4.7	4.7
817 DK GRN/WHT	D13	VSS OUTPUT (4000 PPM)	(5)	(5)
419 BRN/WHT	D14	SERVICE ENGINE SOON LIGHT	0*	B+
	D15	NOT USED		
	D16	NOT USED		

(2)

ENGINE 2.2L LN2

* All voltages shown "0" should read less than .5 volt.
1. Not useable.
2. A/C select "OFF" and engine cooling fan "OFF."
3. Varies depending on temperature.
4. Reads B + for 2 seconds after ignition "ON," then should read 0 volt.
5. Varies with vehicle speed. Refer to Section 8A-33.

DIAGNOSTIC CIRCUIT CHECK — 1992 2.2L ENGINE

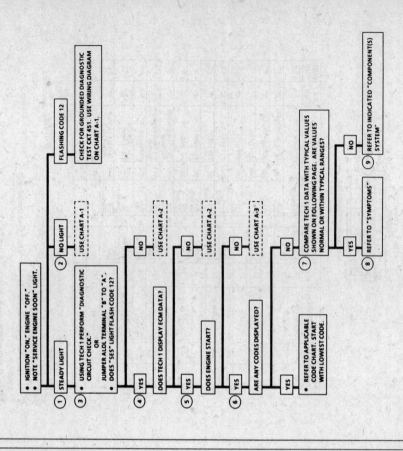

- IGNITION "ON," ENGINE "OFF."
- NOTE "SERVICE ENGINE SOON" LIGHT.

(1) **STEADY LIGHT**

(2) **NO LIGHT** → **FLASHING CODE 12** → USE CHART A-1 / CHECK FOR GROUNDED DIAGNOSTIC TEST CKT 451. USE WIRING DIAGRAM ON CHART A-1.

(3)
- USING TECH 1 PERFORM "DIAGNOSTIC CIRCUIT CHECK."
  OR
- JUMPER ALDL TERMINAL "B" TO "A."
- DOES "SES" LIGHT FLASH CODE 12?

(4) YES / NO → USE CHART A-1

DOES TECH 1 DISPLAY ECM DATA?
(5) YES / NO → USE CHART A-2

DOES ENGINE START?
(6) YES / NO → USE CHART A-2

ARE ANY CODES DISPLAYED?
YES → USE CHART A-3
NO
- REFER TO APPLICABLE CODE CHART. START WITH LOWEST CODE.

(7) COMPARE TECH 1 DATA WITH TYPICAL VALUES SHOWN ON FOLLOWING PAGE. ARE VALUES NORMAL OR WITHIN TYPICAL RANGES?
YES (8) → REFER TO "SYMPTOMS"
NO (9) → REFER TO INDICATED "COMPONENT(S) SYSTEM"

DIAGNOSTIC CIRCUIT CHECK

2.2L (VIN 4) "L" CARLINE (PORT)

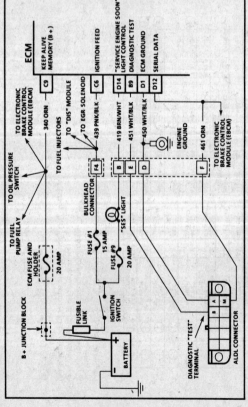

ECM
- KEEP ALIVE MEMORY (B+) — C3
- IGNITION FEED — C6
- "SERVICE ENGINE SOON" LIGHT CONTROL — D14
- DIAGNOSTIC TEST — B9
- ECM GROUND — D1
- SERIAL DATA — D12

B + JUNCTION BLOCK

TO OIL PRESSURE SWITCH
TO FUEL PUMP RELAY
TO ELECTRONIC BRAKE CONTROL MODULE (EBCM)
340 ORN
TO FUEL INJECTORS
TO "DIS" MODULE
TO EGR SOLENOID
439 PNK/BLK
BULKHEAD CONNECTOR — F4 / B / E / D / F
419 BRN/WHT
451 WHT/BLK
450 WHT/BLK
ENGINE GROUND
461 ORN
TO ELECTRONIC BRAKE CONTROL MODULE (EBCM)

ECM FUSE AND HOLDER
20 AMP
FUSE #1
15 AMP
FUSE #9
20 AMP
FUSIBLE LINK
IGNITION SWITCH
BATTERY
"SES" LIGHT
DIAGNOSTIC "TEST" TERMINAL
ALDL CONNECTOR

Circuit Description:

The diagnostic circuit check is an organized approach to identifying a problem created by an electronic engine control system malfunction. It must be the starting point for any driveability complaint diagnosis, because it directs the service technician to the next logical step in diagnosing the complaint. Understanding the chart and using it correctly will reduce diagnostic time and prevent the unnecessary replacement of good parts.

Test Description: Number(s) below refer to circled number(s) on the diagnostic chart.

1. This step is a check for the proper operation of the "Service Engine Soon" light. The "SES" light should be "ON" steady.
2. No "SES" light at this point indicates that there is a problem with the "SES" light circuit or the ECM control of that circuit.
3. This test checks the ability of the ECM to control the "SES" light. With the diagnostic terminal grounded, the "SES" light should flash a Code 12 three times, followed by any trouble code stored in memory. Depending upon the type of ECM, an EEPROM error may result in the inability to flash Code 12.
4. Most of the 6E procedures use a Tech 1 to aid diagnosis, therefore, serial data must be available. If an EEPROM error is present, the ECM may have been able to flash Code 12/51, but not enable serial data.
5. Although the ECM is powered up, a "Cranks But Will Not Run" symptom could exist because of an ECM or system problem.
6. This step will isolate if the customer complaint is a "SES" light or a driveability problem with no "SES" light. Refer to diagnostic code in this section for a list of valid codes. An invalid code may be the result of a faulty "Scan" tool, EEPROM or ECM.
7. Comparison of actual control system data with the typical values is a quick check to determine if any parameter is not within limits. Keep in mind that a base engine problem (i.e. advanced cam timing) may substantially alter sensor values.
8. Installation of a "Scan" tool will provide a good ground path for the ECM and may hide a driveability complaint due to poor ECM grounds.
9. If the actual data is not within the typical values established, the charts in "Symptoms," will provide a functional check of the suspect component or system.

1992 2.2L ENGINE

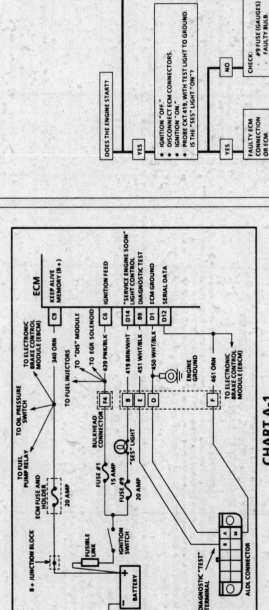

CHART A-1

NO "SERVICE ENGINE SOON" LIGHT
2.2L (VIN 4) "L" CARLINE (PORT)

CHART A-1

NO "SERVICE ENGINE SOON" LIGHT
2.2L (VIN 4) "L" CARLINE (PORT)

Circuit Description:

There should always be a steady "Service Engine Soon" light, when the ignition is "ON" and engine "OFF." Battery voltage is supplied directly to the light bulb. The Electronic Control Module (ECM) will control the light and turn it "ON" by providing a ground path through CKT 419 to the ECM.

Test Description: Number(s) below refer to circled number(s) on the diagnostic chart.

1. Battery feed CKT 340 is protected by a 20 amp fuse next to the B+ junction block.
2. Using a test light connected to B+, probe each of the system ground circuits to be sure a good ground is present. See "ECM Connector Terminal End View" at the beginning of this section for ECM pin locations of ground circuits.

Diagnostic Aids:

If engine runs correctly, check for the following:
- Faulty light bulb.
- CKT 419 open.
- Fuse #9 (Gauges) blown. This will result in no oil or generator lights, seat belt reminder, etc. If "Engine Cranks But Will Not Run," use CHART A-3.

DOES THE ENGINE START?

YES → IS ECM BATTERY FEED CKT 340 AND ECM FUSE OK?

(1)

- YES:
  - IGNITION "OFF."
  - DISCONNECT ECM CONNECTORS.
  - IGNITION "ON."
  - PROBE CKTS 340 & 439 WITH TEST LIGHT TO GROUND.
  - IS THE LIGHT "ON" ON BOTH CIRCUITS?
    - YES → FAULTY ECM GROUNDS OR ECM. (2)
    - NO → LOCATE AND CORRECT SHORT TO GROUND IN CIRCUIT THAT HAD A BLOWN FUSE.

- NO:
  - IGNITION "OFF."
  - DISCONNECT ECM CONNECTORS.
  - IGNITION "ON."
  - PROBE CKT 419, WITH TEST LIGHT TO GROUND.
  - IS THE "SES" LIGHT "ON"?
    - YES → FAULTY ECM CONNECTION OR ECM.
    - NO → CHECK:
      - #9 FUSE (GAUGES)
      - FAULTY BULB.
      - OPEN CKT 419.
      - CKT 419 SHORTED TO VOLTAGE.
      - OPEN IGNITION FEED TO BULB.

YES →
- IGNITION "OFF."
- REPAIR OPEN IN CIRCUIT THAT DID NOT LIGHT THE TEST LIGHT.

(NO branch: REPAIR OPEN IN CIRCUIT THAT DID NOT LIGHT THE TEST LIGHT.)

"AFTER REPAIRS," CONFIRM "CLOSED LOOP" OPERATION AND NO "SERVICE ENGINE SOON" LIGHT.

1992 2.2L ENGINE

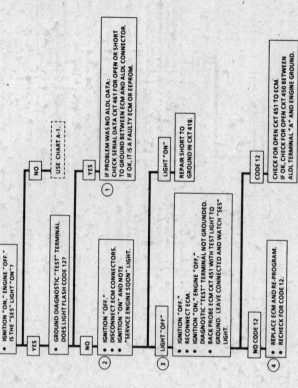

CHART A-2
NO ALDL DATA OR WON'T FLASH CODE 12
"SERVICE ENGINE SOON" LIGHT "ON" STEADY
2.2L (VIN 4) "L" CARLINE (PORT)

- IGNITION "ON," ENGINE "OFF." IS THE "SES" LIGHT "ON"?

  - YES → GROUND DIAGNOSTIC "TEST" TERMINAL. DOES LIGHT FLASH CODE 12?
    - NO → (2) IGNITION "OFF." DISCONNECT ECM CONNECTORS. IGNITION "ON" AND NOTE "SERVICE ENGINE SOON" LIGHT.
      - LIGHT "OFF." → (3) IGNITION "OFF." RECONNECT ECM. IGNITION "ON," ENGINE "OFF." DIAGNOSTIC "TEST" TERMINAL NOT GROUNDED. BACK PROBE ECM CKT 451 WITH TEST LIGHT TO GROUND. LEAVE CONNECTED AND WATCH "SES" LIGHT.
        - NO CODE 12 → (4) REPLACE ECM AND RE-PROGRAM. RECHECK FOR CODE 12.
        - CODE 12 → CHECK FOR OPEN CKT 451 TO ECM. IF OK, CHECK FOR OPEN CKT 450 BETWEEN ALDL TERMINAL "A" AND ENGINE GROUND.
      - LIGHT "ON" → REPAIR SHORT TO GROUND IN CKT 419.
    - YES → (1) IF PROBLEM WAS NO ALDL DATA: CHECK SERIAL DATA CKT 461 FOR OPEN OR SHORT TO GROUND BETWEEN ECM AND ALDL CONNECTOR. IF OK, IT IS A FAULTY ECM OR EEPROM.
  - NO → USE CHART A-1.

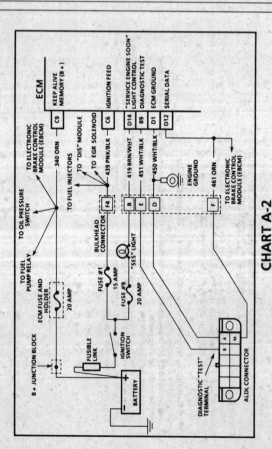

CHART A-2
NO ALDL DATA OR WON'T FLASH CODE 12
"SERVICE ENGINE SOON" LIGHT "ON" STEADY
2.2L (VIN 4) "L" CARLINE (PORT)

Circuit Description:

There should always be a steady "Service Engine Soon" light when the ignition is "ON" and the engine is "OFF." Battery voltage is supplied directly to the light bulb. The Electronic Control Module (ECM) will control the light and turn it "ON" by providing a ground path through CKT 419 to the ECM.

With the diagnostic terminal grounded, the light should flash a Code 12, followed by any trouble code(s) stored in memory. A steady light suggests a short to ground in the light control CKT 419, or an open in diagnostic CKT 451.

Test Description: Number(s) below refer to circled number(s) on the diagnostic chart.

1. If there is a problem with the ECM that causes a "Scan" tool to not read data from the ECM, then the ECM should not flash a Code 12. If Code 12 does flash, be sure that the "Scan" tool is working properly on another vehicle. If the "Scan" is OK, and CKT 461 is functioning properly and CKT 461 may be at fault for the "NO ALDL" symptom.

2. If the light turns "OFF" when the ECM connector is disconnected, then CKT 419 is not shorted to ground.

3. This step will check for an open diagnostic CKT 451.

4. At this point, the "Service Engine Soon" light wiring is OK. The problem is a faulty ECM. If Code 12 does not flash, the ECM should be replaced and reprogrammed. Refer to Electronic Control Module (ECM) and Sensors

1992 2.2L ENGINE

CHART A-3
(Page 1 of 3)
ENGINE CRANKS BUT WON'T RUN
2.2L (VIN 4) "L" CARLINE (PORT)

ECM

C6	IGNITION FEED
A5	INJECTOR DRIVER
A4	PEAK AND HOLD
A12	JUMPER
D8	LOW REFERENCE
D7	HIGH REFERENCE
D6	BYPASS
D5	EST

439 PNK/BLK

INJECTOR JUMPER HARNESS CONNECTOR (GRAY)

467 DK BLU

887 TAN

CRANKSHAFT RELUCTOR

453 BLK/RED
430 PPL/WHT
424 TAN/BLK
423 WHT

CRANKSHAFT SENSOR

450 BLK/WHT

YEL PPL

SHIELD

TO EGR SOLENOID

439 PNK/BLK

439 PNK/BLK

TO IGNITION SWITCH

ECM/FUEL INJECTOR FUSE #1
15 AMP

#1 #2 #3 #4

B+ GND SIGNAL

DIRECT IGNITION SYSTEM (DIS) MODULE

F E D C B A

121 WHT

TO TACHOMETER

COIL ASSEMBLIES

1 4

2 3

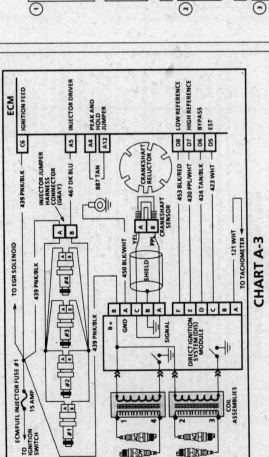

Circuit Description:
Before using this chart, battery condition, engine cranking speed, and fuel quantity should be checked and verified as being OK.

Test Description: Number(s) below refer to circled number(s) on the diagnostic chart.

1. A "Service Engine Soon" light "ON" is a basic test to determine if there is battery and ignition voltage at the ECM.
   - No ALDL data may be the result of an ECM problem, and CHART A-2 will diagnose an ECM problem.
   - If TPS is less than .2 volts, the TPS 5 volt reference circuit could be shorted to ground. If TPS is over 2.5 volts, the ECM could be in the "Clear Flood Mode" which may cause the engine to not start.
   - The "Scan" tool should display rpm during cranking.

2. Because the DIS uses two spark plugs and cables to complete the circuit of each coil, the opposite spark plug cable should be left connected.

3. Nominal resistance of each injector is 11.6 to 12.4 ohms at 20°C (68°F). Resistance will increase slightly at higher temperatures. This test is performed with injectors 1, 2, 3, and 4 in parallel, so measurement will be one forth of the nominal resistance for a single injector.

4. The test light should flash, indicating that the ECM is controlling the injectors. How bright the light flashes is not important.

5. Ignition may have to be cycled "ON" several times to obtain maximum fuel pressure.

6. Damage to the ECM injector driver may occur if any injector resistance measures less than 11.6 ohms (internal short to ignition CKT 439).

Diagnostic Aids:
- Water or contamination in fuel system may cause a no start condition during very cold or freezing weather. The engine may start after approximately 5 minutes in a heated shop.
- An EGR valve sticking open can cause a rich air/fuel ratio during cranking. Unless the ECM enters "Clear Flood Mode" at the first indication of a flooding condition, it may result in a no start condition.
- An A/C pressure sensor with an internal short to ground can cause a no start condition. Disconnect the A/C pressure sensor, if vehicle starts replace faulty sensor.
- A MAP sensor stuck between .5 and 2.5 volts can cause a no start condition. Disconnect the MAP sensor, if vehicle starts replace faulty sensor.

CHART A-3
(Page 1 of 3)
ENGINE CRANKS BUT WON'T RUN
2.2L (VIN 4) "L" CARLINE (PORT)

NOTICE: PFI SYSTEM UNDER PRESSURE. TO AVOID FUEL SPILLAGE, REFER TO FIELD SERVICE PROCEDURES FOR TESTING OR MAKING REPAIRS REQUIRING DISASSEMBLY OF FUEL LINES OR FITTING.

(1) IGNITION "ON." IF "SES" LIGHT IS OFF, USE CHART A-1. INSTALL TECH 1 "SCAN" TOOL. IF NO DATA, USE CHART A-2. CHECK THE FOLLOWING:
- TPS, IF LESS THAN .2 VOLTS OR OVER 2.5 VOLTS AT CLOSED THROTTLE, USE CODE 21 CHART.
- COOLANT, IF BELOW -38° C, USE CODE 14 CHART.
- RPM, IF NO RPM WHILE CRANKING, USE CHART A-3 (PAGE 2 OF 3).

• PROBE FUEL PUMP "TEST" TERMINAL WITH A TEST LIGHT TO B +. IGNITION "OFF" FOR 10 SECONDS. LIGHT SHOULD BE "ON." IGNITION "ON." LIGHT SHOULD GO OUT FOR ABOUT 2 SECONDS AND THEN COME BACK "ON." DOES IT?

→ NO → USE FUEL PUMP RELAY CIRCUIT CHART A-5.

↓ YES

(2) • CRANK ENGINE AND CHECK FOR SPARK WITH ST-125 ON SPARK PLUG CABLES 1 & 2 OR 3 & 4.
• CHECK ONE CABLE AT A TIME. LEAVE THE OTHER CABLES CONNECTED TO PLUGS DURING CRANKING. IS THERE SPARK ON BOTH CABLES?

→ NO → USE CHART A-3 (PAGE 2 OF 3).

↓ YES

(3) • DISCONNECT INJECTOR JUMPER HARNESS AT 2 PIN CONNECTOR. USING DVM MEASURE RESISTANCE BETWEEN CAVITIES "A" AND "B" (INJECTOR SIDE OF HARNESS). RESISTANCE SHOULD BE ABOUT 2.9 TO 3.1 OHMS. IS IT?

→ NO → 3.1 OHMS OR GREATER. → REPAIR OPEN IN HARNESS OR REPLACE ANY INJECTOR(S) THAT MEASURE 12.4 OHMS OR GREATER.

→ NO → 2.9 OHMS OR LESS. → REPAIR SHORT IN HARNESS OR REPLACE ANY INJECTOR(S) THAT MEASURE 11.6 OHMS OR LESS.

↓ YES

(4) • CONNECT INJECTOR TEST LIGHT J34730-28 TO INJECTOR JUMPER HARNESS (ECM SIDE).
• CRANK ENGINE AND OBSERVE TEST LIGHT (SHOULD BLINK). DOES LIGHT BLINK?

→ NO → (6) USE CHART A-3 (PAGE 3 OF 3).

↓ YES

(5) • IGNITION "OFF." INSTALL FUEL PRESSURE GAGE (SEE CHART A-7 PAGE 3 OF 3).
• IGNITION "ON." FUEL PRESSURE SHOULD BE 284-325 kPa (41-47 psi). IS IT?

→ NO → USE CHART A-3 (PAGE 3 OF 3).

↓ YES

USE FUEL SYSTEM DIAGNOSIS CHART A-7.

CHECK FOR FOULED SPARK PLUGS, OR EGR VALVE STUCK OPEN, OR A/C PRESSURE SENSOR SHORTED. SEE "DIAGNOSTICS AIDS" ON FACING PAGE.

1992 2.2L ENGINE

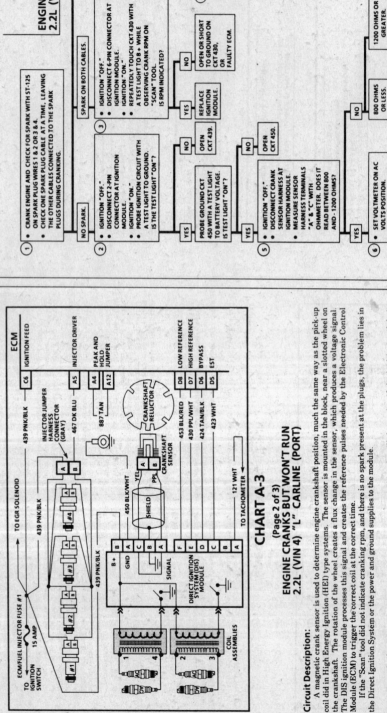

CHART A-3
(Page 2 of 3)
ENGINE CRANKS BUT WON'T RUN
2.2L (VIN 4) "L" CARLINE (PORT)

Circuit Description:

A magnetic crank sensor is used to determine engine crankshaft position, much the same way as the pick-up coil did in High Energy Ignition (HEI) type systems. The sensor is mounted in the block, near a slotted wheel on the crankshaft. The rotation of the wheel creates a flux change in the sensor, which produces a voltage signal. The DIS ignition module processes this signal and creates the reference pulses needed by the Electronic Control Module (ECM) to trigger the correct coil at the correct time.

If the "Scan" tool did not indicate cranking rpm, and there is no spark present at the plugs, the problem lies in the Direct Ignition System or the power and ground supplies to the module.

Test Description: Number(s) below refer to circled number(s) on the diagnostic chart.

1. The Direct Ignition System (DIS) uses two plugs and cables to complete the circuit of each coil. The other spark plug cable in the circuit must be left connected to create a spark.

2. This test will determine if the 12 volt supply and a good ground is available at the DIS module.

3. This test will determine if the ignition module is not generating the reference pulse, or if the wiring or ECM are at fault. By touching and removing a test light to 12 volts on CKT 430, a reference pulse should be generated. If rpm is indicated, the ECM and wiring are OK.

4. This test will determine if the ignition module is not triggering the problem coil, or if the tested coil is at fault. This test could also be performed by substituting a known good coil. The secondary coil winding can be checked with a Digital Voltmeter (DVM). There should be 5,000 to 10,000 ohms across the coil towers. There should not be any continuity from either coil tower to ground.

5. Checks for continuity of the crank sensor and connections.

6. Normal crank sensor voltage output range is .8 to 1.4 volts (800 to 1400 mV) with a fully charged battery and engine at room temperature. Minimum output voltage (slow cranking, low battery) can be as low as .3 volt (300 mV).

1992 2.2L ENGINE

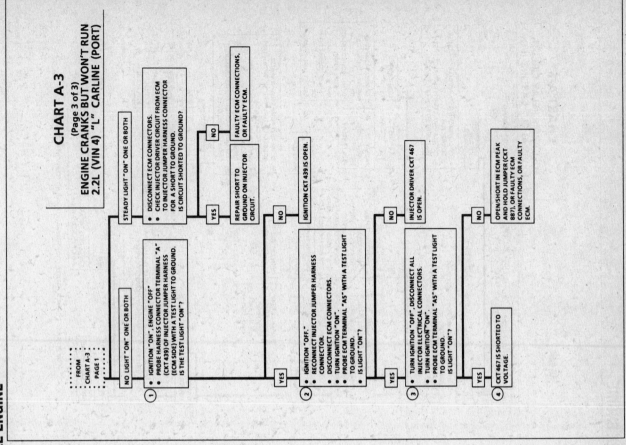

CHART A-3
(Page 3 of 3)
ENGINE CRANKS BUT WON'T RUN
2.2L (VIN 4) "L" CARLINE (PORT)

FROM
CHART A-3
PAGE 1

1 IGNITION "ON", ENGINE "OFF".
• PROBE HARNESS CONNECTOR TERMINAL "A" (CKT 439) OF INJECTOR JUMPER HARNESS (ECM SIDE) WITH A TEST LIGHT TO GROUND. IS THE TEST LIGHT "ON"?

STEADY LIGHT "ON" ONE OR BOTH

• DISCONNECT ECM CONNECTORS.
• CHECK INJECTOR DRIVER CIRCUIT FROM ECM TO INJECTOR JUMPER HARNESS CONNECTOR FOR A SHORT TO GROUND. IS CIRCUIT SHORTED TO GROUND?

NO LIGHT "ON" ONE OR BOTH

NO — FAULTY ECM CONNECTIONS, OR FAULTY ECM.

YES — REPAIR SHORT TO GROUND ON INJECTOR CIRCUIT.

2 IGNITION "OFF."
• RECONNECT INJECTOR JUMPER HARNESS CONNECTOR.
• DISCONNECT ECM CONNECTORS.
• TURN IGNITION "ON".
• PROBE ECM TERMINAL "A5" WITH A TEST LIGHT TO GROUND. IS LIGHT "ON"?

NO — IGNITION CKT 439 IS OPEN.

3 TURN IGNITION "OFF", DISCONNECT ALL INJECTOR ELECTRICAL CONNECTORS.
• TURN IGNITION "ON".
• PROBE ECM TERMINAL "A5" WITH A TEST LIGHT TO GROUND. IS LIGHT "ON"?

NO — INJECTOR DRIVER CKT 467 IS OPEN.

4 CKT 467 IS SHORTED TO VOLTAGE.

NO — OPEN/SHORT IN ECM PEAK AND HOLD JUMPER (CKT 887), OR FAULTY ECM CONNECTIONS, OR FAULTY ECM.

YES
YES
YES

ECM

IGNITION FEED — C6
INJECTOR DRIVER — A5
PEAK AND HOLD JUMPER — A4 TAN, A12
LOW REFERENCE — D8
HIGH REFERENCE — D7
BYPASS — D6
EST — D5

439 PNK/BLK
INJECTOR JUMPER HARNESS CONNECTOR (GRAY)
467 DK BLU
887 TAN
453 BLK/RED
430 PPL/WHT
424 TAN/BLK
423 WHT

TO EGR SOLENOID
439 PNK/BLK
439 PNK/BLK
450 BLK/WHT

CRANKSHAFT RELUCTOR
CRANKSHAFT SENSOR
YEL
PPL
SHIELD

DIRECT IGNITION SYSTEM (DIS) MODULE
B+
GND
SIGNAL

121 WHT — TO TACHOMETER

COIL ASSEMBLIES
1 4
2 3

ECM/FUEL INJECTOR FUSE #1 15 AMP
TO IGNITION SWITCH

#1 #2 #3 #4

CHART A-3
(Page 3 of 3)
ENGINE CRANKS BUT WON'T RUN
2.2L (VIN 4) "L" CARLINE (PORT)

Test Description: Number(s) below refer to circled number(s) on the diagnostic chart.

1. This test checks for ignition voltage at the injector jumper harness connector.

2. Checks for open in CKT 467 from ECM to injector jumper harness connector. The test light has a path to voltage through the injector windings to ignition CKT 439.

3. Checks for short to voltage on CKT 467 from ECM to injectors. Be sure all injectors are disconnected from injector harness connectors.

4. Damage to the ECM injector driver may occur if injector driver CKT 467 shorts to ignition CKT 439.

1992 2.2L ENGINE

CHART A-5
FUEL PUMP RELAY CIRCUIT
2.2L (VIN 4) "L" CARLINE (PORT)

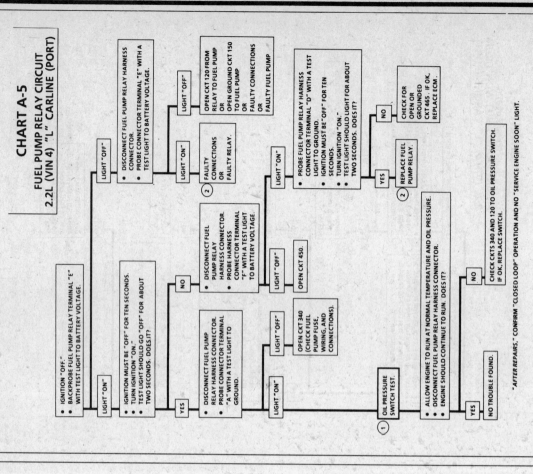

- IGNITION "OFF."
- BACKPROBE FUEL PUMP RELAY TERMINAL "E" WITH TEST LIGHT TO BATTERY VOLTAGE.

LIGHT "OFF"
- DISCONNECT FUEL PUMP RELAY HARNESS CONNECTOR.
- PROBE CONNECTOR TERMINAL "E" WITH A TEST LIGHT TO BATTERY VOLTAGE.

LIGHT "OFF"
- OPEN CKT 120 FROM RELAY TO FUEL PUMP
- OR
- OPEN GROUND CKT 150 TO FUEL PUMP
- OR
- FAULTY CONNECTIONS
- OR
- FAULTY FUEL PUMP

LIGHT "ON"
② FAULTY CONNECTIONS OR FAULTY RELAY.

LIGHT "ON"
- IGNITION MUST BE "OFF" FOR TEN SECONDS.
- TURN IGNITION "ON."
- TEST LIGHT SHOULD GO "OFF" FOR ABOUT TWO SECONDS. DOES IT?

NO
- DISCONNECT FUEL PUMP RELAY HARNESS CONNECTOR. PROBE HARNESS CONNECTOR TERMINAL "E" WITH A TEST LIGHT TO BATTERY VOLTAGE.

LIGHT "OFF" — OPEN CKT 450.

LIGHT "ON"
- DISCONNECT FUEL PUMP RELAY HARNESS CONNECTOR. PROBE CONNECTOR TERMINAL "A" WITH A TEST LIGHT TO GROUND.

LIGHT "OFF" — OPEN CKT 340 (CHECK FUEL PUMP FUSE, WIRING, AND CONNECTIONS).

LIGHT "ON"

YES

LIGHT "ON"
- PROBE FUEL PUMP RELAY HARNESS CONNECTOR TERMINAL "D" WITH A TEST LIGHT TO GROUND.
- IGNITION MUST BE "OFF" FOR TEN SECONDS.
- TURN IGNITION "ON."
- TEST LIGHT SHOULD LIGHT FOR ABOUT TWO SECONDS. DOES IT?

NO — CHECK FOR OPEN OR GROUNDED CKT 465. IF OK, REPLACE ECM.

YES
② REPLACE FUEL PUMP RELAY.

① OIL PRESSURE SWITCH TEST.
- ALLOW ENGINE TO RUN AT NORMAL TEMPERATURE AND OIL PRESSURE.
- DISCONNECT FUEL PUMP RELAY HARNESS CONNECTOR.
- ENGINE SHOULD CONTINUE TO RUN. DOES IT?

NO — CHECK CKTS 340 AND 120 TO OIL PRESSURE SWITCH. IF OK, REPLACE SWITCH.

YES — NO TROUBLE FOUND.

"AFTER REPAIRS," CONFIRM "CLOSED LOOP" OPERATION AND NO "SERVICE ENGINE SOON" LIGHT.

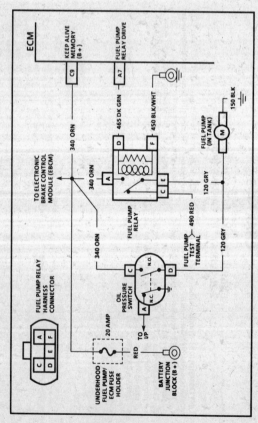

ECM
KEEP ALIVE MEMORY (B+) — C9
FUEL PUMP RELAY DRIVE — A7

340 ORN
340 ORN
340 ORN
465 DK GRN
450 BLK/WHT
490 RED
120 GRY
120 GRY
150 BLK

TO ELECTRONIC BRAKE CONTROL MODULE (EBCM)

FUEL PUMP RELAY

FUEL PUMP RELAY HARNESS CONNECTOR

FUEL PUMP TEST TERMINAL

FUEL PUMP (IN TANK)

OIL PRESSURE SWITCH

UNDERHOOD FUEL PUMP/ ECM FUSE HOLDER

20 AMP

RED — TO I/P

BATTERY JUNCTION BLOCK (B+)

CHART A-5
FUEL PUMP RELAY CIRCUIT
2.2L (VIN 4) "L" CARLINE (PORT)

Circuit Description:

When the ignition switch is turned "ON," the Electronic Control Module (ECM) will activate the fuel pump relay with a 12 volt supply and run the in-tank fuel pump. The fuel pump will operate as long as the engine is cranking or running and the ECM is receiving ignition reference pulses. If there are no ignition reference pulses, the ECM will no longer supply the fuel pump relay signal within 2 seconds after key "ON."

Should the fuel pump relay or the 12 volt relay drive from the ECM fail, the fuel pump will receive supply current through the oil pressure switch back-up circuit.

The fuel pump test terminal is located in the driver's side of the engine compartment. When the engine is stopped, the pump can be turned "ON" by applying battery voltage to the test terminal.

Test Description: Number(s) below refer to circled number(s) on the diagnostic chart.

1. At this point, the fuel pump relay is operating correctly. The back-up circuit through the oil pressure switch is now tested.

2. After the fuel pump relay is replaced, continue with "Oil Pressure Switch Test."

Diagnostic Aids:

An inoperative fuel pump relay can result in long cranking times. The extended crank period is caused by the time necessary for oil pressure to reach the pressure required to close the oil pressure switch and supply the necessary current for the fuel pump.

1992 2.2L ENGINE

CHART A-7
(Page 1 of 3)
FUEL SYSTEM DIAGNOSIS
2.2L (VIN 4) "L" CARLINE (PORT)

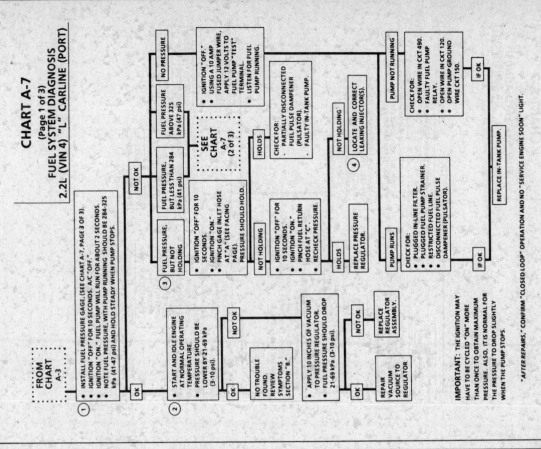

FROM CHART A-3

① INSTALL FUEL PRESSURE GAGE. (SEE CHART A-7, PAGE 3 OF 3).
IGNITION "OFF" FOR 10 SECONDS. A/C "OFF."
IGNITION "ON." FUEL PUMP WILL RUN FOR ABOUT 2 SECONDS.
NOTE FUEL PRESSURE, WITH PUMP RUNNING SHOULD BE 284-325 kPa (41-47 psi) AND HOLD STEADY WHEN PUMP STOPS.

— NOT OK:

FUEL PRESSURE ABOVE 325 kPa (47 psi) → SEE CHART A-7 (2 of 3)

③ FUEL PRESSURE, BUT NOT HOLDING

FUEL PRESSURE, BUT LESS THAN 284 kPa (41 psi):
IGNITION "OFF" FOR 10 SECONDS. IGNITION "ON." PINCH GAGE INLET HOSE AT "A" (SEE FACING PAGE). PRESSURE SHOULD HOLD.
HOLDS → CHECK FOR:
- PARTIALLY DISCONNECTED FUEL PULSE DAMPENER (PULSATOR).
- FAULTY IN-TANK PUMP.
NOT HOLDING:
IGNITION "OFF" FOR 10 SECONDS. IGNITION "ON." PINCH FUEL RETURN HOSE AT "C". RECHECK PRESSURE.
HOLDS → REPLACE PRESSURE REGULATOR.
NOT HOLDING → ④ LOCATE AND CORRECT LEAKING INJECTOR(S).

NO PRESSURE:
IGNITION "OFF." USING A 10 AMP FUSED JUMPER WIRE, APPLY 12 VOLTS TO FUEL PUMP "TEST" TERMINAL. LISTEN FOR FUEL PUMP RUNNING.
PUMP RUNS → CHECK FOR:
• PLUGGED IN-LINE FILTER.
• PLUGGED FUEL PUMP STRAINER.
• RESTRICTED FUEL LINE.
• DISCONNECTED FUEL PULSE DAMPENER (PULSATOR).
IF OK → REPLACE IN-TANK PUMP.
PUMP NOT RUNNING → CHECK FOR:
• OPEN WIRE IN CKT 490.
• FAULTY FUEL PUMP RELAY.
• OPEN WIRE IN CKT 120.
• OPEN PUMP GROUND WIRE CKT 150.
IF OK → ④

— OK:

② START AND IDLE ENGINE AT NORMAL OPERATING TEMPERATURE. PRESSURE SHOULD BE LOWER BY 21-69 kPa (3-10 psi).
OK:
APPLY 10 INCHES OF VACUUM TO PRESSURE REGULATOR. FUEL PRESSURE SHOULD DROP 21-69 kPa (3-10 psi).
OK → REPAIR VACUUM SOURCE TO REGULATOR.
NOT OK → REPLACE REGULATOR ASSEMBLY.
NOT OK → NO TROUBLE FOUND. REVIEW SYMPTOMS SECTION "B."

IMPORTANT: THE IGNITION MAY HAVE TO BE CYCLED "ON" MORE THAN ONCE TO OBTAIN MAXIMUM PRESSURE. ALSO, IT IS NORMAL FOR THE PRESSURE TO DROP SLIGHTLY WHEN THE PUMP STOPS.

"AFTER REPAIRS," CONFIRM "CLOSED LOOP" OPERATION AND NO "SERVICE ENGINE SOON" LIGHT.

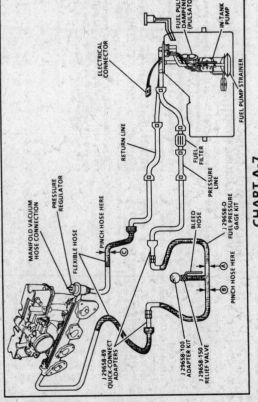

CHART A-7
(Page 1 of 3)
FUEL SYSTEM DIAGNOSIS
2.2L (VIN 4) "L" CARLINE (PORT)

Diagram labels: MANIFOLD VACUUM HOSE CONNECTION — PRESSURE REGULATOR — FLEXIBLE HOSE — PINCH HOSE HERE — RETURN LINE — ELECTRICAL CONNECTOR — FUEL PULSE DAMPENER (PULSATOR) — IN-TANK PUMP — FUEL PUMP STRAINER — FUEL FILTER — PRESSURE LINE — BLEED HOSE — PINCH HOSE HERE — J29658-89 QUICK-CONNECT ADAPTERS — J29658-100 ADAPTER KIT — J29658-150 RELIEF VALVE — J29658-D FUEL PRESSURE GAGE KIT — Ⓐ Ⓑ

Circuit Description:
When the ignition switch is turned "ON," the Electronic Control Module (ECM) will turn "ON" the in-tank fuel pump. It will remain "ON" as long as the engine is cranking or running, and the ECM is receiving reference pulses. If there are no reference pulses, the ECM will shut "OFF" the fuel pump within 2 seconds after ignition "ON" or engine stops.

An electric fuel pump, attached to the fuel sender assembly (inside the fuel tank), pumps fuel through an in-line filter to the fuel passage within the lower manifold assembly. The pump is designed to provide fuel at a pressure above the regulated pressure needed by the injectors. A pressure regulator, attached to the lower manifold assembly, keeps fuel available to the injectors at a regulated pressure. Unused fuel is returned to the fuel tank by a separate line.

Test Description: Number(s) below refer to circled number(s) on the diagnostic chart.
1. Install fuel pressure gage per instructions on page 3 of 3. Ignition "ON" pump pressure should be 284-325 kPa to (41-47 psi). This pressure is controlled by spring pressure within the regulator assembly.
2. When the engine is idling, the manifold pressure is low (high vacuum) and is applied to the fuel regulator diaphragm. This will offset the spring and result in a lower fuel pressure.

This idle pressure will vary somewhat depending on barometric pressure, however, the pressure idling should be less, indicating pressure regulator control.
3. Pressure that continues to fall is caused by one of the following:
• In-tank fuel pump check valve not holding.
• Partially disconnected fuel pulse dampener (pulsator).
• Fuel pressure regulator valve leaking.
• Injector(s) sticking open.
4. An injector sticking open can best be determined by checking for a fouled or saturated spark plug(s).

1992 2.2L ENGINE

CHART A-7
(Page 2 of 3)
FUEL SYSTEM DIAGNOSIS
2.2L (VIN 4) "L" CARLINE (PORT)

FROM CHART A-7 (1 of 3)

① HAS PRESSURE BUT LESS THAN 284 kPa (41 psi)

CHECK FOR RESTRICTED FUEL LINES OR IN-LINE FILTER.

NOT OK → REPLACE FILTER OR REPAIR FUEL LINE AND RECHECK.

OK

② IGNITION "OFF."
• USING A 10 AMP FUSED JUMPER WIRE, APPLY 12 VOLTS TO FUEL PUMP "TEST" TERMINAL.
• GRADUALLY PINCH PRESSURE GAGE OUTLET HOSE AT (B). LOOK FOR PRESSURE ABOVE 325 kPa (47 psi). DO NOT EXCEED 414 kPa (60 psi).

ABOVE 325 kPa (47 psi) → IF LINES ARE OK, REPLACE PRESSURE REGULATOR.

PRESSURE BUT LESS THAN 284 kPa (41 psi)

CHECK FOR:
- FAULTY FUEL PUMP.
- PARTIALLY DISCONNECTED FUEL PULSE DAMPENER (PULSATOR).
- RESTRICTED FUEL PUMP STRAINER.
- INCORRECT FUEL PUMP.

FUEL PRESSURE ABOVE 325 kPa (47 psi)

③ • DISCONNECT ENGINE COMPARTMENT FUEL RETURN LINE QUICK-CONNECT FITTING. (PROCEDURES FOR DISCONNECTING/ CONNECTING QUICK-CONNECT FITTINGS ARE SAME AS THOSE FOR FUEL FEED LINE, SEE PAGE 3 OF 3).
• PLACE OPEN END OF FLEXIBLE HOSE INTO AN APPROVED GASOLINE CONTAINER. NOTE FUEL PRESSURE WITHIN 2 SECONDS AFTER IGNITION IS TURNED "ON."

ABOVE 325 kPa (47 psi) → CHECK FOR RESTRICTED FUEL RETURN LINE FROM FUEL PRESSURE REGULATOR TO POINT WHERE FUEL LINE WAS DISCONNECTED.
IF LINE OK, REPLACE FUEL PRESSURE REGULATOR.

284-325 kPa (41-47 psi) → LOCATE AND CORRECT RESTRICTED FUEL RETURN LINE TO FUEL TANK.

CHART A-7
(Page 2 of 3)
FUEL SYSTEM DIAGNOSIS
2.2L (VIN 4) "L" CARLINE (PORT)

Labels: MANIFOLD VACUUM HOSE CONNECTION, PRESSURE REGULATOR, FLEXIBLE HOSE, PINCH HOSE HERE, ELECTRICAL CONNECTOR, FUEL PULSE DAMPENER (PULSATOR), IN-TANK PUMP, FUEL PUMP STRAINER, RETURN LINE, FUEL FILTER, PRESSURE LINE, BLEED HOSE, J 29658-D FUEL PRESSURE GAGE KIT, PINCH HOSE HERE, J 29658-100 ADAPTER KIT, J 29658-150 RELIEF VALVE, J 29658-89 QUICK-CONNECT ADAPTERS

Test Description: Number(s) below refer to circled number(s) on the diagnostic chart.

1. Pressure below 284 kPa (41 psi) may cause a lean condition and may set a Code 44 or Code 32. It could also cause hard starting cold and poor driveability. Low enough pressure will cause the engine not to run at all. Restricted flow may allow the engine to run at idle, or low speeds, but may cause a surge and stall when more fuel is required, as when accelerating or driving at high speeds.

2. Restricting fuel flow at the fuel pressure gage (at B) causes fuel pressure to build above regulated pressure. With battery voltage applied to the pump "test" terminal, pressure should rise above 325 kPa (47 psi) as the gage outlet hose is restricted.

   NOTICE: Do not allow pressure to exceed 414 kPa (60 psi), as damage to the regulator may result.

3. This test determines if the high fuel pressure is due to a restricted fuel return line, or a faulty fuel pressure regulator. High fuel pressure may cause a rich condition and may set a Code 45.

1992 2.2L ENGINE

CHART A-7
(Page 3 of 3)
FUEL SYSTEM DIAGNOSIS 2.2L (VIN 4) "L" CARLINE (PORT)

FUEL PRESSURE CHECK

Tools Required:
J 29658-D - Fuel Pressure Gage Kit
J 29658-150 - Fuel Pressure Gage Relief Valve
J 29658-100 - TBI Pressure Gage Modification Kit
J 29658-89 - Fuel Pressure Quick Connect Adapters
J 37088 - A - Fuel Line Quick-Connect Separators

CAUTION: To Reduce the Risk of Fire and Personal Injury:
- It is necessary to relieve fuel system pressure before connecting a fuel pressure gage.
- After relieving system pressure, a small amount of fuel may be released when disconnecting the fuel lines. Cover fuel line fittings with a shop towel before disconnecting, to catch any fuel that may leak out. Place towel in approved container when disconnect is completed.
- Do not pinch or restrict nylon fuel lines to avoid severing, which could cause a fuel leak.

NOTICE: If nylon fuel lines become kinked, and cannot be straightened, they must be replaced.

1. Loosen fuel filler cap to relieve fuel tank pressure. (Do not tighten at this time.)
2. Raise vehicle.
3. Disconnect fuel pump electrical connector.
4. Lower vehicle.
5. Start and run engine until fuel supply remaining in fuel pipes is consumed. Engage starter for three seconds to assure relief of any remaining pressure.
6. Disconnect negative battery cable.
7. Locate engine compartment fuel feed quick-connect fitting.
8. Grasp both ends of fitting, twist female end ¼ turn in each direction to loosen any dirt in fitting.

CAUTION: Safety glasses must be worn when using compressed air, as flying dirt particles may cause eye injury.

9. Using compressed air, blow dirt out of quick-connect fitting.
10. Choose correct tool from separator tool set J 37088-A for size of fitting. Insert tool into female end of connector, then push inward to release male connector.
11. If not previously installed, connect Fuel Pressure Gage Relief Valve J 29658-150, to fuel pressure gage hose assembly.
12. Connect 414 kPa (60 psi) gage from TBI Pressure Gage Modification kit J 29658-100 to hose assembly.
13. Connect gage quick-connect adapters J 29658-89 to hose assembly.

CAUTION: To Reduce the Risk of Fire and Personal Injury: Before connecting fuel line quick-connect fittings, always apply a few drops of clean engine oil to the male tube ends. This will ensure proper reconnection and prevent a possible fuel leak. (During normal operation, the O-rings located inside the female connector will swell and may prevent proper reconnection if not lubricated.)

14. Lubricate the male tube end of the fuel line and the gage adapter with engine oil.
15. Connect fuel pressure gage.
    - Push connectors together to cause the retaining tabs/fingers to snap into place.
    - Once installed, pull on both ends of each connection to make sure it is secure.

CHART A-7
(Page 3 of 3)
FUEL SYSTEM DIAGNOSIS
2.2L (VIN 4) "L" CARLINE (PORT)

FUEL PRESSURE CHECK
-continued

16. Connect negative battery cable.
17. Check fuel pressure.
18. Place bleed hose into an approved container and open valve to bleed system pressure.
19. Disconnect negative battery cable.
20. Disconnect fuel pressure gage.
21. Lubricate the male tube end of the fuel line, and reconnect quick-connect fitting.
    - Push connector together to cause the retaining tabs/fingers to snap into place.
    - Once installed, pull on both ends of connection to make sure it is secure.
22. Tighten fuel filler cap.
23. Connect negative battery cable.
24. Cycle ignition "ON" and "OFF" twice, waiting ten seconds between cycles, then check for fuel leaks.

1992 2.2L ENGINE

CODE 13
OXYGEN (O₂) SENSOR CIRCUIT
(OPEN CIRCUIT)
2.2L (VIN 4) "L" CARLINE (PORT)

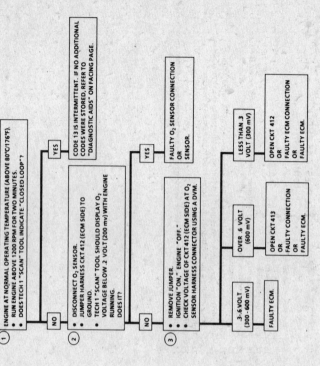

ECM

D11 — O₂ SENSOR SIGNAL — 412 PPL
D10 — O₂ SENSOR GROUND — 413 TAN
C1 — ECM GROUND — 551 TAN/WHT

OXYGEN (O₂) SENSOR
EXHAUST
REAR ENGINE/TRANS GROUND

CODE 13
OXYGEN (O₂) SENSOR CIRCUIT
(OPEN CIRCUIT)
2.2L (VIN 4) "L" CARLINE (PORT)

Circuit Description:

The Electronic Control Module (ECM) supplies a voltage of about .45 volt between terminals "D10" and "D11". (If measured with a 10 megohm digital voltmeter, this may read as low as .32 volt.) When the O₂ sensor reaches operating temperature, it varies this voltage from about .1 volt (exhaust is lean) to about .9 volt (exhaust is rich).

The sensor is like an open circuit and produces no voltage when it is below 316°C (600°F). An open sensor circuit, or cold sensor, causes "Open Loop" operation.

Test Description: Number(s) below refer to circled number(s) on the diagnostic chart.

1. Code 13 will set under the following conditions:
   - Engine at normal operating temperature.
   - At least 2 minutes has elapsed since engine start-up.
   - O₂ signal voltage is steady between 35 and .55 volt.
   - Throttle angle is above 5%.
   - All above conditions are met for 40.3 seconds or more.

   If the conditions for a Code 13 exist, the system will not operate in "Closed Loop."

2. This test determines if the Oxygen (O₂) sensor is the problem or if the ECM and wiring are at fault.

3. In doing this test, use only a 10 megohm digital voltmeter. This test checks the continuity of CKT 412 and CKT 413. If CKT 413 is open, the ECM voltage on CKT 412 will be over .6 volt (600 mV).

Diagnostic Aids:

Normal Tech 1 "Scan" tool O₂ sensor voltage varies between 100 mV to 999 mV (.1 and 1.0 volt) while in "Closed Loop." Code 13 sets in about 40 seconds if sensor signal voltage remains between .35 and .55 volt, but the system will go to "Open Loop" in about 15 seconds.

Verify a clean, tight ground connection for CKT 413. Open CKT 412 or CKT 413 will result in a Code 13. If Code 13 is intermittent, refer to "Symptoms,"

1992 2.2L ENGINE

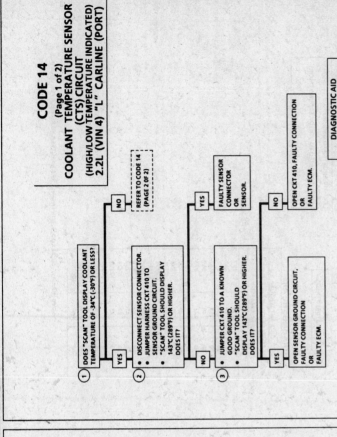

CODE 14
(Page 1 of 2)
COOLANT TEMPERATURE SENSOR (CTS) CIRCUIT
(HIGH/LOW TEMPERATURE INDICATED)
2.2L (VIN 4) "L" CARLINE (PORT)

Circuit Description:

The Coolant Temperature Sensor (CTS) utilizes a thermistor to control the signal voltage to the Electronic Control Module (ECM). The ECM applies a reference voltage on CKT 410 to the sensor. When the engine is cold, the sensor (thermistor) resistance is high. The ECM will then sense a high signal voltage. As the engine warms up, the sensor resistance decreases and the voltage drops. At normal engine operating temperature, the voltage will measure about 1.5 to 2.0 volts at ECM terminal "B4".

Coolant temperature is one of the inputs used to control the following:
- Cooling Fan.
- Fuel Delivery.
- Electronic Spark Timing (EST).
- Idle Air Control (IAC).
- Torque Converter Clutch (TCC).

A second thermistor within the CTS provides a signal to the coolant temperature gage located in the instrument panel.

Test Description: Number(s) below refer to circled number(s) on the diagnostic chart.

1. Code 14 will set if:
   - The engine has been running for 2 minutes.
   - Signal voltage indicates a coolant temperature below -34°C (-30°F).
   OR
   - Signal voltage indicates a coolant temperature above 130°C (275°F) for 3 seconds.
2. If the ECM recognizes the grounded circuit (low voltage) and displays a high temperature, the ECM and wiring are O.K.
3. This test will determine if there is a wiring problem or a faulty ECM. If CKT 455 is open, there may also be other codes stored.

Diagnostic Aids:

The Tech 1 "Scan" tool reads engine temperature in degrees Celsius.

After the engine is started, the temperature should rise steadily to about 90°C (194°F), then stabilize when the thermostat opens.

If the engine has been allowed to cool to an ambient temperature (overnight), coolant temperature and Intake Air Temperature (IAT) may be checked with a "Scan" tool and should read close to each other.

When a Code 14 is set, the ECM will turn "ON" the engine cooling fan.

If Code 14 is intermittent refer to "Symptoms."

Diagnostic flow chart:

1. DOES "SCAN" TOOL DISPLAY COOLANT TEMPERATURE OF -34°C (-30°F) OR LESS?
   - NO → REFER TO CODE 14 (PAGE 2 OF 2)
   - YES →

2. DISCONNECT SENSOR CONNECTOR. JUMPER HARNESS CKT 410 TO SENSOR GROUND CIRCUIT. "SCAN" TOOL SHOULD DISPLAY 143°C (289°F) OR HIGHER. DOES IT?
   - YES → FAULTY SENSOR CONNECTOR OR SENSOR.
   - NO →

3. JUMPER CKT 410 TO A KNOWN GOOD GROUND. "SCAN" TOOL SHOULD DISPLAY 143°C (289°F) OR HIGHER. DOES IT?
   - NO → OPEN CKT 410, FAULTY CONNECTION OR FAULTY ECM.
   - YES → OPEN SENSOR GROUND CIRCUIT, FAULTY CONNECTION OR FAULTY ECM.

DIAGNOSTIC AID
COOLANT SENSOR
TEMPERATURE VS. RESISTANCE VALUES (APPROXIMATE)

°C	°F	OHMS
100	212	177
90	194	241
80	176	332
70	158	467
60	140	667
50	122	973
45	113	1188
40	104	1459
35	95	1802
30	86	2238
25	77	2796
20	68	3520
15	59	4450
10	50	5670
5	41	7280
0	32	9420
-5	23	12300
-10	14	16180
-15	5	21450
-20	-4	28680
-30	-22	52700
-40	-40	100700

"AFTER REPAIRS," REFER TO CODE CRITERIA ON FACING PAGE AND CONFIRM CODE DOES NOT RESET.

1992 2.2L ENGINE

CODE 14
(Page 2 of 2)
COOLANT TEMPERATURE SENSOR (CTS) CIRCUIT
(HIGH/LOW TEMPERATURE INDICATED)
2.2L (VIN 4) "L" CARLINE (PORT)

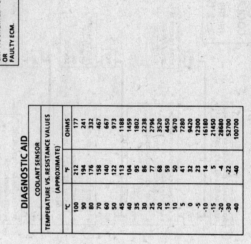

FROM CODE 14 PAGE 1 OF 2

(1) DOES "SCAN" TOOL DISPLAY COOLANT TEMPERATURE OF 143°C (289°F) OR HIGHER?

- **NO** → • CODE 14 IS INTERMITTENT. IF NO ADDITIONAL CODES WERE STORED, REFER TO "DIAGNOSTIC AIDS" ON FACING PAGE.
- **YES** → (2) • DISCONNECT SENSOR CONNECTOR. "SCAN" TOOL SHOULD DISPLAY TEMPERATURE BELOW -34°C (-30°F). DOES IT?
  - **NO** → CKT 410 SHORTED TO GROUND, OR CKT 410 SHORTED TO SENSOR GROUND CIRCUIT OR FAULTY ECM.
  - **YES** → REPLACE COOLANT TEMPERATURE SENSOR.

DIAGNOSTIC AID

COOLANT SENSOR
TEMPERATURE VS. RESISTANCE VALUES
(APPROXIMATE)

°C	°F	OHMS
100	212	177
90	194	241
80	176	332
70	158	467
60	140	667
50	122	973
45	113	1188
40	104	1459
35	95	1802
30	86	2238
25	77	2796
20	68	3520
15	59	4450
10	50	5670
5	41	7280
0	32	9420
-5	23	12300
-10	14	16180
-15	5	21450
-20	-4	28680
-30	-22	52700
-40	-40	100700

"AFTER REPAIRS," CLEAR CODES," RUN ENGINE FOR 5 MINUTES AND RECHECK FOR CODES.

ECM — CTS SIGNAL — 5 VOLT REFERENCE — SENSOR GROUND — B4 — D2 — 410 YEL — 455 PPL — TO A/C PRESSURE SENSOR — TO MAP SENSOR — COOLANT TEMPERATURE SENSOR (CTS) — B A C D — 35 DK GRN — TO COOLANT TEMPERATURE LIGHT — 635 DK GRN/WHT — TO COOLANT TEMP GAGE — CTS CONNECTOR (FRONT VIEW)

CODE 14
(Page 2 of 2)
COOLANT TEMPERATURE SENSOR (CTS) CIRCUIT
(HIGH/LOW TEMPERATURE INDICATED)
2.2L (VIN 4) "L" CARLINE (PORT)

Circuit Description:

The Coolant Temperature Sensor (CTS) utilizes a thermistor to control the signal voltage to the Electronic Control Module (ECM). The ECM applies a reference voltage on CKT 410 to the sensor. When the engine is cold, the sensor (thermistor) resistance is high. The ECM will then sense a high signal voltage.

As the engine warms up, the sensor resistance decreases and the voltage drops. At normal engine operating temperature, the voltage will measure about 1.5 to 2.0 volts at ECM terminal "B4."

Coolant temperature is one of the inputs used to control the following:
- Fuel delivery.
- Electronic Spark Timing (EST).
- Cooling fan.
- Torque Converter Clutch (TCC).
- Idle Air Control (IAC).

Test Description: Number(s) below refer to circled number(s) on the diagnostic chart.

1. Checks to see if code was set as a result of hard failure or intermittent condition.
2. If the ECM recognizes the open circuit (high voltage), and displays a low temperature, the ECM and wiring are OK.

Diagnostic Aids:

The Tech 1 "Scan" tool reads engine temperature in degrees Celsius.

After the engine is started, the temperature should rise steadily to about 90°C (194°F), then stabilize when the thermostat opens.

If the engine has been allowed to cool to an ambient temperature (overnight), coolant temperature and Intake Air Temperature (IAT) may be checked with a "Scan" tool and should read close to each other.

When a Code 14 is set, the ECM will turn "ON" the engine cooling fan.

If Code 14 is intermittent, refer to "Symptoms."

1992 2.2L ENGINE

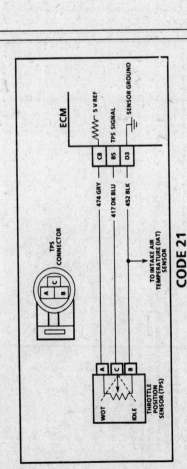

CODE 21
(Page 1 of 2)

THROTTLE POSITION SENSOR (TPS) CIRCUIT
(SIGNAL VOLTAGE HIGH/LOW)
2.2L (VIN 4) "L" CARLINE (PORT)

Circuit Description:

The Throttle Position Sensor (TPS) provides a voltage signal that changes relative to the throttle valve. Signal voltage will vary from .33 to 1.33 volts at idle to about 4.5 volts at Wide Open Throttle (WOT).

The TPS signal is one of the most important inputs used by the Electronic Control Module (ECM) for fuel control and for many of the ECM controlled outputs.

Test Description: Number(s) below refer to circled number(s) on the diagnostic chart.

1. A Code 21 will set under the following conditions:
   - TPS reading above 3.9 volts.
   - MAP reading below 65 kPa.
   - Engine speed less than 1,750 rpm.
   - All of the above conditions present for 5 seconds.

   OR

   - TPS reading below 1.9 volts for 64 seconds. The TPS has an auto zeroing feature. If the voltage reading is within the range of about .33 to 1.33 volts, the ECM will use that value as closed throttle. If the voltage reading is outside of the auto zero range at closed throttle, check for a binding throttle cable or damaged linkage. If OK, continue with diagnosis.

2. If the ECM recognizes the change of state, the ECM and CKTs 474 and 417 are OK.

3. This step isolates a faulty sensor, ECM, or an open CKT 452. If CKT 452 is open, there may also be other codes stored.

Diagnostic Aids:

A "Scan" tool displays throttle position in volts. Closed throttle voltage should be .33 to 1.33 volts. TPS voltage should increase at a steady rate as throttle is moved to WOT.

If Code 21 is intermittent, refer to "Symptoms."

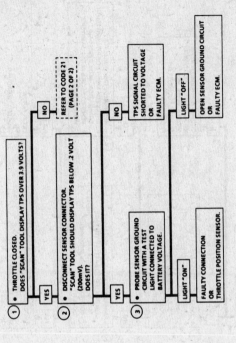

CODE 21
(Page 1 of 2)

THROTTLE POSITION SENSOR (TPS) CIRCUIT
(SIGNAL VOLTAGE HIGH/LOW)
2.2L (VIN 4) "L" CARLINE (PORT)

1. THROTTLE CLOSED.
   DOES "SCAN" TOOL DISPLAY TPS OVER 3.9 VOLTS?

   YES → 2. DISCONNECT SENSOR CONNECTOR.
   "SCAN" TOOL SHOULD DISPLAY TPS BELOW .2 VOLT (200mV).
   DOES IT?

   NO → REFER TO CODE 21 (PAGE 2 OF 2)

   YES → 3. PROBE SENSOR GROUND CIRCUIT WITH A TEST LIGHT CONNECTED TO BATTERY VOLTAGE.

   NO → TPS SIGNAL CIRCUIT SHORTED TO VOLTAGE OR FAULTY ECM.

   LIGHT "ON" → FAULTY CONNECTION OR THROTTLE POSITION SENSOR.

   LIGHT "OFF" → OPEN SENSOR GROUND CIRCUIT OR FAULTY ECM.

1992 2.2L ENGINE

CODE 21
(Page 2 of 2)
THROTTLE POSITION SENSOR (TPS) CIRCUIT
(SIGNAL VOLTAGE HIGH/LOW)
2.2L (VIN 4) "L" CARLINE (PORT)

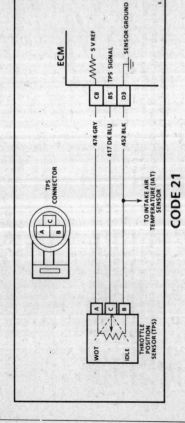

ECM
- C8 — 5 V REF
- B5 — TPS SIGNAL
- D3 — SENSOR GROUND

474 GRY
417 DK BLU
452 BLK

TO INTAKE AIR TEMPERATURE (IAT) SENSOR

TPS CONNECTOR

THROTTLE POSITION SENSOR (TPS)

WOT / IDLE

Diagnostic Chart (from Code 21, Page 1 of 2):

FROM CODE 21 (PAGE 1 of 2).

1. THROTTLE CLOSED. DOES "SCAN" TOOL DISPLAY LESS THAN .19 VOLTS?
   - NO → CODE 21 IS INTERMITTENT. IF NO ADDITIONAL CODES WERE STORED, REFER TO "DIAGNOSTIC AIDS" ON FACING PAGE.
   - YES ↓

2. DISCONNECT TPS SENSOR CONNECTOR. JUMPER 5 VOLT REFERENCE CIRCUIT AND CKT 417 TOGETHER. "SCAN" TOOL SHOULD DISPLAY THROTTLE POSITION OVER 4.0 V (4000 mV). DOES IT?
   - YES → RECONNECT TPS CONNECTOR. CHECK FOR FAULTY OR INTERMITTENT CONNECTION. IF OK, TPS IS FAULTY. REFER TO FACING PAGE FOR SPECIFIC INSTRUCTIONS. (4)
   - NO ↓

3. PROBE CKT 417 WITH A TEST LIGHT CONNECTED TO BATTERY VOLTAGE. "SCAN" TOOL SHOULD DISPLAY THROTTLE POSITION OVER 4.0V (4000 mV). DOES IT?
   - YES → 5 VOLT REFERENCE CIRCUIT OPEN OR SHORTED TO GROUND OR FAULTY CONNECTION OR FAULTY ECM.
   - NO → CKT 417 OPEN OR SHORTED TO GROUND OR SHORTED TO THROTTLE POSITION SENSOR GROUND CIRCUIT OR FAULTY ECM CONNECTION OR FAULTY ECM.

Circuit Description:

The Throttle Position Sensor (TPS) provides a voltage signal that changes relative to the throttle valve. Signal voltage will vary from .33 to 1.33 volts at idle to about 4.5 volts at Wide Open Throttle (WOT).

The TPS signal is one of the most important inputs used by the Electronic Control Module (ECM) for fuel control and for many of the ECM controlled outputs.

Test Description: Number(s) below refer to circled number(s) on the diagnostic chart.

1. This step checks to see if Code 21 is the result of a hard failure or an intermittent condition.

2. This step simulates conditions for a Code 21. If the "Scan" tool displays over 4 volts, the ECM and wiring are OK.

3. This simulates a high signal voltage to check for an open or short in CKT 417. The Tech 1 "Scan" tool will not read battery voltage, but the ECM should recognize the signal on CKT 417.

4. See "Fuel Metering System," Section TPS replacement procedures.

Diagnostic Aids:

A "Scan" tool displays throttle position in volts. Closed throttle voltage should be .33 to 1.33 volts. TPS voltage should increase at a steady rate as throttle is moved to WOT.

If Code 21 is intermittent, refer to "Symptoms,"

1992 2.2L ENGINE

CODE 23
(Page 1 of 2)
INTAKE AIR TEMPERATURE (IAT) SENSOR CIRCUIT
(HIGH/LOW TEMPERATURE INDICATED)
2.2L (VIN 4) "L" CARLINE (PORT)

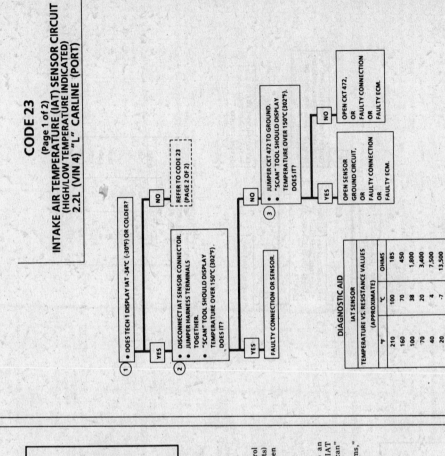

CODE 23
(Page 1 of 2)
INTAKE AIR TEMPERATURE (IAT) SENSOR CIRCUIT
(HIGH/LOW TEMPERATURE INDICATED)
2.2L (VIN 4) "L" CARLINE (PORT)

Circuit Description:

The Intake Air Temperature (IAT) sensor, located in the air cleaner assembly, uses a thermistor to control the signal voltage to the Electronic Control Module (ECM). The ECM applies a reference voltage (4 to 5.5 volts) on CKT 472 to the sensor. When intake air is cold, the sensor (thermistor) resistance is high. The ECM will then sense a high signal voltage. As the air warms, the sensor resistance becomes less and the voltage drops.

Test Description: Number(s) below refer to circled number(s) on the diagnostic chart.

1. A Code 23 will set under the following conditions:
   - Engine running for 2 minutes or longer.
   - Signal voltage indicates an IAT temperature less than -34°C (-30°F).

   OR
   - Signal voltage indicates an IAT temperature greater than 150°C (302°F) for more than 2 seconds.

2. This test simulates conditions for a Code 23. If the "Scan" tool displays a high temperature, the ECM and wiring are OK.

3. This step checks continuity of CKT 472 and CKT 452. If CKT 452 is open, there may be other codes stored.

Diagnostic Aids:

If the engine has been allowed to cool to an ambient temperature (overnight), coolant and IAT temperatures may be checked with a Tech 1 "Scan" tool and should read close to each other.

If Code 23 is intermittent, refer to "Symptoms."

DIAGNOSTIC AID

IAT SENSOR TEMPERATURE VS. RESISTANCE VALUES (APPROXIMATE)		
°F	°C	OHMS
210	100	185
160	70	450
100	38	1,800
70	20	3,400
40	4	7,500
20	-7	13,500
0	-18	25,000
-40	-40	100,700

1992 2.2L ENGINE

CODE 23
(Page 2 of 2)
INTAKE AIR TEMPERATURE (IAT) SENSOR CIRCUIT
(HIGH/LOW TEMPERATURE INDICATED)
2.2L (VIN 4) "L" CARLINE (PORT)

FROM CODE 23 PAGE 1 OF 2

(1) DOES "SCAN" TOOL DISPLAY IAT OF 150°C (302°F) OR HOTTER?

YES → (2) DISCONNECT IAT SENSOR CONNECTOR. "SCAN" TOOL SHOULD DISPLAY TEMPERATURE BELOW -34°C (-30°F). DOES IT?

NO → CODE 23 IS INTERMITTENT. IF NO ADDITIONAL CODES WERE STORED, REFER TO "DIAGNOSTIC AIDS" ON FACING PAGE.

YES → REPLACE IAT SENSOR.

NO → CKT 472 SHORTED TO GROUND, OR TO SENSOR GROUND, OR ECM IS FAULTY.

DIAGNOSTIC AID

IAT SENSOR
TEMPERATURE VS. RESISTANCE VALUES
(APPROXIMATE)

°F	°C	OHMS
210	100	185
160	70	450
100	38	1,800
70	20	3,400
40	4	7,500
20	-7	13,500
0	-18	25,000
-40	-40	100,700

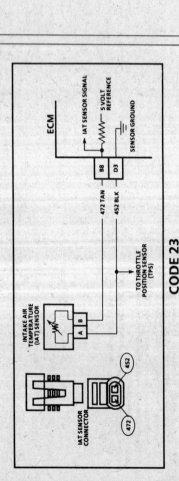

CODE 23
(Page 2 of 2)
INTAKE AIR TEMPERATURE (IAT) SENSOR CIRCUIT
(HIGH/LOW TEMPERATURE INDICATED)
2.2L (VIN 4) "L" CARLINE (PORT)

Circuit Description:

The Intake Air Temperature (IAT) sensor, located in the air cleaner assembly, uses a thermistor to control the signal voltage to the Electronic Control Module (ECM). The ECM applies a reference voltage (4 to 5.5 volts) on CKT 472 to the sensor. When intake air is cold, the sensor (thermistor) resistance is high. Therefore, the ECM will sense a high signal voltage. As the air warms, the sensor resistance becomes less and the voltage drops.

Test Description: Number(s) below refer to circled number(s) on the diagnostic chart.

1. This step determines if Code 23 is the result of a hard failure or an intermittent condition.
2. If the ECM recognizes the open circuit (high voltage) and displays a low temperature, the ECM and wiring are OK.

Diagnostic Aids:

If the engine has been allowed to cool to an ambient temperature (overnight), coolant and IAT temperatures may be checked with a "Scan" tool and should read close to each other.

If Code 23 is intermittent, refer to "Symptoms."

1992 2.2L ENGINE

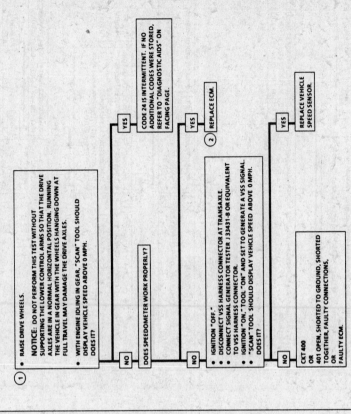

CODE 24

VEHICLE SPEED SENSOR (VSS) CIRCUIT
2.2L (VIN 4) "L" CARLINE (PORT)

Circuit Description:

Vehicle speed information is provided to the Electronic Control Module (ECM) by the Vehicle Speed Sensor (VSS), which is a Permanent Magnet (PM) generator, and it is mounted in the transaxle. The PM generator produces a pulsing voltage, whenever vehicle speed is over about 3 mph. The AC voltage level and the number of pulses increases with vehicle speed. The ECM then converts the pulsing voltage to mph, which is used for calculations, and the mph can be displayed with a "Scan" tool.

The function of VSS buffer used in past model years has been incorporated into the ECM. The ECM then supplies the necessary signal to the instrument panel (4000 pulses per mile) for operating the speedometer and the odometer.

Test Description: Number(s) below refer to circled number(s) on the diagnostic chart.

1. Code 24 will set if vehicle speed equals 0 mph when:
   - Engine speed is between 1400 and 3600 rpm.
   - Low load condition (low MAP voltage), high manifold vacuum).
   - Transaxle not in park or neutral.
   - All above conditions are met for 4 seconds.

   These conditions are met during a road load deceleration.

   Disregard a Code 24 that sets when the drive wheels are not turning. This can be caused by a faulty park/neutral switch circuit.

   The PM generator only produces a signal if the drive wheels are turning greater than 3 mph.

2. At this point, the ECM is not sending vehicle speed data to the "Scan" tool. If the "Scan" tool is connected and functioning properly, the ECM is at fault.

Diagnostic Aids:

"Scan" tool should indicate a vehicle speed whenever the drive wheels are turning greater than 3 mph.

A problem in CKT 817 will not affect the VSS input or the readings on a "Scan" tool.

Check CKTs 400 and 401 for proper connections to be sure they are clean and tight and the harness is routed correctly. Refer to "Intermittents" in "Symptoms."

(A/T) - A faulty or misadjusted Park/Neutral (P/N) switch can result in a false Code 24. Use a "Scan" tool and check for the proper signal while in a drive range. Refer to CHART C-1A for the P/N switch check.

1992 2.2L ENGINE

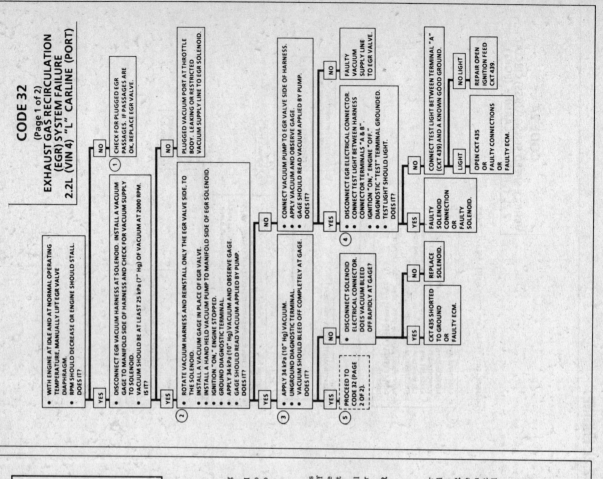

CODE 32

(Page 1 of 2)

EXHAUST GAS RECIRCULATION
(EGR) SYSTEM FAILURE
2.2L (VIN 4) "L" CARLINE (PORT)

① CHECK FOR PLUGGED EGR PASSAGES. IF PASSAGES ARE OK, REPLACE EGR VALVE.

- WITH ENGINE AT IDLE AND AT NORMAL OPERATING TEMPERATURE, MANUALLY LIFT EGR VALVE DIAPHRAGM.
- RPM SHOULD DECREASE OR ENGINE SHOULD STALL. DOES IT?

NO → CHECK FOR PLUGGED EGR PASSAGES. IF PASSAGES ARE OK, REPLACE EGR VALVE.

YES

- DISCONNECT EGR VACUUM HARNESS AT SOLENOID. INSTALL A VACUUM GAGE TO MANIFOLD SIDE OF HARNESS AND CHECK FOR VACUUM SUPPLY TO SOLENOID.
- VACUUM SHOULD BE AT LEAST 25 kPa (7" Hg) OF VACUUM AT 2000 RPM. IS IT?

NO → PLUGGED VACUUM PORT AT THROTTLE BODY, LEAKING OR RESTRICTED VACUUM SUPPLY LINE TO EGR SOLENOID.

②
- ROTATE VACUUM HARNESS AND REINSTALL ONLY THE EGR VALVE SIDE TO THE SOLENOID.
- INSTALL A VACUUM GAGE IN PLACE OF EGR VALVE.
- INSTALL A HAND HELD VACUUM PUMP TO MANIFOLD SIDE OF EGR SOLENOID.
- IGNITION "ON," ENGINE STOPPED.
- GROUND DIAGNOSTIC TERMINAL.
- APPLY 34 kPa (10" Hg) VACUUM AND OBSERVE GAGE. GAGE SHOULD READ VACUUM APPLIED BY PUMP. DOES IT?

③
- APPLY 34 kPa (10" Hg) VACUUM.
- UNGROUND DIAGNOSTIC TERMINAL.
- VACUUM SHOULD BLEED OFF COMPLETELY AT GAGE. DOES IT?

YES →
- CONNECT VACUUM PUMP TO EGR VALVE SIDE OF HARNESS.
- APPLY VACUUM AND OBSERVE GAGE.
- GAGE SHOULD READ VACUUM APPLIED BY PUMP. DOES IT?

NO → FAULTY VACUUM SUPPLY LINE TO EGR VALVE.

YES →
- DISCONNECT EGR ELECTRICAL CONNECTOR.
- CONNECT TEST LIGHT BETWEEN HARNESS CONNECTOR TERMINALS "A & B."
- IGNITION "ON," ENGINE "OFF."
- DIAGNOSTIC "TEST" TERMINAL GROUNDED.
- TEST LIGHT SHOULD LIGHT. DOES IT?

④

NO → CONNECT TEST LIGHT BETWEEN TERMINAL "A" (CKT 439) AND A KNOWN GOOD GROUND.

LIGHT → REPAIR OPEN IGNITION FEED CKT 439.

NO LIGHT → OPEN CKT 435 OR FAULTY CONNECTIONS OR FAULTY ECM.

YES → FAULTY SOLENOID CONNECTION OR FAULTY SOLENOID.

NO →
- DISCONNECT SOLENOID ELECTRICAL CONNECTOR.
- DOES VACUUM BLEED OFF RAPIDLY AT GAGE?

YES → REPLACE SOLENOID.

NO → CKT 435 SHORTED TO GROUND OR FAULTY ECM.

⑤ PROCEED TO CODE 32 (PAGE 2 OF 2).

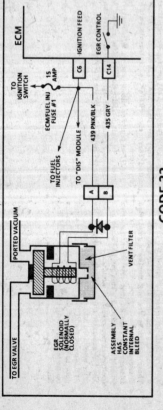

```
TO EGR VALVE
PORTED VACUUM
EGR SOLENOID (NORMALLY CLOSED)
VENT FILTER
ASSEMBLY HAS CONSTANT INTERNAL BLEED

ECM
IGNITION FEED    C6
EGR CONTROL      C14
TO IGNITION SWITCH
15 AMP
ECM/FUEL INJ FUSE #1
TO FUEL INJECTORS
TO "DIS" MODULE
439 PNK/BLK
435 GRY
A    B
```

CODE 32

(Page 1 of 2)

EXHAUST GAS RECIRCULATION (EGR) SYSTEM FAILURE
2.2L (VIN 4) "L" CARLINE (PORT)

Circuit Description:

The Exhaust Gas Recirculation (EGR) system is controlled by the ECM. The ECM controls the vacuum being supplied to the valve by energizing and de-energizing a solenoid.

The ECM uses information from various engine sensors to determine when EGR is necessary. Once the ECM has requested EGR by grounding the solenoid circuit, the ECM will monitor engine operating conditions to determine if exhaust gas flow has entered the intake manifold. When the ECM tests for EGR operation and no change in engine operating conditions is indicated, a Code 32 will set.

Test Description: Number(s) below refer to circled number(s) on the diagnostic chart.

1. Intake Passage: Shut "OFF" engine and remove the EGR valve from the manifold. Plug the exhaust side hole with a suitable stopper. Leaving the intake side hole open, attempt to start the engine. If the engine runs at a high idle (up to 3000 rpm is possible) or starts and stalls, the EGR intake passage is not restricted. If the engine starts and idles normally, the EGR intake passage is restricted.

2. By grounding the diagnostic "test" terminal, the EGR solenoid should be energized and allow vacuum to be applied to the gage. The vacuum at the gage may or may not slowly bleed off. It is important that the gage is able to read the amount of vacuum being applied.

3. When the diagnostic "test" terminal is ungrounded, the vacuum gage should bleed off completely through a vent in the solenoid. The vacuum pump gage may or may not bleed off but this does not indicate a problem.

4. This test will determine if the electrical control part of the system is at fault or if the connector or solenoid is at fault.

5. At this point, it has been determined that the EGR solenoid, and the ECM and the vacuum supply are OK.

Diagnostic Aids:

Vacuum lines should be thoroughly checked for proper routing. Refer to "Vehicle Emission Control Information" label.

The Code 32 chart is a functional check of the EGR system. If the EGR system works properly but a Code 32 has been set, check other items that could result in high block learn values during a cruise condition at approximately 55 mph. Low fuel pressure or lean fuel injector(s) may set a Code 32.

1992 2.2L ENGINE

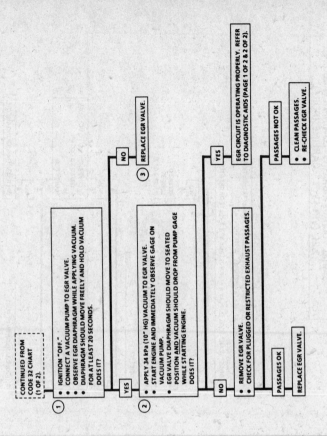

CODE 32
(Page 2 of 2)
EXHAUST GAS RECIRCULATION (EGR) SYSTEM FAILURE
2.2L (VIN 4) "L" CARLINE (PORT)

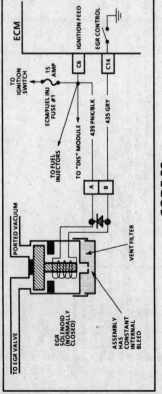

CODE 32
(Page 2 of 2)
EXHAUST GAS RECIRCULATION (EGR) SYSTEM FAILURE
2.2L (VIN 4) "L" CARLINE (PORT)

Circuit Description:

The Exhaust Gas Recirculation (EGR) system is controlled by the ECM. The ECM controls the vacuum being supplied to the valve by energizing and de-energizing a solenoid.

The ECM uses information from various engine sensors to determine when EGR is necessary. Once the ECM has requested EGR by grounding the solenoid circuit, the ECM will monitor engine operating conditions to determine if exhaust gas flow has entered the intake manifold. When the ECM tests for EGR operation and no change in engine operating conditions is indicated, a Code 32 will set.

Test Description: Number(s) below refer to circled number(s) on the diagnostic chart.

1. The remaining tests check the ability of the EGR valve to interact with the exhaust system. This system uses a negative backpressure EGR valve which should hold vacuum with engine "OFF."

2. When engine is started, exhaust backpressure at the base of the EGR valve should open the valve's internal bleed and vent the applied vacuum allowing the valve to seat.

3. Suction from shop exhaust hoses can alter backpressure and may affect the functional check of the EGR valve.

Diagnostic Aids:

Low fuel pressure or lean fuel injectors may cause a Code 32 to set. Use Chart A-7. If fuel pressure is normal, perform the injector balance test, Chart C2-A.

1992 2.2L ENGINE

CODE 33
(Page 1 of 2)
MANIFOLD ABSOLUTE PRESSURE (MAP) SENSOR CIRCUIT
(SIGNAL VOLTAGE HIGH/LOW - LOW/HIGH VACUUM)
2.2L (VIN 4) "L" CARLINE (PORT)

1
- IF ENGINE IDLE IS ROUGH, UNSTABLE, OR INCORRECT, CORRECT CONDITION BEFORE USING CHART. SEE "SYMPTOMS" IN SECTION "B".
- ENGINE IDLING.
- DOES "SCAN" TOOL DISPLAY A MAP VOLTAGE OF 3.7 VOLTS OR GREATER?

YES → | NO → REFER TO CODE 33 (PAGE 2 OF 2).

2
- DISCONNECT MAP SENSOR ELECTRICAL CONNECTOR.
- ENGINE IDLING.
- "SCAN" TOOL SHOULD READ A VOLTAGE OF .3 VOLT OR LESS.
- DOES IT?

YES → | NO → CKT 432 SHORTED TO VOLTAGE, SHORTED TO CKT 416 OR FAULTY ECM.

- PROBE SENSOR GROUND CIRCUIT WITH A TEST LIGHT TO BATTERY VOLTAGE. TEST LIGHT SHOULD LIGHT. DOES IT?

YES → PLUGGED SENSOR INLET PORT OR LEAKING SENSOR SEAL OR FAULTY MAP SENSOR.

NO → OPEN SENSOR GROUND CIRCUIT.

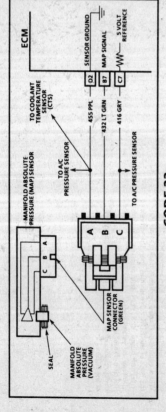

MANIFOLD ABSOLUTE PRESSURE (MAP) SENSOR
TO A/C PRESSURE SENSOR
TO COOLANT TEMPERATURE SENSOR (CTS)
MAP SENSOR CONNECTOR (GREEN)
TO A/C PRESSURE SENSOR
SEAL
MANIFOLD ABSOLUTE PRESSURE (VACUUM)

ECM
SENSOR GROUND — 455 PPL — D2
MAP SIGNAL — 432 LT GRN — B7
5 VOLT REFERENCE — 416 GRY — C7
A   B   C

CODE 33
(Page 1 of 2)
MANIFOLD ABSOLUTE PRESSURE (MAP) SENSOR CIRCUIT
(SIGNAL VOLTAGE HIGH/LOW - LOW/HIGH VACUUM)
2.2L (VIN 4) "L" CARLINE (PORT)

Circuit Description:
The Manifold Absolute Pressure (MAP) sensor responds to changes in manifold pressure (vacuum). The ECM receives this information as a signal voltage that will vary from about 1 to 1.5 volts at closed throttle (idle), to about 4.5 volts at Wide Open Throttle (WOT) (low vacuum).

If the MAP sensor fails, the Electronic Control Module (ECM) will substitute a fixed MAP value based on engine rpm and use the Throttle Position Sensor (TPS) to control fuel delivery.

Test Description: Number(s) below refer to circled number(s) on the diagnostic chart.
1. A Code 33 will set under the following conditions:
   - The engine is running.
   - MAP signal indicates greater than 3.7 volts (80 kPa).
   - Throttle position is less than 5%.
   - These conditions exist for a time period longer than 5 seconds.

   OR
   - MAP signal indicates less than .3 volt (15 kPa).
   - Engine speed is less than 1200 rpm's and TPS position is greater than 15%.
2. If the ECM recognizes the change, the ECM and CKTs 416 and 432 are OK. If CKT 455 is open, there may also be other codes stored.

Diagnostic Aids:
With the ignition "ON" and the engine stopped, the manifold pressure is equal to atmospheric pressure and the signal voltage will be high. This information is used by the ECM as an indication of vehicle altitude and is referred to as BARO. Comparison of this BARO reading with a known good vehicle with the same sensor is a good way to check accuracy of a "suspect" sensor. Reading should be within ± .4 volt.

If Code 33 is intermittent, refer to "Symptoms,"

1992 2.2L ENGINE

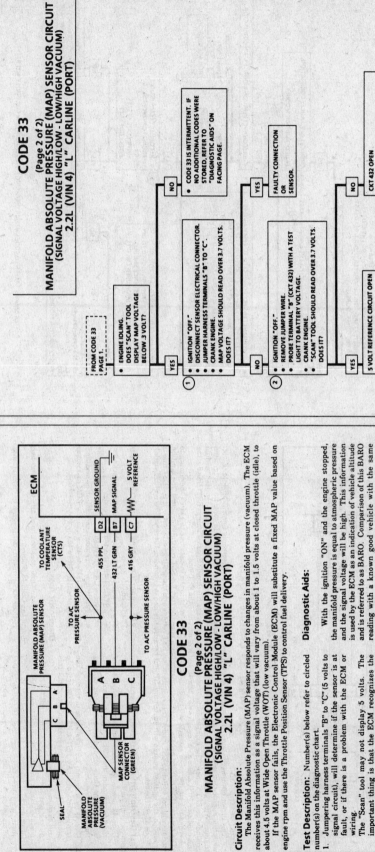

CODE 33
(Page 2 of 2)

MANIFOLD ABSOLUTE PRESSURE (MAP) SENSOR CIRCUIT
(SIGNAL VOLTAGE HIGH/LOW - LOW/HIGH VACUUM)
2.2L (VIN 4) "L" CARLINE (PORT)

Circuit Description:

The Manifold Absolute Pressure (MAP) sensor responds to changes in manifold pressure (vacuum). The ECM receives this information as a signal voltage that will vary from about 1 to 1.5 volts at closed throttle (idle), to about 4.5 volts at Wide Open Throttle (WOT) (low vacuum).

If the MAP sensor fails, the Electronic Control Module (ECM) will substitute a fixed MAP value based on engine rpm and use the Throttle Position Sensor (TPS) to control fuel delivery.

Test Description: Number(s) below refer to circled number(s) on the diagnostic chart.

1. Jumpering harness terminals "B" to "C" (5 volts to signal circuit), will determine if the sensor is at fault, or if there is a problem with the ECM or wiring.

   The "Scan" tool may not display 5 volts. The important thing is that the ECM recognizes the voltage as more than 4 volts, indicating that the ECM CKTs 432, and 416 are OK.

2. This step determines if CKT 416 or CKT 432 is faulty. The "Scan" tool will not display battery voltage, but should indicate over 4 volts.

Diagnostic Aids:

With the ignition "ON" and the engine stopped, the manifold pressure is equal to atmospheric pressure and the signal voltage will be high. This information is used by the ECM as an indication of vehicle altitude and is referred to as BARO. Comparison of this BARO reading with a known good vehicle with the same sensor is a good way to check accuracy of a "suspect" sensor. Reading should be within ± .4 volt.

If Code 33 is intermittent, refer to "Symptoms,"

1992 2.2L ENGINE

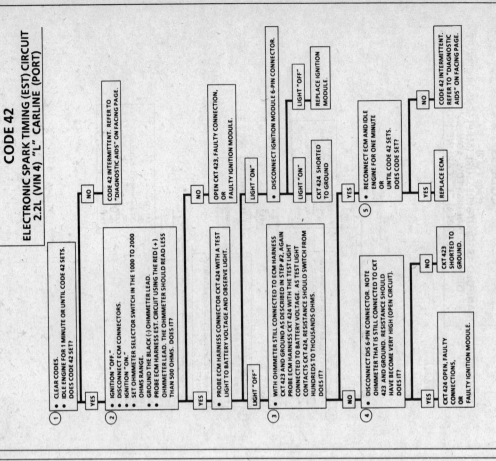

CODE 42
ELECTRONIC SPARK TIMING (EST) CIRCUIT
2.2L (VIN 4) "L" CARLINE (PORT)

(1)
- CLEAR CODES.
- IDLE ENGINE FOR 1 MINUTE OR UNTIL CODE 42 SETS.
  DOES CODE 42 SET?

NO → CODE 42 INTERMITTENT. REFER TO "DIAGNOSTIC AIDS" ON FACING PAGE.

YES ↓

(2)
- IGNITION "OFF."
- DISCONNECT ECM CONNECTORS.
- IGNITION "ON."
- SET OHMMETER SELECTOR SWITCH IN THE 1000 TO 2000 OHMS RANGE.
- GROUND THE BLACK (-) OHMMETER LEAD.
- PROBE ECM HARNESS EST. CIRCUIT USING THE RED (+) OHMMETER LEAD. THE OHMMETER SHOULD READ LESS THAN 500 OHMS. DOES IT?

NO → OPEN CKT 423, FAULTY CONNECTION, OR FAULTY IGNITION MODULE.

YES ↓

- PROBE ECM HARNESS CONNECTOR CKT 424 WITH A TEST LIGHT TO BATTERY VOLTAGE AND OBSERVE LIGHT.

LIGHT "OFF" ← → LIGHT "ON"

(3)
- WITH OHMMETER STILL CONNECTED TO ECM HARNESS CKT 423 AND GROUND AS DESCRIBED IN STEP #2, AGAIN PROBE ECM HARNESS CKT 424 WITH THE TEST LIGHT CONNECTED TO BATTERY VOLTAGE. AS TEST LIGHT CONTACTS CKT 424, RESISTANCE SHOULD SWITCH FROM HUNDREDS TO THOUSANDS OHMS. DOES IT?

LIGHT "ON" ←

CKT 424 SHORTED TO GROUND

- DISCONNECT IGNITION MODULE 6-PIN CONNECTOR.

LIGHT "OFF" → REPLACE IGNITION MODULE.

NO ↓

(4)
- DISCONNECT DIS 6-PIN CONNECTOR. NOTE OHMMETER THAT IS STILL CONNECTED TO CKT 423 AND GROUND. RESISTANCE SHOULD HAVE BECOME VERY HIGH (OPEN CIRCUIT). DOES IT?

YES → CKT 424 OPEN, FAULTY CONNECTIONS, OR FAULTY IGNITION MODULE.

NO → CKT 423 SHORTED TO GROUND.

↓

(5)
- RECONNECT ECM AND IDLE ENGINE FOR ONE MINUTE OR UNTIL CODE 42 SETS. DOES CODE SET?

YES → REPLACE ECM.

NO → CODE 42 INTERMITTENT. REFER TO "DIAGNOSTIC AIDS" ON FACING PAGE.

"AFTER REPAIRS," REFER TO CODE CRITERIA ON FACING PAGE AND CONFIRM CODE DOES NOT RESET.

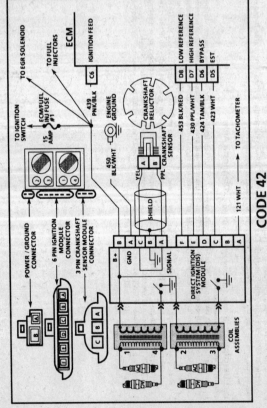

CODE 42
ELECTRONIC SPARK TIMING (EST) CIRCUIT
2.2L (VIN 4) "L" CARLINE (PORT)

Circuit Description:

The Direct Ignition System (DIS) module sends a reference signal to the Electronic Control Module (ECM). While the engine is cranking, the DIS module controls the ignition timing. When the system is running on the ignition module (no voltage on the bypass line), the ignition module grounds the EST signal. The ECM expects to sense no voltage on the Electronic Spark Timing (EST) line during this condition. If it senses a voltage, it sets Code 42 and will not enter the EST mode.

When the engine speed exceeds 400 rpm, the ECM applies 5 volts to the bypass line to switch the timing to ECM control (EST). If the bypass line is open or grounded, once the rpm for EST control is reached, the ignition module will not switch to EST mode. This results in low EST voltage and the setting of Code 42. If the EST line is grounded, the ignition module will switch to EST, but because the line is grounded, there will be no EST signal. A Code 42 will be set.

Test Description: Number(s) below refer to circled number(s) on the diagnostic chart.

1. Code 42 means the ECM has sensed an open or short to ground in the EST or bypass circuits. This test confirms Code 42 and that the fault causing the code is present.

2. Checks for a normal EST ground path through the ignition module. An EST CKT 423, shorted to ground, will also read less than 500 ohms, but this will be checked later.

3. As the test light voltage contacts CKT 424, the module should switch, causing the ohmmeter to "overrange" if the meter is in the 1000 to 2000 ohms position. Selecting the 10,000 to 20,000 ohms position will indicate a reading above 5000 ohms.

4. The important thing is that the module "switched."
   - The module did not switch and this step checks for:
     - EST CKT 423 shorted to ground.
     - Bypass CKT 424 open.
     - Faulty ignition module connection or module.

5. Confirms that Code 42 is a faulty ECM and not an intermittent in CKTs 423 or 424.

Diagnostic Aids:

The "Scan" tool does not have any ability to help diagnose a Code 42 problem.

If Code 42 is intermittent, refer to "Symptoms," ohms.

1992 2.2L ENGINE

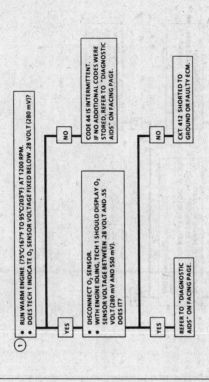

CODE 44

OXYGEN (O_2) SENSOR CIRCUIT
(LEAN EXHAUST INDICATED)
2.2L (VIN 4) "L" CARLINE (PORT)

1
- RUN WARM ENGINE (75°C/167°F TO 95°C/203°F) AT 1200 RPM.
- DOES TECH 1 INDICATE O_2 SENSOR VOLTAGE FIXED BELOW .28 VOLT (280 mV)?

YES →
- DISCONNECT O_2 SENSOR.
- WITH ENGINE IDLING, TECH 1 SHOULD DISPLAY O_2 SENSOR VOLTAGE BETWEEN .28 VOLT AND .55 VOLT (280 mV AND 550 mV).
- DOES IT?

NO →
CODE 44 IS INTERMITTENT.
IF NO ADDITIONAL CODES WERE STORED, REFER TO "DIAGNOSTIC AIDS" ON FACING PAGE.

YES →
REFER TO "DIAGNOSTIC AIDS" ON FACING PAGE.

NO →
CKT 412 SHORTED TO GROUND OR FAULTY ECM.

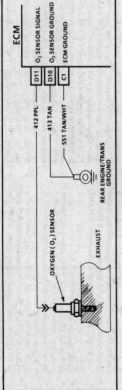

OXYGEN (O_2) SENSOR

EXHAUST

REAR ENGINE/TRANS GROUND

412 PPL → D11 — O_2 SENSOR SIGNAL
413 TAN → D10 — O_2 SENSOR GROUND
551 TAN/WHT → C1 — ECM GROUND

ECM

CODE 44

OXYGEN (O_2) SENSOR CIRCUIT
(LEAN EXHAUST INDICATED)
2.2L (VIN 4) "L" CARLINE (PORT)

Circuit Description:

The Electronic Control Module (ECM) supplies a voltage of about .45 volt between terminals "D10" and "D11". (If measured with a 10 megohm digital voltmeter, this may read as low as .32 volt.)

When the O_2 sensor reaches operating temperature, it varies this voltage from about .1 volt (exhaust is lean) to about .9 volt (exhaust is rich).

The sensor is like an open circuit and produces no voltage when it is below 316°C (600°F). An open sensor circuit, or cold sensor, causes "Open Loop" operation.

Test Description: Number(s) below refer to circled number(s) on the diagnostic chart.

1. Code 44 is set when the O_2 sensor signal voltage on CKT 412 remains below .27 volt for 25 seconds or more.

Diagnostic Aids:

Using the "Scan" tool, observe the block learn value at different engine speeds. If the conditions for Code 44 exists, the block learn values will be around 150 or higher.

Check the following possible causes:

- O_2 Sensor Wire - Sensor pigtail may be mispositioned and contacting the exhaust manifold. Check for ground in wire between connector and sensor.

- Fuel Contamination - Water, even in small amounts, near the in-tank fuel pump inlet can be delivered to the injectors. The water causes a lean exhaust and can set a Code 44.

- Fuel Pressure - System will be lean if fuel pressure is too low. It may be necessary to monitor fuel pressure while driving the vehicle at various road speeds and/or loads to confirm. See "Fuel System Diagnosis," CHART A-7.

- Exhaust Leaks - If there is an exhaust leak, the engine can cause outside air to be pulled into the exhaust and past the sensor. Vacuum or crankcase leaks can cause a lean condition.

- If Code 44 is intermittent, refer to "Symptoms," Section "6E3-B".

- A cracked or otherwise damaged O_2 sensor may set an intermittent Code 44.

1992 2.2L ENGINE

CODE 45

OXYGEN (O₂) SENSOR CIRCUIT
(RICH EXHAUST INDICATED)
2.2L (VIN 4) "L" CARLINE (PORT)

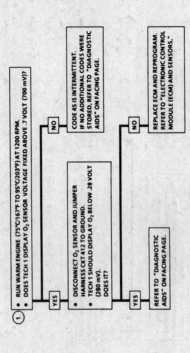

① • RUN WARM ENGINE (75°C/167°F TO 95°C/203°F) AT 1200 RPM.
• DOES TECH 1 DISPLAY O₂ SENSOR VOLTAGE FIXED ABOVE .7 VOLT (700 mV)?

YES → • DISCONNECT O₂ SENSOR AND JUMPER HARNESS CKT 412 TO GROUND.
• TECH 1 SHOULD DISPLAY O₂ BELOW .28 VOLT (280 mV).
DOES IT?

NO → CODE 45 IS INTERMITTENT. IF NO ADDITIONAL CODES WERE STORED, REFER TO "DIAGNOSTIC AIDS" ON FACING PAGE.

YES → REFER TO "DIAGNOSTIC AIDS" ON FACING PAGE.

NO → REPLACE ECM AND REPROGRAM. REFER TO "ELECTRONIC CONTROL MODULE (ECM) AND SENSORS."

CODE 45

OXYGEN (O₂) SENSOR CIRCUIT
(RICH EXHAUST INDICATED)
2.2L (VIN 4) "L" CARLINE (PORT)

Circuit Description:

The Electronic Control Module (ECM) supplies a voltage of about .45 volt between terminals "D10" and "D11". (If measured with a 10 megohm digital voltmeter, this may read as low as .32 volt.) When the Oxygen (O₂) sensor reaches operating temperature, it varies this voltage from about .1 volt (exhaust is lean) to about .9 volt (exhaust is rich).

The sensor is like an open circuit and produces no voltage when it is below 316°C (600°F). An open sensor circuit, or cold sensor, causes "Open Loop" operation.

Test Description: Number(s) below refer to circled number(s) on the diagnostic chart.

1. Code 45 is set when the O₂ sensor signal voltage on CKT 412 remains above .7 volt under the following conditions:
   • Engine run time after start is 2 minutes or more.
   • System is operating in "Closed Loop."
   • Throttle angle is greater than 5%.
   • Above conditions exist for 51 seconds or more.

Diagnostic Aids:

Code 45, or rich exhaust, is most likely caused by one of the following:

• Fuel Pressure - System will go rich, if pressure is too high. The ECM can compensate for some increase. However, if it gets too high, a Code 45 will be set. See "Fuel System Diagnosis" CHART A-7.

• Leaking Injector - See CHART A-7.

• An open ground CKT 453 - May result in induced electrical "noise." The ECM interprets this "noise" as reference pulses. The additional pulses result in a higher than actual engine speed signal. The ECM then delivers too much fuel causing the system to go rich. The engine tachometer will also show higher than actual engine speed, which can help in diagnosing this problem.

• Canister Purge - Check for fuel saturation. If full of fuel, check canister control and hoses.

• See "Canister Purge."

• MAP Sensor - An output that causes the ECM to sense a higher than normal manifold pressure (low vacuum) can cause the system to go rich. Disconnecting the Manifold Absolute Pressure (MAP) sensor will allow the ECM to set a fixed value for the MAP sensor. Substitute a different MAP sensor if the rich condition is gone, while the sensor is disconnected.

• TPS - An intermittent Throttle Position Sensor (TPS) output will cause the system to operate richly due to a false indication of the engine accelerating.

• O₂ Sensor Contamination - Inspect Oxygen (O₂) sensor for silicone contamination from fuel, or use of improper RTV sealant. The sensor may have a white, powdery coating and result in a high but false signal voltage (rich exhaust indication). The ECM will then reduce the amount of fuel delivered to the engine causing a severe surge driveability problem.

• EGR Valve - Exhaust Gas Recirculation (EGR) sticking open at idle is usually accompanied by a rough idle and/or stall condition.

If Code 45 is intermittent, refer to "Symptoms," Section "6E3-B".

• Engine Oil Contamination - Fuel fouled engine oil could cause the O₂ sensor to sense a rich air/fuel mixture and set a Code 45.

ECM

D11	O₂ SENSOR SIGNAL
D10	O₂ SENSOR GROUND
C1	ECM GROUND

412 PPL
413 TAN
551 TAN/WHT

OXYGEN (O₂) SENSOR

EXHAUST

REAR ENGINE/TRANS GROUND

1992 2.2L ENGINE

ECM

+5V
A/C PRESSURE SIGNAL
SENSOR GROUND
A/C REQUEST SIGNAL
A/C RELAY CONTROL DRIVER

C7
B6
D2
D9
C12

416 GRY
380 GRY/RED
455 PPL
66 LT GRN
459 DK GRN/WHT

TO MANIFOLD ABSOLUTE PRESSURE (MAP) SENSOR

TO COOLANT TEMPERATURE SENSOR (CTS)

TO MAP SENSOR

A/C PRESSURE SENSOR

B
C
A

IGNITION SWITCH

FUSE #8
25 AMP

59 DK GRN

A/C SELECT SWITCH

66 LT GRN

A
E
D
F

A/C COMPRESSOR RELAY

TO COOLING FAN RELAY

39 PNK/BLK

REFER TO SECTION 8A-11 FOR COMPLETE ILLUSTRATION OF BRANCH CIRCUITS

150 BLK

B
A

A/C COMPRESSOR CLUTCH

TO IGNITION SWITCH

FUSE #9
20 AMP

CODE 66
A/C PRESSURE SENSOR CIRCUIT
2.2L (VIN 4) "L" CARLINE (PORT)

Circuit Description:

The A/C pressure sensor responds to changes in A/C refrigerant system high side pressure. This input indicates how much load the A/C compressor is putting on the engine and is one of the factors used by the ECM to determine IAC valve position for idle speed control. The circuit consists of a 5 volt reference and a ground, both provided by the ECM, and a signal line to the ECM. The signal is a voltage which is proportional to the pressure. The sensor's range of operation is 0 to 454 psi. At 0 psi, the signal will be about .1 volt, varying up to about 4.9 volts at 454 psi or above. Code 66 sets if the voltage is above 4.9 volts (454 psi) or below .3 volt (7.5 psi) for 5 seconds or more. The A/C compressor is disabled by the ECM if fault is currently present.

Test Description: Number(s) below refer to circled number(s) on the diagnostic chart.

1. This step checks the voltage signal being received by the ECM from the A/C pressure sensor. The normal operating range is between .1 volt and 4.9 volts.
2. Checks to see if the high voltage signal is from a shorted sensor or a short to voltage in the circuit. Normally, disconnecting the sensor would make a normal circuit go to near zero volt.
3. Checks to see if low voltage signal is from the sensor or the circuit. Jumpering the sensor signal CKT 380 to 5 volts, checks the circuit, connections, and ECM.
4. This step checks to see if the low voltage signal was due to an open in the sensor circuit or the 5 volt reference circuit since the prior step eliminated the pressure sensor.

Diagnostic Aids:

Code 66 sets when signal voltage falls outside the normal possible range of the sensor and is not due to a refrigerant system problem. If problem is intermittent, check for opens or shorts in harness or poor connections.

CODE 51
EEPROM OR ECM FAILURE
2.2L (VIN 4) "L" CARLINE (PORT)

CODE 51
ECM FAILURE
(ECM FAILED OR EEPROM FAILURE)

CHECK THAT ALL ECM CONNECTIONS ARE GOOD.
IF OK, CLEAR MEMORY AND RECHECK ECM.
IF CODE 51 REAPPEARS, REPLACE ECM AND REPROGRAM.
FOR ECM REPLACEMENT AND REPROGRAMMING REFER TO SECTION C1 "ECM AND SENSORS"

1992 2.2L ENGINE

CHART C-2A
INJECTOR BALANCE TEST
2.2L (VIN 4) "L" CARLINE (PORT)

NOTICE: The entire test should NOT be repeated more than once without running the engine to prevent flooding. (This includes any retest on faulty injectors.)

The fuel pressure test in Section "A" Chart A-7, should be completed prior to this test.

Step 1. If engine is at operating temperature, allow a 10 minute "cool down" period then connect fuel pressure gauge and injector tester.
1. Ignition "OFF."
2. Connect fuel pressure gauge and injector tester.
3. Ignition "ON."
4. Bleed off air in gauge. Repeat until all air is bled from gauge.

Step 2. Run test:
1. Ignition "OFF" for 10 seconds.
2. Ignition "ON". Record gauge pressure. (Pressure must hold steady, if not see the Fuel System diagnosis, Chart A-7.
3. Turn injector on, by depressing button on injector tester, and note pressure at the instant the gauge needle stops.

Step 3. 1. Repeat step 2 on all injectors and record pressure drop on each. Retest injectors that appear faulty (Any injectors that have a 10 kPa (1.5 psi) difference, either more or less, in pressure from the average). If no problem is found, review "Symptoms"

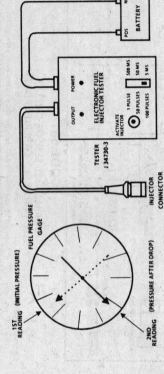

BATTERY — NEG, POS

ELECTRONIC FUEL INJECTOR TESTER
POWER · OUTPUT
ACTIVATE INJECTOR
1 PULSE · 500 MS
50 PULSES · 50 MS
100 PULSES · 5 MS

TESTER J 34730-3

INJECTOR CONNECTOR

FUEL PRESSURE GAGE

1ST READING (INITIAL PRESSURE)
2ND READING (PRESSURE AFTER DROP)

EXAMPLE

CYLINDER	1	2	3
1ST READING	293 kPa (43 psi)	293 kPa (43 psi)	293 kPa (43 psi)
2ND READING	131 kPa (19 psi)	115 kPa (17 psi)	145 kPa (21 psi)
AMOUNT OF DROP	162 kPa (24 psi)	178 kPa (26 psi)	148 kPa (21 psi)
	OK	FAULTY, RICH (TOO MUCH FUEL DROP)	FAULTY, LEAN (TOO LITTLE FUEL DROP)

CODE 66
A/C PRESSURE SENSOR CIRCUIT
2.2L (VIN 4) "L" CARLINE (PORT)

1. KEY "ON," ENGINE NOT RUNNING. NOTE "SCAN" VOLTAGE FOR A/C PRESSURE SENSOR.

- BELOW .3 VOLT
- BETWEEN .3 VOLT AND 4.9 VOLTS. → FAULT IS NOT PRESENT AT THIS TIME. SEE "DIAGNOSTIC AIDS."
- ABOVE 4.9 VOLTS

BELOW .3 VOLT branch:

3. DISCONNECT A/C PRESSURE SENSOR CONNECTOR. JUMPER TERMINALS "C" AND "B". DOES "SCAN" DISPLAY ABOVE 4.6 VOLTS?

- YES → CHECK SENSOR TERMINAL CONNECTIONS. IF OK, REPLACE A/C PRESSURE SENSOR.
- NO →

4. REMOVE JUMPER. CONNECT VOLTMETER FROM TERMINAL "C" TO "B". IS VOLTAGE ABOUT 5 VOLTS?

- YES → CHECK FOR OPEN IN CKT 380. IF OK, CHECK FOR POOR CONNECTION AT ECM TERMINAL "B6". IF OK, REPLACE ECM.
- NO → BACK PROBE ECM TERMINAL "C7" WITH VOLTMETER TO GROUND. IS VOLTAGE ABOUT 5 VOLTS?
  - YES → REPAIR OPEN IN CKT 416.
  - NO → CHECK FOR POOR CONNECTION AT ECM TERMINAL "C7" OR SHORT TO GROUND IN CKT 416. IF OK, ECM IS FAULTY.

ABOVE 4.9 VOLTS branch:

2. DISCONNECT A/C PRESSURE SENSOR ELECTRICAL CONNECTOR. DOES "SCAN" DISPLAY LESS THAN 1 VOLT?

- YES → CHECK FOR OPEN IN SENSOR GROUND CIRCUIT. IF NOT OPEN, CHECK FOR POOR SENSOR TERMINAL CONNECTIONS. IF OK, REPLACE A/C PRESSURE SENSOR.
- NO → CHECK FOR SHORT TO VOLTAGE IN SENSOR GROUND CIRCUIT. IF NOT SHORTED, REPLACE ECM.

1992 2.2L ENGINE

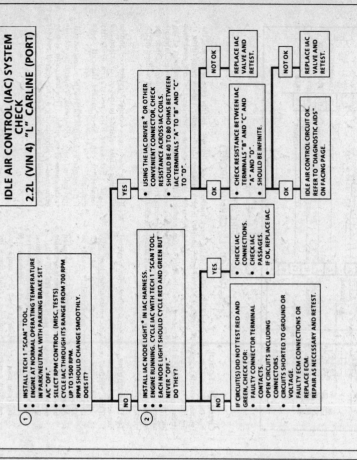

CHART C-2C
IDLE AIR CONTROL (IAC) SYSTEM CHECK
2.2L (VIN 4) "L" CARLINE (PORT)

①
- INSTALL TECH 1 "SCAN" TOOL.
- ENGINE AT NORMAL OPERATING TEMPERATURE IN PARK/NEUTRAL WITH PARKING BRAKE SET.
- A/C "OFF".
- SELECT RPM CONTROL. (MISC. TESTS)
- CYCLE IAC THROUGH ITS RANGE FROM 700 RPM UP TO 1500 RPM.
- RPM SHOULD CHANGE SMOOTHLY. DOES IT?

②
- INSTALL IAC NODE LIGHT * IN IAC HARNESS.
- ENGINE RUNNING, CYCLE IAC WITH TECH 1 "SCAN TOOL.
- EACH NODE LIGHT SHOULD CYCLE RED AND GREEN BUT NEVER "OFF."
- DO THEY?

NO →

- IF CIRCUIT(S) DID NOT TEST RED AND GREEN, CHECK FOR:
- FAULTY CONNECTOR TERMINAL CONTACTS.
- OPEN CIRCUITS INCLUDING CONNECTORS.
- CIRCUITS SHORTED TO GROUND OR VOLTAGE.
- FAULTY ECM CONNECTIONS OR REPLACE ECM.
- REPAIR AS NECESSARY AND RETEST.

YES →
- CHECK IAC CONNECTIONS.
- CHECK IAC PASSAGES.
- IF OK, REPLACE IAC.

YES →
- USING THE IAC DRIVER * OR OTHER CONVENIENT CONNECTOR, CHECK RESISTANCE ACROSS IAC COILS.
- SHOULD BE 40 TO 80 OHMS BETWEEN IAC TERMINALS "A" TO "B" AND "C" TO "D".

OK →
- CHECK RESISTANCE BETWEEN IAC TERMINALS "B" AND "C" AND "A" AND "D".
- SHOULD BE INFINITE.

NOT OK → REPLACE IAC VALVE AND RETEST.

OK →
IDLE AIR CONTROL CIRCUIT OK. REFER TO "DIAGNOSTIC AIDS" ON FACING PAGE.

NOT OK → REPLACE IAC VALVE AND RETEST.

* IAC DRIVER AND NODE LIGHT REQUIRED KIT 222-L FROM: CONCEPT TECHNOLOGY, INC. J 37027 FROM: KENT-MOORE, INC.

CLEAR CODES, CONFIRM "CLOSED LOOP" OPERATION, NO "SERVICE ENGINE SOON" LIGHT, PERFORM IAC RESET PROCEDURE PER APPLICABLE SERVICE MANUAL AND VERIFY CONTROLLED IDLE SPEED IS CORRECT.

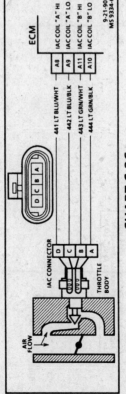

ECM

A8	IAC COIL "A" HI
A9	IAC COIL "A" LO
A11	IAC COIL "B" HI
A10	IAC COIL "B" LO

9-21-90
MS 9334-6E

441 LT BLU/WHT
442 LT BLU/BLK
443 LT GRN/WHT
444 LT GRN/BLK

CHART C-2C
IDLE AIR CONTROL (IAC) SYSTEM CHECK
2.2L (VIN 4) "L" CARLINE (PORT)

Circuit Description:

The ECM controls engine idle speed with the IAC valve. To increase idle speed, the ECM retracts the IAC valve pintle away from its seat, allowing more air to bypass the throttle bore. To decrease idle speed, it extends the IAC valve towards its seat, reducing air flow. A Tech 1 "Scan" tool will read the ECM commands to the IAC valve in counts. Higher the counts indicate more air bypass (higher idle). The lower the counts indicate less air is allowed to bypass (lower idle).

Test Description: Number(s) below refer to circled numbers on the diagnostic chart.

1. The Tech 1 rpm control mode is used to extend and retract the IAC valve. The valve should move smoothly within the specified range. If the idle speed commanded (IAC extended) too low (below 700 rpm), the engine may stall. This may be normal and would not indicate a problem. Retracting the IAC beyond its controlled range (above 1500 rpm) will cause a delay before the rpms start dropping. This too is normal.

2. This test uses the Tech 1 to command the IAC controlled idle speed. The ECM issues commands to obtain commanded idle speed. The node lights each should flash red and green to indicate a good circuit as the ECM issues commands. While the sequence of color is not important if either light is "OFF" or does not flash red and green, check the circuits for faults, beginning with poor terminal contacts.

Diagnostic Aids:

A slow, unstable, or fast idle may be caused by a non-IAC system problem that cannot be overcome by the IAC system. Out of control range IAC "Scan" tool counts will be above 60 if idle is too low, and zero counts if idle is too high. The following checks should be made to repair a non-IAC system problem:

- **Vacuum Leak (High Idle)**
  If idle is too high, stop the engine. Fully extend (low) IAC with tester. Start engine. If idle speed is above 800 rpm, locate and correct vacuum leak including PCV system. Also check for binding of throttle blade or linkage.

- **System Too Lean (High Air/Fuel Ratio)**
  The idle speed may be too high or too low. Engine speed may vary up and down and disconnecting the IAC valve does not help. Code 44 may be set. "Scan" O₂ voltage will be less than 300 mV (.3 volt). Check for low regulated fuel pressure, water in the fuel or a restricted injector.

- **System Too Rich (Low Air/Fuel Ratio)**
  The idle speed will be too low. "Scan" tool IAC counts will usually be above 80. System is obviously rich and may exhibit black smoke in exhaust.
  "Scan" tool O₂ voltage will be fixed above 800 mV (.8 volt).
  Check for high fuel pressure, leaking or sticking injector. Silicone contaminated O₂ sensors "Scan" voltage will be slow to respond.

- **Throttle Body**
  Remove IAC valve and inspect bore for foreign material.

- **IAC Valve Electrical Connections.**
  IAC valve connections should be carefully checked for proper contact.

- **PCV Valve.**
  An incorrect or faulty PCV valve may result in an incorrect idle speed.
  Refer to "Rough, Unstable, Incorrect Idle, or Stalling" in "Symptoms."
  If intermittent poor driveability or idle symptoms are resolved by disconnecting the IAC, carefully recheck connections, valve terminal resistance, or replace IAC.

AIR FLOW

IAC CONNECTOR

THROTTLE BODY

D C B A

1992 2.2L ENGINE

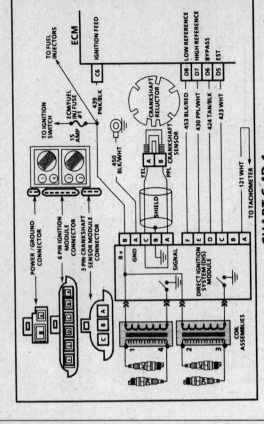

CHART C-4D-1
"DIS" MISFIRE AT IDLE
2.2L (VIN 4) "L" CARLINE (PORT)

Circuit Description:

The Direct Ignition System (DIS) uses a waste spark method of distribution. In this type of system, the ignition module triggers the number 1/4 coil pair resulting in both number 1 and number 4 spark plugs firing at the same time. Number 1 cylinder is on the compression stroke at the same time number 4 is on the exhaust stroke, resulting in a lower energy requirement to fire number 4 spark plug. This leaves the remainder of the high voltage to be used to fire number 1 spark plug. The crank sensor is remotely mounted beside the module/coil assembly and protrudes through the block to within approximately .050" of the crankshaft reluctor. Since the reluctor is a machined portion of the crankshaft and the crankshaft sensor is mounted in a fixed position on the block, timing adjustments are not possible or necessary.

Test Description: Number(s) below refer to circled number(s) on the diagnostic chart.

1. If the "Misfire" complaint exists under load only, the diagnostic chart on page 2 must be used. Engine rpm should drop approximately equally on all plug leads.

2. A spark tester, such as a ST-125, must be used because it is essential to verify adequate available secondary voltage at the spark plug (25,000 volts).

3. If the spark jumps the tester gap after grounding the opposite plug cable, it indicates excessive resistance in the plug which was bypassed. A faulty or poor connection at that plug could also result in a misfire condition. Also, check for carbon deposits inside the spark plug boot.

4. If carbon tracking is evident, replace coil and be sure plug cables relating to that coil are clean and tight. Excessive wire resistance or faulty connections could have caused the coil to be damaged.

5. If the no spark condition follows the suspected coil, that coil is faulty. Otherwise, the ignition module is the cause of no spark. This test could also be performed by substituting a known good coil for the one causing the no spark condition.

CHART C-3
CANISTER PURGE VALVE CHECK
(NON-ECM CONTROLLED)
2.2L (VIN 4) "L" CARLINE (PORT)

- DISCONNECT THE VACUUM HOSE AT THE PURGE VALVE LABELED "CONTROL VAC."
- START ENGINE AND IDLE.
- MANIFOLD VACUUM SHOULD BE PRESENT AT THE DISCONNECTED HOSE.

IS IT?

- **YES**
- **NO** → REPAIR PLUGGED OR LEAKING MANIFOLD VACUUM SOURCE.

- REMOVE PURGE VALVE.
- APPLY A CLEAN SHORT HOSE TO THE TUBE LABELED "PURGE VAC" OF THE VALVE AND BLOW INTO THE HOSE. NO AIR SHOULD PASS THROUGH THE VALVE.

DOES VALVE HOLD?

- **YES**
- **NO** → REPLACE VALVE.

- INSTALL A HAND VACUUM PUMP TO THE TUBE LABELED "CONTROL VAC."
- APPLY 51 kPa (15" Hg) VACUUM THE DIAPHRAGM SHOULD HOLD VACUUM FOR AT LEAST 20 SECONDS.

DOES IT?

- **YES**
- **NO** → REPLACE VALVE.

- WITH THE VACUUM STILL APPLIED TO THE "CONTROL VAC" TUBE, AGAIN TRY TO BLOW INTO A CLEAN HOSE ON THE TUBE LABELED "PURGE VAC" OF THE VALVE. AIR SHOULD PASS THROUGH FREELY.

DOES IT?

- **YES**
- **NO** → REPLACE VALVE.

VALVE OK.

CHECK ALL EMISSION CONTROL LINES, HOSES AND FITTINGS FOR BLOCKAGE, LEAKAGE OR DETERIORATION AND REPAIR AS NECESSARY.

1992 2.2L ENGINE

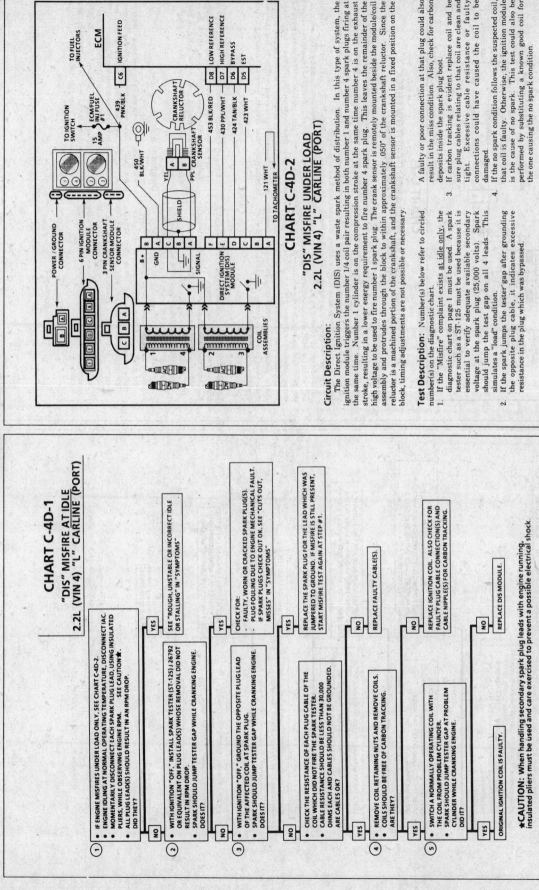

ECM

- TO FUEL INJECTORS
- C6 IGNITION FEED
- D8 LOW REFERENCE
- D7 HIGH REFERENCE
- D6 BYPASS
- D5 EST

- TO IGNITION SWITCH
- ECM/FUEL INJ FUSE #1
- 15 AMP
- 439 PNK/BLK
- 450 BLK/WHT

- POWER / GROUND CONNECTOR
- 6 PIN IGNITION MODULE CONNECTOR
- 3 PIN CRANKSHAFT SENSOR MODULE CONNECTOR

- CRANKSHAFT RELUCTOR
- PPL CRANKSHAFT SENSOR
- YEL A / B
- SHIELD
- 453 BLK/RED
- 430 PPL/WHT
- 424 TAN/BLK
- 423 WHT
- 121 WHT
- TO TACHOMETER

- B+ B
- GND A
- SIGNAL B A
- DIRECT IGNITION SYSTEM (DIS) MODULE
- F E D C B A

- COIL ASSEMBLIES
- 1 4
- 2 3

CHART C-4D-2
"DIS" MISFIRE UNDER LOAD
2.2L (VIN 4) "L" CARLINE (PORT)

Circuit Description:

The Direct Ignition System (DIS) uses a waste spark method of distribution. In this type of system, the ignition module triggers the number 1/4 coil pair resulting in both number 1 and number 4 spark plugs firing at the same time. Number 1 cylinder is on the compression stroke at the same time number 4 is on the exhaust stroke, resulting in a lower energy requirement to fire number 4 spark plug. This leaves the remainder of the high voltage to be used to fire number 1 spark plug. The crank sensor is remotely mounted beside the module/coil assembly and protrudes through the block to within approximately .050" of the crankshaft reluctor. Since the reluctor is a machined portion of the crankshaft, and the crankshaft sensor is mounted in a fixed position on the block, timing adjustments are not possible or necessary.

Test Description: Number(s) below refer to circled number(s) on the diagnostic chart.

1. If the "Misfire" complaint exists at idle only, the diagnostic chart on page 1 must be used. A spark tester such as a ST-125 must be used because it is essential to verify adequate available secondary voltage at the spark plug (25,000 volts). Spark should jump the test gap on all 4 leads. This simulates a "load" condition.

2. If the spark jumps the tester gap after grounding the opposite plug cable, it indicates excessive resistance in the plug which was bypassed.

A faulty or poor connection at that plug could also result in the miss condition. Also, check for carbon deposits inside the spark plug boot.

3. If carbon tracking is evident replace coil and be sure plug cables relating to that coil are clean and tight. Excessive cable resistance or faulty connections could have caused the coil to be damaged.

4. If the no spark condition follows the suspected coil, that coil is faulty. Otherwise, the ignition module is the cause of no spark. This test could also be performed by substituting a known good coil for the one causing the no spark condition.

CHART C-4D-1
"DIS" MISFIRE AT IDLE
2.2L (VIN 4) "L" CARLINE (PORT)

① • IF ENGINE MISFIRES UNDER LOAD ONLY, SEE CHART C-4D-2.
   • ENGINE IDLING AT NORMAL OPERATING TEMPERATURE, DISCONNECT IAC.
   • MOMENTARILY DISCONNECT EACH SPARK PLUG LEAD, USING INSULATED PLIERS, WHILE OBSERVING ENGINE RPM.   SEE CAUTION★.
   • ALL PLUG LEAD(S) SHOULD RESULT IN AN RPM DROP.
   DID THEY?

   YES → SEE "ROUGH, UNSTABLE OR INCORRECT IDLE OR STALLING" IN "SYMPTOMS"

   NO

② • WITH IGNITION "OFF," INSTALL SPARK TESTER (ST-125) 26792 OR EQUIVALENT ON PLUG LEAD(S) WHOSE REMOVAL DID NOT RESULT IN RPM DROP.
   • SPARK SHOULD JUMP TESTER GAP WHILE CRANKING ENGINE. DOES IT?

   YES → CHECK FOR:
   - FAULTY, WORN OR CRACKED SPARK PLUG(S).
   - PLUG FOULING DUE TO ENGINE MECHANICAL FAULT. IF SPARK PLUGS CHECK OUT OK. SEE "CUTS OUT, MISSES" IN "SYMPTOMS"

   NO

③ • WITH IGNITION "OFF," GROUND THE OPPOSITE PLUG LEAD OF THE AFFECTED COIL AT SPARK PLUG.
   • SPARK SHOULD JUMP TESTER GAP WHILE CRANKING ENGINE. DOES IT?

   YES → REPLACE THE SPARK PLUG FOR THE LEAD WHICH WAS JUMPERED TO GROUND. IF MISFIRE IS STILL PRESENT, START MISFIRE TEST AGAIN AT STEP #1.

   NO

④ • CHECK THE RESISTANCE OF EACH PLUG CABLE OF THE COIL WHICH DID NOT FIRE THE SPARK TESTER.
   • CABLE RESISTANCE SHOULD BE LESS THAN 30,000 OHMS EACH AND CABLES SHOULD NOT BE GROUNDED. ARE CABLES OK?

   NO → REPLACE FAULTY CABLE(S).

   YES

   • REMOVE COIL RETAINING NUTS AND REMOVE COILS.
   • COILS SHOULD BE FREE OF CARBON TRACKING. ARE THEY?

   NO → REPLACE IGNITION COIL. ALSO CHECK FOR FAULTY PLUG CABLE CONNECTION(S) AND CABLE NIPPLE(S) FOR CARBON TRACKING.

   YES

⑤ • SWITCH A NORMALLY OPERATING COIL WITH THE COIL FROM PROBLEM CYLINDER.
   • SPARK SHOULD JUMP TESTER GAP AT PROBLEM CYLINDER WHILE CRANKING ENGINE. DID IT?

   NO → REPLACE DIS MODULE.

   YES

   ORIGINAL IGNITION COIL IS FAULTY.

★**CAUTION:** When handling secondary spark plug leads with engine running, insulated pliers must be used and care exercised to prevent a possible electrical shock.

"*AFTER REPAIRS,*" CONFIRM "CLOSED LOOP" OPERATION AND NO "SERVICE ENGINE SOON" LIGHT.

1992 2.2L ENGINE

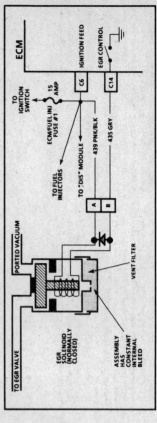

CHART C-7

EXHAUST GAS RECIRCULATION (EGR) FLOW CHECK
2.2L (VIN 4) "L" CARLINE (PORT)

Circuit Description:

A properly operating EGR system will directly affect the air/fuel mixture requirements of the engine. Since the exhaust gas introduced into the air/fuel mixture cannot be used in combustion (contains very little oxygen), less fuel is required to maintain a correct air/fuel ratio. If the EGR system were to fail in a closed position, the exhaust gas would be replaced with air, and the air/fuel mixture would be leaner. The ECM would compensate for the lean condition by adding fuel, resulting in higher block learn values.

The fuel control on this engine is conducted within 4 block learn cells. Since EGR is not used at idle, the idle cell would not be affected by EGR system operation. The other block learn cells are affected by EGR operation, and, when the EGR system is operating properly, the block learn values in all cells should be close to the same. If the EGR system becomes inoperative, the block learn values in the open throttle cells would change to compensate for the resulting lean mixtures, but the block learn value in the closed throttle cell would not change.

The difference in block learn values between the idle (closed throttle) cell and cell 2 is used to monitor EGR system performance. When the difference between the two block learn values is greater than 10 and the block learn value in cell 2 is greater than 135 Code 32 is set. The system operates in block learn cell 2 during a cruise condition at approximately 55 mph.

Test Description: Number(s) below refer to circled number(s) on the diagnostic chart.

1. Codes should be diagnosed using appropriate chart before preparing a functional check. If Codes 14, 21, 23, 32, or 33 are set, use those charts first.
2. The tail pipe ventilation hose must be removed for this test. The ventilation hose can sometimes cause a good EGR valve to fail this test.
3. **Intake Passage:** Shut "OFF" engine and remove the EGR valve from the manifold. Plug the exhaust side hole with a suitable stopper. Leaving the intake side hole open, attempt to start the engine. If the engine runs at a high idle (up to 3000 rpm is possible) or starts and stalls, the EGR intake passage is not restricted. If the engine starts and idles normally, the EGR intake passage is restricted.

Exhaust Passage: With EGR valve still removed, plug the intake side hole with a suitable stopper. With the exhaust side hole open, check for the presence of exhaust gas. If no exhaust gas is present, the EGR exhaust side passage is restricted.

Diagnostic Aids:

This chart is a functional check of the EGR system. If the EGR system works properly, check other items that result in high block learn values in block learn cell 2, but not in the closed throttle cell.

Incorrect fuel pressure or lean/rich fuel injectors can also cause incorrect block learn values. See "Fuel Pressure Test" in CHART A-7. If fuel pressure checks out OK, proceed to "Fuel Injector Balance Test" in CHART C-2A.

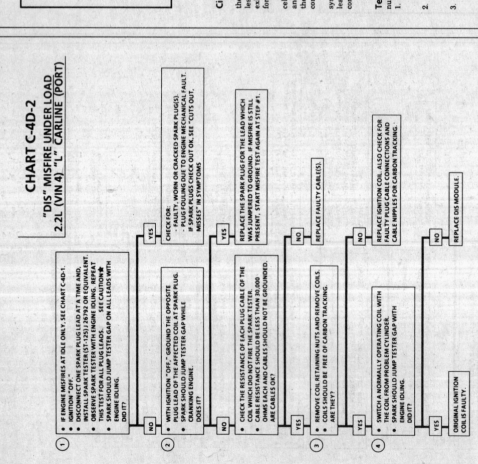

CHART C-4D-2

"DIS" MISFIRE UNDER LOAD
2.2L (VIN 4) "L" CARLINE (PORT)

1. • IF ENGINE MISFIRES AT IDLE ONLY, SEE CHART C-4D-1.
   • IGNITION "OFF."
   • DISCONNECT ONE SPARK PLUG LEAD AT A TIME AND, INSTALL SPARK TESTER (ST-125) J 26792 OR EQUIVALENT.
   • OBSERVE SPARK TESTER WITH ENGINE IDLING. REPEAT THIS TEST FOR ALL PLUG LEADS.   SEE CAUTION★
   • SPARK SHOULD JUMP TESTER GAP ON ALL LEADS WITH ENGINE IDLING.
   DID IT?

   YES → CHECK FOR:
   - FAULTY, WORN OR CRACKED SPARK PLUG(S).
   - PLUG FOULING DUE TO ENGINE MECHANICAL FAULT.
   IF SPARK PLUGS CHECK OUT OK. SEE "CUTS OUT, MISSES" IN SYMPTOMS

   NO
   2. • WITH IGNITION "OFF," GROUND THE OPPOSITE PLUG LEAD OF THE AFFECTED COIL AT SPARK PLUG.
   • SPARK SHOULD JUMP TESTER GAP WHILE CRANKING ENGINE.
   DOES IT?

   YES → REPLACE THE SPARK PLUG FOR THE LEAD WHICH WAS JUMPERED TO GROUND. IF MISFIRE IS STILL PRESENT, START MISFIRE TEST AGAIN AT STEP #1.

   NO
   • CHECK THE RESISTANCE OF EACH CABLE OF THE COIL WHICH DID NOT FIRE THE SPARK TESTER.
   • CABLE RESISTANCE SHOULD BE LESS THAN 30,000 OHMS EACH AND CABLES SHOULD NOT BE GROUNDED.
   ARE CABLES OK?

   YES → REPLACE FAULTY CABLE(S).

   NO
   3. • REMOVE COIL RETAINING NUTS AND REMOVE COILS.
   • COILS SHOULD BE FREE OF CARBON TRACKING.
   ARE THEY?

   NO → REPLACE IGNITION COIL. ALSO CHECK FOR FAULTY PLUG CABLE CONNECTIONS AND CABLE NIPPLES FOR CARBON TRACKING.

   YES
   4. • SWITCH A NORMALLY OPERATING COIL WITH THE COIL FROM PROBLEM CYLINDER.
   • SPARK SHOULD JUMP TESTER GAP WITH ENGINE IDLING.
   DID IT?

   YES → ORIGINAL IGNITION COIL IS FAULTY.

   NO → REPLACE DIS MODULE.

★**CAUTION:** When handling secondary spark plug leads with engine running, insulated pliers must be used and care exercised to prevent a possible electrical shock.

"AFTER REPAIRS," CONFIRM "CLOSED LOOP" OPERATION AND NO "SERVICE ENGINE SOON" LIGHT.

1992 2.2L ENGINE

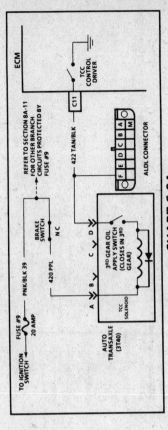

ECM

TCC CONTROL DRIVER

C11

REFER TO SECTION 8A-11 FOR OTHER BRANCH CIRCUITS PROTECTED BY FUSE #9

422 TAN/BLK

ALDL CONNECTOR

F E D C B A M

TO IGNITION SWITCH

FUSE #9 20 AMP

PNK/BLK 39

BRAKE SWITCH

N C

420 PPL

A B C D

3RD GEAR OIL APPLY SWITCH (CLOSES IN 3RD GEAR)

TCC SOLENOID

AUTO TRANSAXLE (3T40)

CHART C-8A
TORQUE CONVERTER CLUTCH (TCC)
(ELECTRICAL DIAGNOSIS)
2.2L (VIN 4) "L" CARLINE (PORT)

Circuit Description:

The purpose of the automatic transmission/transaxle Torque Converter Clutch (TCC) feature is to eliminate the power loss of the torque converter stage when the vehicle is in a cruise condition. This allows the convenience of the automatic transmission/transaxle and the fuel economy of a manual transmission.

Test Description: Number(s) below refer to circled number(s) on the diagnostic chart.

1. This test should be performed with the aid of a helper, to operate the Tech 1 and observe the rpm fluctuation.

2. Entering the "Field Service Mode" forces the ECM to close the TCC control driver circuit completing the path for current which should light the test light.

3. Perform this test with the aid of a helper. The 3rd gear switch must be engaged while measuring the TCC solenoid resistance.

Fused battery ignition is supplied to the TCC solenoid through the brake switch. The ECM will engage TCC by grounding CKT 422 to energize the solenoid.

TCC will engage when:
- Vehicle speed above 35 km/h (22 mph).
- Engine at normal operating temperature (above 70°C, 158°F).
- Throttle position sensor output not changing, indicating a steady road speed.
- Brake switch closed.

CHART C-7
EXHAUST GAS RECIRCULATION (EGR) FLOW CHECK
2.2L (VIN 4) "L" CARLINE (PORT)

1. "SCAN" TROUBLE CODES. IF CODES ARE PRESENT, REFER TO THOSE CODE CHARTS FIRST.

- WITH ENGINE AT IDLE, MANUALLY LIFT THE EGR VALVE DIAPHRAGM. RPM SHOULD DECREASE OR ENGINE STALL.
  - DOES IT?

YES ↓

2. IGNITION "OFF."
- DISCONNECT VACUUM LINE FROM EGR VALVE.
- APPLY 34 kPa (10 Hg.) OF VACUUM TO THE EGR VALVE AND OBSERVE EGR VALVE DIAPHRAGM. SHOULD MOVE.
  - DOES IT?

NO → 3. CHECK EGR VALVE, GASKETS, AND ALL PASSAGES FOR DAMAGE, LEAKAGE, OR PLUGGING. IF OK, REPLACE EGR VALVE.

YES ↓

- RECONNECT VACUUM LINE TO EGR VALVE.
- START ENGINE AND IDLE.
- OBSERVE EGR VALVE DIAPHRAGM WHILE SNAPPING THE THROTTLE FROM IDLE TO WIDE OPEN THROTTLE AND BACK TO IDLE. THE EGR VALVE SHOULD OPEN ON ENGINE DECELERATION.
  - DOES IT?

NO → REPLACE EGR VALVE.

YES ↓

EGR SYSTEM IS OK, NO PROBLEM FOUND. SEE "DIAGNOSTIC AIDS" ON FACING PAGE.

NO → USE CODE 32 CHART.

1992 2.2L ENGINE

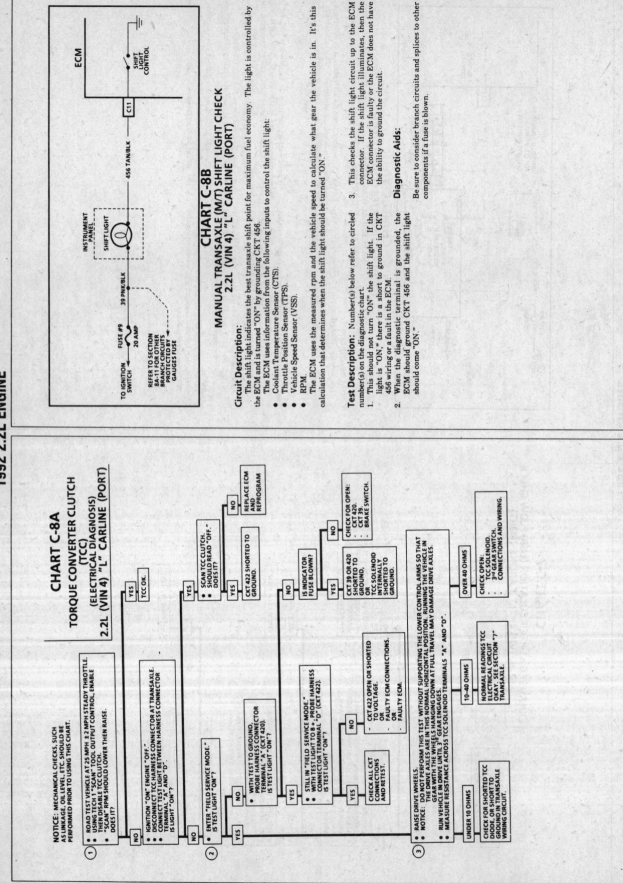

CHART C-8B
MANUAL TRANSAXLE (M/T) SHIFT LIGHT CHECK
2.2L (VIN 4) "L" CARLINE (PORT)

Circuit Description:

The shift light indicates the best transaxle shift point for maximum fuel economy. The light is controlled by the ECM and is turned "ON" by grounding CKT 456.

The ECM uses information from the following inputs to control the shift light:

• Coolant Temperature Sensor (CTS).
• Throttle Position Sensor (TPS).
• Vehicle Speed Sensor (VSS).
• RPM.

The ECM uses the measured rpm and the vehicle speed to calculate what gear the vehicle is in. It's this calculation that determines when the shift light should be turned "ON."

Test Description: Number(s) below refer to circled number(s) on the diagnostic chart.

1. This should not turn "ON" the shift light. If the light is "ON," there is a short to ground in CKT 456 wiring or a fault in the ECM.

2. When the diagnostic terminal is grounded, the ECM should ground CKT 456 and the shift light should come "ON."

3. This checks the shift light circuit up to the ECM connector. If the shift light illuminates, then the ECM connector is faulty or the ECM does not have the ability to ground the circuit.

Diagnostic Aids:

Be sure to consider branch circuits and splices to other components if a fuse is blown.

CHART C-8A
TORQUE CONVERTER CLUTCH (TCC)
(ELECTRICAL DIAGNOSIS)
2.2L (VIN 4) "L" CARLINE (PORT)

1992 2.2L ENGINE

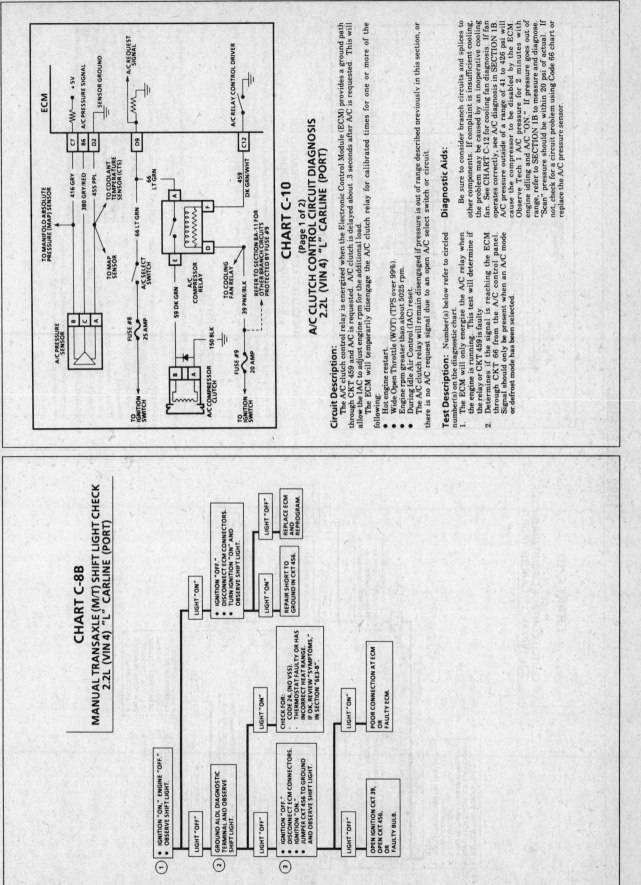

ECM

C7 — 416 GRY — TO MANIFOLD ABSOLUTE PRESSURE (MAP) SENSOR
+5V
B6 — A/C PRESSURE SIGNAL — 380 GRY/RED
D2 — SENSOR GROUND — 455 PPL
TO MAP SENSOR
D9 — A/C REQUEST SIGNAL — 66 LT GRN — TO COOLANT TEMPERATURE SENSOR (CTS)
C12 — A/C RELAY CONTROL DRIVER — 459 DK GRN/WHT

A/C PRESSURE SENSOR
B C A
FUSE #8 25 AMP
TO IGNITION SWITCH

A/C SELECT SWITCH
66 LT GRN
59 DK GRN

A/C COMPRESSOR RELAY
A F
E D

TO COOLING FAN RELAY
39 PNK/BLK
REFER TO SECTION 8A-11 FOR OTHER BRANCH CIRCUITS PROTECTED BY FUSE #9

150 BLK

A/C COMPRESSOR CLUTCH
B A
FUSE #9 20 AMP
TO IGNITION SWITCH

CHART C-10
(Page 1 of 2)
A/C CLUTCH CONTROL CIRCUIT CIRCUIT DIAGNOSIS
2.2L (VIN 4) "L" CARLINE (PORT)

Circuit Description:
The A/C clutch control relay is energized when the Electronic Control Module (ECM) provides a ground path through CKT 459 and A/C is requested. A/C clutch is delayed about 3 seconds after A/C is requested. This will allow the IAC to adjust engine rpm for the additional load.

The ECM will temporarily disengage the A/C clutch relay for calibrated times for one or more of the following:
- Hot engine restart.
- Wide Open Throttle (WOT) (TPS over 99%).
- Engine rpm greater than about 5025 rpm.
- During Idle Air Control (IAC) reset.

The A/C clutch relay will remain disengaged if pressure is out of range described previously in this section, or there is no A/C request signal due to an open A/C select switch or circuit.

Test Description: Number(s) below refer to circled number(s) on the diagnostic chart.
1. The ECM will only energize the A/C relay when the engine is running. This test will determine if the relay or CKT 459 is faulty.
2. Determines if the signal is reaching the ECM through CKT 66 from the A/C control panel. Signal should only be present when an A/C mode or defrost mode has been selected.

Diagnostic Aids:
Be sure to consider branch circuits and splices to other components. If complaint is insufficient cooling, the problem may be caused by an inoperative cooling fan. See CHART C-12 for cooling fan diagnosis. If fan operates correctly, see A/C diagnosis in SECTION 1B. A/C pressure outside of a range of 41 to 426 psi will cause the compressor to be disabled by the ECM. Observe Tech 1 A/C pressure for 2 minutes with engine idling and A/C "ON." If pressure goes out of range, refer to SECTION 1B to measure and diagnose. "Scan" pressure should be within 20 psi of actual. If not, check for a circuit problem using Code 66 chart or replace the A/C pressure sensor.

CHART C-8B
MANUAL TRANSAXLE (M/T) SHIFT LIGHT CHECK
2.2L (VIN 4) "L" CARLINE (PORT)

1.
- IGNITION "ON," ENGINE "OFF."
- OBSERVE SHIFT LIGHT.

LIGHT "OFF"

2.
- GROUND ALDL DIAGNOSTIC TERMINAL AND OBSERVE SHIFT LIGHT.

LIGHT "OFF"

- IGNITION "OFF."
- DISCONNECT ECM CONNECTORS.
- IGNITION "ON."
- JUMPER CKT 456 TO GROUND AND OBSERVE SHIFT LIGHT.

LIGHT "OFF"

OPEN IGNITION CKT 39, OR OPEN CKT 456, OR FAULTY BULB.

LIGHT "ON"

3.
- IGNITION "OFF."
- DISCONNECT ECM CONNECTORS.
- IGNITION "ON." TURN IGNITION "ON" AND OBSERVE SHIFT LIGHT.

LIGHT "ON"

REPAIR SHORT TO GROUND IN CKT 456.

LIGHT "OFF"

REPLACE ECM AND REPROGRAM.

CHECK FOR:
- CODE 24 (NO VSS).
- THERMOSTAT FAULTY OR HAS INCORRECT HEAT RANGE.
IF OK, REVIEW "SYMPTOMS," IN SECTION "6E3-B".

LIGHT "ON"

POOR CONNECTION AT ECM OR FAULTY ECM.

1992 2.2L ENGINE

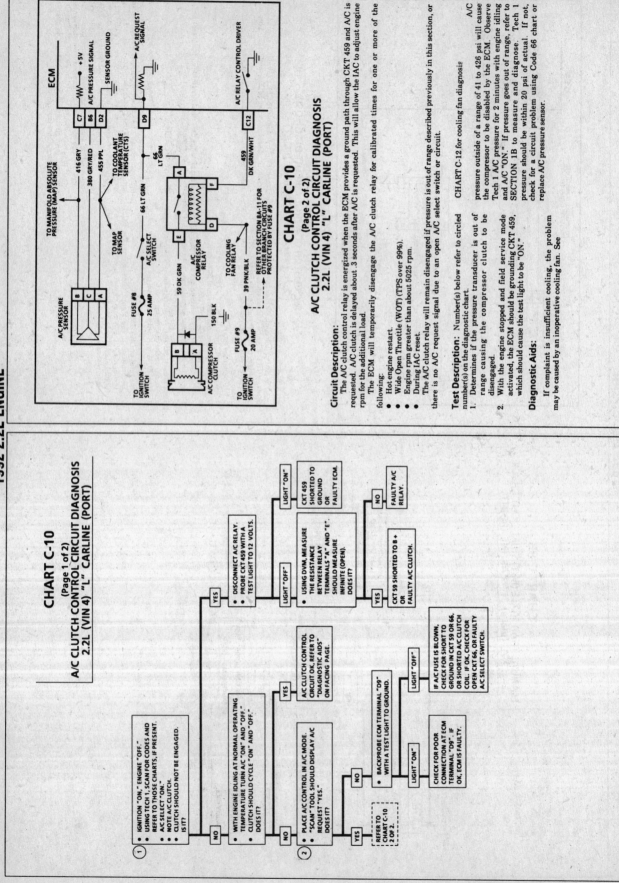

CHART C-10
(Page 1 of 2)
A/C CLUTCH CONTROL CIRCUIT DIAGNOSIS
2.2L (VIN 4) "L" CARLINE (PORT)

CHART C-10
(Page 2 of 2)
A/C CLUTCH CONTROL CIRCUIT DIAGNOSIS
2.2L (VIN 4) "L" CARLINE (PORT)

Circuit Description:

The A/C clutch control relay is energized when the ECM provides a ground path through CKT 459 and A/C is requested. A/C clutch is delayed about .3 seconds after A/C is requested. This will allow the IAC to adjust engine rpm for the additional load.

The ECM will temporarily disengage the A/C clutch relay for calibrated times for one or more of the following:

- Hot engine restart.
- Wide Open Throttle (WOT) (TPS over 99%).
- Engine rpm greater than about 5025 rpm.
- During IAC reset.

The A/C clutch relay will remain disengaged if pressure is out of range described previously in this section, or there is no A/C request signal due to an open A/C select switch or circuit.

Test Description: Number(s) below refer to circled number(s) on the diagnostic chart.

1. Determines if the pressure transducer is out of range causing the compressor clutch to be disengaged.

2. With the engine stopped and field service mode activated, the ECM should be grounding CKT 459, which should cause the test light to be "ON."

Diagnostic Aids:

If complaint is insufficient cooling, the problem may be caused by an inoperative cooling fan. See CHART C-12 for cooling fan diagnosis.

A/C pressure outside of a range of 41 to 426 psi will cause the compressor to be disabled by the ECM. Observe Tech 1 A/C pressure for 2 minutes with engine idling and A/C "ON." If pressure goes out of range, refer to SECTION 1B to measure and diagnose. Tech 1 pressure should be within 20 psi of actual. If not, check for a circuit problem using Code 66 chart or replace A/C pressure sensor.

1992 2.2L ENGINE

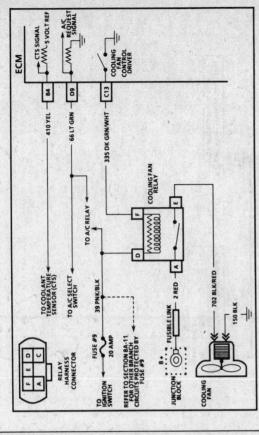

CHART C-12
ECM CONTROLLED COOLING FAN
2.2L (VIN 4) "L" CARLINE (PORT)

Circuit Description:

Battery voltage to operate the cooling fan motor is supplied to relay by CKT 2. Ignition voltage to energize the relay is supplied to relay by CKT 39. When the ECM grounds CKT 335, the relay is energized and the cooling fan is turned "ON." When the engine is running, the ECM will turn the cooling fan "ON" if:

- A/C is "ON."
- Coolant temperature greater than 106°C (223°F).
- Code 14, coolant sensor failure.

Diagnostic Aids:

If the owner complained of an overheating problem, it must be determined if the complaint was due to an actual boil over, or the hot light, or temperature gage indicated overheating.

If the gage or light indicates overheating, but no boil over is detected, the gage circuit should be checked. The gage accuracy can also be checked by comparing the coolant sensor reading using a "Scan" tool and comparing its reading with the gage reading.

If the engine is actually overheating and the gage indicates overheating, but the cooling fan is not coming "ON," the coolant sensor has probably shifted out of calibration and should be replaced.

CHART C-10
(2 of 2)
A/C CLUTCH CONTROL CIRCUIT DIAGNOSIS
2.2L (VIN 4) "L" CARLINE (PORT)

1
- IGNITION "ON," A/C "ON."
- ENGINE "OFF."
- "SCAN" A/C PRESSURE.

PRESSURE IS BETWEEN 41 LBS - 426 LBS

PRESSURE IS LESS THAN 41 LBS OR GREATER THAN 426 LBS.

- INSTALL A/C MANIFOLD GAGE SET AS DESCRIBED IN A/C SECTION 1B.
- ARE "SCAN" PRESSURES WITHIN 20 LBS OF HIGH SIDE PRESSURE?

NO → REPLACE A/C PRESSURE SENSOR AND RECHECK.

YES → REFER TO A/C SECTION 1B FOR A/C DIAGNOSIS.

- DISCONNECT A/C RELAY.
- PROBE CKTS 39 & 66 WITH TEST LIGHT TO GROUND.

LIGHT "ON" BOTH

NO LIGHT, ONE OR BOTH → REPAIR OPEN IN CIRCUIT THAT DID NOT LIGHT.

- JUMPER CKT 66 TO CKT 59.
  DOES A/C CLUTCH ENGAGE?

NO → CHECK:
- OPEN CKT 59 TO CLUTCH.
- FAULTY CLUTCH COIL.
- OPEN GROUND TO CLUTCH.

YES →

2
- IGNITION "ON." ENGINE STOPPED. ACTIVATE FIELD SERVICE MODE.
- PROBE CKT 459 WITH A TEST LIGHT TO 12 VOLTS.

LIGHT "OFF" → OPEN CKT 459, FAULTY CONNECTION, OR ECM.

LIGHT "ON" → FAULTY RELAY.

1992 2.2L ENGINE

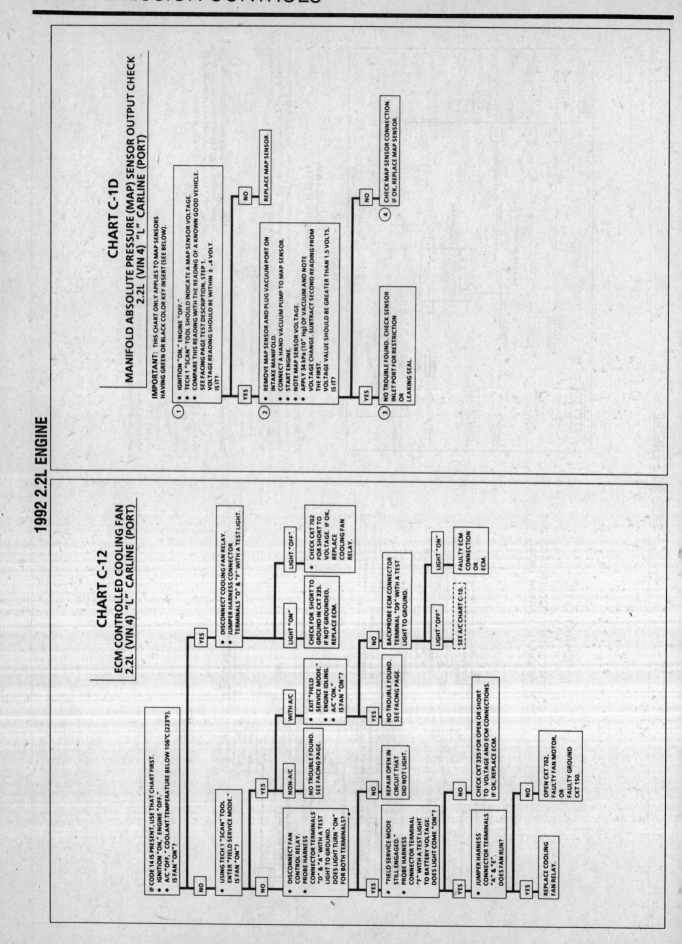

CHART C-1D
MANIFOLD ABSOLUTE PRESSURE (MAP) SENSOR OUTPUT CHECK
2.2L (VIN 4) "L" CARLINE (PORT)

IMPORTANT: THIS CHART ONLY APPLIES TO MAP SENSORS HAVING GREEN OR BLACK COLOR KEY INSERT (SEE BELOW).

①
- IGNITION "ON," ENGINE "OFF."
- TECH 1 "SCAN" TOOL SHOULD INDICATE A MAP SENSOR VOLTAGE.
- COMPARE THIS READING WITH THE READING OF A KNOWN GOOD VEHICLE. SEE FACING PAGE TEST DESCRIPTION, STEP 1.

VOLTAGE READING SHOULD BE WITHIN ± .4 VOLT. IS IT?

NO → REPLACE MAP SENSOR.

YES →

②
- REMOVE MAP SENSOR AND PLUG VACUUM PORT ON INTAKE MANIFOLD.
- CONNECT A HAND VACUUM PUMP TO MAP SENSOR.
- START ENGINE.
- NOTE MAP SENSOR VOLTAGE.
- APPLY 34 kPa (10" Hg) OF VACUUM AND NOTE VOLTAGE CHANGE. SUBTRACT SECOND READING FROM THE FIRST.

VOLTAGE VALUE SHOULD BE GREATER THAN 1.5 VOLTS. IS IT?

NO → ④ CHECK MAP SENSOR CONNECTION. IF OK, REPLACE MAP SENSOR.

YES →

③ NO TROUBLE FOUND. CHECK SENSOR INLET PORT FOR RESTRICTION OR LEAKING SEAL.

CHART C-12
ECM CONTROLLED COOLING FAN
2.2L (VIN 4) "L" CARLINE (PORT)

IF CODE 14 IS PRESENT, USE THAT CHART FIRST.
- IGNITION "ON," ENGINE "OFF."
- A/C "OFF." COOLANT TEMPERATURE BELOW 106°C (223°F).

IS FAN "ON"?

YES →
- DISCONNECT COOLING FAN RELAY.
- JUMPER HARNESS CONNECTOR TERMINALS "D" & "F" WITH A TEST LIGHT.

LIGHT "ON" →
CHECK FOR SHORT TO GROUND IN CKT 335. IF NOT GROUNDED, REPLACE ECM.

LIGHT "OFF" →
CHECK CKT 702 FOR SHORT TO VOLTAGE. IF OK, REPLACE COOLING FAN RELAY.

NO →
USING TECH 1 "SCAN" TOOL ENTER "FIELD SERVICE MODE." IS FAN "ON"?

YES →
WITH A/C →
- EXIT "FIELD SERVICE MODE." ENGINE IDLING.
- A/C "ON." IS FAN "ON"?

YES → NO TROUBLE FOUND. SEE FACING PAGE.

NON-A/C → NO TROUBLE FOUND. SEE FACING PAGE.

NO →
BACKPROBE ECM CONNECTOR TERMINAL "D9" WITH A TEST LIGHT TO GROUND.

LIGHT "ON" → FAULTY ECM CONNECTION OR ECM.

LIGHT "OFF" → SEE A/C CHART C-10.

NO →
- DISCONNECT FAN CONTROL RELAY.
- PROBE HARNESS CONNECTOR TERMINALS "D" & "A" WITH A TEST LIGHT TO GROUND. DOES LIGHT TURN "ON" FOR BOTH TERMINALS?

YES →
"FIELD SERVICE MODE" STILL ENGAGED.
- PROBE HARNESS CONNECTOR TERMINAL "F" WITH A TEST LIGHT TO BATTERY VOLTAGE. DOES LIGHT COME "ON"?

NO → REPAIR OPEN IN CIRCUIT THAT DID NOT LIGHT.

YES →
- JUMPER HARNESS CONNECTOR TERMINALS "A" & "E." DOES FAN RUN?

NO → CHECK CKT 335 FOR OPEN OR SHORT TO VOLTAGE AND ECM CONNECTIONS. IF OK, REPLACE ECM.

YES → REPLACE COOLING FAN RELAY.

NO → OPEN CKT 702, FAULTY FAN MOTOR, OR FAULTY GROUND CKT 150.

1992 2.2L ENGINE

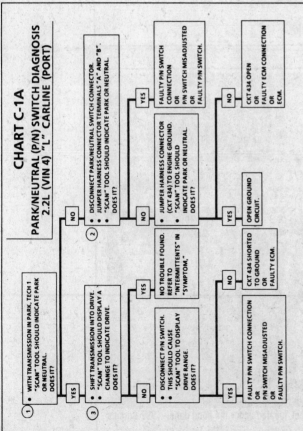

CHART C-1D

MANIFOLD ABSOLUTE PRESSURE (MAP) SENSOR OUTPUT CHECK
2.2L (VIN 4) "L" CARLINE (PORT)

Circuit Description:

The Manifold Absolute Pressure (MAP) sensor measures the changes in the intake manifold pressure which result from engine load (intake manifold vacuum) and rpm changes; and converts these into a voltage output. The ECM sends a 5 volts reference voltage to the MAP sensor. As the manifold pressure changes, the output voltage of the sensor also changes. By monitoring the sensor output voltage, the ECM knows the manifold pressure. A lower pressure (low voltage) output voltage will be about 1 to 2 volts at idle. While higher pressure (high voltage) output voltage will be about 4 to 4.8 at Wide Open Throttle (WOT). The MAP sensor is also used, under certain conditions, to measure barometric pressure, allowing the ECM to make adjustments for altitude changes. The ECM uses the MAP sensor to control fuel delivery and ignition timing.

Test Description: Number(s) below refer to circled number(s) on the diagnostic chart.

Important
- Be sure to use the same Diagnostic Test Equipment for all measurements.

1. When comparing "Scan" readings to a known good vehicle, it is important to compare vehicles that use a MAP sensor having the same color insert and the same "Hot Stamped" number.

2. Applying 34 kPa (10" Hg) vacuum to the MAP sensor should result in voltage readings of 1.5 to 2.1 volts less than the voltage in Step 1. Upon applying vacuum to the sensor, the change in voltage should be instantaneous. A slow voltage change indicates a faulty sensor.

3. Check vacuum source to sensor for leaking or restriction. Be sure that no other vacuum devices are connected to the MAP vacuum source.

   NOTICE: Make sure electrical connector remains securely fastened.

4. Remove sensor from the intake plenum and twist sensor **(by hand only)** to check for intermittent connection. Output changes greater than .10 volt indicate a faulty sensor or connection. If OK, replace sensor.

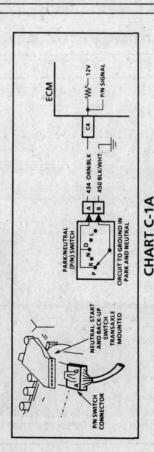

CHART C-1A

PARK/NEUTRAL (P/N) SWITCH DIAGNOSIS
2.2L (VIN 4) "L" CARLINE (PORT)

Circuit Description:

The Park/Neutral (P/N) switch contacts are a part of the neutral start switch and are closed to ground in park or neutral, and open in drive ranges.

The ECM supplies ignition voltage through a current limiting resistor to CKT 434 and senses a closed switch, when the voltage on CKT 434 drops to less than one volt.

The ECM uses the P/N signal as one of the inputs to control idle air control and VSS diagnostics.

Test Description: Number(s) below refer to circled number(s) on the diagnostic chart.

1. Checks for a closed switch to ground in park position. Different makes of "Scan" tools will read P/N differently. Refer to tool operations manual for type of display used.

2. Checks for an open switch in drive range.

3. Be sure "Scan" tool indicates drive, even while wiggling shifter to test for an intermittent or misadjusted switch in drive range.

CHART C-1A
PARK/NEUTRAL (P/N) SWITCH DIAGNOSIS
2.2L (VIN 4) "L" CARLINE (PORT)

1. • WITH TRANSMISSION IN PARK, TECH 1 "SCAN" TOOL SHOULD INDICATE PARK OR NEUTRAL.
   DOES IT?

   NO → ② DISCONNECT PARK/NEUTRAL SWITCH CONNECTOR.
   JUMPER HARNESS CONNECTOR TERMINALS "A" AND "B".
   "SCAN" TOOL SHOULD INDICATE PARK OR NEUTRAL.
   DOES IT?

   YES → FAULTY P/N SWITCH CONNECTION OR P/N SWITCH MISADJUSTED OR FAULTY P/N SWITCH.

   NO → JUMPER HARNESS CONNECTOR (CKT 434) TO ENGINE GROUND. "SCAN" TOOL SHOULD INDICATE PARK OR NEUTRAL. DOES IT?

   YES → FAULTY P/N SWITCH CONNECTION OR P/N SWITCH MISADJUSTED OR FAULTY P/N SWITCH.

   NO → CKT 434 OPEN OR FAULTY ECM CONNECTION OR ECM.

   YES ↓

3. • SHIFT TRANSMISSION INTO DRIVE. "SCAN" TOOL SHOULD DISPLAY A CHANGE TO INDICATE DRIVE. DOES IT?

   YES → NO TROUBLE FOUND. REFER TO "INTERMITTENTS" IN "SYMPTOM."

   NO → • DISCONNECT P/N SWITCH. THIS SHOULD CAUSE "SCAN" TOOL TO DISPLAY DRIVE RANGE. DOES IT?

   YES → CKT 434 SHORTED TO GROUND OR FAULTY ECM.

   NO → FAULTY P/N SWITCH CONNECTION OR P/N SWITCH MISADJUSTED OR FAULTY P/N SWITCH.

   YES → OPEN GROUND CIRCUIT.

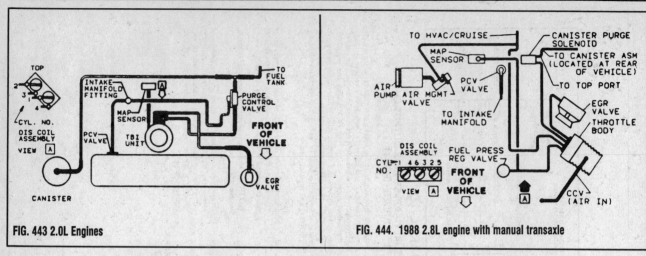

FIG. 443 2.0L Engines

FIG. 444. 1988 2.8L engine with manual transaxle

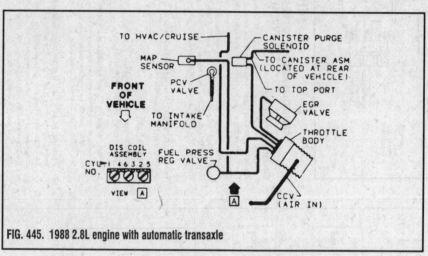

FIG. 445. 1988 2.8L engine with automatic transaxle

FIG. 443A Typical Emission Control Information label, located under the hood panel–1992 Corsica shown

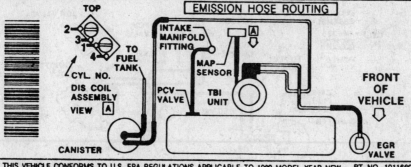

DAC
2.0 LITER
K1G2.0V5JFG0
KAO-1E

VEHICLE EMISSION CONTROL INFORMATION
GENERAL MOTORS CORPORATION [GM]

CATALYST
BPEGR/ORC

IDLE AIR SPEED SCREW IS PRESET AND SEALED AT FACTORY. PROVISION FOR ADJUSTMENT DURING TUNE UP IS NOT PROVIDED. DO NOT ATTEMPT ADJUSTMENT.

IDLE SPEEDS ARE AUTOMATICALLY CONTROLLED. DO NOT ATTEMPT ADJUSTMENTS.

IGNITION TIMING IS AUTOMATICALLY CONTROLLED AND IS NOT ADJUSTABLE.

SEE SERVICE MANUAL AND MAINTENANCE SCHEDULE FOR ADDITIONAL INFORMATION.

SPARK PLUG GAP (IN.) 0.035

EMISSION HOSE ROUTING

THIS VEHICLE CONFORMS TO U.S. EPA REGULATIONS APPLICABLE TO 1989 MODEL YEAR NEW PASSENGER CARS. HOWEVER, IF THIS VEHICLE IS BUILT FOR USE IN CANADA IT DOES NOT COMPLY WITH U.S. EPA FUEL LABELING REGULATIONS.

PT. NO. 10116606
PRINTED IN U.S.A.

FIG. 446. 1989 2.0L engine—Federal

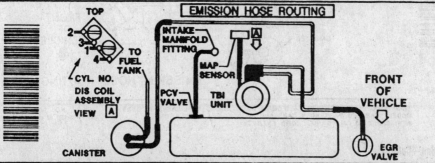

DAD
2.0 LITER
K1G2.0W5JFG5
KAO-1G

VEHICLE EMISSION CONTROL INFORMATION
GENERAL MOTORS CORPORATION [GM]

CATALYST
BPEGR/TWC

IDLE AIR SPEED SCREW IS PRESET AND SEALED AT FACTORY. PROVISION FOR ADJUSTMENT DURING TUNE UP IS NOT PROVIDED. DO NOT ATTEMPT ADJUSTMENT.

IDLE SPEEDS ARE AUTOMATICALLY CONTROLLED. DO NOT ATTEMPT ADJUSTMENTS.

IGNITION TIMING IS AUTOMATICALLY CONTROLLED AND IS NOT ADJUSTABLE.

SEE SERVICE MANUAL AND MAINTENANCE SCHEDULE FOR ADDITIONAL INFORMATION.

SPARK PLUG GAP (IN.) 0.035

EMISSION HOSE ROUTING

THIS VEHICLE CONFORMS TO CALIFORNIA REGULATIONS APPLICABLE TO 1989 MODEL YEAR NEW PASSENGER CARS AND TO U.S. EPA REGULATIONS APPLICABLE TO CALIFORNIA.

PT. NO. 10116607
PRINTED IN U.S.A.

FIG. 447. 1989 2.0L engine—California

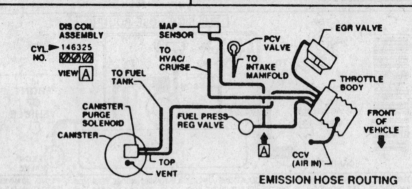

DMH
2.8 LITER
K1G3.1W8XGZ9
KB0-1L

VEHICLE EMMISSION CONTROL INFORMATION
General Motors Corporation [GM]

CATALYST
EGR/TWC
MANUAL TRANS.

IDLE AIR SPEED SCREW IS PRESET AND SEALED AT FACTORY. PROVISION FOR ADJUSTMENT DURING TUNE UP IS NOT PROVIDED. DO NOT ATTEMPT ADJUSTMENT.

IDLE SPEEDS ARE AUTOMATICALLY CONTROLLED. DO NOT ATTEMPT ADJUSTMENTS.

IGNITION TIMING IS AUTOMATICALLY CONTROLLED AND NOT ADJUSTABLE. SEE SERVICE MANUAL AND MAINTENANCE SCHEDULE FOR ADDITIONAL INFORMATION.

SPARK PLUG GAP (IN.) 0.045

NOTE DAMAGE TO HEADS MAY RESULT IF ENGINE IS NOT ALLOWED TO COOL BEFORE REMOVING SPARK PLUGS.

EMISSION HOSE ROUTING

THIS VEHICLE CONFORMS TO CALIFORNIA REGULATIONS APPLICABLE TO 1989 MODEL YEAR NEW PASSENGER CARS AND TO U S EPA REGULATIONS

PT NO 10120400
PRINTED IN U.S.A.

FIG. 448. 1989 2.8L engine with manual transaxle—California

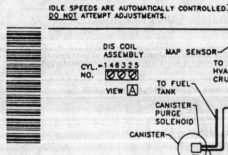
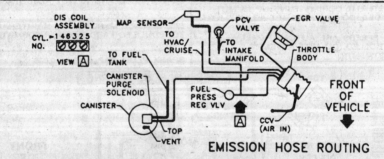

DBD
2.8 LITER
K1G3.1W8XGZ9
KB0-1L

VEHICLE EMISSION CONTROL INFORMATION
GENERAL MOTORS CORPORATION [GM]

CATALYST
EGR/TWC

IDLE AIR SPEED SCREW IS PRESET AND SEALED AT FACTORY. PROVISION FOR ADJUSTMENT DURING TUNE UP IS NOT PROVIDED. DO NOT ATTEMPT ADJUSTMENT.

IDLE SPEEDS ARE AUTOMATICALLY CONTROLLED. DO NOT ATTEMPT ADJUSTMENTS.

IGNITION TIMING IS AUTOMATICALLY CONTROLLED AND IS NOT ADJUSTABLE. SEE SERVICE MANUAL AND MAINTENANCE SCHEDULE FOR ADDITIONAL INFORMATION.

SPARK PLUG GAP (IN.) 0.045

NOTE DAMAGE TO HEADS MAY RESULT IF ENGINE IS NOT ALLOWED TO COOL BEFORE REMOVING SPARK PLUGS.

EMISSION HOSE ROUTING

THIS VEHICLE CONFORMS TO CALIFORNIA REGULATIONS APPLICABLE TO 1989 MODEL YEAR NEW PASSENGER CARS AND TO U.S. EPA REGULATIONS APPLICABLE TO CALIFORNIA. (OBD EXEMPT)

PT. NO. 10116627
PRINTED IN U.S.A.

FIG. 449. 1989 2.8L engine—California

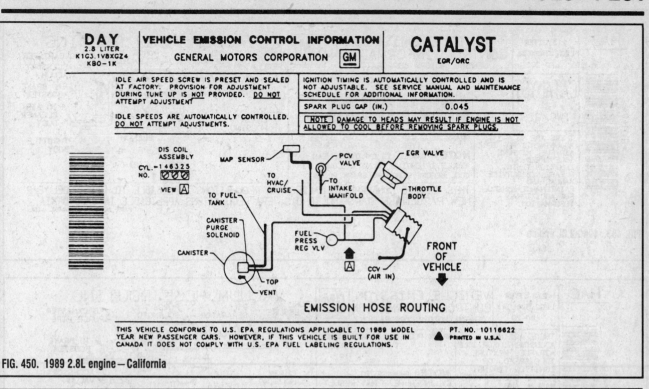

FIG. 450. 1989 2.8L engine—California

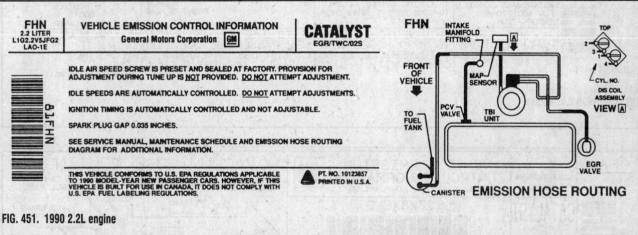

FIG. 451. 1990 2.2L engine

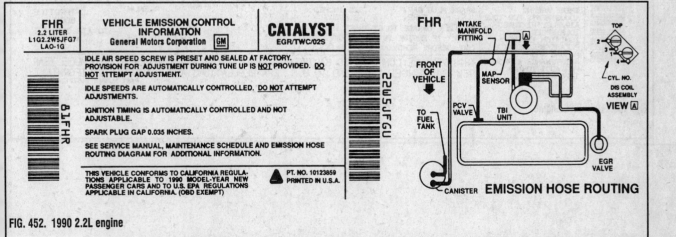

FIG. 452. 1990 2.2L engine

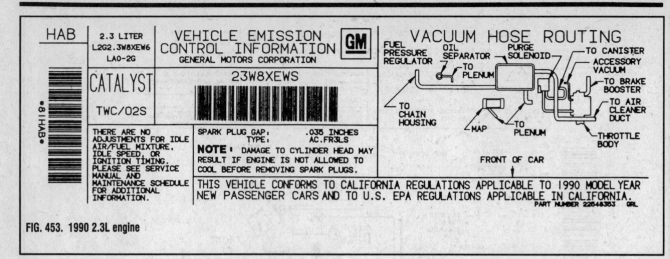

FIG. 453. 1990 2.3L engine

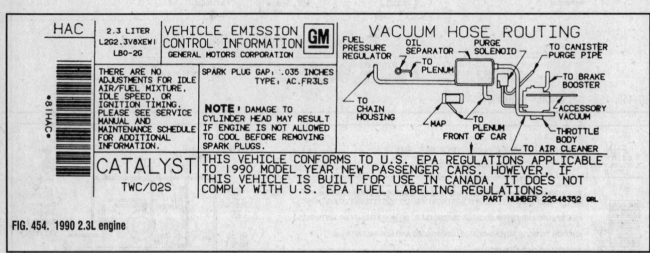

FIG. 454. 1990 2.3L engine

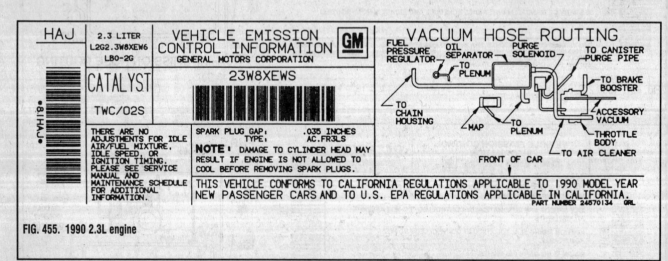

FIG. 455. 1990 2.3L engine

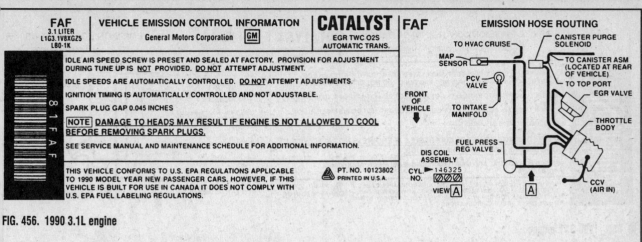

FAF
3.1 LITER
L1G3.1V8XGZ5
LB0-1K

VEHICLE EMISSION CONTROL INFORMATION
General Motors Corporation GM

CATALYST
EGR TWC O2S
AUTOMATIC TRANS.

FAF

EMISSION HOSE ROUTING

IDLE AIR SPEED SCREW IS PRESET AND SEALED AT FACTORY. PROVISION FOR ADJUSTMENT DURING TUNE UP IS NOT PROVIDED. DO NOT ATTEMPT ADJUSTMENT.

IDLE SPEEDS ARE AUTOMATICALLY CONTROLLED. DO NOT ATTEMPT ADJUSTMENTS.

IGNITION TIMING IS AUTOMATICALLY CONTROLLED AND NOT ADJUSTABLE.

SPARK PLUG GAP 0.045 INCHES

NOTE DAMAGE TO HEADS MAY RESULT IF ENGINE IS NOT ALLOWED TO COOL BEFORE REMOVING SPARK PLUGS.

SEE SERVICE MANUAL AND MAINTENANCE SCHEDULE FOR ADDITIONAL INFORMATION.

THIS VEHICLE CONFORMS TO U.S. EPA REGULATIONS APPLICABLE TO 1990 MODEL YEAR NEW PASSENGER CARS. HOWEVER, IF THIS VEHICLE IS BUILT FOR USE IN CANADA IT DOES NOT COMPLY WITH U.S. EPA FUEL LABELING REGULATIONS.

PT. NO. 10123802
PRINTED IN U.S.A.

FIG. 456. 1990 3.1L engine

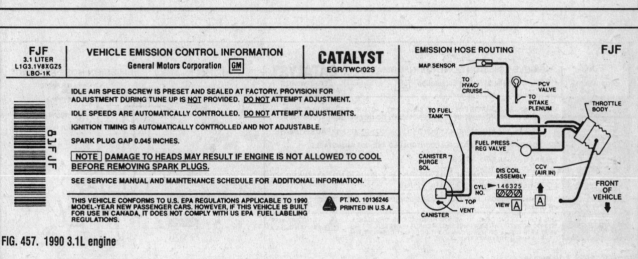

FJF
3.1 LITER
L1G3.1V8XGZ5
LB0-1K

VEHICLE EMISSION CONTROL INFORMATION
General Motors Corporation GM

CATALYST
EGR/TWC/02S

EMISSION HOSE ROUTING

FJF

IDLE AIR SPEED SCREW IS PRESET AND SEALED AT FACTORY. PROVISION FOR ADJUSTMENT DURING TUNE UP IS NOT PROVIDED. DO NOT ATTEMPT ADJUSTMENT.

IDLE SPEEDS ARE AUTOMATICALLY CONTROLLED. DO NOT ATTEMPT ADJUSTMENTS.

IGNITION TIMING IS AUTOMATICALLY CONTROLLED AND NOT ADJUSTABLE.

SPARK PLUG GAP 0.045 INCHES.

NOTE DAMAGE TO HEADS MAY RESULT IF ENGINE IS NOT ALLOWED TO COOL BEFORE REMOVING SPARK PLUGS.

SEE SERVICE MANUAL AND MAINTENANCE SCHEDULE FOR ADDITIONAL INFORMATION.

THIS VEHICLE CONFORMS TO U.S. EPA REGULATIONS APPLICABLE TO 1990 MODEL-YEAR NEW PASSENGER CARS. HOWEVER, IF THIS VEHICLE IS BUILT FOR USE IN CANADA, IT DOES NOT COMPLY WITH US EPA FUEL LABELING REGULATIONS.

PT. NO. 10136246
PRINTED IN U.S.A.

FIG. 457. 1990 3.1L engine

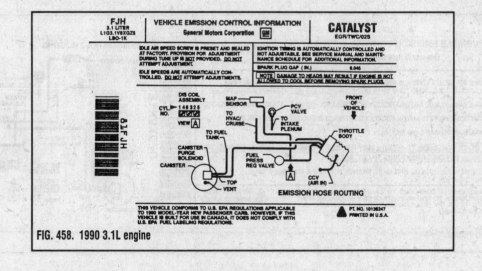

FJH
3.1 LITER
L1G3.1V8XGZ5
LB0-1K

VEHICLE EMISSION CONTROL INFORMATION
General Motors Corporation GM

CATALYST
EGR/TWC/02S

IDLE AIR SPEED SCREW IS PRESET AND SEALED AT FACTORY. PROVISION FOR ADJUSTMENT DURING TUNE UP IS NOT PROVIDED. DO NOT ATTEMPT ADJUSTMENT.

IDLE SPEEDS ARE AUTOMATICALLY CONTROLLED. DO NOT ATTEMPT ADJUSTMENTS.

IGNITION TIMING IS AUTOMATICALLY CONTROLLED AND NOT ADJUSTABLE. SEE SERVICE MANUAL AND MAINTENANCE SCHEDULE FOR ADDITIONAL INFORMATION.

SPARK PLUG GAP (IN.) 0.045

NOTE DAMAGE TO HEADS MAY RESULT IF ENGINE IS NOT ALLOWED TO COOL BEFORE REMOVING SPARK PLUGS.

EMISSION HOSE ROUTING

THIS VEHICLE CONFORMS TO U.S. EPA REGULATIONS APPLICABLE TO 1990 MODEL-YEAR NEW PASSENGER CARS. HOWEVER, IF THIS VEHICLE IS BUILT FOR USE IN CANADA, IT DOES NOT COMPLY WITH U.S. EPA FUEL LABELING REGULATIONS.

PT. NO. 10136247
PRINTED IN U.S.A.

FIG. 458. 1990 3.1L engine

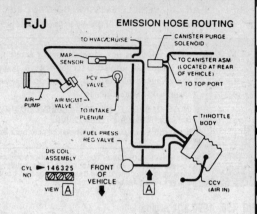

FIG. 459. 1990 3.1L engine

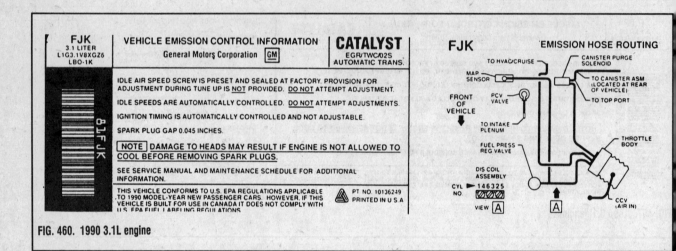

FIG. 460. 1990 3.1L engine

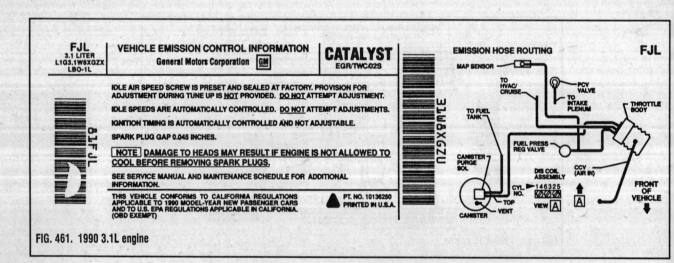

FIG. 461. 1990 3.1L engine

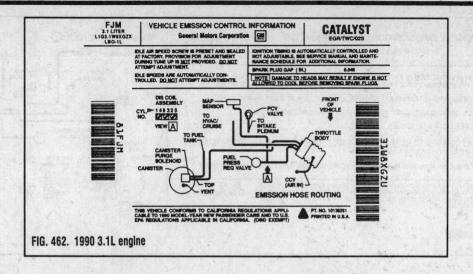

FIG. 462. 1990 3.1L engine

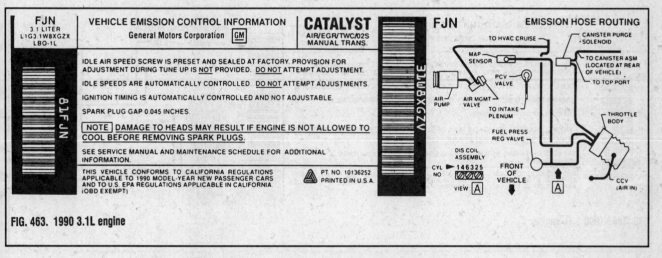

FIG. 463. 1990 3.1L engine

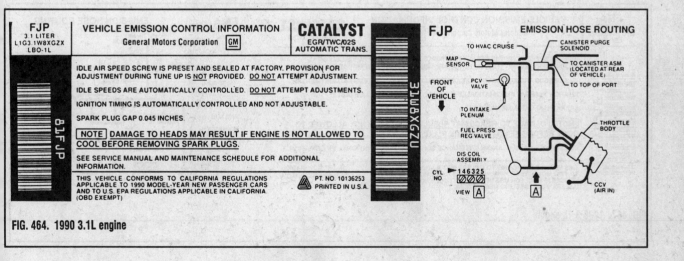

FIG. 464. 1990 3.1L engine

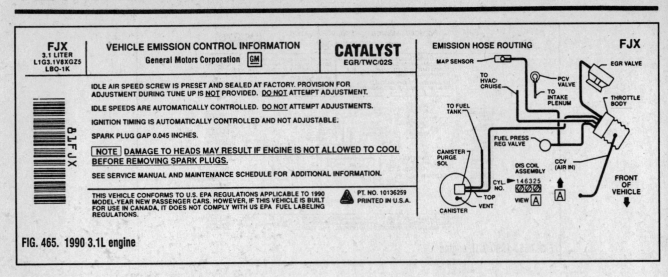

FIG. 465. 1990 3.1L engine

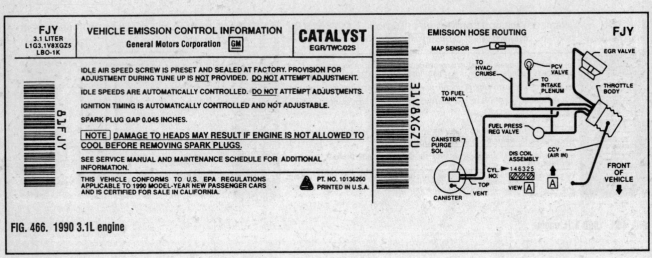

FIG. 466. 1990 3.1L engine

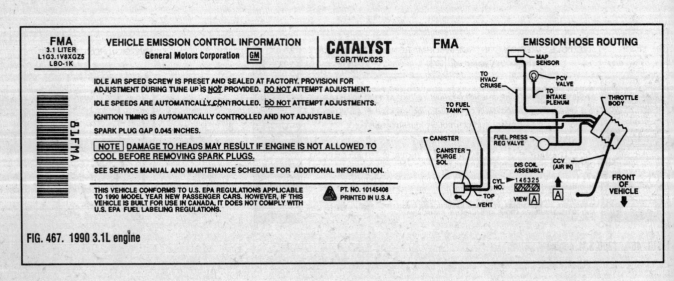

FIG. 467. 1990 3.1L engine

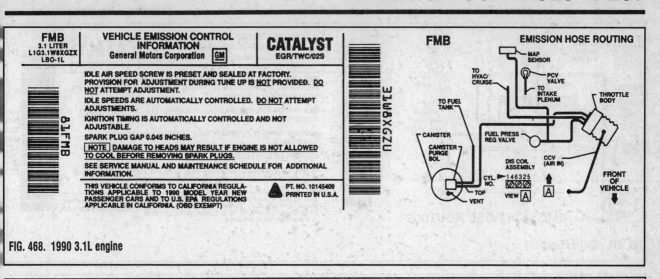

FIG. 468. 1990 3.1L engine

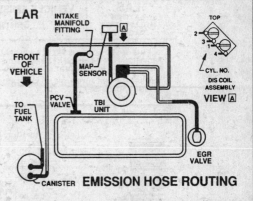

FIG. 469. 1991 2.2L engine

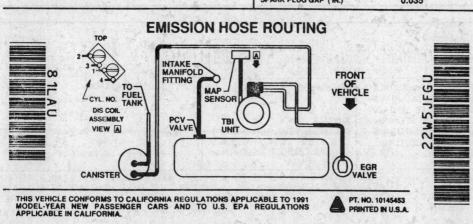

FIG. 470. 1991 2.2L engine

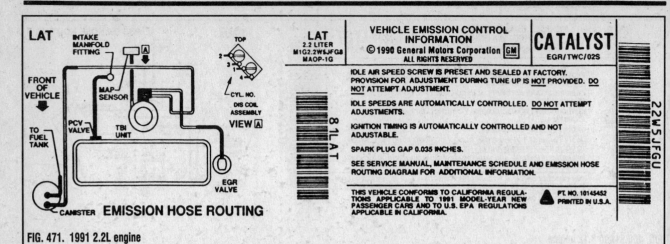

FIG. 471. 1991 2.2L engine

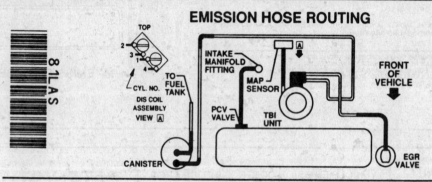

FIG. 472. 1991 2.2L engine

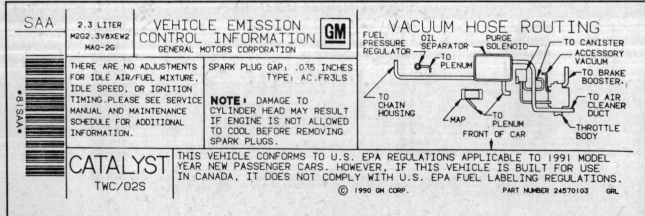

FIG. 473. 1991 2.3L engine

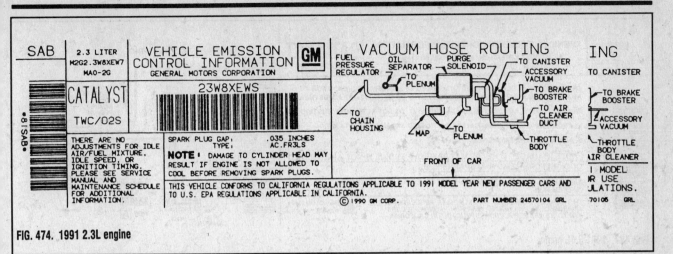

FIG. 474. 1991 2.3L engine

FIG. 475. 1991 2.3L engine

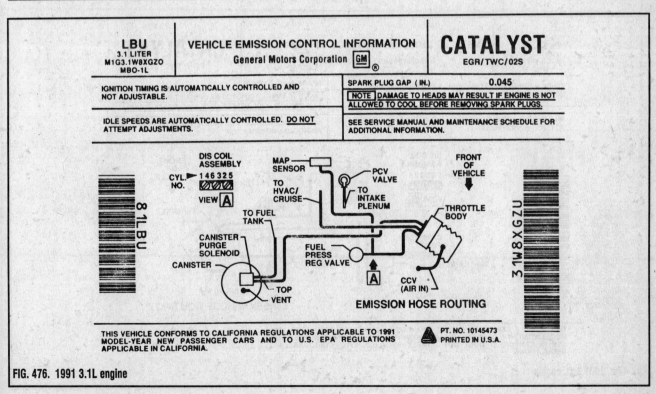

FIG. 476. 1991 3.1L engine

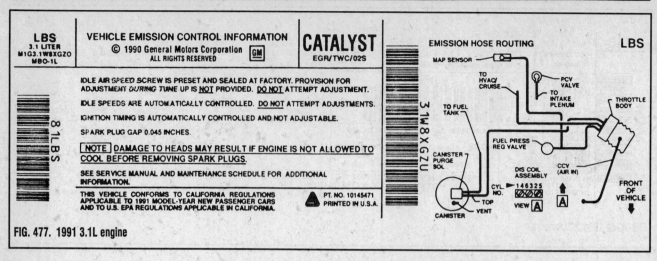

FIG. 477. 1991 3.1L engine

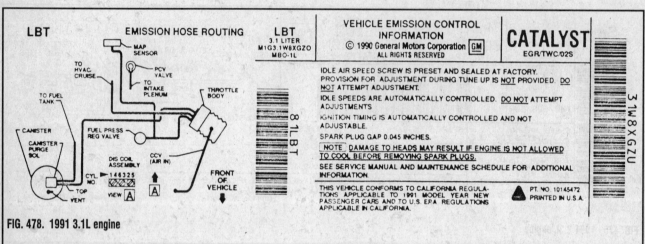

FIG. 478. 1991 3.1L engine

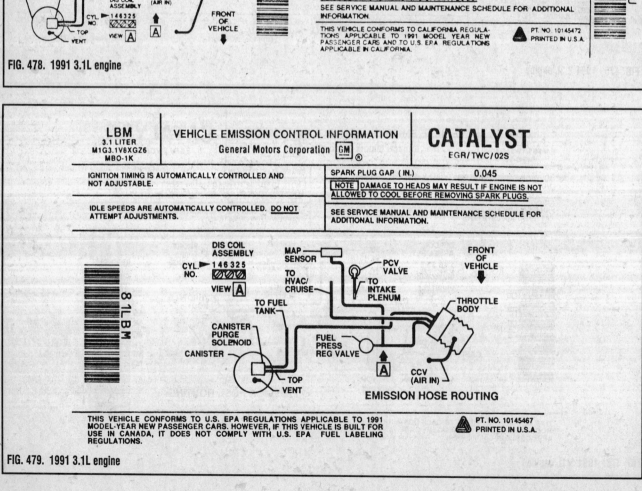

FIG. 479. 1991 3.1L engine

c. If the fuel pipes were disconnect from the fuel rail, remove the fuel inlet and return tube O-ring seals and tube seals and discard.

16. Assemble as follows:

a. Lubricate new injector O-ring seals with clean engine oil, and install on the injectors.

b. Install new injector retaining clips, if necessary.

c. If separated from the fuel rail, install the injector(s) into the fuel rail injector sockets, with the electrical connector facing outward. Push in far enough to engage the retainer clip over the fuel rail extrusion flange.

d. If the fuel pipes were disconnected from the fuel rail, install new inlet and return tube O-ring seals. Lubricate the seals with clean engine oil.

17. If the fuel rail was disconnected from the fuel pipes, apply a few drops of clean engine oil to the male end of the fuel pipes and reconnect the fuel pipes to the rail at this time.

18. Install the return pipe to the regulator, aligning the bracket. Apply Loctite® 262, or equivalent, to the threads of the fuel return pipe bracket screw and tighten to 53 inch lbs. (6.0 Nm).

19. Using a back-up wrench, install the fuel inlet nut to 22 ft. lbs. (30 Nm).

20. Position the fuel rail over the cylinder head, and connect the injector electrical connectors. Rotate the injector(s) as required to avoid stretching the wire harness.

21. Install the fuel rail assembly to the cylinder head and tighten the attaching bolts to 19 ft. lbs. (26 Nm).

22. Install the vacuum hose to the pressure regulator.

23. If the front engine fuel pipes are being replaced, install new pipe O-rings, coated with clean engine oil.

24. Install the inlet and return pipe connections using a back-up wrench, and tighten to 20 ft. lbs. (27 Nm).

25. Install the fuel pipe clamp bolt and tighten to 106 inch lbs. (12 Nm).

26. Install the hose to the bottom of the crankcase ventilation oil/air separator.

27. Position the separator and canister purge solenoid over the attaching bosses.

28. Install the separator and solenoid attaching bolts and tighten to 71 inch lbs.

29. Connect the hoses to the front and the sides of the separator.

30. Tighten the fuel filler cap and connect the negative battery cable.

Fuel Injectors

REMOVAL & INSTALLATION

♦ SEE FIGS 37-39

1. Relieve the fuel system pressure.
2. Disconnect the negative battery cable.
3. Remove the fuel rail assembly from the cylinder head.

➡ **It is not necessary to separate the rail from the fuel pipes.**

4. Remove the injector retaining clip by spreading the open end of the clip slightly and removing from the rail.
5. Remove the injector(s).
6. Remove the O-rings from both ends of the injectors.

To install:

➡ **Each injector is calibrated with a different flow rate. Replace with the identical part numbers.**

7. Install new O-ring seals and lubricate with engine oil.
8. Place new injector retaining clips on the injector assembly. Position the clip on the right side of the injector electrical connector.
9. Install the injector assembly(ies) into the fuel rail socket(s) with the electrical connector facing outward. Push in far enough to engage the retainer clip over the rail extrusion flange.
10. Install the fuel rail assembly.

Pressure Regulator Assembly

REMOVAL & INSTALLATION

♦ SEE FIGS 35-39

1. Relieve the fuel system pressure.
2. Disconnect the negative battery cable.
3. Remove the fuel rail assembly from the cylinder head.
4. Remove the pressure regulator attaching screws.
5. Twist back and forth and remove the regulator from the fuel rail.

To install:

6. Lubricate the new rail to the regulator inlet fitting O-ring seal with clean engine oil and install in the regulator.

7. Install the pressure regulator by aligning the retainer and spacer assembly mounting holes and tightening the retaining screws, with thread locking material, to 49 inch lbs. (5.5 Nm) for 1990 and 102 inch lbs. (11.5 Nm) for 1991–92.

Throttle Body Assembly

REMOVAL & INSTALLATION

♦ SEE FIGS 40-43

1. Relieve the fuel system pressure.
2. Disconnect the negative battery cable.
3. Partially drain the radiator enough to allow the coolant hoses at the throttle body to be removed.
4. Disconnect the air cleaner duct to the throttle body.
5. Disconnect the electrical connectors from the IAC valve and TPS.
6. Disconnect the vacuum hoses at the throttle body.
7. Disconnect the throttle, cruise and transmission control cables to the throttle body.
8. Remove the accelerator cable bracket attaching nut and bolt.
9. Disconnect the power brake vacuum hose at the throttle body.
10. Remove the throttle body attaching bolt and stud.
11. Loosen the throttle body from the manifold.
12. Disconnect the coolant lines and remove the throttle body and gasket from the manifold.

To install:

13. Reposition the throttle body next to the manifold and reconnect the coolant hoses.
14. Install a new mounting gasket and tighten the bolt and stud and tighten the bolts to 19 ft. lbs (26 Nm).
15. Connect the power brake vacuum hose at the throttle body.
16. Connect the throttle, cruise and transmission control cables to the throttle body.
17. Remove the accelerator cable bracket attaching nut and bolt and tighten the nut to 18 ft. lbs (25 Nm) and the bolt to 106 inch lbs. (12 Nm).
18. Connect the vacuum hoses at the throttle body.
19. Connect the electrical connectors to the IAC valve and TPS.

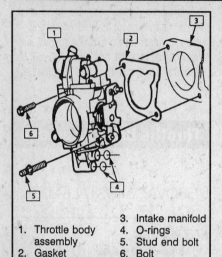

1. Throttle body assembly
2. Gasket
3. Intake manifold
4. O-rings
5. Stud end bolt
6. Bolt

FIG. 40 Throttle body removal on the ASDF fuel injection system — 1990–91 2.3L engine

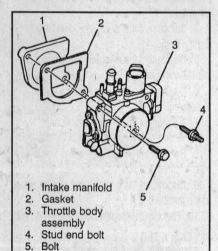

1. Intake manifold
2. Gasket
3. Throttle body assembly
4. Stud end bolt
5. Bolt

FIG. 41 Throttle body removal on the ASDF fuel injection system — 1992 2.3L engine

20. Connect the air cleaner duct to the throttle body.

21. Refill the radiator.

22. Connect the negative battery cable.

23. With the engine off, check to see that the accelerator pedal is free.

24. Reset the IAC pintle position as follows:

a. Turn the ignition switch to the **ON** position (engine **OFF)**.

b. Ground the diagnostic test terminal for 5 seconds.

c. Remove the ground.

d. Turn the ignition switch to the **OFF** position for 10 seconds.

e. Start the engine and check for proper idle information.

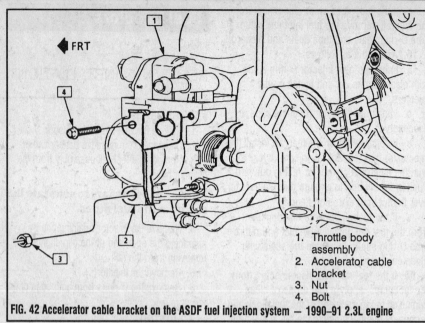

◀ **FRT**

1. Throttle body assembly
2. Accelerator cable bracket
3. Nut
4. Bolt

FIG. 42 Accelerator cable bracket on the ASDF fuel injection system — 1990–91 2.3L engine

Throttle Position Sensor

REMOVAL & INSTALLATION

◆ SEE FIG 46

1. Disconnect the electrical connector from the TPS.

2. Remove the TPS attaching screws and remove the TPS.

To install:

3. With the throttle valve closed, position the TPS on the throttle shaft, than align with the screw holes.

➡ **If replacing the TPS, install new screws that are supplied with the TPS service package.**

4. Tighten the TPS attaching screws to 18 inch lbs. (2.0 Nm).

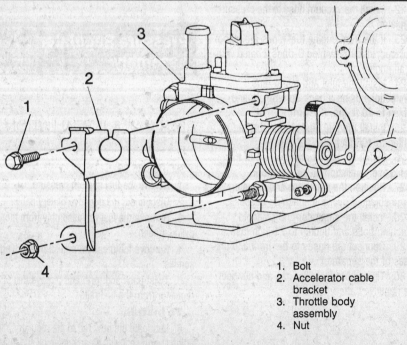

1. Bolt
2. Accelerator cable bracket
3. Throttle body assembly
4. Nut

FIG. 43 Accelerator cable bracket on the ASDF fuel injection system — 1992 2.3L engine

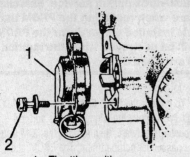

1. Throttle position
sensor (TPS)
2. TPS attaching screw

FIG. 46 Throttle position sensor (TPS) installation on the ASDF fuel injection system 1990–92 2.3L engine

Idle Air Control (IAC) Valve

REMOVAL & INSTALLATION

◆ SEE FIG 47
1. Disconnect the electrical connector from the idle air control valve.
2. Remove the retaining screws and remove the IAC valve.

✸ WARNING

Before installing a new idle air control valve, measure the distance that the valve extends from the tip of the valve pintle and the flange mounting surface. The distance should be no greater than

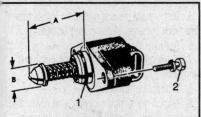

1. IAC valve O-ring
2. IAC valve attaching screw
3. Distance of pintle extension
4. Diameter of pintle

FIG. 47 Idle air control (IAC) valve (TPS) installation on the ASDF fuel injection system 1990–92 2.3L engine

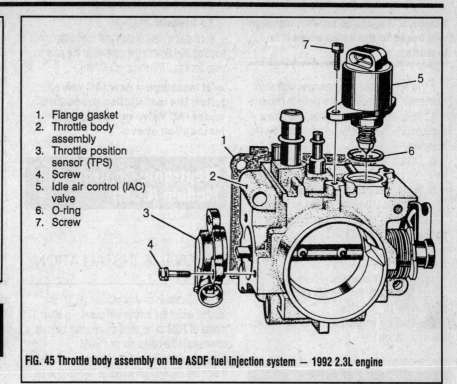

1. Flange gasket
2. Throttle body assembly
3. Throttle position sensor (TPS)
4. Screw
5. Idle air control (IAC) valve
6. O-ring
7. Screw

FIG. 45 Throttle body assembly on the ASDF fuel injection system — 1992 2.3L engine

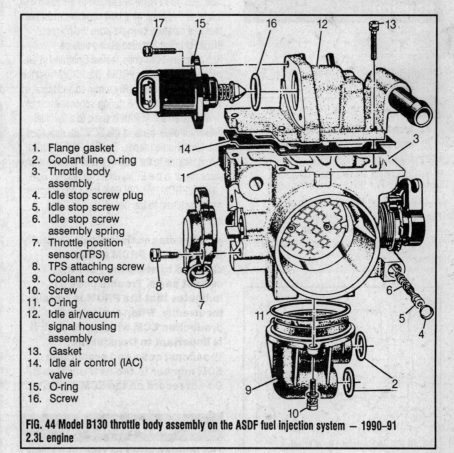

1. Flange gasket
2. Coolant line O-ring
3. Throttle body assembly
4. Idle stop screw plug
5. Idle stop screw
6. Idle stop screw assembly spring
7. Throttle position sensor (TPS)
8. TPS attaching screw
9. Coolant cover
10. Screw
11. O-ring
12. Idle air/vacuum signal housing assembly
13. Gasket
14. Idle air control (IAC) valve
15. O-ring
16. Screw

FIG. 44 Model B130 throttle body assembly on the ASDF fuel injection system — 1990–91 2.3L engine

28mm. If it extends too far, damage will occur to the valve when it is installed.

3. To adjust, exert firm pressure, with slight side to side movement, on the pintle to retract it.

4. To complete the installation, use a new seal lubricated with engine oil and install the IAC assembly.

5. Tighten the screws to 27 inch lbs. (3.0 Nm).

6. Install the electrical connector.

7. Reset the IAC pintle position as follows:

a. Turn the ignition switch to the **ON** position (engine **OFF**).

b. Ground the diagnostic test terminal for 5 seconds.

c. Remove the ground.

d. Turn the ignition switch to the **OFF** position for 10 seconds.

e. Start the engine and check for proper idle information.

Idle Air/Vacuum Signal Housing

REMOVAL & INSTALLATION

♦ SEE FIG 48

1. Disconnect the negative battery cable.

2. Disconnect the vacuum connections at the idle air/vacuum signal housing.

3. Disconnect the IAC valve electrical connection.

4. Remove the IAC valve assembly as described earlier in this section.

5. Remove the idle air/vacuum signal housing screws, and remove the housing and gasket.

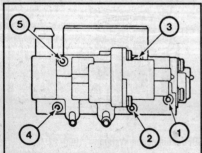

FIG. 48 Idle air/vacuum signal housing assembly screw tightening sequence on the ASDF fuel injection system — 1990–91 2.3L engine

To install:

6. Install a new gasket and reposition the housing and tighten the screws in the proper sequence to 27 inch lbs. (3.0 Nm).

➡ **If installing a new IAC valve, follow the installation procedure under IAC Valve removal and installation above.**

Electronic Control Module (ECM)

REMOVAL & INSTALLATION

The electronic control module (ECM) is located under the instrument panel. To allow 1 model of ECM to be used on different models, a device called a calibrator or PROM (Programmable Read Only Memory) is installed inside the ECM which contains information on the vehicle weight, engine, transmission, axle ratio, etc. The PROM is specific to the exact model and replacement part numbers must be checked carefully to make sure the correct PROM is being installed during service. Replacement ECM units (called Controllers) are supplied WITHOUT a PROM. The PROM from the old ECM must be carefully removed and installed in the replacement unit during service. Another device called a CALPAK is used to allow fuel delivery if other parts of the ECM are damaged (the Limp Home mode). The CALPAK is similar in appearance to the PROM and is located in the same place in the ECM, under an access cover. Like the PROM, the CALPAK must be removed and transferred to the new ECM unit being installed.

➡ **If the diagnosis indicates a faulty ECM unit, the PROM should be checked to see if they are the correct parts. Trouble code 51 indicates that the PROM is installed incorrectly. When replacing the production ECM with a new part, it is important to transfer the Broadcast code and production ECM number to the new part label. Do not record on the ECM cover.**

❄ CAUTION

The ignition must be OFF whenever disconnecting or connecting the ECM electrical harness. It is possible to install a PROM backwards during service. Exercise care when replacing the PROM that it is installed correctly, or the PROM will be destroyed when the ignition is switched ON.

To remove the ECM, first disconnect the battery. Remove the wiring harness and mounting hardware, then remove the ECM from the passenger compartment. The PROM and CALPAK are located under the access cover on the top of the control unit. Using the rocker type PROM removal tool, or equivalent, engage 1 end of the PROM carrier with the hook end of the tool. Press on the vertical bar end of the tool and rock the engaged end of the PROM carrier up as far as possible. Engage the opposite end of the PROM carrier in the same manner and rock this end up as far as possible. Repeat this process until the PROM carrier and PROM are free of the socket. The PROM carrier should only be removed with the removal tool or damage to the PROM or PROM socket may occur.

Fuel Tank

REMOVAL & INSTALLATION

1988–89

♦ SEE FIG. 49

1. Relieve the fuel system pressure as outlined earlier in this section.

2. Disconnect the negative cable at the battery.

3. Raise and support the car.

4. Drain the tank. There is no drain plug; remaining fuel in the tank must be siphoned through the fuel feed line (the line to the fuel pump), because of the restrictor in the filler neck.

5. Disconnect the hose and the vapor return hose from the level sending unit fittings.

6. Remove the ground wire screw.

7. Unplug the level sending unit electrical connector.

8. Disconnect the vent hose.

9. Unbolt the support straps, and lower and remove the tank. Installation is the reverse of removal. Tighten the front retaining strap bolts to 26 ft. lbs. (35 Nm) and the rear strap bolts to 8 ft. lbs. (11 Nm).

1991–92

♦ SEE FIG. 50

1. Relieve the fuel system pressure as outlined earlier in this section.

2. Disconnect the negative cable at the battery.

3. Raise and support the car.

4. Drain the tank. There is no drain plug; remaining fuel in the tank must be siphoned through the fuel filler tube.

5. Remove the exhaust pipe rubber hangers.

6. Remove the muffler hanger attaching bolts.

7. Remove the heat shield attaching screws and remove the heat shield.

8. Remove the filler tube and clamp at the fuel tank.

9. Disconnect the fuel tank vent tube and clamp at the fuel tank vent hose.

10. Disconnect the electrical connector.

11. Disconnect the vapor connecting hose from the fuel level meter.

12. If the nylon feed or return connecting lines become kinked, and cannot be straightened, they must be replaced as follows:

a. Grasp the fuel level meter fuel feed tube and nylon fuel feed connecting line quick

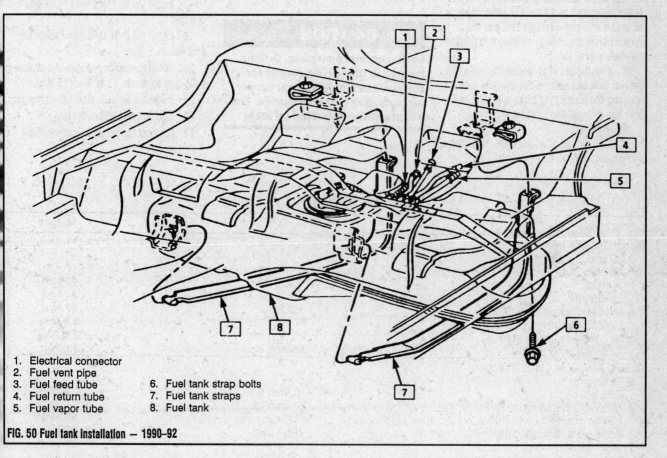

1. Electrical connector
2. Fuel vent pipe
3. Fuel feed tube
4. Fuel return tube
5. Fuel vapor tube
6. Fuel tank strap bolts
7. Fuel tank straps
8. Fuel tank

FIG. 50 Fuel tank installation — 1990–92

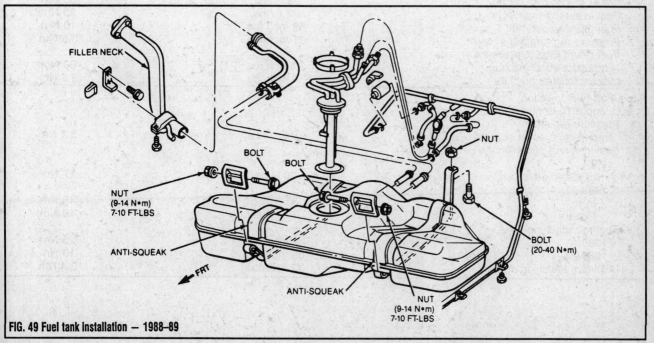

FIG. 49 Fuel tank installation — 1988–89

connect fitting and twist the quick connect fitting 1/4 turn in each direction to loosen any dirt within the fitting. Repeat for the return nylon fuel connecting line fitting.

b. For the fuel return quick connect fittings, squeeze the plastic tabs of the male end connector and pull the connection apart.

c. For the fuel feed quick connect fitting, select the correct tool from J 37088 tool set or its equivalent, and insert the tool into the female connector, then push inward to release the male connector.

13. With the aid of an assistant, support the fuel tank and remove the rear fuel tank retaining strap attaching bolts, fuel tank and both fuel tank retaining straps.

To install:

14. With the aid of an assistant, position and support the fuel tank and install the retaining strap attaching bolts. Tighten to 22 ft. lbs. (30 Nm).

15. Connect the nylon fuel feed and return connecting line quick connect fittings to the fuel level meter as follow:

a. Apply a few drops of clean engine oil to the male tube ends of the engine fuel feed and return pipes.

❄ CAUTION

During normal operation, O-rings, located in the female connector will swell and may prevent proper reconnection if not lubricated. This will prevent a possible fuel leak.

b. Push the connectors together to cause the retaining the retaining tabs/fingers to snap into place. Pull on both ends of each connection to make sure they are secure. Repeat for the other fitting.

16. Install the vapor connecting hose.

17. Install the electrical connector.

18. Install the fuel tank vent hose and clamp.

19. Install the heat shield and attaching screws.

20. Install the muffler hanger and attaching bolts and tighten to 11 ft. lbs. (15 Nm).

21. Install the exhaust pipe rubber hangers.

22. Add fuel and install the cap.

23. Connect the negative battery cable.

TORQUE SPECIFICATIONS

Component	U.S.	Metric
Model 700 TBI Injection		
2.0L and 2.2L Engines		
Throttle body mounting		
1988:	17 ft. lbs.	23 Nm
1989-91:	18 ft. lbs.	24 Nm
Inlet and outlet tube nuts:	20 ft. lbs.	27 Nm
Injector retainer:	27 inch lbs.	3.0 Nm
IAC valve retaining screws:	27 inch lbs.	3.0 Nm
TPS attaching screws:	18 inch lbs.	2.0 Nm
Bottom Feed Port (BFP) Injection		
2.2L Engine		
TPS attaching screws:	18 inch lbs.	2.0 Nm
IAC valve retaining screws:	27 inch lbs.	3.0 Nm
Upper manifold bolts/studs:	22 ft. lbs.	30 Nm
Accelerator bracket bolts/nuts:	18 ft. lbs.	25 Nm
EGR transfer nuts:	20 ft. lbs.	27 Nm
Lower manifold stud nuts:	22 ft. lbs.	30 Nm
Fuel inlet pipe retaining nut:	22 ft. lbs.	30 Nm
Fuel pipe support nut:	89 inch lbs.	10 Nm
Pressure reg. bracket screw:	31 inch lbs.	3.5 Nm
Fuel return pipe to pressure		
regulator attaching nut:	22 inch lbs.	30 Nm
Injector retainer bracket:	31 inch lbs.	3.5 Nm
Multi-Port Fuel Injection		
2.8L and 3.1L Engines		
Pressure regulator		
mounting bracket screws:	28 inch lbs.	3.2 Nm
Fuel inlet and outlet fittings		
1988		
Inlet and outlet:	20 ft lbs.	27 Nm
1989-92		
Inlet:	35 ft. lbs.	48 Nm
Outlet:	30 ft. lbs.	40 Nm
Fuel rail attaching bolts		
1988:	19 ft. lbs.	25 Nm
1989-92:	88 inch lbs.	10 Nm
IAC valve attaching screws:	30 inch lbs.	3.4 Nm

6

CHASSIS ELECTRICAL

UNDERSTANDING AND TROUBLESHOOTING ELECTRICAL SYSTEMS

With the rate at which both import and domestic manufacturers are incorporating electronic control systems into their production lines, it won't be long before every new vehicle is equipped with one or more on-board computer. These electronic components (with no moving parts) should theoretically last the life of the vehicle, provided nothing external happens to damage the circuits or memory chips.

While it is true that electronic components should never wear out, in the real world malfunctions do occur. It is also true that any computer-based system is extremely sensitive to electrical voltages and cannot tolerate careless or haphazard testing or service procedures. An inexperienced individual can literally do major damage looking for a minor problem by using the wrong kind of test equipment or connecting test leads or connectors with the ignition switch ON. When selecting test equipment, make sure the manufacturers instructions state that the tester is compatible with whatever type of electronic control system is being serviced. Read all instructions carefully and double check all test points before installing probes or making any test connections.

The following section outlines basic diagnosis techniques for dealing with computerized automotive control systems. Along with a general explanation of the various types of test equipment available to aid in servicing modern electronic automotive systems, basic repair techniques for wiring harnesses and connectors is given. Read the basic information before attempting any repairs or testing on any computerized system, to provide the background of information necessary to avoid the most common and obvious mistakes that can cost both time and money. Although the replacement and testing procedures are simple in themselves, the systems are not, and unless one has a thorough understanding of all components and their function within a particular computerized control system, the logical test sequence these systems demand cannot be followed. Minor malfunctions can make a big difference, so it is important to know how each component affects the operation of the overall electronic system to find the ultimate cause of a problem without replacing good components unnecessarily. It is not enough to use the correct test equipment; the test equipment must be used correctly.

Safety Precautions

❊❊ CAUTION

Whenever working on or around any computer based microprocessor control system, always observe these general precautions to prevent the possibility of personal injury or damage to electronic components.

• Never install or remove battery cables with the key ON or the engine running. Jumper cables should be connected with the key OFF to avoid power surges that can damage electronic control units. Engines equipped with computer controlled systems should avoid both giving and getting jump starts due to the possibility of serious damage to components from arcing in the engine compartment when connections are made with the ignition ON.

• Always remove the battery cables before charging the battery. Never use a high output charger on an installed battery or attempt to use any type of "hot shot" (24 volt) starting aid.

• Exercise care when inserting test probes into connectors to insure good connections without damaging the connector or spreading the pins. Always probe connectors from the rear (wire) side, NOT the pin side, to avoid accidental shorting of terminals during test procedures.

• Never remove or attach wiring harness connectors with the ignition switch ON, especially to an electronic control unit.

• Do not drop any components during service procedures and never apply 12 volts directly to any component (like a solenoid or relay) unless instructed specifically to do so. Some component electrical windings are designed to safely handle only 4 or 5 volts and can be destroyed in seconds if 12 volts are applied directly to the connector.

• Remove the electronic control unit if the vehicle is to be placed in an environment where temperatures exceed approximately 176°F (80°C), such as a paint spray booth or when arc or gas welding near the control unit location in the car.

ORGANIZED TROUBLESHOOTING

When diagnosing a specific problem, organized troubleshooting is a must. The complexity of a modern automobile demands that you approach any problem in a logical, organized manner. There are certain troubleshooting techniques that are standard:

1. Establish when the problem occurs. Does the problem appear only under certain conditions? Were there any noises, odors, or other unusual symptoms?

2. Isolate the problem area. To do this, make some simple tests and observations; then eliminate the systems that are working properly. Check for obvious problems such as broken wires, dirty connections or split or disconnected vacuum hoses. Always check the obvious before assuming something complicated is the cause.

3. Test for problems systematically to determine the cause once the problem area is isolated. Are all the components functioning properly? Is there power going to electrical switches and motors? Is there vacuum at vacuum switches and/or actuators? Is there a mechanical problem such as bent linkage or loose mounting screws? Doing careful, systematic checks will often turn up most causes on the first inspection without wasting time checking components that have little or no relationship to the problem.

4. Test all repairs after the work is done to make sure that the problem is fixed. Some causes can be traced to more than one component, so a careful verification of repair work is important to pick up additional malfunctions that may cause a problem to reappear or a different problem to arise. A blown fuse, for example, is a simple problem that may require more than another fuse to repair. If you don't look for a problem that caused a fuse to blow, for example, a shorted wire may go undetected.

Experience has shown that most problems tend to be the result of a fairly simple and obvious cause, such as loose or corroded connectors or air leaks in the intake system; making careful inspection of components during testing essential to quick and accurate troubleshooting. Special, hand held computerized testers designed specifically for diagnosing the system are available from a variety of aftermarket sources, as well as from the vehicle manufacturer, but care should be taken that any test equipment being used is designed to diagnose that particular computer controlled system accurately without damaging the control unit (ECU) or components being tested.

➡ **Pinpointing the exact cause of trouble in an electrical system can sometimes only be accomplished by the use of special test equipment. The following describes commonly used test equipment and explains how to put it to best use in diagnosis. In addition to the information covered below, the manufacturer's instructions booklet provided with the tester should be read and clearly understood before attempting any test procedures.**

TEST EQUIPMENT

Jumper Wires

Jumper wires are simple, yet extremely valuable, pieces of test equipment. Jumper wires are merely wires that are used to bypass sections of a circuit. The simplest type of jumper wire is merely a length of multistrand wire with an alligator clip at each end. Jumper wires are usually fabricated from lengths of standard automotive wire and whatever type of connector (alligator clip, spade connector or pin connector) that is required for the particular vehicle being tested. The well equipped tool box will have several different styles of jumper wires in several different lengths. Some jumper wires are made with three or more terminals coming from a common splice for special purpose testing. In cramped, hard-to-reach areas it is advisable to have insulated boots over the jumper wire terminals in order to prevent accidental grounding, sparks, and possible fire, especially when testing fuel system components.

Jumper wires are used primarily to locate open electrical circuits, on either the ground (-) side of the circuit or on the hot (+) side. If an electrical component fails to operate, connect the jumper wire between the component and a good ground. If the component operates only with the jumper installed, the ground circuit is open. If the ground circuit is good, but the component does not operate, the circuit between the power feed and component is open. You can sometimes connect the jumper wire directly from the battery to the hot terminal of the component, but first make sure the component uses 12 volts in operation. Some electrical components, such as fuel injectors, are

designed to operate on about 4 volts and running 12 volts directly to the injector terminals can burn out the wiring. By inserting an inline fuseholder between a set of test leads, a fused jumper wire can be used for bypassing open circuits. Use a 5 amp fuse to provide protection against voltage spikes. When in doubt, use a voltmeter to check the voltage input to the component and measure how much voltage is being applied normally. By moving the jumper wire successively back from the lamp toward the power source, you can isolate the area of the circuit where the open is located. When the component stops functioning, or the power is cut off, the open is in the segment of wire between the jumper and the point previously tested.

✳✳ CAUTION

Never use jumpers made from wire that is of lighter gauge than used in the circuit under test. If the jumper wire is of too small gauge, it may overheat and possibly melt. Never use jumpers to bypass high resistance loads (such as motors) in a circuit. Bypassing resistances, in effect, creates a short circuit which may, in turn, cause damage and fire. Never use a jumper for anything other than temporary bypassing of components in a circuit.

12 Volt Test Light

The 12 volt test light is used to check circuits and components while electrical current is flowing through them. It is used for voltage and ground tests. Twelve volt test lights come in different styles but all have three main parts; a ground clip, a probe, and a light. The most commonly used 12 volt test lights have pick-type probes. To use a 12 volt test light, connect the ground clip to a good ground and probe wherever necessary with the pick. The pick should be sharp so that it can penetrate wire insulation to make contact with the wire, without making a large hole in the insulation. The wrap-around light is handy in hard to reach areas or where it is difficult to support a wire to push a probe pick into it. To use the wrap around light, hook the wire to probed with the hook and pull the trigger. A small pick will be forced through the wire insulation into the wire core.

✳✳ CAUTION

Do not use a test light to probe electronic ignition spark plug or coil wires. Never use a pick-type test light to probe wiring on computer controlled systems unless specifically instructed to do so. Any wire insulation that is pierced by the test light probe should be taped and sealed with silicone after testing.

Like the jumper wire, the 12 volt test light is used to isolate opens in circuits. But, whereas the jumper wire is used to bypass the open to operate the load, the 12 volt test light is used to locate the presence of voltage in a circuit. If the test light glows, you know that there is power up to that point; if the 12 volt test light does not glow when its probe is inserted into the wire or connector, you know that there is an open circuit (no power). Move the test light in successive steps back toward the power source until the light in the handle does glow. When it does glow, the open is between the probe and point previously probed.

➡ **The test light does not detect that 12 volts (or any particular amount of voltage) is present; it only detects that some voltage is present. It is advisable before using the test light to touch its terminals across the battery posts to make sure the light is operating properly.**

Self-Powered Test Light

The self-powered test light usually contains a 1.5 volt penlight battery. One type of self-powered test light is similar in design to the 12 volt test light. This type has both the battery and the light in the handle and pick-type probe tip. The second type has the light toward the open tip, so that the light illuminates the contact point. The self-powered test light is dual purpose piece of test equipment. It can be used to test for either open or short circuits when power is isolated from the circuit (continuity test). A powered test light should not be used on any computer controlled system or component unless specifically instructed to do so. Many engine sensors can be destroyed by even this small amount of voltage applied directly to the terminals.

Open Circuit Testing

To use the self-powered test light to check for open circuits, first isolate the circuit from the vehicle's 12 volt power source by disconnecting the battery or wiring harness connector. Connect the test light ground clip to a good ground and probe sections of the circuit sequentially with the test light. (start from either end of the circuit). If the light is out, the open is between the probe and the circuit ground. If the light is on, the open is between the probe and end of the circuit toward the power source.

Short Circuit Testing

By isolating the circuit both from power and from ground, and using a self-powered test light, you can check for shorts to ground in the circuit. Isolate the circuit from power and ground. Connect the test light ground clip to a good ground and probe any easy-to-reach test point in the circuit. If the light comes on, there is a short somewhere in the circuit. To isolate the short, probe a test point at either end of the isolated circuit (the light should be on). Leave the test light probe connected and open connectors, switches, remove parts, etc., sequentially, until the light goes out. When the light goes out, the short is between the last circuit component opened and the previous circuit opened.

➡ The 1.5 volt battery in the test light does not provide much current. A weak battery may not provide enough power to illuminate the test light even when a complete circuit is made (especially if there are high resistances in the circuit). Always make sure that the test battery is strong. To check the battery, briefly touch the ground clip to the probe; if the light glows brightly the battery is strong enough for testing. Never use a self-powered test light to perform checks for opens or shorts when power is applied to the electrical system under test. The 12 volt vehicle power will quickly burn out the 1.5 volt light bulb in the test light.

Voltmeter

A voltmeter is used to measure voltage at any point in a circuit, or to measure the voltage drop across any part of a circuit. It can also be used to check continuity in a wire or circuit by indicating current flow from one end to the other. Voltmeters usually have various scales on the meter dial and a selector switch to allow the selection of different voltages. The voltmeter has a positive and a negative lead. To avoid damage to the meter, always connect the negative lead to the negative (-) side of circuit (to ground or nearest the ground side of the circuit) and connect the positive lead to the positive (+) side of the circuit (to the power source or the nearest power source). Note that the negative voltmeter

lead will always be black and that the positive voltmeter will always be some color other than black (usually red). Depending on how the voltmeter is connected into the circuit, it has several uses.

A voltmeter can be connected either in parallel or in series with a circuit and it has a very high resistance to current flow. When connected in parallel, only a small amount of current will flow through the voltmeter current path; the rest will flow through the normal circuit current path and the circuit will work normally. When the voltmeter is connected in series with a circuit, only a small amount of current can flow through the circuit. The circuit will not work properly, but the voltmeter reading will show if the circuit is complete or not.

Available Voltage Measurement

Set the voltmeter selector switch to the 20V position and connect the meter negative lead to the negative post of the battery. Connect the positive meter lead to the positive post of the battery and turn the ignition switch ON to provide a load. Read the voltage on the meter or digital display. A well charged battery should register over 12 volts. If the meter reads below 11.5 volts, the battery power may be insufficient to operate the electrical system properly. This test determines voltage available from the battery and should be the first step in any electrical trouble diagnosis procedure. Many electrical problems, especially on computer controlled systems, can be caused by a low state of charge in the battery. Excessive corrosion at the battery cable terminals can cause a poor contact that will prevent proper charging and full battery current flow.

Normal battery voltage is 12 volts when fully charged. When the battery is supplying current to one or more circuits it is said to be "under load". When everything is off the electrical system is under a "no-load" condition. A fully charged battery may show about 12.5 volts at no load; will drop to 12 volts under medium load; and will drop even lower under heavy load. If the battery is partially discharged the voltage decrease under heavy load may be excessive, even though the battery shows 12 volts or more at no load. When allowed to discharge further, the battery's available voltage under load will decrease more severely. For this reason, it is important that the battery be fully charged during all testing procedures to avoid errors in diagnosis and incorrect test results.

Voltage Drop

When current flows through a resistance, the voltage beyond the resistance is reduced (the larger the current, the greater the reduction in

voltage). When no current is flowing, there is no voltage drop because there is no current flow. All points in the circuit which are connected to the power source are at the same voltage as the power source. The total voltage drop always equals the total source voltage. In a long circuit with many connectors, a series of small, unwanted voltage drops due to corrosion at the connectors can add up to a total loss of voltage which impairs the operation of the normal loads in the circuit.

INDIRECT COMPUTATION OF VOLTAGE DROPS

1. Set the voltmeter selector switch to the 20 volt position.
2. Connect the meter negative lead to a good ground.
3. Probe all resistances in the circuit with the positive meter lead.
4. Operate the circuit in all modes and observe the voltage readings.

DIRECT MEASUREMENT OF VOLTAGE DROPS

1. Set the voltmeter switch to the 20 volt position.
2. Connect the voltmeter negative lead to the ground side of the resistance load to be measured.
3. Connect the positive lead to the positive side of the resistance or load to be measured.
4. Read the voltage drop directly on the 20 volt scale.

Too high a voltage indicates too high a resistance. If, for example, a blower motor runs too slowly, you can determine if there is too high a resistance in the resistor pack. By taking voltage drop readings in all parts of the circuit, you can isolate the problem. Too low a voltage drop indicates too low a resistance. If, for example, a blower motor runs too fast in the MED and/or LOW position, the problem can be isolated in the resistor pack by taking voltage drop readings in all parts of the circuit to locate a possibly shorted resistor. The maximum allowable voltage drop under load is critical, especially if there is more than one high resistance problem in a circuit because all voltage drops are cumulative. A small drop is normal due to the resistance of the conductors.

HIGH RESISTANCE TESTING

1. Set the voltmeter selector switch to the 4 volt position.
2. Connect the voltmeter positive lead to the positive post of the battery.
3. Turn on the headlights and heater blower to provide a load.
4. Probe various points in the circuit with the negative voltmeter lead.

5. Read the voltage drop on the 4 volt scale. Some average maximum allowable voltage drops are:

    FUSE PANEL — 7 volts
    IGNITION SWITCH — 5volts
    HEADLIGHT SWITCH — 7 volts
    IGNITION COIL (+) — 5 volts
    ANY OTHER LOAD — 1.3 volts

➡ **Voltage drops are all measured while a load is operating; without current flow, there will be no voltage drop.**

Ohmmeter

The ohmmeter is designed to read resistance (ohms) in a circuit or component. Although there are several different styles of ohmmeters, all will usually have a selector switch which permits the measurement of different ranges of resistance (usually the selector switch allows the multiplication of the meter reading by 10, 100, 1000, and 10,000). A calibration knob allows the meter to be set at zero for accurate measurement. Since all ohmmeters are powered by an internal battery (usually 9 volts), the ohmmeter can be used as a self-powered test light. When the ohmmeter is connected, current from the ohmmeter flows through the circuit or component being tested. Since the ohmmeter's internal resistance and voltage are known values, the amount of current flow through the meter depends on the resistance of the circuit or component being tested.

The ohmmeter can be used to perform continuity test for opens or shorts (either by observation of the meter needle or as a self-powered test light), and to read actual resistance in a circuit. It should be noted that the ohmmeter is used to check the resistance of a component or wire while there is no voltage applied to the circuit. Current flow from an outside voltage source (such as the vehicle battery) can damage the ohmmeter, so the circuit or component should be isolated from the vehicle electrical system before any testing is done. Since the ohmmeter uses its own voltage source, either lead can be connected to any test point.

➡ **When checking diodes or other solid state components, the ohmmeter leads can only be connected one way in order to measure current flow in a single direction. Make sure the positive (+) and negative (-) terminal connections are as described in the test procedures to verify the one-way diode operation.**

In using the meter for making continuity checks, do not be concerned with the actual resistance readings. Zero resistance, or any resistance readings, indicate continuity in the circuit. Infinite resistance indicates an open in the circuit. A high resistance reading where there should be none indicates a problem in the circuit. Checks for short circuits are made in the same manner as checks for open circuits except that the circuit must be isolated from both power and normal ground. Infinite resistance indicates no continuity to ground, while zero resistance indicates a dead short to ground.

RESISTANCE MEASUREMENT

The batteries in an ohmmeter will weaken with age and temperature, so the ohmmeter must be calibrated or "zeroed" before taking measurements. To zero the meter, place the selector switch in its lowest range and touch the two ohmmeter leads together. Turn the calibration knob until the meter needle is exactly on zero.

➡ **All analog (needle) type ohmmeters must be zeroed before use, but some digital ohmmeter models are automatically calibrated when the switch is turned on. Self-calibrating digital ohmmeters do not have an adjusting knob, but its a good idea to check for a zero readout before use by touching the leads together. All computer controlled systems require the use of a digital ohmmeter with at least 10 megohms impedance for testing. Before any test procedures are attempted, make sure the ohmmeter used is compatible with the electrical system or damage to the on-board computer could result.**

To measure resistance, first isolate the circuit from the vehicle power source by disconnecting the battery cables or the harness connector. Make sure the key is OFF when disconnecting any components or the battery. Where necessary, also isolate at least one side of the circuit to be checked to avoid reading parallel resistances. Parallel circuit resistances will always give a lower reading than the actual resistance of either of the branches. When measuring the resistance of parallel circuits, the total resistance will always be lower than the smallest resistance in the circuit. Connect the meter leads to both sides of the circuit (wire or component) and read the actual measured ohms on the meter scale. Make sure the selector switch is set to the proper ohm scale for the

circuit being tested to avoid misreading the ohmmeter test value.

Ammeters

An ammeter measures the amount of current flowing through a circuit in units called amperes or amps. Amperes are units of electron flow which indicate how fast the electrons are flowing through the circuit. Since Ohms Law dictates that current flow in a circuit is equal to the circuit voltage divided by the total circuit resistance, increasing voltage also increases the current level (amps). Likewise, any decrease in resistance will increase the amount of amps in a circuit. At normal operating voltage, most circuits have a characteristic amount of amperes, called "current draw" which can be measured using an ammeter. By referring to a specified current draw rating, measuring the amperes, and comparing the two values, one can determine what is happening within the circuit to aid in diagnosis. An open circuit, for example, will not allow any current to flow so the ammeter reading will be zero. More current flows through a heavily loaded circuit or when the charging system is operating.

An ammeter is always connected in series with the circuit being tested. All of the current that normally flows through the circuit must also flow through the ammeter; if there is any other path for the current to follow, the ammeter reading will not be accurate. The ammeter itself has very little resistance to current flow and therefore will not affect the circuit, but it will measure current draw only when the circuit is closed and electricity is flowing. Excessive current draw can blow fuses and drain the battery, while a reduced current draw can cause motors to run slowly, lights to dim and other components to not operate properly. The ammeter can help diagnose these conditions by locating the cause of the high or low reading.

Multimeters

Different combinations of test meters can be built into a single unit designed for specific tests. Some of the more common combination test devices are known as Volt/Amp testers, Tach/Dwell meters, or Digital Multimeters. The Volt/

Amp tester is used for charging system, starting system or battery tests and consists of a voltmeter, an ammeter and a variable resistance carbon pile. The voltmeter will usually have at least two ranges for use with 6, 12 and 24 volt systems. The ammeter also has more than one range for testing various levels of battery loads and starter current draw and the carbon pile can be adjusted to offer different amounts of resistance. The Volt/Amp tester has heavy leads to carry large amounts of current and many later models have an inductive ammeter pickup that clamps around the wire to simplify test connections. On some models, the ammeter also has a zero-center scale to allow testing of charging and starting systems without switching leads or polarity. A digital multimeter is a voltmeter, ammeter and ohmmeter combined in an instrument which gives a digital readout. These are often used when testing solid state circuits because of their high input impedance (usually 10 megohms or more).

The tach/dwell meter combines a tachometer and a dwell (cam angle) meter and is a specialized kind of voltmeter. The tachometer scale is marked to show engine speed in rpm and the dwell scale is marked to show degrees of distributor shaft rotation. In most electronic ignition systems, dwell is determined by the control unit, but the dwell meter can also be used to check the duty cycle (operation) of some electronic engine control systems. Some tach/dwell meters are powered by an internal battery, while others take their power from the car battery in use. The battery powered testers usually require calibration much like an ohmmeter before testing.

Special Test Equipment

A variety of diagnostic tools are available to help troubleshoot and repair computerized engine control systems. The most sophisticated of these devices are the console type engine analyzers that usually occupy a garage service bay, but there are several types of aftermarket electronic testers available that will allow quick circuit tests of the engine control system by plugging directly into a special connector located in the engine compartment or under the dashboard. Several tool and equipment manufacturers offer simple, hand held testers that measure various circuit voltage levels on command to check all system components for proper operation. Although these testers usually cost about $300-$500, consider that the average computer control unit (or ECM) can cost just as much and the money saved by not replacing perfectly good sensors or components in an attempt to correct a problem could justify the purchase price of a special diagnostic tester the first time it's used.

These computerized testers can allow quick and easy test measurements while the engine is operating or while the car is being driven. In addition, the on-board computer memory can be read to access any stored trouble codes; in effect allowing the computer to tell you where it hurts and aid trouble diagnosis by pinpointing exactly which circuit or component is malfunctioning. In the same manner, repairs can be tested to make sure the problem has been corrected. The biggest advantage these special testers have is their relatively easy hookups that minimize or eliminate the chances of making the wrong connections and getting false voltage readings or damaging the computer accidentally.

➡ **It should be remembered that these testers check voltage levels in circuits; they don't detect mechanical problems or failed components if the circuit voltage falls within the preprogrammed limits stored in the tester PROM unit. Also, most of the hand held testers are designed to work only on one or two systems made by a specific manufacturer.**

A variety of aftermarket testers are available to help diagnose different computerized control systems. Owatonna Tool Company (OTC), for example, markets a device called the OTC Monitor which plugs directly into the assembly line diagnostic link (ALDL). The OTC tester makes diagnosis a simple matter of pressing the correct buttons and, by changing the internal PROM or inserting a different diagnosis cartridge, it will work on any model from full size to subcompact, over a wide range of years. An adapter is supplied with the tester to allow connection to all types of ALDL links, regardless of the number of pin terminals used. By inserting an updated PROM into the OTC tester, it can be easily updated to diagnose any new modifications of computerized control systems.

Wiring Harnesses

The average automobile contains about 1/2 mile of wiring, with hundreds of individual connections. To protect the many wires from damage and to keep them from becoming a confusing tangle, they are organized into bundles, enclosed in plastic or taped together and called wire harnesses. Different wiring harnesses serve different parts of the vehicle. Individual wires are color coded to help trace them through a harness where sections are hidden from view.

A loose or corroded connection or a replacement wire that is too small for the circuit will add extra resistance and an additional voltage drop to the circuit. A ten percent voltage drop can result in slow or erratic motor operation, for example, even though the circuit is complete. Automotive wiring or circuit conductors can be in any one of three forms:

1. Single strand wire
2. Multistrand wire
3. Printed circuitry

Single strand wire has a solid metal core and is usually used inside such components as alternators, motors, relays and other devices. Multistrand wire has a core made of many small strands of wire twisted together into a single conductor. Most of the wiring in an automotive electrical system is made up of multistrand wire, either as a single conductor or grouped together in a harness. All wiring is color coded on the insulator, either as a solid color or as a colored wire with an identification stripe. A printed circuit is a thin film of copper or other conductor that is printed on an insulator backing. Occasionally, a printed circuit is sandwiched between two sheets of plastic for more protection and flexibility. A complete printed circuit, consisting of conductors, insulating material and connectors for lamps or other components is called a printed circuit board. Printed circuitry is used in place of individual wires or harnesses in places where space is limited, such as behind instrument panels.

Wire Gauge

Since computer controlled automotive electrical systems are very sensitive to changes in resistance, the selection of properly sized wires is critical when systems are repaired. The wire gauge number is an expression of the cross section area of the conductor. The most common system for expressing wire size is the American Wire Gauge (AWG) system.

Wire cross section area is measured in circular mils. A mil is $\frac{1}{1000}$ in. (0.001 in. [0.0254mm]); a circular mil is the area of a circle one mil in diameter. For example, a conductor $\frac{1}{4}$ in. (6mm) in diameter is 0.250 in. or 250 mils. The circular mil cross section area of the wire is 250 squared (250^2) or 62,500 circular mils. Imported car models usually use metric wire gauge designations, which is simply the cross section area of the conductor in square millimeters (mm^2).

Gauge numbers are assigned to conductors of various cross section areas. As gauge number increases, area decreases and the conductor becomes smaller. A 5 gauge conductor is smaller than a 1 gauge conductor and a 10 gauge is smaller than a 5 gauge. As the cross section area of a conductor decreases, resistance increases and so does the gauge number. A conductor with a higher gauge number will carry less current than a conductor with a lower gauge number.

➡ **Gauge wire size refers to the size of the conductor, not the size of the complete wire. It is possible to have two wires of the same gauge with different diameters because one may have thicker insulation than the other.**

12 volt automotive electrical systems generally use 10, 12, 14, 16 and 18 gauge wire. Main power distribution circuits and larger accessories usually use 10 and 12 gauge wire. Battery cables are usually 4 or 6 gauge, although 1 and 2 gauge wires are occasionally used. Wire length must also be considered when making repairs to a circuit. As conductor length increases, so does resistance. An 18 gauge wire, for example, can carry a 10 amp load for 10 feet without excessive voltage drop; however if a 15 foot wire is required for the same 10 amp load, it must be a 16 gauge wire.

An electrical schematic shows the electrical current paths when a circuit is operating properly. It is essential to understand how a circuit works before trying to figure out why it doesn't. Schematics break the entire electrical system down into individual circuits and show only one particular circuit. In a schematic, no attempt is made to represent wiring and components as they physically appear on the vehicle; switches and other components are shown as simply as possible. Face views of harness connectors show the cavity or terminal locations in all multi-pin connectors to help locate test points.

If you need to backprobe a connector while it is on the component, the order of the terminals must be mentally reversed. The wire color code can help in this situation, as well as a keyway, lock tab or other reference mark.

➡ **Wiring diagrams are not included in this book. As trucks have become more complex and available with longer option lists, wiring diagrams have grown in size and complexity. It has become almost impossible to provide a readable reproduction of a wiring diagram in a book this size. Information on ordering wiring diagrams from the vehicle manufacturer can be found in the owner's manual.**

WIRING REPAIR

Soldering is a quick, efficient method of joining metals permanently. Everyone who has the occasion to make wiring repairs should know how to solder. Electrical connections that are soldered are far less likely to come apart and will conduct electricity much better than connections that are only "pig-tailed" together. The most popular (and preferred) method of soldering is with an electrical soldering gun. Soldering irons are available in many sizes and wattage ratings. Irons with higher wattage ratings deliver higher temperatures and recover lost heat faster. A small soldering iron rated for no more than 50 watts is recommended, especially on electrical systems where excess heat can damage the components being soldered.

There are three ingredients necessary for successful soldering; proper flux, good solder and sufficient heat. A soldering flux is necessary to clean the metal of tarnish, prepare it for soldering and to enable the solder to spread into tiny crevices. When soldering, always use a resin flux or resin core solder which is non-corrosive and will not attract moisture once the job is finished. Other types of flux (acid core) will leave a residue that will attract moisture and cause the wires to corrode. Tin is a unique metal with a low melting point. In a molten state, it dissolves and alloys easily with many metals. Solder is made by mixing tin with lead. The most common proportions are 40/60, 50/50 and 60/40, with the percentage of tin listed first. Low priced solders usually contain less tin, making them very difficult for a beginner to use because more heat is required to melt the solder. A common solder is 40/60 which is well suited for all-around general use, but 60/40 melts easier, has more tin for a better joint and is preferred for electrical work.

Soldering Techniques

Successful soldering requires that the metals to be joined be heated to a temperature that will melt the solder — usually 360-460°F (182-238°C). Contrary to popular belief, the purpose of the soldering iron is not to melt the solder itself, but to heat the parts being soldered to a temperature high enough to melt the solder when it is touched to the work. Melting flux-cored solder on the soldering iron will usually destroy the effectiveness of the flux.

➡ **Soldering tips are made of copper for good heat conductivity, but must be "tinned" regularly for quick transference of heat to the project and to prevent the solder from sticking to the iron. To "tin"** **the iron, simply heat it and touch the flux-cored solder to the tip; the solder will flow over the hot tip. Wipe the excess off with a clean rag, but be careful as the iron will be hot.**

After some use, the tip may become pitted. If so, simply dress the tip smooth with a smooth file and "tin" the tip again. An old saying holds that "metals well cleaned are half soldered." Flux-cored solder will remove oxides but rust, bits of insulation and oil or grease must be removed with a wire brush or emery cloth. For maximum strength in soldered parts, the joint must start off clean and tight. Weak joints will result in gaps too wide for the solder to bridge.

If a separate soldering flux is used, it should be brushed or swabbed on only those areas that are to be soldered. Most solders contain a core of flux and separate fluxing is unnecessary. Hold the work to be soldered firmly. It is best to solder on a wooden board, because a metal vise will only rob the piece to be soldered of heat and make it difficult to melt the solder. Hold the soldering tip with the broadest face against the work to be soldered. Apply solder under the tip close to the work, using enough solder to give a heavy film between the iron and the piece being soldered, while moving slowly and making sure the solder melts properly. Keep the work level or the solder will run to the lowest part and favor the thicker parts, because these require more heat to melt the solder. If the soldering tip overheats (the solder coating on the face of the tip burns up), it should be retinned. Once the soldering is completed, let the soldered joint stand until cool. Tape and seal all soldered wire splices after the repair has cooled.

Wire Harness and Connectors

The on-board computer (ECM) wire harness electrically connects the control unit to the various solenoids, switches and sensors used by the control system. Most connectors in the engine compartment or otherwise exposed to the elements are protected against moisture and dirt which could create oxidation and deposits on the terminals. This protection is important because of the very low voltage and current levels used by the computer and sensors. All connectors have a lock which secures the male and female terminals together, with a secondary lock holding the seal and terminal into the connector. Both terminal locks must be released when disconnecting ECM connectors.

These special connectors are weather-proof and all repairs require the use of a special terminal and the tool required to service it. This tool is used to remove the pin and sleeve terminals. If removal is attempted with an ordinary pick, there is a good chance that the terminal will be bent or deformed. Unlike standard blade type terminals, these terminals cannot be straightened once they are bent. Make certain that the connectors are properly seated and all of the sealing rings in place when connecting leads. On some models, a hinge-type flap provides a backup or secondary locking feature for the terminals. Most secondary locks are used to improve the connector reliability by retaining the terminals if the small terminal lock tangs are not positioned properly.

Molded-on connectors require complete replacement of the connection. This means splicing a new connector assembly into the harness. All splices in on-board computer systems should be soldered to insure proper contact. Use care when probing the connections or replacing terminals in them as it is possible to short between opposite terminals. If this happens to the wrong terminal pair, it is possible to damage certain components. Always use jumper wires between connectors for circuit checking and never probe through weatherproof seals.

Open circuits are often difficult to locate by sight because corrosion or terminal misalignment are hidden by the connectors. Merely wiggling a connector on a sensor or in the wiring harness may correct the open circuit condition. This should always be considered when an open circuit or a failed sensor is indicated. Intermittent problems may also be caused by oxidized or loose connections. When using a circuit tester for diagnosis, always probe connections from the wire side. Be careful not to damage sealed connectors with test probes.

All wiring harnesses should be replaced with identical parts, using the same gauge wire and connectors. When signal wires are spliced into a harness, use wire with high temperature insulation only. With the low voltage and current levels found in the system, it is important that the best possible connection at all wire splices be made by soldering the splices together. It is seldom necessary to replace a complete harness. If replacement is necessary, pay close attention to insure proper harness routing. Secure the harness with suitable plastic wire clamps to prevent vibrations from causing the harness to wear in spots or contact any hot components.

➡ **Weatherproof connectors cannot be replaced with standard connectors. Instructions are provided with replacement connector and terminal packages. Some wire harnesses have mounting indicators (usually pieces of colored tape) to mark where the harness is to be secured.**

In making wiring repairs, it's important that you always replace damaged wires with wires that are the same gauge as the wire being replaced. The heavier the wire, the smaller the gauge number. Wires are color-coded to aid in identification and whenever possible the same color coded wire should be used for replacement. A wire stripping and crimping tool is necessary to install solderless terminal connectors. Test all crimps by pulling on the wires; it should not be possible to pull the wires out of a good crimp.

Wires which are open, exposed or otherwise damaged are repaired by simple splicing. Where possible, if the wiring harness is accessible and the damaged place in the wire can be located, it is best to open the harness and check for all possible damage. In an inaccessible harness, the wire must be bypassed with a new insert, usually taped to the outside of the old harness.

When replacing fusible links, be sure to use fusible link wire, NOT ordinary automotive wire. Make sure the fusible segment is of the same gauge and construction as the one being replaced and double the stripped end when crimping the terminal connector for a good contact. The melted (open) fusible link segment of the wiring harness should be cut off as close to the harness as possible, then a new segment spliced in as described. In the case of a damaged fusible link that feeds two harness wires, the harness connections should be replaced with two fusible link wires so that each circuit will have its own separate protection.

➡ **Most of the problems caused in the wiring harness are due to bad ground connections. Always check all vehicle ground connections for corrosion or looseness before performing any power feed checks to eliminate the chance of a bad ground affecting the circuit.**

Repairing Hard Shell Connectors

Unlike molded connectors, the terminal contacts in hard shell connectors can be replaced. Weatherproof hard-shell connectors with the leads molded into the shell have non-replaceable terminal ends. Replacement usually involves the use of a special terminal removal tool that depress the locking tangs (barbs) on the connector terminal and allow the connector to be removed from the rear of the shell. The connector shell should be replaced if it shows any evidence of burning, melting, cracks, or breaks. Replace individual terminals that are burnt, corroded, distorted or loose.

➡ **The insulation crimp must be tight to prevent the insulation from sliding back on the wire when the wire is pulled. The insulation must**

be visibly compressed under the crimp tabs, and the ends of the crimp should be turned in for a firm grip on the insulation.

The wire crimp must be made with all wire strands inside the crimp. The terminal must be fully compressed on the wire strands with the ends of the crimp tabs turned in to make a firm grip on the wire. Check all connections with an ohmmeter to insure a good contact. There should be no measurable resistance between the wire and the terminal when connected.

Mechanical Test Equipment

Vacuum Gauge

Most gauges are graduated in inches of mercury (in.Hg), although a device called a manometer reads vacuum in inches of water (in. H_2O). The normal vacuum reading usually varies between 18 and 22 in.Hg at sea level. To test engine vacuum, the vacuum gauge must be connected to a source of manifold vacuum. Many engines have a plug in the intake manifold which can be removed and replaced with an adapter fitting. Connect the vacuum gauge to the fitting with a suitable rubber hose or, if no manifold plug is available, connect the vacuum gauge to any device using manifold vacuum, such as EGR valves, etc. The vacuum gauge can be used to determine if enough vacuum is reaching a component to allow its actuation.

Hand Vacuum Pump

Small, hand-held vacuum pumps come in a variety of designs. Most have a built-in vacuum gauge and allow the component to be tested without removing it from the vehicle. Operate the pump lever or plunger to apply the correct amount of vacuum required for the test specified in the diagnosis routines. The level of vacuum in inches of Mercury (in.Hg) is indicated on the pump gauge. For some testing, an additional vacuum gauge may be necessary.

Intake manifold vacuum is used to operate various systems and devices on late model vehicles. To correctly diagnose and solve problems in vacuum control systems, a vacuum source is necessary for testing. In some cases, vacuum can be taken from the intake manifold when the engine is running, but vacuum is normally provided by a hand vacuum pump. These hand vacuum pumps have a built-in vacuum gauge that allow testing while the device is still attached to the component. For some tests, an additional vacuum gauge may be necessary.

HEATER

Blower Motor

REMOVAL & INSTALLATION

1988-89
♦ SEE FIG. 1
1. Disconnect the negative battery cable.
2. Disconnect the electrical connections at the blower motor and blower resistor.
3. Remove the plastic water shield from the right side of the cowl.
3. On vehicles equipped with V6 engine and air conditioning, it may be necessary to remove the alternator.
4. Remove the blower motor retaining screws and then pull the blower motor and cage out.
5. Hold the blower motor cage and remove the cage retaining nut from the blower motor shaft.
6. Remove the blower motor and cage.
7. Installation is the reverse of removal.

1990-92
♦ SEE FIG. 1
1. Disconnect the negative battery cable.
2. Disconnect the electrical connections at the blower motor.
3. On vehicles equipped with the 3.1L V6 engine, remove the alternator.
4. Disconnect the motor cooling tube.
5. Disconnect the motor returning screws and remove the motor and fan assembly.
6. Remove the nut from the blower motor shaft and remove the fan.

➡ On 1991-92 models, the blower motor and fan is serviced as an assembly.

To install:
7. Install the fan onto the blower motor shaft and install the nut.
8. Install the blower motor and retaining screws.
9. Install the motor cooling tube.
10. On vehicles equipped with the 3.1L V6 engine, install the alternator.
11. Connect the electrical connections to the blower motor.
12. Connect the negative battery cable.

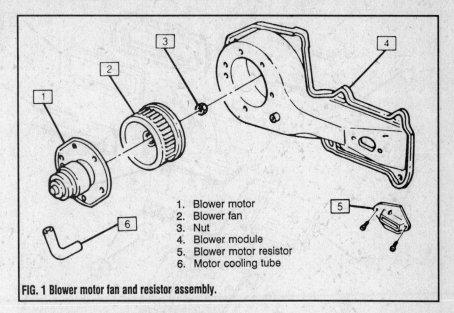

1. Blower motor
2. Blower fan
3. Nut
4. Blower module
5. Blower motor resistor
6. Motor cooling tube

FIG. 1 Blower motor fan and resistor assembly.

Heater Core

REMOVAL & INSTALLATION

Cars Without Air Conditioning

1988-90
♦ SEE FIG. 2
1. Disconnect the negative battery cable and drain the cooling system.

✳ CAUTION

When draining the coolant, keep in mind that cats and dogs are attracted by the ethylene glycol antifreeze, and are quite likely to drink any that is left in an uncovered container or in puddles on the ground. This will prove fatal in sufficient quantity. Always drain the coolant into a sealable container. Coolant should be reused unless it is contaminated or several years old.

2. Remove the heater inlet and outlet hoses from the heater core.
3. Remove the heater outlet deflector.
4. Remove the retaining screws and then remove the heater core cover.
5. Remove the heater core retaining straps and then remove the heater core.
6. Installation is the reverse of removal.

1991
♦ SEE FIG. 3
1. Disconnect the negative battery cable and drain the cooling system.
2. Disable the SIR system. Please refer to Section 8 in the steering section for disabling the Supplemental Inflatable Restraint (SIR) system.
3. Remove the instrument panel as outlined in this section.
4. Remove the screws and floor outlet, turning clockwise and to the right to release from the rear floor air outlet.
5. Drain the cooling system.
6. Raise the vehicle and support it safely.
7. Disconnect the heater hoses from the heater core.
8. Disconnect the drain tube elbow from the heater core cover.
9. Lower the vehicle.
10. Remove the screws and remove the heater core cover.
11. Remove the core screws, clamps and heater core from the vehicle.

To install:
12. Reposition the heater core and install the straps and screws.

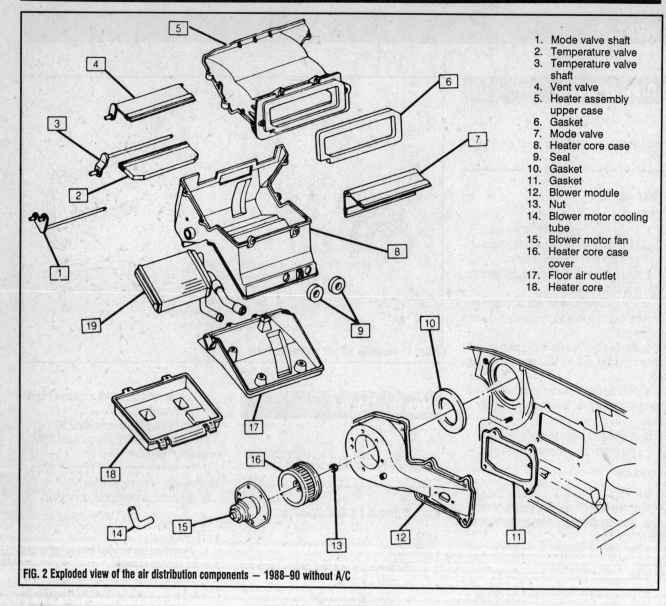

1. Mode valve shaft
2. Temperature valve
3. Temperature valve shaft
4. Vent valve
5. Heater assembly upper case
6. Gasket
7. Mode valve
8. Heater core case
9. Seal
10. Gasket
11. Gasket
12. Blower module
13. Nut
14. Blower motor cooling tube
15. Blower motor fan
16. Heater core case cover
17. Floor air outlet
18. Heater core

FIG. 2 Exploded view of the air distribution components — 1988–90 without A/C

13. Install the heater core cover and attaching screws.
14. Install the floor outlet and retaining screws.
15. Install the instrument panel.
16. Raise the vehicle and support it safely.
17. Install the heater hoses to the heater core.
18. Lower the vehicle.
19. Fill the cooling system.
20. Enable the SIR system. Please refer to Section 8 in the steering section for enabling the Supplemental Inflatable Restraint (SIR) system.

1992
▶ SEE FIG. 3

1. Disconnect the negative battery cable and drain the cooling system.
2. Disable the SIR system. Please refer to Section 8 in the steering section for disabling the Supplemental Inflatable Restraint (SIR) system.

3. Remove the radio as outlined in this section.
4. Reach through the radio opening and release the heater core cover from the retention clips.
5. Remove the screws and floor outlet, turning clockwise and to the right to release from the rear floor air outlet.
6. Drain the cooling system.
7. Raise the vehicle and support it safely.
8. Disconnect the heater hoses from the heater core.
9. Disconnect the drain tube elbow from the heater core cover.
10. Lower the vehicle.
11. Remove the screws and remove the heater core cover.
12. Remove the core screws, clamps and heater core from the vehicle.

To install:
13. Reposition the heater core and install the straps and screws.
14. Install the heater core cover and attaching screws.
15. Reach through the radio opening, position the cover under the retention clips.
16. Install the radio.
14. Install the floor outlet and retaining screws.
15. Raise the vehicle and support it safely.
16. Install the heater hoses to the heater core.
17. Lower the vehicle.
18. Fill the cooling system.
19. Enable the SIR system. Please refer to Section 8 in the steering section for enabling the Supplemental Inflatable Restraint (SIR) system.

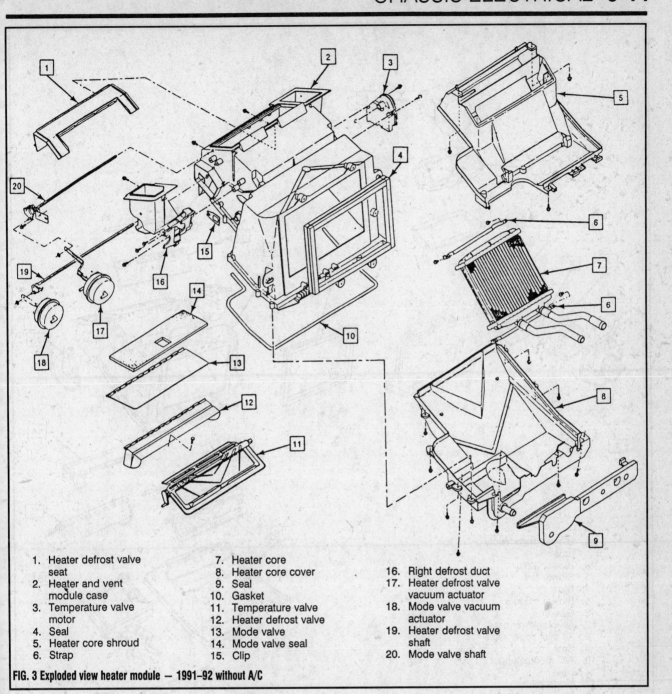

1. Heater defrost valve seat
2. Heater and vent module case
3. Temperature valve motor
4. Seal
5. Heater core shroud
6. Strap
7. Heater core
8. Heater core cover
9. Seal
10. Gasket
11. Temperature valve
12. Heater defrost valve
13. Mode valve
14. Mode valve seal
15. Clip
16. Right defrost duct
17. Heater defrost valve vacuum actuator
18. Mode valve vacuum actuator
19. Heater defrost valve shaft
20. Mode valve shaft

FIG. 3 Exploded view heater module — 1991-92 without A/C

Cars With Air Conditioning

1988-90

▶ SEE FIG. 4

1. Disconnect the negative battery cable and drain the cooling system.

> ❄ **CAUTION**
>
> **When draining the coolant, keep in mind that cats and dogs are attracted by the ethylene glycol antifreeze, and are quite likely to drink any that is left in an uncovered container or in puddles on the ground. This will prove fatal in sufficent quantity. Always drain the coolant into a sealable container. Coolant should be reused unless it is contaminated or several years old.**

2. Raise and support the front of the vehicle.
3. Disconnect the drain tube from the heater case.

4. Remove the heater hoses from the heater core.

5. Lower the car. Remove the right and left hush panels, the steering column trim cover, the heater outlet duct and the glove box.

6. Remove the heater core cover. Be sure to pull the cover straight to the rear so as not to damage the drain tube.

7. Remove the heater core clamps and then remove the core.

8. Reverse the above procedure to install (refer to Section 1), and fill the cooling system.

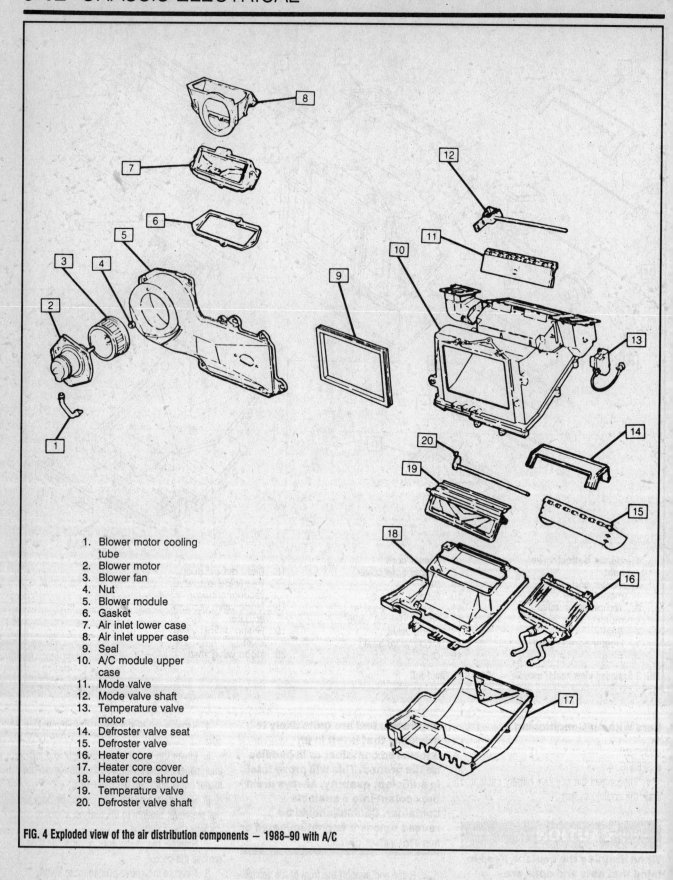

1. Blower motor cooling tube
2. Blower motor
3. Blower fan
4. Nut
5. Blower module
6. Gasket
7. Air inlet lower case
8. Air inlet upper case
9. Seal
10. A/C module upper case
11. Mode valve
12. Mode valve shaft
13. Temperature valve motor
14. Defroster valve seat
15. Defroster valve
16. Heater core
17. Heater core cover
18. Heater core shroud
19. Temperature valve
20. Defroster valve shaft

FIG. 4 Exploded view of the air distribution components — 1988–90 with A/C

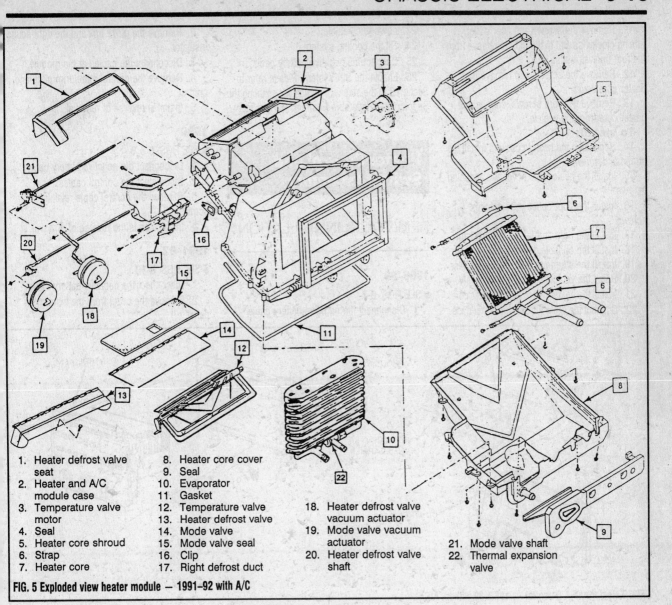

1. Heater defrost valve seat
2. Heater and A/C module case
3. Temperature valve motor
4. Seal
5. Heater core shroud
6. Strap
7. Heater core
8. Heater core cover
9. Seal
10. Evaporator
11. Gasket
12. Temperature valve
13. Heater defrost valve
14. Mode valve
15. Mode valve seal
16. Clip
17. Right defrost duct
18. Heater defrost valve vacuum actuator
19. Mode valve vacuum actuator
20. Heater defrost valve shaft
21. Mode valve shaft
22. Thermal expansion valve

FIG. 5 Exploded view heater module — 1991–92 with A/C

1991

♦ SEE FIG. 5

1. Disconnect the negative battery cable and drain the cooling system.

2. Disable the SIR system. Please refer to Section 8 in the steering section for disabling the Supplemental Inflatable Restraint (SIR) system.

3. Remove the instrument panel as outlined in this section.

4. Remove the screws and floor outlet, turning clockwise and to the right to release from the rear floor air outlet.

5. Drain the cooling system.

6. Raise the vehicle and support it safely.

7. Disconnect the heater hoses from the heater core.

8. Disconnect the drain tube elbow from the heater core cover.

9. Lower the vehicle.

10. Remove the screws and remove the heater core cover.

11. Remove the core screws, clamps and heater core from the vehicle.

To install:

12. Reposition the heater core and install the straps and screws.

13. Install the heater core cover and attaching screws.

14. Install the floor outlet and retaining screws.

15. Install the instrument panel.

16. Raise the vehicle and support it safely.

17. Install the heater hoses to the heater core.

18. Lower the vehicle.

19. Fill the cooling system.

20. Enable the SIR system. Please refer to Section 8 in the steering section for enabling the Supplemental Inflatable Restraint (SIR) system.

1992

♦ SEE FIG. 5

1. Disable the SIR system. Please refer to Section 8 in the steering section for disabling the Supplemental Inflatable Restraint (SIR) system.

2. Disconnect the negative battery cable and drain the cooling system.

3. Drain the cooling system.

4. Raise the vehicle and support it safely.

5. Disconnect the drain tube from the heater case.

6. Disconnect the heater hoses from the heater core.

7. Lower the vehicle.

8. Remove the console, if equipped.

9. Remove the right and left sound insulators.

10. Remove the steering column opening filler.

6-14 CHASSIS ELECTRICAL

11. Remove the screws and floor outlet, turning clockwise and to the right to release from the rear floor air outlet.

12. Remove the screws and remove the heater core cover.

13. Remove the core screws, clamps and heater core from the vehicle.

To install:

14. Reposition the heater core and install the straps and screws.

15. Install the heater core cover and attaching screws.

16. Install the floor outlet and retaining screws.

17. Install the right and left sound insulators.

18. Install the console, if equipped.

19. Install the steering column opening filler.

20. Raise the vehicle and support it safely.

21. Install the heater hoses to the heater core.

22. Connect the drain tube to the heater case.

23. Lower the vehicle.

24. Fill the cooling system.

25. Connect the negative battery cable.

26. Enable the SIR system. Please refer to Section 8 in the steering section for enabling the Supplemental Inflatable Restraint (SIR) system.

Heater Control and Switch Assembly

REMOVAL & INSTALLATION

1988–89

▶ SEE FIGS. 6-7

1. Disconnect the negative battery cable.

2. Remove the glove box and the right sound insulator.

3. Disconnect the cables at the module.

4. Remove the control panel trim plate and control.

5. Install in reverse of removal.

1990

▶ SEE FIGS. 6 & 8

1. Disconnect the negative battery cable.

2. Disconnect the control cables.

3. Remove the control cable retaining screws.

4. Installation is the reverse of removal.

1991–92

▶ SEE FIGS. 9-10

1. Disconnect the negative battery cable.

2. Remove the bezel from the instrument panel.

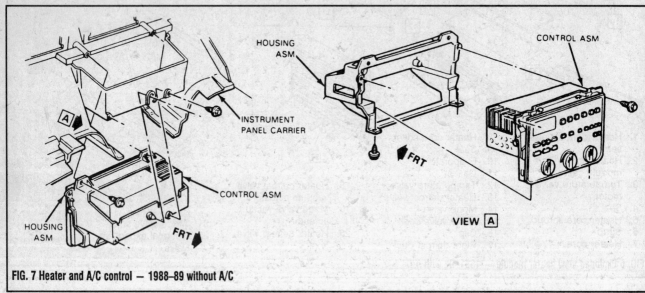

FIG. 7 Heater and A/C control — 1988–89 without A/C

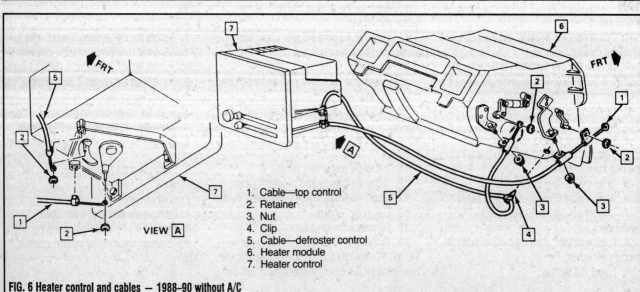

1. Cable—top control
2. Retainer
3. Nut
4. Clip
5. Cable—defroster control
6. Heater module
7. Heater control

FIG. 6 Heater control and cables — 1988–90 without A/C

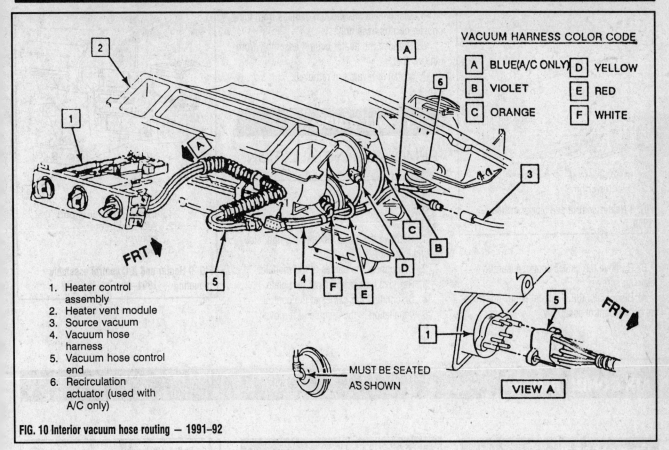

VACUUM HARNESS COLOR CODE

A	BLUE(A/C ONLY)	D	YELLOW
B	VIOLET	E	RED
C	ORANGE	F	WHITE

MUST BE SEATED AS SHOWN

VIEW A

FRT

1. Heater control assembly
2. Heater vent module
3. Source vacuum
4. Vacuum hose harness
5. Vacuum hose control end
6. Recirculation actuator (used with A/C only)

FIG. 10 Interior vacuum hose routing — 1991–92

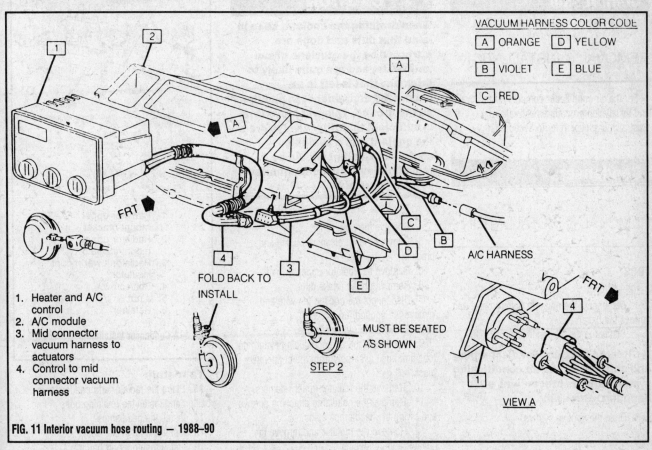

VACUUM HARNESS COLOR CODE

A	ORANGE	D	YELLOW
B	VIOLET	E	BLUE
C	RED		

A/C HARNESS

FOLD BACK TO INSTALL

MUST BE SEATED AS SHOWN

STEP 2

VIEW A

FRT

1. Heater and A/C control
2. A/C module
3. Mid connector vacuum harness to actuators
4. Control to mid connector vacuum harness

FIG. 11 Interior vacuum hose routing — 1988–90

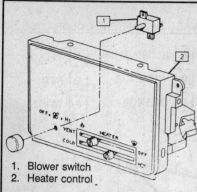

1. Blower switch
2. Heater control

FIG. 8 Heater control and blower switch — 1990

3. Remove the heater control assembly retaining screws.

4. Disconnect the electrical connector from the heater control assembly.

5. Disconnect the vacuum harness from the heater control assembly.

6. Remove the heater control assembly from the vehicle.

7. Install in reverse of removal.

Control Cables

REMOVAL & INSTALLATION

1988–89

♦ SEE FIG. 6

1. Remove the glove box and the right side sound insulator.

2. Disconnect the cables at the module.

3. Remove he control panel trim plate.

4. Disconnect the cables at the control.

5. Installation is the reverse of removal.

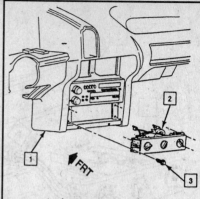

1. Instrument panel pad
2. A/C and heater control
3. Bolt

FIG. 9 Heater and A/C control assembly mounting — 1991–92

AIR CONDITIONER

Compressor

REMOVAL & INSTALLATION

For the air conditioner compressor removal and installation procedures and related illustrations, please refer to Section 3.

Condenser

REMOVAL & INSTALLATION

1988

♦ SEE FIG. 11A

1. Disconnect the negative battery cable and remove the battery.

2. Discharge the air conditioning system.

➡ **Refer to Section 1 for discharging and charging of the air conditioning system and the precautions of handling refrigerant.**

3. Drain the cooling system.

❊❊ CAUTION

When draining the coolant, keep in mind that cats and dogs are attracted by the ethylene glycol antifreeze, and are quite likely to drink any that is left in an uncovered container or in puddles on the ground. This will prove fatal in sufficient quantity. Always drain the coolant into a sealable container. Coolant should be reused unless it is contaminated or several years old.

4. Remove the air cleaner.

5. Remove the air cleaner housing and bracket.

6. Remove the radiator upper air baffle.

6. Remove the air intake duct.

7. Disconnect the cooling fan wire and remove the cooling fan.

8. Remove the radiator hoses.

9. Disconnect the air conditioning evaporator tube and hose assembly from the condenser block.

10. Remove the radiator upper retainers.

11. Remove the headlamp attaching screws and swing the headlamps aside.

12. Remove the radiator and remove the radiator and condenser.

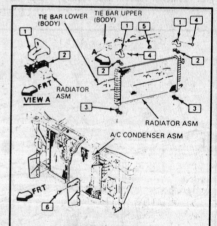

1. Radiator upper mount bracket
2. Radiator upper mount insulator
3. Radiator lower mount insulator
4. Bolt/screw
5. J nut
6. Retainer

FIG. 11A Condenser installation — 1989

To Install:

13. Place the radiator and condenser in position and install the retaining bolts.

14. Install the headlamps.

15. Install the air intake duct.

16. Install the upper air baffle.

17. Install the upper retainers.
18. Install the fan and wire.
19. Install the radiator hoses.
20. Connect the air conditioning evaporator tube and hose assembly to the condenser block.
21. Install the air cleaner housing and bracket.
22. Install the air cleaner.
23. Fill the cooling system.
24. Install the battery.
25. Evacuate and charge the air conditioning system. Refer to Section 1.

1989–90

♦ SEE FIG. 4

1. Disconnect the negative battery cable and remove the battery.
2. Discharge the air conditioning system.

➡ **Refer to Section 1 for discharging and charging of the air conditioning system and the precautions of handling refrigerant.**

3. Remove the top splash guard.
4. Remove the grille support brackets.
5. Remove the hood latch assembly.
6. Remove the radiator air baffle.
7. Remove the air horn extension.
8. Remove the condenser bracket bolts.
9. Disconnect the condenser lines and remove the condenser, upward in front of the radiator while tilting the driver's side upward.

To Install:

10. Place the condenser in position and install the retaining bolts.
11. Lubricate the O-rings and install the lines to the condenser.
12. If replacing the condenser, add 1 fl. oz. of refrigerant oil to the system.
13. Evacuate the system.
14. Install the hood latch assembly.
15. Install the grille support brackets.
16. Install the small air deflector.
17. Install the grille air baffle.
18. Install the top splash guard.
19. Charge the air conditioning system. Refer to Section 1.

1991–92

♦ SEE FIG. 11B-11D

1. Disable the SIR system. Please refer to Section 8 in the steering section for disabling the Supplemental Inflatable Restraint (SIR) system.
2. Disconnect the negative battery cable.
3. Discharge the A/C system. Refer to Section 1.
4. Remove the radiator air baffle.
5. Remove the air cleaner assembly.
6. Remove the engine cooling fan.

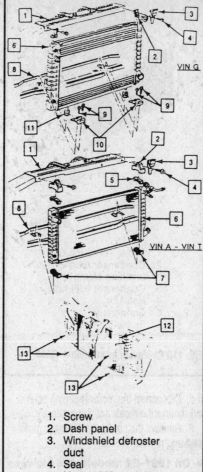

1. Screw
2. Dash panel
3. Windshield defroster duct
4. Seal
5. Heater A/C module
6. Clip

FIG. 11B Condenser installation — 1991

7. Disconnect the forward discriminating sensor. If necessary to remove the sensor, proceed as follows:
   a. With the SIR system disabled, remove the right outer upper radiator baffle.
   b. Disconnect the sensor electrical connection.
   c. The sensor and bracket are attached to the upper radiator tie bar. Use care when handling.
8. Disconnect the evaporator tube from the condenser outlet.
9. Disconnect the A/C compressor and condenser hose from the condenser outlet.
10. Remove the screws attaching the condenser to the radiator.
11. Remove the bolts and radiator upper mounting brackets.
12. Remove the condenser from the vehicle by tipping the radiator toward the engine.

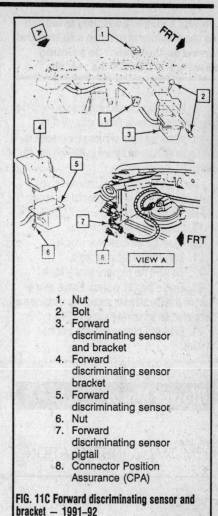

1. Nut
2. Bolt
3. Forward discriminating sensor and bracket
4. Forward discriminating sensor bracket
5. Forward discriminating sensor
6. Nut
7. Forward discriminating sensor pigtail
8. Connector Position Assurance (CPA)

FIG. 11C Forward discriminating sensor and bracket — 1991–92

To Install:

13. Install the condenser to the vehicle by tipping the radiator toward the engine.
14. Install the radiator upper mounting bracket and bolts and tighten to 66 inch lbs. (7.5 Nm).
15. Install the screws attaching the condenser to the radiator and tighten to 53 inch lbs. 6 Nm).
16. Connect the A/C compressor and condenser hose to the condenser inlet and tighten the fitting to 18 ft. lbs. (24 Nm).
17. Connect the evaporator tube to the condenser outlet and tighten the fitting to 18 ft. lbs. (24 Nm).
18. Connect the forward discriminating sensor. If removed, install the sensor as follows:

❄ CAUTION

Proper operation of the forward discriminating sensor and the SIR system, requires that the sensor

and its bracket be rigidly attached to the vehicle structure and that the arrow on the sensor be pointing toward the front of the vehicle.

    a. Install the nuts securing the sensor to the bracket and tighten to 80 inch lbs. (9 Nm).

    b. Install the bolts securing the bracket to the upper tie bar and tighten to 80 inch lbs. (9 Nm).

    b. Install the electrical connections and make sure the wire is secured into the upper radiator tie bar with the clips.

19. Install the engine cooling fan.
20. Install the air cleaner assembly.
21. Install the radiator air baffle.
22. Connect the negative battery cable.
23. Enable the SIR system. Please refer to Section 8 in the steering section for enabling the Supplemental Inflatable Restraint (SIR) system.
24. Evacuate, charge and leak test the system.

Blower Motor

REMOVAL & INSTALLATION

1988–89

♦ SEE FIG. 1

1. Disconnect the negative battery cable.
2. Disconnect the electrical connections at the blower motor and blower resistor.
3. Remove the plastic water shield from the right side of the cowl.
3. On vehicles equipped with V6 engine and air conditioning, it may be necessary to remove the alternator.
4. Remove the blower motor retaining screws and then pull the blower motor and cage out.
5. Hold the blower motor cage and remove the cage retaining nut from the blower motor shaft.
6. Remove the blower motor and cage.
7. Installation is the reverse of removal.

1990–92

♦ SEE FIG. 1

1. Disconnect the negative battery cable.
2. Disconnect the electrical connections at the blower motor.
3. On vehicles equipped with the 3.1L V6 engine, remove the alternator.
4. Disconnect the motor cooling tube.

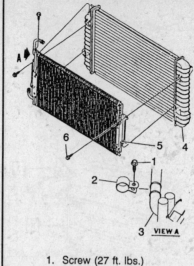

1. Screw (27 ft. lbs.)
2. Condenser tube retaining clamp
3. Condenser inlet tube
4. Radiator
5. Condenser
6. Screw (54 ft. lbs.)

FIG. 11D Condenser installation — 1992

5. Disconnect the motor returning screws and remove the motor and fan assembly.
6. Remove the nut from the blower motor shaft and remove the fan.

➡ **On 1991–92 models, the blower motor and fan is serviced as an assembly.**

To install:

7. Install the fan onto the blower motor shaft and install the nut.
8. Install the blower motor and retaining screws.
9. Install the motor cooling tube.
10. On vehicles equipped with the 3.1L V6 engine, install the alternator.
11. Connect the electrical connections to the blower motor.
12. Connect the negative battery cable.

A/C Control Assembly

REMOVAL & INSTALLATION

1988–90

1. Disconnect the negative battery cable.
2. Unsnap the radio trim ring.

3. Remove the four screws retaining the radio.
4. Disconnect the electrical and vacuum harness from the back of the radio.
5. Remove the four screws securing the heater and A/C control to the radio face plate.
6. Install in reverse of above.

1991–92

♦ SEE FIGS. 9-10

1. Disconnect the negative battery cable.
2. Remove the control bezel from the instrument panel.
3. Remove the control assembly retaining screws.
4. Disconnect the electrical connector from the heater control assembly.
5. Disconnect the vacuum harness from the heater control assembly.
6. Remove the heater and A/C control assembly from the vehicle.
7. Install in reverse of removal.

Evaporator Core

REMOVAL & INSTALLATION

1988–90

♦ SEE FIG.

1. Disconnect the negative battery cable drain the cooling system and discharge the A/C system.

➡ **Refer to Section 1 for Discharging, Charging and Evacuation of the A/C systems**

2. Jack up the car and support it safely.
3. Disconnect the heater hoses and evaporator lines at the heater core and evaporator core.
4. Remove the drain tube.
5. Remove the right hand and left hand hush panels, steering column trim cover, heater outlet duct and glove box.
6. Remove the heater core cover by pulling straight rearward on the cover to avoid breaking the drain tube.
7. Remove the heater core clamps and remove the heater core.
8. Remove the screws holding the defroster vacuum actuator to the module case.
9. Remove the evaporator cover and remove the evaporator core.

To install:
10. Reposition the core and install the cover.

11. Install the screws holding the defroster vacuum actuator to the module case.

12. Install the heater core clamps and cover.

13. Install the right hand and left hand hush panels, steering column trim cover, heater outlet duct and glove box.

14. Install the drain tube.

15. Connect the heater hoses and evaporator lines at the heater core and evaporator core.

16. Lower the car and charge the A/C system (refer to Section 1), and fill the cooling system.

1991
♦ SEE FIG. 5

1. Disconnect the negative battery cable and discharge the A/C system.

➡ **Refer to Section 1 for Discharging, Charging and Evacuation of the A/C systems**

2. Disable the SIR system. Please refer to Section 8 in the steering section for disabling the Supplemental Inflatable Restraint (SIR) system.

3. Remove the instrument panel as outlined in this section.

4. Remove the screws and floor outlet, turning clockwise and to the right to release from the rear floor air outlet.

5. Raise the vehicle and support it safely.

6. Remove the bolt from the mating block at the A/C module.

7. Remove the bolt from the tube retaining clamp on vehicles equipped with the 2.3L engine only.

8. Disconnect the drain tube from the heater case.

9. Lower the vehicle.

10. Remove the screws and remove the heater core cover.

11. Remove the core screws, clamps and gently lower the heater core.

12. Remove the screws from the evaporator cover.

13. Remove the screw from the evaporator securing clamp and remove the evaporator from the vehicle.

To install:

12. Reposition the evaporator and install the securing clamp.

13. Install the evaporator cover and retaining screws.

14. Raise the vehicle and support it safely.

15. Connect the drain tube to the heater case.

16. Install the bolt to the mating block at the A/C module.

17. Install the bolt to the tube retaining clamp on vehicles equipped with the 2.3L engine only.

18. Lower the vehicle.

19. Install the floor outlet and retaining screws.

20. Install the instrument panel.

20. Enable the SIR system. Please refer to Section 8 in the steering section for enabling the Supplemental Inflatable Restraint (SIR) system.

21. Evacuate, charge and leak test the A/C system.

1992
♦ SEE FIG. 5

1. Disconnect the negative battery cable and discharge the A/C system.

➡ **Refer to Section 1 for Discharging, Charging and Evacuation of the A/C systems**

2. Disable the SIR system. Please refer to Section 8 in the steering section for disabling the Supplemental Inflatable Restraint (SIR) system.

3. Raise the vehicle and support it safely.

4. Remove the front exhaust shield.

5. Remove the cradle cross brace. Remove 3 of the bolts and swing to one side.

6. Disconnect the lines from the evaporator and discard the O-rings.

7. Lower the vehicle.

8. Remove the right side under dash insulator panel.

9. Disconnect the electrical junction box at the heater core cover.

10. Remove the left side insulator panel.

11. Remove the steering column opening filler.

12. Remove the screws and floor outlet duct.

13. Remove the screws and remove the heater core cover.

14. Remove the core screws, clamps and heater core and carefully leave the heater core suspended.

15. Remove the evaporator assembly.

To install:

16. Reposition and install the evaporator.

17. Install the heater core cover and attaching screws.

18. Install the floor outlet and retaining screws.

19. Install the steering column opening filler.

20. Install the left sound insulator.

21. Connect the electrical junction box at the heater core cover.

22. Install the right side under dash insulator panel.

23. Raise the vehicle and support it safely.

24. Connect the lines to the evaporator and use new the O-rings.

25. Install the cradle cross brace 3 reining bolts.

26. Install the front exhaust shield.

27. Lower the vehicle.

28. Enable the SIR system. Please refer to Section 8 in the steering section for disabling the Supplemental Inflatable Restraint (SIR) system.

29. Connect the negative battery cable.

30. Evacuate, charge and leak test the A/C system.

REMOVAL & INSTALLATION

1988-90
♦ SEE FIG. 12

➡ **The accumulator assembly should only be replaced when the shell is perforated and a refrigerant leak is found.**

1. Disconnect the negative battery cable.

2. Discharge the A/C system.

3. Disconnect the refrigerant lines at the accumulator.

4. Remove the bracket and remove the accumulator.

To install:

➡ **Drain and measure the old oil from the accumulator and replace the same amount of new oil that was drained plus 2 fl. oz. to compensate for that retained by the original accumulator dessicant. If no oil can be drained from the old accumulator, add 2 fl. oz. of new oil to the new accumulator.**

5. Install the bracket and the accumulator.

6. Connect the refrigerant lines to the accumulator.

7. Connect the negative battery cable.

8. Charge the A/C system.

1991
♦ SEE FIG. 12

➡ **The accumulator assembly should only be replaced when the shell is perforated and a refrigerant leak is found.**

1. Disconnect the negative battery cable.

2. Discharge the A/C system.

3. Disconnect the A/C compressor and condenser hose at the accumulator outlet.

4. Raise the vehicle and support it safely.

5. Disconnect the A/C accumulator tube from the accumulator inlet.

6. Remove the bracket bolt and remove the accumulator.

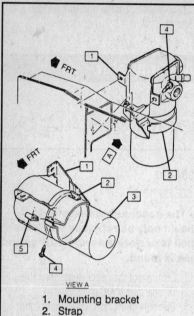

VIEW A

1. Mounting bracket
2. Strap
3. Accumulator
4. Bolt (53 inch lbs.)
5. Nut

FIG. 12 Accumulator mounting — 1988–90

To install:

➡ **Drain and measure the old oil from the accumulator and replace the same amount of new oil that was drained plus 2 fl. oz. to compensate for that retained by the original accumulator dessicant. If no oil can be drained from the old accumulator, add 2 fl. oz. of new oil to the new accumulator.**

7. Install the bracket and the accumulator and tighten the bolt to 62 inch lbs. (7 Nm).

8. Connect the A/C accumulator tube to the accumulator inlet and tighten the fitting to 30 ft. lbs. (41 Nm).
9. Lower the vehicle.
10. Connect the A/C compressor and condenser hose to the accumulator outlet and tighten the fitting to 30 ft. lbs. (41 Nm).
11. Evacuate, charge and leak test the A/C system.

Receiver Dehydrator

REMOVAL & INSTALLATION

1992

▶ SEE FIG. 13

➡ **The receiver dehydrator assembly should only be replaced when the shell is perforated and a refrigerant leak is found.**

1. Disconnect the negative battery cable.
2. Discharge the A/C system.
3. Raise the vehicle and support it safely.
4. Remove the right front tire and wheel assembly.
5. Partially remove the splash shield.
6. Disconnect both lines at the receiver dehydrator and discard the O-ring seals.
7. Remove the receiver dehydrator bracket bolts and remove the receiver dehydrator.

To install:

8. If installing a new receiver dehydrator, add 3.5 fl. oz. of new oil to the new receiver dehydrator.

9. Install the receiver dehydrator to the bracket and install the retaining bolt.
10. Connect both lines at the receiver dehydrator and use new O-ring seals.
11. Install the splash shield.
12. Install the tire and wheel assembly.
13. Lower the vehicle.
14. Connect the negative battery cable.
15. Evacuate, charge and leak test the A/C system.

Thermal Expansion Valve

REMOVAL & INSTALLATION

1992

▶ SEE FIG. 14

1. Discharge the A/C system.

➡ **Refer to Section 1 for Discharging, Charging and Evacuation of the A/C systems**

2. Disable the SIR system. Please refer to Section 8 in the steering section for disabling the Supplemental Inflatable Restraint (SIR) system.
3. Disconnect the negative battery cable.
4. Remove the right side under dash insulator panel.
5. Disconnect the electrical junction box at the heater core cover.
6. Remove the left side insulator panel.
7. Remove the steering column opening filler.

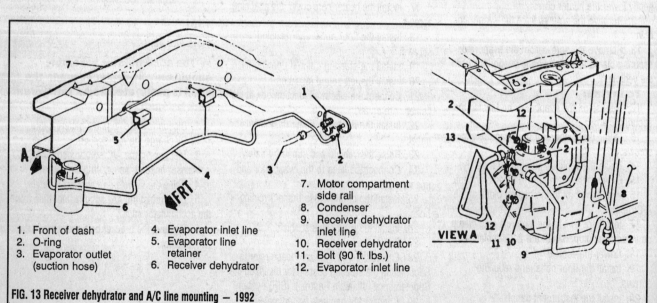

1. Front of dash
2. O-ring
3. Evaporator outlet (suction hose)
4. Evaporator inlet line
5. Evaporator line retainer
6. Receiver dehydrator
7. Motor compartment side rail
8. Condenser
9. Receiver dehydrator inlet line
10. Receiver dehydrator
11. Bolt (90 ft. lbs.)
12. Evaporator inlet line

VIEW A

FIG. 13 Receiver dehydrator and A/C line mounting — 1992

8. Partially remove the shift console if equipped to gain access to the floor duct and heater core cover.

9. Remove the screws and floor outlet duct.

10. Remove the screws and remove the heater core cover.

11. Remove the core screws, clamps and heater core and carefully leave the heater core suspended.

12. Remove the insulation tape from the valve fittings and remove the thermal expansion valve.

To install:

13. Install the thermal expansion valve including new tape.

14. Install the heater core shroud, straps and cover.

15. Without running the engine, evacuate and partially recharge the system with 1 lb. of R-12 refrigerant. Leak test the fittings.

16. Install the floor outlet and retaining screws.

17. Install the steering column opening filler.

18. Install the left sound insulator.

19. Connect the electrical junction box at the heater core cover.

20. Install the right side under dash insulator panel.

21. Install the floor console.

22. Connect the negative battery cable.

23. Enable the SIR system. Please refer to Section 8 in the steering section for disabling the Supplemental Inflatable Restraint (SIR) system.

24. Complete charging the A/C system.

Heater and A/C Vacuum Actuator

REMOVAL & INSTALLATION

1988–90

▶ SEE FIG. 11

1. Remove the glove box and steering column trim cover.

2. Remove the right and left hush panels and heater outlet duct.

3. Remove the actuator to bracket nuts and remove the actuator.

4. Installation is the reverse of removal.

Defrost Vacuum Actuator

REMOVAL & INSTALLATION

1988–90

▶ SEE FIG. 11

1. Remove the glove box.

2. Remove the right and left hush panels and heater outlet duct.

3. Remove the vacuum actuator bracket from the module.

4. Installation is the reverse of removal.

Recirculation Vacuum Actuator

REMOVAL & INSTALLATION

1988–90

▶ SEE FIG. 11

1. Remove the glove box and the right side hush panel.

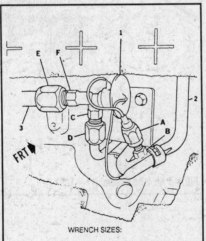

WRENCH SIZES:

A.	15mm	D.	19mm
B.	9/16"	E.	23mm
C.	13mm	F.	16mm

1. Thermal expansion valve
2. Evaporator outlet line
3. Evaporator inlet line

FIG. 14 Thermal expansion valve installation 1992

2. Remove the ECM mounting bracket screws and lower the ECM for access.

3. Remove the vacuum actuator.

4. Installation is the reverse of removal.

Heater Defrost Valve Vacuum Actuator

REMOVAL & INSTALLATION

1991

▶ SEE FIG. 10

1. Remove the right side sound insulator.

2. Remove the instrument panel compartment.

3. Remove the push-on retainer attaching the vacuum actuator to the valve.

4. Disconnect the vacuum hose from the actuator.

5. Remove the instrument panel center support bracket.

6. Unclip and remove the vacuum actuator from the vehicle.

To install:

7. Clip the vacuum actuator into position.

8. Connect the vacuum hose to the actuator.

9. Install the push-on retainer attaching vacuum actuator to the valve.

10. Install the instrument panel center support bracket.

11. Install the instrument panel compartment.

12. Install the right side sound insulator.

Mode Valve Vacuum Actuator

REMOVAL & INSTALLATION

1991

▶ SEE FIG. 10

1. Disable the SIR system. Please refer to Section 8 in the steering section for disabling the Supplemental Inflatable Restraint (SIR) system.

2. Remove the instrument panel assembly.

3. Remove the push-on retainer attaching the vacuum actuator to the valve.

4. Disconnect the vacuum hose from the actuator.

5. Unclip and remove the vacuum actuator from the vehicle.

To install:

6. Clip the vacuum actuator into position.

7. Connect the vacuum hose to the actuator.

8. Install the push-on retainer attaching the vacuum actuator to the valve.

9. Install the instrument panel.

10. Enable the SIR system. Please refer to Section 8 in the steering section for enabling the Supplemental Inflatable Restraint (SIR) system.

Air Inlet Valve Vacuum Actuator

REMOVAL & INSTALLATION

1991

♦ SEE FIG. 10 & 15

1. Disable the SIR system. Please refer to Section 8 in the steering section for disabling the Supplemental Inflatable Restraint (SIR) system.

2. Remove the right side sound insulator.

3. Remove the instrument panel compartment.

4. Remove the push-on retainer attaching the vacuum actuator to the valve.

5. Disconnect the vacuum hose from the actuator.

6. Remove the actuator retaining nuts, disengage it from the valve and remove the vacuum actuator from the vehicle.

To install:

7. Install the vacuum actuator into position, engaging it to the valve. Install and tighten the retaining nuts.

8. Connect the vacuum hose to the actuator.

9. Install the push-on retainer attaching the vacuum actuator to the valve.

10. Install the instrument panel compartment.

11. Enable the SIR system. Please refer to Section 8 in the steering section for enabling the Supplemental Inflatable Restraint (SIR) system.

Heater and Vent Valve Vacuum Actuator

REMOVAL & INSTALLATION

1992

♦ SEE FIG. 5

1. Remove the right side sound insulator.

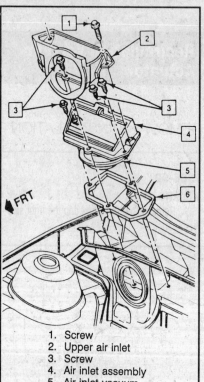

1. Screw
2. Upper air inlet
3. Screw
4. Air inlet assembly
5. Air inlet vacuum actuator
6. Gasket

FIG. 15 Air inlet assembly — 1991

2. Remove the instrument panel compartment.

3. Remove the push-on retainer attaching the vacuum actuator to the valve.

4. Disconnect the vacuum hose from the actuator.

5. Remove the instrument panel center support bracket.

6. Remove the vacuum actuator from the vehicle.

To install:

7. Clip the vacuum actuator into position.

8. Connect the vacuum hose to the actuator.

9. Install the push-on retainer attaching the vacuum actuator to the valve.

10. Install the instrument panel center support bracket.

11. Install the instrument panel compartment.

12. Install the right side sound insulator.

Defrost Vacuum Actuator

REMOVAL & INSTALLATION

1. Remove the right and left side sound insulator.

2. Remove the console, if equipped.

3. Remove the floor air outlet duct.

4. Remove the vacuum actuator bracket from the module.

5. Disconnect the vacuum actuator from the bracket.

To install:

6. Connect the vacuum actuator to the bracket.

7. Install the vacuum actuator bracket to the module.

8. Install the floor air outlet duct.

9. Install the console, if equipped.

10. Install the right and left side sound insulator.

CRUISE CONTROL

Cruise Control Module

REMOVAL & INSTALLATION

1988–92

♦ SEE FIGS. 16-17
1. Remove the right side sound insulator.
2. Remove the instrument panel glovebox.
3. Disconnect the module connector.
4. Remove the 2 retaining bolts.
5. On 1990–92 Canadian models only, remove the daytime running light module bracket.
6. Remove the cruise control module.

To install:

7. Install the cruise control module.
8. Install the daytime running light module bracket, on 1990–92 Canadian models only.
9. Install the 2 retaining bolts and tighten to 17 inch lbs. (1.9 Nm).
10. Connect the module connector.
11. Install the instrument panel glovebox.
12. Install the right side sound insulator.

Cruise Control Servo

REMOVAL & INSTALLATION

1988–92

♦ SEE FIGS. 18-20
1. Remove the cable retainer and disconnect the cable from the servo.
2. Disconnect the servo vacuum hose.
3. Remove the servo to bracket retaining screws and remove the servo.
4. Installation is the reverse of removal. Tighten the servo to bracket retaining screw to

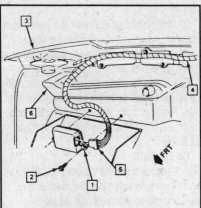

1. Module
2. Bolt/screw
3. Instrument panel
4. Instrument panel harness
5. Cruise control module connector
6. Air distribution duct

FIG. 16 Cruise control module installation — 1988–89

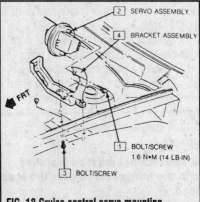

1. BOLT/SCREW 1.6 N•M (14 LB-IN)
2. SERVO ASSEMBLY
3. BOLT/SCREW
4. BRACKET ASSEMBLY

FIG. 18 Cruise control servo mounting — 1988–91 except 2.3L engine

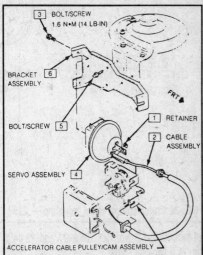

FIG. 19 Cruise control servo mounting — 1990–91 2.3L engine

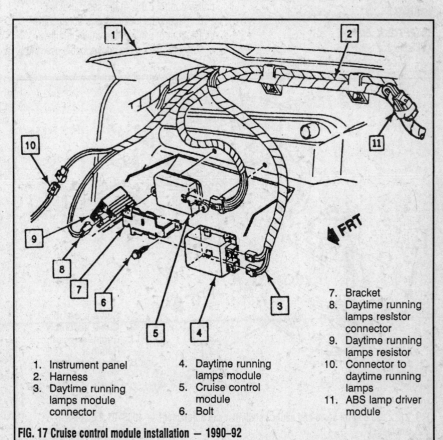

1. Instrument panel
2. Harness
3. Daytime running lamps module connector
4. Daytime running lamps module
5. Cruise control module
6. Bolt
7. Bracket
8. Daytime running lamps resistor connector
9. Daytime running lamps resistor
10. Connector to daytime running lamps
11. ABS lamp driver module

FIG. 17 Cruise control module installation — 1990–92

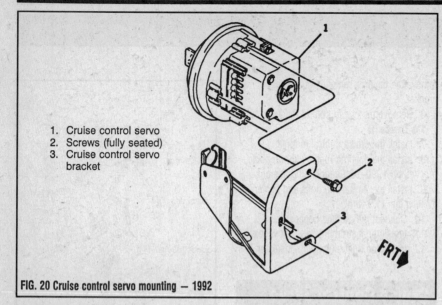

1. Cruise control servo
2. Screws (fully seated)
3. Cruise control servo bracket

FIG. 20 Cruise control servo mounting — 1992

14 inch lbs. (1.6 Nm) for 1988–91 and 12 inch lbs. (1.5 Nm) for 1992.

Cruise Control Cable

REMOVAL & INSTALLATION

1988–91

EXCEPT 2.3L ENGINE
♦ SEE FIGS. 21-22
1. Disconnect the retainer at the servo blade.

2. Release the locking tangs and disconnect the cruise control cable at the servo bracket.
3. Remove the retainer at the throttle body.
4. Release the locking tangs and disconnect the cruise control cable at the engine bracket.
5. Remove the cruise control cable.

To install:
6. Route the cruise control cable between servo and engine bracket.
7. Secure the locking tangs and connect the cruise control cable at the servo bracket.
8. Secure the locking tangs connect the cruise control cable at the engine bracket.
9. Install the cruise control cable over the stud on the throttle lever so the stud engages the slot in the cable end, securing with the retainer.

➡ **Do not stretch the cable to make a particular tab hole connect to a cable pin. This will prevent the engine from returning to idle.**

10. Install the cruise control cable into a selected cruise control servo blade hole based on minimum cable slack securing with the retainer.

➡ **The retainer must be installed with the tang secured over the stud head.**

2.3L ENGINE
♦ SEE FIGS. 23
1. Remove the air cleaner and intake ductwork.
2. Remove the strut tower bracket nuts and lift and hold the servo and bracket assembly and hold.
3. Remove the accelerator cable pulley/cam assembly cover bolt and remove the cover.
4. Release the locking tangs and disconnect the cruise control cable at the servo bracket.
5. Pull back on the pulley/cam lever then side the cruise control cable off the pulley/cam lever.
6. Release the locking tangs and disconnect the cruise control cable from the pulley/cam assembly.

To install:
7. Connect the cruise control cable to the pulley/cam assembly by pulling back on the lever and sliding the cable into the slot.
8. Connect the cruise control cable to the pulley/cam assembly and secure the locking tangs.

➡ **The locking tangs must be expanded and locked to the attached holes.**

9. Install the accelerator cable pulley/cam assembly cover and tighten the bolt to 14 inch lbs. (1.6 Nm).
10. Install the servo and bracket assembly and tighten the strut tower bracket nuts to 18 ft. lbs. (25 Nm).
11. Connect the cruise control cable to the servo bracket and secure the locking tangs.
12. Install the cruise control cable into a selected cruise control servo blade hole based on minimum cable slack securing with the retainer.
13. Install the air cleaner and intake ductwork.

➡ **The retainer must be installed with the tang secured over the stud head.**

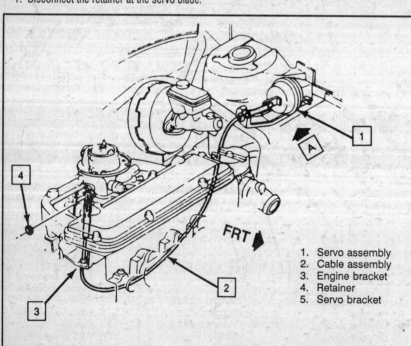

1. Servo assembly
2. Cable assembly
3. Engine bracket
4. Retainer
5. Servo bracket

FIG. 21 Cruise control servo and cable installation and adjustment — 1988–91 2.0L and 2.2L engines

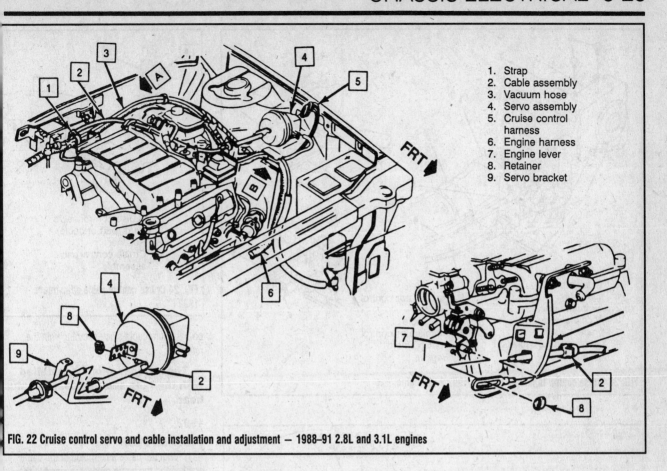

1. Strap
2. Cable assembly
3. Vacuum hose
4. Servo assembly
5. Cruise control harness
6. Engine harness
7. Engine lever
8. Retainer
9. Servo bracket

FIG. 22 Cruise control servo and cable installation and adjustment — 1988–91 2.8L and 3.1L engines

Cruise Control Cable

ADJUSTMENT

1988–91

EXCEPT 2.3L ENGINE

▶ SEE FIGS. 21-22

1. Disconnect the retainer at the servo blade.
2. Remove the cruise control cable from the servo blade.

➡ **Do not stretch the cable to make a particular tab hole connect to a cable pin. This will prevent the engine from returning to idle.**

3. Install the cruise control cable into a selected cruise control servo blade hole based on minimum cable slack securing with the retainer.

➡ **The retainer must be installed with the tang secured over the stud head.**

2.3L ENGINE

▶ SEE FIGS. 23

1. Remove the air cleaner and intake ductwork.

2. Remove the retainer at the servo blade.
3. Disconnect the cable at the servo blade.
4. Install the cruise control cable into a selected cruise control servo blade hole based

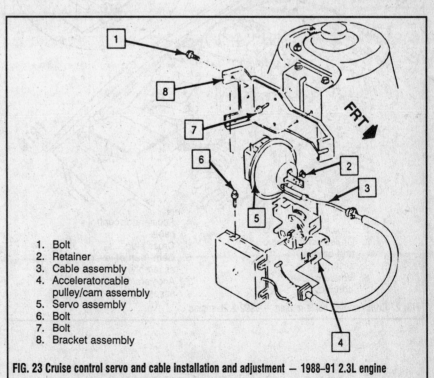

1. Bolt
2. Retainer
3. Cable assembly
4. Accelerator cable pulley/cam assembly
5. Servo assembly
6. Bolt
7. Bolt
8. Bracket assembly

FIG. 23 Cruise control servo and cable installation and adjustment — 1988–91 2.3L engine

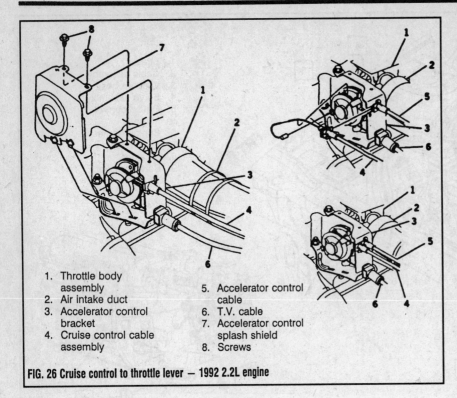

1. Throttle body assembly
2. Air intake duct
3. Accelerator control bracket
4. Cruise control cable assembly
5. Accelerator control cable
6. T.V. cable
7. Accelerator control splash shield
8. Screws

FIG. 26 Cruise control to throttle lever — 1992 2.2L engine

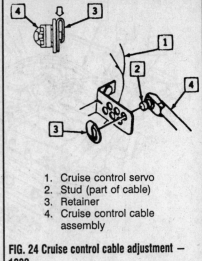

1. Cruise control servo
2. Stud (part of cable)
3. Retainer
4. Cruise control cable assembly

FIG. 24 Cruise control cable adjustment — 1992

on minimum cable slack securing with the retainer.

➡ **The retainer must be installed with the tang secured over the stud head.**

1992

▶ SEE FIGS. 24-28

1. With the cable assembled in the cable bracket and the servo bracket, assemble the cable to the throttle body lever stud with the retainer.

2. Pull the servo assembly end of the cable towards the servo without moving the throttle body lever.

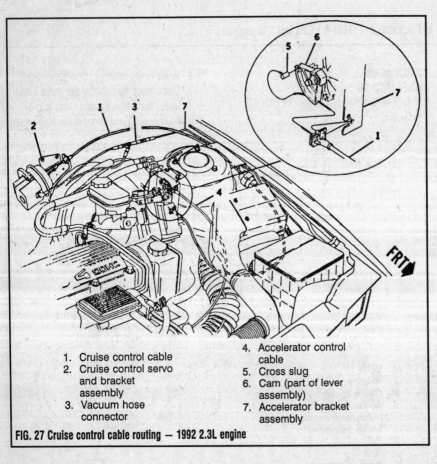

1. Cruise control cable
2. Cruise control servo and bracket assembly
3. Vacuum hose connector
4. Accelerator control cable
5. Cross slug
6. Cam (part of lever assembly)
7. Accelerator bracket assembly

FIG. 27 Cruise control cable routing — 1992 2.3L engine

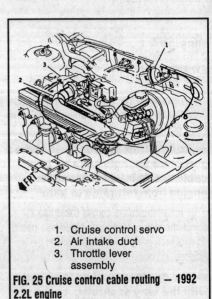

1. Cruise control servo
2. Air intake duct
3. Throttle lever assembly

FIG. 25 Cruise control cable routing — 1992 2.2L engine

3. If one of the 6 holes in the servo assembly lines up with the cable pin, connect the pin to the tab with the retainer.

4. If one of the 6 holes does not line up with the pin, move the cable away from the servo assembly until the next closest tab hole lines up. Connect the pin to the tab with the retainer.

➡ **Do not stretch the cable to make a particular tab hole connect to a cable pin. This will prevent the engine from returning to idle.**

Cruise Control Clutch Switch

REMOVAL & INSTALLATION

◆ SEE FIG. 29

1. Disconnect the negative battery cable.
2. Remove the lower, left trim panel. Locate the switch on the clutch pedal support.
3. Disconnect the electrical connector from the switch and remove the switch by twisting it out of the tubular retaining clip.

To Install:

4. Using a new retaining clip, install the switch and connect the electrical connector.
5. To adjust the switch, pull back on the clutch pedal, push the switch through the retaining clip noting the clicks; repeat this procedure until no more clicks can be heard.
6. Connect the negative battery cable and check the switch operation.

ADJUSTMENT

1. Disconnect the negative battery cable.
2. Remove the lower, left trim panel and locate the switch on the clutch pedal support.
3. Disconnect the electrical connector from the switch and remove the switch by twisting it out of the tubular retaining clip.
4. Pull back on the clutch pedal and push the switch through the retaining clip noting the clicks; repeat this procedure until no more clicks can be heard.
5. Connect the electrical connector to the switch.
6. Connect the negative battery cable and check the switch operation.

Brake Pedal Switch, Vacuum Release Valve and TCC Switch/ Vacuum Release Valve

REMOVAL & INSTALLATION

◆ SEE FIG. 30-31

1. Disconnect the negative battery cable.
2. Remove the lower, left trim panel. Locate the switch(s) on the brake pedal support.
3. Disconnect the electrical connector and vacuum hose from the switch(s) and remove the switch(s) by twisting it out of the tubular retaining clip.

To Install:

4. Using a new retaining clip, install the switch(s) and connect the electrical connector and vacuum hose.
5. To adjust the switch, pull back on the brake pedal, push the switch through the retaining clip noting the clicks; repeat this procedure until no more clicks can be heard.

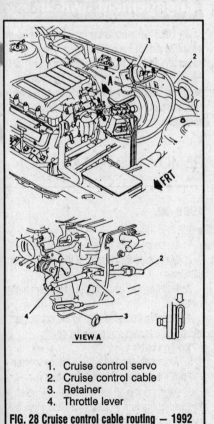

1. Cruise control servo
2. Cruise control cable
3. Retainer
4. Throttle lever

FIG. 28 Cruise control cable routing — 1992 3.1L engine

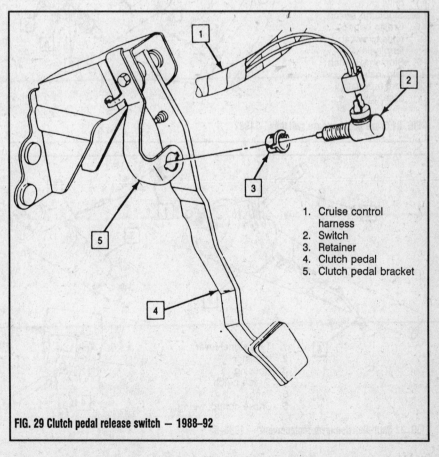

1. Cruise control harness
2. Switch
3. Retainer
4. Clutch pedal
5. Clutch pedal bracket

FIG. 29 Clutch pedal release switch — 1988–92

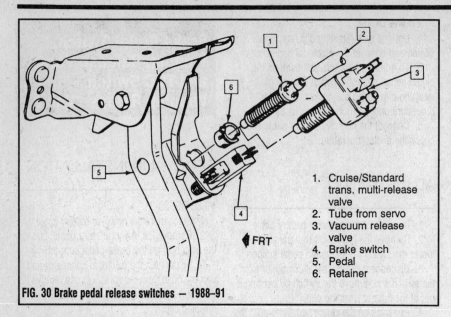

1. Cruise/Standard trans. multi-release valve
2. Tube from servo
3. Vacuum release valve
4. Brake switch
5. Pedal
6. Retainer

↑ FRT

FIG. 30 Brake pedal release switches — 1988–91

1. Brake pedal mounting bracket
2. Cruise control vacuum release valve (manual trans. only)
3. Torque converter clutch terminals
4. TCC and cruise control release switch/valve (automatic trans. only)
5. Stoplamp switch
6. Cruise control release switch terminals
7. Stoplamp switch terminals
8. Brake pedal assembly

FIG. 31 Brake pedal release switches — 1992

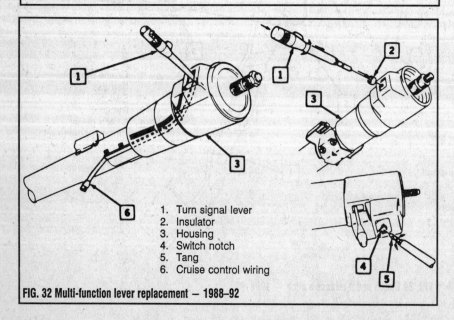

1. Turn signal lever
2. Insulator
3. Housing
4. Switch notch
5. Tang
6. Cruise control wiring

FIG. 32 Multi-function lever replacement — 1988–92

6. Connect the negative battery cable and check the switch operation.

Set/Coast and Resume/Accel Switch

REMOVAL & INSTALLATION

1988–90

1. Disconnect the negative battery cable.
2. Remove the horn pad. Two screws on all but the GT models, GT models just pull off.
3. Remove the retainer, nut and steering wheel as outlined in Steering, Section 8 .
4. Disconnect the electrical connectors.
5. Remove the horn switch, GT only.

To install:

6. Install the horn switch, GT only.
7. Connect the electrical connectors.
8. Install steering wheel, nut and retainer as outlined in Steering, Section 8.
9. Install the horn pad. Two screws on all but the GT models, GT models just push on.

Engagement Switch

On 1988–90 models the cruise control on-off switch is part of the multi-function lever assembly. and not serviced separately. On 1991–92 models, all the cruise control function switches, including resume and accelerate (R/A) etc., are part of the multi-function lever assembly.

REMOVAL & INSTALLATION

1988–92

♦ SEE FIG. 32

1. Disconnect the negative battery cable.
2. Make sure the lever is in the center or off position.
3. Pull the lever straight out of the turn signal switch.
4. Attach mechanics wire to the connector and pull the harness through the column.

To install:

5. Attach mechanics wire to the connector and pull the harness through the column.
6. Align the tab on the lever with the notch in the pivot of the turn signal switch and push the lever straight into the turn signal switch.
7. Connect the negative battery cable.

ENTERTAINMENT SYSTEMS

Radio

REMOVAL & INSTALLATION

1988–90

◆ SEE FIGS. 33-35

The radio is part of the accessory center, which also includes the heater and air conditioning controls.

1. Disconnect the negative battery cable.

2. Remove left side sound insulator attaching screws and remove the insulator from the lower dash.

3. On the Beretta, remove the lower trim panel screws and pull the trim panel out to release the taps at the top and remove the trim panel.

4. On Corsica, the trim panel has no attaching screws. Carefully pull the trim panel out and release it from the retaining taps and remove the trim panel.

5. Remove the accessory center attaching screws from the top and from the bottom.

6. Pull the accessory center away from the carrier.

7. On vehicles with air conditioning, remove the electrical and vacuum harness from the back of the heater and air conditioning control assembly.

8. On vehicles without air conditioning, remove the cables from the control module.

9. Disconnect the antenna connection and unplug a label the attaching electrical connections.

10. Pull the accessory center assembly from the dash.

11. Place the assembly on a clean working area.

12. Remove all controls knobs by pulling off.

13. Remove the screws attaching the trim plate to the radio. Separate the radio from the trim plate.

To install:

14. Assemble the radio to the trim plate and accessory center. Install the attaching screws.

15. Install the knobs by pushing in place.

16. Position the accessory center assembly to the dash and connect the electrical harness connections.

17. On vehicles with air conditioning, connect the electrical and vacuum harnesses at the rear of the heater and air conditioning control assembly.

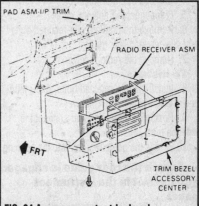

FIG. 34 Accessory center trim bezel — 1988–90 Beretta

18. On vehicles without air conditioning, connect the control cables to the control module.

19. Connect the antenna lead to the radio.

20. Slide the accessory center into place in the dash. Install the attaching screws at top and bottom.

21. Install the trim panel in place.

22. Install the left side sound insulator to lower dash and cowl and install the attaching screws.

23. Connect the negative battery cable.

1991–92

◆ SEE FIG. 36

1. Disconnect the negative battery cable.

2. Remove the accessory center bezel by inserting a flat blade tool to separate the bezel from the panel and disengage the clips. Remove the bezel.

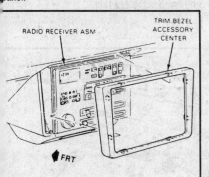

FIG. 33 Accessory center trim bezel — 1988–90 Corsica

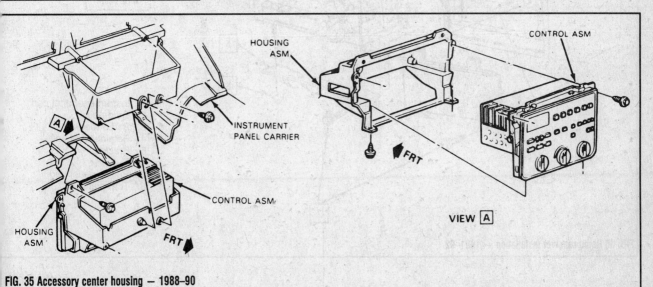

FIG. 35 Accessory center housing — 1988–90

➡ **If equipped with air conditioning, the outlets need not be removed prior to removing the bezel.**

3. Remove the bracket-to-panel screws.
4. Remove the radio receiver.
5. Disconnect the antenna cable.
6. Remove the bracket, clip-retained bolts and clip-retained rear guide.
7. Remove the radio receiver.

To install:

8. Install the clip-retained bolts, rear guide and bracket to the radio receiver.
9. Position the receiver and connect the antenna lead.
10. Press the guide receiver into the opening.

➡ **Ensure the rear guide is engaged into the slot in the instrument panel.**

11. Install the attaching screws.
12. Place the trim bezel into position, align the clips to the holes in the panel and press in to secure.
13. Connect the negative battery cable.

Front Speakers

REMOVAL & INSTALLATION

1988–90

1. Using a suitable too, carefully pry off the grille.
2. Remove the screws retaining the speaker to the instrument panel.
3. Disconnect the electrical connection and remove the speaker.

To install:

4. Reposition the speaker and connect the electrical connection.
5. Install the screws retaining the speaker to the instrument panel.
6. Press the speaker grille into place.

1991–92

◆ SEE FIG. 37
The shroud side trim panels incorporate the front speakers.

❊❊❊ CAUTION

The following procedure requires operations to be performed around the Supplemental Inflatable Restraint (SIR) system wiring and/ or components. Use care not to damage these components.

1. Remove the shroud side trim panel as follows:
   a. Remove the sound insulator.
   b. Remove the carpet retainer.
   c. Remove the upper screw from the hood release bracket.
   d. Loosen the instrument panel sound insulator.
   e. Remove the stud to bracket on the dash panel.
   f. Slide the panel toward the rear of the vehicle to disengage the retainer from the floor bracket (left side), or stud (right side).
   g. Disconnect the speaker wire.
2. Remove the speaker to trim panel bolts and remove the speaker.

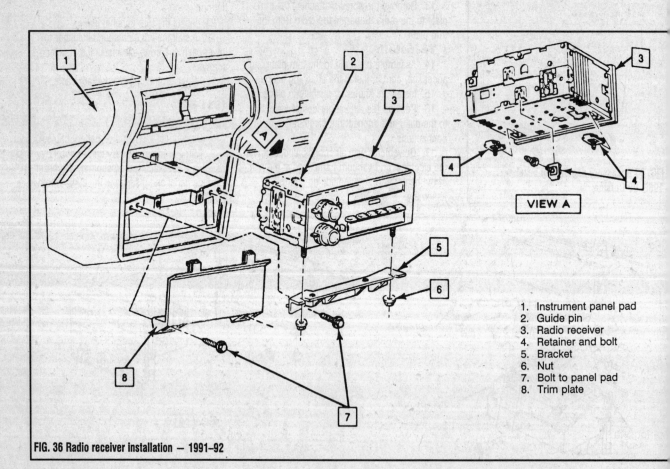

1. Instrument panel pad
2. Guide pin
3. Radio receiver
4. Retainer and bolt
5. Bracket
6. Nut
7. Bolt to panel pad
8. Trim plate

FIG. 36 Radio receiver installation — 1991–92

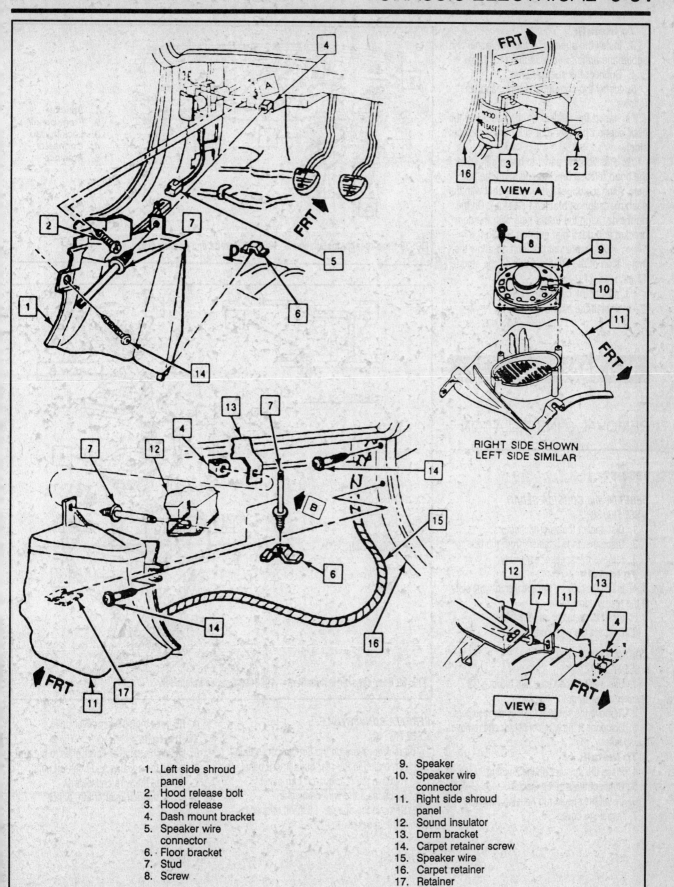

1. Left side shroud panel
2. Hood release bolt
3. Hood release
4. Dash mount bracket
5. Speaker wire connector
6. Floor bracket
7. Stud
8. Screw
9. Speaker
10. Speaker wire connector
11. Right side shroud panel
12. Sound insulator
13. Derm bracket
14. Carpet retainer screw
15. Speaker wire
16. Carpet retainer
17. Retainer

FIG. 37 Front shroud side trim panel and speaker installation — 1991–92

To install:

3. Install the speaker to the trim panel and tighten the bolts to 16 inch lbs. (1.8 Nm).

4. Connect the speaker wire.

5. Install the shroud side trim panel as follows:

   a. Insert the retainer on the panel into the floor support bracket (left side), or stud (right side).

   b. Position the panel to hinge pillar over the hood release bracket and align the bolt hole. Align the upper hole in the panel with the dash mat support bracket (left side). On the right side, align the upper hole with the derm bracket and dash mat support bracket.

   c. Apply sufficient pressure to allow the installation of the stud and tighten the stud to 17 inch lbs. (1.9 Nm).

   d. Install the carpet retainer.

   e. Install the sound insulator.

Rear Speakers

REMOVAL & INSTALLATION

1988–92

BERETTA and CORSICA SEDAN
◆ SEE FIG. 38

1. Disconnect the wire connectors.
2. Disconnect the retainers from the tab.
3. remove the speaker assembly.

To install:

4. Insert the tabs on the speaker into the slots in the rear window panel.
5. Insert the retainer into the tab.
6. Connect the wire connectors.

CORSICA HATCHBACK
◆ SEE FIG. 39

1. Use a flat bladed tool, and remove the speaker cover from the housing.
2. Remove the speaker to housing fasteners.
3. Disconnect the wire connector and remove the speaker.

To install:

4. Place the speaker on the housing.
5. Connect the wire connector.
6. Install the speaker to housing fasteners.
7. Install the cover.

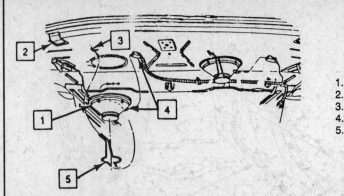

1. Speaker
2. Front panel
3. Locking tab
4. Connector
5. Retainer

FIG. 38 Rear speaker installation — 1988–92 Beretta and Corsica sedan

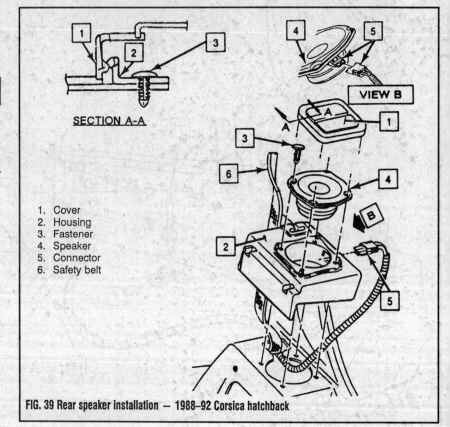

1. Cover
2. Housing
3. Fastener
4. Speaker
5. Connector
6. Safety belt

SECTION A-A

VIEW B

FIG. 39 Rear speaker installation — 1988–92 Corsica hatchback

BERETTA CONVERTIBLE
◆ SEE FIG. 40

The rear speakers on the Beretta convertible are incorporated in the rear quarter trim panel.

1. Remove the rear quarter trim panel.
2. Disconnect the wire connector.
3. Remove the speaker push-on nuts and remove the speaker.

4. Remove the speaker cover grille.

To install:

5. Install the speaker cover grille to the trim.
6. Install the speaker and push-on nuts.
7. Connect the wire connector.
8. Install the rear quarter trim panel.

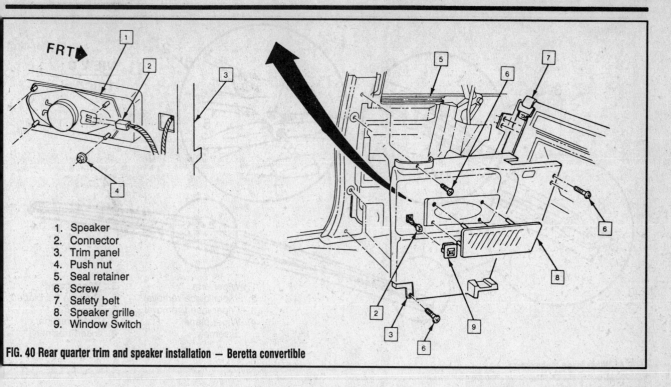

1. Speaker
2. Connector
3. Trim panel
4. Push nut
5. Seal retainer
6. Screw
7. Safety belt
8. Speaker grille
9. Window Switch

FIG. 40 Rear quarter trim and speaker installation — Beretta convertible

WINDSHIELD WIPERS AND WASHERS

Wiper Blade

REMOVAL & INSTALLATION

▶ SEE FIG. 41

The wiper blade is retained to the wiper arm pin by spring tension. To remove the blade assembly, insert a pry tool and depress the pivot spring and remove the blade from the arm. Replacement procedures for the wiper blade inserts are detailed in Section 1.

Wiper Arm

REMOVAL & INSTALLATION

1988–89

▶ SEE FIG. 42

1. With the wipers **ON** turn the ignition **OFF** when the wiper arm is at the mid-wipe position.

2. Lift the wiper arm from the windshield and pull the retaining latch.
3. Remove the arm from the transmission shaft.

To Install:

4. Install the arm on the transmission shaft.
5. Push the retaining latch in and return the arm to the windshield.
6. Park the wipers.

1990–92

▶ SEE FIG. 43-46

1. Turn the ignition **ON**, place the wiper system in the park position, then turn the ignition **OFF**.
2. Disconnect the washer hose from the plastic connector.
3. Remove the plastic cap at the wiper arm shaft.

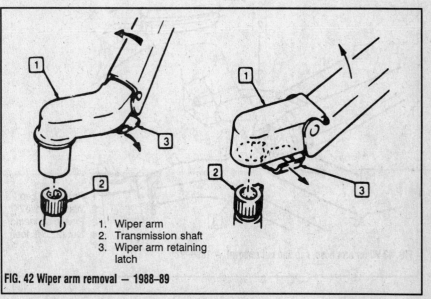

1. Wiper arm
2. Transmission shaft
3. Wiper arm retaining latch

FIG. 42 Wiper arm removal — 1988–89

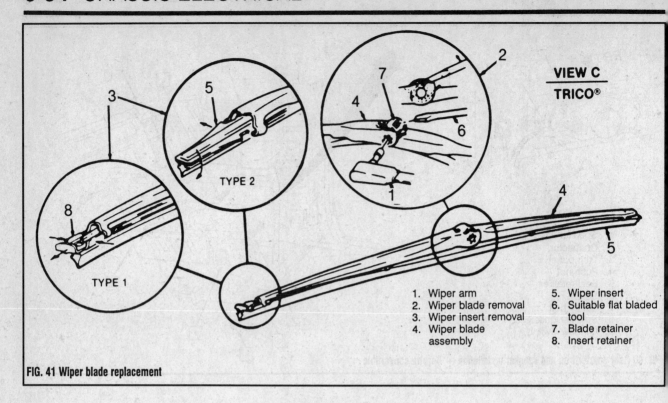

1. Wiper arm
2. Wiper blade removal
3. Wiper insert removal
4. Wiper blade assembly
5. Wiper insert
6. Suitable flat bladed tool
7. Blade retainer
8. Insert retainer

FIG. 41 Wiper blade replacement

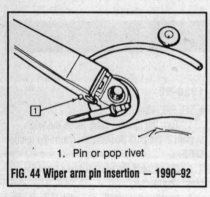

1. Pin or pop rivet

FIG. 44 Wiper arm pin insertion — 1990-92

4. Lift the wiper arm and insert a suitable pin completely through the 2 holes, located next the pivot of the arm.

5. Remove the nut securing the wiper arm.

6. Remove the arm by lifting off the shaft, using an up and down rocking motion.

To install:

7. Install the new wiper arm 1 in. (25mm) below the park ramp.

8. Remove the pivot prevention pin from the wiper arm.

9. Install a new nut with a torque wrench. The torque MUST be 14.7-17.7 ft. lbs. (20-27 Nm).

10. Run the wiper system and check for a correct wiper pattern. The left side blade tip should wipe to a limit of 1.5 in. (38mm) from the outside edge of the glass. The right side blade should overlap slightly into the left side wipe pattern.

11. Connect the washer hose to the plastic connector.

12. Install the plastic cap.

Linkage

REMOVAL & INSTALLATION

▶ SEE FIG. 47-48

1. Raise the hood.

2. Remove the wiper arms.

3. Loosen (but do not remove) the drive link-to-crank arm attaching nuts.

4. Remove the air inlet screen/panel.

5. Remove the linkage-to-body retaining screws and remove the linkage through the access hole in the shroud upper panel.

6. Installation is the reverse of removal.

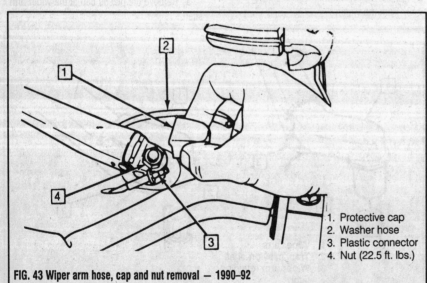

1. Protective cap
2. Washer hose
3. Plastic connector
4. Nut (22.5 ft. lbs.)

FIG. 43 Wiper arm hose, cap and nut removal — 1990-92

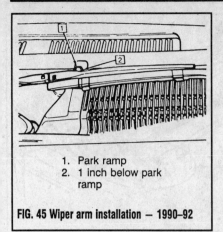

1. Park ramp
2. 1 inch below park ramp

FIG. 45 Wiper arm installation — 1990–92

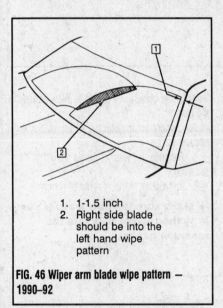

1. 1-1.5 inch
2. Right side blade should be into the left hand wipe pattern

FIG. 46 Wiper arm blade wipe pattern — 1990–92

Wiper Motor

REMOVAL & INSTALLATION

♦ SEE FIGS. 47-48

1. Disconnect the negative battery cable.
2. Remove the left and right side wiper arms.
3. Remove the air inlet screen/panel.
4. Disconnect the wiper motor drive link from the crank arm.
5. Disconnect the electrical connectors and washer hoses.
6. Remove the wiper motor-to-chassis bolts and the wiper motor by guiding the crank arm through the hole.
7. Remove the crank arm from the motor.

FIG. 43A A plastic cap protects the wiper arm retaining nut–1991–1992 shown

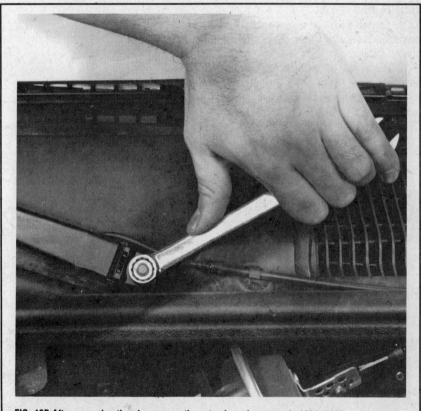

FIG. 43B After removing the pin, remove the nut using a box wrench–1991–1992

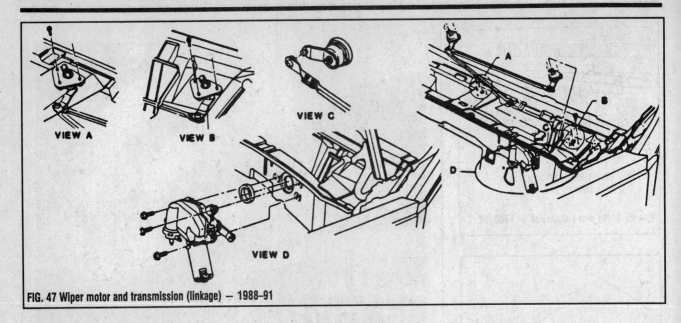

FIG. 47 Wiper motor and transmission (linkage) — 1988-91

To install:

8. Install the crank arm on the new wiper motor shaft and install the attaching nut.

9. Install the wiper motor while guiding the crank arm through cowl opening.

10. Install the wiper motor to the chassis and install the attaching bolts.

11. Connect the blower motor electrical connectors to the wiper harness connectors and connect the washer hoses.

12. Connect the wiper arm drive link to the crank arm.

13. Install the top vent screen/panel in place to the cowl area.

14. Install the left and right wiper arms.

15. Connect the negative battery cable.

Windshield Washer Pump and/or Reservoir

REMOVAL & INSTALLATION

1988-91

◆ SEE FIG. 49

1. Remove the washer solvent from the reservoir.

2. Remove the reservoir screws.

3. Disconnect the electrical connectors and hose.

4. Remove the washer pump from the reservoir.

5. Installation is the reverse of removal.

➡ **Make sure the new washer pump is pushed all the way into the reservoir gasket.**

1992

◆ SEE FIG. 50

1. Remove the washer solvent from the reservoir.

2. Remove the panel screws to allow the inner fender panel to be pulled to allow access to the pump.

3. Disconnect the electrical connectors and hose.

4. Remove the washer pump from the reservoir.

5. Installation is the reverse of removal.

➡ **Make sure the new washer pump is pushed all the way into the reservoir gasket.**

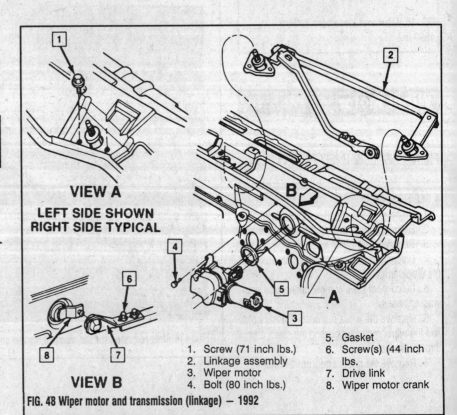

VIEW A
LEFT SIDE SHOWN RIGHT SIDE TYPICAL

VIEW B

1. Screw (71 inch lbs.)
2. Linkage assembly
3. Wiper motor
4. Bolt (80 inch lbs.)
5. Gasket
6. Screw(s) (44 inch lbs.)
7. Drive link
8. Wiper motor crank

FIG. 48 Wiper motor and transmission (linkage) — 1992

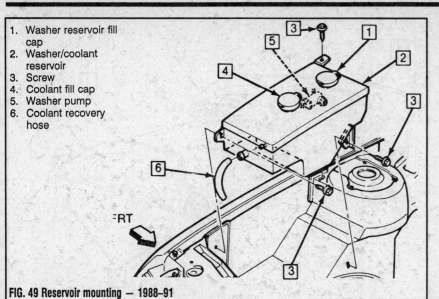

1. Washer reservoir fill cap
2. Washer/coolant reservoir
3. Screw
4. Coolant fill cap
5. Washer pump
6. Coolant recovery hose

FIG. 49 Reservoir mounting — 1988–91

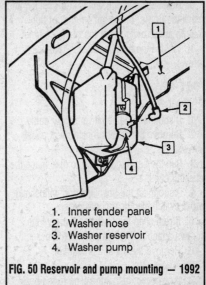

1. Inner fender panel
2. Washer hose
3. Washer reservoir
4. Washer pump

FIG. 50 Reservoir and pump mounting — 1992

INSTRUMENTS AND SWITCHES

Instrument Cluster Bezel

REMOVAL & INSTALLATION

1988–89

► SEE FIG. 51-52

1. Disconnect the negative battery cable.
2. Remove the left side sound insulator attaching screws and remove the insulator from the lower dash and cowl.

3. Remove the 2 screws from the top of the trim cover. Remove the trim cover.
4. Remove the 2 bolts from the upper part of the column and bolt(s) from the lower part of the column. Lower and support the column to prevent tension on the flex joint.
5. Remove the instrument cluster trim panel attaching hardware. Pull the trim panel rearward.

6. Disconnect the electrical connectors.
7. Remove the trim panel.
To install:
8. Position the instrument cluster trim panel close to the wiring harness and connect the electrical connectors. Install the cluster trim panel and attaching hardware.

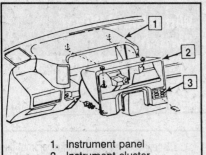

1. Instrument panel
2. Instrument cluster bezel
3. driver information center

FIG. 51 Instrument cluster bezel — 1988–90 Beretta

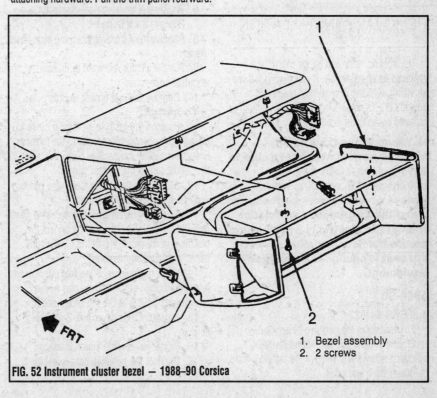

1. Bezel assembly
2. 2 screws

FIG. 52 Instrument cluster bezel — 1988–90 Corsica

9. Raise the steering wheel into position and install the bolt(s) at the bottom part of the column and 2 bolts at the top of the column.

10. Install the trim cover and 2 attaching screws.

1991–92

♦ SEE FIG. 53

1. Disconnect the negative battery cable.
2. Remove the bezel-to-instrument panel screws.
3. Pull the bezel to the rear to disengage the retaining clips.
4. Disconnect the headlight and windshield wiper switch electrical connectors.
5. If removing the switches, remove the screws attaching the switches to the bezel.
6. Remove the clips, as required.

To install:

7. If removed, install the clips to the bezel.
8. If removed, install the headlight and windshield wiper switches to the bezel and install the attaching screws.
9. Install the switch knobs.
10. Connect the electrical connectors.
11. Position the bezel and press in to engage the retaining clips.
12. Install the instrument panel-to-bezel screws.
13. Connect the negative battery cable.

Instrument Cluster

REMOVAL & INSTALLATION

The speedometer and gauge cluster are replaced as an assembly. If any part(s) require servicing, with the exception of bulbs and sockets, the cluster will have to be exchanged or repaired by an authorized service center.

➡ **Whenever working on any electronic equipment, make sure to have a clean, static free environment in which to work. Always cover the work surface with a mat that is grounded and static free. Static electricity from walking across the floor or sliding across a car seat is enough to damage any equipment.**

1988–90

♦ SEE FIG. 51-52

1. Disconnect the negative battery cable.
2. Remove the left side sound insulator attaching screws and remove the insulator from the lower dash and cowl.

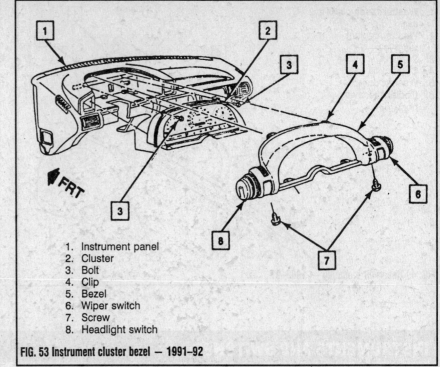

1. Instrument panel
2. Cluster
3. Bolt
4. Clip
5. Bezel
6. Wiper switch
7. Screw
8. Headlight switch

FIG. 53 Instrument cluster bezel — 1991–92

3. Remove the 2 screws from the top of the trim cover. Remove the trim cover.
4. Remove the 2 bolts from the upper part of the column and bolt(s) from the lower part of the column. Lower and support the column to prevent tension on the flex joint.
5. Remove the instrument cluster trim panel attaching hardware. Pull the trim panel rearward.
6. Disconnect the electrical connectors.
7. Remove the trim panel.
8. Remove the 4 screws attaching instrument cluster.
9. Pull the cluster rearward to disconnect the electrical connectors.
10. Remove the instrument cluster.

To install:

11. Position the instrument cluster close to the wiring harness and connect to the harness. Ensure the cluster connectors plug in securely to the connectors in the cluster carrier.
12. Slide the instrument cluster into position and install the mounting screws.
13. Position the instrument cluster trim panel close to the wiring harness and connect the electrical connectors. Install the cluster trim panel and attaching hardware.
14. Raise the steering wheel into position and install the bolt(s) at the bottom part of the column and 2 bolts at the top of the column.
15. Install the trim cover and 2 attaching screws.
16. Install the left side sound insulator.
17. Connect the negative battery cable.

1991–92

♦ SEE FIG. 53

1. Disconnect the negative battery cable.
2. Remove the instrument cluster bezel.
3. Remove the instrument cluster-to-instrument panel attaching screws.
4. Remove the instrument cluster. The electrical connector will release as the cluster is removed.

To install:

5. Carefully, install the instrument cluster. The electrical connector will align and engage as the cluster is pushed into position.
6. Install the instrument cluster bezel.
7. Connect the negative battery cable.

Windshield Wiper Switch

REMOVAL & INSTALLATION

1. Disconnect the negative terminal from the battery.
2. Remove the switch by gently prying behind the switch.
3. Disconnect and label the wiring.

4. Connect the wires to the new switch and press it into the instrument panel to the same depth as the old switch.

5. Reconnect the negative battery cable and check the wiper operation.

Headlight Switch

REMOVAL & INSTALLATION

1988–90

▶ SEE FIG. 54

1. Disconnect the negative battery cable.
2. Remove the switch by gently prying behind the switch.
3. Disconnect and label the wiring.

To install:

4. Connect the wires to the new switch and press it into the instrument panel.
5. Connect the negative battery cable and test the switch operation.

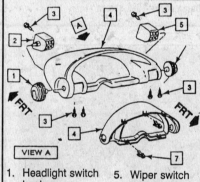

1. Headlight switch knob
2. Headlight switch
3. Screw
4. Bezel
5. Wiper switch
6. Wiper switch knob
7. Clip

FIG. 55 Exploded view of cluster bezel, headlight and windshield wiper switch — 1991–92

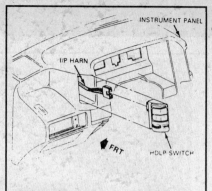

FIG. 54 Headlight switch installation — 1988–90

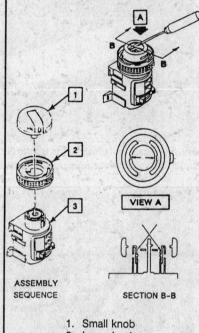

ASSEMBLY SEQUENCE

SECTION B-B

1. Small knob
2. Large knob
3. Switch

FIG. 56 Headlight and windshield wiper switch installation — 1991–92

1991–92

▶ SEE FIG. 55-56

1. Disconnect the negative battery cable.
2. Remove the instrument cluster bezel.
3. Squeeze the small knob at the side and pull straight out.
4. Insert a small flat blade into the slots adjacent to the center of the inner knob to disengage the knob from the switch.
5. Remove the screws attaching the switch to the bezel.
6. Remove the switch.

To install:

7. Install the switch to the bezel. Install the attaching screws.
8. Position the inner knob on the switch. Ensure the tabs are lined up with the slots and press to secure the knob.
9. Position the outer knob on the switch and align the D-shaped hole in the knob to the shaft on the switch and press to secure the knob.
10. Install the instrument cluster bezel.
11. Connect the negative battery cable.

Clock

REMOVAL & INSTALLATION

The clock is part of the radio. If the clock is found to be defective the radio will have to be removed and sent to an authorized facility for clock repair.

Back-Up Light Switch

The Back-Up/Neutral Start switch procedure is located in Section 7.

Ignition Switch

The ignition switch is located in the steering column and is covered in Section 8.

LIGHTING

Headlights

REMOVAL & INSTALLATION

◆ SEE FIGS. 57-58

Sealed beams are not used, instead composite style headlamps (which contain replacement bulbs) are used. The bulb located inside the headlamp assembly, can be removed from under the hood.

• Turn off the lamp switch and allow the bulb to cool before changing bulbs. Leave the lamp switch **OFF** until bulb replacement.
• Wear eye protection.
• Handle the bulb by the base and avoid touching the glass.
• Keep dirt and moisture off of the bulb.
• Carefully place the old bulb in the new bulb's carton and dispose of properly.
• Keep halogen bulbs out of reach of children.

1. Open the hood.
2. Turn the two lock tabs in the cover shroud above the headlamp and fold the cover back.
3. Remove the two large thumb screws and move the lamp forward.
4. Rotate the socket and bulb at the back of the lamp assembly and remove the socket.
5. Disconnect the wiring connector at the bulb and replace the bulb.
6. Installation is the reverse of removal.

FIG. 57A Rotate the locking tabs to remove the headlamp cover–1992 shown

FIG. 57B Remove the 2 headlamp retaining thumb screws and rotate the headlamp assembly forward–1992 shown

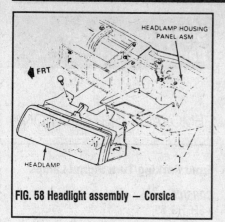

FIG. 58 Headlight assembly — Corsica

HEADLIGHT AIMING

Headlights should be checked for proper aim during your annual state inspection (each state has its own headlight aiming laws). If your state doesn't require state inspection, you should ideally have headlight aim checked annually, especially if you travel on rough road surfaces often. Headlights that are not aimed properly can create a dangerous situation by blinding oncoming drivers and by not illuminating the road properly for you. A universal do-it-yourself procedure that can be used in a pinch is given here, although it is not intended as the true method; expensive aiming tools are needed for that. If the headlights don't come close to straight ahead when aiming, something is properly broken; in fact if they are so far off as to catch your attention in the first place, a support piece probably broke.

1. Park the car on a level surface, at least 25 ft. from a wall that is perpendicular to the ground surface. Make sure there is no excess weight in the trunk, unless you normally travel with that amount of weight in the car. Bounce the car a few times to settle the suspension.

2. Measure and record the distance from the ground to the center of each headlight lens.

3. Measure and record the distance between lens centers (from one side to the other side).

4. Turn the headlights on and adjust so the hot-spots (lit area of most concentrated intensity) are the same height from the ground and distance from each other that the lens centers were in Steps 2 and 3. Adjusting screws are located on the inner side (horizontal aim) and top (vertical aim)of the lens.

5. Adjust each headlight so the hot-spot drops about 1 in. (25mm).

6. Adjust each headlight so it points to the right about 1 in. (25mm) on the wall; this will prevent glare in an oncoming driver's eyes.

7. Take your car to a service station and see how good you did!

FIG. 57C With the headlamp assembly forward, disconnect the electrical connector–1992 shown

FIG. 57D The headlamp bulb is easily removed from the back of the headlamp assembly–1992 shown

FIG. 57E Headlamp assembly removal–1992 shown

Signal and Marker Lamps

REMOVAL & INSTALLATION

Front Parking/Turn Signal Lamps

CORSICA

◆ SEE FIG. 59

1. Disconnect the negative battery cable.
2. Disconnect the socket by reaching from under the vehicle. pressing the tab (inner bulb) and twisting.
3. Use a socket wrench with a long extension, reach through the hole in the front fascia and remove the 1 bolt from the bottom of the light assembly.
4. Working through the light opening in the front fascia, remove the 2 bolts at the front of the assembly.
5. Carefully remove the lamp assembly through the front fascia opening.

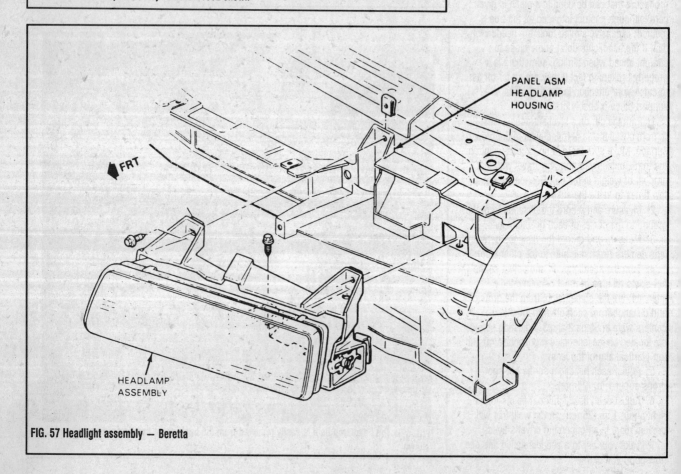

PANEL ASM HEADLAMP HOUSING

FRT

HEADLAMP ASSEMBLY

FIG. 57 Headlight assembly — Beretta

To install:

6. Install the lamp assembly, making sure the bolt holes on the top are above the bolt holes in the fascia.

7. Install the 2 bolts at the front of the assembly but do not fully tighten until the bottom bolt is installed.

8. Install the 1 bolt at the bottom of the assembly.

9. Install the socket assembly and connect the negative battery cable.

BERETTA

♦ SEE FIG. 60

1. Disconnect the negative battery cable.

2. Remove the headlight assembly as outlined earlier.

3. Disconnect the radiator to grille covers.

4. Remove the 12 bolts holding the headlight mounting panel.

➡ **The 2 center bolts can be loosened rather than be removed.**

5. Remove the wiring harness clips to the headlamp panel.

6. Remove the headlight mounting panel with the grille attached.

7. Remove the front energy absorber and rear shim as outlined in the Bumper removal procedure, Section 10.

8. Disconnect the socket by reaching from under the vehicle. pressing the tab (inner bulb) and twisting.

9. Remove the 2 screws from the bottom of the assembly.

10. Remove the 1 screw from the upper rear of the assembly and remove the lamp assembly.

To install:

11. Install the lamp assembly and 3 retaining screws.

12. Install the socket assembly.

13. Install the front energy absorber and rear shim as outlined in the Bumper removal procedure, Section 10.

14. Reposition the headlight mounting panel with the grille attached.

15. Install the wiring harness clips to the headlamp panel.

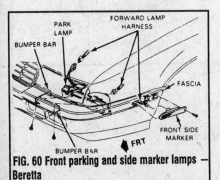

FIG. 60 Front parking and side marker lamps — Beretta

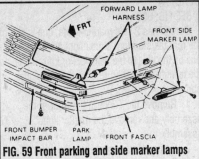

FIG. 59 Front parking and side marker lamps Corsica

16. Install the 12 bolts holding the headlight mounting panel.

17. Connect the radiator to grille covers.

18. Install the headlight assembly.

19. Connect the negative battery cable.

Rear Tail/Stop/Turn Signal

♦ SEE FIG. 61-62

※ WARNING

Take care to prevent water leaks if the sealing surfaces are disturbed. Damaged gaskets must be replaced and sealer used as necessary.

1. Disconnect the negative battery cable.

2. Open the trunk and remove the rear compartment inner trim, if so equipped.

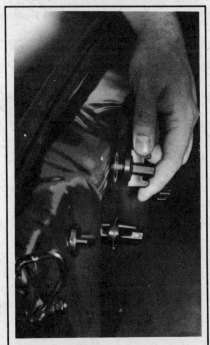

FIG. 61A Removing the tail lamp assembly wingnuts–1992 shown

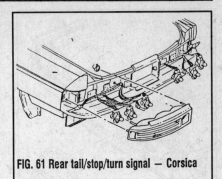

FIG. 61 Rear tail/stop/turn signal — Corsica

3. Remove the 3 wing nuts, (4 on the Corsica), holding the tailamp assembly.

4. Remove the tailamp assembly by pulling straight back.

5. Remove the socket from the assembly.

6. Remove the bulb(s) from the socket(s), if replacing.

To install:

7. Install the socket from the assembly.

8. Install the bulb(s) from the socket(s), if replacing.

9. Install the tailamp assembly and install the 3 wing nuts, (4 on the Corsica), holding the tailamp assembly.

➡ **Check for proper sealing before tightening the wingnuts.**

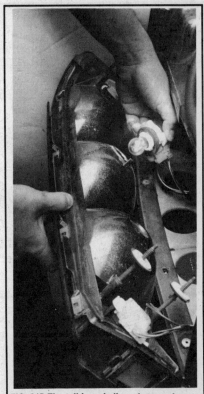

FIG. 61B The tail lamp bulb sockets unplug from the rear of the tail lamp assemblies–1992 shown

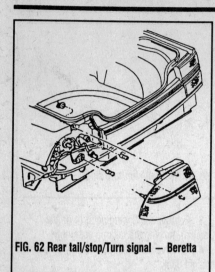

FIG. 62 Rear tail/stop/Turn signal — Beretta

10. Install the rear compartment inner trim, if so equipped.

11. Disconnect the negative battery cable.

Rear Side Marker Light

CORSICA

▶ SEE FIG. 62

The rear side marker lights are part of the rear tail/stop/turn signal light assembly. Refer to the procedure above.

BERETTA

▶ SEE FIG. 63

Beretta has 2 side marker lights, one is part of the rear tail/stop/turn signal light assembly and one on the side of the vehicle. For information on the taillight assembly, refer to the procedure above.

1. Remove the Torx® at the front of the assembly and remove the marker light assembly.
2. Remove the socket from the assembly.
3. Remove the bulb, if replacing.
4. Installation is the reverse of removal.

Front Side Marker Light

1. Remove the Torx® at the front of the assembly and remove the marker light assembly.
2. Remove the socket from the assembly.
3. Remove the bulb, if replacing.
4. Installation is the reverse of removal.

Center High Mounted Stoplight

EXCEPT LUGGAGE CARRIER, HATCHBACK OR CONVERTIBLE

▶ SEE FIG. 64

1. Remove one screw from each side of the light base.
2. Slide the assembly rearward.

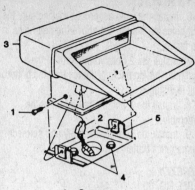

1. Screws
2. Connector
3. Lamp
4. Screws
5. Support

FIG. 64 Center high mounted stop light

3. Disconnect the electrical connector, by carefully opening the tab.
4. Remove the light assembly.
5. Installation is the reverse of removal.

WITH LUGGAGE CARRIER

▶ SEE FIG. 64

1. Open the trunk and remove the nuts holding the luggage carrier outer supports.

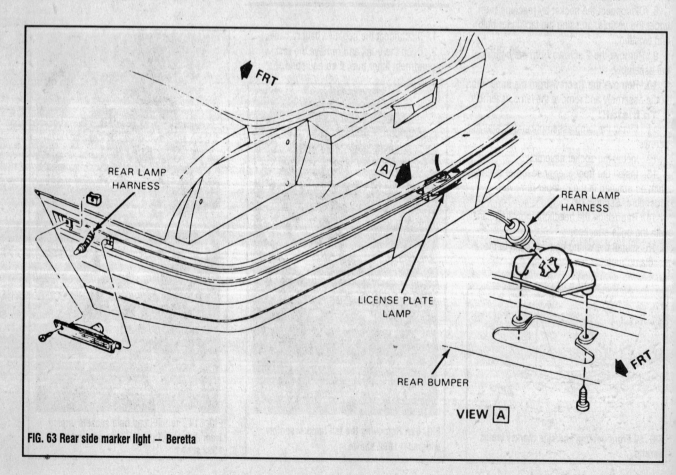

FIG. 63 Rear side marker light — Beretta

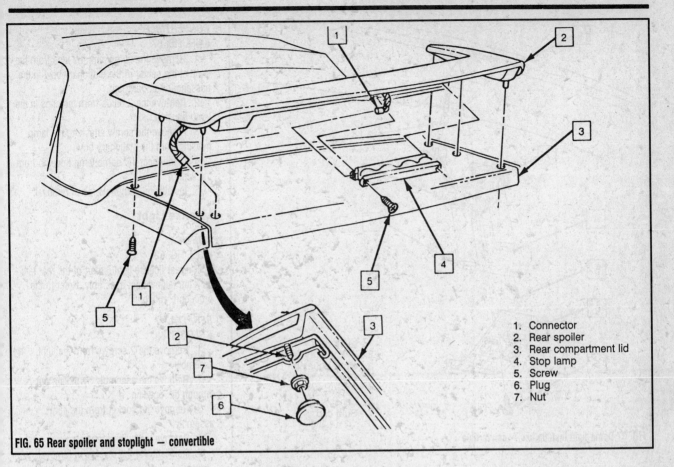

1. Connector
2. Rear spoiler
3. Rear compartment lid
4. Stop lamp
5. Screw
6. Plug
7. Nut

FIG. 65 Rear spoiler and stoplight — convertible

2. Remove the luggage carrier outer supports and crossbar.

3. Remove the gasket on the bottom of the light assembly.

4. Remove the 2 nuts from the light assembly.

5. Remove the light assembly.

6. Disconnect the electrical connector.

To install:

7. Connect the electrical connector.

8. Install the light assembly.

9. Install the 2 nuts to the light assembly.

10 Install the gasket on the bottom of the light assembly.

11. Install the luggage carrier outer supports and crossbar.

12. Install the nuts holding the luggage carrier outer supports.

WITH HATCHBACK

▶ SEE FIG. 64

1. Remove the interior finish panel.

2. Remove the 2 nuts from the light assembly.

3. Slide out the assembly.

4. Disconnect the electrical connector, by carefully opening the tab.

5. Remove the light assembly and replace the bulb, as necessary.

6. Installation is the reverse of removal.

CONVERTIBLE

▶ SEE FIG. 65

1. Remove the screws securing the stoplamp to the spoiler.

2. Pull the stoplamp away and disconnect the wiring from the lamp.

3. Remove the stoplamp assembly.

4. Installation is the reverse of removal.

Dome Light

EXCEPT CONVERTIBLE

▶ SEE FIG. 66

1. Remove the courtesy lamps fuse.

2. Remove the lens by pulling down.

3. Remove the 2 clips by loosening slightly with a suitable prying tool, then pull with pliers.

4. Remove the assembly by lowering the rear and pulling backward to release the clip at the front.

To install:

5. Install the assembly, making sure the clip on the front goes over the bracket.

6. Install the 2 clips by pushing into place.

7. Install the lens and the fuse.

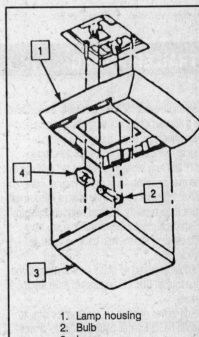

1. Lamp housing
2. Bulb
3. Lens
4. Retainer clip

FIG. 66 Dome light installation — except convertible

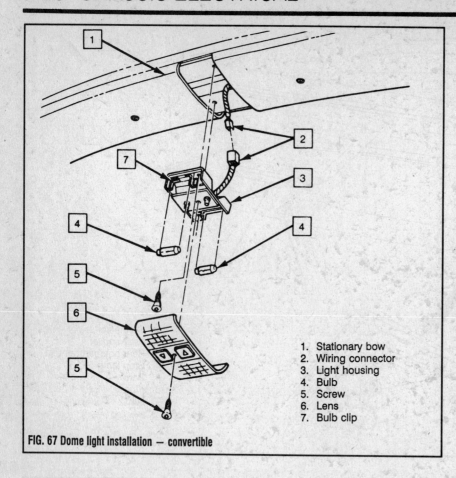

1. Stationary bow
2. Wiring connector
3. Light housing
4. Bulb
5. Screw
6. Lens
7. Bulb clip

FIG. 67 Dome light installation — convertible

CONVERTIBLE
♦ SEE FIG. 67

1. Remove the screw and the lens from the lamp at the center of the stationary bow in the passenger compartment.

2. Remove the 2 bulbs from the clips in the lamp housing.

3. Remove the screw attaching the lamp housing from the stationary bow.

4. Disconnect the dome lamp housing from the wiring.

5. Installation is the reverse of removal.

License Light

CORSICA
♦ SEE FIG. 62

The rear license light is part of the rear tail/stop/turn signal light assembly. Refer to the procedure above.

BERETTA
♦ SEE FIG. 63

1. Remove the 2 screws from the light assembly.

2. Remove the assembly by pulling out through the opening.

3. Remove the socket from the light assembly.

4. Remove the bulb, if replacing.

5. Installation is the reverse of removal.

TRAILER WIRING

Wiring the car for towing is fairly easy. There are a number of good wiring kits available and these should be used, rather than trying to design your own. All trailers will need brake lights and turn signals as well as tail lights and side marker lights. Most states require extra marker lights for overly wide trailers. Also, most states have recently required back-up lights for trailers, and most trailer manufacturers have been building trailers with back-up lights for several years.

Additionally, some Class I, most Class II and just about all Class III trailers will have electric brakes.

Add to this number an accessories wire, to operate trailer internal equipment or to charge the trailer's battery, and you can have as many as 7 wires in the harness.

Determine the equipment on your trailer and buy the wiring kit necessary. The kit will contain all the wires needed, plus a plug adapter set which included the female plug, mounted on the bumper or hitch, and the male plug, wired into, or plugged into the trailer harness.

When installing the kit, follow the manufacturer's instructions. The color coding of the wires is standard throughout the industry.

One point to note, some domestic vehicles, and most imported vehicles, have separate turn signals. On most domestic vehicles, the brake lights and rear turn signals operate with the same bulb. For those vehicles with separate turn signals, you can purchase an isolation unit so that the brake lights won't blink whenever the turn signals are operated, or, you can go to your local electronics supply house and buy 4 diodes to wire in series with the brake and turn signal bulbs. Diodes will isolate the brake and turn signals. The choice is yours. The isolation units are simple and quick to install, but far more expensive than the diodes. The diodes, however, require more work to install properly, since they require the cutting of each bulb's wire and soldering in place of the diode.

One final point, the best kits are those with a spring loaded cover on the vehicle mounted socket. This cover prevents dirt and moisture from corroding the terminals. Never let the vehicle socket hang loosely. Always mount it securely to the bumper or hitch.

➡ **For more information on towing a trailer please refer to Section 1.**

LIGHT BULB CHART

EXTERIOR LIGHTS	Trade No.
Back-up Lights	1156
Center High-Mounted Stop-Light	
Except Luggage Carrier Mounted	1057
Luggage Carrier Mounted	577
Hatchback (Corsica)	557
Front Parking/Turn Signal Lights	2057NA
Parking Only (Beretta)	194NA
Headlights	
Low-Beam	9006
High-Beam	9005
License Plate Lights	194
Rear Tail/Stop/Turn Signal Lights	2057
Taillight Only (Corsica)	194
Sidemarker Lights (Front and Rear)	194
Trunk Light	91707
INTERIOR LIGHTS	**Trade No.**
Heater and A/C Controls	194
Ashtray	
Console	161
Instrument Panel	168
Cargo Light	211-2
Cluster Lighting	194/168
Courtesy Lights	161
Dome/Reading Lights	561/906
Gear Selector Indicator	74
Headlight High-Beam Indicator	74
Indicator Lights	74
Service Engine Soon Warning	168
Over-Head Console (Courtesy/Reading)	562
Turn Signal Indicators	74

CIRCUIT PROTECTION

Fusible Links

A fusible link is a protective device used in an electrical circuit. When the current increases beyond a certain amperage, the fusible metal of the wire link melts, thus breaking the electrical circuit and preventing further damage to other components and wiring. Whenever a fusible link is melted because of a short circuit, correct the cause before installing a new one.

To replace a fusible link, cut off the burned link beyond the original splice. Replace the link with a new one of the same rating. If the splice has two wires, two repair links are required, one for each wire. Connect the new fusible link to the wires, then crimp securely.

✳✳ WARNING

Use only replacements of the same electrical capacity as the original, available from your dealer. Replacements of a different electrical value will not provide adequate system protection.

Fuses

Fuses protect all the major electrical systems in the car. In case of an electrical overload, the fuse melts, breaking the circuit and stopping the flow of electricity.

If a fuse blows, the cause should be investigated and corrected before the installation of a new fuse. This, however, is easier to say than to do. Because each fuse protects a limited number of components, your job is narrowed down somewhat. Begin your investigation by

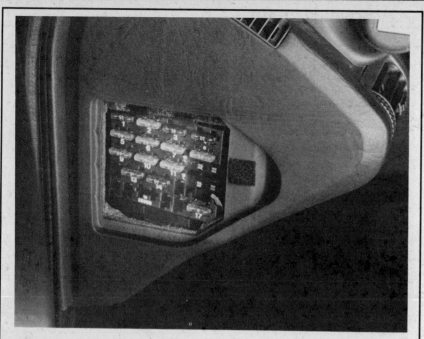

FIG. 68A The fusebox, shown with the cover removed, is located at the driver's side end of the instrument panel–1992 shown

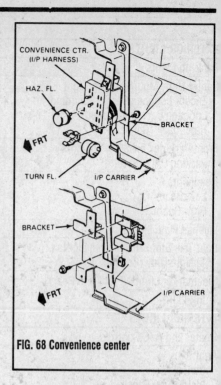

FIG. 68 Convenience center

looking for obvious fraying, loose connections, breaks in insulation, etc. Use the techniques outlined at the beginning of this Section. Electrical problems are almost always a real headache to solve, but if you are patient and persistent, and approach the problem logically (that is, don't start replacing electrical components randomly), you will eventually find the solution.

The amperage of each fuse and the circuit it protects are marked on the fusebox, which is located under the left end (driver's side) of the instrument panel. Remove the cover by pulling out from the bottom.

Circuit Breakers

The headlights are protected by a circuit breaker in the headlamp switch. If the circuit breaker trips, the headlights will either flash on and off, or stay off altogether. The circuit breaker resets automatically after the overload is removed.

The windshield wipers are also protected by a circuit breaker. If the motor overheats, the circuit breaker will trip, remaining off until the motor cools or the overload is removed. One common cause of overheating is operation of the wipers in heavy snow.

The circuit breakers for the power door locks and power windows are located in the fuse box.

Flashers

The hazard flasher is located in the convenience center', under the dash, to the left side of the steering column. The horn relay and the buzzer assembly may be found here also. The turn signal flasher is mounted in a clip above the convenience center. In all cases, replacement is made by unplugging the old unit and plugging in a new one.

TORQUE SPECIFICATIONS

Component	U.S.	Metric
Forward discriminating sensor (air bag system)		
1991-92:	80 inch lbs.	9 Nm
Accumulator bracket bolt:	62 inch lbs.	7 Nm
A/C compressor & condenser hose to accumulator outlet fitting:	30 ft. lbs.	41 Nm
Cruise control servo to bracket		
1988-91:	14 inch lbs.	1.6 Nm
1992:	12 inch lbs.	1.5 Nm
Front speaker to trim panel		
1991-92:	16 inch lbs.	1.8 Nm
Wiper arm pivot nut		
1990-92:	17.7 ft. lbs.	20-27 Nm

Troubleshooting Basic Turn Signal and Flasher Problems

Most problems in the turn signals or flasher system can be reduced to defective flashers or bulbs, which are easily replaced. Occasionally, problems in the turn signals are traced to the switch in the steering column, which will require professional service.

F = Front   R = Rear   ● = Lights off   o = Lights on

Problem		Solution
Turn signals light, but do not flash		• Replace the flasher
No turn signals light on either side		• Check the fuse. Replace if defective. • Check the flasher by substitution • Check for open circuit, short circuit or poor ground
Both turn signals on one side don't work		• Check for bad bulbs • Check for bad ground in both housings
One turn signal light on one side doesn't work		• Check and/or replace bulb • Check for corrosion in socket. Clean contacts. • Check for poor ground at socket
Turn signal flashes too fast or too slow		• Check any bulb on the side flashing too fast. A heavy-duty bulb is probably installed in place of a regular bulb. • Check the bulb flashing too slow. A standard bulb was probably installed in place of a heavy-duty bulb. • Check for loose connections or corrosion at the bulb socket
Indicator lights don't work in either direction		• Check if the turn signals are working • Check the dash indicator lights • Check the flasher by substitution

Troubleshooting Basic Turn Signal and Flasher Problems

Most problems in the turn signals or flasher system can be reduced to defective flashers or bulbs, which are easily replaced. Occasionally, problems in the turn signals are traced to the switch in the steering column, which will require professional service.

F = Front   R = Rear   ● = Lights off   o = Lights on

Problem		Solution

One indicator light doesn't light		• On systems with 1 dash indicator: See if the lights work on the same side. Often the filaments have been reversed in systems combining stoplights with taillights and turn signals. Check the flasher by substitution
		• On systems with 2 indicators: Check the bulbs on the same side
		  Check the indicator light bulb
		  Check the flasher by substitution

Troubleshooting Basic Windshield Wiper Problems

Problem	Cause	Solution
Electric Wipers		
Wipers do not operate— Wiper motor heats up or hums	• Internal motor defect • Bent or damaged linkage • Arms improperly installed on linking pivots	• Replace motor • Repair or replace linkage • Position linkage in park and reinstall wiper arms
Electric Wipers		
Wipers do not operate— No current to motor	• Fuse or circuit breaker blown • Loose, open or broken wiring • Defective switch • Defective or corroded terminals • No ground circuit for motor or switch	• Replace fuse or circuit breaker • Repair wiring and connections • Replace switch • Replace or clean terminals • Repair ground circuits
Wipers do not operate— Motor runs	• Linkage disconnected or broken	• Connect wiper linkage or replace broken linkage
Vacuum Wipers		
Wipers do not operate	• Control switch or cable inoperative • Loss of engine vacuum to wiper motor (broken hoses, low engine vacuum, defective vacuum/fuel pump) • Linkage broken or disconnected • Defective wiper motor	• Repair or replace switch or cable • Check vacuum lines, engine vacuum and fuel pump • Repair linkage • Replace wiper motor
Wipers stop on engine acceleration	• Leaking vacuum hoses • Dry windshield • Oversize wiper blades • Defective vacuum/fuel pump	• Repair or replace hoses • Wet windshield with washers • Replace with proper size wiper blades • Replace pump

Troubleshooting Basic Lighting Problems

Problem	Cause	Solution
Lights		
One or more lights don't work, but others do	• Defective bulb(s) • Blown fuse(s) • Dirty fuse clips or light sockets • Poor ground circuit	• Replace bulb(s) • Replace fuse(s) • Clean connections • Run ground wire from light socket housing to car frame
Lights burn out quickly	• Incorrect voltage regulator setting or defective regulator • Poor battery/alternator connections	• Replace voltage regulator • Check battery/alternator connections
Lights go dim	• Low/discharged battery • Alternator not charging • Corroded sockets or connections • Low voltage output	• Check battery • Check drive belt tension; repair or replace alternator • Clean bulb and socket contacts and connections • Replace voltage regulator
Lights flicker	• Loose connection • Poor ground • Circuit breaker operating (short circuit)	• Tighten all connections • Run ground wire from light housing to car frame • Check connections and look for bare wires
Lights "flare"—Some flare is normal on acceleration—if excessive, see "Lights Burn Out Quickly"	• High voltage setting	• Replace voltage regulator
Lights glare—approaching drivers are blinded	• Lights adjusted too high • Rear springs or shocks sagging • Rear tires soft	• Have headlights aimed • Check rear springs/shocks • Check/correct rear tire pressure
Turn Signals		
Turn signals don't work in either direction	• Blown fuse • Defective flasher • Loose connection	• Replace fuse • Replace flasher • Check/tighten all connections
Right (or left) turn signal only won't work	• Bulb burned out • Right (or left) indicator bulb burned out • Short circuit	• Replace bulb • Check/replace indicator bulb • Check/repair wiring
Flasher rate too slow or too fast	• Incorrect wattage bulb • Incorrect flasher	• Flasher bulb • Replace flasher (use a variable load flasher if you pull a trailer)
Indicator lights do not flash (burn steadily)	• Burned out bulb • Defective flasher	• Replace bulb • Replace flasher
Indicator lights do not light at all	• Burned out indicator bulb • Defective flasher	• Replace indicator bulb • Replace flasher

Troubleshooting Basic Dash Gauge Problems

Problem	Cause	Solution
Coolant Temperature Gauge		
Gauge reads erratically or not at all	• Loose or dirty connections • Defective sending unit • Defective gauge	• Clean/tighten connections • Bi-metal gauge: remove the wire from the sending unit. Ground the wire for an instant. If the gauge registers, replace the sending unit. • Magnetic gauge: disconnect the wire at the sending unit. With ignition ON gauge should register COLD. Ground the wire; gauge should register HOT.
Ammeter Gauge—Turn Headlights ON (do not start engine). Note reaction		
Ammeter shows charge Ammeter shows discharge Ammeter does not move	• Connections reversed on gauge • Ammeter is OK • Loose connections or faulty wiring • Defective gauge	• Reinstall connections • Nothing • Check/correct wiring • Replace gauge
Oil Pressure Gauge		
Gauge does not register or is inaccurate	• On mechanical gauge, Bourdon tube may be bent or kinked • Low oil pressure • Defective gauge • Defective wiring • Defective sending unit	• Check tube for kinks or bends preventing oil from reaching the gauge • Remove sending unit. Idle the engine briefly. If no oil flows from sending unit hole, problem is in engine. • Remove the wire from the sending unit and ground it for an instant with the ignition ON. A good gauge will go to the top of the scale. • Check the wiring to the gauge. If it's OK and the gauge doesn't register when grounded, replace the gauge. • If the wiring is OK and the gauge functions when grounded, replace the sending unit
All Gauges		
All gauges do not operate All gauges read low or erratically All gauges pegged	• Blown fuse • Defective instrument regulator • Defective or dirty instrument voltage regulator • Loss of ground between instrument voltage regulator and car • Defective instrument regulator	• Replace fuse • Replace instrument voltage regulator • Clean contacts or replace • Check ground • Replace regulator

Troubleshooting Basic Dash Gauge Problems

Problem	Cause	Solution
Warning Lights		
Light(s) do not come on when ignition is ON, but engine is not started	• Defective bulb • Defective wire • Defective sending unit	• Replace bulb • Check wire from light to sending unit • Disconnect the wire from the sending unit and ground it. Replace the sending unit if the light comes on with the ignition ON.
Light comes on with engine running	• Problem in individual system • Defective sending unit	• Check system • Check sending unit (see above)

Troubleshooting the Heater

Problem	Cause	Solution
Blower motor will not turn at any speed	• Blown fuse • Loose connection • Defective ground • Faulty switch • Faulty motor • Faulty resistor	• Replace fuse • Inspect and tighten • Clean and tighten • Replace switch • Replace motor • Replace resistor
Blower motor turns at one speed only	• Faulty switch • Faulty resistor	• Replace switch • Replace resistor
Blower motor turns but does not circulate air	• Intake blocked • Fan not secured to the motor shaft	• Clean intake • Tighten security
Heater will not heat	• Coolant does not reach proper temperature • Heater core blocked internally • Heater core air-bound • Blend-air door not in proper position	• Check and replace thermostat if necessary • Flush or replace core if necessary • Purge air from core • Adjust cable
Heater will not defrost	• Control cable adjustment incorrect • Defroster hose damaged	• Adjust control cable • Replace defroster hose

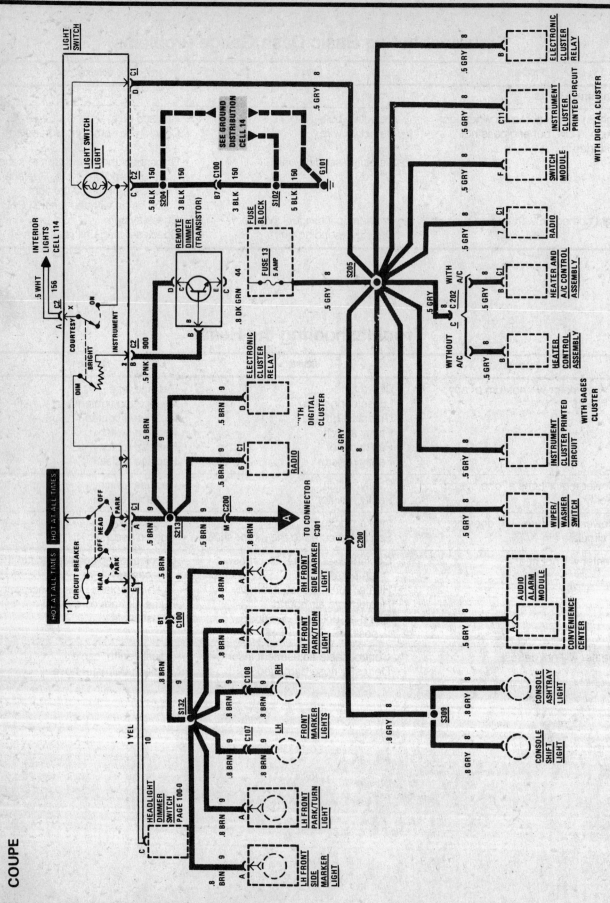

COUPE

Light switch details (coupe)-1988–89 Corsica and Beretta

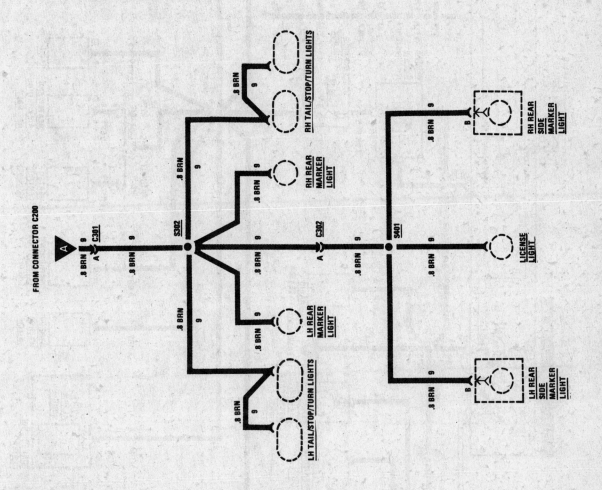

2 DOOR

FROM CONNECTOR C200

A

.8 BRN

A C301 B

.8 BRN

S302

.8 BRN

RH TAIL/STOP/TURN LIGHTS

.8 BRN

RH REAR MARKER LIGHT

A C302

.8 BRN

S401

.8 BRN

LICENSE LIGHT

.8 BRN

LH REAR MARKER LIGHT

.8 BRN

LH TAIL/STOP/TURN LIGHTS

.8 BRN

B RH REAR SIDE MARKER LIGHT

.8 BRN

B LH REAR SIDE MARKER LIGHT

Light switch details (2 door)-1988–89 Corsica and Beretta

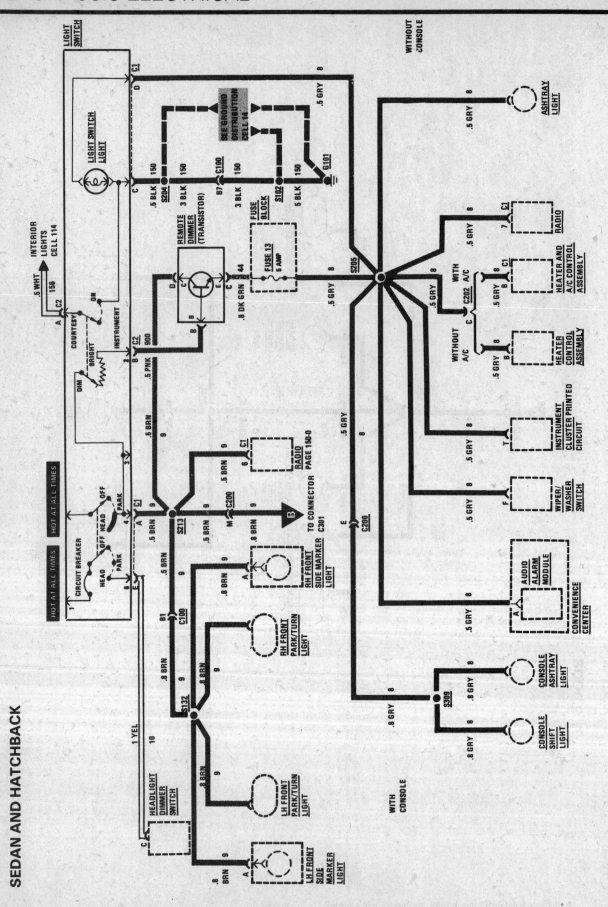

Light switch details (sedan and hatchback)-1988–89 Corsica and Beretta

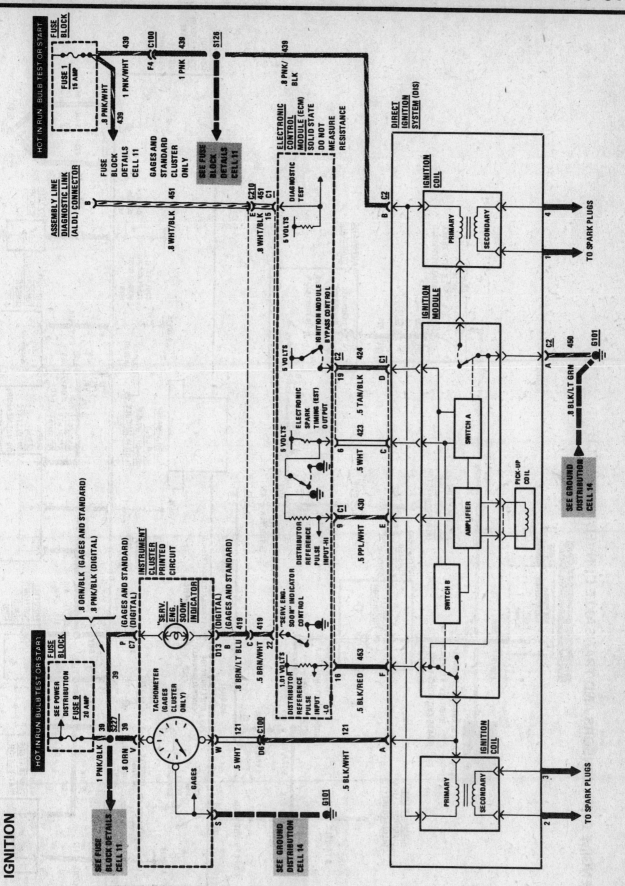

Electronic fuel injection: (2.0L 4 cyl., ignition)-1988–89 Corsica and Beretta

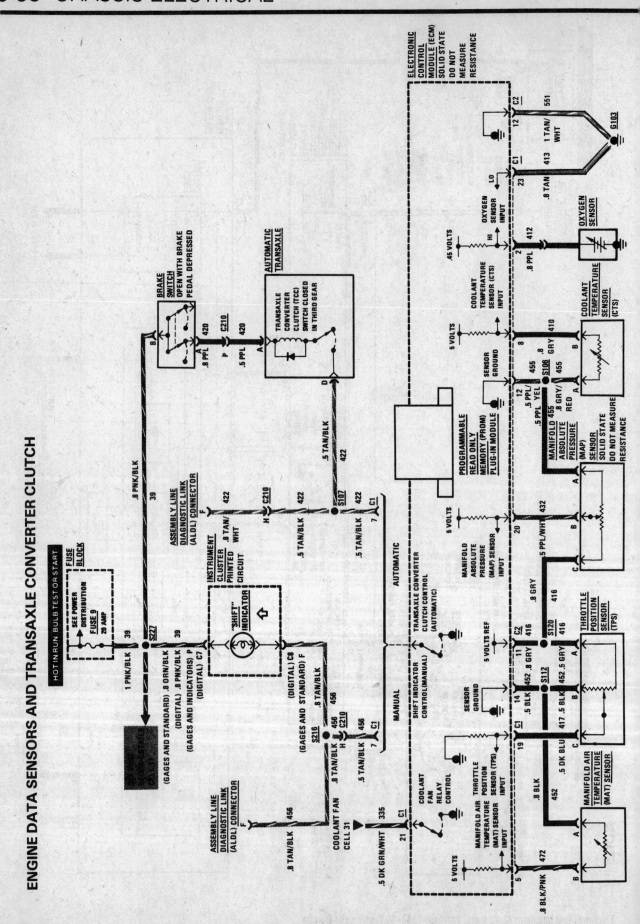

ENGINE DATA SENSORS AND TRANSAXLE CONVERTER CLUTCH

Electronic fuel injection: (2.0L 4 cyl., data sensors and transaxle converter clutch)-1988–89 Corsica and Beretta

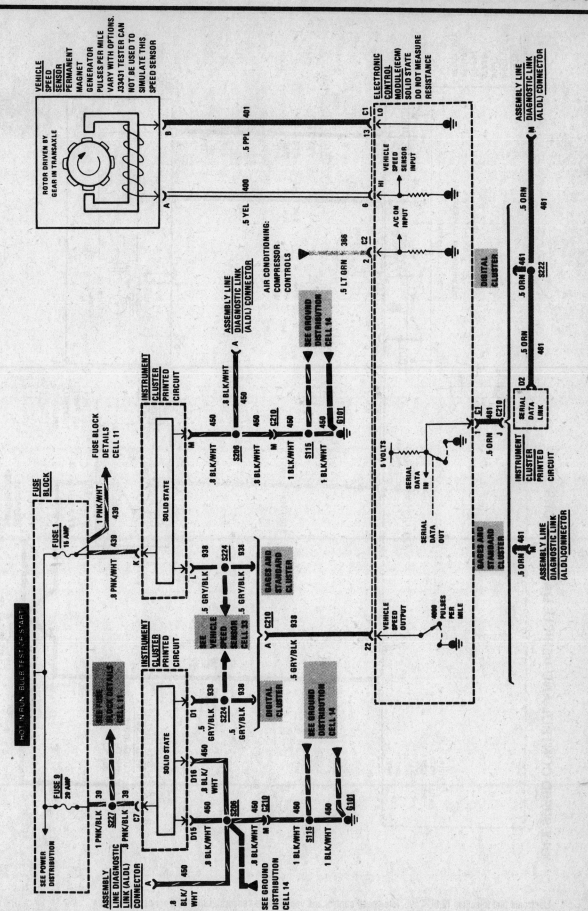

VEHICLE SPEED SENSOR

Electronic fuel injection: (2.0L 4 cyl., vehicle speed sensor)-1988–89 Corsica and Beretta

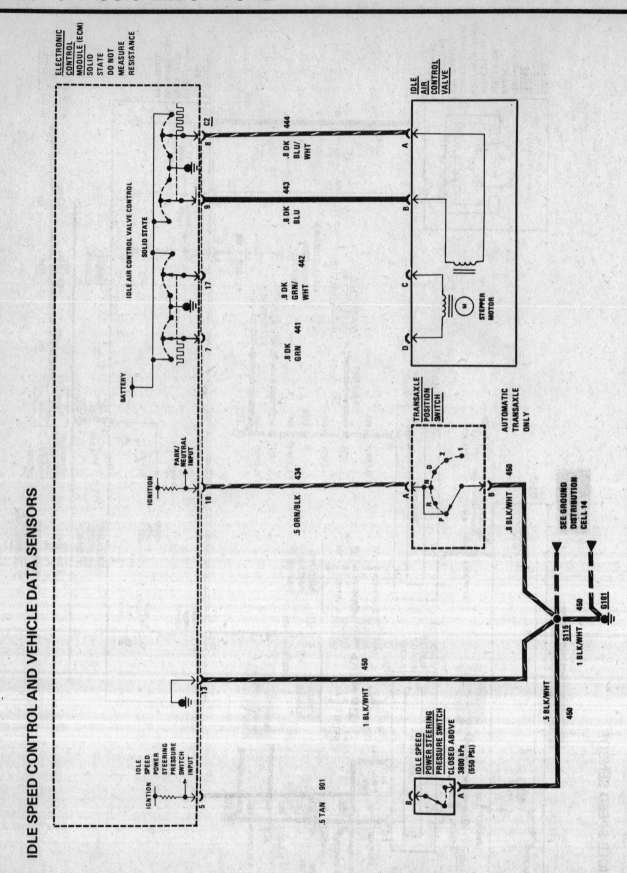

IDLE SPEED CONTROL AND VEHICLE DATA SENSORS

Electronic fuel injection: (2.0L 4 cyl., idle speed control and vehicle data sensors)-1988–89 Corsica and Beretta

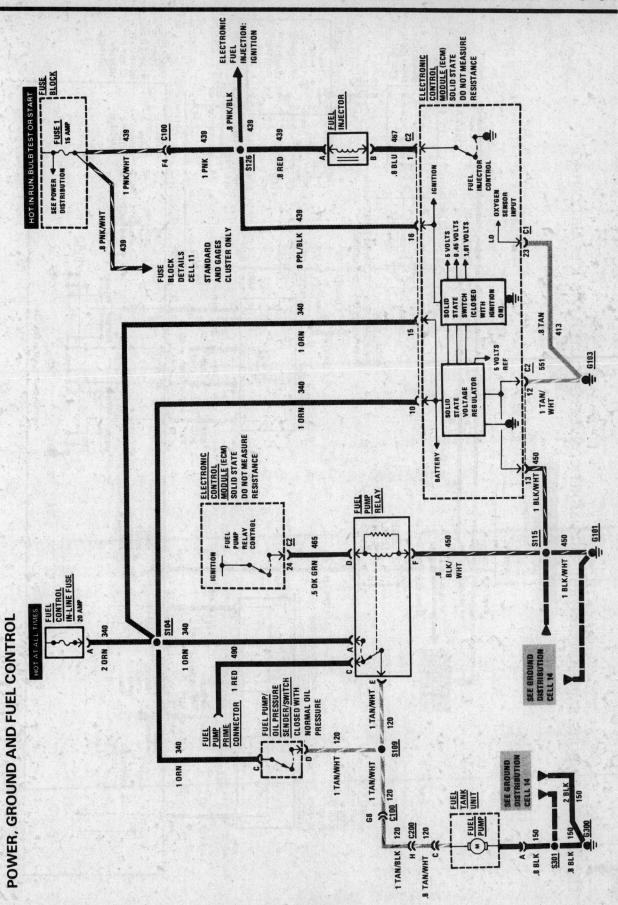

POWER, GROUND AND FUEL CONTROL

Electronic fuel injection: (2.0L 4 cyl., power, ground and fuel control) -1988–89 Corsica and Beretta

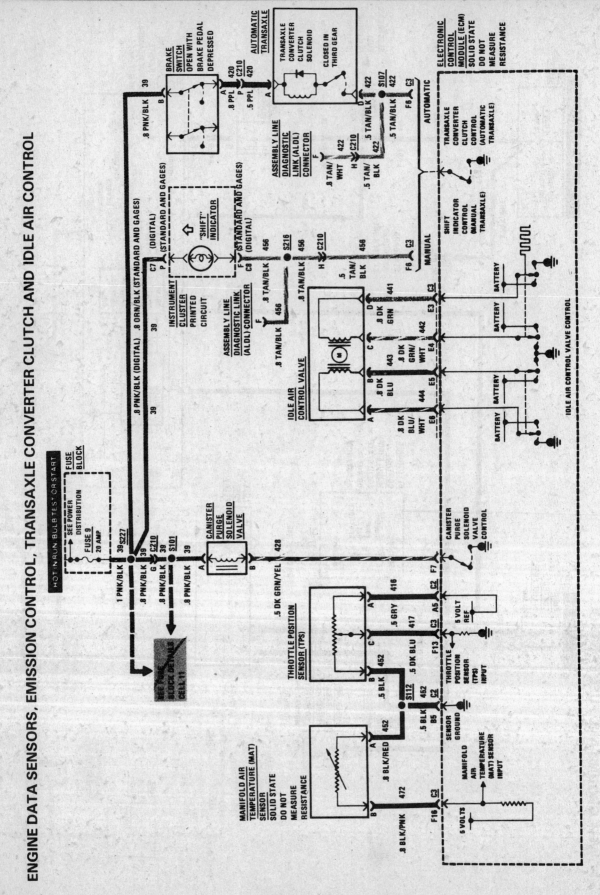

ENGINE DATA SENSORS, EMISSION CONTROL, TRANSAXLE CONVERTER CLUTCH AND IDLE AIR CONTROL

Multi-port fuel injection: (2.8L V6 engine data sensors, emission control, transaxle converter clutch and idle air control)-1988–89 Corsica and Beretta

ENGINE DATA SENSORS

ELECTRONIC CONTROL MODULE (ECM) SOLID STATE DO NOT MEASURE RESISTANCE

G104

D1 C1   1 TAN/WHT   551

E15 C3   413

E16   .8 TAN

LO   OXYGEN SENSOR INPUT

HI   OXYGEN SENSOR INPUT

.45 VOLTS

E14   .8 PPL   412   OXYGEN SENSOR

5 VOLTS

F9   .8 DK BLU   496   DETONATION SENSOR

DETONATION SENSOR INPUT

5 VOLTS

E16   .8 GRY   410   COOLANT TEMPERATURE SENSOR (CTS)

COOLANT TEMPERATURE SENSOR (CTS) INPUT

B

A   .8 GRY/RED   455   MANIFOLD ABSOLUTE PRESSURE (MAP) SENSOR SOLID STATE DO NOT MEASURE RESISTANCE

SENSOR GROUND

MANIFOLD ABSOLUTE PRESSURE (MAP) SENSOR INPUT

C2   B6   455   .5 PPL/YEL   S106   455   .5 PPL   A

5 V REFERENCE

C3   F15   474   432   .5 PPL/WHT   B

A4   C2   474   .5 GRY/RED   S118   .5 GRY/RED   C   474

.8 GRY/RED   474   B   EGR ELECTRONIC VACUUM REGULATOR VALVE (EVRV) SOLID STATE DO NOT MEASURE RESISTANCE

C   450   S115   450   G101

.5 BLK/WHT   1 BLK/WHT

SEE GROUND DISTRIBUTION CELL 14

EGR VALVE POSITION INPUT

C2   A3   911   E

EGR SOLENOID CONTROL IGNITION

C3   C1   435   .5 PNK   A

E9   .5 GRY

S101   .8 PNK/BLK   39   D

HOT IN RUN, BULB TEST OR START

FUSE BLOCK

SEE POWER DISTRIBUTION

FUSE 9 20 AMP

1 PNK/BLK   S227   39   .8 PNK/BLK   C210   G   39   .8 PNK/BLK   S101

SEE FUSE BLOCK DETAILS CELL 11

Multi-port fuel injection: (2.8L V6 engine data sensors)-1988–89 Corsica and Beretta

POWER, GROUNDS, FUEL CONTROL AND INJECTORS

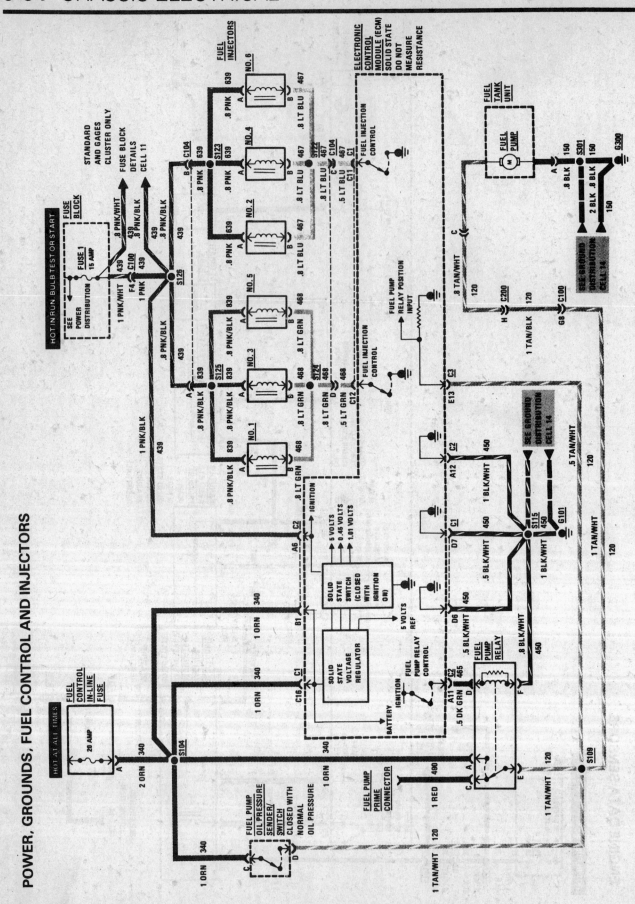

Multi-port fuel injection: (2.8L V6 engine fuel control and injectors) -1988–89 Corsica and Beretta

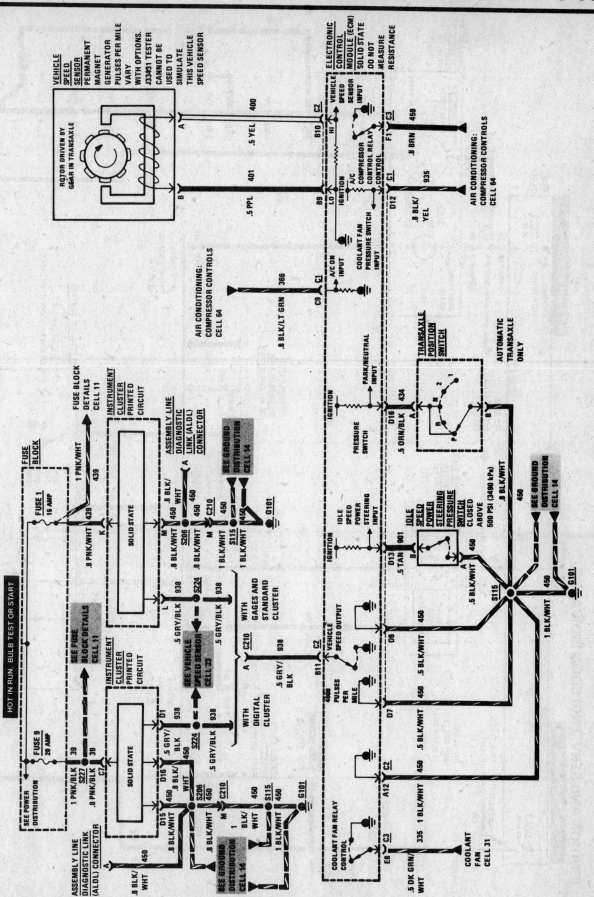

VEHICLE DATA SENSORS AND VEHICLE SPEED SENSOR

Multi-port fuel injection: (2.8L V6 engine vehicle speed sensors)-1988–89 Corsica and Beretta

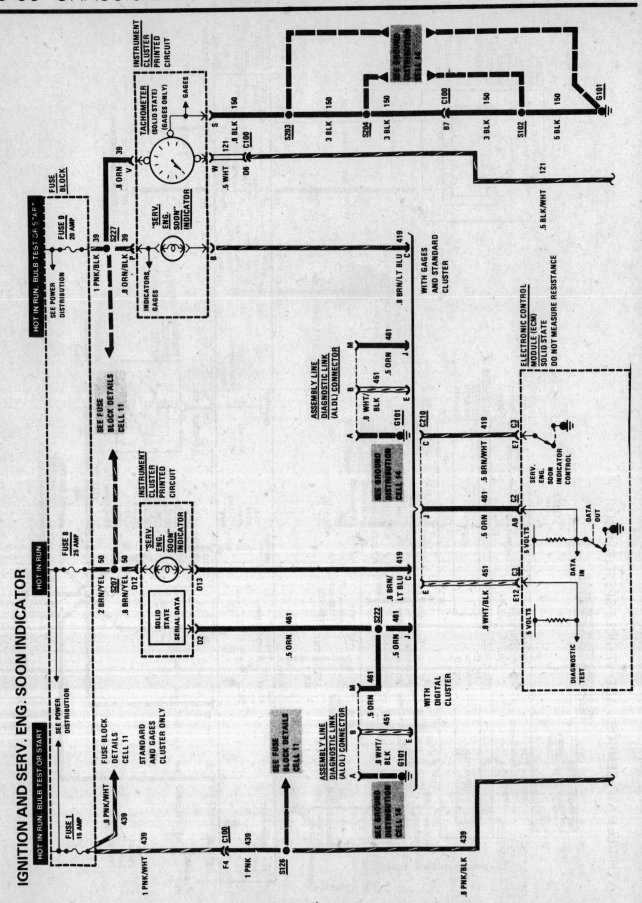

Multi-port fuel injection: (2.8L V6 engine ignition and service engine soon indicator)-1988–89 Corsica and Beretta

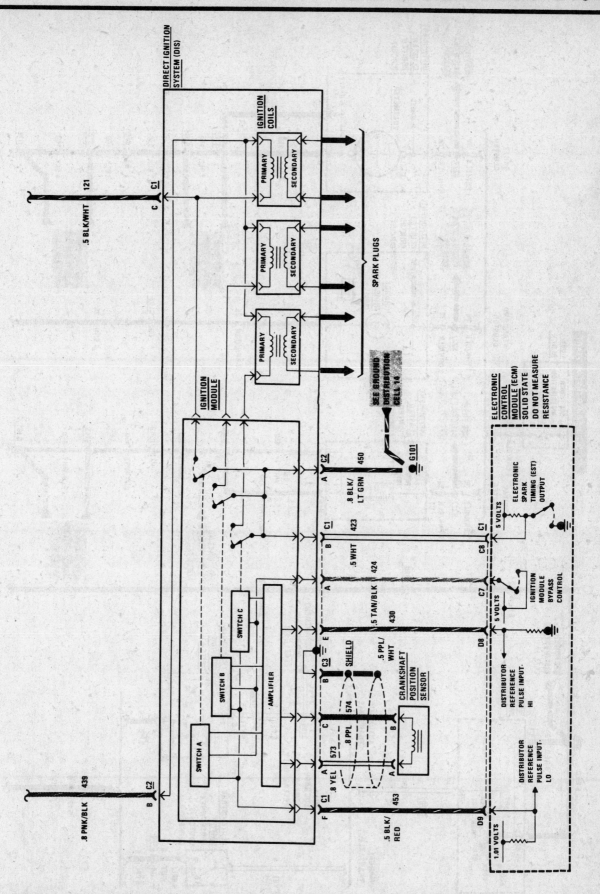

Multi-port fuel injection: (2.8L V6 engine ignition and service engine soon indicator cont.)-1988–89 Corsica and Beretta

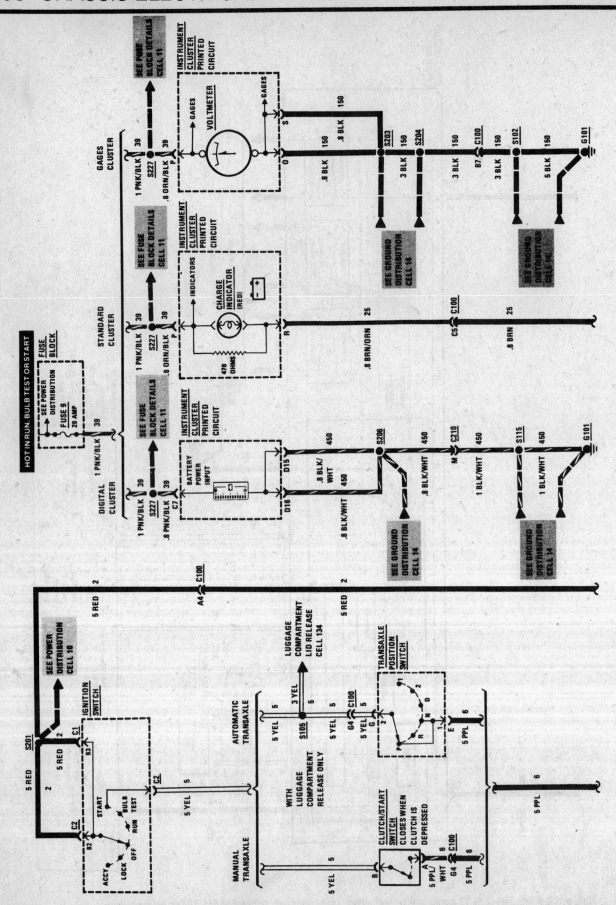

Starter and charging system-1988–89 Corsica and Beretta

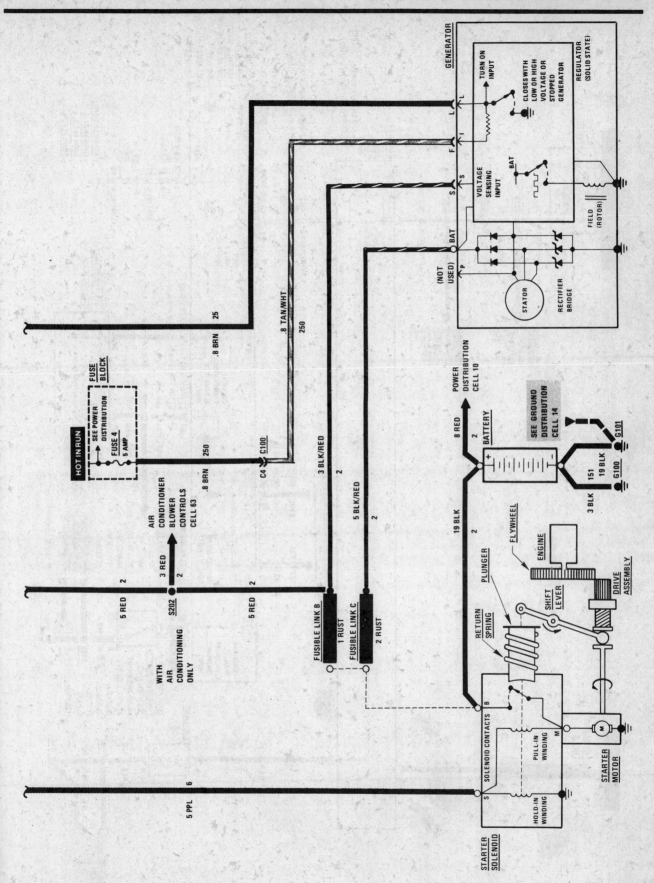

Starter and charging system (cont.)-1988–89 Corsica and Beretta

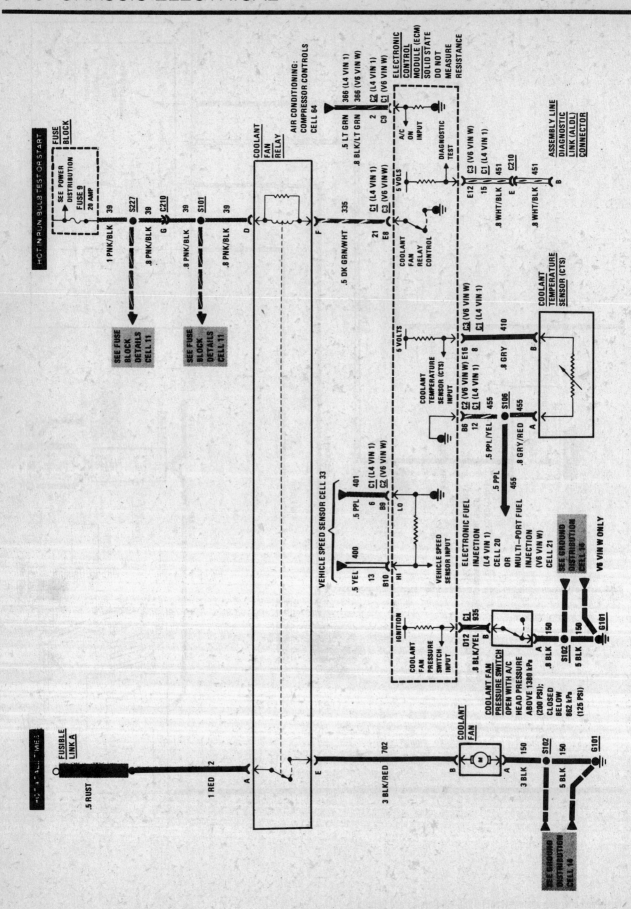

Coolant fan-1988–89 Corsica and Beretta

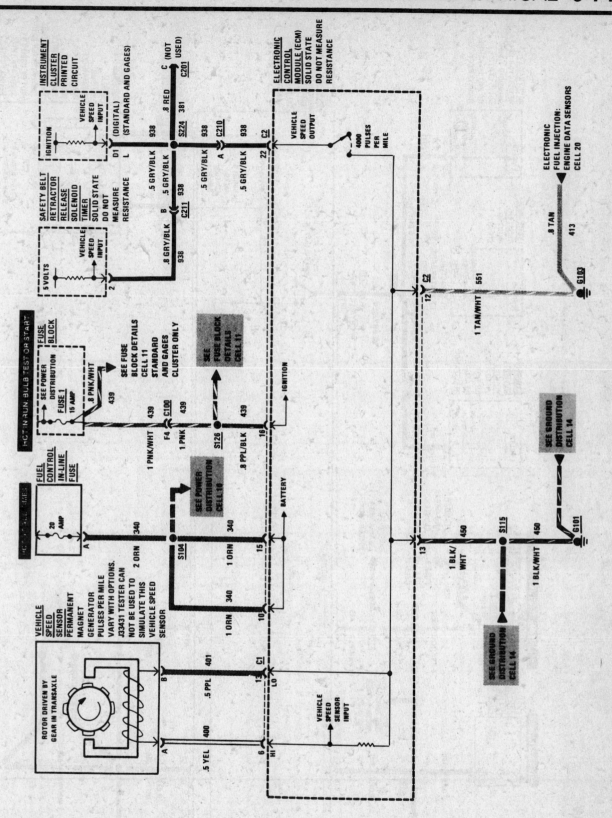

L4 VIN 1

Vehicle speed sensor: (permanent magnet generator, 2.0L 4 cyl. engine)-1988–89 Corsica and Beretta

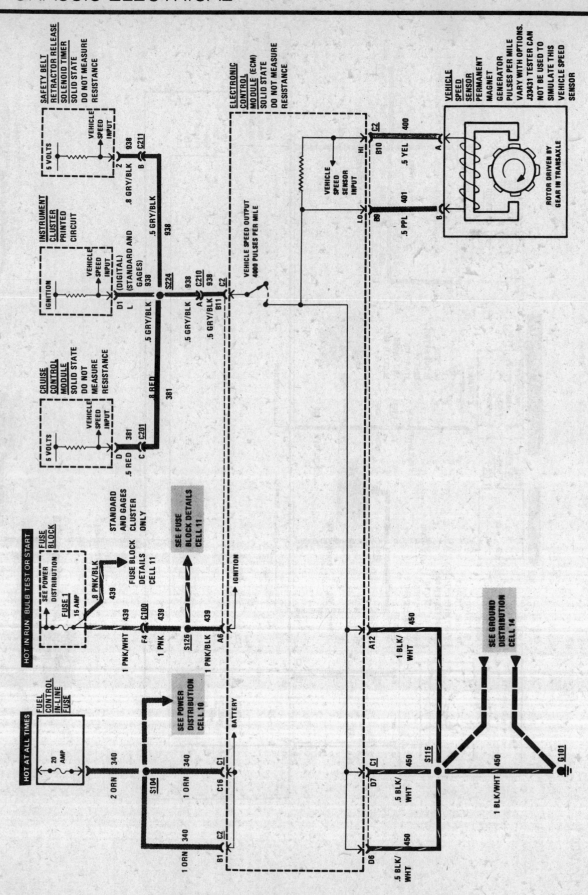

V6 VIN W

Vehicle speed sensor: (permanent magnet generator, 2.8L V6 engine)-1988–89 Corsica and Beretta

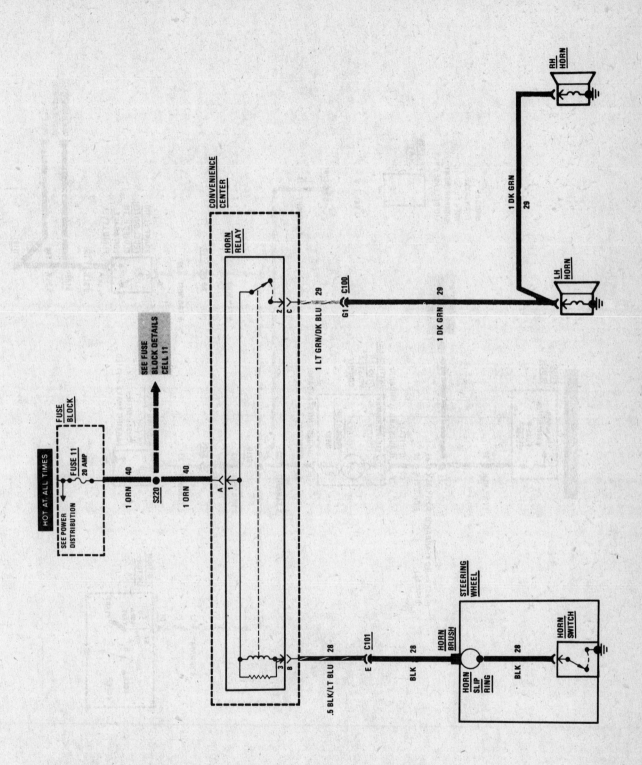

Horns-1988–89 Corsica and Beretta

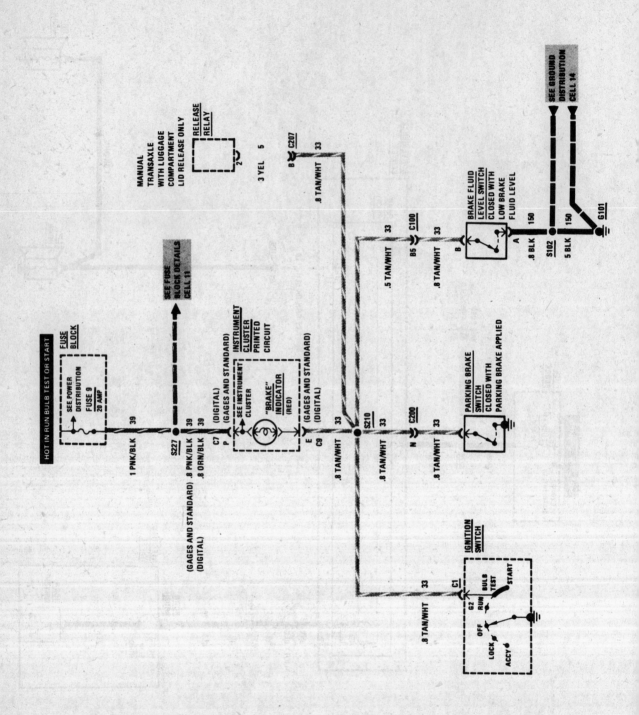

Brake warning system-1988–89 Corsica and Beretta

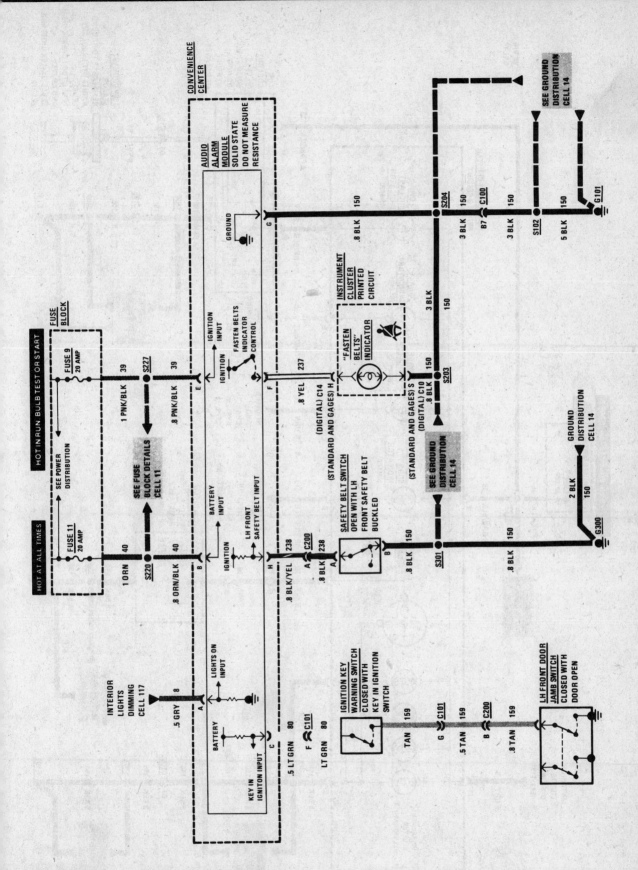

Warnings and alarms: (chime)-1988–89 Corsica and Beretta

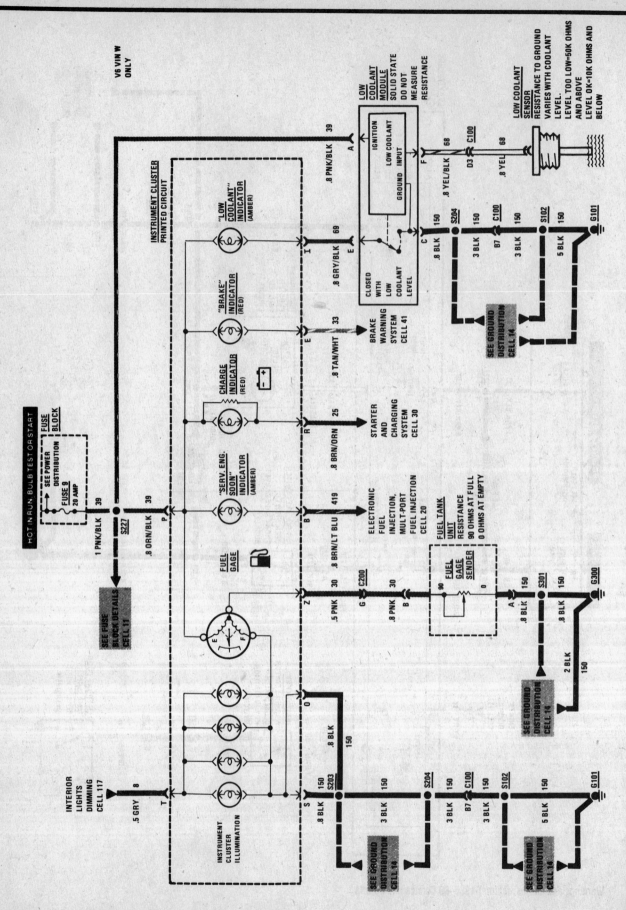

Instrument panel (indicators cluster)-1988–89 Corsica and Beretta

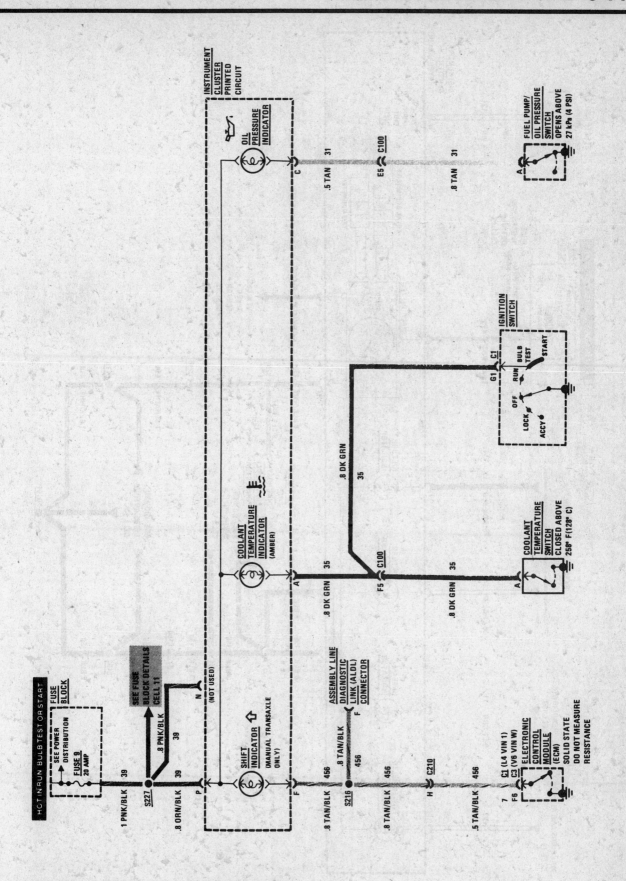

Instrument panel (indicators cluster)-1988–89 Corsica and Beretta

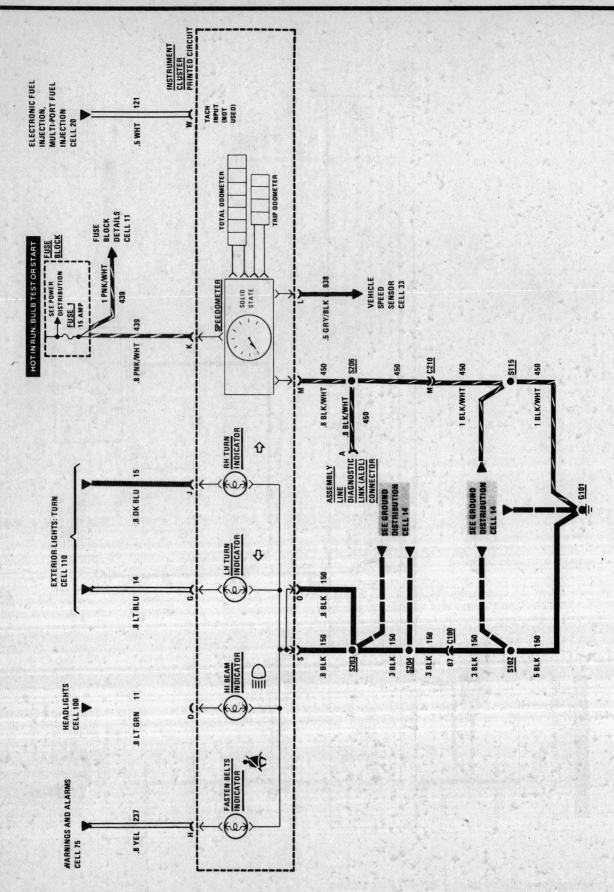

Instrument panel (indicators cluster)-1988–89 Corsica and Beretta

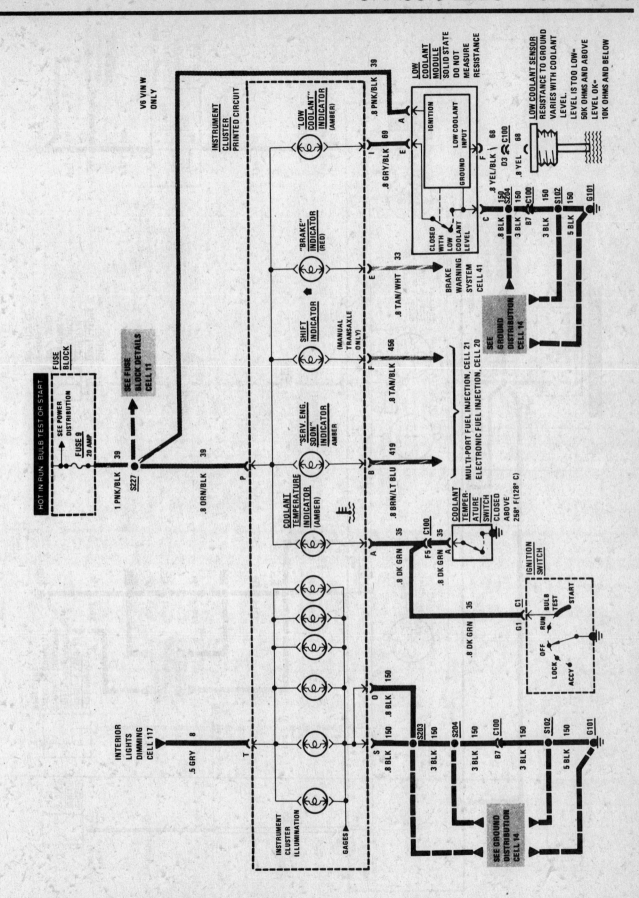

Instrument panel (gages cluster)-1988–89 Corsica and Beretta

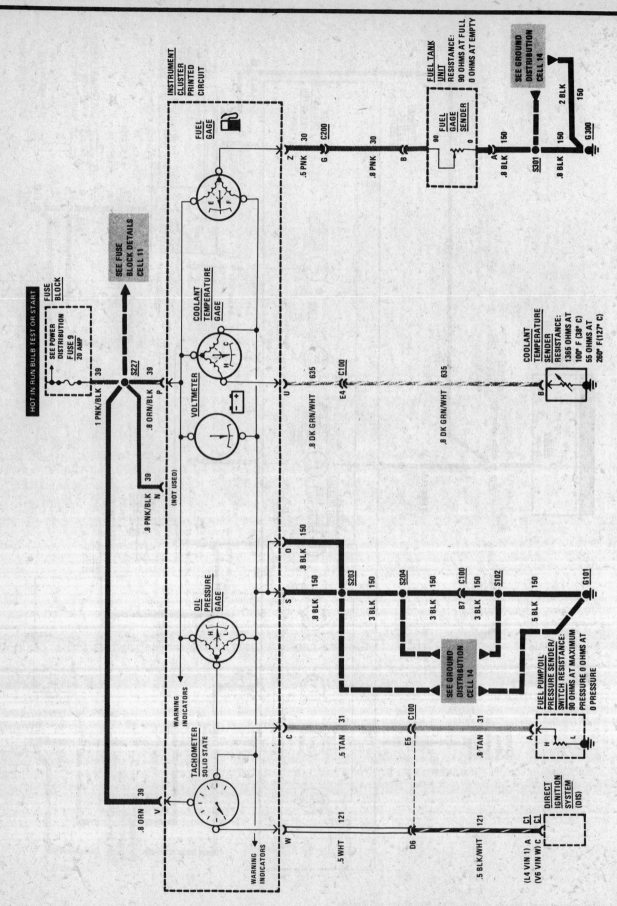

Instrument panel (gages cluster)-1988–89 Corsica and Beretta

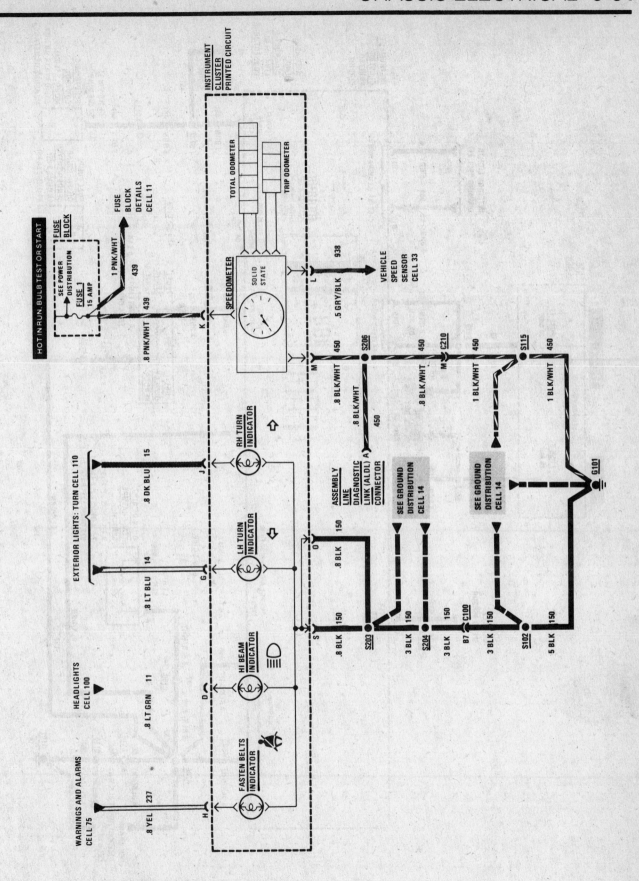

Instrument panel (gages cluster)-1988–89 Corsica and Beretta

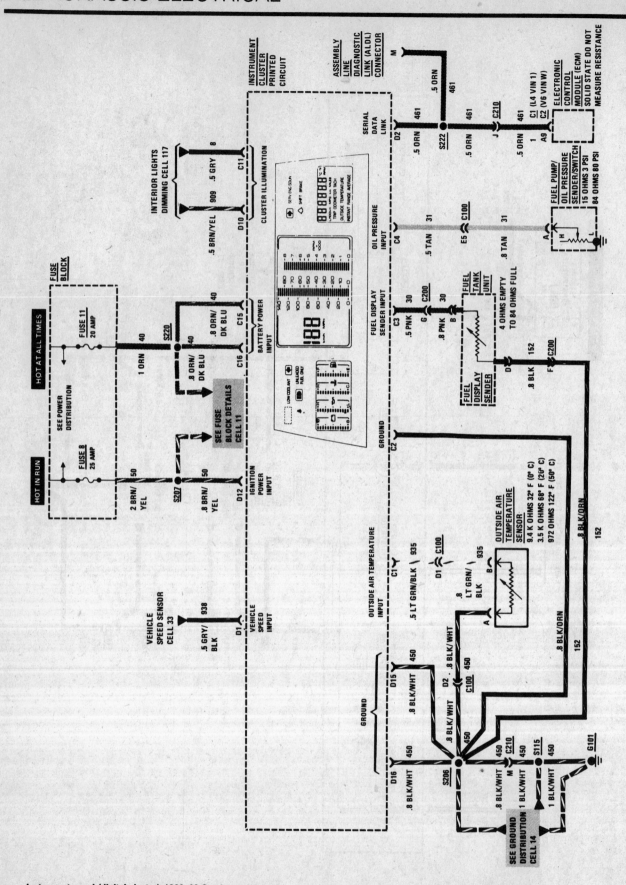

Instrument panel (digital cluster)-1988–89 Corsica and Beretta

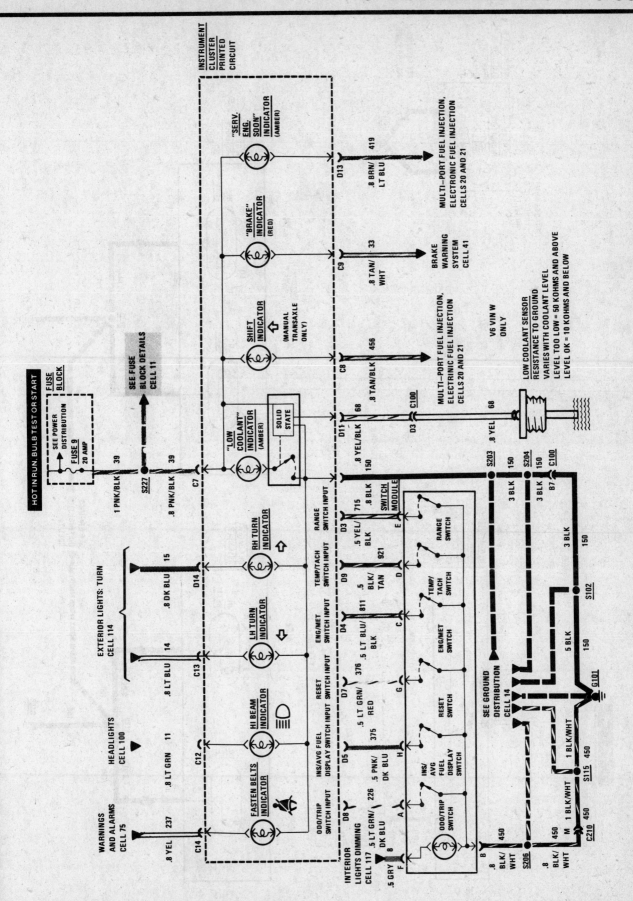

Instrument panel (digital cluster)-1988–89 Corsica and Beretta

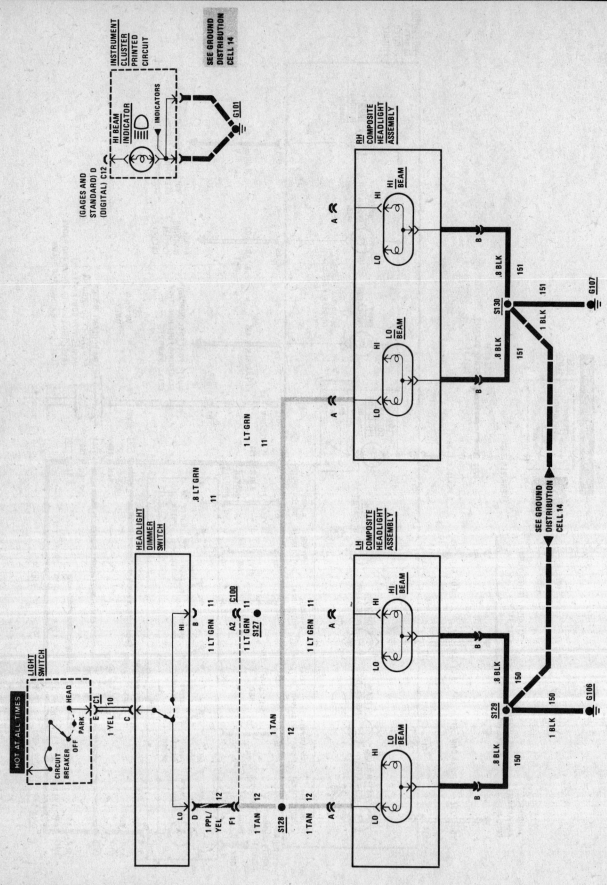

Headlights-1988–89 Corsica and Beretta

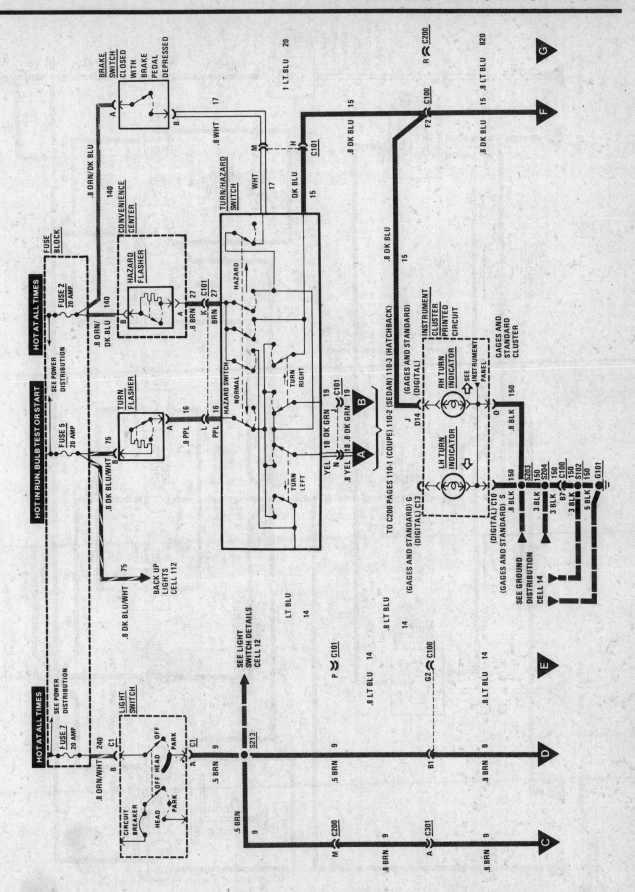

Exterior lights: (turn/hazard/stop/tail/marker/license/park)-1988–89 Corsica and Beretta

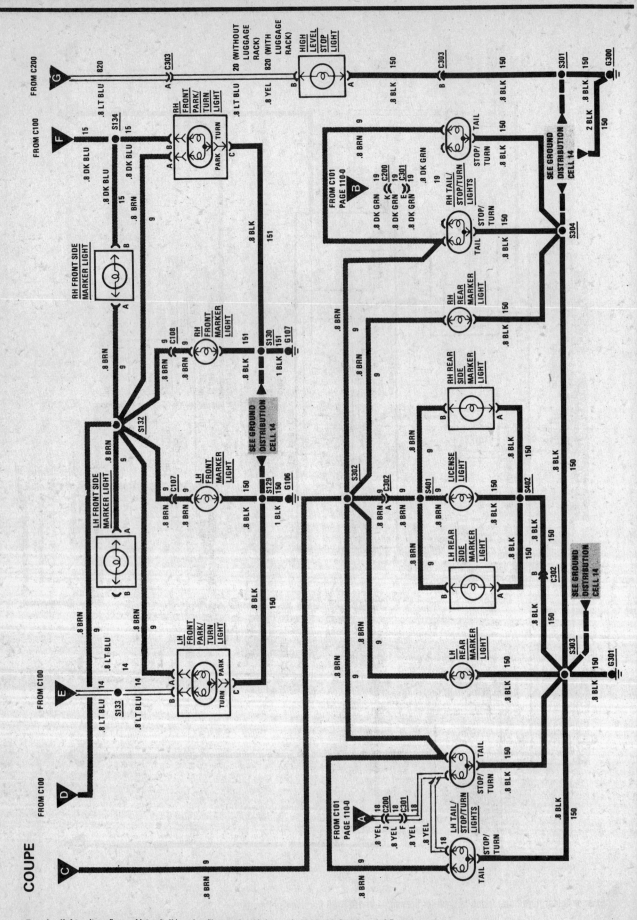

Exterior lights: (turn/hazard/stop/tail/marker/license/park) (coupe)-1988–89 Corsica and Beretta

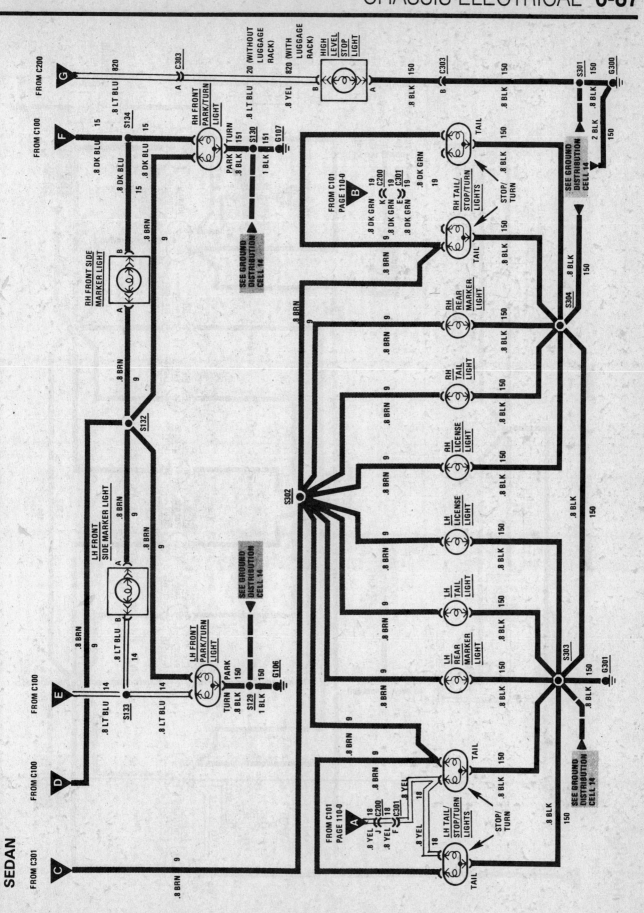

SEDAN

Exterior lights: (turn/hazard/stop/tail/marker/license/park) (sedan)-1988–89 Corsica and Beretta

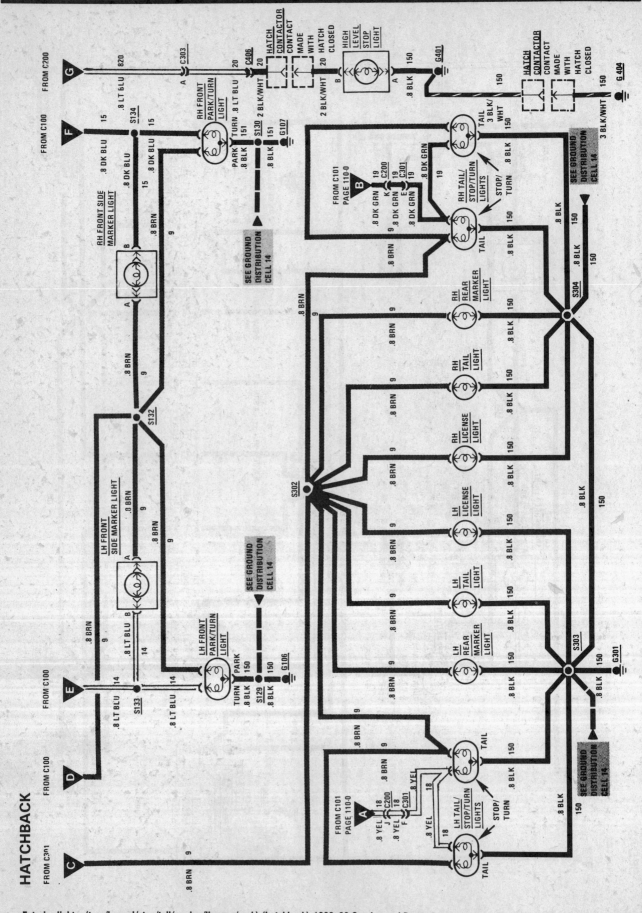

HATCHBACK

Exterior lights: (turn/hazard/stop/tail/marker/license/park) (hatchback)-1988–89 Corsica and Beretta

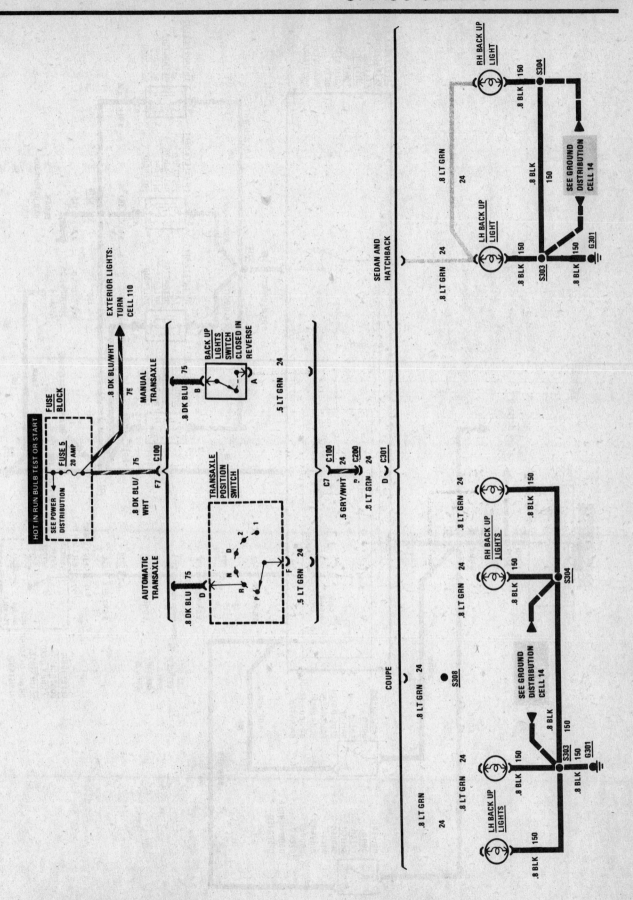

Backup lights-1988–89 Corsica and Beretta

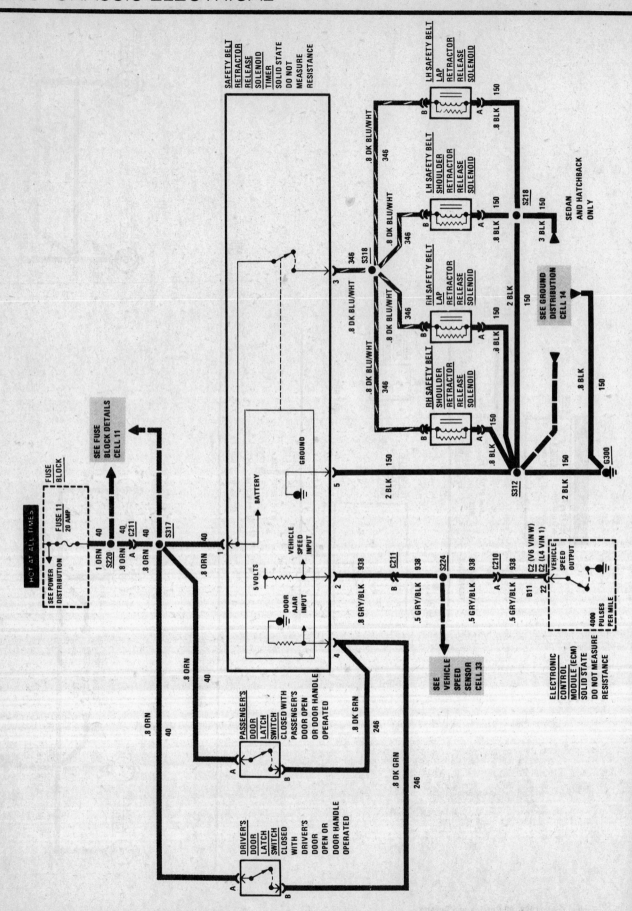

Passive restraint system-1988–89 Corsica and Beretta

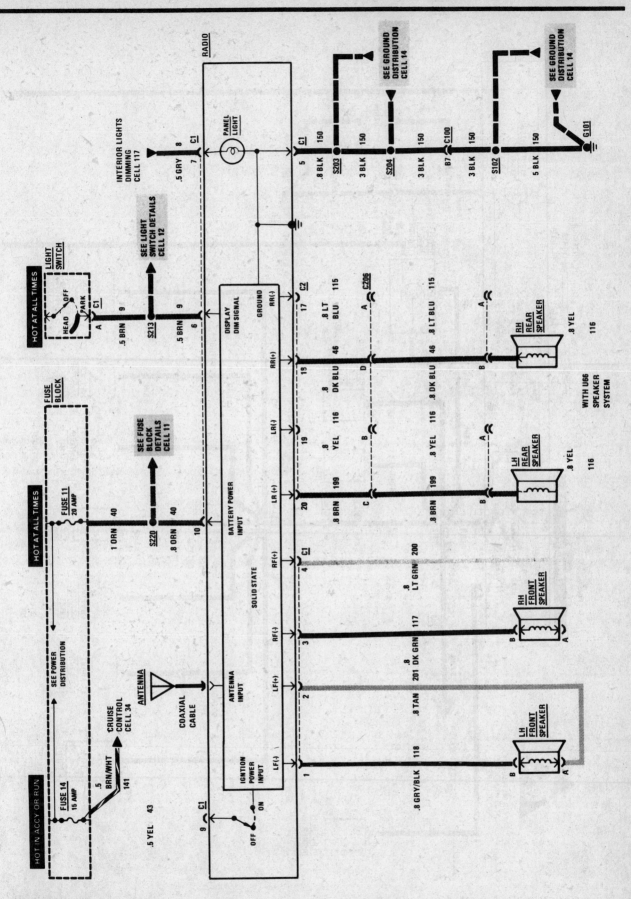

Radio-1988–89 Corsica and Beretta

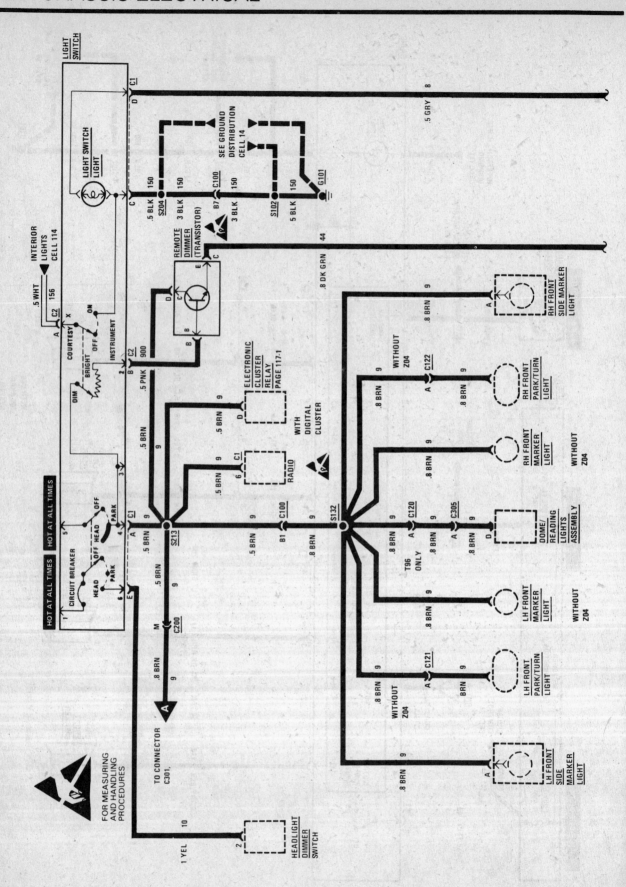

Light switch details (coupe)-1990 Corsica and Beretta

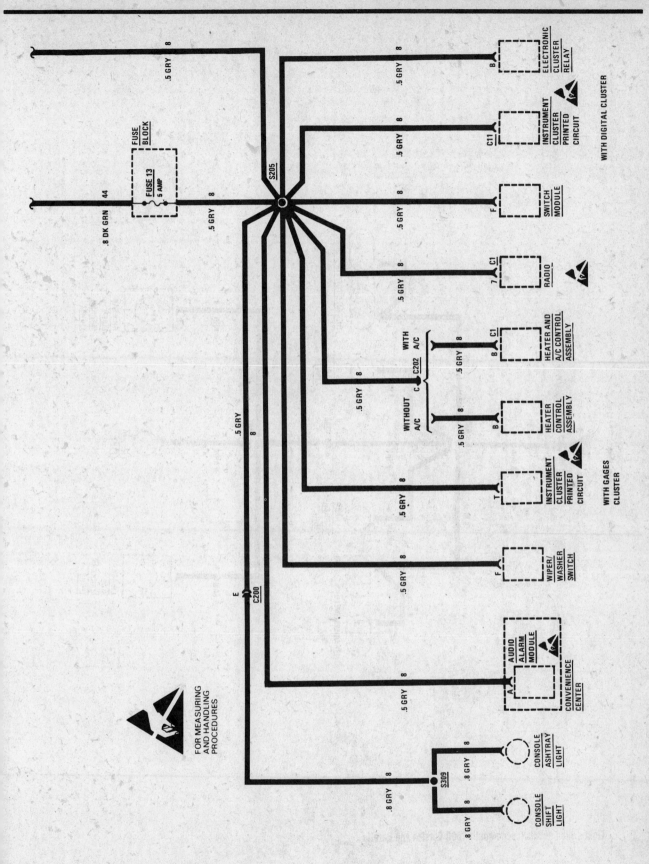

Light switch details (coupe cont.)-1990 Corsica and Beretta

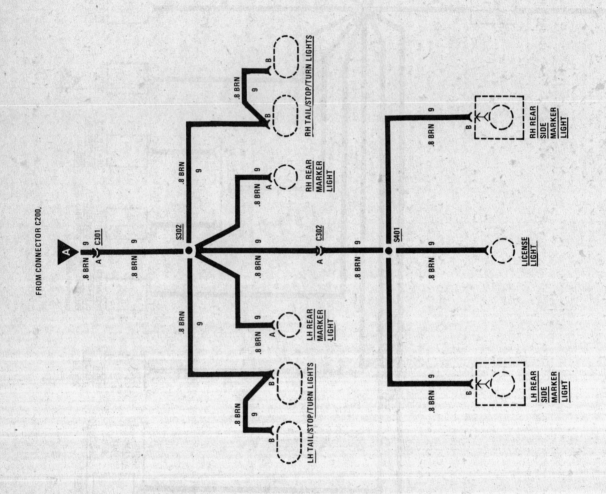

Light switch details (coupe cont.)-1990 Corsica and Beretta

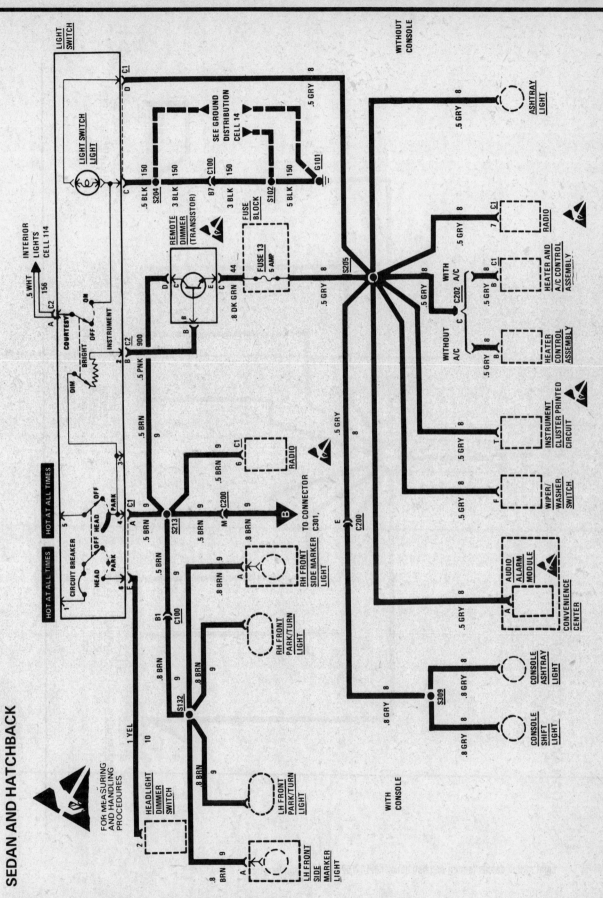

SEDAN AND HATCHBACK

Light switch details (sedan and hatchback)-1990 Corsica and Beretta

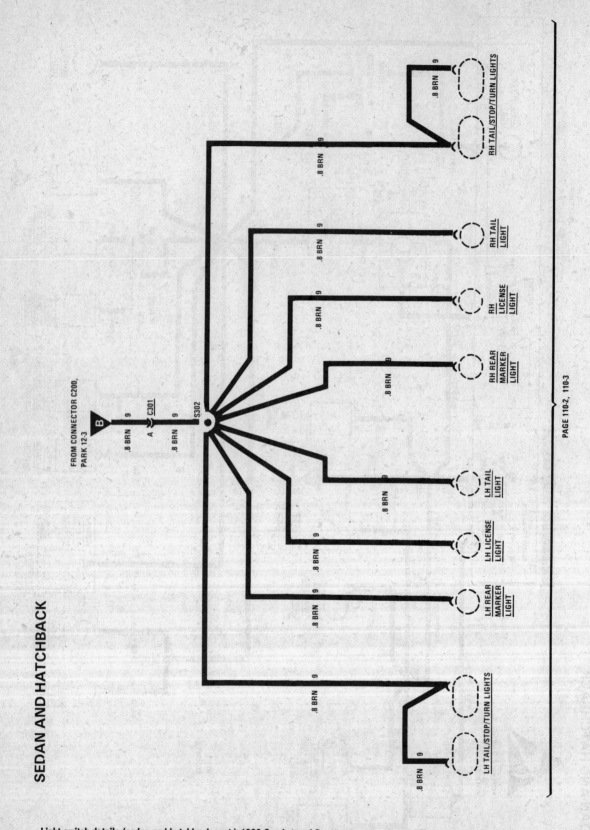

SEDAN AND HATCHBACK

FROM CONNECTOR C200, PARK 12-3

B .8 BRN 9 A C301 9 .8 BRN S302

RH TAIL/STOP/TURN LIGHTS
.8 BRN 9
.8 BRN 9

RH TAIL LIGHT
.8 BRN 9

RH LICENSE LIGHT
.8 BRN 9

RH REAR MARKER LIGHT
.8 BRN 9

LH TAIL LIGHT
.8 BRN 9

LH LICENSE LIGHT
.8 BRN 9

LH REAR MARKER LIGHT
.8 BRN 9

LH TAIL/STOP/TURN LIGHTS
.8 BRN 9
.8 BRN 9

PAGE 110-2, 110-3

Light switch details (sedan and hatchback cont.)-1990 Corsica and Beretta

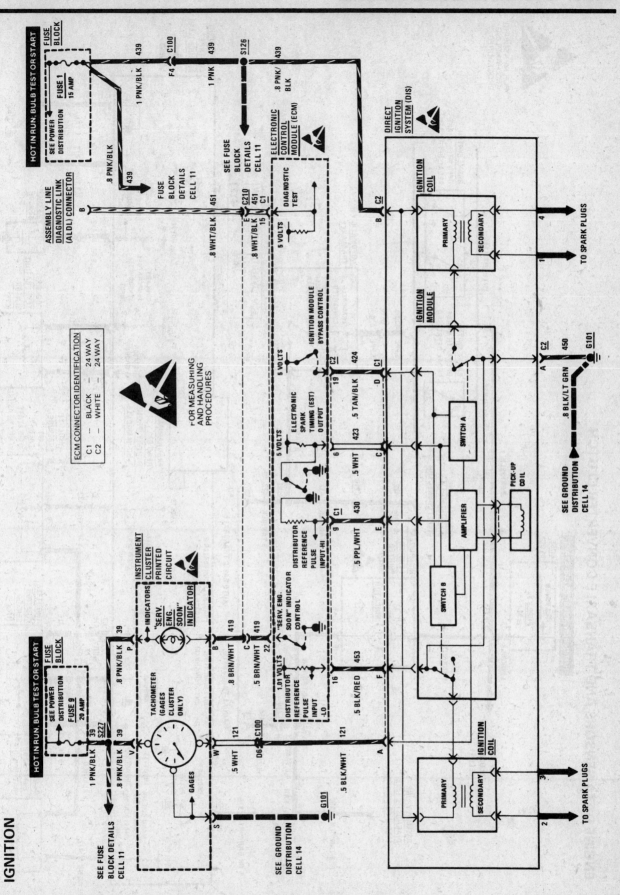

IGNITION

Electronic fuel injection: (2.2L 4 cyl., ignition)-1990 Corsica and Beretta

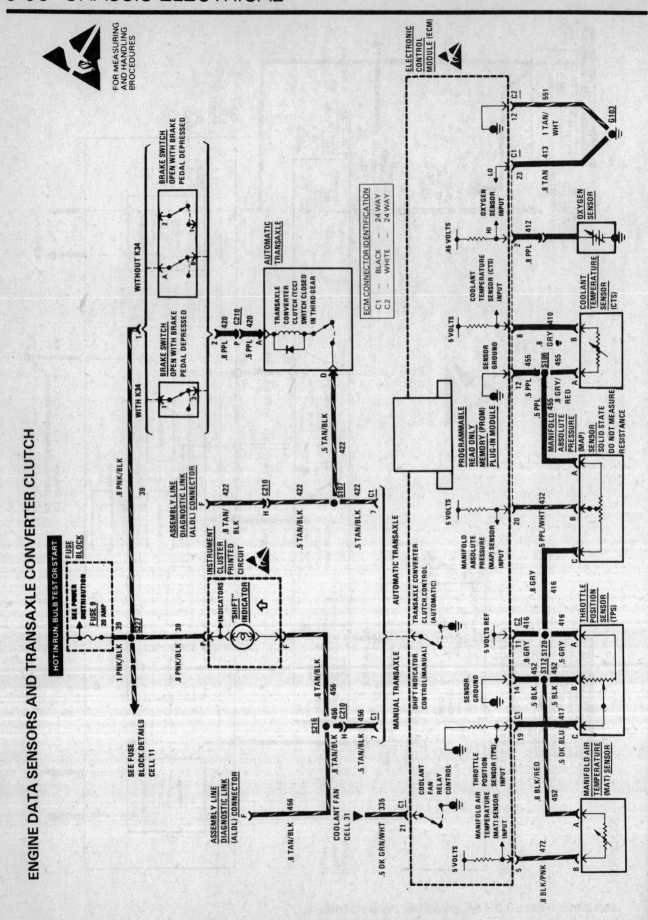

ENGINE DATA SENSORS AND TRANSAXLE CONVERTER CLUTCH

Electronic fuel injection: (2.2L 4 cyl., data sensors and transaxle converter clutch)-1990 Corsica and Beretta

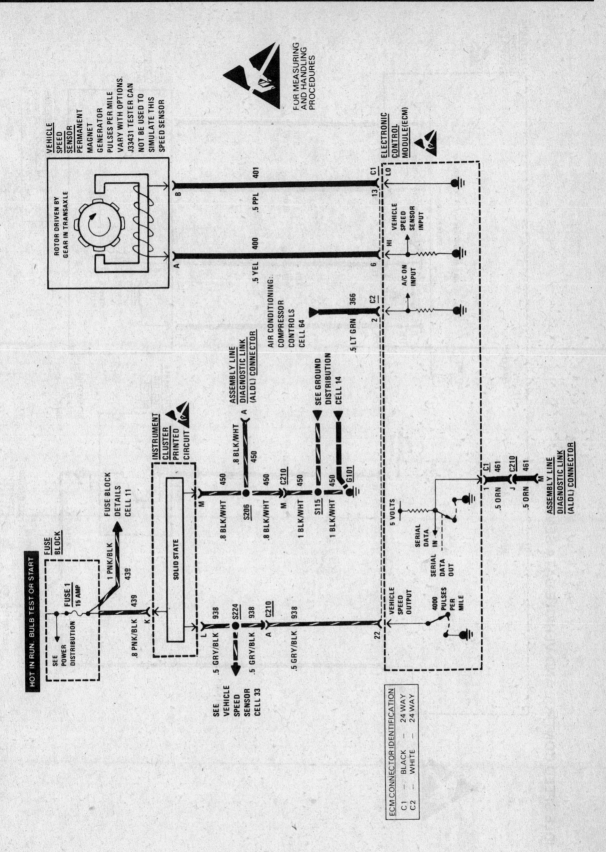

VEHICLE SPEED SENSOR

Electronic fuel injection: (2.2L 4 cyl., vehicle speed sensor)-1990 Corsica and Beretta

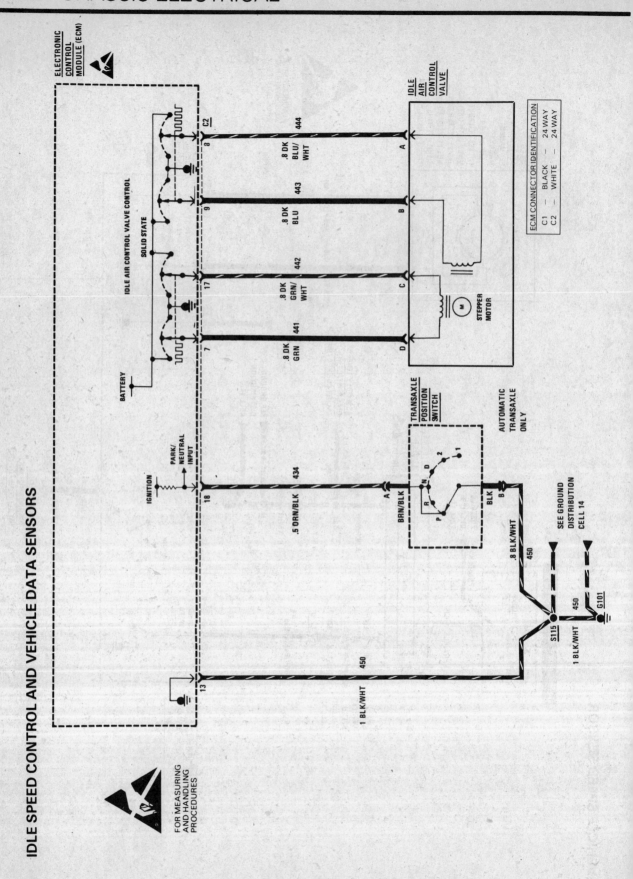

Electronic fuel injection: (2.2L 4 cyl., idle speed control and vehicle data sensors)-1990 Corsica and Beretta

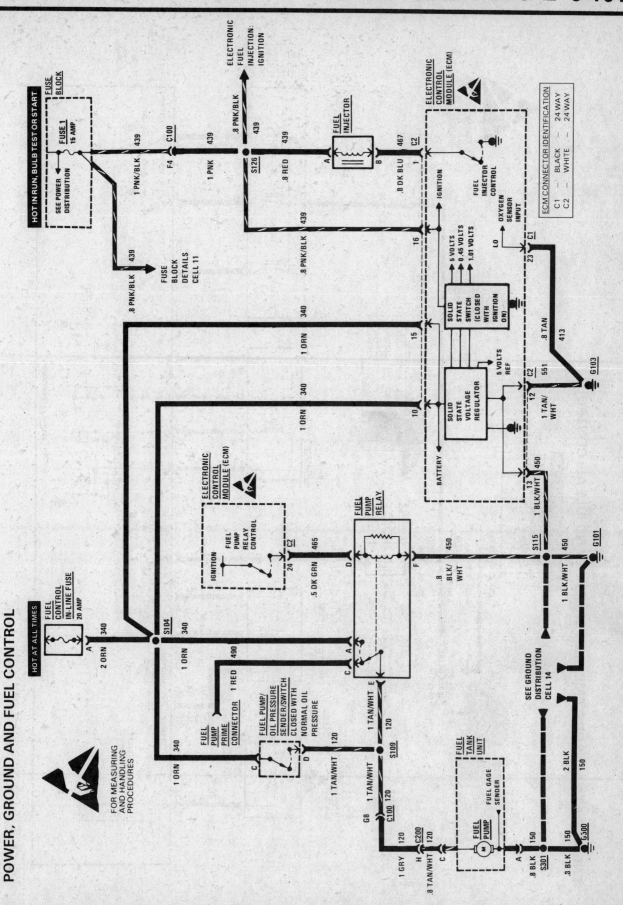

POWER, GROUND AND FUEL CONTROL

Electronic fuel injection: (2.2L 4 cyl., power, ground and fuel control) -1990 Corsica and Beretta

ENGINE DATA SENSORS, EMISSION CONTROL AND IDLE AIR CONTROL

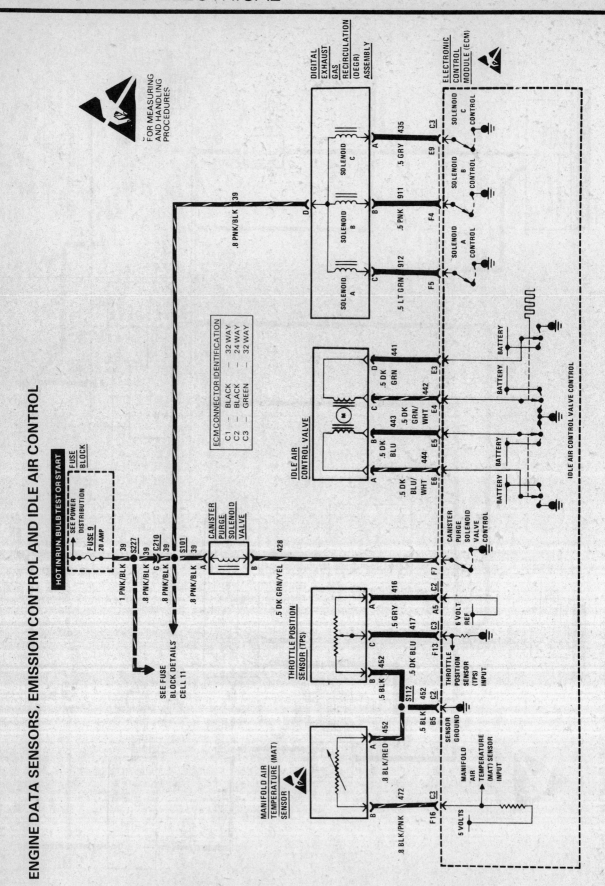

Multi-port fuel injection: (3.1L V6 engine data sensors, emission control and idle air control)-1990 Corsica and Beretta

ENGINE DATA SENSORS

FOR MEASURING
AND HANDLING
PROCEDURES

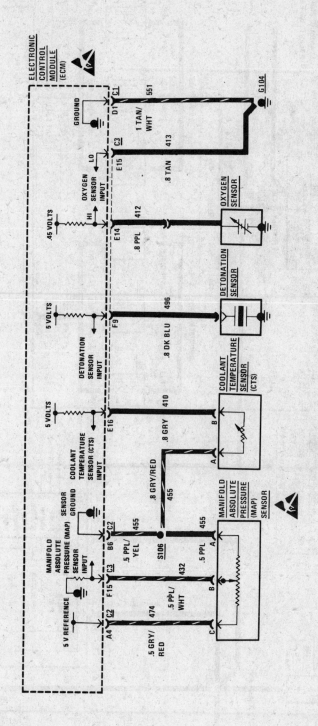

Multi-port fuel injection: (3.1L V6 engine data sensors)-1990 Corsica and Beretta

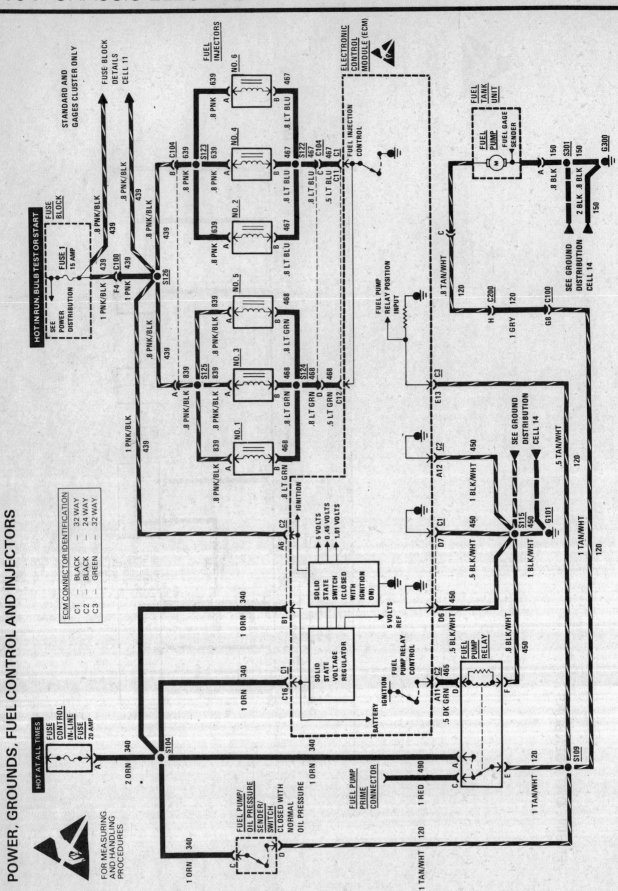

POWER, GROUNDS, FUEL CONTROL AND INJECTORS

Multi-port fuel injection: (3.1L V6 engine fuel control and injectors) -1990 Corsica and Beretta

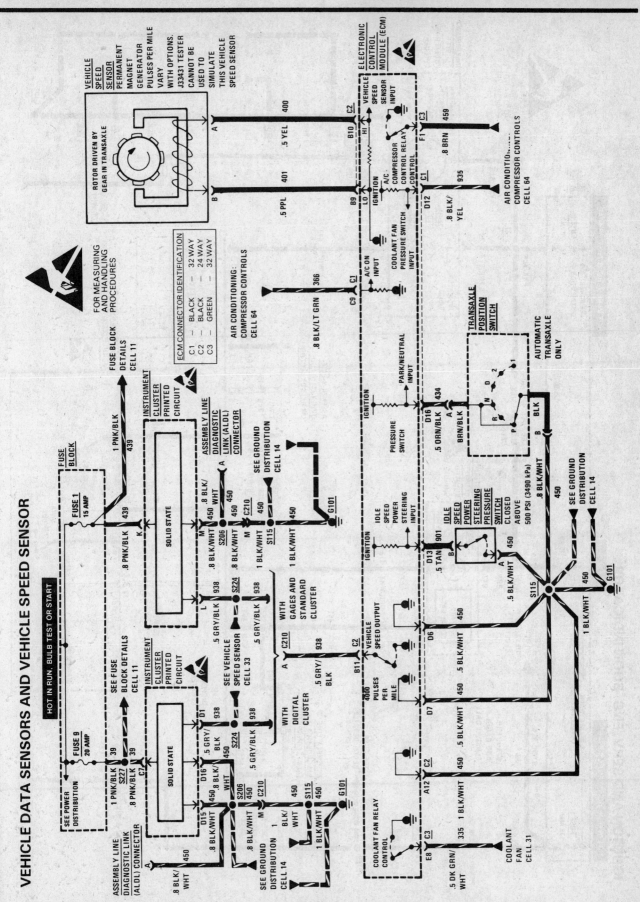

Multi-port fuel injection: (3.1L V6 engine vehicle data sensors and vehicle speed sensors)-1990 Corsica and Beretta

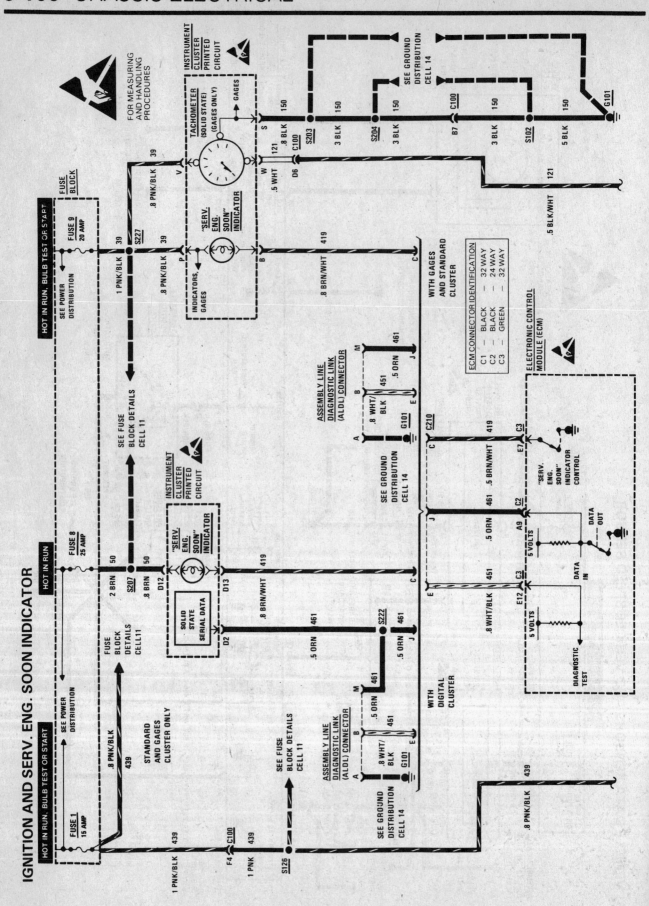

Multi-port fuel injection: (3.1L V6 engine ignition and service engine soon indicator)-1990 Corsica and Beretta

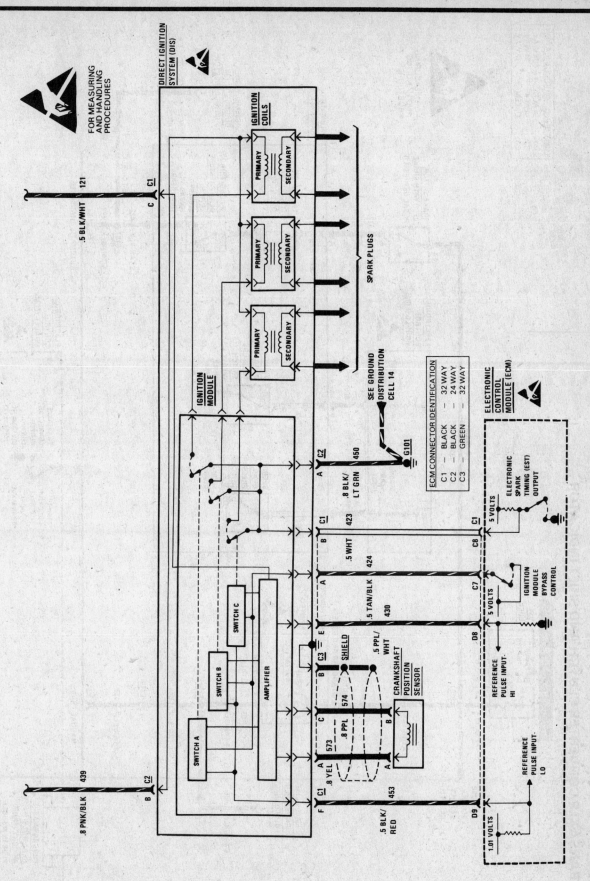

Multi-port fuel injection: (3.1L V6 engine ignition and service engine soon indicator cont.)-1990 Corsica and Beretta

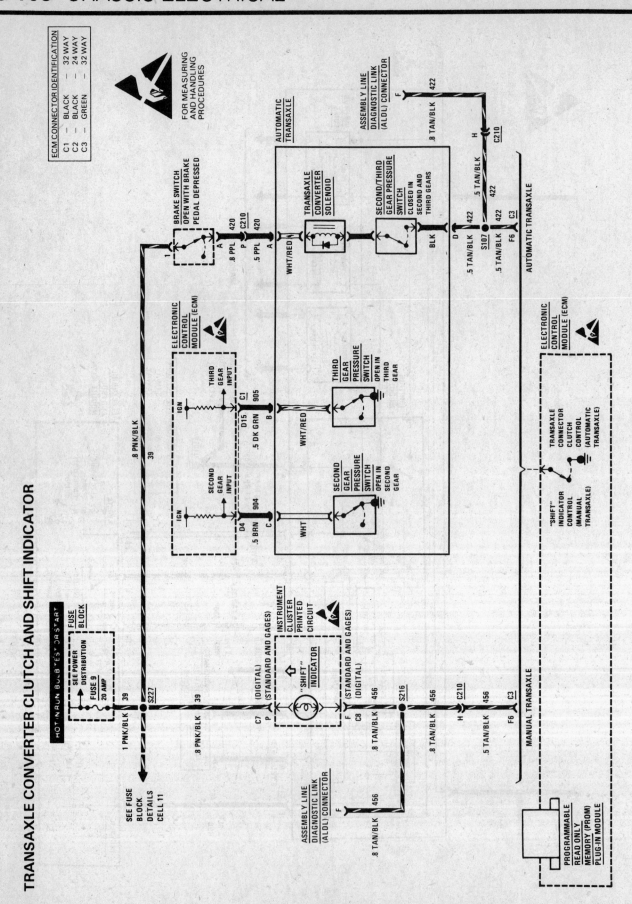

Multi-port fuel injection: (3.1L V6 engine transaxle converter clutch and shift indicator)-1990 Corsica and Beretta

POWER AND GROUNDS

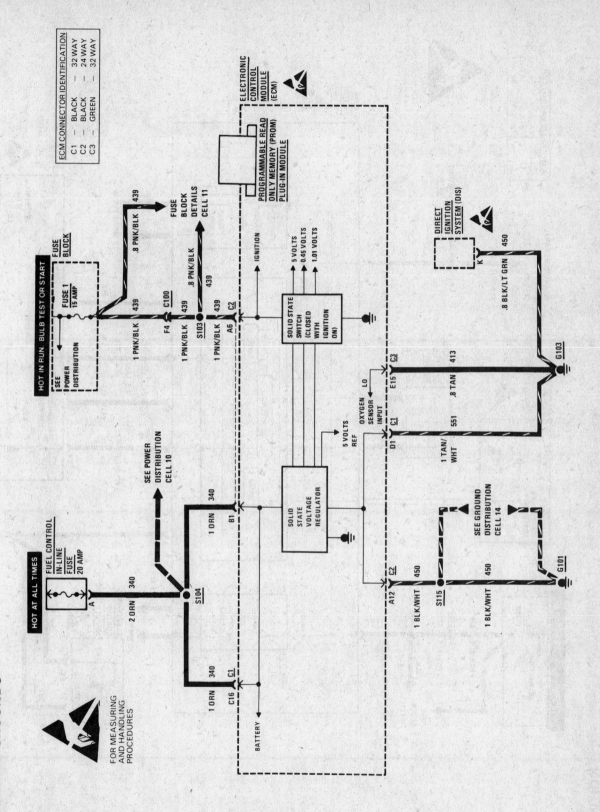

Electronic fuel injection: (2.3L 4 cyl., power and grounds)-1990 Corsica and Beretta

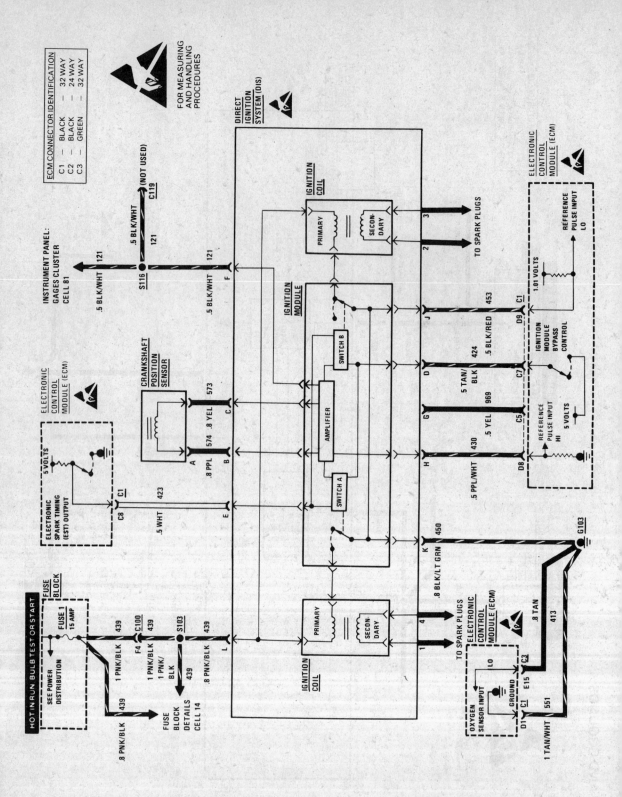

IGNITION

Electronic fuel injection: (2.3L 4 cyl., ignition)-1990 Corsica and Beretta

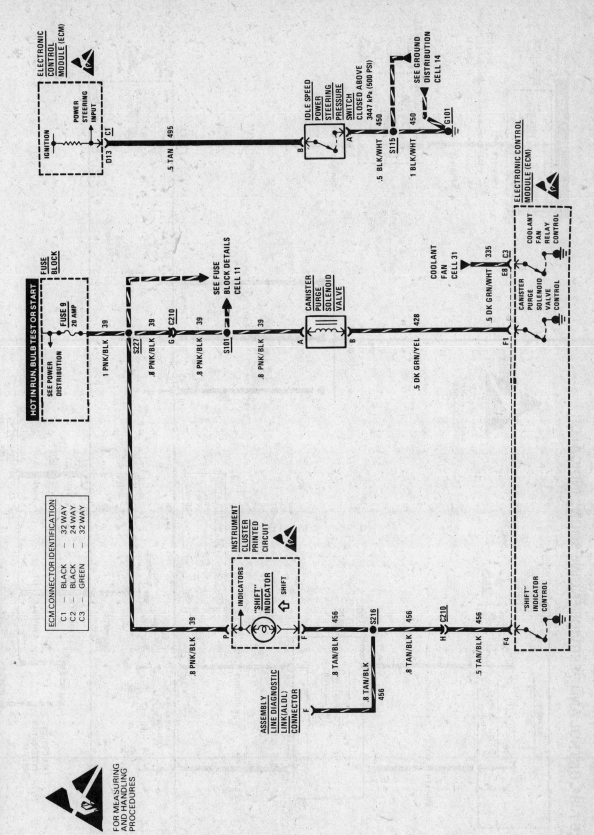

SHIFT INDICATOR AND VEHICLE DATA SENSORS

Electronic fuel injection: (2.3L 4 cyl., shift indicator and vehicle speed sensors)-1990 Corsica and Beretta

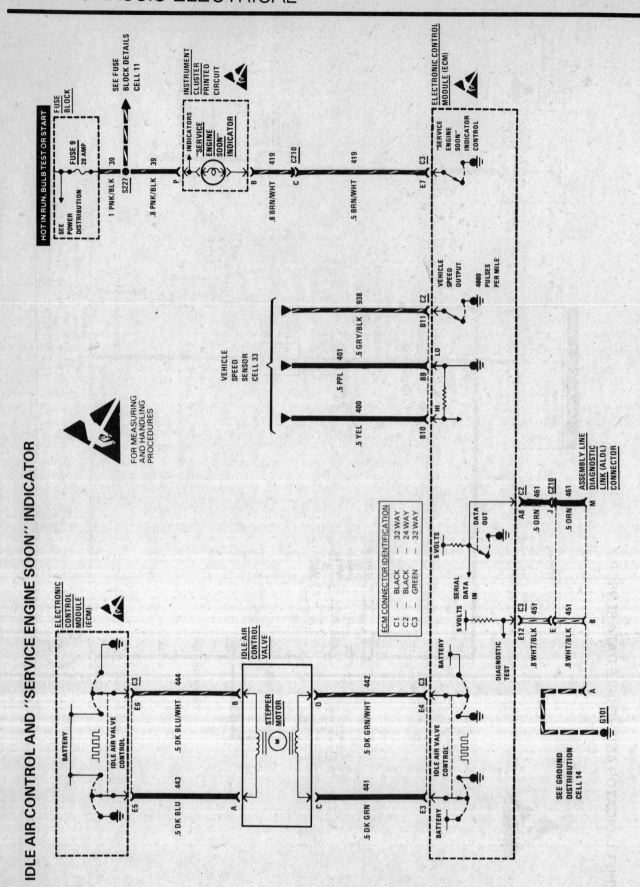

IDLE AIR CONTROL AND "SERVICE ENGINE SOON" INDICATOR

Electronic fuel injection: (2.3L 4 cyl., idle air control and service engine soon indicator)-1990 Corsica and Beretta

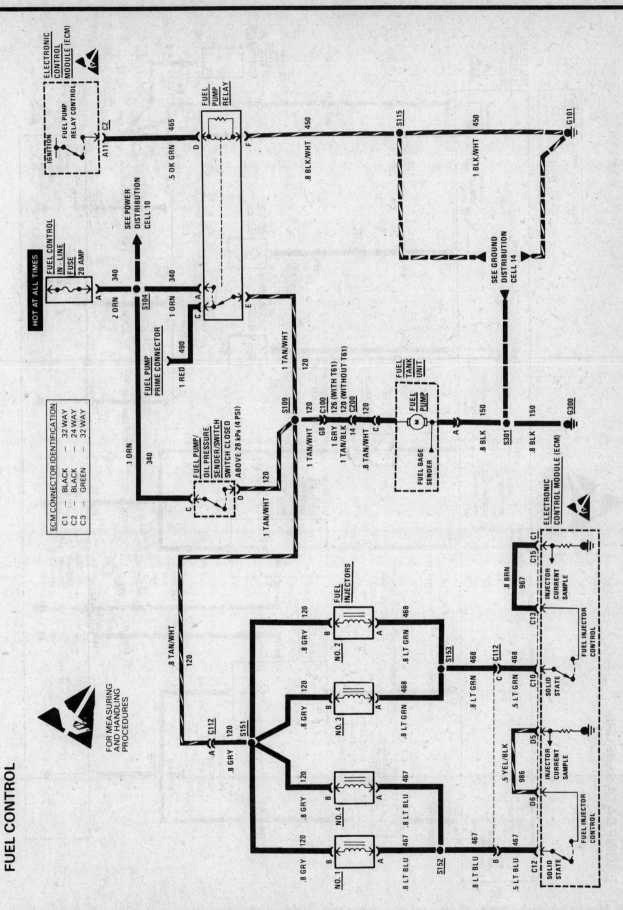

FUEL CONTROL

Electronic fuel injection: (2.3L 4 cyl., fuel control)-1990 Corsica and Beretta

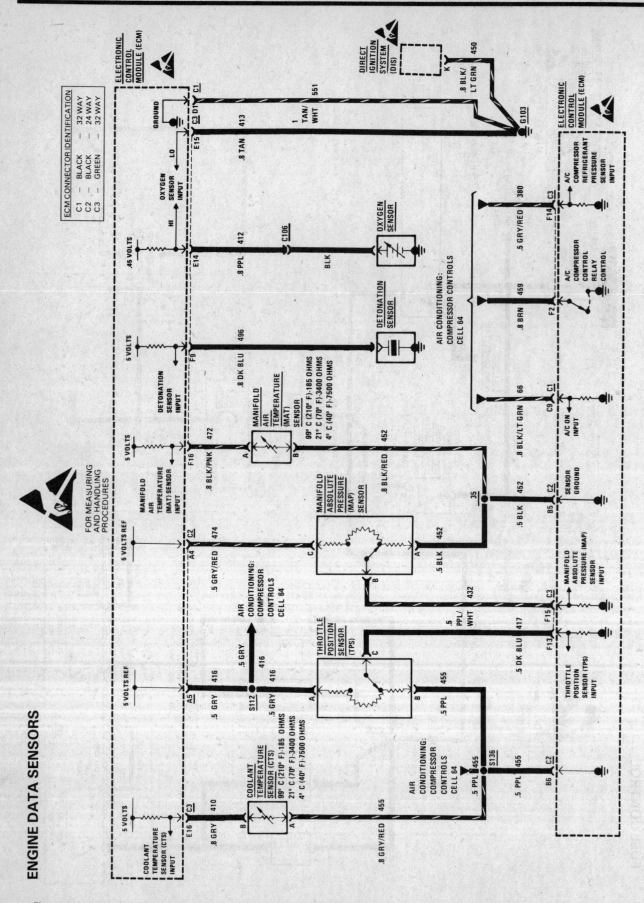

ENGINE DATA SENSORS

Electronic fuel injection: (2.3L 4 cyl., engine data sensors) -1990 Corsica and Beretta

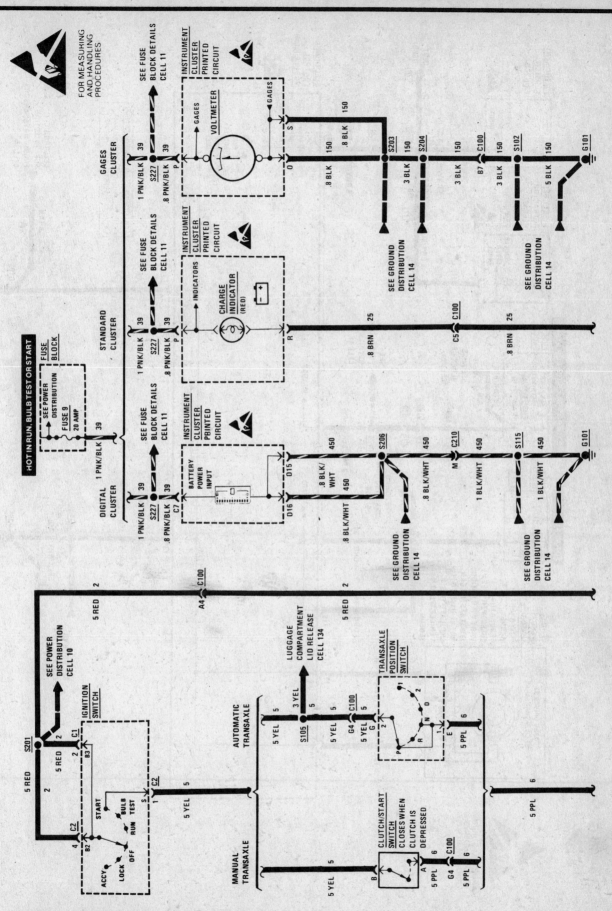

Starter and charging system-1990 Corsica and Beretta

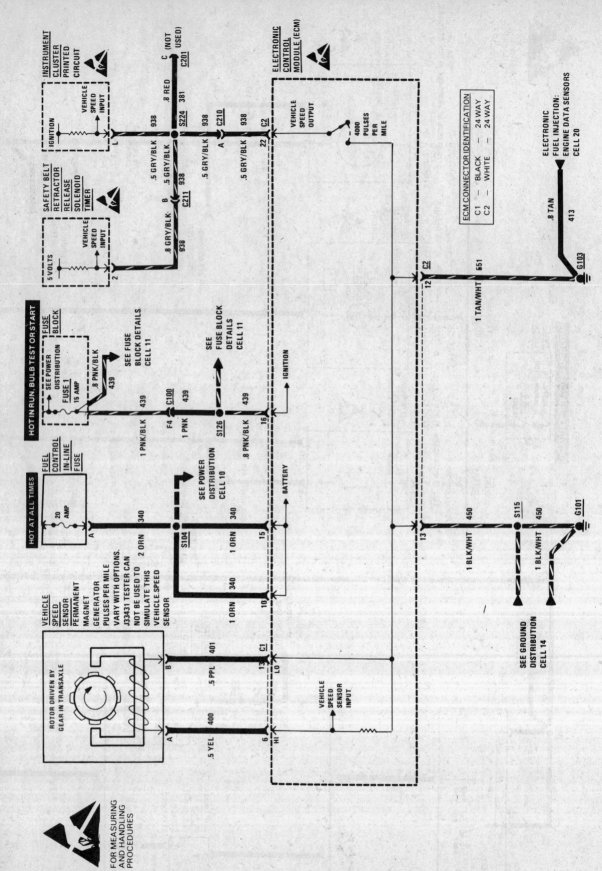

Vehicle speed sensor: (permanent magnet generator, 2.2L 4 cyl. engine)-1990 Corsica and Beretta

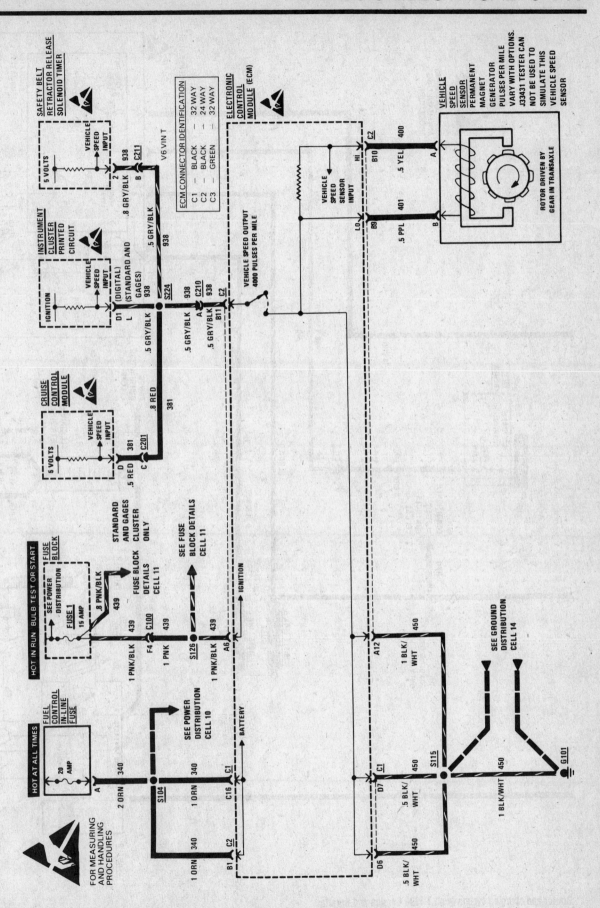

Vehicle speed sensor: (permanent magnet generator, 3.1L V6 engine)-1990 Corsica and Beretta

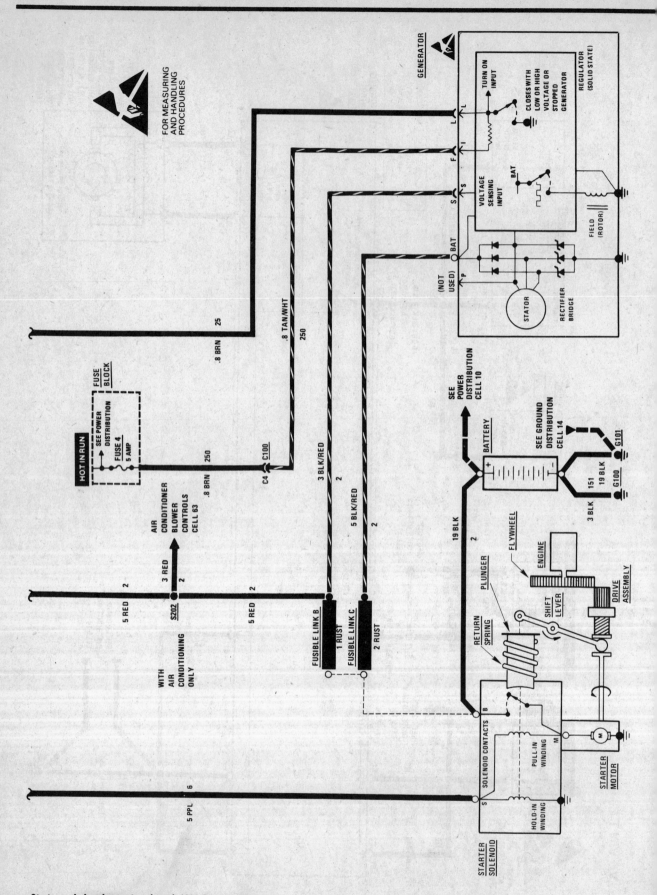

Starter and charging system (cont.)-1990 Corsica and Beretta

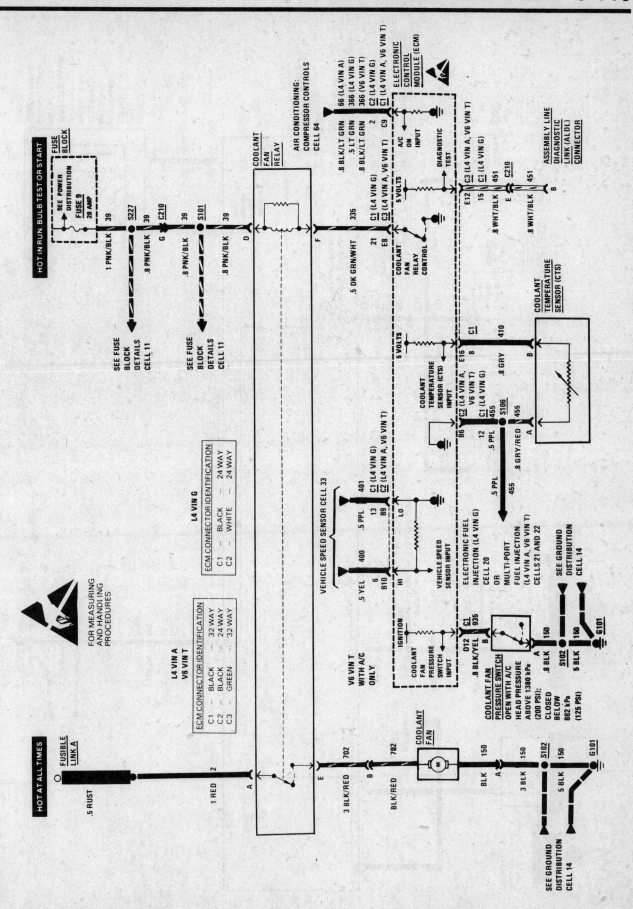

Coolant fan-1990 Corsica and Beretta

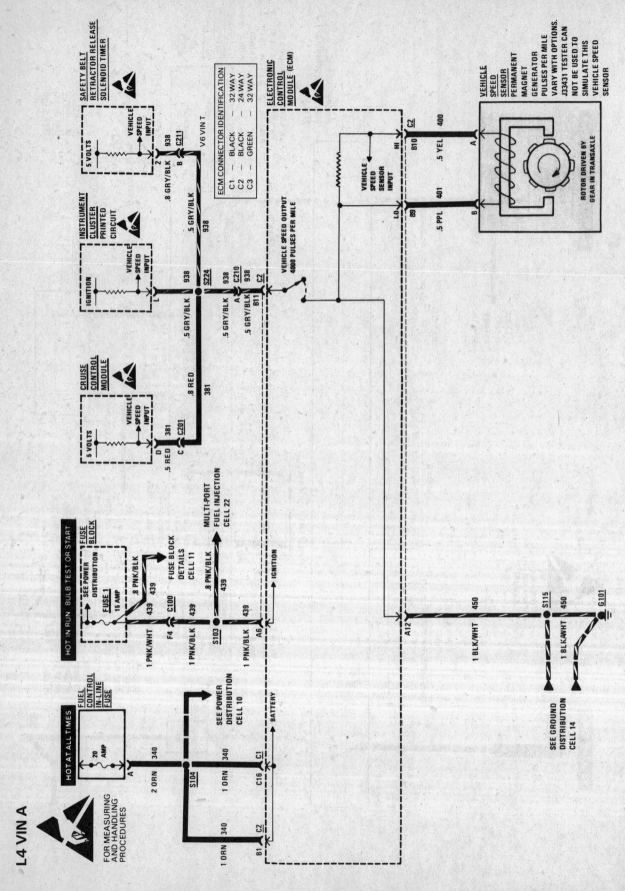

Vehicle speed sensor: (permanent magnet generator, 2.3L 4 cyl. engine)-1990 Corsica and Beretta

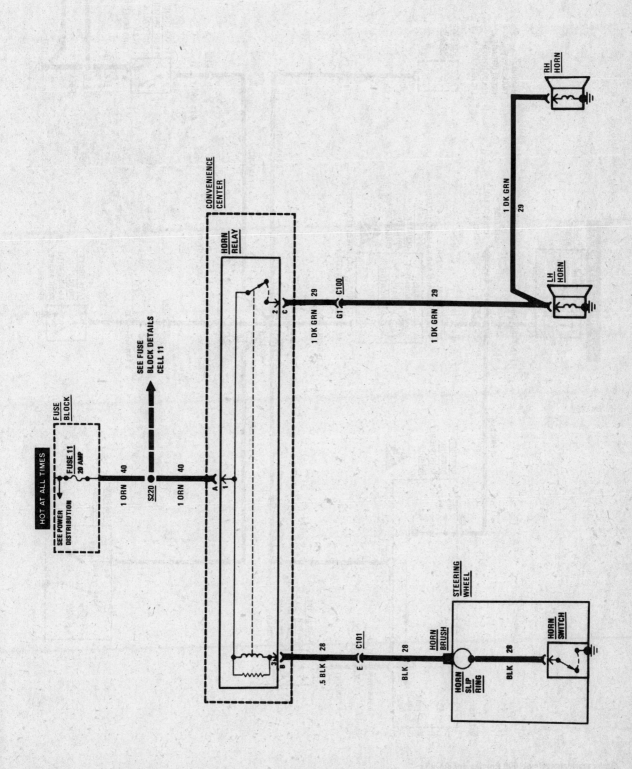

Horns-1990 Corsica and Beretta

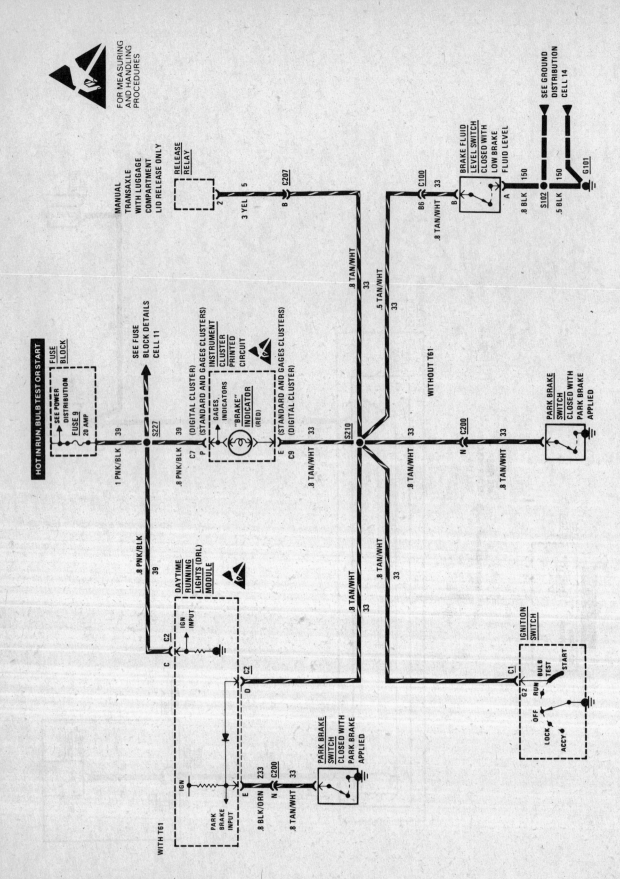

Brake warning system-1990 Corsica and Beretta

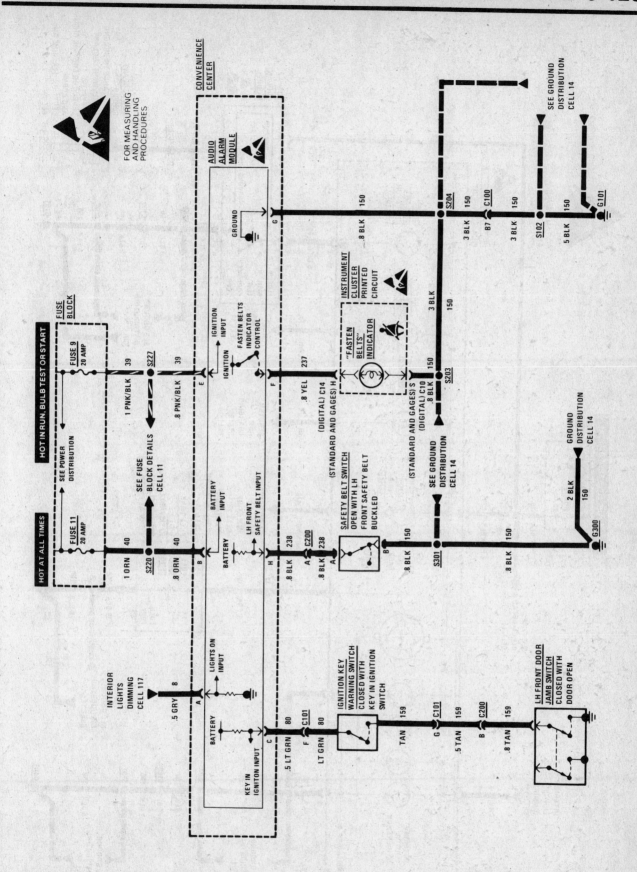

Warnings and alarms: (chime)-1990 Corsica and Beretta

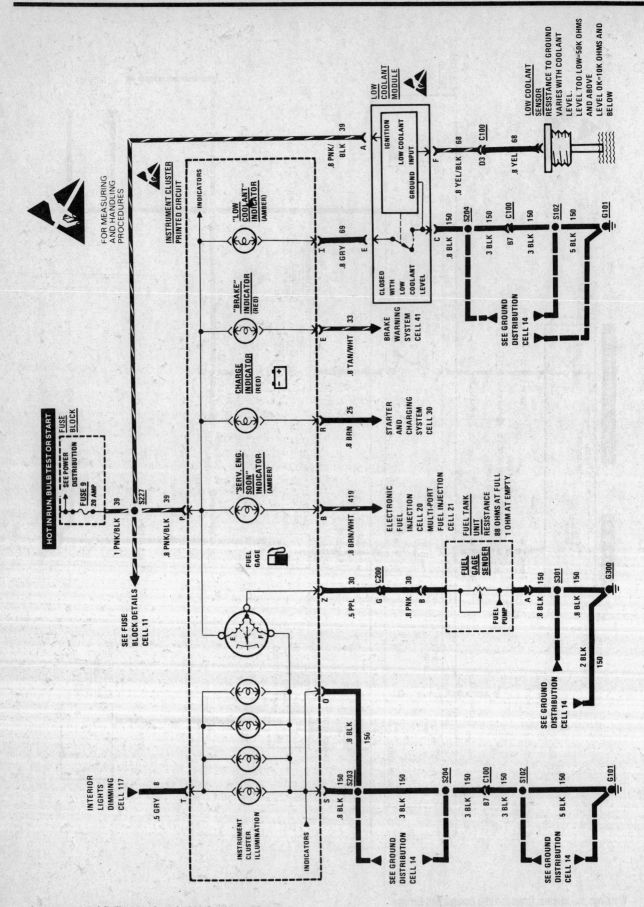

Instrument panel (indicators cluster)-1990 Corsica and Beretta

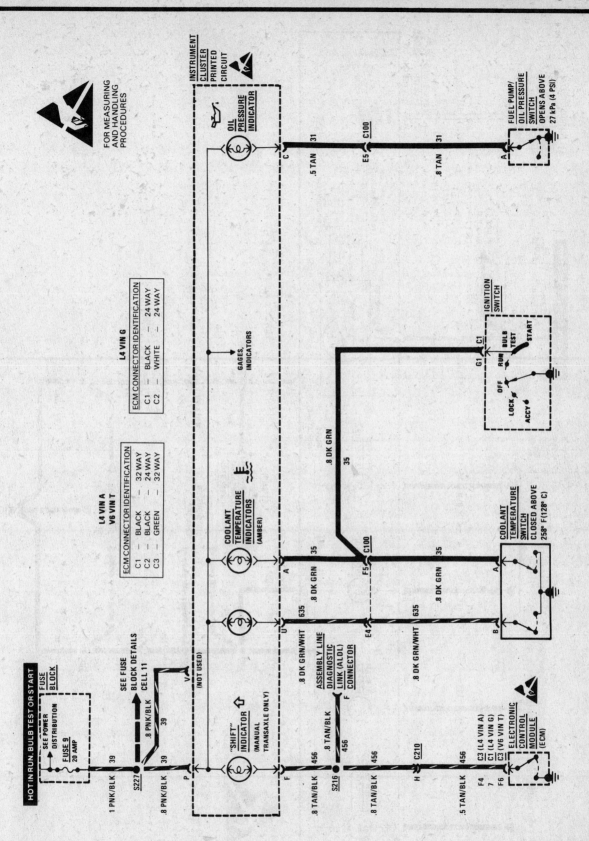

Instrument panel (indicators cluster)-1990 Corsica and Beretta

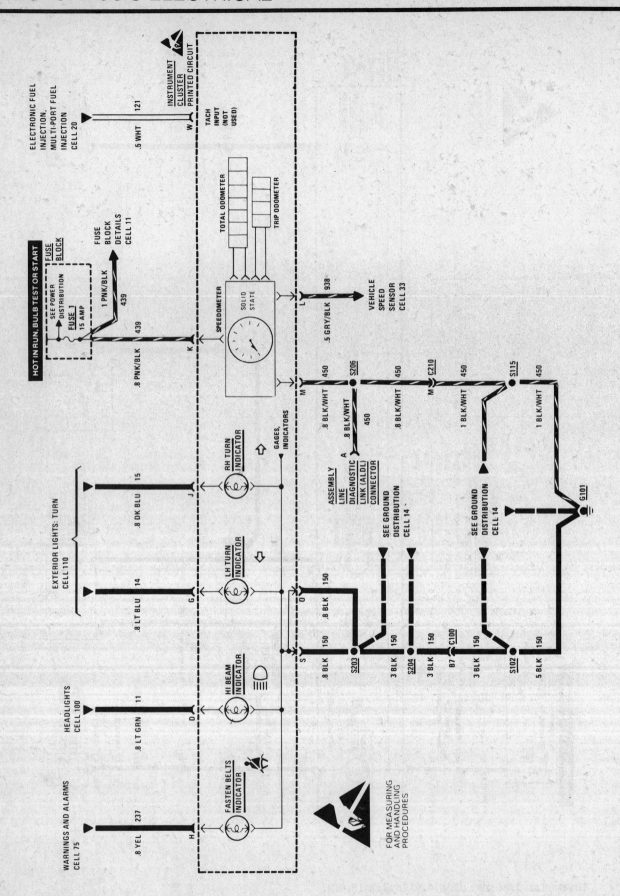

Instrument panel (indicators cluster)-1990 Corsica and Beretta

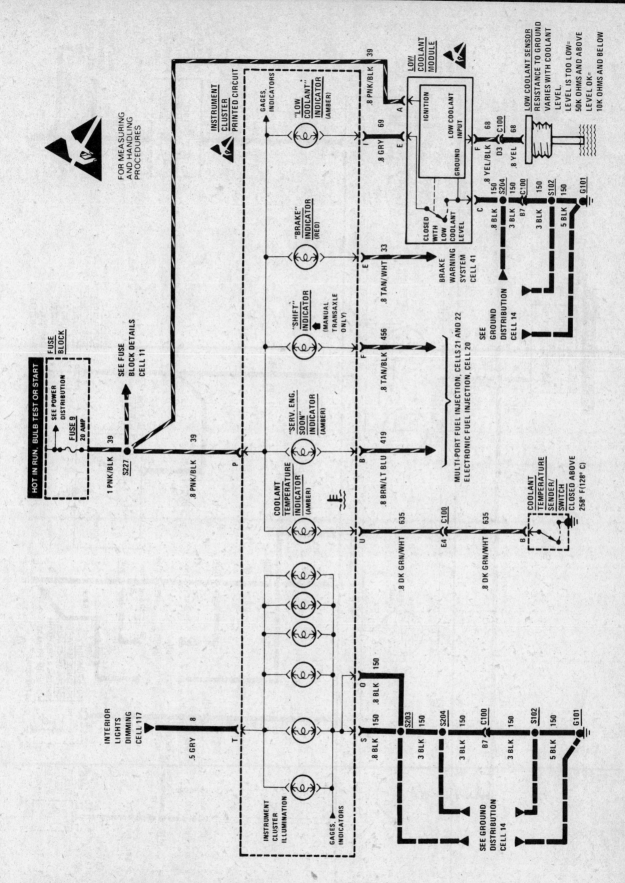

Instrument panel (gages cluster)-1990 Corsica and Beretta

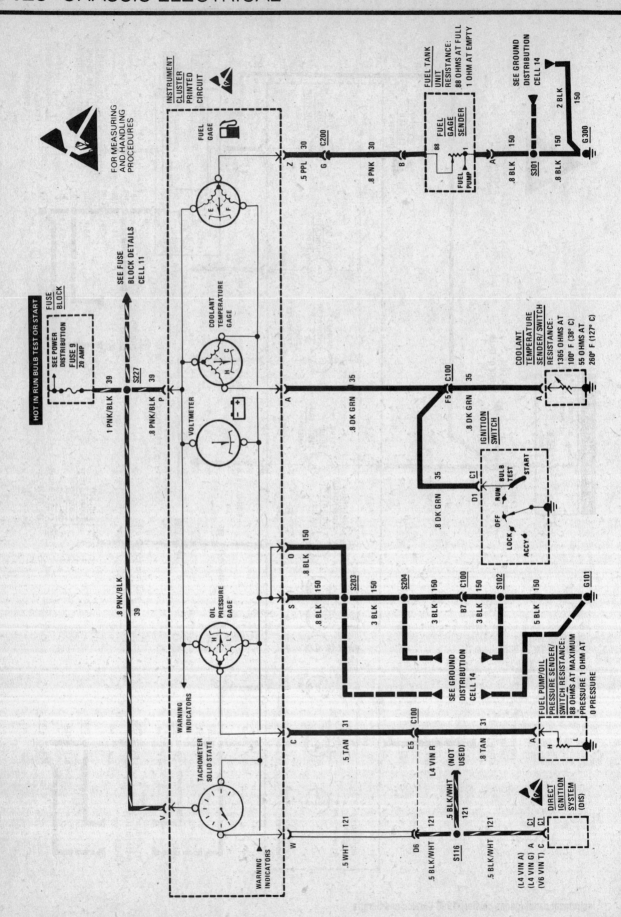

Instrument panel (gages cluster)-1990 Corsica and Beretta

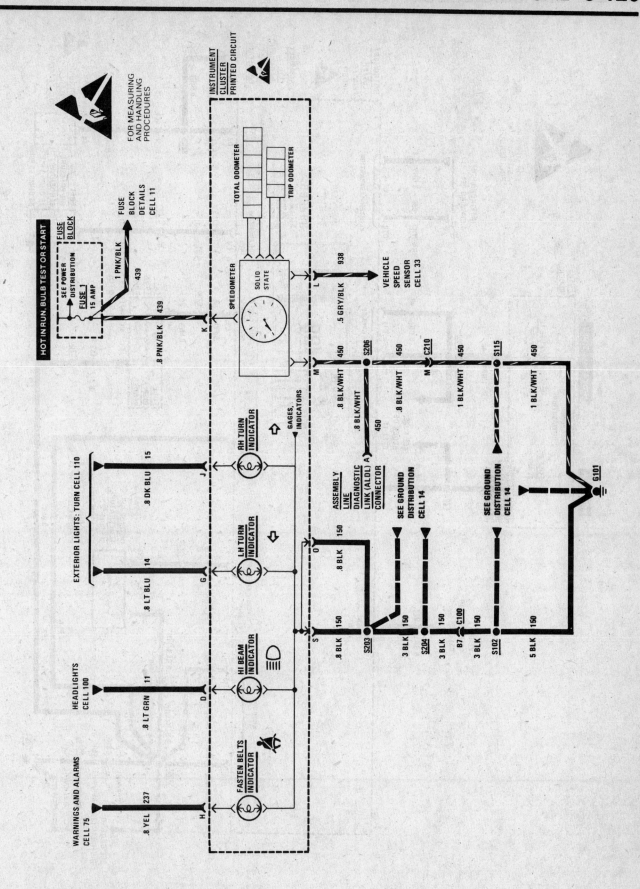

Instrument panel (gages cluster)-1990 Corsica and Beretta

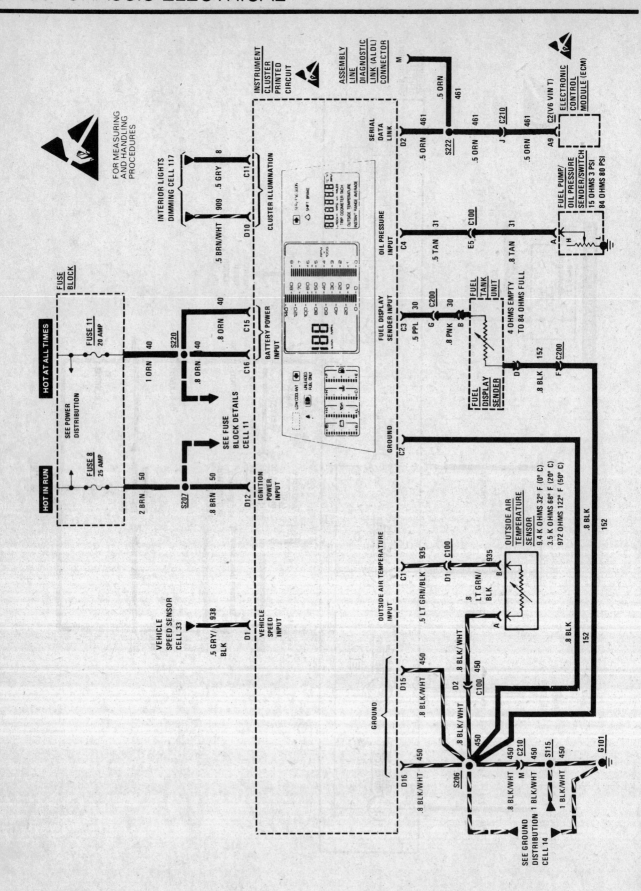

Instrument panel (digital cluster)-1990 Corsica and Beretta

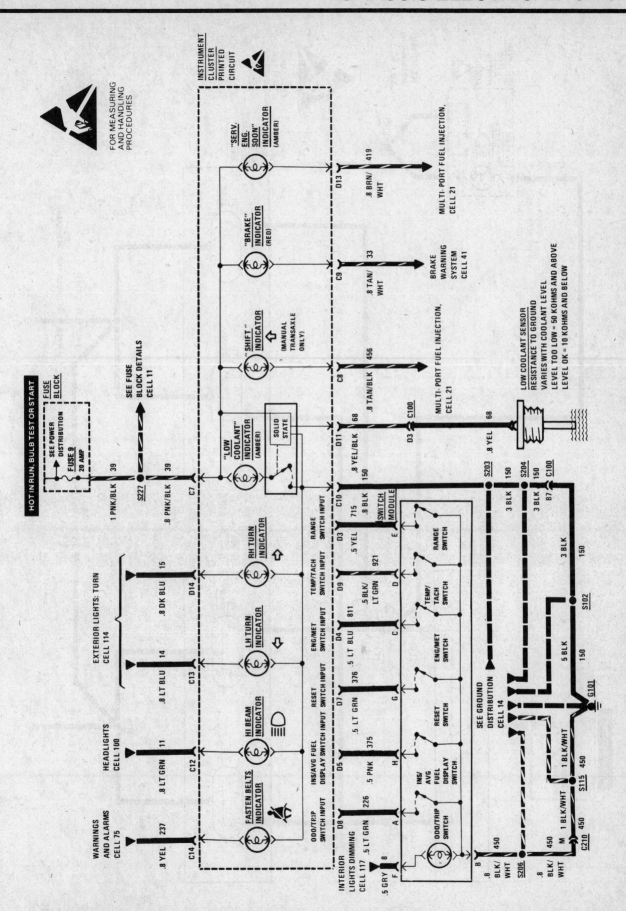

Instrument panel (digital cluster)-1990 Corsica and Beretta

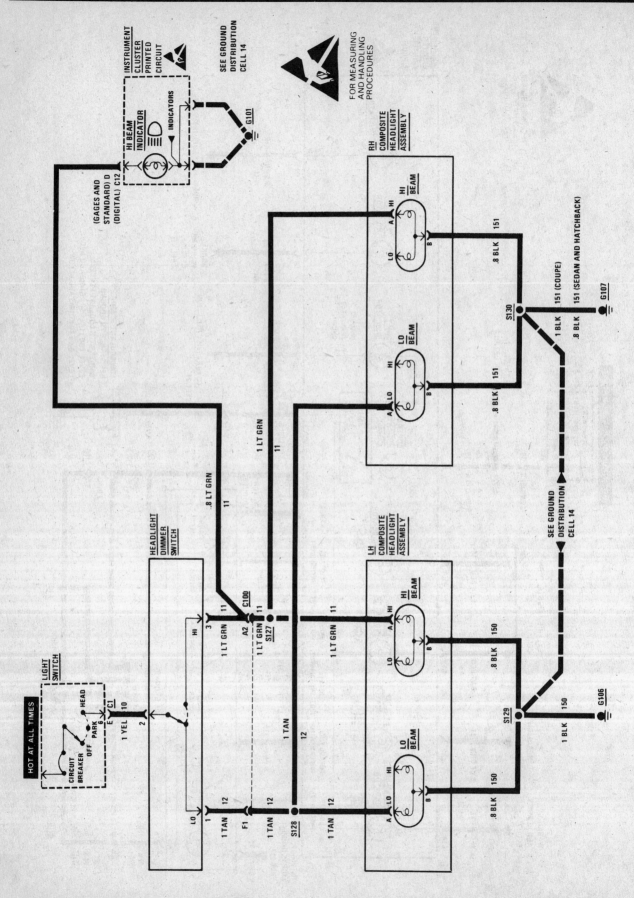

Headlights (without fog lights)-1990 Corsica and Beretta

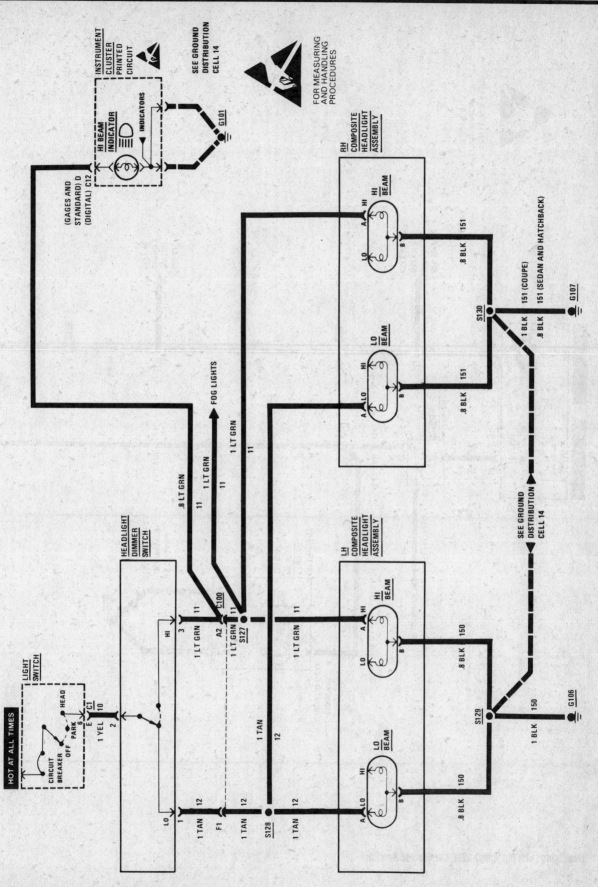

Headlights (with fog lights)-1990 Corsica and Beretta

FOR MEASURING
AND HANDLING
PROCEDURES

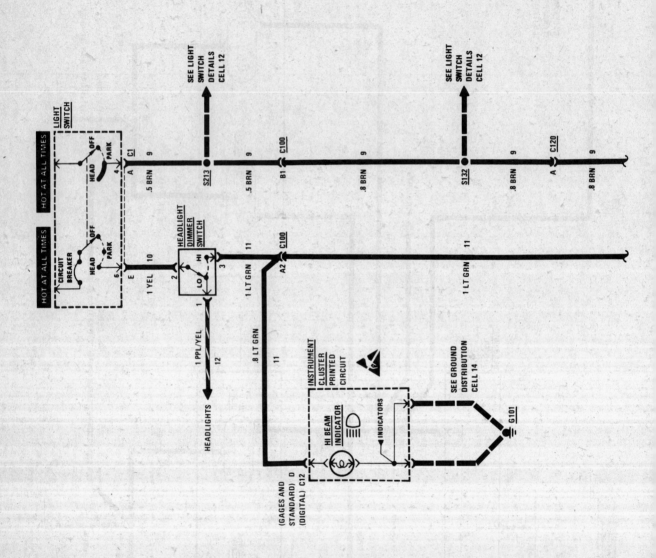

Headlights (with fog lights)-1990 Corsica and Beretta

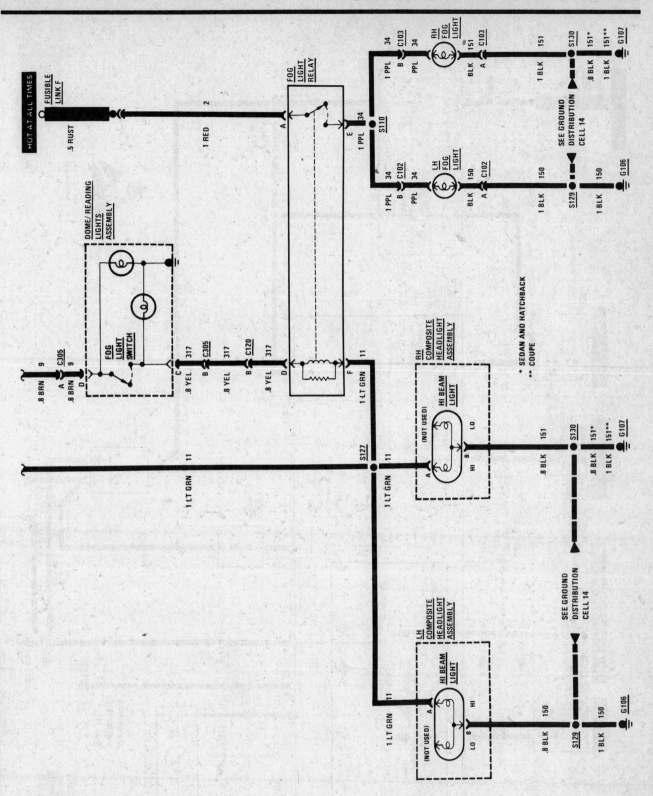

Headlights (with fog lights)-1990 Corsica and Beretta

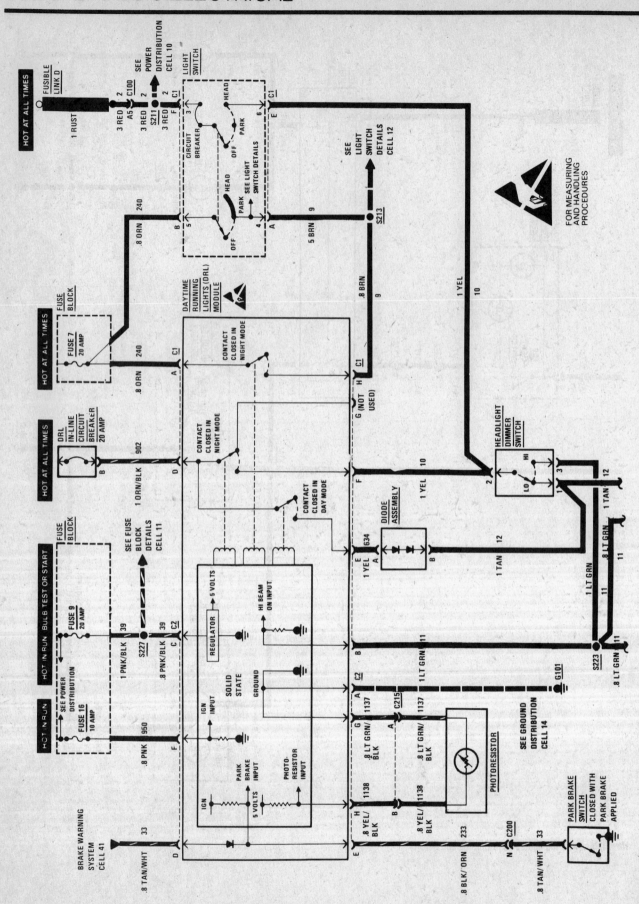

Headlights (with daytime running lights)-1990 Corsica and Beretta

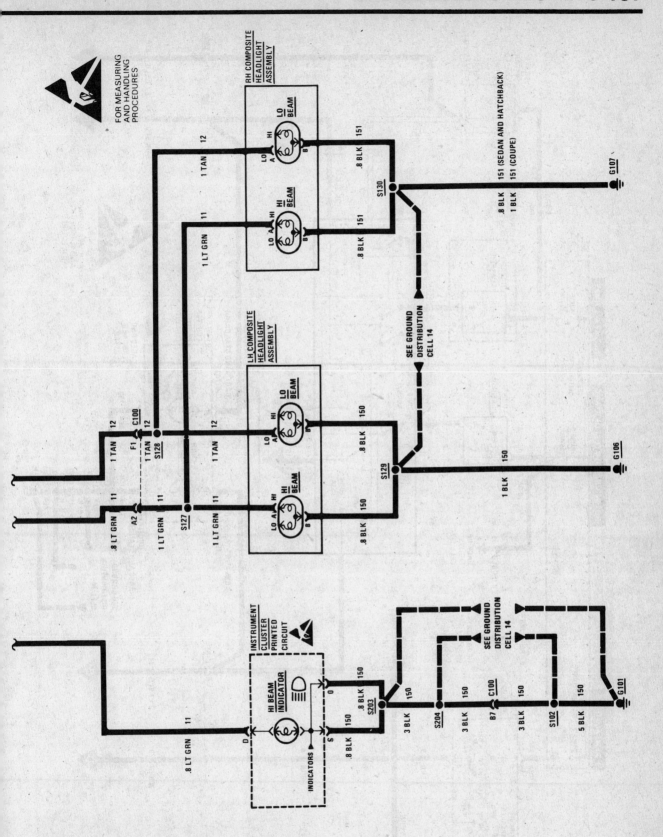

Headlights (with daytime running lights)-1990 Corsica and Beretta

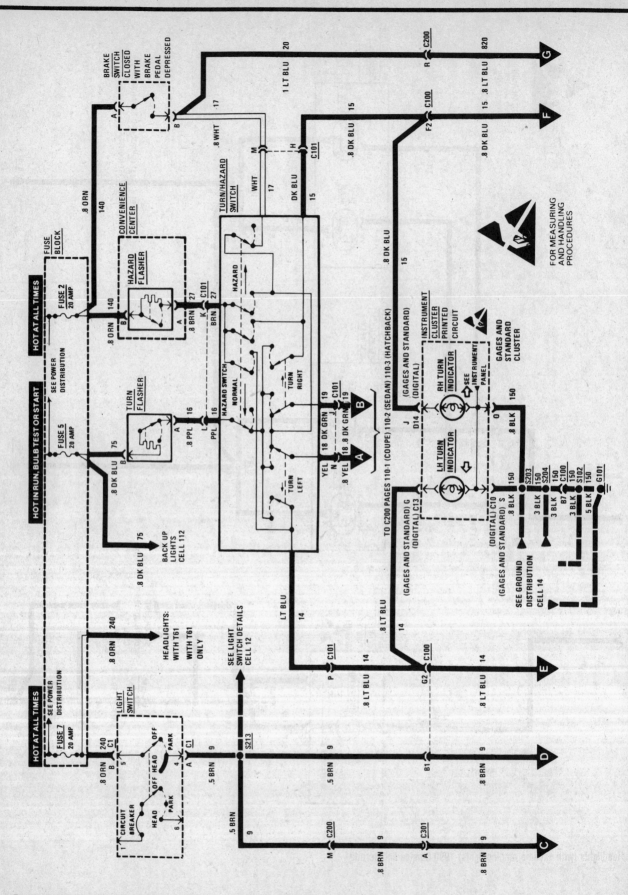

Exterior lights: (turn/hazard/stop/tail/marker/license/park)-1990 Corsica and Beretta

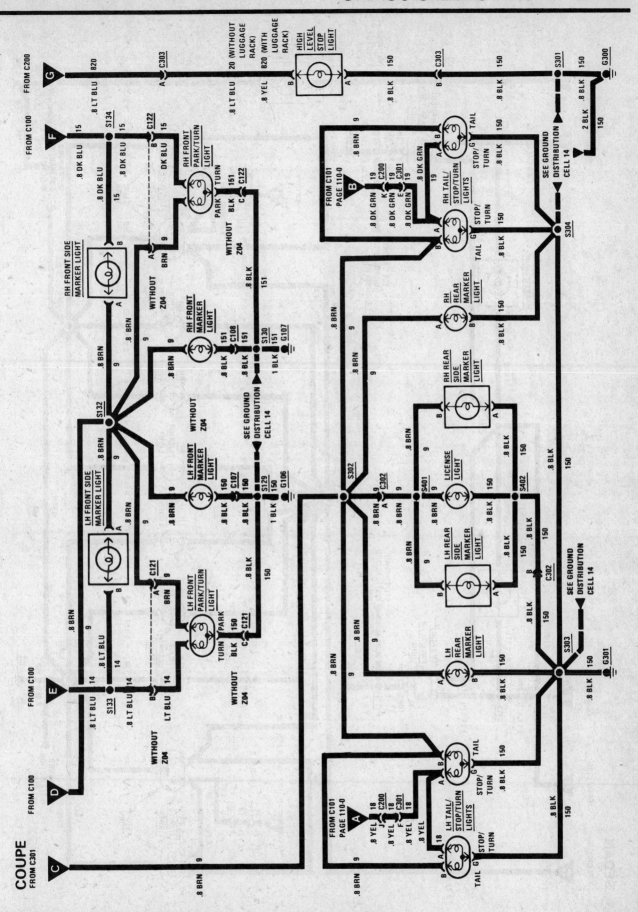

Exterior lights: (turn/hazard/stop/tail/marker/license/park) (coupe)-1990 Corsica and Beretta

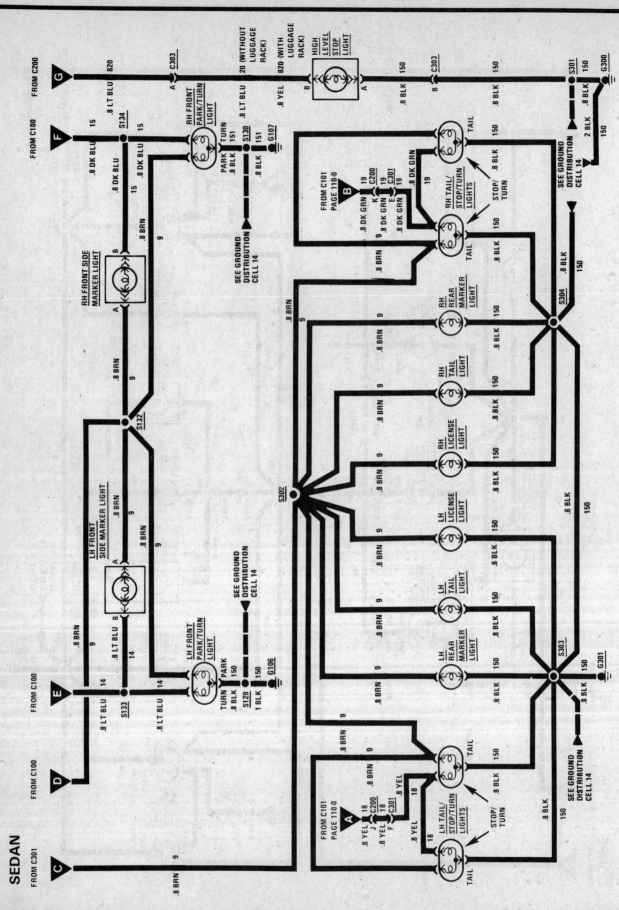

SEDAN

Exterior lights: (turn/hazard/stop/tail/marker/license/park) (sedan)-1990 Corsica and Beretta

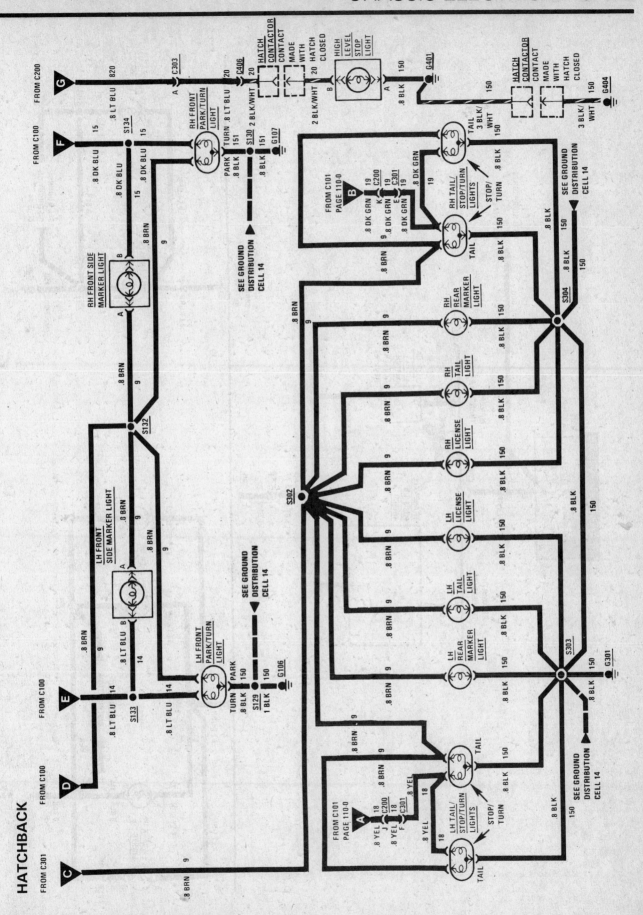

HATCHBACK

Exterior lights: (turn/hazard/stop/tail/marker/license/park) (hatchback)-1990 Corsica and Beretta

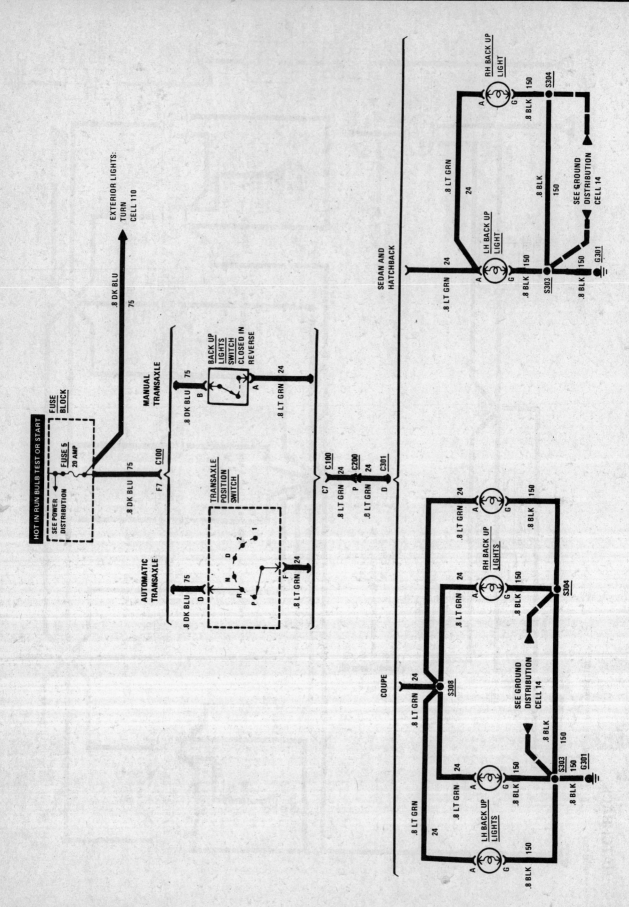

Backup lights-1990 Corsica and Beretta

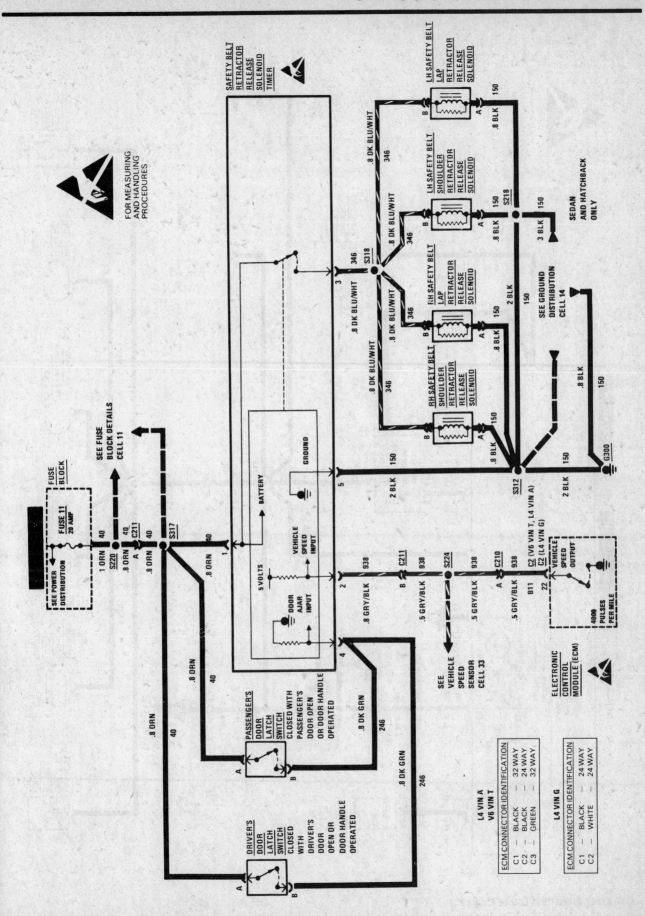

Automatic safety belts-1990 Corsica and Beretta

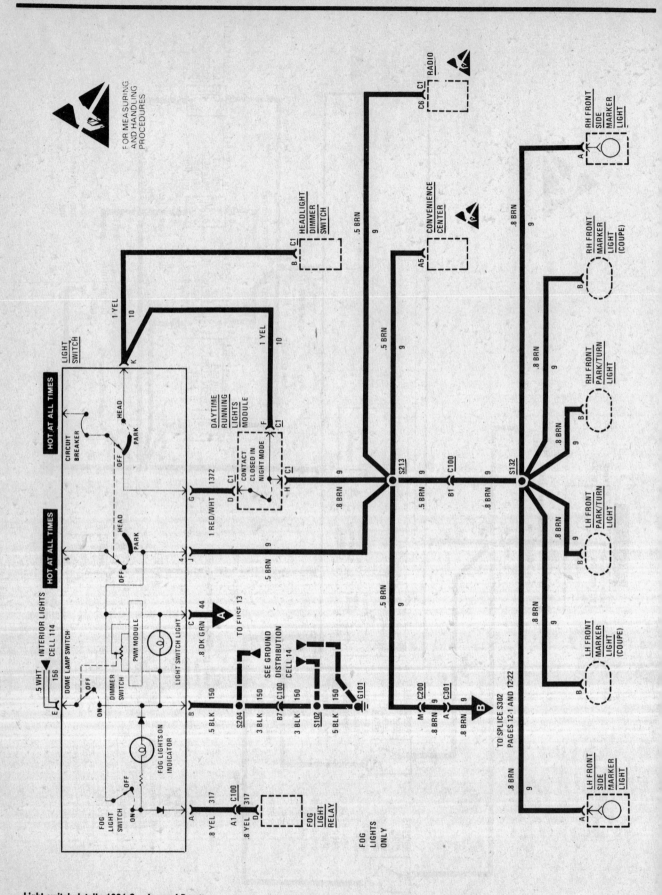

Light switch details-1991 Corsica and Beretta

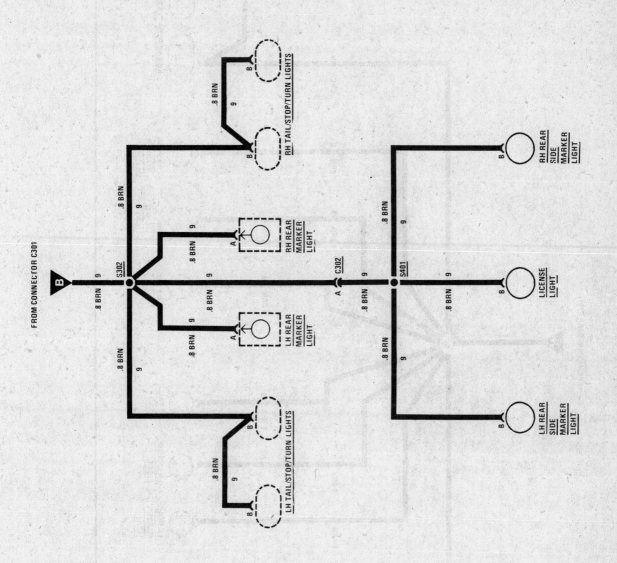

Light switch details (coupe)-1991 Corsica and Beretta

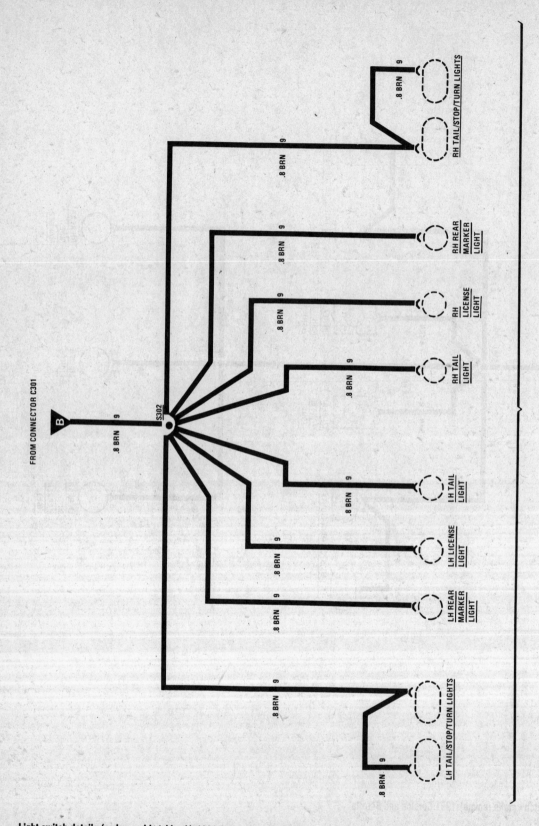

Light switch details (sedan and hatchback)-1991 Corsica and Beretta

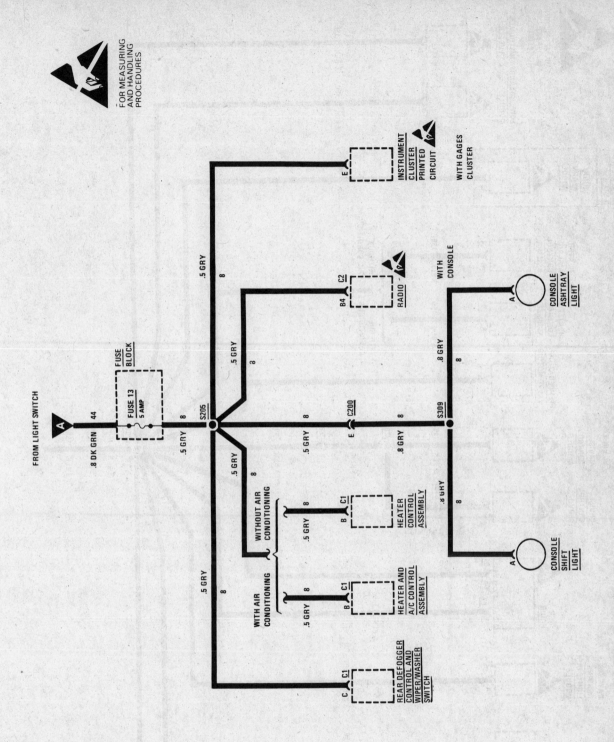

Light switch details (sedan and hatchback cont.)-1991 Corsica and Beretta

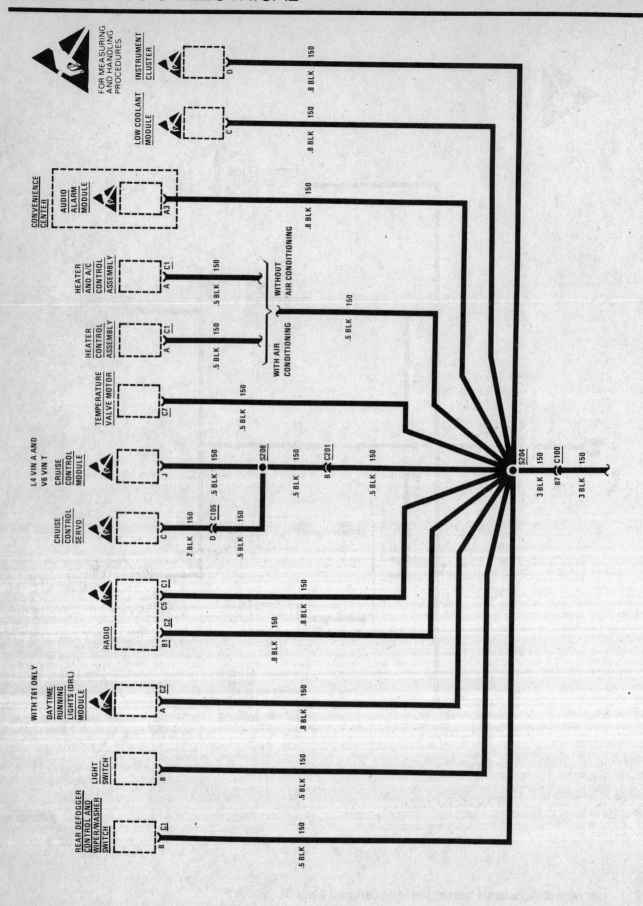

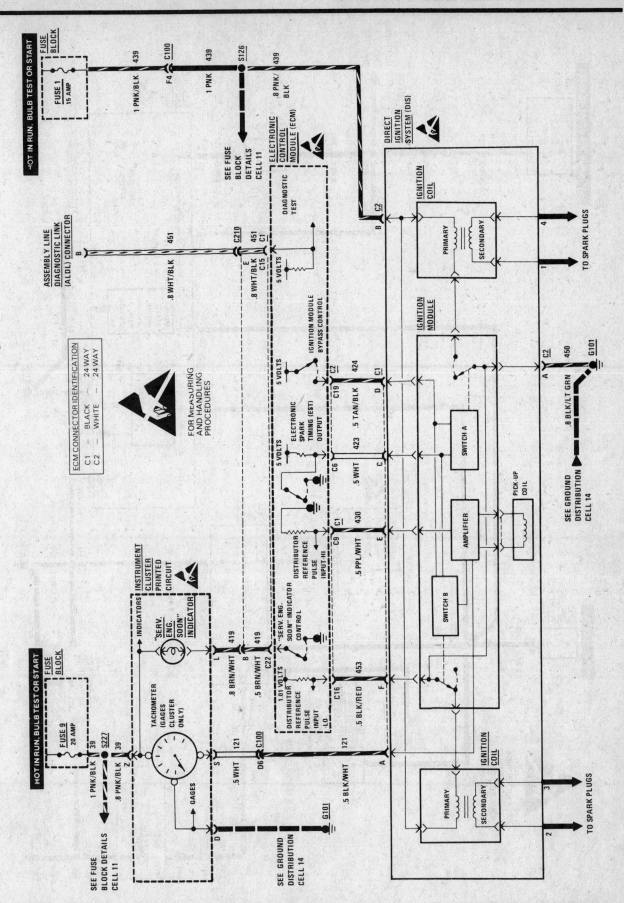

Electronic fuel injection: (2.2L 4 cyl., ignition)-1991 Corsica and Beretta

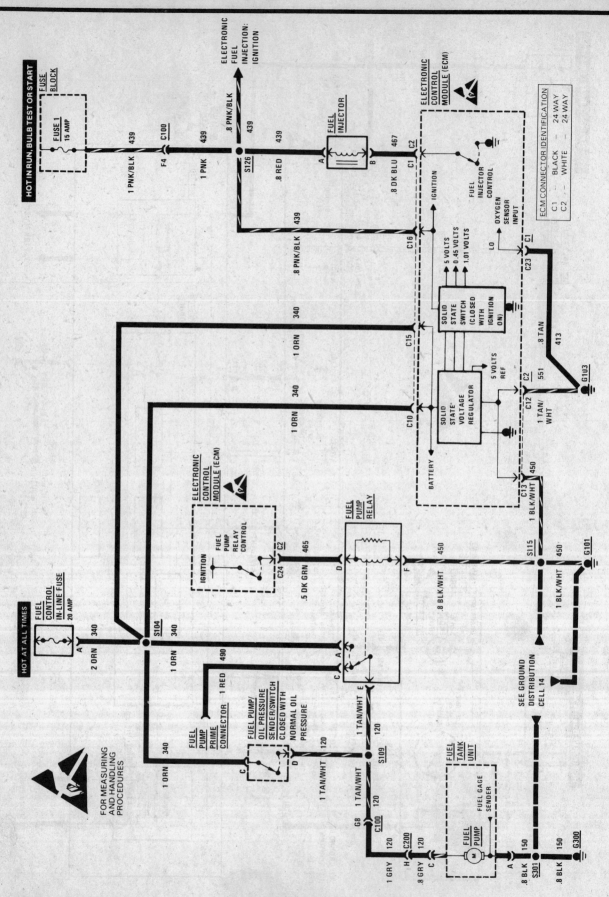

Electronic fuel injection: (2.2L 4 cyl., power, ground and fuel control) -1991 Corsica and Beretta

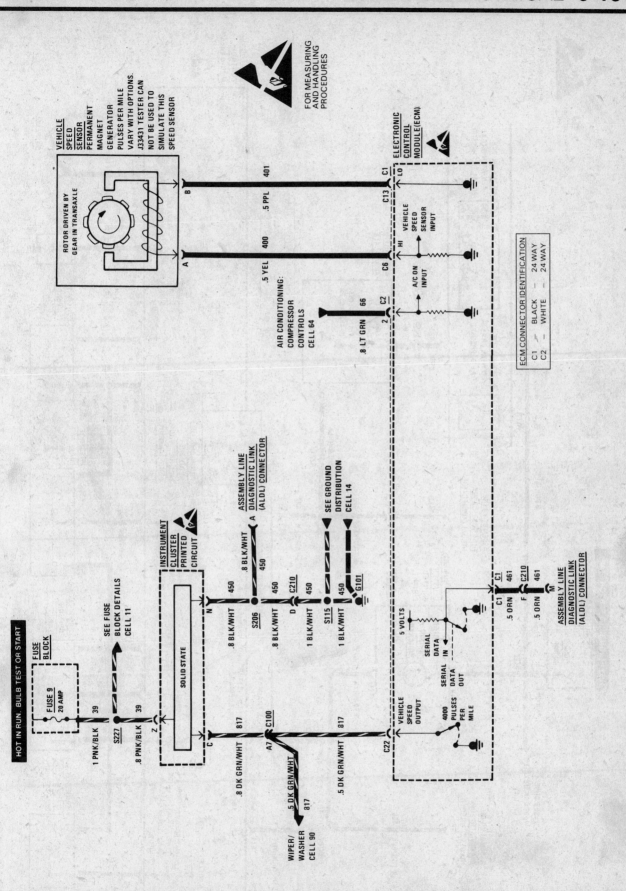

Electronic fuel injection: (2.2L 4 cyl., vehicle speed sensor)-1991 Corsica and Beretta

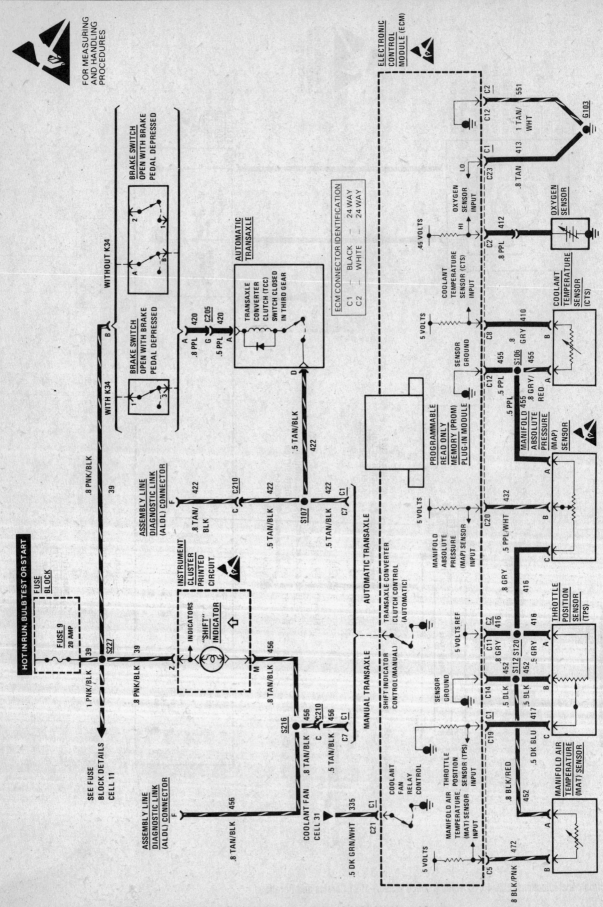

Electronic fuel injection: (2.2L 4 cyl., data sensors and transaxle converter clutch)-1991 Corsica and Beretta

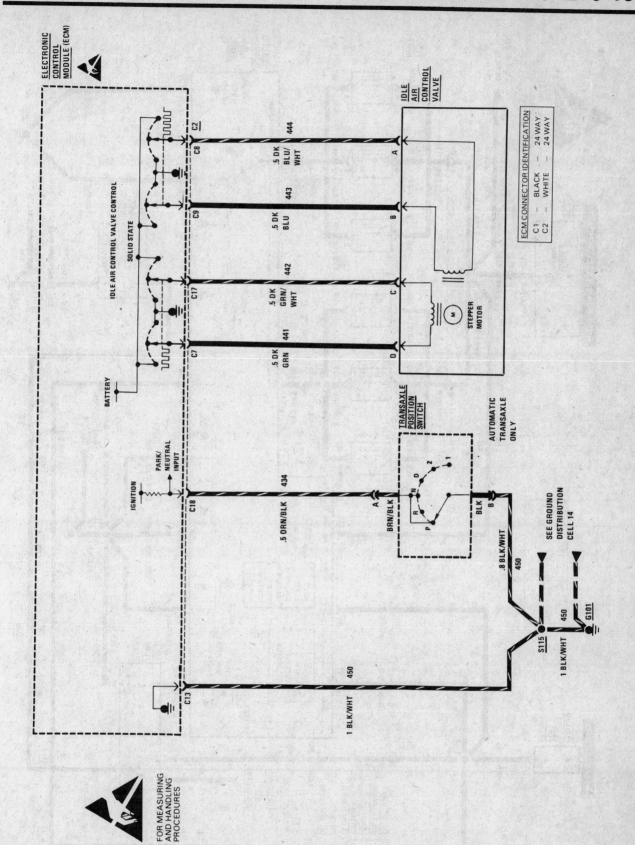

Electronic fuel injection: (2.2L 4 cyl., idle speed control and vehicle data sensors)-1991 Corsica and Beretta

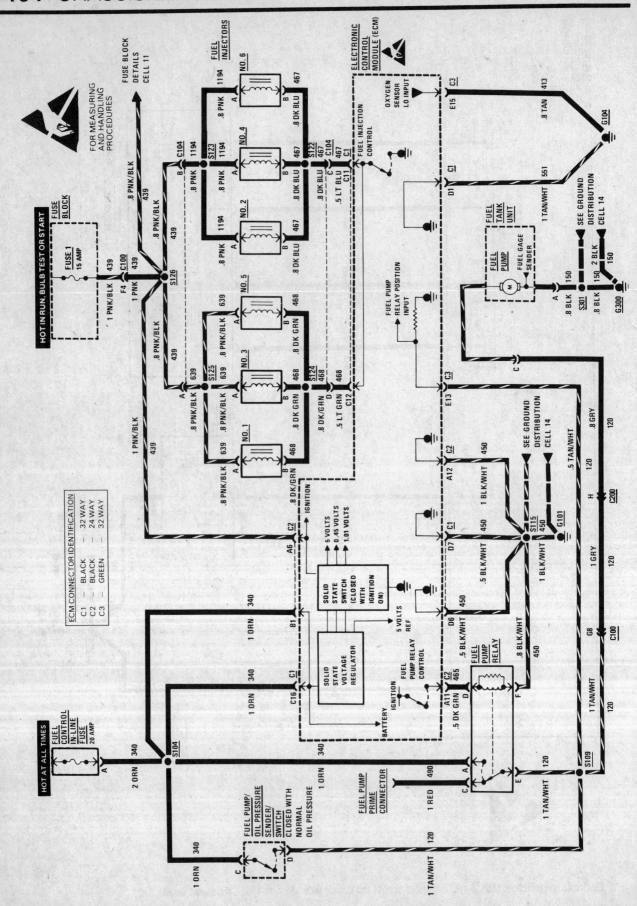

Multi-port fuel injection: (3.1L V6 engine, power grounds, fuel control and injectors) -1991 Corsica and Beretta

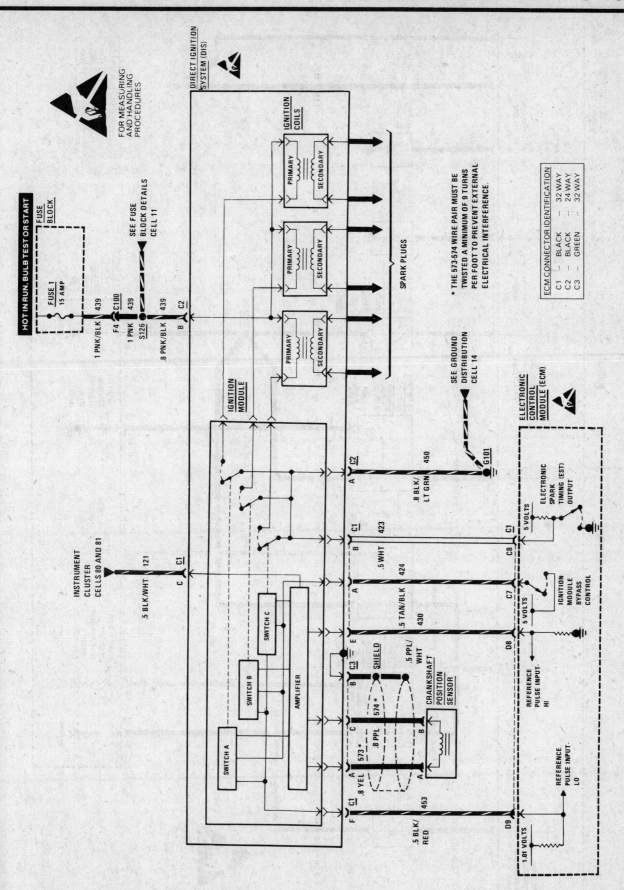

Multi-port fuel injection: (3.1L V6 engine, ignition)-1991 Corsica and Beretta

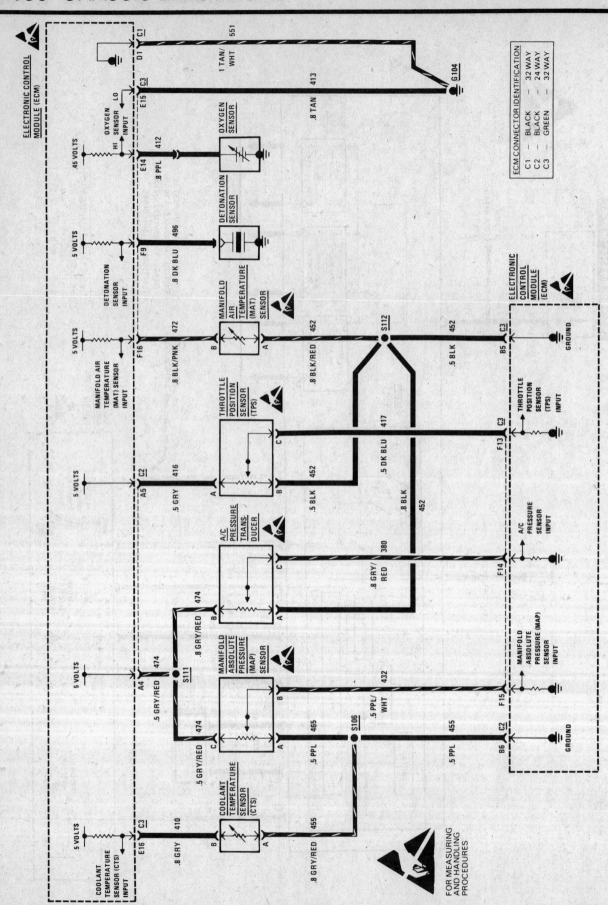

Multi-port fuel injection: (3.1L V6 engine, data sensors)-1991 Corsica and Beretta

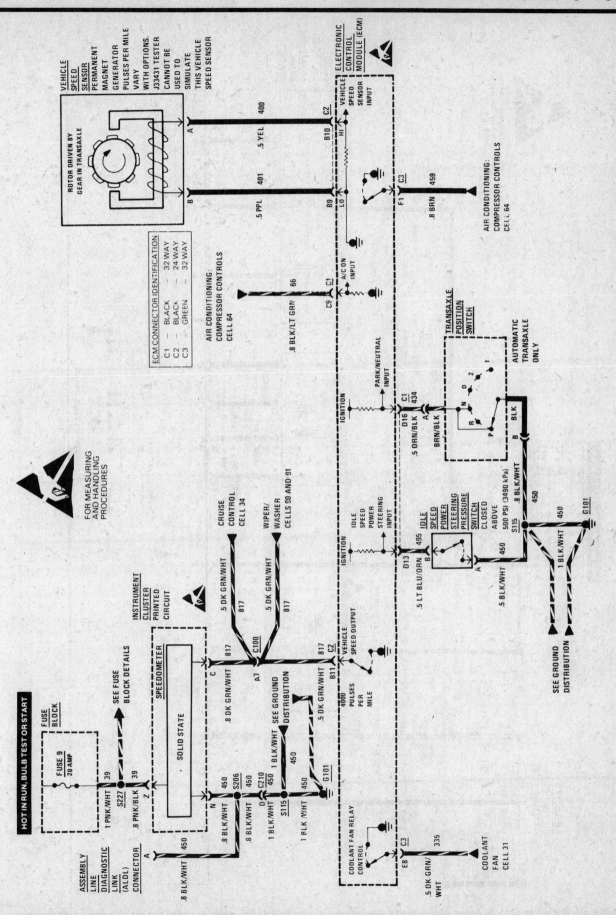

Multi-port fuel injection: (3.1L V6 engine, vehicle data sensors and vehicle speed sensors)-1991 Corsica and Beretta

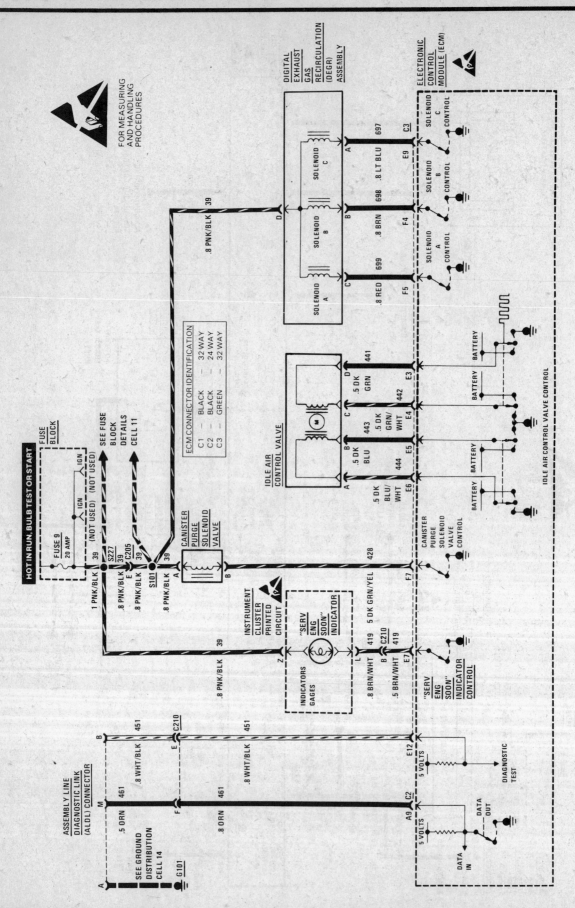

Multi-port fuel injection: (3.1L V6 engine, service engine soon indicator, diagnostic data line, emission control and idle air control)-1991 Corsica and Beretta

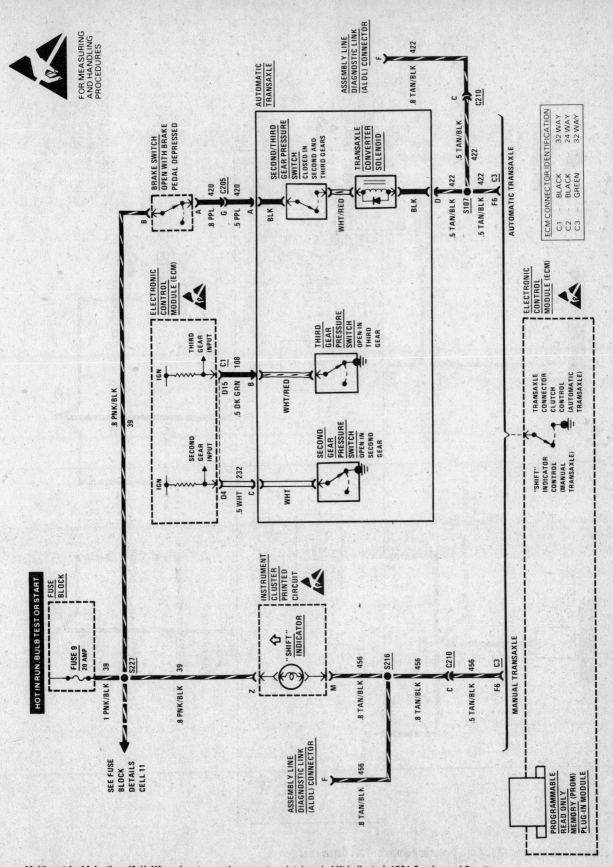

Multi-port fuel injection: (3.1L V6 engine, transaxle converter clutch and shift indicator)-1991 Corsica and Beretta

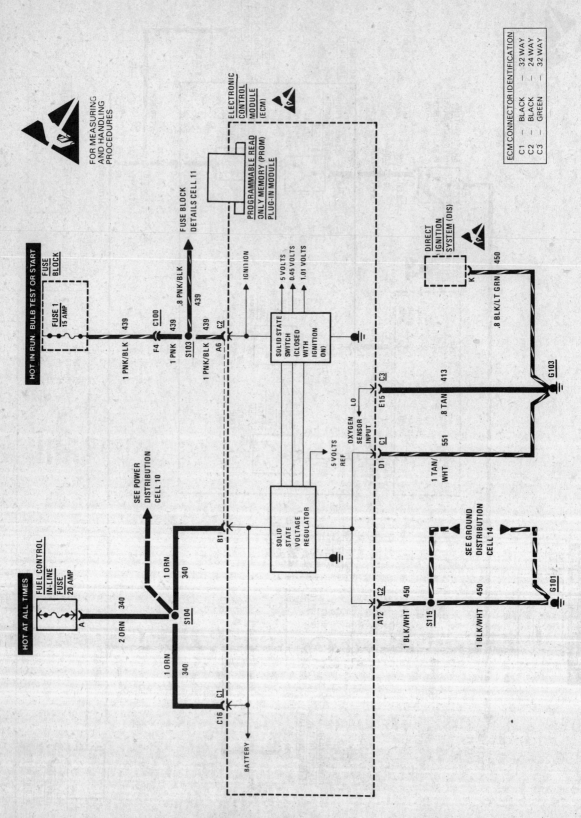

Electronic fuel injection: (2.3L 4 cyl., power and grounds)-1991 Corsica and Beretta

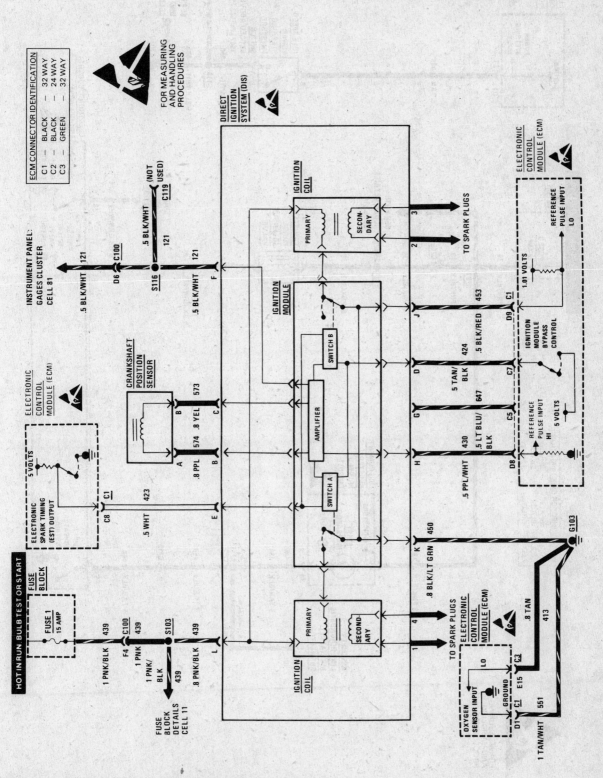

Electronic fuel injection: (2.3L 4 cyl., ignition)-1991 Corsica and Beretta

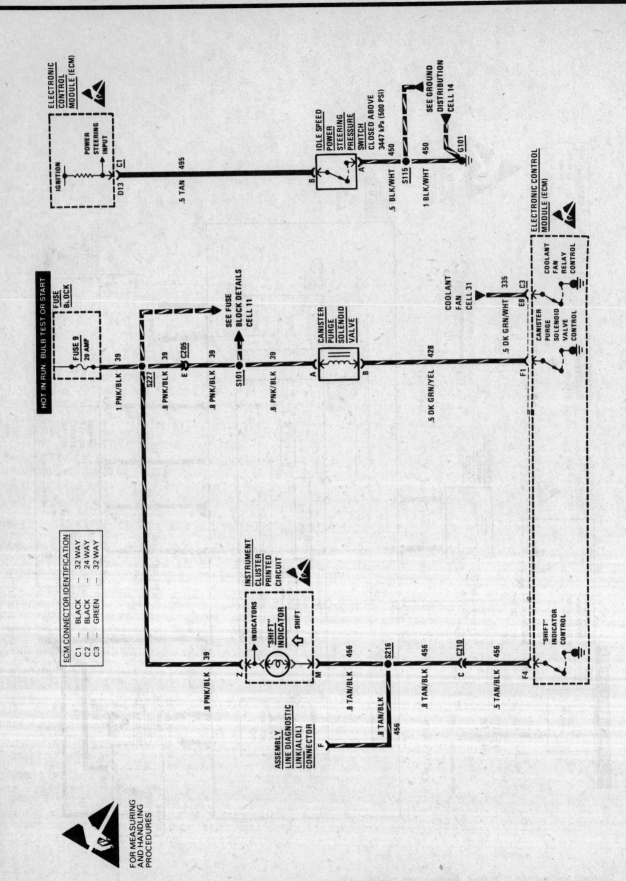

Electronic fuel injection: (2.3L 4 cyl., shift indicator and vehicle speed sensors)-1991 Corsica and Beretta

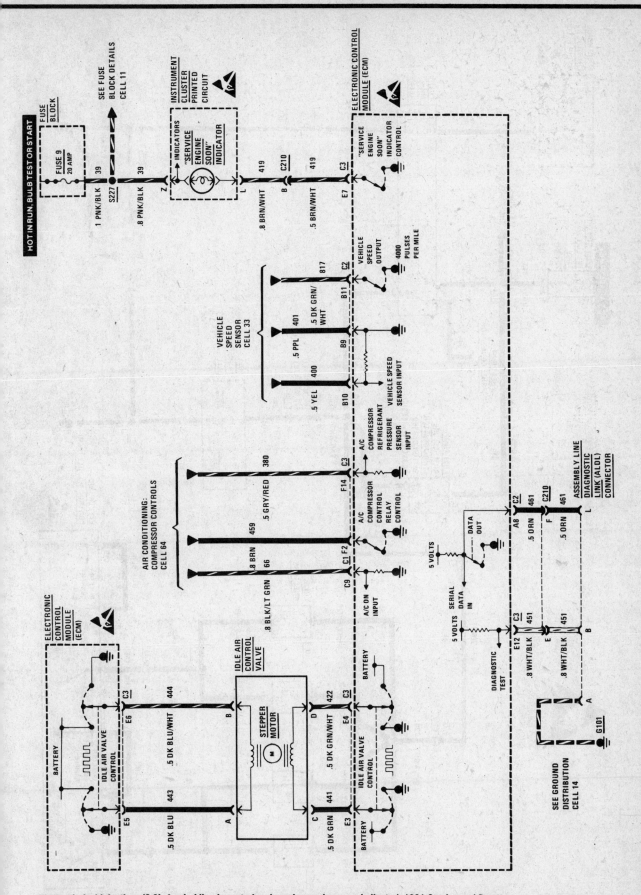

Electronic fuel injection: (2.3L 4 cyl., idle air control and service engine soon indicator)-1991 Corsica and Beretta

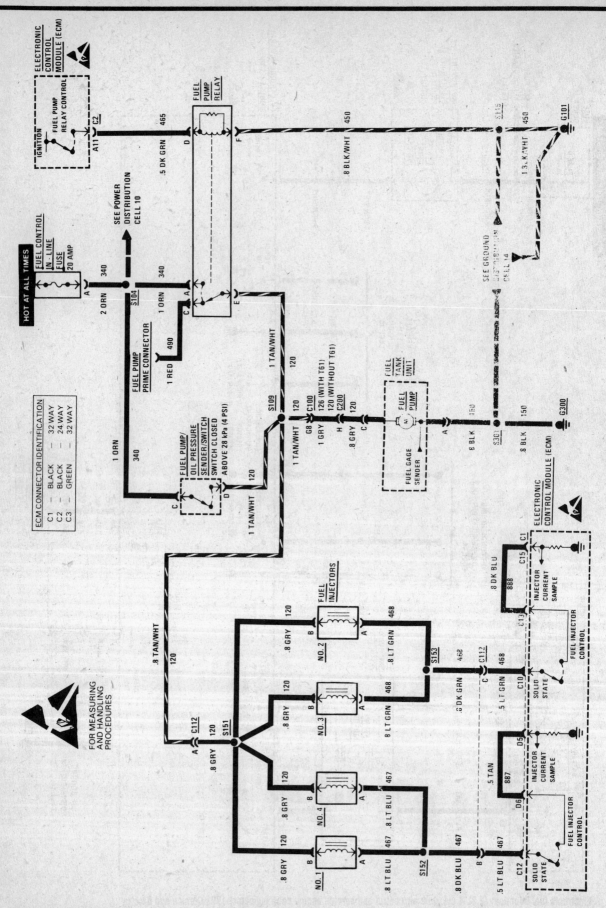

Electronic fuel injection: (2.3L 4 cyl., fuel control)-1991 Corsica and Beretta

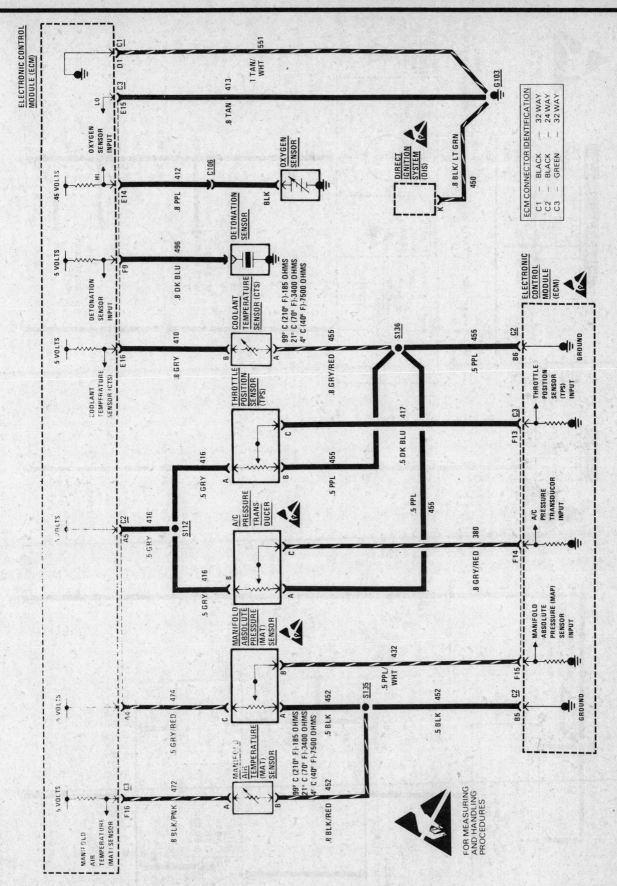

Electronic fuel injection: (2.3L 4 cyl., engine data sensors) -1991 Corsica and Beretta

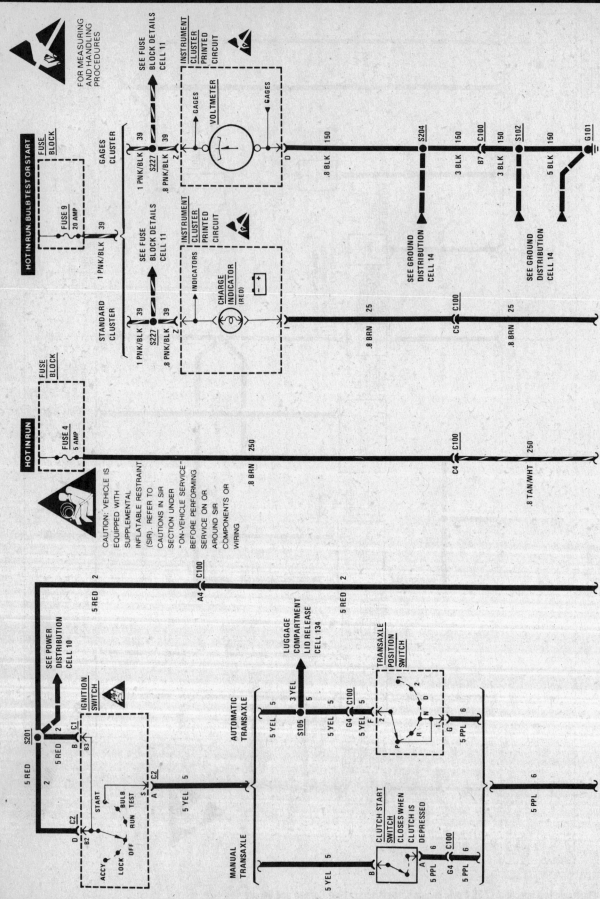

Starter and charging system-1991 Corsica and Beretta

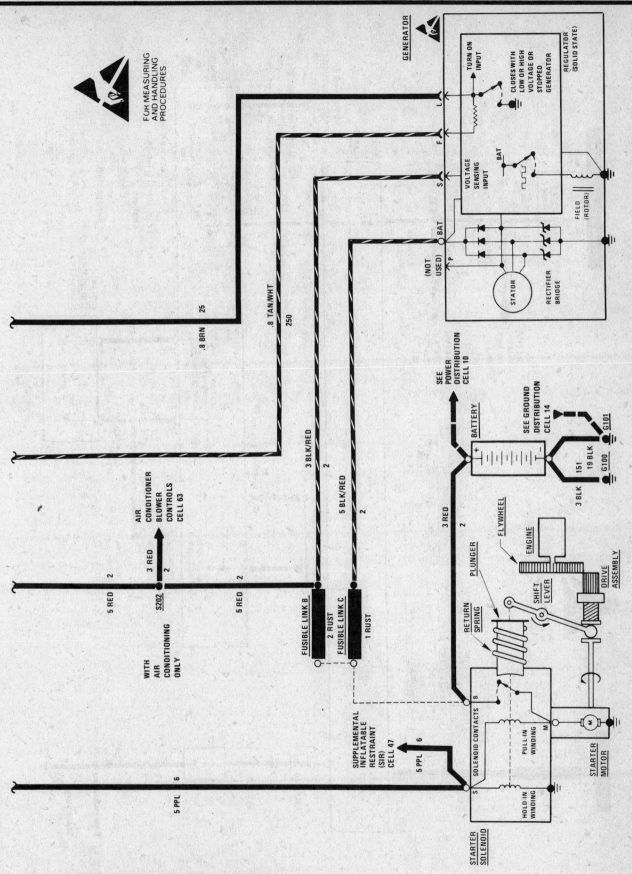

Starter and charging system (cont.)-1991 Corsica and Beretta

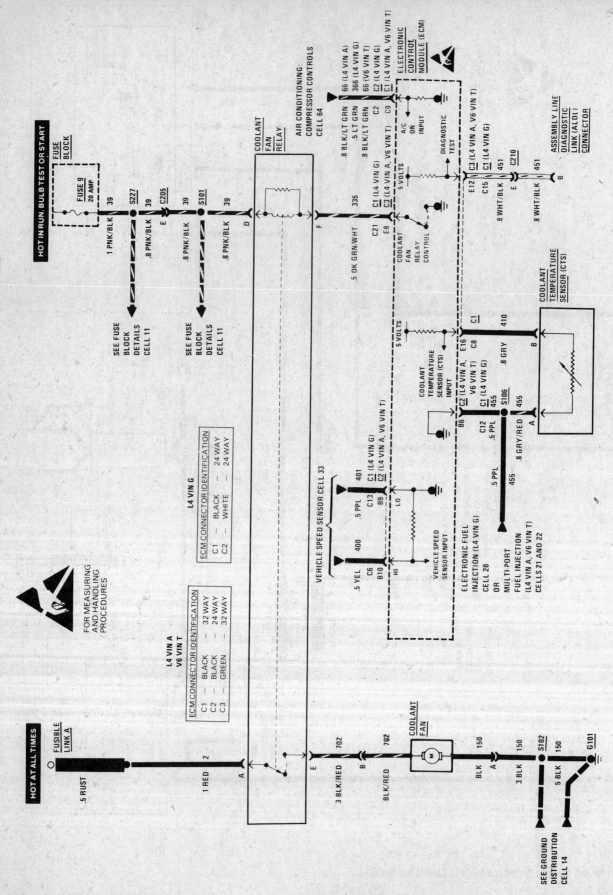

Coolant fan-1991 Corsica and Beretta

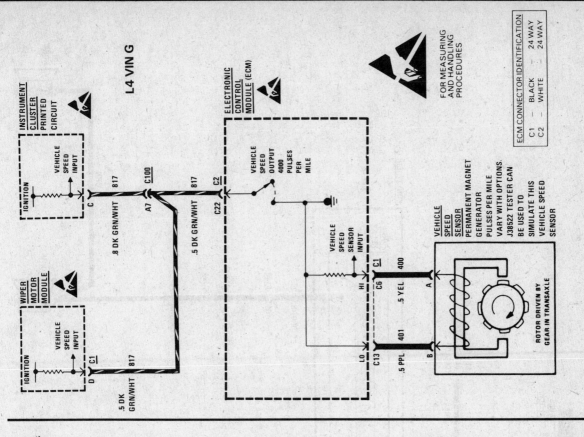

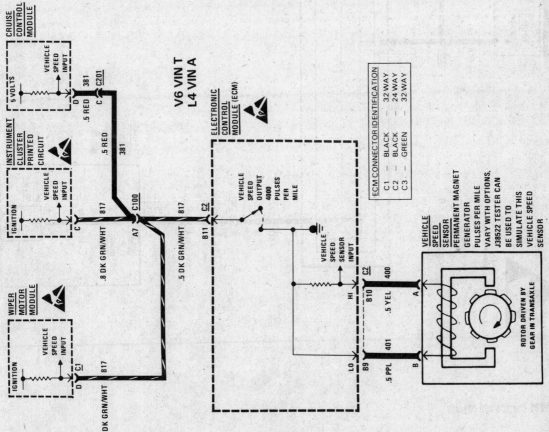

Vehicle speed sensor: (permanent magnet generator)-1991 Corsica and Beretta

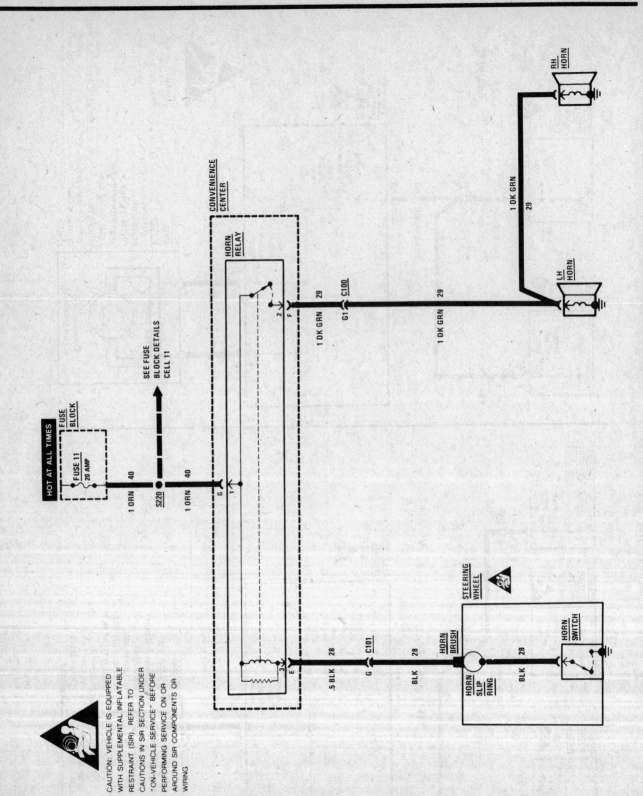

Horns-1991 Corsica and Beretta

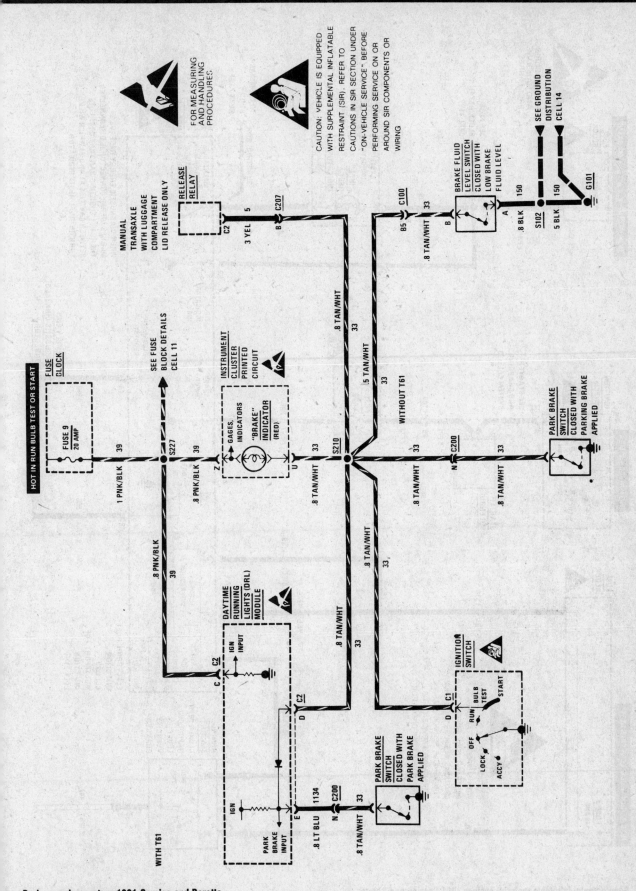

Brake warning system-1991 Corsica and Beretta

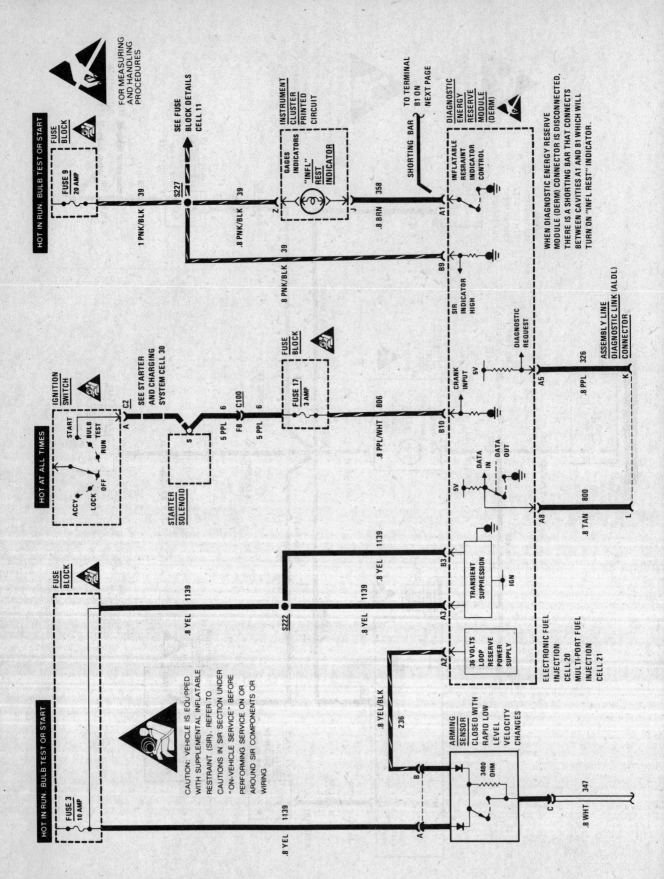

Supplemental inflatable restraint system-1991 Corsica and Beretta

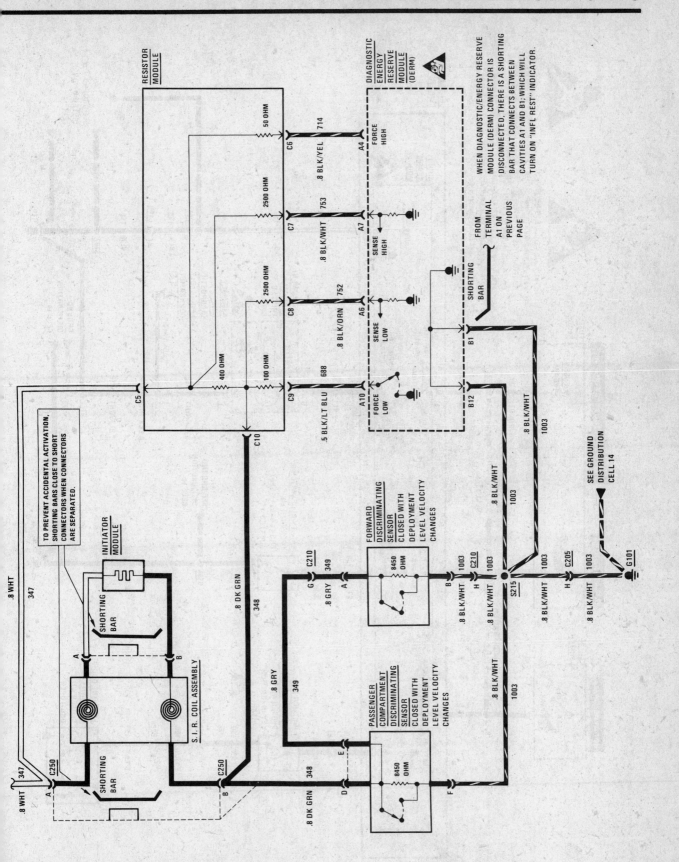

Supplemental inflatable restraint system cont.-1991 Corsica and Beretta

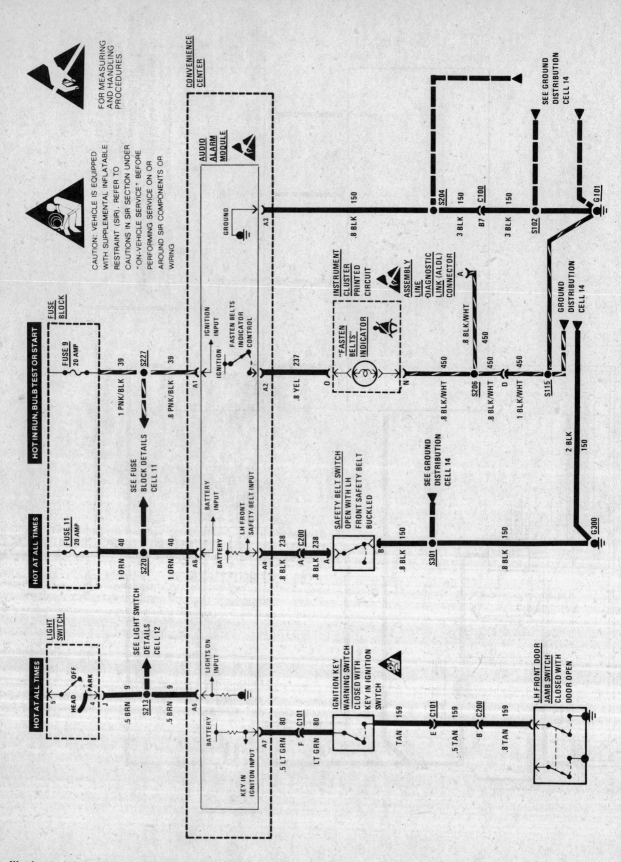

Warnings and alarms: (chime)-1991 Corsica and Beretta

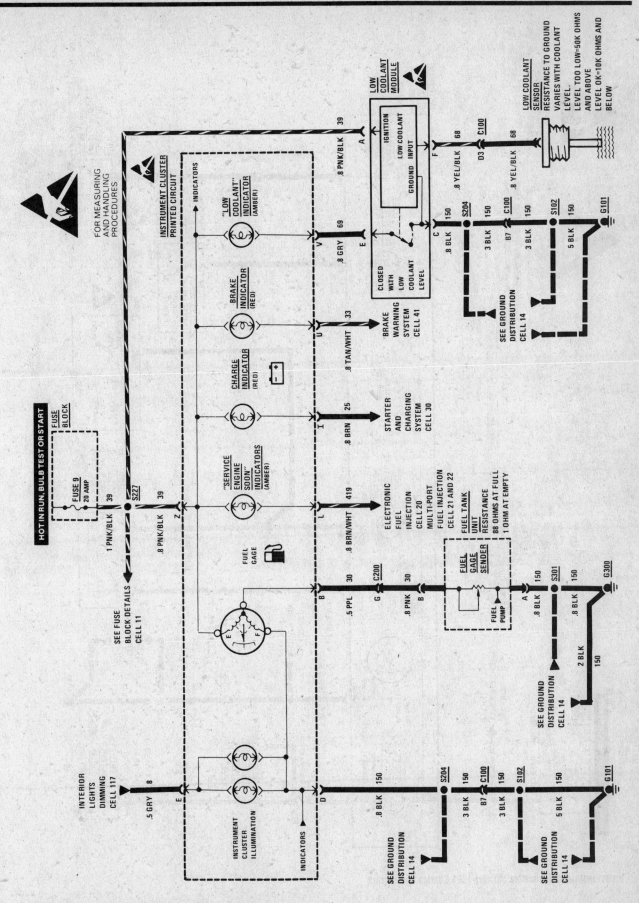

Instrument panel (indicators cluster)-1991 Corsica and Beretta

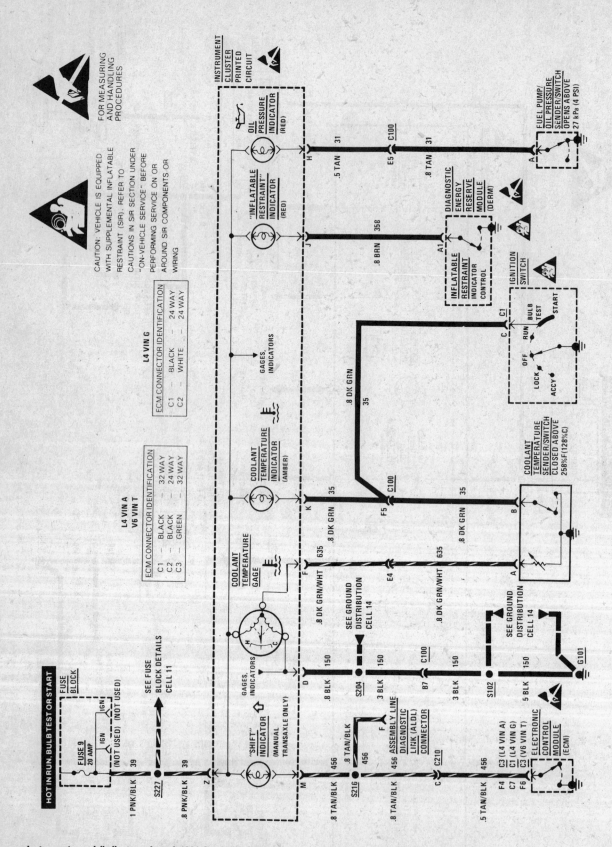

Instrument panel (indicators cluster)-1991 Corsica and Beretta

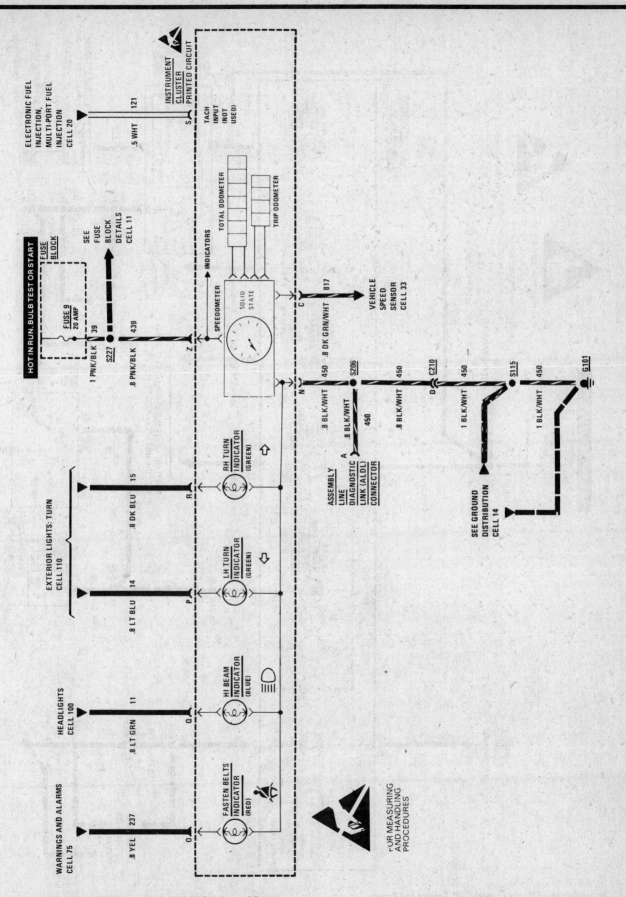

Instrument panel (indicators cluster)-1991 Corsica and Beretta

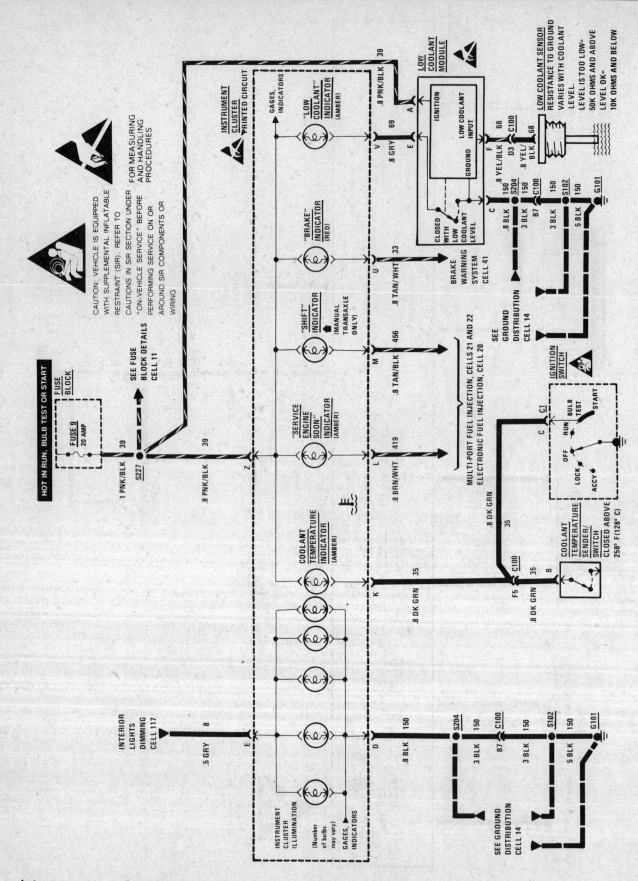

Instrument panel (gages cluster)-1991 Corsica and Beretta

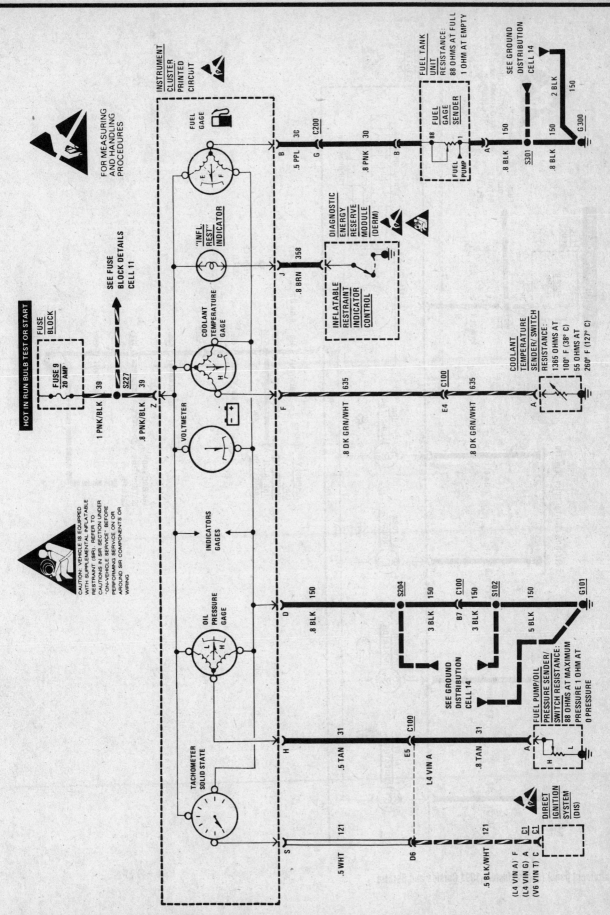

Instrument panel (gages cluster)-1991 Corsica and Beretta

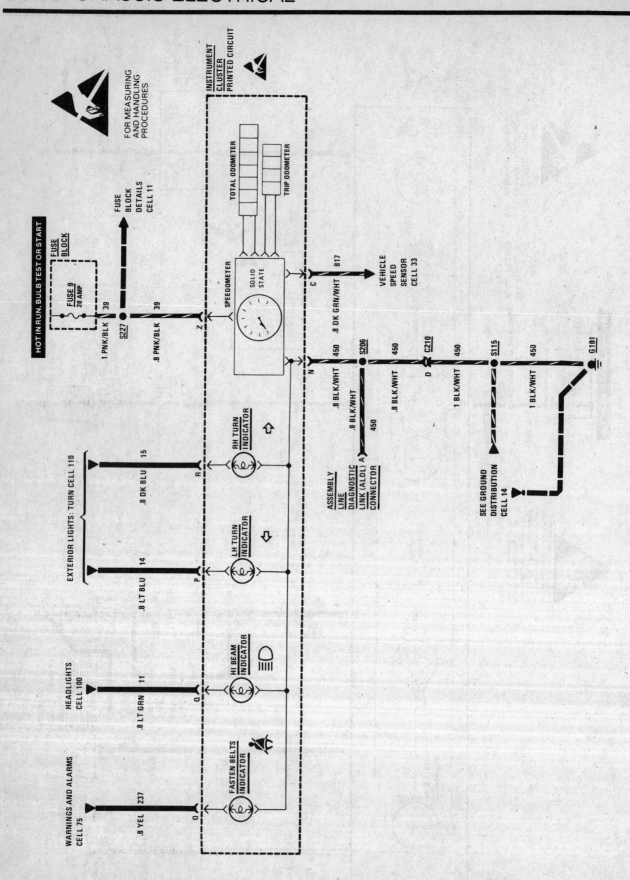

Instrument panel (gages cluster)-1991 Corsica and Beretta

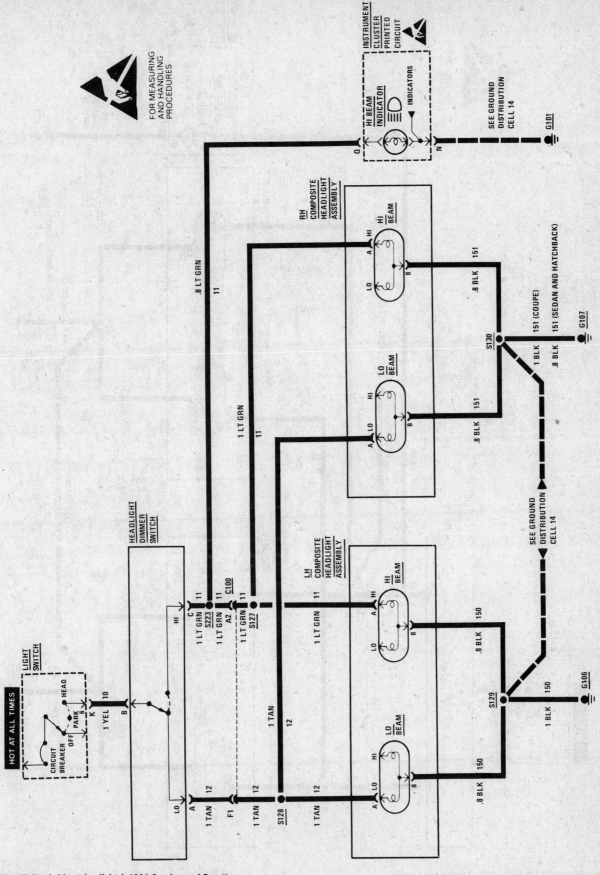

Headlights (without fog lights)-1991 Corsica and Beretta

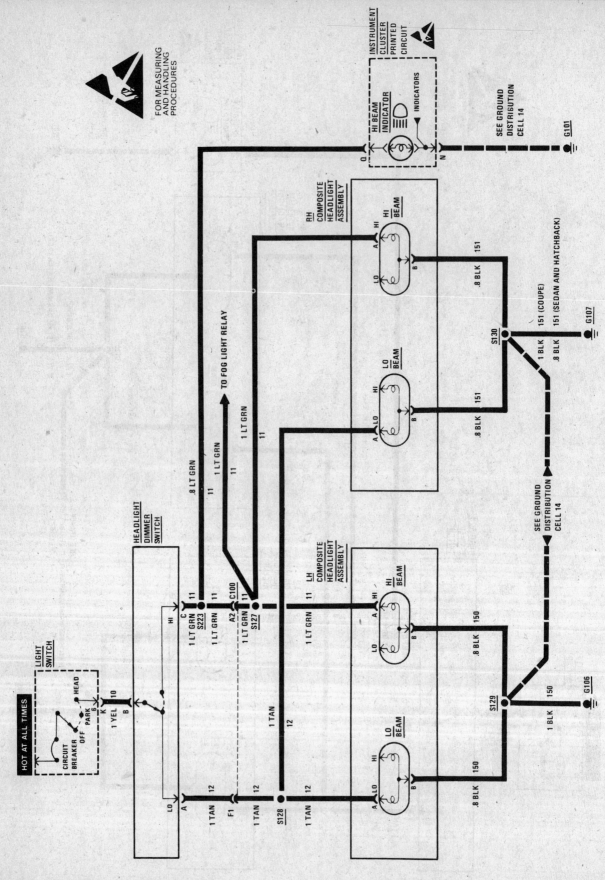

Headlights (with fog lights)-1991 Corsica and Beretta

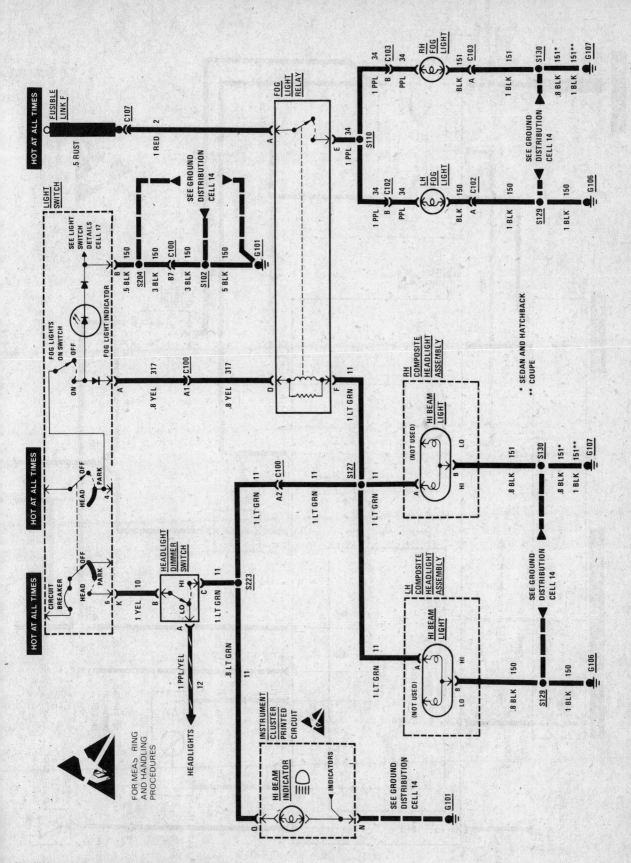

Headlights (with fog lights)-1991 Corsica and Beretta

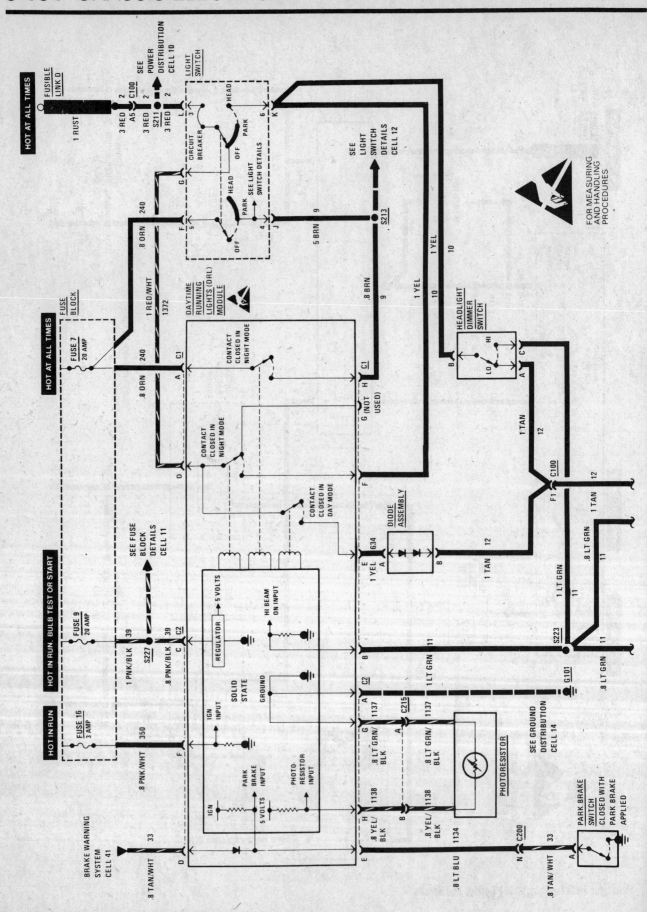

Headlights (with daytime running lights)-1991 Corsica and Beretta

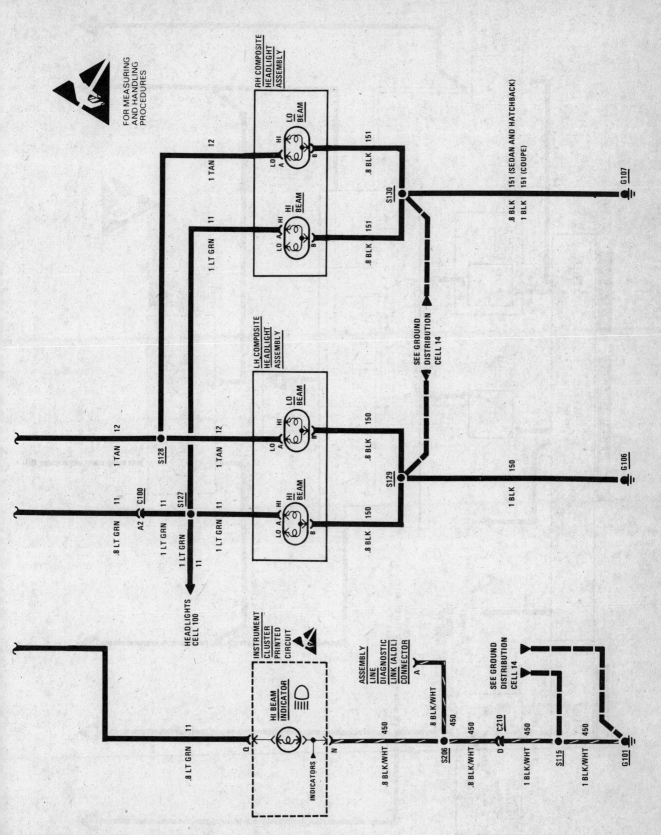

Headlights (with daytime running lights)-1991 Corsica and Beretta

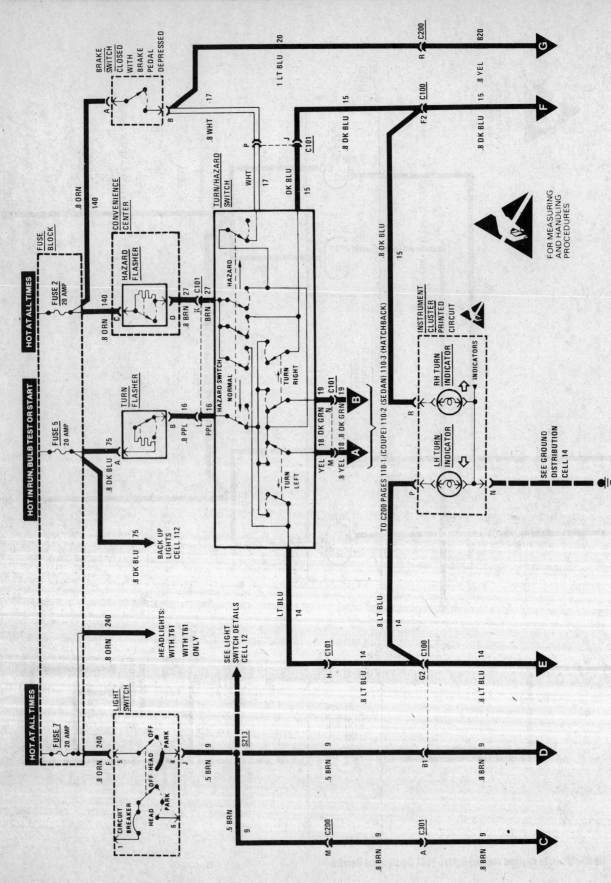

Exterior lights: (turn/hazard/stop/tail/marker/license/park)-1991 Corsica and Beretta

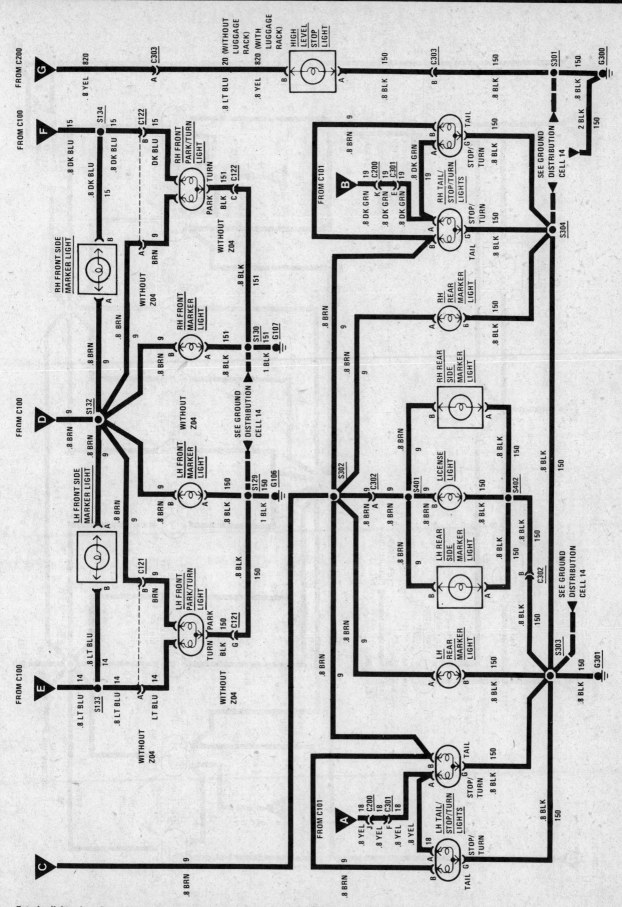

Exterior lights: (turn/hazard/stop/tail/marker/license/park) (coupe)-1991 Corsica and Beretta

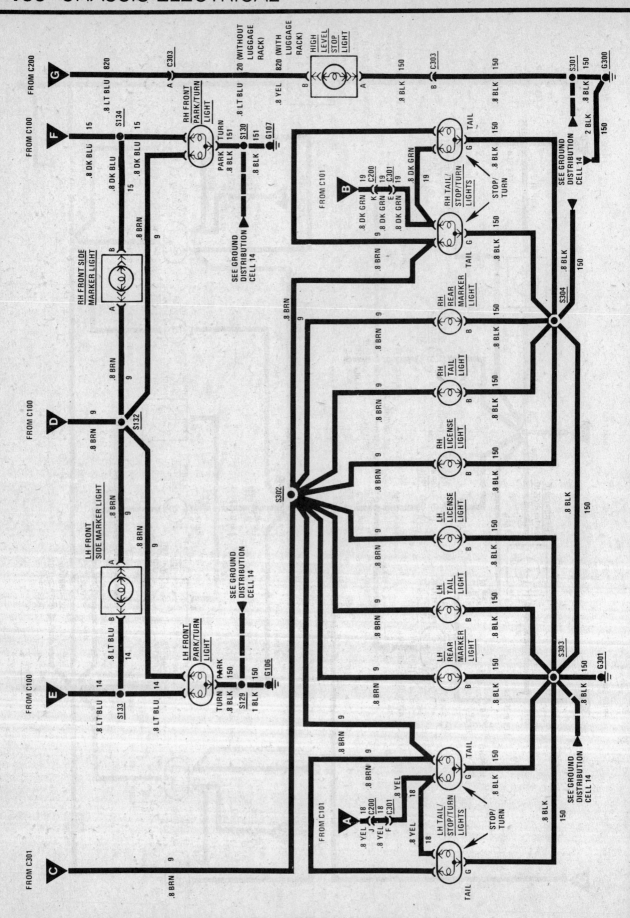

Exterior lights: (turn/hazard/stop/tail/marker/license/park) (sedan)-1991 Corsica and Beretta

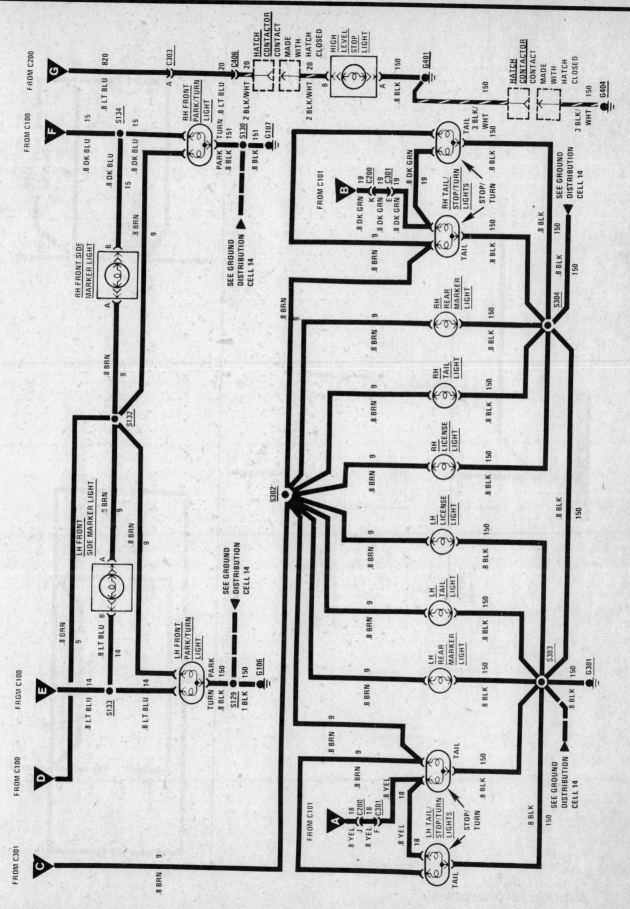

Exterior lights: (turn/hazard/stop/tail/marker/license/park) (hatchback)-1991 Corsica and Beretta

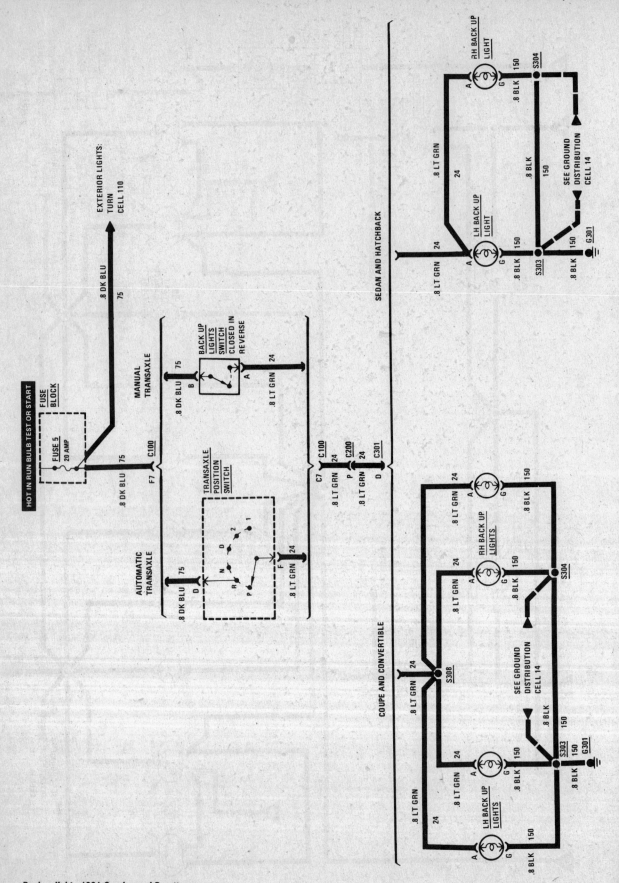

Backup lights-1991 Corsica and Beretta

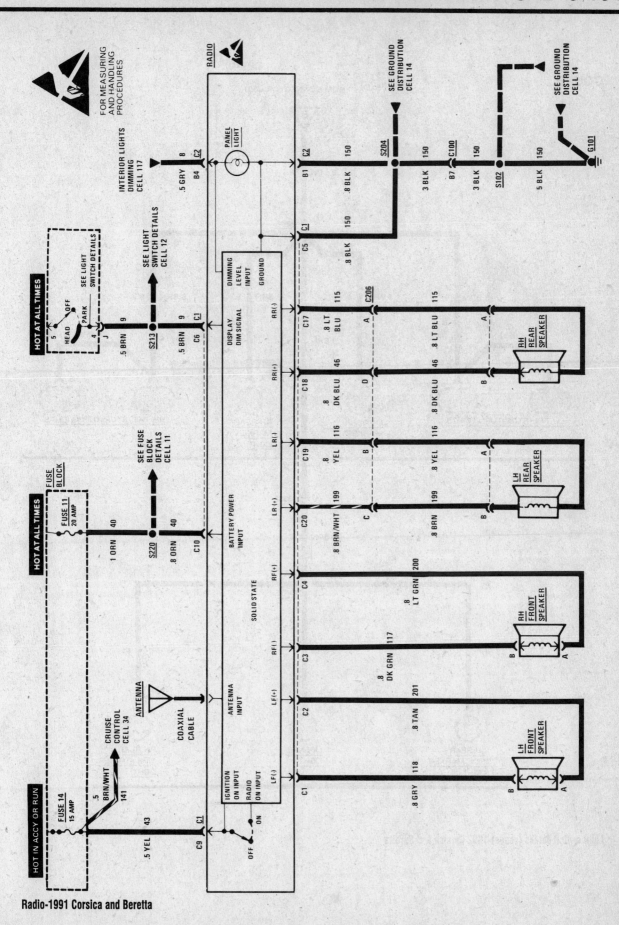

Radio—1991 Corsica and Beretta

COUPE

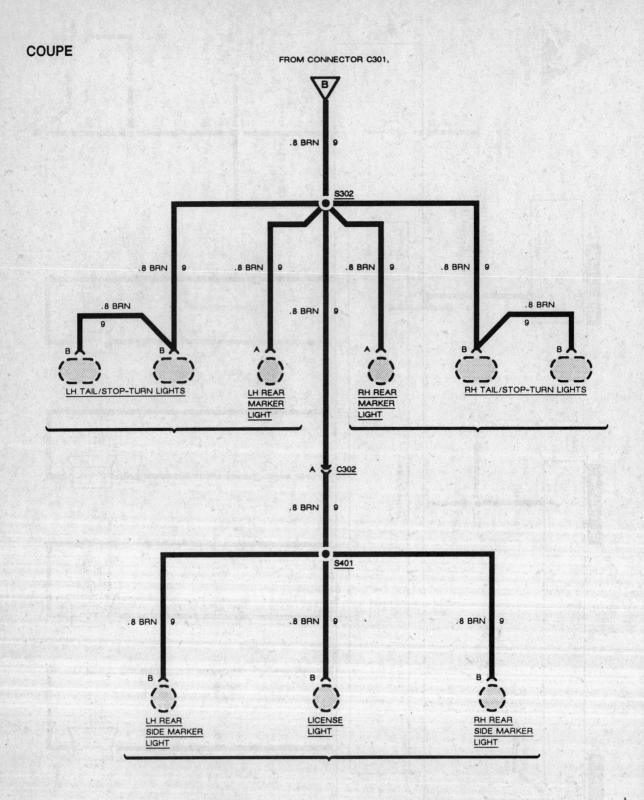

FROM CONNECTOR C301,

.8 BRN 9

S302

.8 BRN 9 .8 BRN 9 .8 BRN 9 .8 BRN 9

.8 BRN .8 BRN 9 .8 BRN

9 9

B B A A B B

LH TAIL/STOP-TURN LIGHTS LH REAR MARKER LIGHT RH REAR MARKER LIGHT RH TAIL/STOP-TURN LIGHTS

A C302

.8 BRN 9

S401

.8 BRN 9 .8 BRN 9 .8 BRN 9

B B B

LH REAR SIDE MARKER LIGHT LICENSE LIGHT RH REAR SIDE MARKER LIGHT

Light switch details (coupe)-1992 Corsica and Beretta

SEDAN

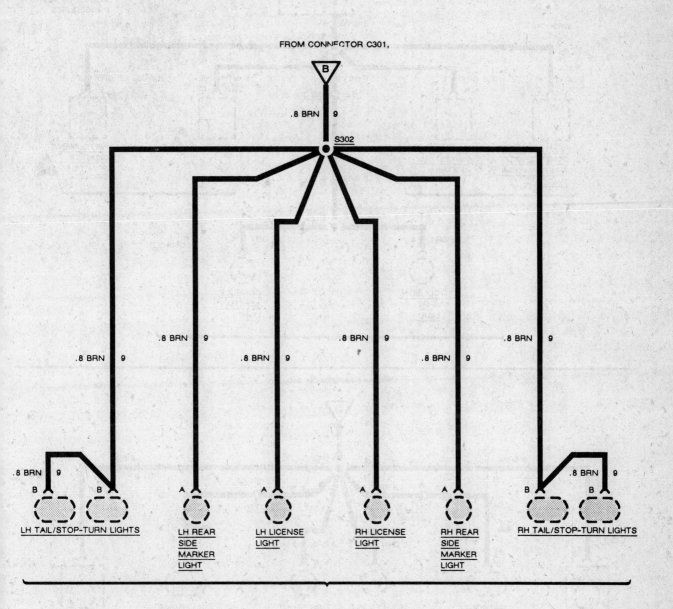

FROM CONNECTOR C301,

B

.8 BRN 9

S302

.8 BRN 9   .8 BRN 9   .8 BRN 9

.8 BRN 9   .8 BRN 9   .8 BRN 9   .8 BRN 9

.8 BRN 9   .8 BRN 9

B   B   A   A   A   A   B   B

LH TAIL/STOP-TURN LIGHTS   LH REAR SIDE MARKER LIGHT   LH LICENSE LIGHT   RH LICENSE LIGHT   RH REAR SIDE MARKER LIGHT   RH TAIL/STOP-TURN LIGHTS

Light switch details (sedan)-1992 Corsica and Beretta

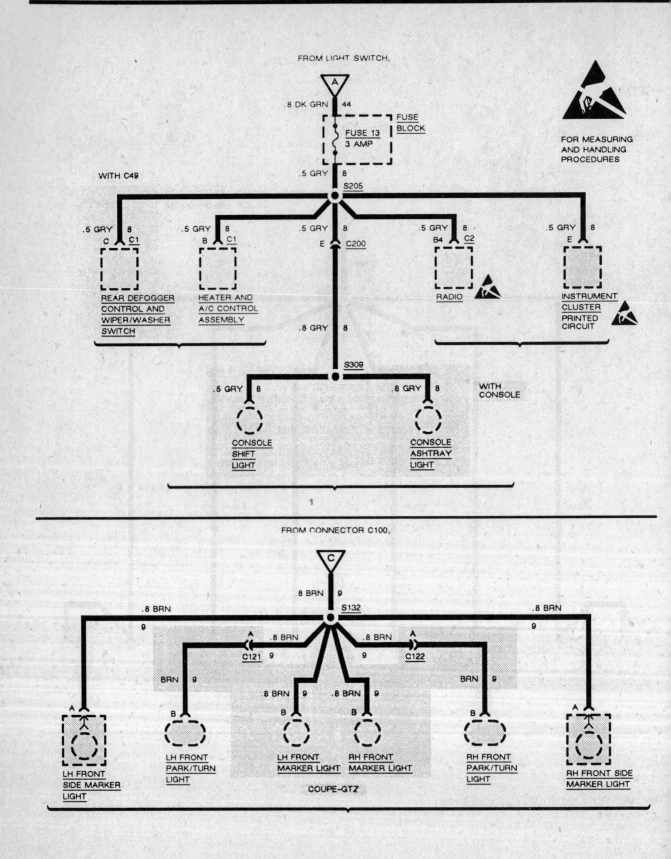

Light switch details (sedan and coupe cont.)-1992 Corsica and Beretta

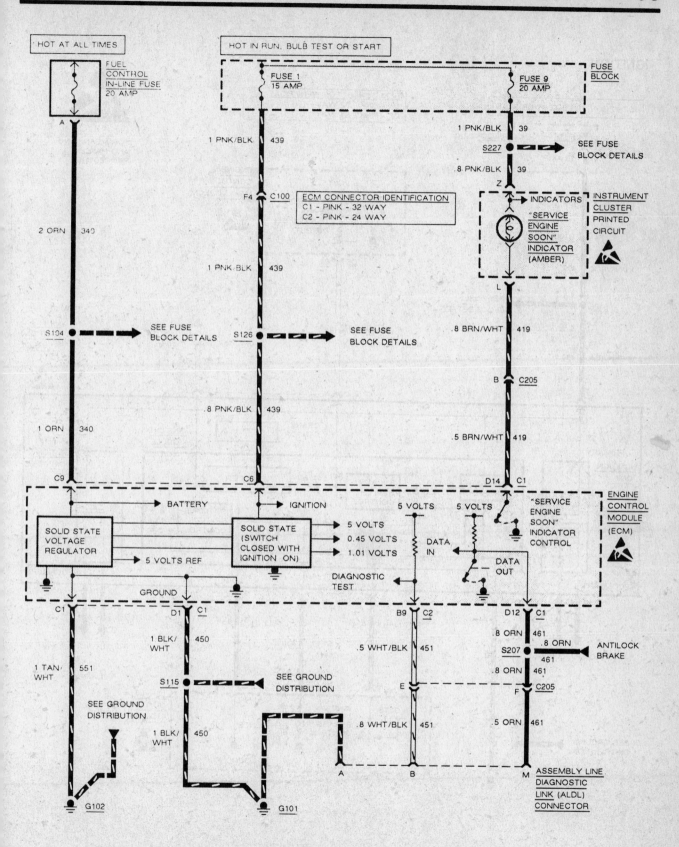

Electronic fuel injection: (2.2L 4 cyl., power, grounds and 'Service Engine Soon' indicator) -1992 Corsica and Beretta

IGNITION

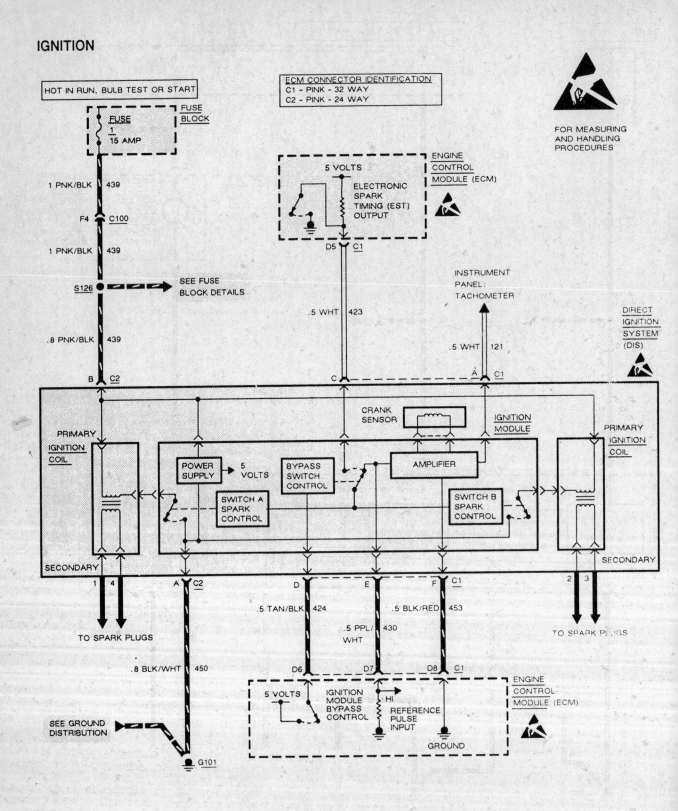

Electronic fuel injection: (2.2L 4 cyl., ignition)-1992 Corsica and Beretta

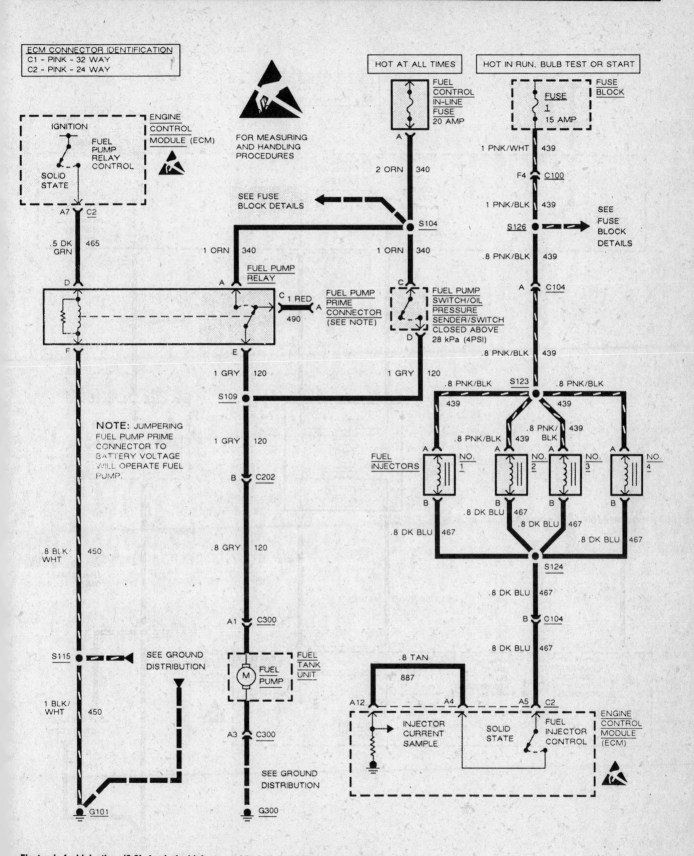

Electronic fuel injection: (2.2L 4 cyl., fuel injector and fuel control)-1992 Corsica and Beretta

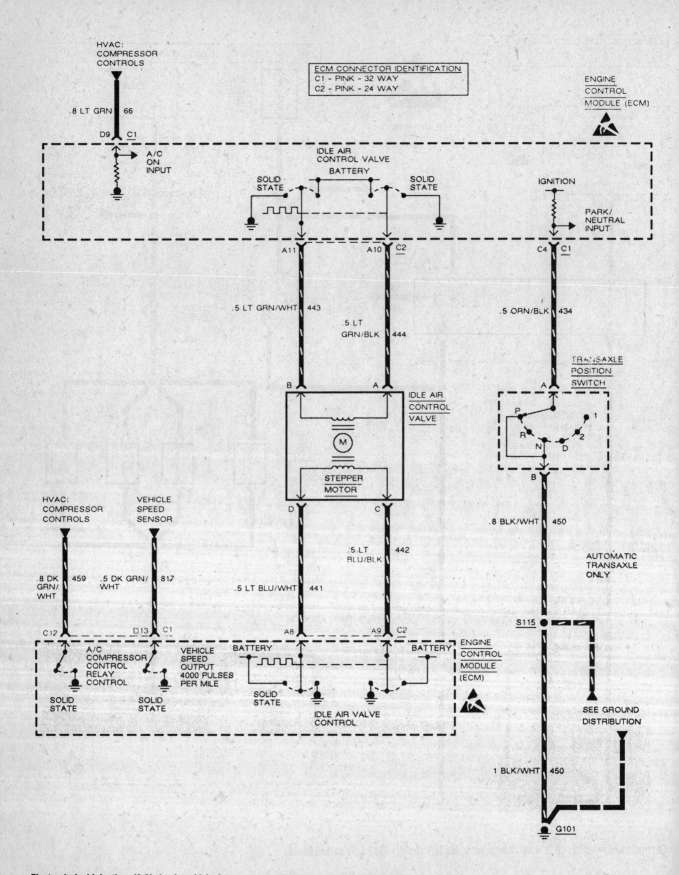

Electronic fuel injection: (2.2L 4 cyl., vehicle data sensors and idle air control)-1992 Corsica and Beretta

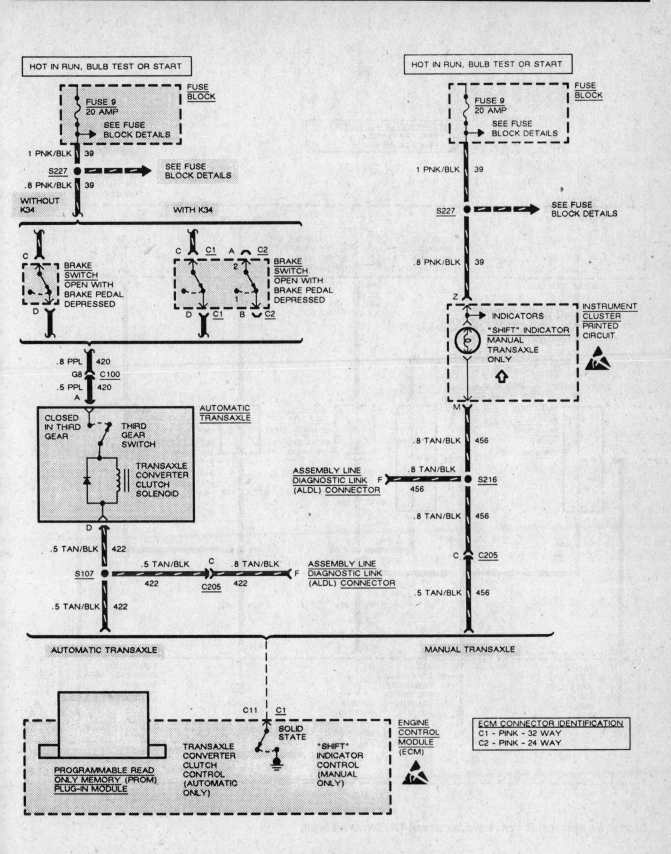

Electronic fuel injection: (2.2L 4 cyl., transaxle converter clutch/shift indicator)-1992 Corsica and Beretta

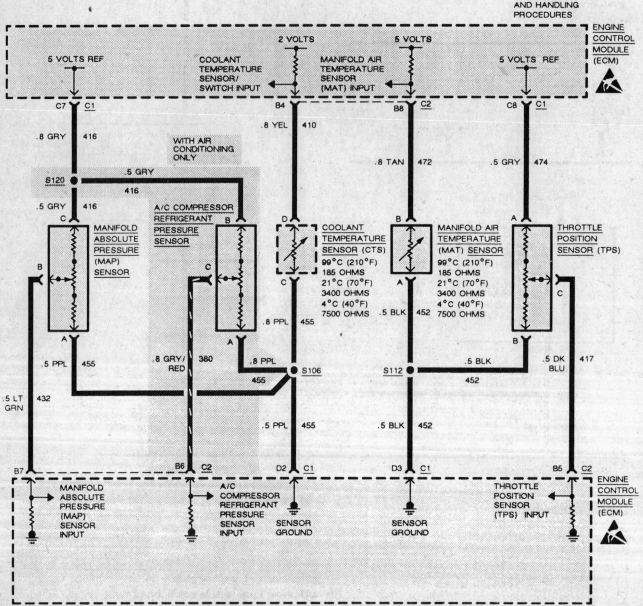

Electronic fuel injection: (2.2L 4 cyl., engine data sensors)-1992 Corsica and Beretta

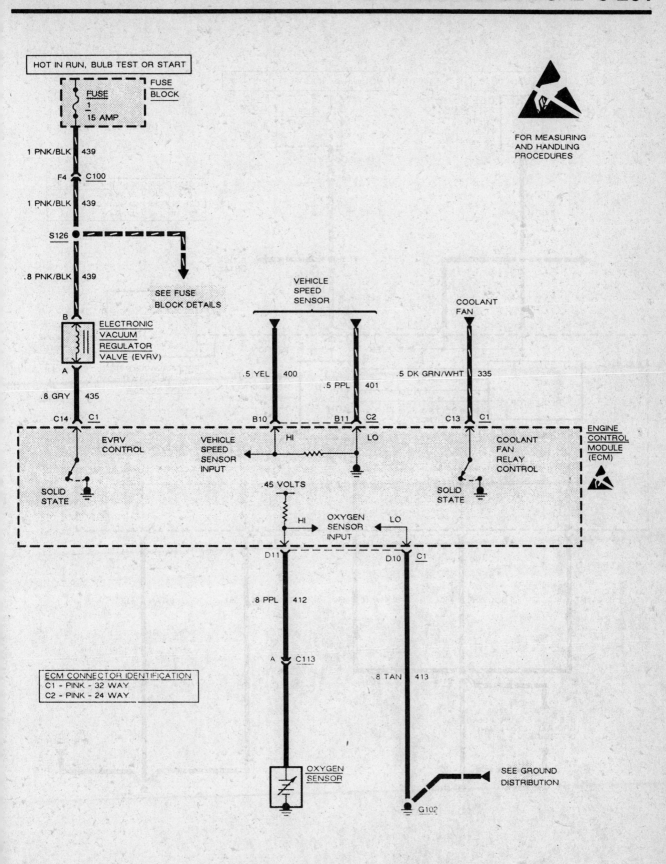

Electronic fuel injection: (2.2L 4 cyl., vehicle data sensors)-1992 Corsica and Beretta

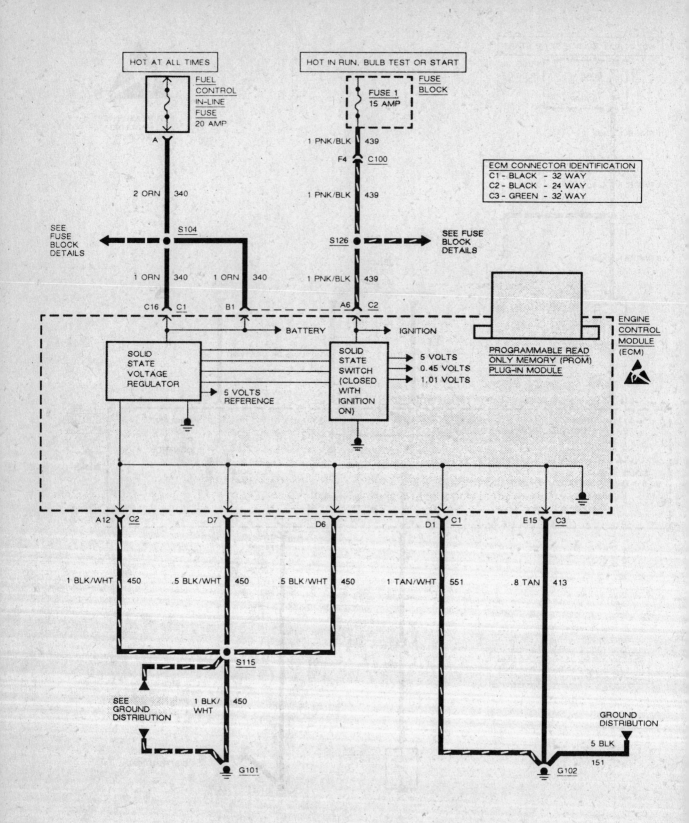

Multi-port fuel injection: (3.1L V6 engine, power and grounds) -1992 Corsica and Beretta

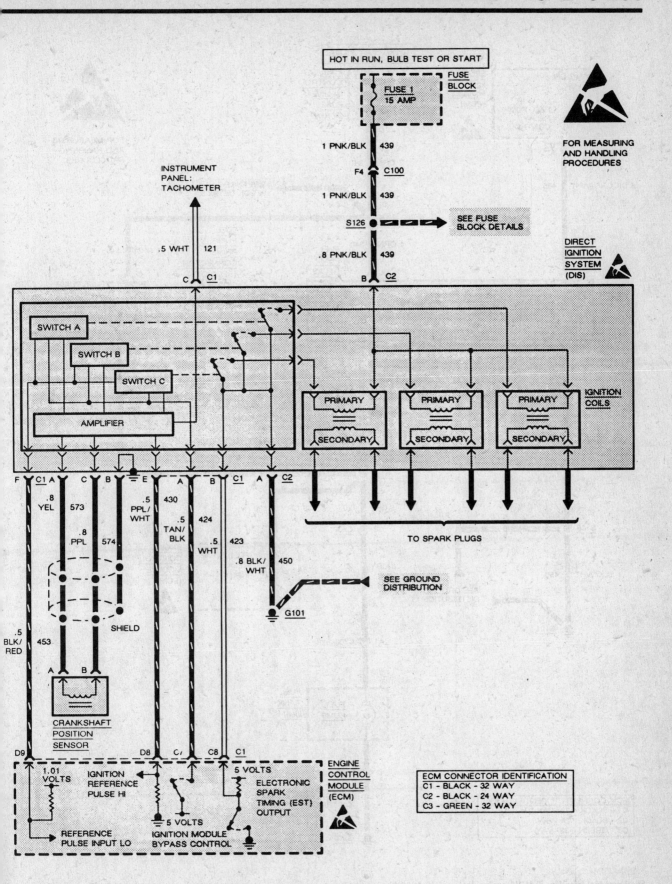

Multi-port fuel injection: (3.1L V6 engine, ignition)-1992 Corsica and Beretta

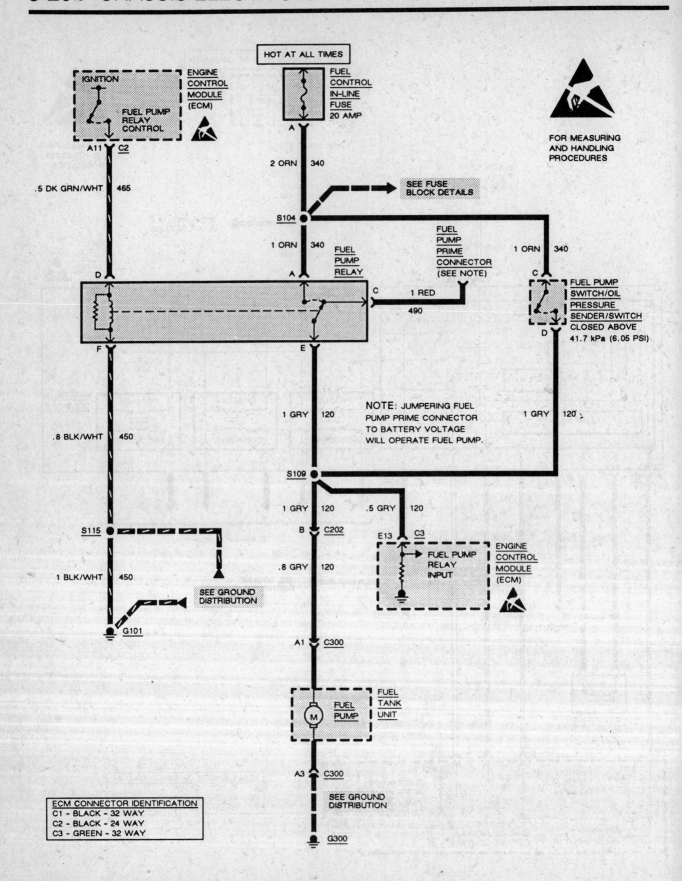

Multi-port fuel injection: (3.1L V6 engine, fuel control)-1992 Corsica and Beretta

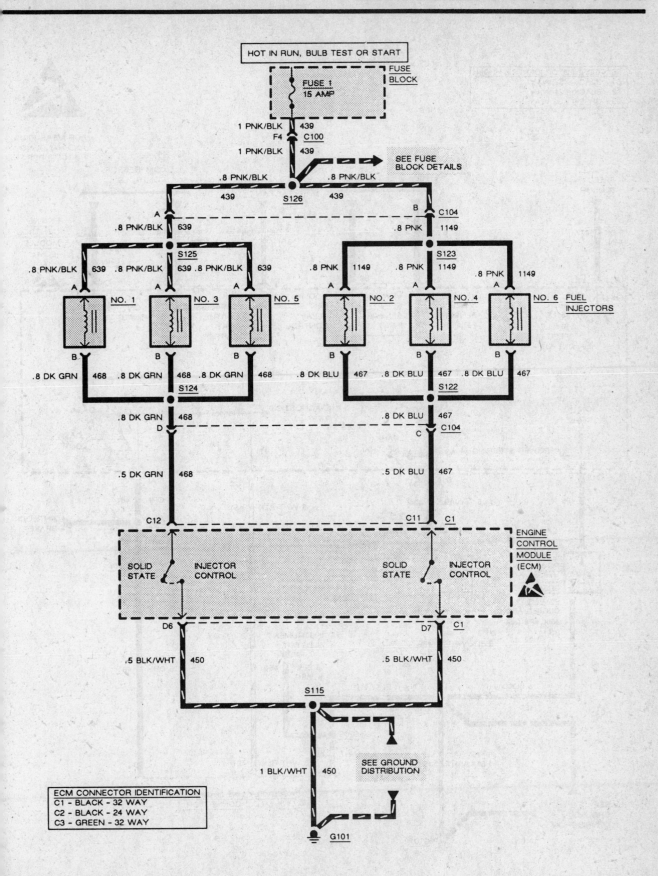

Multi-port fuel injection: (3.1L V6 engine, fuel injectors)-1992 Corsica and Beretta

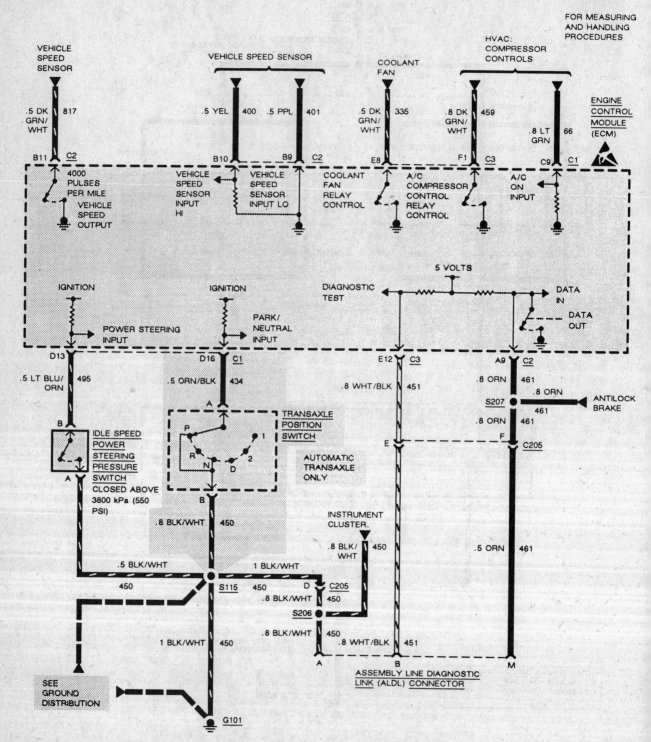

Multi-port fuel injection: (3.1L V6 engine, power and grounds)-1992 Corsica and Beretta

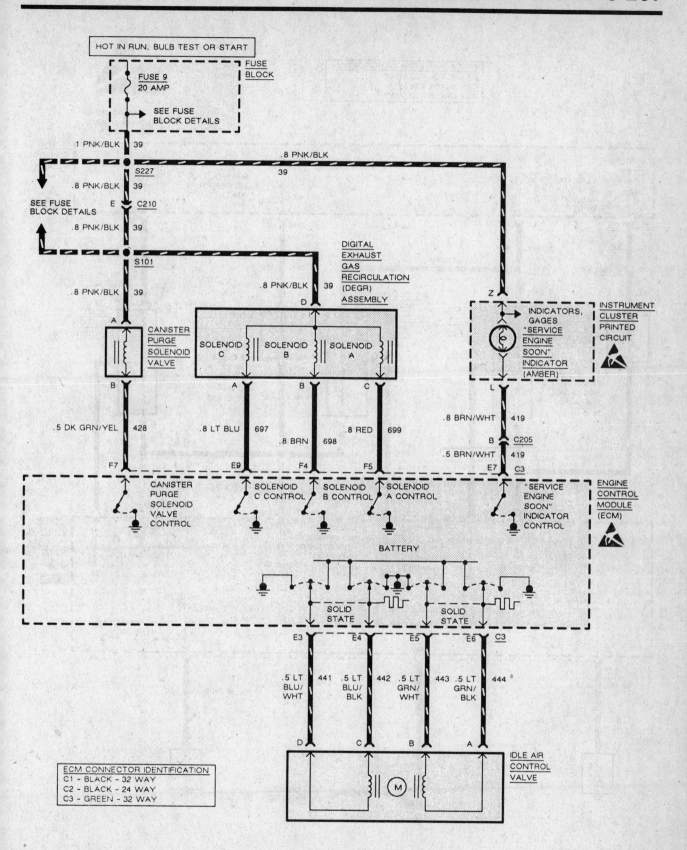

Multi-port fuel injection: (3.1L V6 engine, 'Service Engine Soon' indicator)-1992 Corsica and Beretta

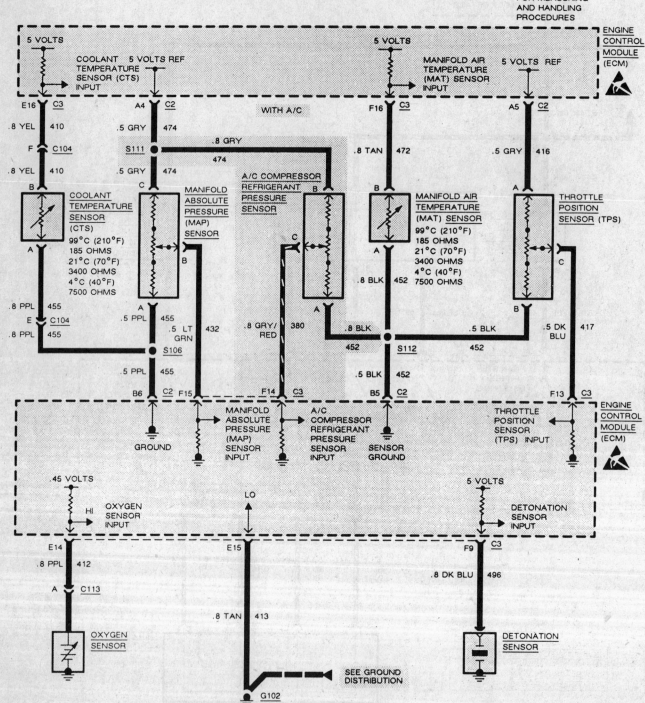

Multi-port fuel injection: (3.1L V6 engine, Engine data sensors)-1992 Corsica and Beretta

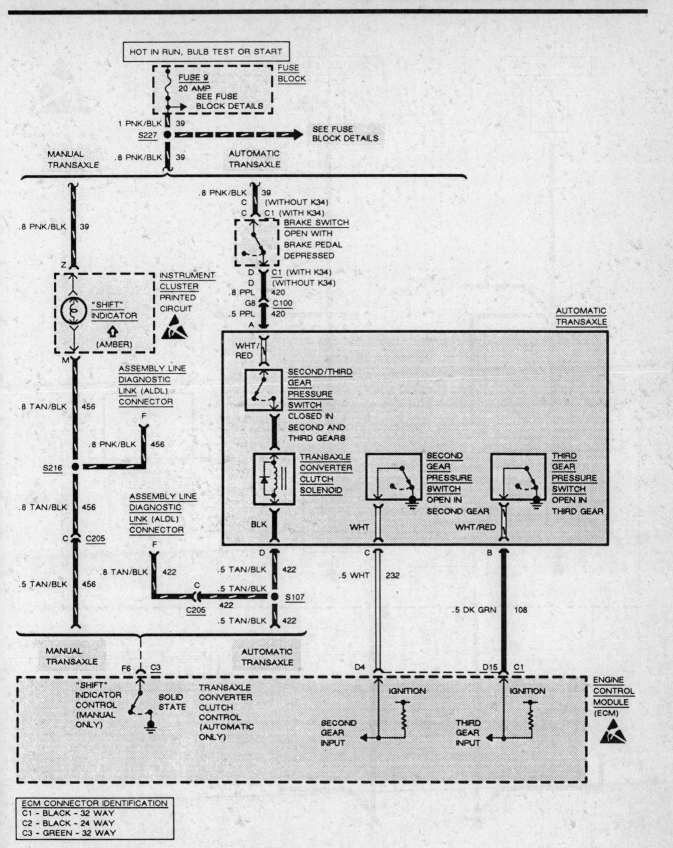

Multi-port fuel injection: (3.1L V6 engine, Transaxle converter clutch/'Shift' indicator)-1992 Corsica and Beretta

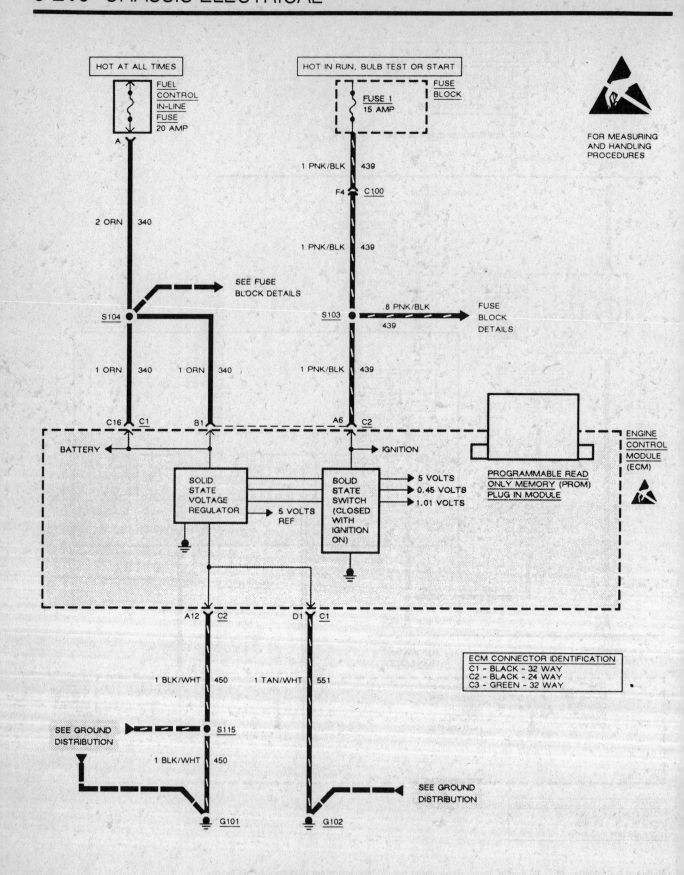

Electronic fuel injection: (2.3L 4 cyl., power and grounds)-1992 Corsica and Beretta

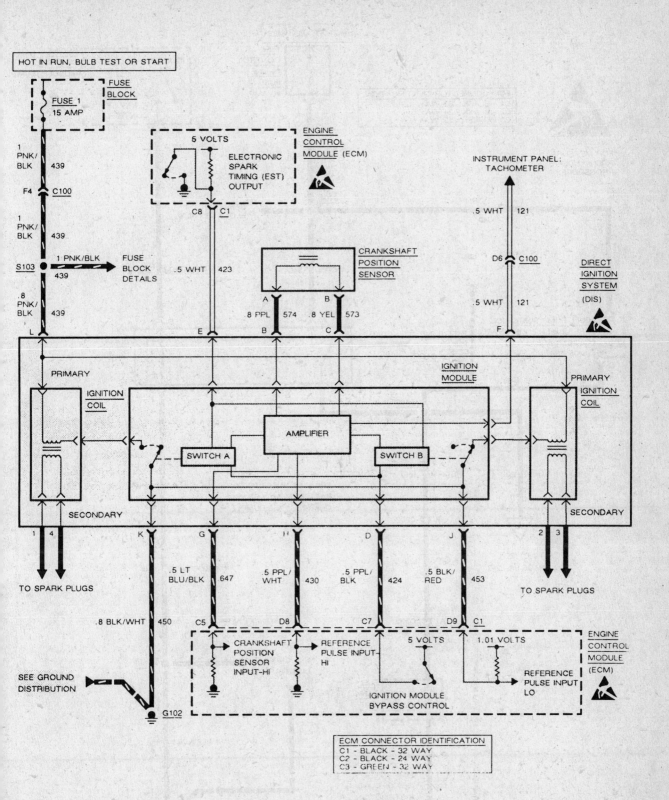

Electronic fuel injection: (2.3L 4 cyl., ignition)-1992 Corsica and Beretta

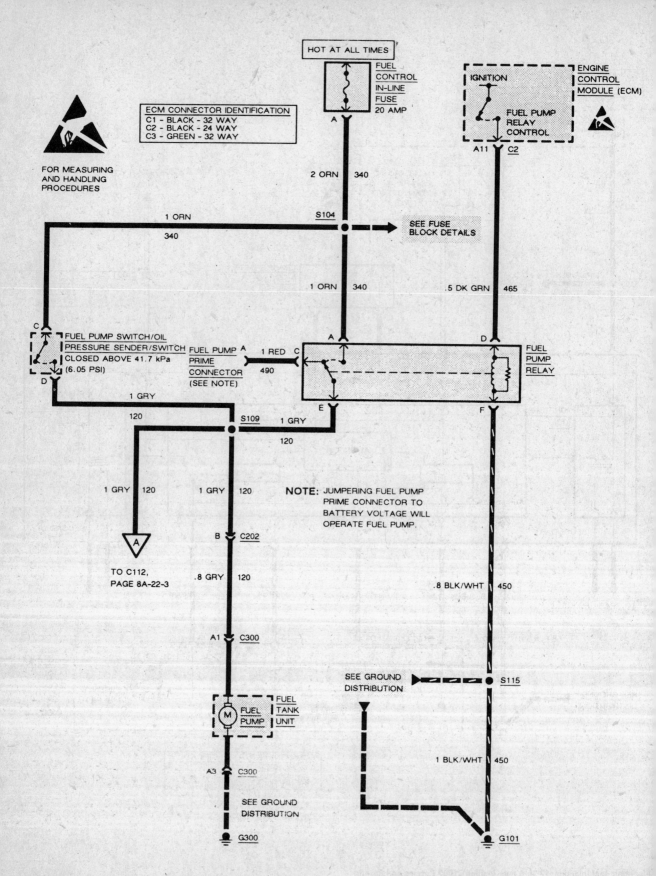

ECM CONNECTOR IDENTIFICATION
C1 - BLACK - 32 WAY
C2 - BLACK - 24 WAY
C3 - GREEN - 32 WAY

FOR MEASURING
AND HANDLING
PROCEDURES

HOT AT ALL TIMES

FUEL
CONTROL
IN-LINE
FUSE
20 AMP

ENGINE
CONTROL
MODULE (ECM)

IGNITION

FUEL PUMP
RELAY
CONTROL

A11   C2

2 ORN   340

1 ORN
340

S104

SEE FUSE
BLOCK DETAILS

1 ORN   340

.5 DK GRN   465

FUEL PUMP SWITCH/OIL
PRESSURE SENDER/SWITCH
CLOSED ABOVE 41.7 kPa
(6.05 PSI)

FUEL PUMP
PRIME
CONNECTOR
(SEE NOTE)

1 RED
490

FUEL
PUMP
RELAY

1 GRY
120

S109   1 GRY
120

NOTE: JUMPERING FUEL PUMP
PRIME CONNECTOR TO
BATTERY VOLTAGE WILL
OPERATE FUEL PUMP.

1 GRY   120

1 GRY   120

TO C112,
PAGE 8A-22-3

B   C202

.8 GRY   120

.8 BLK/WHT   450

A1   C300

SEE GROUND
DISTRIBUTION

S115

FUEL
TANK
UNIT

FUEL
PUMP

1 BLK/WHT   450

A3   C300

SEE GROUND
DISTRIBUTION

G300

G101

Electronic fuel injection: (2.3L 4 cyl, fuel control)-1992 Corsica and Beretta

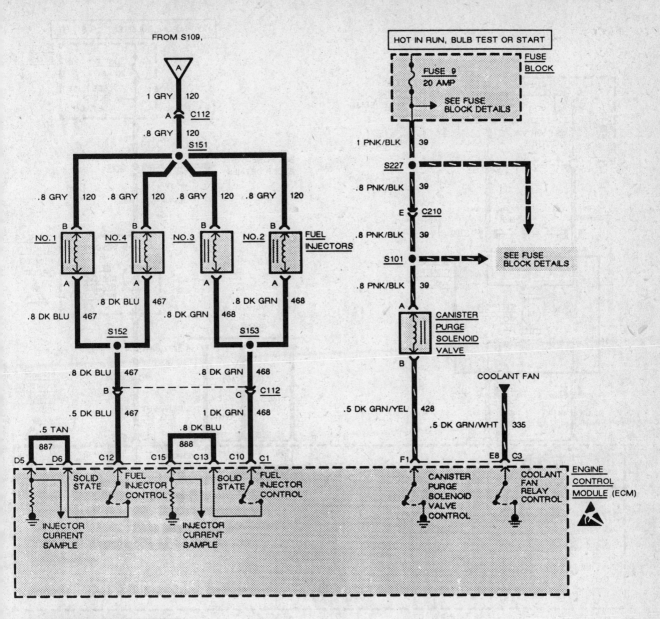

Electronic fuel injection: (2.3L 4 cyl., injectors and vehicle data sensors)-1992 Corsica and Beretta

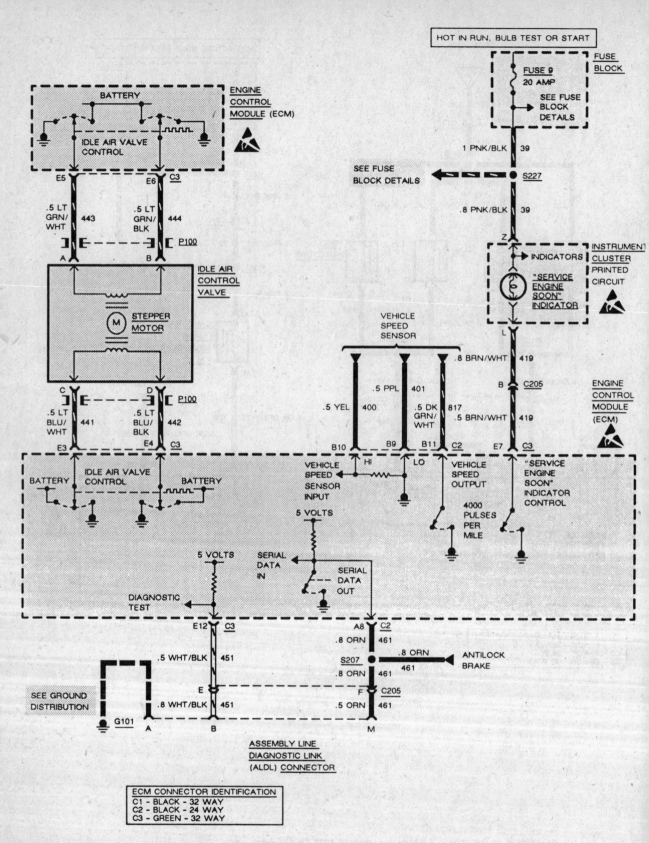

Electronic fuel injection: (2.3L 4 cyl., idle air control and 'Service Engine Soon' indicator)-1992 Corsica and Beretta

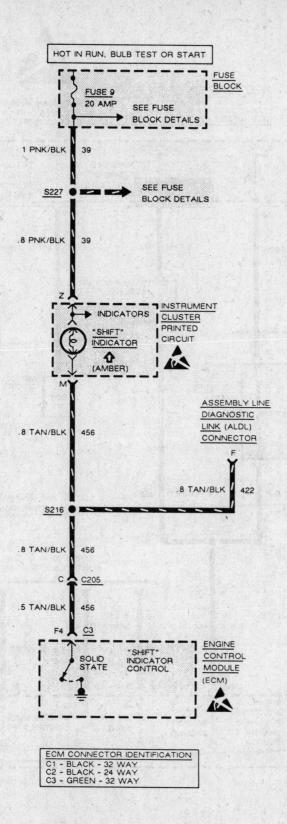

HOT IN RUN, BULB TEST OR START

FUSE BLOCK

FUSE 9 20 AMP SEE FUSE BLOCK DETAILS

FOR MEASURING AND HANDLING PROCEDURES

1 PNK/BLK 39

S227 SEE FUSE BLOCK DETAILS

.8 PNK/BLK 39

Z

INSTRUMENT CLUSTER PRINTED CIRCUIT

INDICATORS

"SHIFT" INDICATOR

(AMBER)

M

ASSEMBLY LINE DIAGNOSTIC LINK (ALDL) CONNECTOR

.8 TAN/BLK 456

F

.8 TAN/BLK 422

S216

.8 TAN/BLK 456

C C205

.5 TAN/BLK 456

F4 C3

ENGINE CONTROL MODULE (ECM)

SOLID STATE

"SHIFT" INDICATOR CONTROL

ECM CONNECTOR IDENTIFICATION
C1 – BLACK – 32 WAY
C2 – BLACK – 24 WAY
C3 – GREEN – 32 WAY

Electronic fuel injection: (2.3L 4 cyl., 'Shift' indicator)-1992 Corsica and Beretta

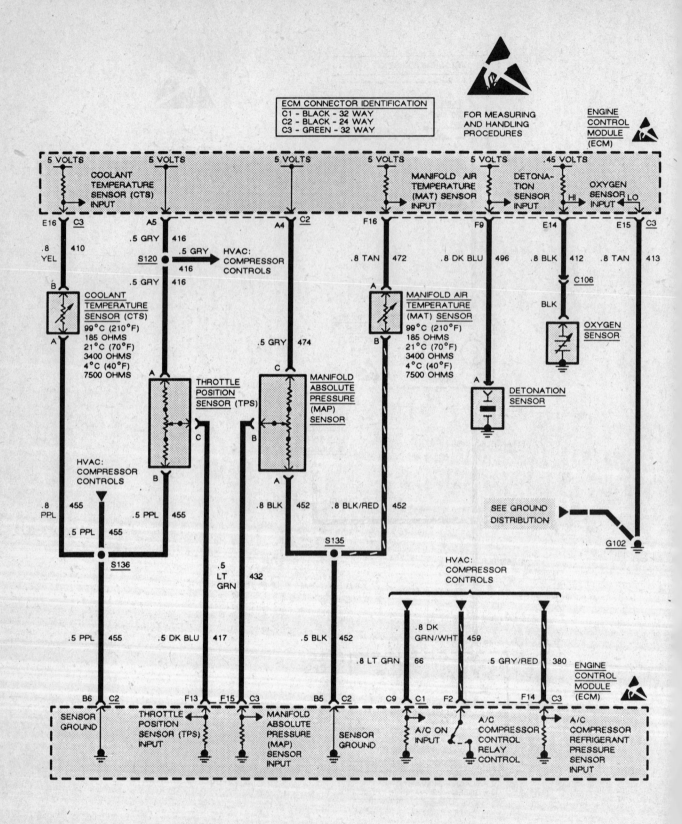

Electronic fuel injection: (2.3L 4 cyl., engine data sensors) -1992 Corsica and Beretta

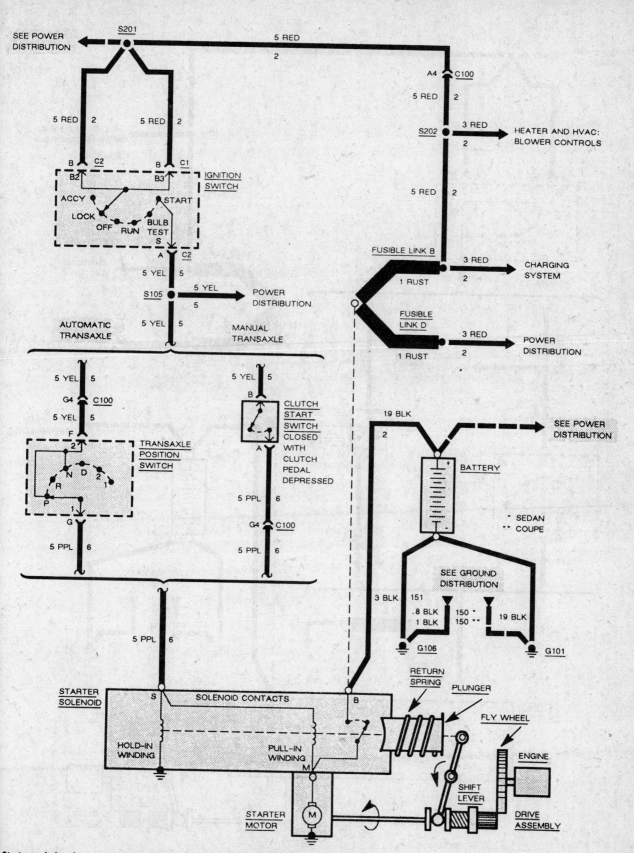

Starter and charging system (early production)-1992 Corsica and Beretta

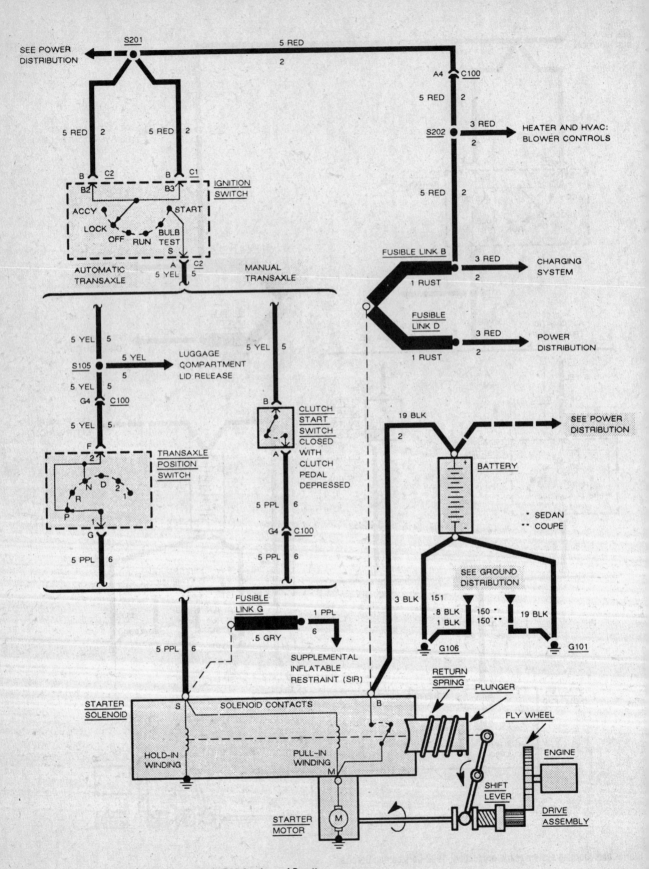

Starter and charging system (Late production)-1992 Corsica and Beretta

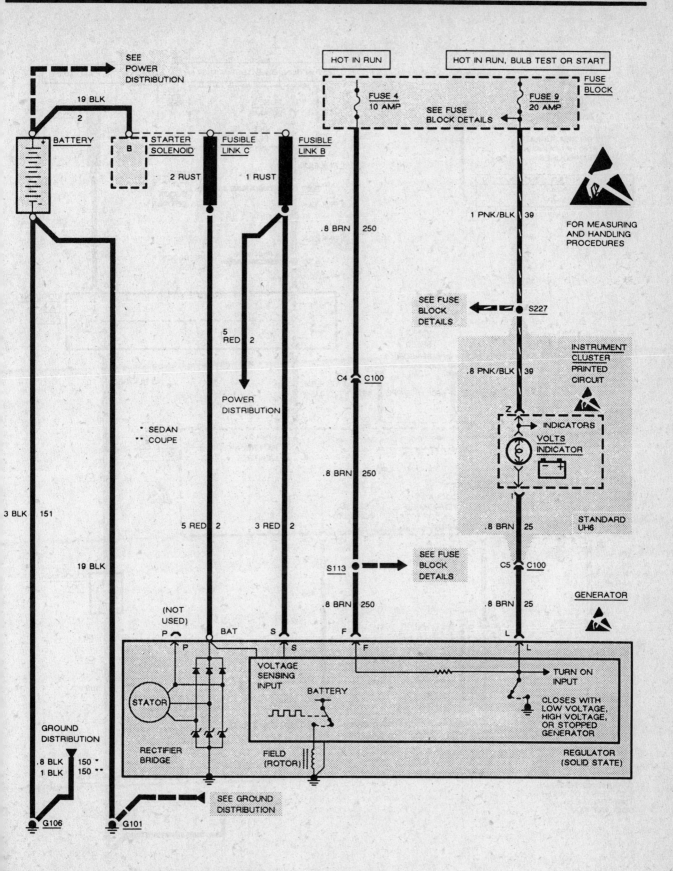

Starter and charging system (Cont.)-1992 Corsica and Beretta

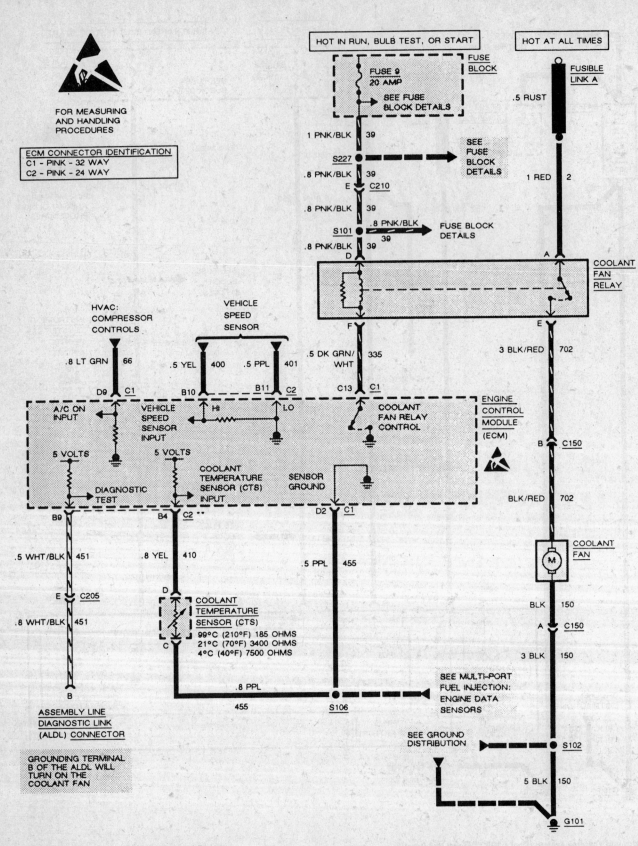

Coolant fan, 2.2L engine-1992 Corsica and Beretta

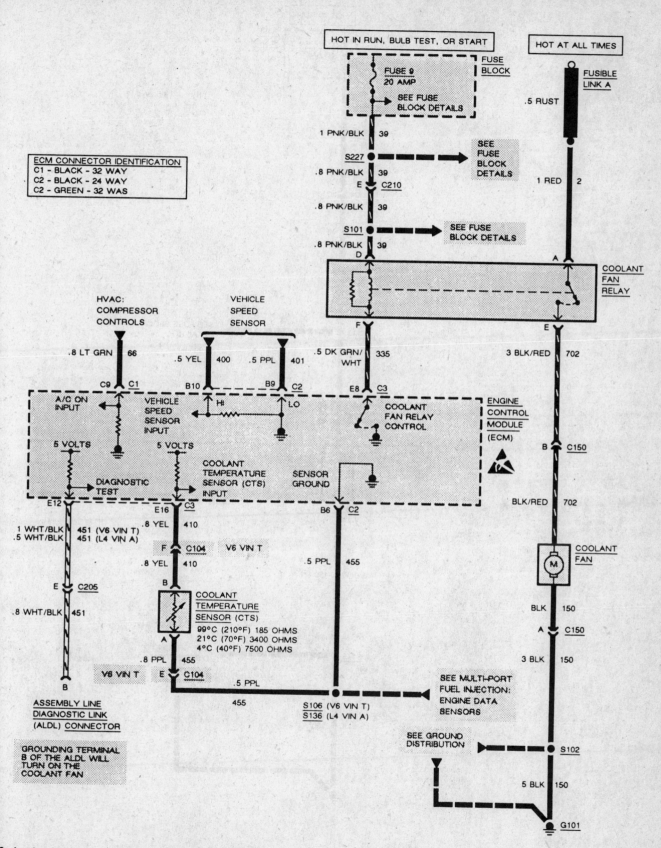

Coolant fan, 2.3L and 3.1L engines-1992 Corsica and Beretta

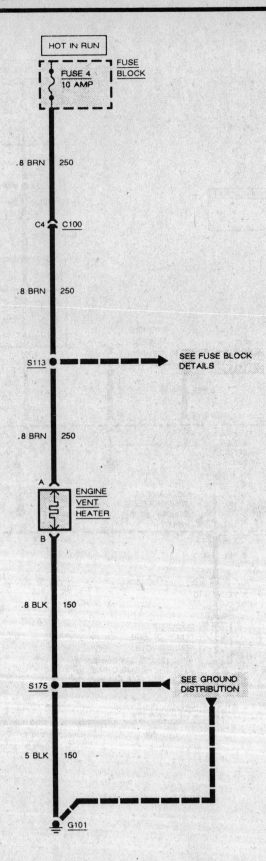

HOT IN RUN

FUSE 4
10 AMP

FUSE
BLOCK

.8 BRN | 250

C4 | C100

.8 BRN | 250

S113 → SEE FUSE BLOCK DETAILS

.8 BRN | 250

A

ENGINE
VENT
HEATER

B

.8 BLK | 150

S175 → SEE GROUND DISTRIBUTION

5 BLK | 150

G101

Engine vent heater-1992 Corsica and Beretta

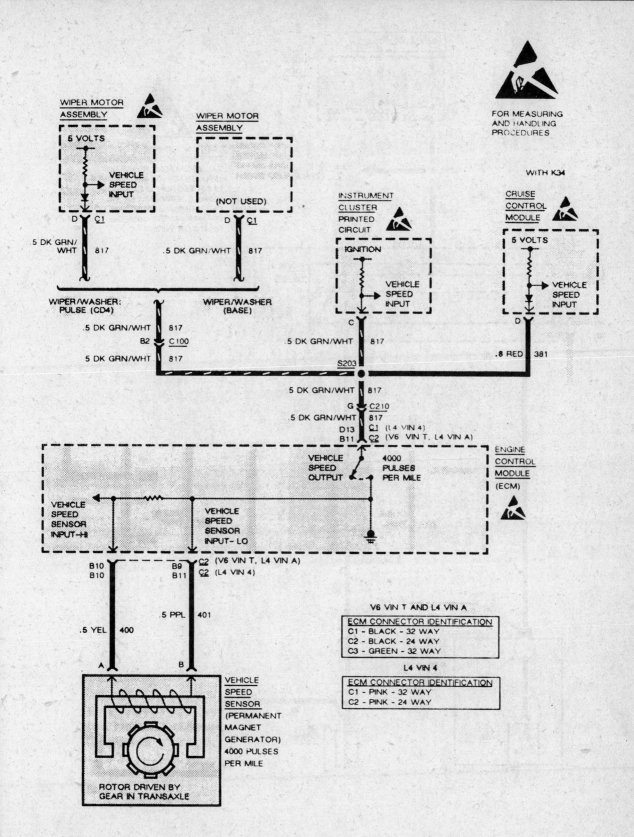

Vehicle speed sensor: Permanant Magnet Generator-1992 Corsica and Beretta

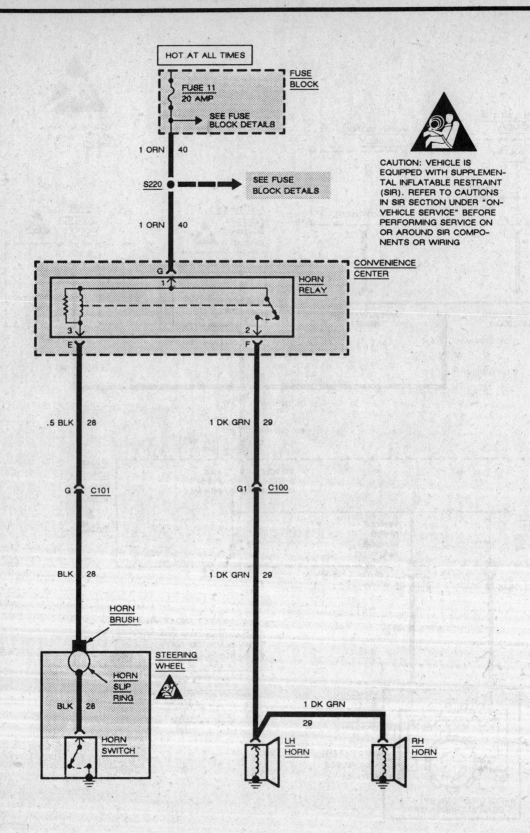

Horns-1992 Corsica and Beretta

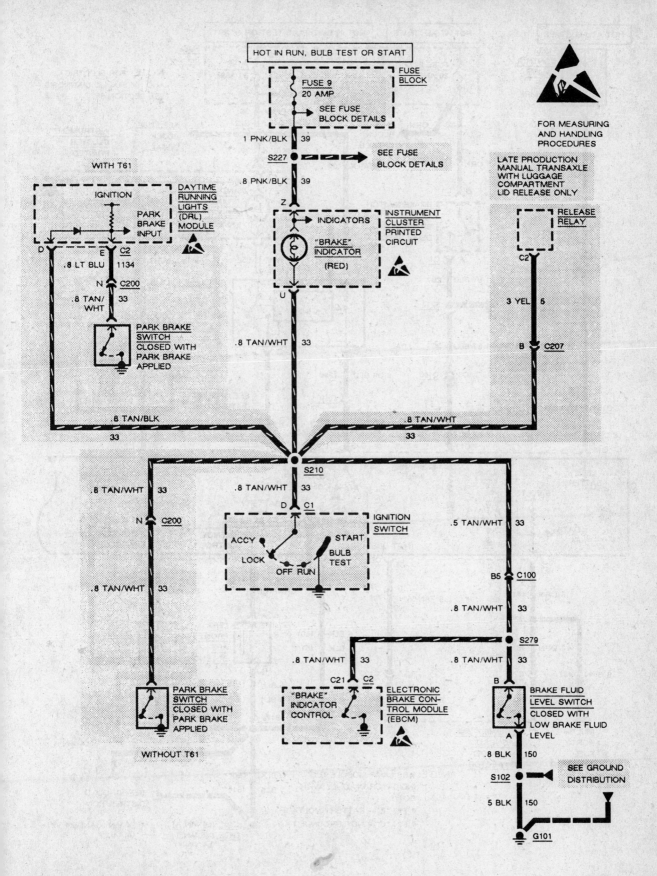

Brake warning system-1992 Corsica and Beretta

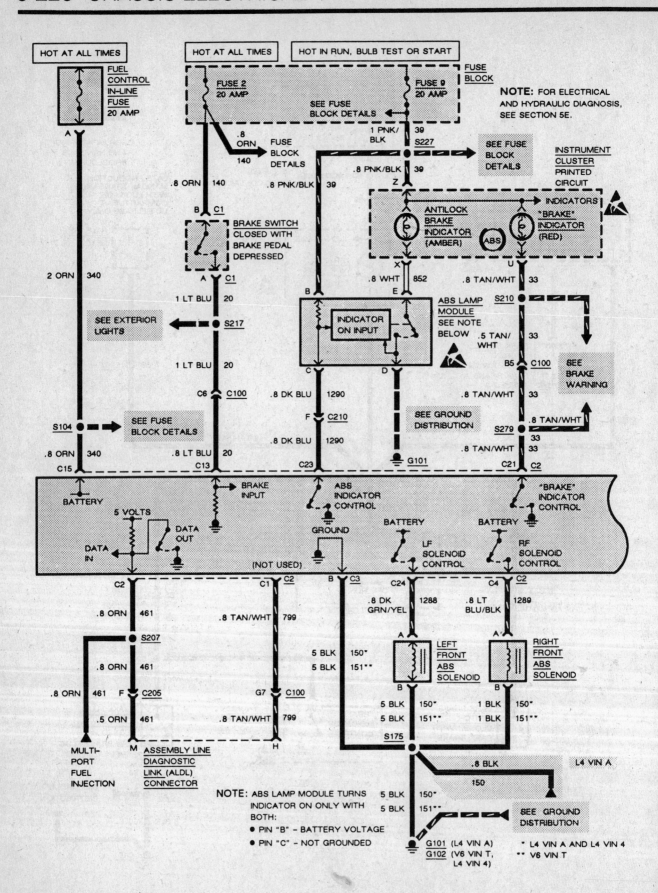

Anti-lock brake-1992 Corsica and Beretta

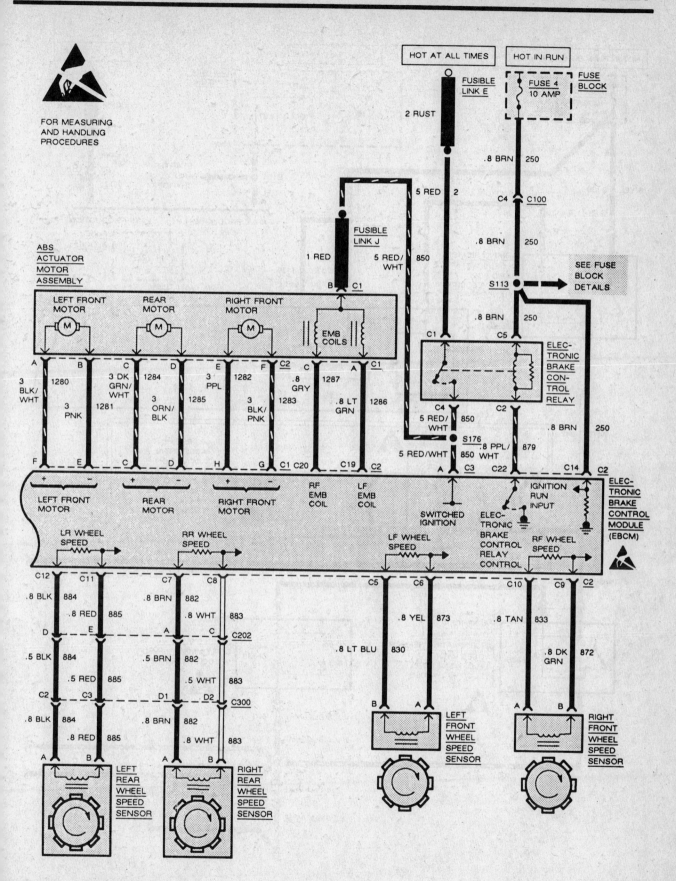

FOR MEASURING
AND HANDLING
PROCEDURES

Anti-lock brake (cont.)-1992 Corsica and Beretta

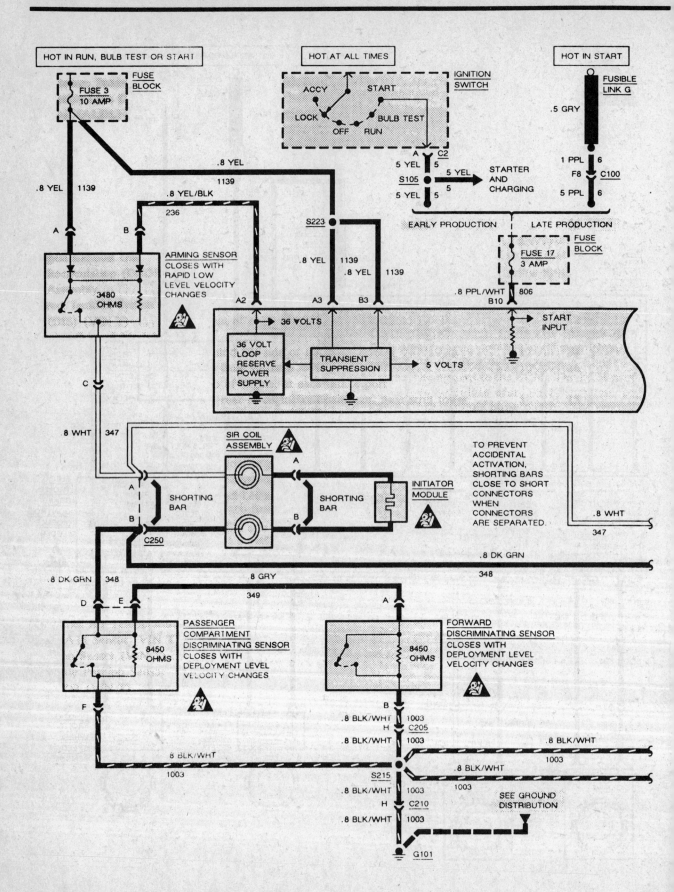

Supplemental inflatable restraint system-1992 Corsica and Beretta

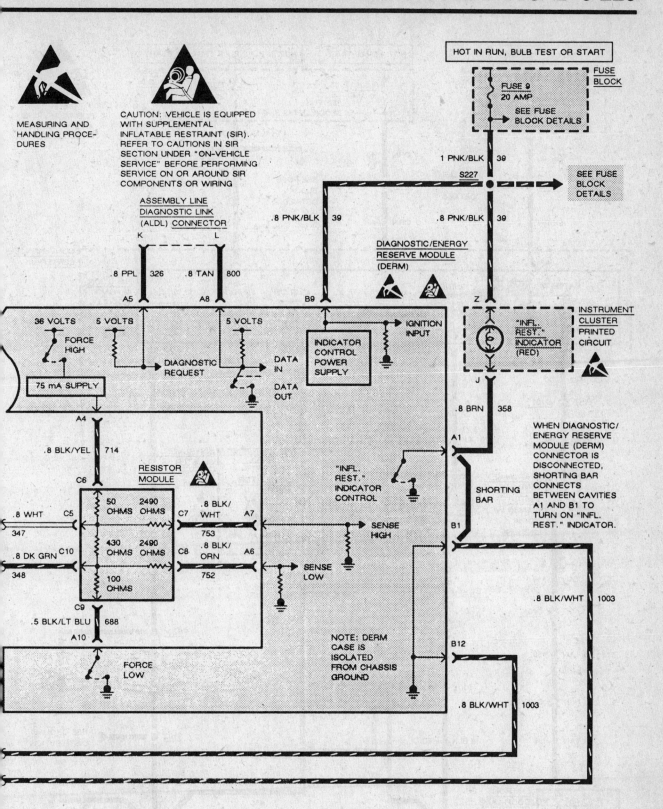

MEASURING AND HANDLING PROCE-DURES

CAUTION: VEHICLE IS EQUIPPED WITH SUPPLEMENTAL INFLATABLE RESTRAINT (SIR). REFER TO CAUTIONS IN SIR SECTION UNDER "ON-VEHICLE SERVICE" BEFORE PERFORMING SERVICE ON OR AROUND SIR COMPONENTS OR WIRING

HOT IN RUN, BULB TEST OR START

FUSE BLOCK

FUSE 9 20 AMP

SEE FUSE BLOCK DETAILS

1 PNK/BLK 39

S227

SEE FUSE BLOCK DETAILS

.8 PNK/BLK 39

.8 PNK/BLK 39

ASSEMBLY LINE DIAGNOSTIC LINK (ALDL) CONNECTOR

K   L

.8 PPL 326   .8 TAN 800

DIAGNOSTIC/ENERGY RESERVE MODULE (DERM)

A5   A8   B9   Z

36 VOLTS   5 VOLTS   5 VOLTS

FORCE HIGH

75 mA SUPPLY

DIAGNOSTIC REQUEST

DATA IN

DATA OUT

INDICATOR CONTROL POWER SUPPLY

IGNITION INPUT

"INFL. REST." INDICATOR (RED)

INSTRUMENT CLUSTER PRINTED CIRCUIT

J

A4

.8 BLK/YEL 714

.8 BRN 358

A1

WHEN DIAGNOSTIC/ ENERGY RESERVE MODULE (DERM) CONNECTOR IS DISCONNECTED, SHORTING BAR CONNECTS BETWEEN CAVITIES A1 AND B1 TO TURN ON "INFL. REST." INDICATOR.

C6

RESISTOR MODULE

SHORTING BAR

.8 WHT   C5   50 OHMS   2490 OHMS   C7   .8 BLK/ WHT   A7
347   753

SENSE HIGH

B1

.8 DK GRN   C10   430 OHMS   2490 OHMS   C8   .8 BLK/ ORN   A6
348   752

SENSE LOW

"INFL. REST." INDICATOR CONTROL

100 OHMS

C9

.5 BLK/LT BLU 688

.8 BLK/WHT 1003

A10

FORCE LOW

NOTE: DERM CASE IS ISOLATED FROM CHASSIS GROUND

B12

.8 BLK/WHT 1003

upplemental inflatable restraint system cont.-1992 Corsica and Beretta

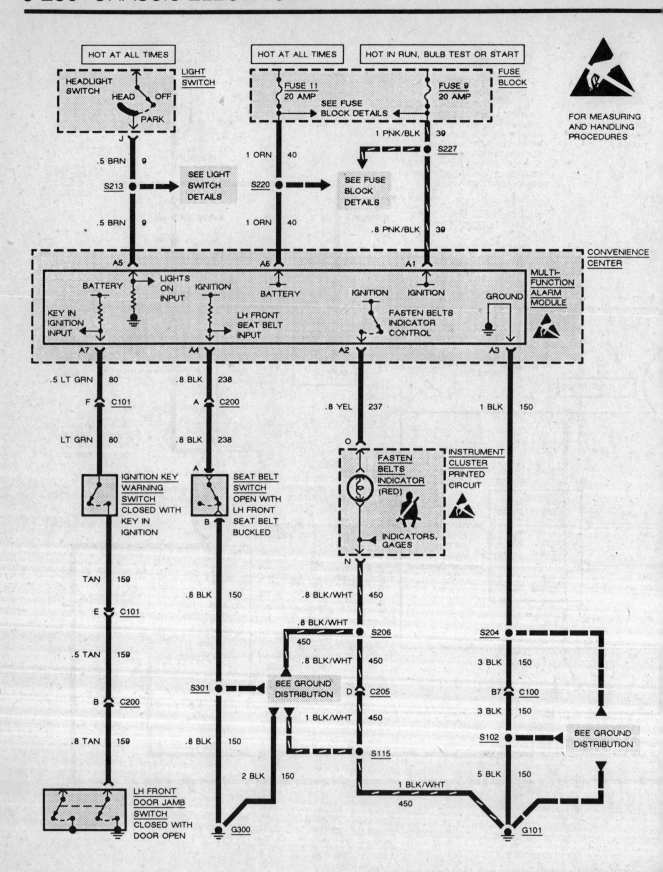

Warnings and alarms: (chime)-1992 Corsica and Beretta

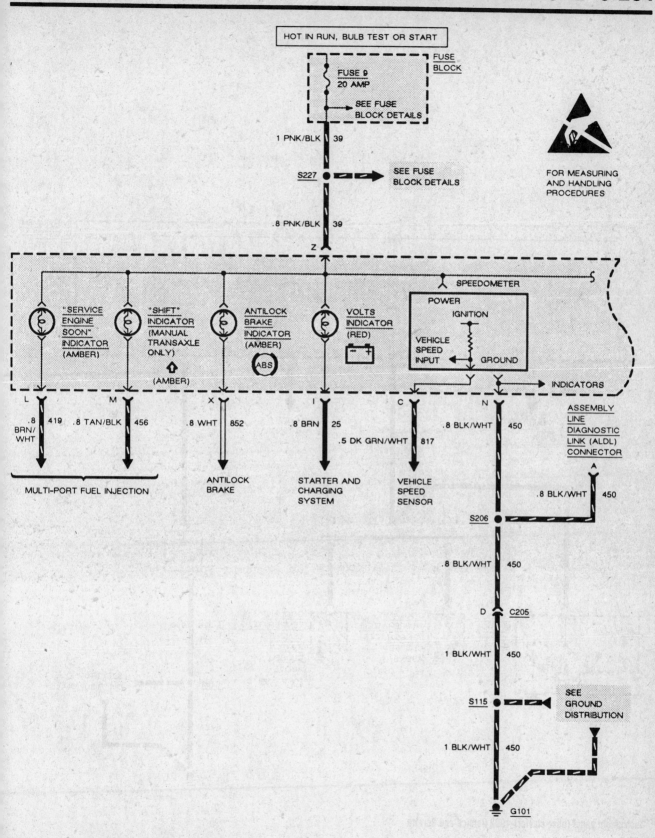

Instrument panel (base cluster)-1992 Corsica and Beretta

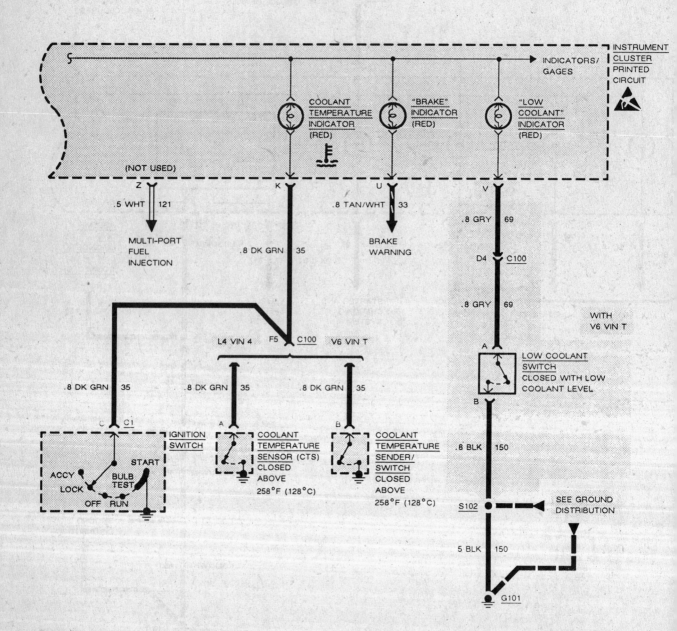

Instrument panel (base cluster)-1992 Corsica and Beretta

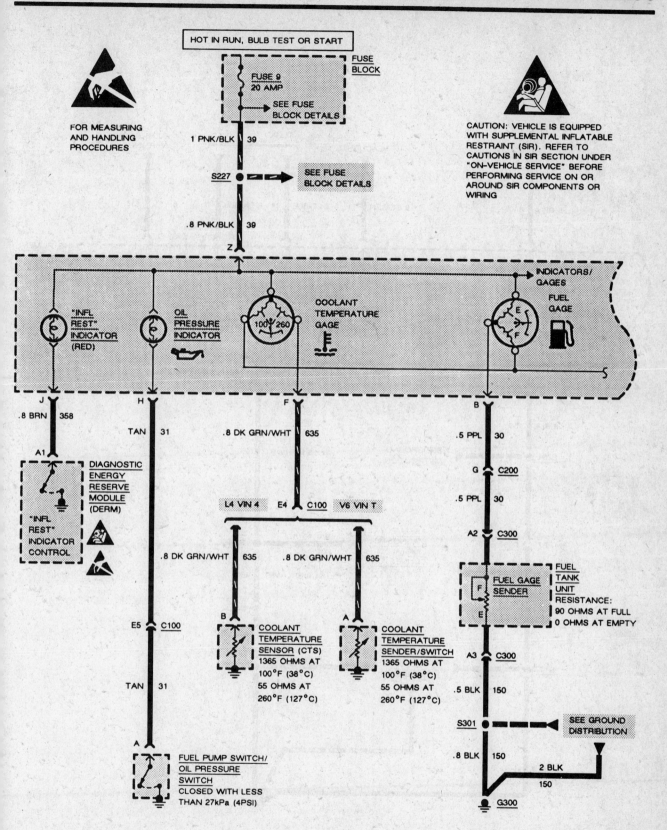

HOT IN RUN, BULB TEST OR START

FOR MEASURING
AND HANDLING
PROCEDURES

FUSE
BLOCK

FUSE 9
20 AMP

SEE FUSE
BLOCK DETAILS

CAUTION: VEHICLE IS EQUIPPED
WITH SUPPLEMENTAL INFLATABLE
RESTRAINT (SIR). REFER TO
CAUTIONS IN SIR SECTION UNDER
"ON-VEHICLE SERVICE" BEFORE
PERFORMING SERVICE ON OR
AROUND SIR COMPONENTS OR
WIRING

1 PNK/BLK   39

S227   SEE FUSE
BLOCK DETAILS

.8 PNK/BLK   39

Z

INDICATORS/
GAGES

"INFL
REST"
INDICATOR
(RED)

OIL
PRESSURE
INDICATOR

COOLANT
TEMPERATURE
GAGE
100   260

FUEL
GAGE
E
F

J   H   F   B

.8 BRN   358   TAN   31   .8 DK GRN/WHT   635   .5 PPL   30

A1   G   C200

DIAGNOSTIC
ENERGY
RESERVE
MODULE
(DERM)   .5 PPL   30

L4 VIN 4   E4   C100   V6 VIN T   A2   C300

"INFL
REST"
INDICATOR
CONTROL

.8 DK GRN/WHT   635   .8 DK GRN/WHT   635

FUEL
GAGE
SENDER

FUEL
TANK
UNIT
RESISTANCE:
90 OHMS AT FULL
0 OHMS AT EMPTY

E5   C100

B   A

COOLANT
TEMPERATURE
SENDER (CTS)
1365 OHMS AT
100°F (38°C)
55 OHMS AT
260°F (127°C)

COOLANT
TEMPERATURE
SENDER/SWITCH
1365 OHMS AT
100°F (38°C)
55 OHMS AT
260°F (127°C)

A3   C300

.5 BLK   150

TAN   31

S301   SEE GROUND
DISTRIBUTION

.8 BLK   150

A
FUEL PUMP SWITCH/
OIL PRESSURE
SWITCH
CLOSED WITH LESS
THAN 27kPa (4PSI)

2 BLK
150

G300

Instrument panel (base cluster)-1992 Corsica and Beretta

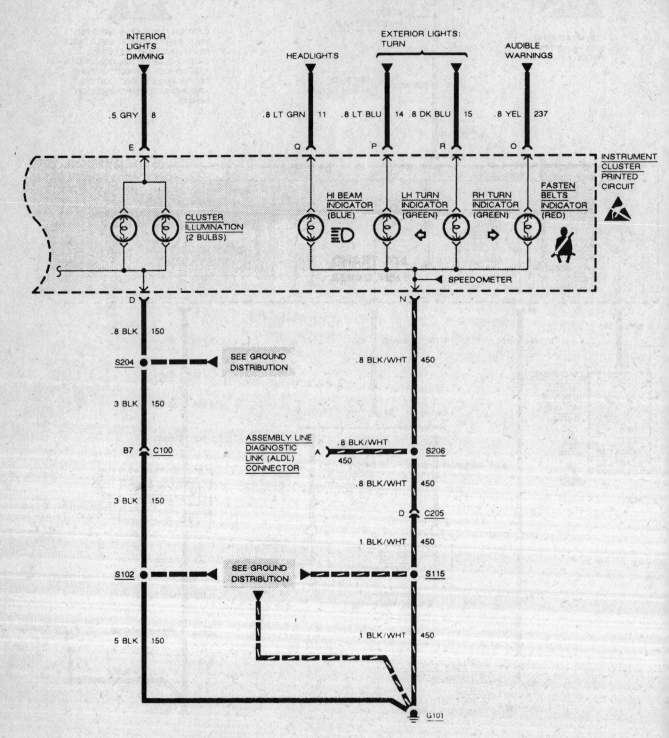

Instrument panel (base cluster)-1992 Corsica and Beretta

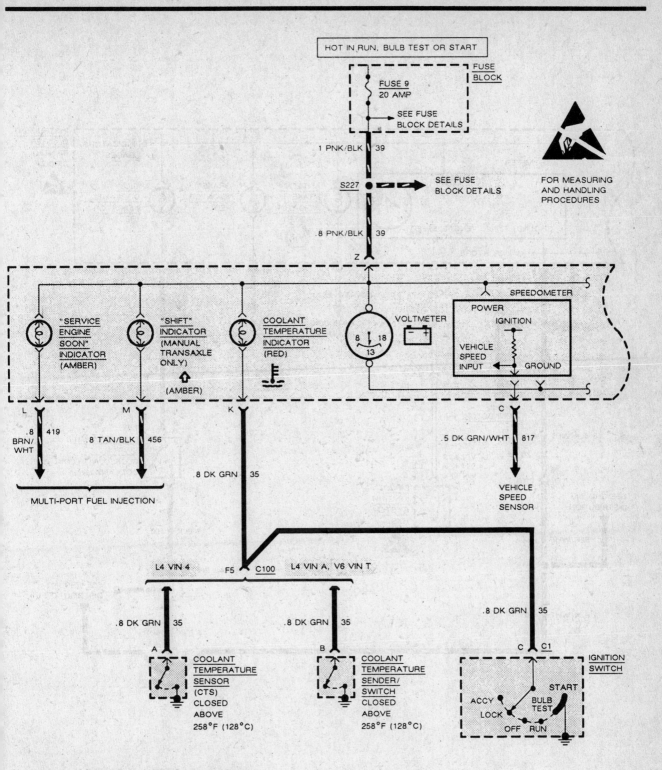

HOT IN RUN, BULB TEST OR START

FUSE BLOCK

FUSE 9
20 AMP

SEE FUSE BLOCK DETAILS

1 PNK/BLK 39

S227 → SEE FUSE BLOCK DETAILS

FOR MEASURING AND HANDLING PROCEDURES

.8 PNK/BLK 39

Z

"SERVICE ENGINE SOON" INDICATOR (AMBER)

"SHIFT" INDICATOR (MANUAL TRANSAXLE ONLY) (AMBER)

COOLANT TEMPERATURE INDICATOR (RED)

VOLTMETER

8 18
13

SPEEDOMETER

POWER
IGNITION
VEHICLE SPEED INPUT
GROUND

L
M
K
C

.8 BRN/WHT 419

.8 TAN/BLK 456

.8 DK GRN 35

.5 DK GRN/WHT 817

MULTI-PORT FUEL INJECTION

VEHICLE SPEED SENSOR

L4 VIN 4
F5
C100
L4 VIN A, V6 VIN T

.8 DK GRN 35

.8 DK GRN 35

.8 DK GRN 35

A
COOLANT TEMPERATURE SENSOR (CTS) CLOSED ABOVE 258°F (128°C)

B
COOLANT TEMPERATURE SENDER/SWITCH CLOSED ABOVE 258°F (128°C)

C C1
IGNITION SWITCH

ACCY
LOCK
OFF RUN
BULB TEST
START

Instrument panel (gages cluster)-1992 Corsica and Beretta

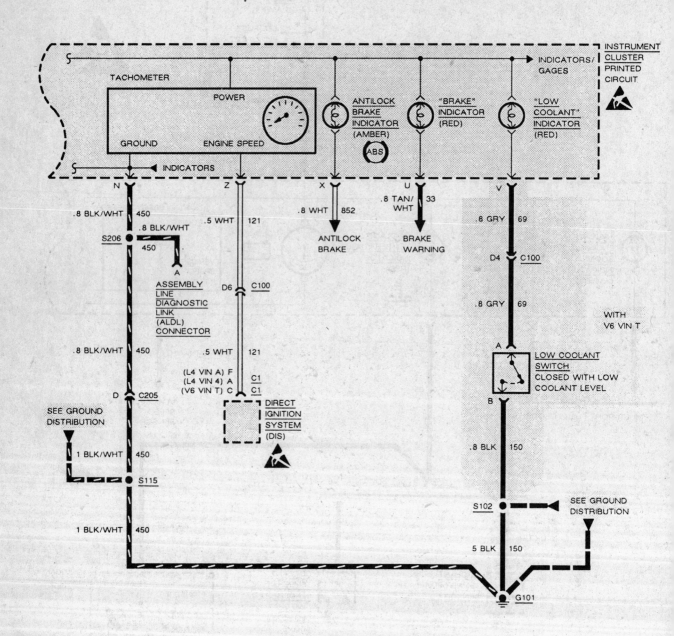

Instrument panel (gages cluster)-1992 Corsica and Beretta

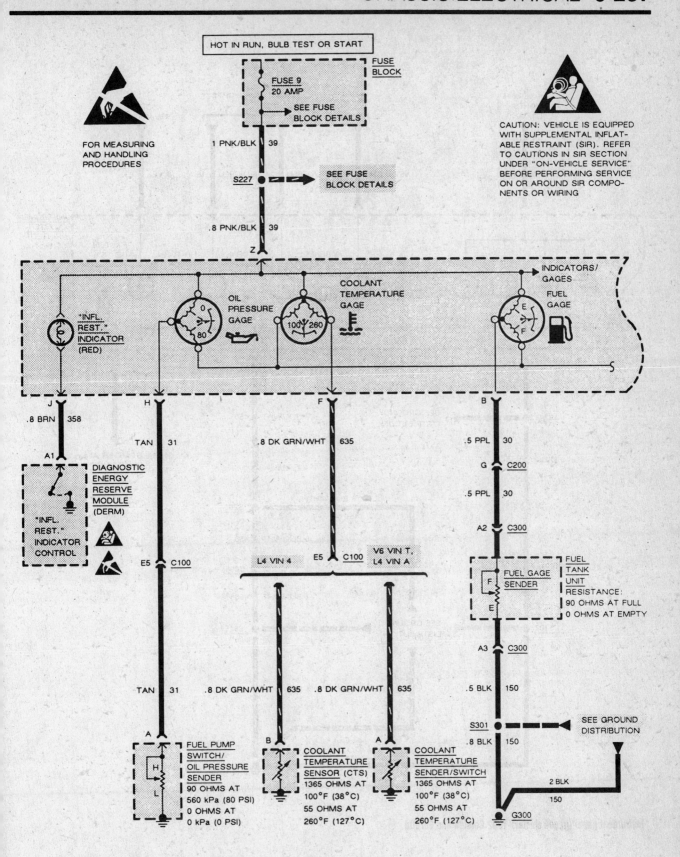

Instrument panel (gages cluster)-1992 Corsica and Beretta

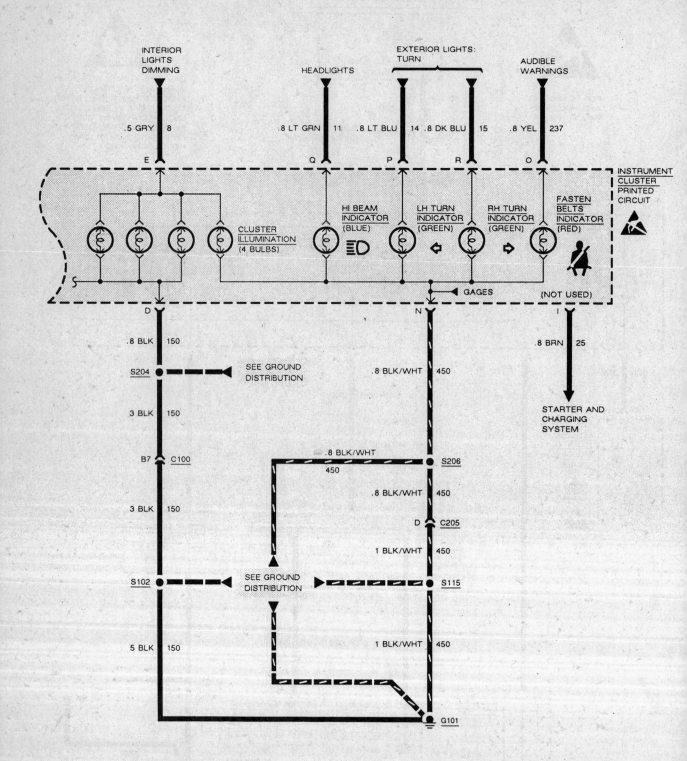

Instrument panel (gages cluster)-1992 Corsica and Beretta

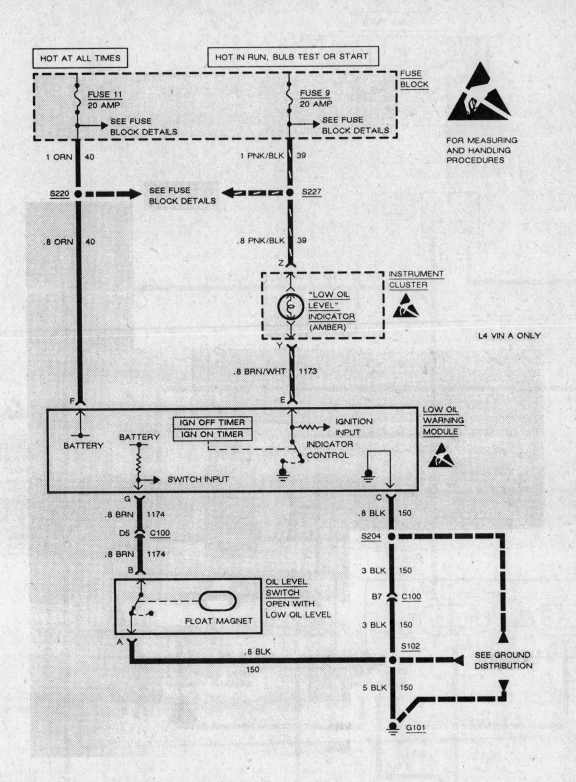

Instrument panel (gages cluster)-1992 Corsica and Beretta

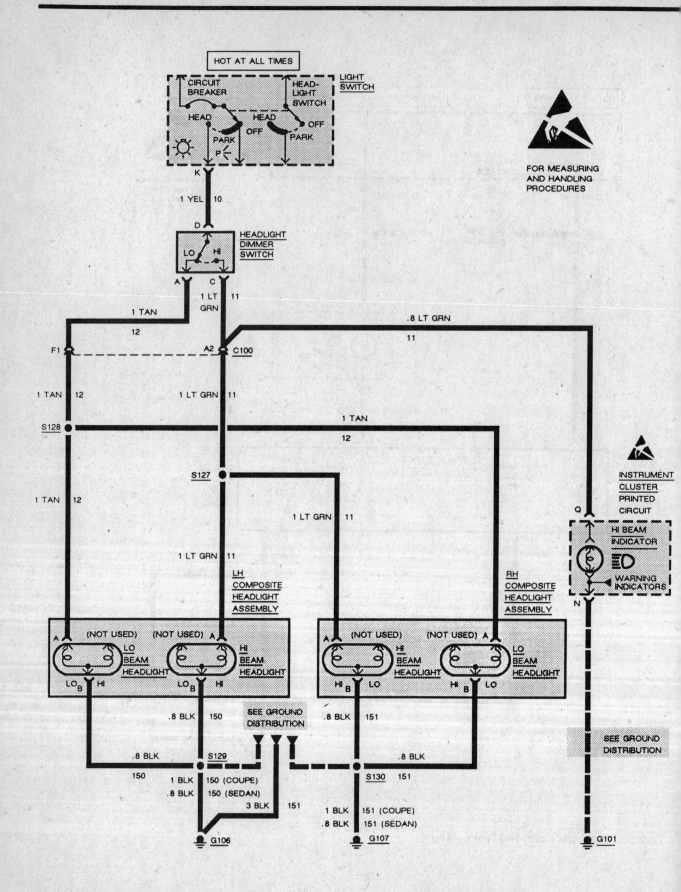

Headlights (without fog lights)-1992 Corsica and Beretta

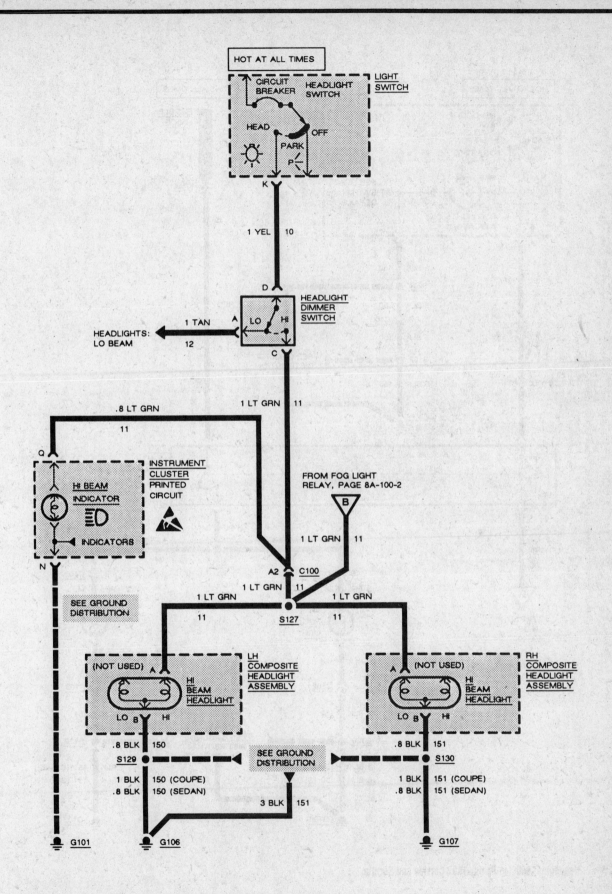

Headlights (with fog lights)-1992 Corsica and Beretta

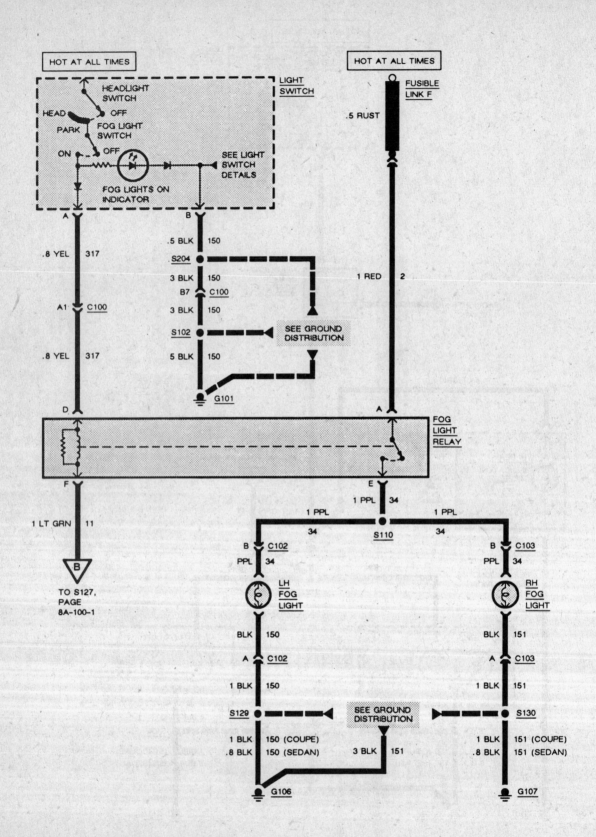

Headlights (with fog lights)-1992 Corsica and Beretta

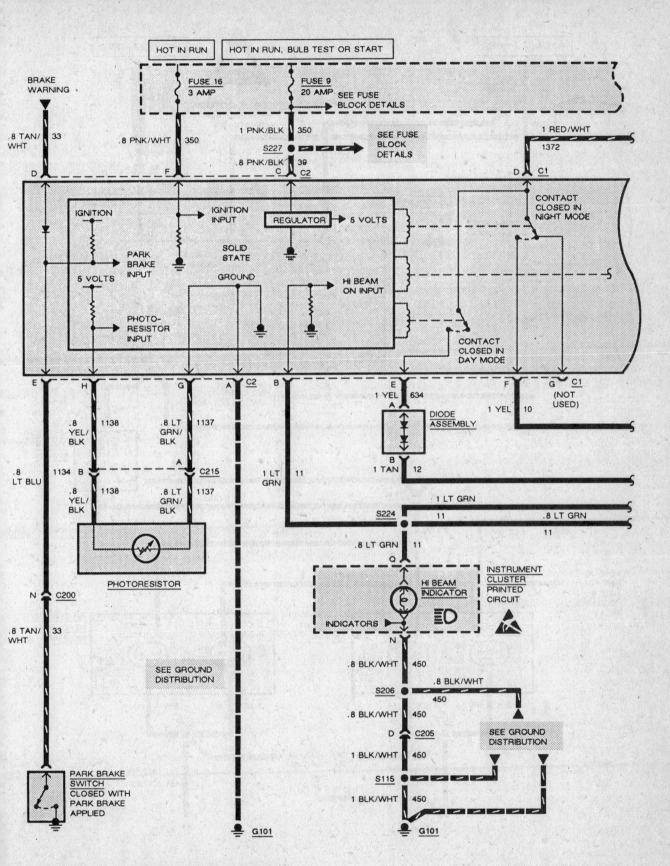

Headlights (with daytime running lights)-1992 Corsica and Beretta

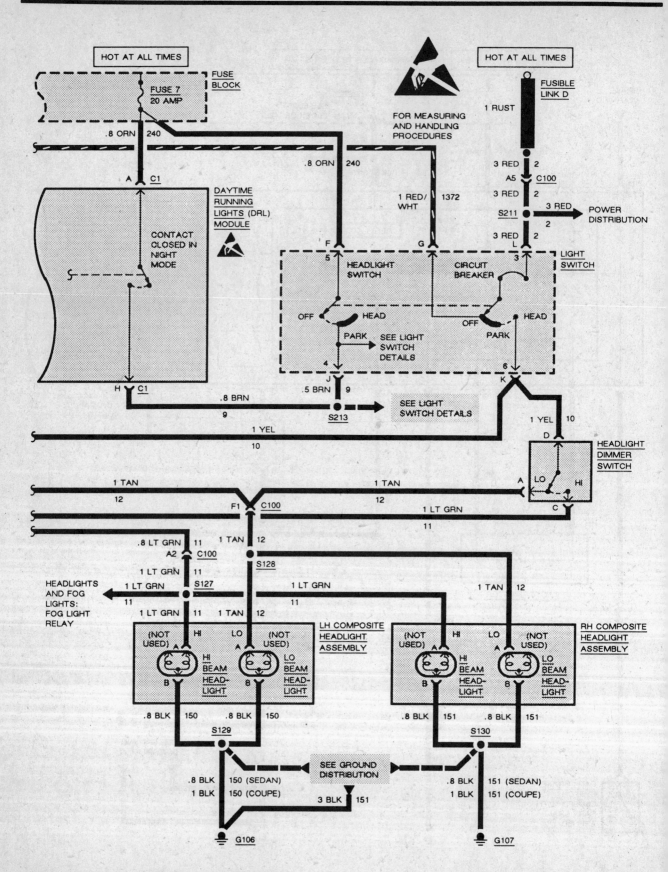

Headlights (with daytime running lights)-1992 Corsica and Beretta

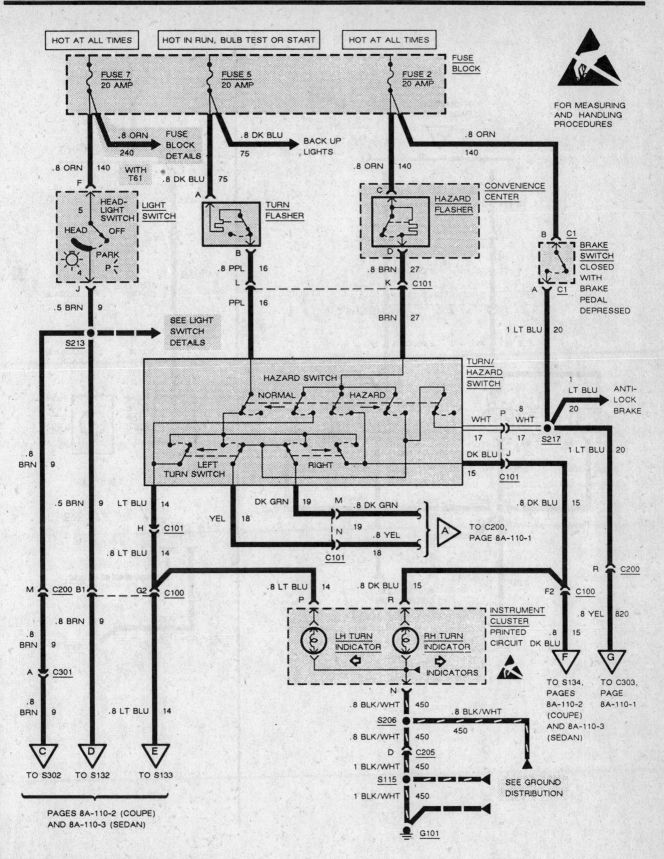

Exterior lights: (hazard)-1992 Corsica and Beretta

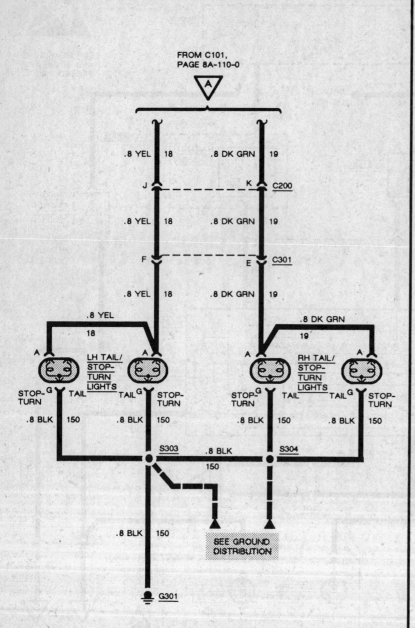

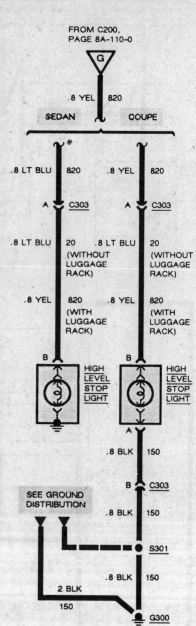

Exterior lights: (Stop-turn/high level stop)-1992 Corsica and Beretta

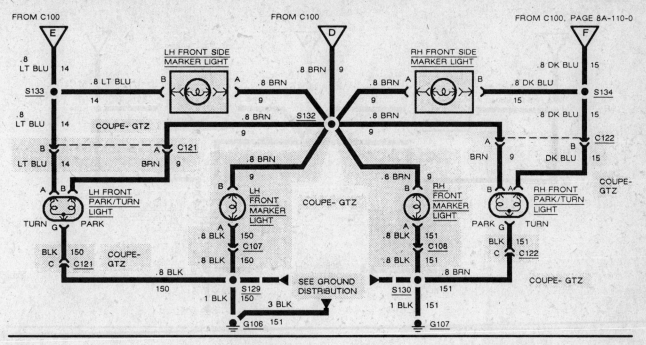

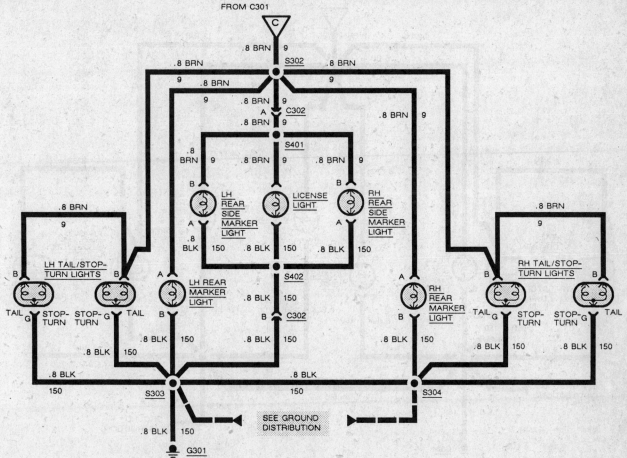

Exterior lights: (Park/tail/marker/license/turn) (coupe-1992 Corsica and Beretta)

SEDAN

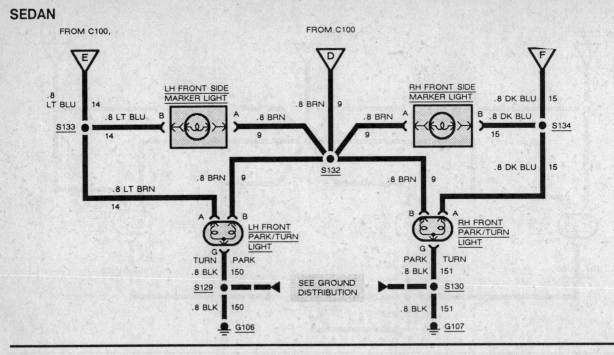

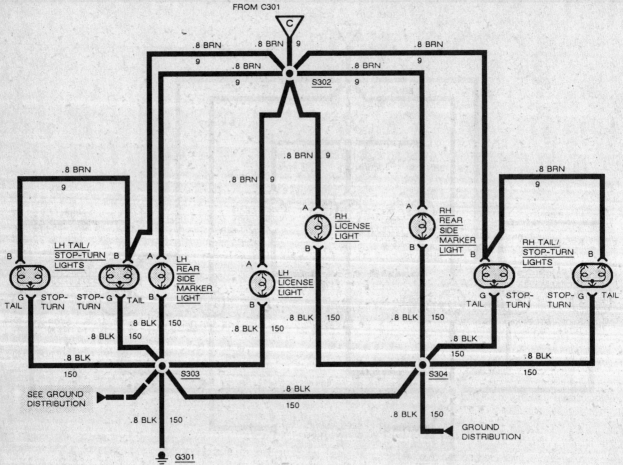

Exterior lights: (Park/tail/marker/license/turn) (sedan-1992 Corsica and Beretta)

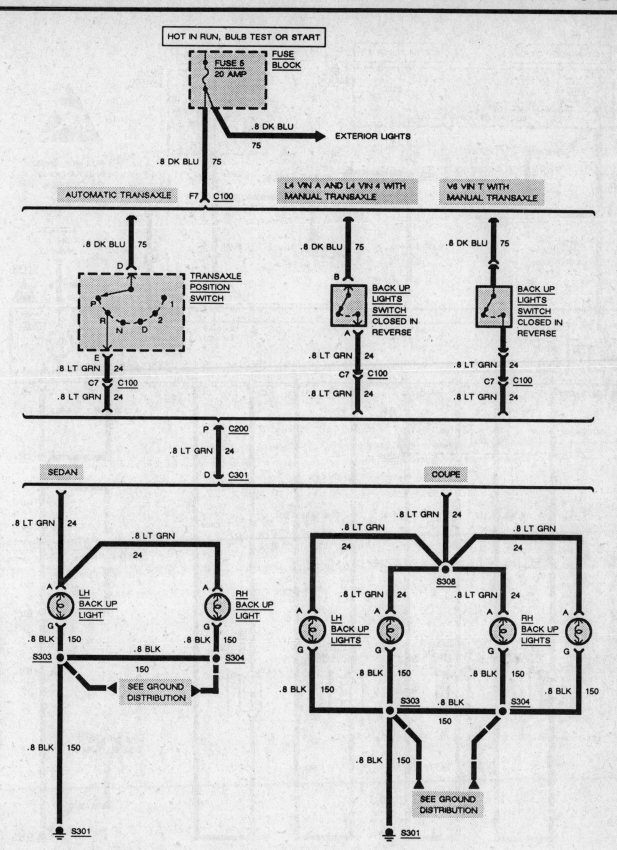

Backup lights-1992 Corsica and Beretta

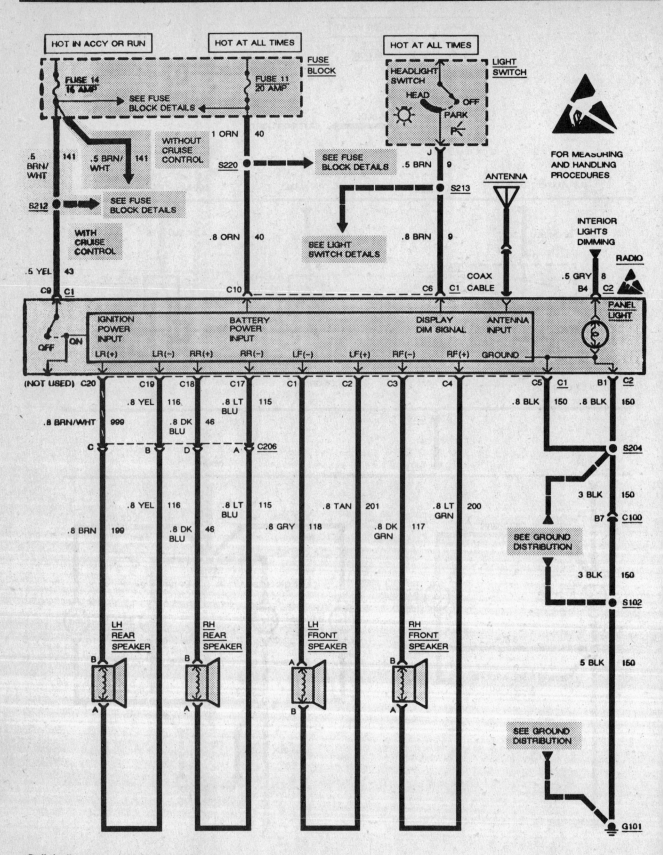

Radio/audio systems-1992 Corsica and Beretta

7

DRIVE
TRAIN

MANUAL TRANSAXLE

Understanding the Transaxle

Because of the way an internal combustion engine breathes, it can produce torque, or twisting force, only within a narrow speed range. Most modern, overhead valve engines must turn at about 2,500 rpm to produce their peak torque. By 4,500 rpm they are producing so little torque that continued increases in engine speed produce no power increases.

The torque peak on overhead camshaft engines is, generally, much higher, but much narrower.

The manual transmission and clutch are employed to vary the relationship between engine speed and the speed of the wheels so that adequate engine power can be produced under all circumstances. The clutch allows engine torque to be applied to the transmission input shaft gradually, due to mechanical slippage. The car can, consequently, be started smoothly from a full stop.

The transmission changes the ratio between the rotating speeds of the engine and the wheels by the use of gears. 4-speed or 5-speed transmissions are most common. The lower gears allow full engine power to be applied to the wheels during acceleration at low speeds.

The transmission contains a mainshaft which passes all the way through the transmission, from the clutch to the halfshafts. This shaft is separated at 1 point, so that front and rear portions can turn at different speeds.

Power is transmitted by a countershaft in the lower gears and reverse. The gears of the countershaft mesh with gears on the mainshaft, allowing power to be carried from one to the other. All the countershaft gears are integral with that shaft, while several of the mainshaft gears can either rotate independently of the shaft or be locked to it. Shifting from one gear to the next causes one of the gears to be freed from rotating with the shaft and locks another to it. Gears are locked and unlocked by internal dog clutches which slide between the center of the gear and the shaft. The forward gears usually employ synchronizers; friction members which smoothly bring gear and shaft to the same speed before the toothed dog clutches are engaged.

The clutch is operating properly if:

1. It will stall the engine when released with the vehicle held stationary.

2. The shift lever can be moved freely between 1st and reverse gears when the vehicle is stationary and the clutch disengaged.

A clutch pedal free-play adjustment is incorporated in the linkage. If there is about 1–2 in. (25–50mm) of motion before the pedal begins to release the clutch, it is adjusted properly. Inadequate free-play wears all parts of the clutch releasing mechanisms and may cause slippage. Excessive free-play may cause inadequate release and hard shifting of gears.

Some clutches use a hydraulic system in place of mechanical linkage. If the clutch fails to release, fill the clutch master cylinder with fluid to the proper level and pump the clutch pedal to fill the system with fluid. Bleed the system in the same way as a brake system. If leaks are located, tighten loose connections or overhaul the master or slave cylinder as necessary.

Front wheel drive cars do not have conventional rear axles or driveshafts. Instead, power is transmitted from the engine to a transaxle, or a combination of transmission and drive axle, in one unit. Both the transmission and drive axle accomplish the same function as their counterparts in a front engine/rear drive axle design. The difference is in the location of the components.

In place of a conventional driveshaft, a front wheel drive design uses 2 driveshafts, sometimes called halfshafts, which couple the drive axle portion of the transaxle to the wheels. Universal joints or constant velocity joints are used just as they would in a rear wheel drive design.

Linkage Adjustment

No adjustments are possible on the manual transaxle shifting cables or linkage. If the

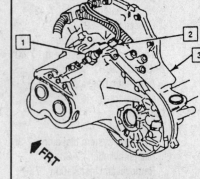

1. Back-up light switch
2. Connector
3. Transaxle

FIG. 1 Back-up light switch — except Isuzu transaxle

transaxle is not engaging completely, check for stretched cables or broken shifter components or a faulty transaxle.

Back-Up Light Switch

REMOVAL & INSTALLATION

▶ SEE FIG. 1-2

The switch is located in the top of the transaxle case accessible in the engine compartment.

1. Disconnect the negative battery cable.
2. Unplug the switch harness.
3. Unscrew the switch.

To install:

4. Use pipe sealant on the threads and tighten

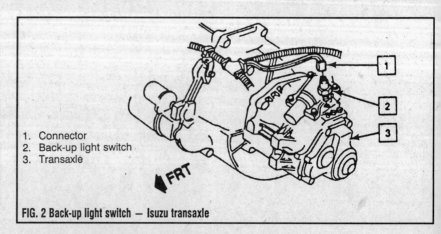

1. Connector
2. Back-up light switch
3. Transaxle

FIG. 2 Back-up light switch — Isuzu transaxle

• 6 ft. lbs. Tighten the switch to 84 inch lbs. (9 Nm) for 1988–90 and to 24 ft. lbs. (33 Nm) for 1991–92.

5. Install the back-up lamp connector.

6. Connect the negative battery cable.

Manual Transaxle

REMOVAL & INSTALLATION

► **Before performing any maintenance that requires the removal of the slave cylinder, transaxle or clutch housing, the clutch master cylinder push rod must first be disconnected from the clutch pedal. Failure to disconnect the push rod will result in permanent damage to the slave cylinder if the clutch pedal is depressed with the slave cylinder disconnected.**

Except Isuzu Transaxle

SEE FIGS. 3-20

1. Disconnect the negative terminal from the battery.

2. Using the Engine Support Fixture tool No. J–28467 or equivalent and Adapter tool No. J–35953 or equivalent, install them on the engine and raise the engine enough to take the engine weight off of the engine mounts.

3. Remove the left side sound insulator.

4. Disconnect the clutch master cylinder push rod from the clutch pedal.

5. Remove the air cleaner and duct assembly.

6. Disconnect the clutch slave cylinder-to-transaxle support bolts and position the cylinder aside.

7. Remove the transaxle-to-mount through bolt.

8. Raise and support the front of the vehicle.

9. Remove the 2 exhaust crossover bolts at the right side manifold.

10. Lower the vehicle. Remove the left side exhaust manifold.

11. Disconnect the transaxle mounting bracket.

12. Disconnect the shifter cables.

13. Remove the upper transaxle-to-engine bolts.

14. Raise and support the front of the vehicle.

15. Remove the left front tire assembly and the left side inner splash shield.

16. Remove the transaxle strut and bracket.

17. Place a drain pan under the transaxle, remove the drain plug and drain the fluid from the transaxle.

18. Remove the clutch housing cover bolts.

19. Disconnect the speedometer wire.

20. From the left suspension support and control arm, disconnect the stabilizer shaft.

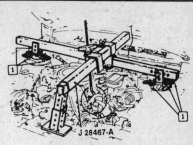

1. Thread onto strut attaching bolts above nuts-3 per side

FIG. 4 FIG. Installation of the engine support tool — 1988–92 with 2.0L and 2.2L engines

21. Remove the left suspension support mounting bolts and move the support aside.

22. Disconnect both halfshafts from the transaxle and remove the left halfshaft from the vehicle.

23. Using a transmission jack, attach it to and support the transaxle.

24. Remove the remaining transaxle-to-engine bolts.

25. Slide the transaxle away from the engine, lower it and remove the right side halfshaft.

To Install:

1. When installing, guide the right side halfshaft into the transaxle while it is being installed in the vehicle.

2. Torque the transaxle-to-engine bolts to 60 ft. lbs., the transaxle mount-to-body bolt to 80 ft. lbs.

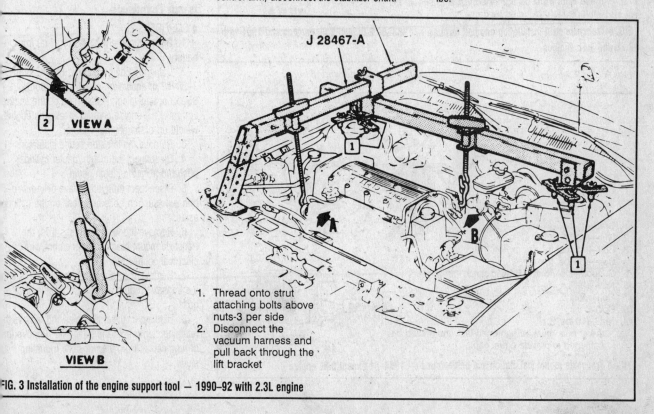

VIEW A

J 28467-A

VIEW B

1. Thread onto strut attaching bolts above nuts-3 per side
2. Disconnect the vacuum harness and pull back through the lift bracket

FIG. 3 Installation of the engine support tool — 1990–92 with 2.3L engine

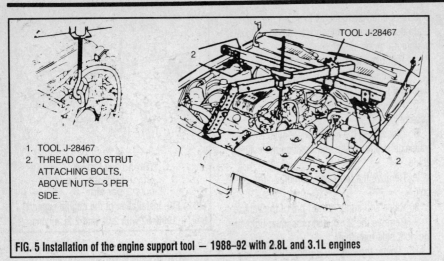

1. TOOL J-28467
2. THREAD ONTO STRUT ATTACHING BOLTS, ABOVE NUTS—3 PER SIDE.

FIG. 5 Installation of the engine support tool — 1988–92 with 2.8L and 3.1L engines

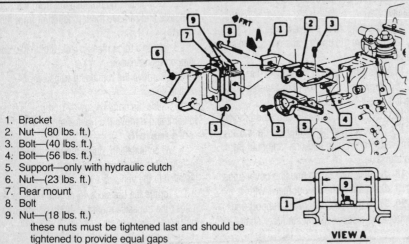

1. Bracket
2. Nut—(80 lbs. ft.)
3. Bolt—(40 lbs. ft.)
4. Bolt—(56 lbs. ft.)
5. Support—only with hydraulic clutch
6. Nut—(23 lbs. ft.)
7. Rear mount
8. Bolt
9. Nut—(18 lbs. ft.)
    these nuts must be tightened last and should be tightened to provide equal gaps

FIG. 6 Transaxle strut installation and bolt torques — 1988–89 2.0L and 2.8L engines and 1991 with 2.2L and 3.1L engines

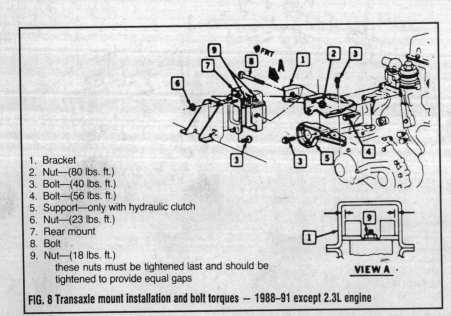

1. Bracket
2. Nut—(80 lbs. ft.)
3. Bolt—(40 lbs. ft.)
4. Bolt—(56 lbs. ft.)
5. Support—only with hydraulic clutch
6. Nut—(23 lbs. ft.)
7. Rear mount
8. Bolt
9. Nut—(18 lbs. ft.)
    these nuts must be tightened last and should be tightened to provide equal gaps

FIG. 8 Transaxle mount installation and bolt torques — 1988–91 except 2.3L engine

3. Install the left halfshaft into its bore at the transaxle then seat both halfshafts at the transaxle.

4. Install the left suspension support mounting bolts.

5. Connect the stabilizer shaft to the left suspension support and control arm.

6. Connect the speedometer wire.

7. Connect the clutch housing cover bolts.

8. Install the transaxle strut and bracket.

9. Install the left front tire assembly and the left side inner splash shield.

10. Lower the car.

11. Install the upper transaxle to engine bolts and torque to 55 ft. lbs. (75 Nm).

12. Install the shift cables.

13. Install the transaxle mount bracket and torque to the specifications illustrated.

14. Install the L.H. exhaust manifold.

15. Raise the car and install the exhaust crossover bolts at the R.H. manifold.

16. Lower the car.

17. Install the transaxle mount thru bolt and torque to the specifications illustrated.

18. Install the clutch slave cylinder to the support bracket.

19. Install the air cleaner and the air intake duct assembly.

20. Remove the engine support fixture.

21. Connect the clutch master cylinder push rod to the clutch pedal.

22. Install the left side sound insulator.

23. Install the negative battery cable.

Isuzu Transaxle

▶ SEE FIGS. 3-20

1. Disconnect the negative terminal from the battery.

2. Using the Engine Support Fixture tool No. J–28467 or equivalent and Adapter tool No. J–35953 or equivalent, install them on the engine and raise the engine enough to take the engine weight off of the engine mounts.

3. Remove the left side sound insulator.

4. Disconnect the clutch master cylinder push rod from the clutch pedal.

5. Disconnect the clutch slave cylinder-to-transaxle support bolts and position the cylinder aside.

6. Remove the wiring harness from the transaxle mount bracket and the shift wire electrical connector.

7. Remove the transaxle-to-mount bolts and the transaxle mount bracket-to-chassis nuts/bolts.

8. Disconnect the shift cables and remove the retaining clamp from the transaxle. Remove the ground cables from the transaxle mounting studs.

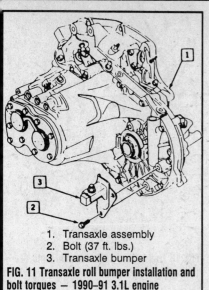

1. Transaxle assembly
2. Bolt (37 ft. lbs.)
3. Transaxle bumper

FIG. 11 Transaxle roll bumper installation and bolt torques — 1990–91 3.1L engine

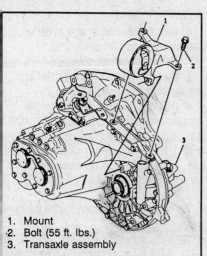

1. Mount
2. Bolt (55 ft. lbs.)
3. Transaxle assembly

FIG. 13 Rear transaxle mount to transaxle installation and bolt torques — 1992 all engines

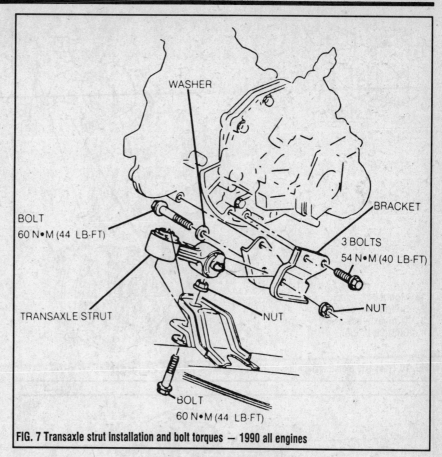

WASHER

BRACKET

BOLT
60 N•M (44 LB·FT)

3 BOLTS
54 N•M (40 LB·FT)

TRANSAXLE STRUT

NUT

NUT

BOLT
60 N•M (44 LB·FT)

FIG. 7 Transaxle strut installation and bolt torques — 1990 all engines

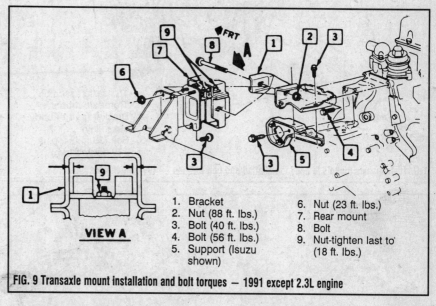

VIEW A

1. Bracket
2. Nut (88 ft. lbs.)
3. Bolt (40 ft. lbs.)
4. Bolt (56 ft. lbs.)
5. Support (Isuzu shown)
6. Nut (23 ft. lbs.)
7. Rear mount
8. Bolt
9. Nut-tighten last to (18 ft. lbs.)

FIG. 9 Transaxle mount installation and bolt torques — 1991 except 2.3L engine

9. Raise and support the front of the vehicle.

10. Remove the left front tire assembly and the left side inner splash shield.

11. Remove the transaxle front strut and bracket.

12. Remove the clutch housing cover bolts. Disconnect the speedometer wire connector.

13. From the left suspension support and control arm, disconnect the stabilizer shaft.

14. Remove the left suspension support mounting bolts and move the support aside.

15. Disconnect both halfshafts from the transaxle and remove the left halfshaft from the vehicle.

16. Place a drain pan under the transaxle, remove the drain plug and drain the fluid from the transaxle.

17. Using a transmission jack, attach it to and support the transaxle.

18. Remove the transaxle-to-engine bolts.

19. Slide the transaxle away from the engine, lower it and remove the right side halfshaft.

To Install:

1. When installing, guide the right side halfshaft into the transaxle while it is being installed in the vehicle.

2. Install and torque the transaxle-to-engine bolts to 55 ft. lbs. (75 Nm)

3. Install the left halfshaft into its bore at the transaxle then seat both halfshafts at the transaxle.

4. Install the left suspension support mounting bolts.

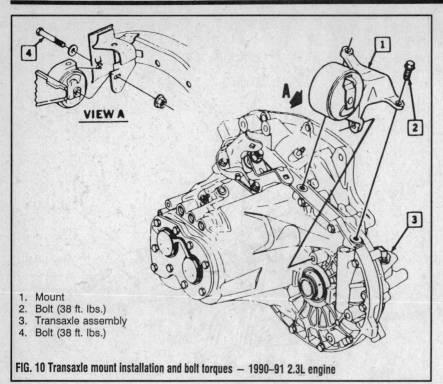

1. Mount
2. Bolt (38 ft. lbs.)
3. Transaxle assembly
4. Bolt (38 ft. lbs.)

FIG. 10 Transaxle mount installation and bolt torques — 1990–91 2.3L engine

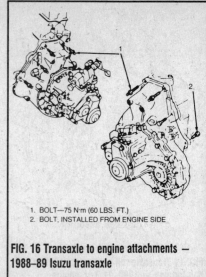

1. BOLT—75 N·m (60 LBS. FT.)
2. BOLT, INSTALLED FROM ENGINE SIDE

FIG. 16 Transaxle to engine attachments — 1988–89 Isuzu transaxle

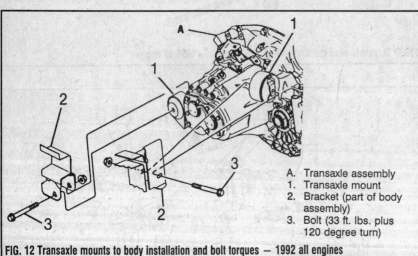

A. Transaxle assembly
1. Transaxle mount
2. Bracket (part of body assembly)
3. Bolt (33 ft. lbs. plus 120 degree turn)

FIG. 12 Transaxle mounts to body installation and bolt torques — 1992 all engines

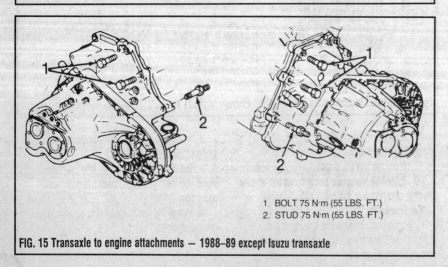

1. BOLT 75 N·m (55 LBS. FT.)
2. STUD 75 N·m (55 LBS. FT.)

FIG. 15 Transaxle to engine attachments — 1988–89 except Isuzu transaxle

5. Connect the stabilizer shaft to the left suspension support and control arm.

6. Connect the speedometer wire.

7. Connect the clutch housing cover bolts and tighten to 89 inch lbs. (10 Nm).

8. Install the transaxle strut and bracket. Torque the transaxle strut to body bolt to 40 ft. lbs. (54 Nm) and the transaxle strut to transaxle to 50 ft. lbs. (68 Nm). See applicable illustration.

9. Install the left front tire assembly and the left side inner splash shield.

10. Lower the car.

11. Install the ground cables at the transaxle mounting studs.

12. Install the wires for the shift light.

13. Install the slave cylinder to the transaxle bracket aligning the push rod into the pocket of the clutch release lever and installing the retaining nuts and tighten evenly.

14. Install the transaxle mount bracket. Tighten the rear mount bracket to transaxle to 40 ft. lbs. (54 Nm). See applicable illustration.

15. Install the transaxle mount to side frame and tighten to 23 ft. lbs. (30 Nm). See applicable illustration.

16. Install the wire harness at the mount bracket.

17. Install the bolt attaching the mount to the transaxle bracket and tighten to 88 ft. lbs. (120 Nm). See applicable illustration.

18. Remove the engine support.

19. Install the shift cables.

20. Connect the negative cable at the battery.

Isuzu 5-Speed Overhaul

♦ SEE FIG. 21-22

Transaxle Case

DISASSEMBLY

1. Remove the clutch release bearing. Attach the transaxle to the transaxle holding fixture tool No. J–33366.

2. Remove the 7 rear cover bolts and the cover.

3. Remove the control box assembly together with the four bolts from the case.

4. Shift the transaxle into gear, then remove the 5th speed drive and the driven gear retaining nuts from the input and the output shaft. Shift the transaxle back into Neutral and aligning the detents on the shift rails.

5. Remove the detent spring retaining bolts for the 1st-2nd, the 3rd-4th and the Reverse-5th speeds. Remove the detent springs and the detent balls. Remove the Reverse detent spring retaining bolts, the spring and the detent.

6. Place the 5th speed synchronizer in Neutral, then remove the roll pin from the 5th gear shift fork and the 5th gear synchronizer hub, the sleeve, the roller bearing and the gear. Remove the shift fork as an assembly from the output shaft. Remove the 5th speed gear from the input shaft.

7. Remove the Torx® bolts from the bearing retainer, then the bearing retainer and the shims from the input and the output shafts.

8. Remove the Reverse idler shaft-to-case bolt.

9. Using tools No. J–22888 and J–22888–30, remove the output shaft collar and the thrust washer.

10. Remove the transaxle case-to-clutch housing bolts and separate the cases.

11. Remove the Reverse idler gear and the Reverse idler shaft.

12. Lift the 5th gear shaft. With the detent aligned facing the same way, remove the 5th and the Reverse shafts at the same time.

13. Using a punch and a hammer, remove the roll pin from the 1–2 shift fork. Slide the shaft upward to clear the housing, then remove the fork and the shaft from the case.

14. Remove the cotter pin, then remove the pin and the Reverse shift lever.

15. Remove the input and the output shafts with the 3–4 shift fork and the shaft as an assembly.

16. Remove the differential case assembly.

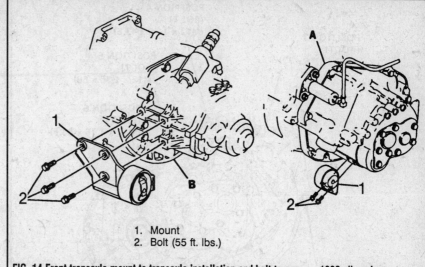

1. Mount
2. Bolt (55 ft. lbs.)

FIG. 14 Front transaxle mount to transaxle installation and bolt torques — 1992 all engines

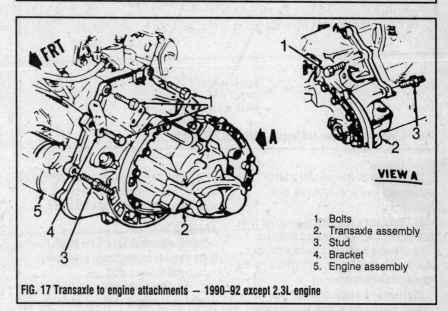

1. Bolts
2. Transaxle assembly
3. Stud
4. Bracket
5. Engine assembly

FIG. 17 Transaxle to engine attachments — 1990–92 except 2.3L engine

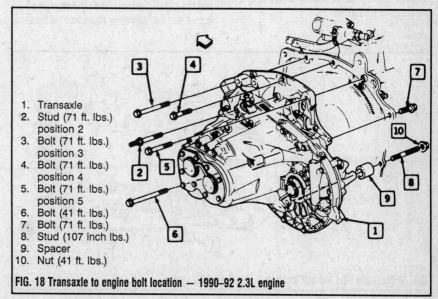

1. Transaxle
2. Stud (71 ft. lbs.) position 2
3. Bolt (71 ft. lbs.) position 3
4. Bolt (71 ft. lbs.) position 4
5. Bolt (71 ft. lbs.) position 5
6. Bolt (41 ft. lbs.)
7. Bolt (71 ft. lbs.)
8. Stud (107 inch lbs.)
9. Spacer
10. Nut (41 ft. lbs.)

FIG. 18 Transaxle to engine bolt location — 1990–92 2.3L engine

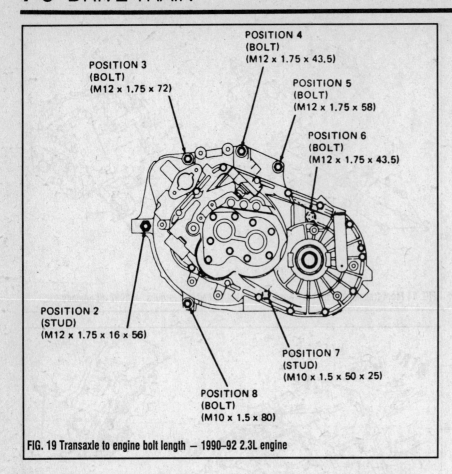

POSITION 3
(BOLT)
(M12 x 1.75 x 72)

POSITION 4
(BOLT)
(M12 x 1.75 x 43.5)

POSITION 5
(BOLT)
(M12 x 1.75 x 58)

POSITION 6
(BOLT)
(M12 x 1.75 x 43.5)

POSITION 2
(STUD)
(M12 x 1.75 x 16 x 56)

POSITION 7
(STUD)
(M10 x 1.5 x 50 x 25)

POSITION 8
(BOLT)
(M10 x 1.5 x 80)

FIG. 19 Transaxle to engine bolt length — 1990–92 2.3L engine

17. Remove the Reverse shift bracket together with the four bolts and the three interlock pins.

18. Remove the rear bearing outer race from the transaxle case, then the input shaft race.

19. Remove the outer races from the input shaft front bearing, the output shaft front and the differential side bearings.

20. Remove the input shaft seal from the housing, then the clutch shaft seal only when replacement is required.

21. Drive the bushing toward the inside of the housing, then remove the fork assembly only when replacing the clutch fork assembly.

ASSEMBLY

Before reassembly, attach the clutch housing to the transaxle holding fixture (if removed).

1. Install the input shaft seal.

2. Install the front outer bearing races for the input shaft, the output shaft and the differential into the clutch housing. Press the input, the output and the differential races into the housing.

3. Apply grease to the three interlock pins and install them on the clutch housing.

4. Install the Reverse shift bracket on the clutch housing. Use the 3rd-4th shift rod to align the bracket to the housing. Install and torque the retaining bolts. Make sure the rod operates smoothly after installation.

5. Install the differential assembly first, then the input and the output shaft with the 3rd-4th shift fork and the shaft together as an assembly into the clutch housing.

➡ **Make sure the interlock pin is in the 3rd-4th shifter shaft before installing.**

6. The 3rd-4th shift shaft is installed into the raised collar of the Reverse shift lever bracket.

7. Install the 1-2 shift fork onto the synchronizer sleeve and insert the shifter shaft into the Reverse shift lever bracket. Align the hole in the fork with the shaft and install the roll pin.

8. Install the Reverse lever on the shift bracket.

9. Install the Reverse and the 5th gear shifter shaft; engage the Reverse shaft with the Reverse shift lever at the same time.

➡ **Make sure the interlock pin is in the 5th gear shifter shaft before installing.**

10. Install the Reverse idler shaft with the gear into the clutch housing.

➡ **Make sure the Reverse lever is engaged in the gear collar.**

11. Using tool No. J–33373, measure and determine the shim size.

a. Position the outer bearing races on the input, the output and the differential bearings. Position the shim selection gauges on the bearing races. The three gauges are identified: Input, Output and Differential.

b. Place the 7 spacers (provided with the tool No. J–33373) evenly around the clutch housing perimeter.

c. Install the bearing and the shim retainer on the transaxle case. Torque the bolts to 11–16 ft. lbs.

d. Carefully position the transaxle case over the gauges and on the spacers. Install the bolts (provided in the tool kit) and tighten the bolts alternately until the case is seated on the spacers, then torque the bolts to 10 ft. lbs.

e. Rotate each gauge to seat the bearings. Rotate the differential case through three revolutions in each direction.

f. With the three gauges compressed, measure the gap between the outer sleeve and the base pad using the available shim sizes.

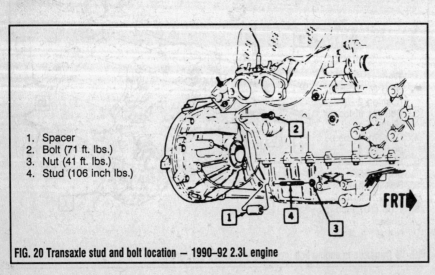

1. Spacer
2. Bolt (71 ft. lbs.)
3. Nut (41 ft. lbs.)
4. Stud (106 inch lbs.)

FIG. 20 Transaxle stud and bolt location — 1990–92 2.3L engine

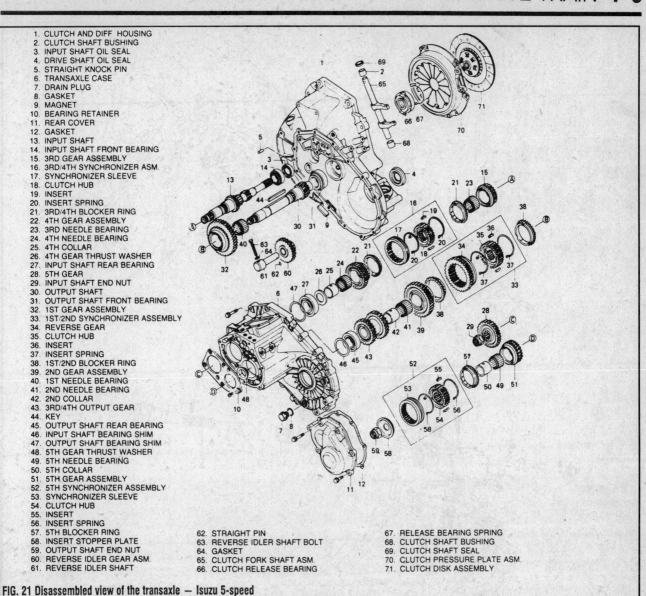

1. CLUTCH AND DIFF HOUSING
2. CLUTCH SHAFT BUSHING
3. INPUT SHAFT OIL SEAL
4. DRIVE SHAFT OIL SEAL
5. STRAIGHT KNOCK PIN
6. TRANSAXLE CASE
7. DRAIN PLUG
8. GASKET
9. MAGNET
10. BEARING RETAINER
11. REAR COVER
12. GASKET
13. INPUT SHAFT
14. INPUT SHAFT FRONT BEARING
15. 3RD GEAR ASSEMBLY
16. 3RD/4TH SYNCHRONIZER ASM.
17. SYNCHRONIZER SLEEVE
18. CLUTCH HUB
19. INSERT
20. INSERT SPRING
21. 3RD/4TH BLOCKER RING
22. 4TH GEAR ASSEMBLY
23. 3RD NEEDLE BEARING
24. 4TH NEEDLE BEARING
25. 4TH COLLAR
26. 4TH GEAR THRUST WASHER
27. INPUT SHAFT REAR BEARING
28. 5TH GEAR
29. INPUT SHAFT END NUT
30. OUTPUT SHAFT
31. OUTPUT SHAFT FRONT BEARING
32. 1ST GEAR ASSEMBLY
33. 1ST/2ND SYNCHRONIZER ASSEMBLY
34. REVERSE GEAR
35. CLUTCH HUB
36. INSERT
37. INSERT SPRING
38. 1ST/2ND BLOCKER RING
39. 2ND GEAR ASSEMBLY
40. 1ST NEEDLE BEARING
41. 2ND NEEDLE BEARING
42. 2ND COLLAR
43. 3RD/4TH OUTPUT GEAR
44. KEY
45. OUTPUT SHAFT REAR BEARING
46. INPUT SHAFT BEARING SHIM
47. OUTPUT SHAFT BEARING SHIM
48. 5TH GEAR THRUST WASHER
49. 5TH NEEDLE BEARING
50. 5TH COLLAR
51. 5TH GEAR ASSEMBLY
52. 5TH SYNCHRONIZER ASSEMBLY
53. SYNCHRONIZER SLEEVE
54. CLUTCH HUB
55. INSERT
56. INSERT SPRING
57. 5TH BLOCKER RING
58. INSERT STOPPER PLATE
59. OUTPUT SHAFT END NUT
60. REVERSE IDLER GEAR ASM.
61. REVERSE IDLER SHAFT

62. STRAIGHT PIN
63. REVERSE IDLER SHAFT BOLT
64. GASKET
65. CLUTCH FORK SHAFT ASM.
66. CLUTCH RELEASE BEARING

67. RELEASE BEARING SPRING
68. CLUTCH SHAFT BUSHING
69. CLUTCH SHAFT SEAL
70. CLUTCH PRESSURE PLATE ASM.
71. CLUTCH DISK ASSEMBLY

FIG. 21 Disassembled view of the transaxle — Isuzu 5-speed

Use the largest shim that can be placed into the gap and drawn through without binding; this will be the correct shim for the bearing being measured.

g. When each of the three shims selected, remove the transaxle case, the spacers and the three gauges.

12. Position the shim selected for the input, the output and the differential into the bearing race bores in the transaxle case.

13. Using tool No. J–24256–A, J–8092 and an arbor press, install the rear input shaft bearing race; press the bearing until it is seated in its bore.

14. Using tool No. J–33370, J–8092 and an arbor press, install the rear output shaft bearing; press the bearing until it is seated in its bore.

15. Using tool No. J–8611–01, J–8092 and an arbor press, install the rear differential case bearing race; press the bearing until it is seated in its bore.

16. Apply a 1/8 in. (3mm) bead of Loctite® 514 to the mating surfaces of the clutch housing and the transaxle case.

17. Be sure the magnet is installed in the transaxle case.

18. Install the case on the clutch housing and the Reverse idle shaft bolt into the case, then torque the bolt to 22–33 ft. lbs.

19. Install the 14 case bolts and torque them to 22–33 ft. lbs. (in a diagonal sequence).

20. Install the drive axle seals.

21. Install the thrust washer and the collar to the output shaft.

22. Install the 5th gear to the input shaft. Install the needle bearing, the 5th gear, the blocking ring, the hub/sleeve assembly (with the shift fork in its groove) and the backing plate on the output shaft. Align the shift fork on the shifter shaft and install the roll pin.

23. Install the Reverse detent balls and the springs, then the 1st-2nd, the 3rd-4th and the 5th speed gears. Install the bolts and torque to 15–21 ft. lbs.

24. Apply Loctite® 262 to the input and the output shaft threads. Install new retaining nuts and torque to 87–101 ft. lbs.; stake the nuts after reaching the final torque.

25. Install the gasket and the control box assembly on the transaxle case, then torque the bolts to 11–16 ft. lbs.

➡ **Make sure the transaxle shifts properly before installing the rear cover.**

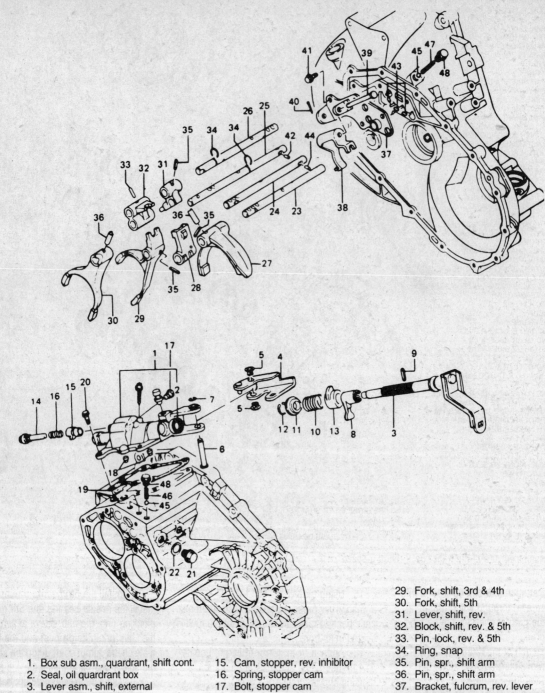

1. Box sub asm., quardrant, shift cont.
2. Seal, oil quardrant box
3. Lever asm., shift, external
4. Lever asm., select, external
5. Bush, select lever
6. Pin, slect lever
7. Ring, snap, select lever
8. Lever, shift, internal
9. Pin, spring, internal lever
10. Spring, select stop, 1st & 2nd
11. Seat, spring select stop
12. Ring, snap, spring seat
13. Stopper, rev. inhibitor
14. Bolt, rev. inhibitor

15. Cam, stopper, rev. inhibitor
16. Spring, stopper cam
17. Bolt, stopper cam
18. Pin, knock, quardrant box
19. Gasket, quardrant box
20. Bolt, quardrant box
21. Plug, screw
22. Gasket, plug
23. Shaft, arm, gear shift, 1st & 2nd
24. Shaft, arm, gear shift, 3rd & 4th
25. Shaft, arm, gear shift, 5th
26. Shaft, arm, gear shift, rev.
27. Fork, shift, 1st & 2nd
28. Block, shift, 1st & 2nd

29. Fork, shift, 3rd & 4th
30. Fork, shift, 5th
31. Lever, shift, rev.
32. Block, shift, rev. & 5th
33. Pin, lock, rev. & 5th
34. Ring, snap
35. Pin, spr., shift arm
36. Pin, spr., shift arm
37. Bracket, fulcrum, rev. lever
38. Lever, shift rev.
39. Pin, fulcrum brkt., rev. shift
40. Cotter pin, snap, fulcrum pin
41. bolt, fulcrum brkt.
42. Pin, lock, 5th shaft
43. Pin, inter lock
44. Pin, lock, 3rd & 4th shaft
45. Ball, detent, gear shift
46. Spring, detent ball
47. Spring, detent ball, rev.
48. Plug, detent spring

FIG. 22 Disassembled view of the transaxle shift linkage — Isuzu 5-speed

26. Install the gasket and the rear cover with the 7 bolts, then torque the bolts to 11–16 ft. lbs.

27. Install the clutch fork assembly (if removed). Using tool No. J–28412, install the bushing into the upper hole. Install the oil seal. Before installing the bushing, apply grease to both the interior and the exterior.

28. Install the clutch release bearing.

Input Shaft

DISASSEMBLY

1. Using tool No. J–22912–01 and an arbor press, remove the front bearing.

2. Pull out the rear bearing 4th gear, the 3rd–4th synchronizer assembly and 3rd gear as an assembly.

➡ **This procedure requires a arbor press and tool No. J–22912–01.**

3. Remove the outer parts from, the input shaft.

Output Shaft

DISASSEMBLY

1. Using tool No. J–22227–A and an arbor press, remove the front bearing.

2. Using tool No. J–22912–01 and an arbor press, remove the rear bearing and the 3rd-4th gear as an assembly.

3. Remove the key, the 2nd gear, the needle bearing and the blocking ring.

4. Using an arbor press, remove the collar, the Reverse gear assembly and the 1st gear as an assembly.

All Except Isuzu Overhaul

◆ SEE FIGS. 23-25

Axle Shaft Seal

REPLACEMENT

➡ **To perform this procedure, you will need a seal installer backed up by a driver handle. Use GM Part Nos. J–26938 and J–8092 or the equivalent.**

1. Disconnect the negative battery cable. Remove the axle from the car as described in the appropriate car section.

2. Carefully pry the old axle seal out of the transaxle.

3. Put the new seal onto the seal installer and then assemble the driver handle to the installer's outer end. Drive the seal in, being careful to keep the handle perpendicular to the seal aperture so that it will be located squarely.

4. Install the driveshaft as described in the car section. Recheck the fluid level and, if necessary, refill the axle with fluid.

Clutch Shaft and Bushing

REPLACEMENT

➡ **To perform this procedure, you will need the following GM parts or their equivalent: Bushing remover/installer J–36037; bushing remover J–36032; bushing installer J–36033; a slide hammer J–23907; and a drive handle J–36190.**

❊❊ CAUTION

Whenever removing the clutch lever assembly, FIRST disconnect the clutch master cylinder pushrod at the clutch pedal. FAILURE TO DO THIS MAY RESULT IN PERMANENT DAMAGE TO THE SLAVE CYLINDER, if the clutch pedal is depressed while the lever is disconnected.

1. Remove the transaxle from the car as described in the appropriate car section.

2. Remove the clutch release lever from the end of the clutch shaft. Then, pull out the clutch shaft seal.

3. Drive the upper clutch shaft bushing into the transaxle housing with a hammer and the bushing remover/installer. Then, turn the clutch shaft slightly for clearance and remove it from the clutch housing.

4. Install the bushing remover and slide hammer, engaging the second step on the bushing remover below the bushing and then tighten the screw to expand the legs and force the bushing out of its position in the housing. Then, remove the bushing and tools.

5. Install the lower bushing by slipping it onto the end of tool 36033 or equivalent. Slide the tool and new bushing through the upper bushing bore and down into the lower bore, and then use the slide hammer to force the bushing fully into the bore.

6. Install the clutch shaft.

7. Install the upper bushing with J–36037 or equivalent. Tap the busing into the bore until the line on the tool is flush with the housing surface.

8. Install the dust seal. Then, install the clutch release lever, torquing the through bolt to 37 ft. lbs.

9. Reinstall the transaxle. Check the fluid level and, if necessary, add fluid.

Shift Shaft Seal

REPLACEMENT

➡ **To perform this procedure, you will need a seal installer GM tool No. J–35823 or equivalent.**

1. Loosen the pinch bolt on the shift shaft lever. Then, remove the lever from the shaft.

2. Slide the cylindrical seal off the shaft.

3. Use the seal installer to install the seal onto the shaft. Then, install the pinch bolts and torque the through bolt/nut to 20 ft. lbs.

Disassembly of Transaxle

EXTERNAL LINKAGE REMOVAL

❊❊ CAUTION

The shift shaft must NOT turn during the next step, or the transmission may be damaged.

1. Fit a large wrench onto the shift lever to keep it from turning; then, unscrew the nut located at the top of the shift shaft.

2. Remove the washer, lever, pivot pin, and pivot.

3. Remove the pin and then the collar located just below the shift lever.

4. Remove the bolts that hold the shift lever bracket to the transaxle case and then remove the bracket.

5. Unscrew and remove the fluid level indicator and then the washer underneath it.

6. Remove the electronic speedometer signal unit, the retainer mounting bolt, and the retainer.

SHIFT RAIL DETENT AND CLUTCH AND DIFFERENTIAL HOUSING DISASSEMBLY

1. Remove the clutch throwout bearing. Puncture the detent holder cover near its center and then use an awl or similar tool to pry it off.

2. Earlier models only have an interlock plate. If the transaxle has this piece, remove the 2 interlock plate mounting bolts and then remove the interlock plate.

3. Remove the detent holder, springs (4), and interlock pins (2).

4. Remove the four detent balls.

5. Remove the reverse shift rail bushing by prying it loose via the 2 slots using small prying instruments.

SHIFT SHAFT DETENT COMPONENTS AND TRANSMISSION HOUSING DISASSEMBLY

1. Remove the snapring which retains the shift shaft cover and then remove the cover.

2. Remove the screw which retains the 5th/reverse bias outer spring seat and then remove the spring seat itself. Then, remove the bias spring and inner spring seat.

SEPARATING THE TRANSMISSION CASE AND CLUTCH HOUSING

1. Remove the 15 transmission case retaining bolts. Then separate the clutch housing from the transmission case.

2. Lift the differential gear assembly (complete with roller bearings on both sides) out of the transmission case.

3. Remove the magnet from the transmission case.

4. Remove the bearing from the upper end of the output shaft.

REMOVAL OF SHIFT SHAFT COMPONENTS

1. Place a rag or other means of catching the shift shaft pin underneath he shift shaft, and then use a thin object and a hammer to tap the shift shaft pin out of the shaft.

2. Remove the shift shaft, catching the four rollers and 2 shift shaft pins as you remove it. Then, remove the 1st/2nd bias spring.

2. Remove the shift lever and reverse lever from the case.

REMOVAL OF GEAR CLUSTER SUPPORT COMPONENTS

➡ **Removal of the output cluster gear retainer requires a special hex socket, J36031 or equivalent.**

1. First, push downward on the 3rd/4th shift rail to engage 4th gear. Then, do the same for the reverse shift rail to engage reverse.

2. Remove the nine retaining bolts from the transmission end plate. Then remove the end plate.

3. Remove and retain the selective shim from the groove in the housing on the output shaft side.

4. Remove the oil shield located in the center of the same area of the housing; then unscrew and remove the output gear cluster retainer, turning it **clockwise** in order to do so.

5. Remove the input gear cluster retainer using the same tool (rotation is normal). Then, shift both shift rails back to neutral.

REMOVAL OF GEAR CLUSTERS

➡ **To perform this procedure, you'll need: a hydraulic press, a gear cluster and transmission case assembly and disassembly pallet, Tool No. J–36182–1 or equivalent; 2**

disassembly adapters J–36282–2 or equivalent, and a J–36185 gear cluster remover.

1. Slide the adapters onto the 2 pegs on either side of the press. Position the pallet and adapters in the press. Then, position the transaxle case and gear cluster assembly onto the pallet and adapters. Make sure the pilots at the ends of the shift rails and input and output shafts align with the corresponding holes in the fixture.

2. Position the gear cluster remover on top of the shaft support bearings and pilot surfaces.

3. Locate the ram of the press squarely on top of the gear cluster remover. Then, press the shafts and gear clusters out of the transaxle case.

REMOVAL OF SHIFT RAILS

4. Remove the transmission case from the press. Remove the 1-2 shift rail assembly. Then, remove the lock pin from the assembly.

5. Remove the 3-4 rail assembly. Remove the 5th gear rail assembly. Finally, remove the reverse rail assembly.

6. Remove the shift gate. Disengage and then remove the shift gate roller.

DISASSEMBLY AND INSPECTION

➡ **You'll need an oven that will produce 250°F. and hold gear assemblies or the gear cluster and other small parts to reassemble the unit. You'll also need hot tap water to heat the speedometer gear prior to assembly. To disassemble and reassemble the input shaft, you'll need a hydraulic press, a J–22912–01 gear remover/installer, a press tube J–36183 or equivalent and a reducer J–36184 for the input/output shaft gears. Use a heavy assembly lubricant, part No. 1052931 or equivalent to pre-lube parts during assembly for protection until the gearbox lubricates itself and is broken in.**

INPUT SHAFT DISASSEMBLY AND ASSEMBLY

➡ **Before disassembly, carefully identify and label the blocker rings for 3rd and 4th gears, as they are easily confused during assembly.**

1. Remove the snapring from the top of the shaft. Position the shaft with the snapring groove upward and the lower end inserted into the press tube and reducer. Center the top of the shaft under the press ram. Press the shaft downward and out of the gears and associated parts.

Remove the gear, bearing, race, 2 blocking rings, and the synchronizer assembly and associated gear.

2. Remove the 3rd gear bearing.

3. Clean all parts in a safe solvent and air dry them. Then inspect as follows:

a. Inspect the shaft for spline wear or cracks and replace it if any are visible.

b. Inspect the gear teeth for scuffing, nicks, burrs, or breaks and replace gears that show such defects.

c. Inspect the bearings by rotating them slowly and checking for roughness in rotation, burrs or pits, and replace as necessary.

d. Inspect the bearing races and shaft bearing surfaces for scoring, wear, or overheating and replace parts as necessary.

e. Inspect the snapring for nicks, distortion, or wear and replace if any of these conditions exist.

f. See the head below referring to "Synchronizer Disassembly and Inspection". Inspect the synchronizer as described there, and replace defective parts.

g. Very slight defects in all parts except bearings can sometimes be removed with a soft stone or crocus cloth. It is permissible to clean up and re-use parts in this manner if only a small amount of metal must be removed.

4. Heat the 5th gear assembly and bearing race for 10 minutes in an oven preheated to 250°F.

5. Prelube all parts on wear surfaces as the assembly proceeds. While the gear is heating, assemble the two 3rd gear bearings and then the 3rd gear to the shaft. Install the 3rd gear with the cone upward. Then, install the blocking ring.

6. Assemble the shaft into the press tube and reducer and position the remover/installer so that the two, small diameter permanent gears near the bottom of the shaft straddle the installer. Position the assembly onto the press so that the shaft protrudes down through the hole in the press bed.

7. Install the two 3rd gear bearings, 3rd gear (with the cone upward) and synchronizer blocking ring onto the shaft. Position the synchronizer onto the top of the shaft with the side marked "3rd gear" and the small outside diameter groove of the sleeve toward the 3rd gear. Position the gear installer on top of the synchronizer unit. Start the press operation cautiously and watch the position of the synchronizer. Stop the press before the synchronizer unit tangs touch those on the gears. Then, lift the 3rd gear blocking ring and 3rd gear so that their tangs fit into the tangs on the synchronizer. Then, press the

synchronizer on until it is seated. Carefully remove any shavings that may have been created during the pressing operation.

8. Install the bearing race (preheated) and the bearing. Install the 4th gear blocking ring.

9. Install the 4th gear, cone downward.

10. Install the shaft assembly into the press tube and reducer and position the assembly squarely on the press. Install the 5th gear (preheated) on top, flat side down. Press the gear into position and install the snapring.

OUTPUT SHAFT DISASSEMBLY AND ASSEMBLY

⇒ To perform this procedure, you will need: a press of at least 15 tons capacity; an input/output shaft gear remover/installer J-22912-01 or equivalent; a J-36183 or equivalent input/output shaft gears press tube; a J-36184 input/output shaft press tube installer; and an oven that will produce 250°F. and old gear assemblies or the gear cluster and other small parts. Before proceeding with disassembly, identify and label the blocking rings for 5th, 2nd, and 1st gears. They must be reinstalled in the correct positions. Use a heavy assembly lubricant, part No. 1052931 or equivalent to pre-lube parts during assembly for protection until the gearbox lubricates itself and is broken in.

1. Install the gear remover/installer and shaft assembly into the press. The remover/installer has a tang which must locate in the shifting fork groove of the reverse/5th gear synchronizer assembly. The remover/installer rests on the press bed.

2. Press the shaft downward so the reverse/5th gear synchronizer assembly is pressed off the top. Then, remove the shaft from the press and remove: the blocker ring, 5th speed gear, 5th gear bearing, thrust washer, and thrust washer positioner ball.

3. Using snapring pliers, open and then work the snapring off the shaft.

4. Install the shaft in the press, supported via the lower side of the 1st speed gear by the input/output shaft gears press tube, resting on the press bed. Use the press ram, resting against the top of the shaft, to force the shaft downward (this will require at least 15 tons pressure) and force the 1st gear and parts above it off the shaft. Separate the following parts from the shaft: 2nd gear, bearing, bearing race, 1-2 synchronizer, blocking rings, 3-4 gear cluster, 1st gear, bearing, caged thrust bearing, and thrust washer.

5. Clean all parts in a safe solvent and air dry them. Then inspect as follows:

a. Inspect the shaft for spline wear or cracks and replace it if any are visible.

b. Inspect the gear teeth for scuffing, nicks, burrs, or breaks and replace gears that show such defects.

c. Inspect the bearings by rotating them slowly and checking for roughness in rotation, burrs or pits, and replace as necessary.

d. Inspect the bearing races and shaft bearing surfaces for scoring, wear, or overheating and replace parts as necessary.

e. Inspect the snapring for nicks, distortion, or wear and replace if any of these conditions exist.

f. See the head below referring to "Synchronizer Disassembly and Inspection". Inspect the synchronizer as described there, and replace defective parts.

g. Very slight defects in all parts except bearings can sometimes be removed with a soft stone or crocus cloth. It is permissible to clean up and re-use parts in this manner if only a small amount of metal must be removed.

6. Put the 2nd gear bearing race, and the 3rd-4th gear cluster in an oven at 250°F. The race requires at least 10 minutes preheating before assembly and the gear cluster at least 20 minutes preheating.

7. Install the thrust washer onto the shaft, **chamfer downward**. Then, install the caged thrust bearing, **needles downward**.

8. Install the 1st gear bearing. Then, install the 1st gear, cone upward. Install the 1st gear blocking ring.

9. Position the shaft into the press with the bottom protruding through the press bed. Locate the 1-2 synchronizer assembly on top of the shaft, with the side marked "1st" and the smaller outside diameter groove on the sleeve facing 1st gear. Use the J-36183 or equivalent input/output shaft gears press tube and the J-36184 input/output shaft press tube installer. Start pressing the synchronizer assembly onto the shaft, but stop before the tangs of the gear and synchronizer touch. Lift and rotate the blocking ring and gear **making sure the thrust washer stays downward in position** in order to engage the tangs. Then, continue the pressing operation until the synchronizer assembly is seated. Carefully remove all metal shavings.

10. Install the 2nd gear bearing race (preheated), 2nd gear bearing, and 2nd gear **with the cone downward**.

11. Position the preheated 3rd-4th gear cluster onto the shaft. Make sure the larger outside diameter gear is below the smaller one.

Use the press and press tube reducer to press the cluster into position.

12. Install the snapring with snapring pliers. Then, install the thrust washer positioning ball, holding it in position with petroleum jelly. Install the thrust washer, aligning the slot in it with the ball.

13. Install the 5th gear bearing and then install the 5th gear, with the cone upward. Install the 5th gear blocking ring.

14. Position the shaft in the press. Position the reverse gear/5th synchronizer assembly onto the shaft. Position the input/output shaft gear press tube and press tube reducer on top of the synchronizer assembly. Start pressing the synchronizer assembly onto the shaft, but stop before the tangs of the gear and synchronizer touch. Lift and rotate the blocking ring and gear **making sure the thrust washer stays downward in position** in order to engage the tangs. Then, continue the pressing operation until the synchronizer assembly is seated. Carefully remove all metal shavings.

DISASSEMBLY AND ASSEMBLY OF THE REVERSE IDLER GEAR

1. Remove the bolt which runs through the transmission case and into the reverse idler gear sliding spindle shaft. Then, remove the shift rail, gear, shaft, and bracket.

2. Remove the reverse idler gear shift rail, detent ball and spring.

3. Clean all parts in a safe solvent and air dry them. Then inspect as follows:

a. Inspect the shaft for scoring, wear or cracks or signs of overheating and replace it if any are visible.

b. Inspect the gear teeth for scuffing, nicks, burrs, or breaks and replace gears that show such defects.

c. Inspect the bushing inside the gear, checking for scores, burrs, out-of-roundness, or overheating, and replace as necessary.

d. Very slight defects in all parts except bearings can sometimes be removed with a soft stone or crocus cloth. It is permissible to clean up and re-use parts in this manner if only a small amount of metal must be removed.

4. Assemble all parts as described in the following steps, lubricating wear surfaces with a lubricant designed to protect the parts till they become lubricated by normal gearbox operation such as GM part No. 1052931.

5. Install the detent spring and ball into the reverse idler bracket.

6. Install the shift rail into the reverse idler gear bracket. Then, install the reverse idler gear onto the shaft with the slot in the gear facing the threaded hole in the shaft.

7. Install the entire assembly into the transaxle. Then, install the fastening bolt and torque it to 16 ft. lbs.

DISASSEMBLY AND ASSEMBLY OF THE TRANSMISSION CASE

➡ **To perform this procedure, you will need the following special tools or equivalent: J–8092 universal driver handle; J–23907 slide hammer and adapter set; J–36027 shift shaft bearing remover; J–36029 shift rail bushing remover and installer; J–36032 clutch shaft inner bushing and reverse shift rail remover; J–36034 sliding sleeve bushing remover and installer; J–36039 shift detent lever bushing remover and installer; J–36181 differential bearing cup remover; J–36190 universal driver handle. Throughout this disassembly procedure, note that it is not necessary to remove bushings or bearings as a matter of routine. Inspect the bearing or bushing and the mating surface of the corresponding shaft. Inspect bushings for scores, burrs, out-of-round wear, or bluing (from overheating). Remove the bearing or bushing and replace it and the corresponding part only if there is evidence of damage or it is clear that the part is worn out.**

1. Remove the snapring and plug from the rear of the sliding sleeve bore. Then, remove the screw-in spring retainer, the spring, and the sliding sleeve. Remove (if necessary) the sliding sleeve bushing with J–36034 and J–36190 or equivalent.

2. Remove the detent lever. If its wear surface is scored or worn, also remove the bushing it rides in with J–36039 and J–36190 or equivalent.

3. Pry out the shift shaft seal with a small, flat-bladed screwdriver.

4. If necessary, remove the shift shaft bearing with J–36027 and J–36190 or equivalent.

5. Remove the axle shaft seal. As necessary, remove the outer race for the differential carrier support bearing with J–36181 and J–8092. Then, remove the three shift rail plugs from the transmission case.

6. (As necessary) remove the input shaft support bearing. Remove the output shaft support bearing.

7. Remove (as necessary) the three shift rail bushings with J–36029 and J–31690. Use the small end of the J–36029–2 adapter in the bushing.

8. As necessary, remove the reverse shift rail bushing with J–36032 and J–23907. Remove the stud that screws into the top of one of the shift rail bushing bores.

9. Inspect the case as follows:
   a. Inspect the bearing race bores for wear, scratches, or grooves.
   b. Inspect the gear teeth for scuffing, nicks, burrs, or breaks and replace gears that show such defects.
   c. Inspect the bushings for scoring, burrs or pits, out-of-round or evidence of overheating (bluing) and replace as necessary.
   d. Inspect the case for cracks, the threaded openings in the case for damaged threads, and the mounting faces for nicks, burrs, or scratches. Replace the case if it is cracked. Clean up damaged threads with a used tap of the correct size (a brand-new tap will cut oversize threads).
   e. Very slight defects in all parts except bearings can sometimes be removed with a soft stone or crocus cloth. It is permissible to clean up and re-use parts in this manner if only a small amount of metal must be removed.

➡ **The following special tools or equivalent designs from other sources are required to reassemble the case: J–26938 differential seal and race installer; J–35823 shift shaft seal installer; J–36209 shift rail bushing remover/installer; J–36034 sliding sleeve bushing remover/installer; J–36039 shift detent lever remover/installer; J–36189 shift shaft bearing installer; J–26190 universal driver handle.**

1. If it has been removed, install the shift shaft bearing with J–36189 and J–36190. Install the shift shaft seal with J–35823.

2. If it they been removed, install the three shift rail bushings. In doing this, install the bearings on the J–36029–2 adapter and retain them with the J–36029–1.

3. If it has been removed, install the reverse rail bushing with J–36030 and J–36190.

4. Install the differential carrier support outer bearing race with J–26938.

5. Install the axle seals with J–26938.

6. Install the three shift rail plugs into the case, screwing them in just until they are even with the surface of the case.

7. If it has been removed, install the detent lever bushing with J–36039 and J–36190. Then, install the detent lever.

8. If it has been removed, install the sliding sleeve bushing with J–36034 and J–36190.

9. Install the sliding sleeve bushing with J–36034 and J–36190. Then, install the sliding sleeve, spring, and retaining screw, torquing the retaining screw to 32 ft. lbs.

10. Install the plug into the sliding sleeve bore, and then install the snapring, flat side up.

11. Install the stud with the chamfer outward, torquing to 15 ft. lbs.

➡ **To perform this procedure you will need the following special tools or equivalent designs from other sources: a hydraulic press; a J–8092 universal driver handle; J–23907 slide hammer and adapter set; J–35824 input bearing assembly remover and installer; J–36029 shift rail bushing remover/installer; J–36032 clutch shaft inner bushing/reverse shift rail remover; J–36037 clutch shaft upper bushing remover/installer; J–36038 output shaft race bearing remover; J–36181 differential; bearing cup remover. Throughout this disassembly procedure, note that it is not necessary to remove bushings or bearings as a matter of routine. Inspect the bearing or bushing and the mating surface of the corresponding shaft. Inspect bushings for scores, burrs, out-of-round wear, or bluing (from overheating). Remove the bearing or bushing and replace it and the corresponding part only if there is evidence of damage or it is clear that the part is worn out.**

1. Remove the 2 axle bearing race retainer bolts and the retainer. Remove the race with J–36038 and J–23907.

2. Remove the bolts, washers, spacer, and interlock plate.

3. Remove its mounting bolt and the reverse rail guide.

4. Remove the rear axle seal.

5. Remove the differential bearing race and selective shim pack with J–36181 and J–8092.

6. With a small screwdriver, pry out the clutch shaft seal.

7. Remove the upper bushing for the outer end of the clutch shaft with J–36037. Then, remove the clutch shaft itself. Remove the inner clutch shaft bushing with the J–36032 and J–23907.

8. Place the assembly in a hydraulic press. Fit the J–35824 into the end of the bearing sleeve assembly. Then, press the sleeve out of the case via the outer end of the special tool.

9. Remove the shift rail bushings by inserting the small end of the J–36029–2 adapter into each bushing.

10. Remove the drain plug and washer. Remove the breather assembly.

11. Inspect the assembly as follows:

a. Clean all parts in solvent and allow them to dry.

b. Inspect the housing bearing race bore for wear, scratches or grooves.

c. Inspect the case for cracks, damaged threads, or nicks, burrs, or scratches in the mounting faces.

d. Replace the case if there are any cracks. Very slight defects can sometimes be removed with a soft stone or crocus cloth. It is permissible to clean up and re-use the case in this manner if only a small amount of metal must be removed.

➡ **The following tools are required to reassemble the case: a hydraulic press; a J–8092 universal drive handle; a J–23423–A differential/output shaft bearing cup installer; a J–35824 input bearing assembly remover/installer; a J–36029 shift rail bushing installer; a J–36033 clutch shaft inner bushing installer; a J–36037 clutch shaft upper bushing remover/installer; a J–36190 universal driver handle; and Loctite 242® or equivalent. Do not install the differential bearing race and axle seal until later, when the bearing is shimmed for proper preload.**

1. Install the drain plug with a new washer, and torque it to 18 ft. lbs.

2. As necessary, install new shift rail bushings. Use tools J–36029 and J–36190, placing the bushing on the J–36029–2 adapter and retaining them between the –1 and –2 sections of the tool. **Make sure the bushings do not protrude into the transmission case side of the clutch housing** .

3. Coat the outside diameter with a small amount of Loctite 242® or equivalent. **Make sure the Oil seepage hole faces DOWNWARD inside the clutch housing.** Then, install a new bearing sleeve assembly with a hydraulic press and J–35842.

4. As necessary, install a new inner clutch shaft bushing with J–36033 and J–36190. Then, install the clutch shaft.

5. As necessary, install a new outer clutch shaft bushing with J–36037. Make sure the bushing is positioned so that the outer end is flush with the bottom of the seal bore.

6. Install a new clutch shaft seal.

7. Install a new reverse rail guide with the short side going into its bore, and then install the retaining bolt, torquing to 15 ft. lbs.

8. Install a new output shaft bearing race, with J–23423–A and J–8092, **aligning cutouts in the race with the slots in the case** .

9. Install the output shaft retainer and bolts, torquing to 15 ft. lbs.

10. Coat the retaining bolts with Loctite 242® or equivalent and install the interlock plate, spacers, washers, and retaining bolts, torquing to 15 ft. lbs. Install the breather assembly.

SYNCHRONIZER DISASSEMBLY, INSPECTION, AND ASSEMBLY

1. Wrap each unit tightly in a shop rag to retain parts. Press the center hub of each unit through the sleeve to disassemble.

2. Clean all parts with solvent and then allow them to air dry. Inspect each unit as follows:

a. Inspect all hub and ring teeth for excess wear, scuffing, nicks, burrs, or actual breakage and replace defective parts.

b. Check synchronizer keys for either wear or distortion and replace those which are found to be defective.

c. Check the detent balls and retaining springs for distortion, cracks or wear. Replace defective parts.

d. Very slight defects in all parts except bearings can sometimes be removed with a soft stone or crocus cloth. It is permissible to clean up and re-use parts in this manner if only a small amount of metal must be removed.

3. Assemble the 1st/2nd and 3rd/4th synchronizer assemblies as follows:

a. Position the synchronizer sleeve with the smaller outside diameter groove upward. Position the hub with the side marked "1st" upward on the 1st/2nd synchronizer and the side marked "3rd" upward on the 3rd/4th synchronizer. Turn the sleeve so that the ball detents in the sleeve will correspond with the ball and spring pockets in the hub. Then, slide the sleeve onto the hub.

b. Insert each spring into its corresponding key. Lift the sleeve just enough to provide clearance and then install each of these assemblies into the sleeve/hub assembly with the bevel cut on the key facing the sleeve. Slip each ball into the hole in the end of the key, depress it with a flat bladed screwdriver and rock the sleeve downward and over the ball to retain it. When all three spring, key, and ball assemblies are installed,

slide the sleeve downward until the balls click into position in the detents inside the sleeve.

4. Assemble the 5th synchronizer assembly as follows:

a. Position the gear with the integral synchronizer hub upward. Insert each detent spring into the indentation in the rear of one of the semi-circular keys. Position each key with the semi-circle downward and the teeth outward. Insert each key/spring assembly into one of the slots in the integral hub.

b. Position the synchronizer sleeve with the teeth upward and oriented to align the spring pockets in the hub with the ball detents in the sleeve.

c. Slide the sleeve far enough onto the hub to retain the keys. Position each ball into the indentation in the end of one of the keys, depress it with the blade of a conventional screwdriver, and then rock that area of the sleeve down just far enough to retain the ball. When all the balls are retained by the sleeve, slide it downward until the balls click into position in the detents.

INSPECTION OF SHIFT RAIL AND FORK ASSEMBLIES

Clean all parts in solvent and allow them to air dry. Inspect the shafts for wear or scoring. Inspect the forks for wear, scoring or distortion (bends). Inspect the levers for wear or distortion such as bending. Replace parts as necessary. Note that the major rail/fork assemblies are replaceable only as complete units. Individual parts are not serviced.

DIFFERENTIAL AND RING GEAR DISASSEMBLY AND ASSEMBLY

➡ **To perform this procedure, you will need the following GM special tools or equivalent designs from other sources: J–2241–11 or J–23598 side bearing puller adapter; J–22888 bearing remover; (2) J–22888–35 bearing remover leg.**

1. Remove the ten ring gear bolts and then separate the ring gear from the differential carrier assembly.

2. Remove the differential bearings with the bearing remover and the side bearing puller adapter.

3. Remove the speedometer cable or sending unit drive gear (it cannot be removed without breaking it).

4. Remove the bolt and washer that retain the cross-differential pin. Slide the pin out and then remove the 2 side differential gears and the 2 differential pinion gears, each with its own washer.

5. Inspect the differential components as follows:

a. Clean all parts in solvent and allow them to air dry.

b. Inspect gears for scuffed, nicked, burred, or broken teeth.

c. Inspect the carrier for distortion, out-of-round bores, and scoring and replace it if any of these conditions is present.

d. Inspect the differential bearings for roughness of rotation, burrs, or pits.

e. Inspect the 2 sets of 2 thrust washers for wear, scuffing, nicks, or burrs.

f. Very slight defects can sometimes be removed with a soft stone or crocus cloth. It is permissible to clean up and re-use parts in this manner if only a small amount of metal must be removed. Clean up or, if necessary, replace defective parts.

➡ **To assemble the differential and ring gear, you will need the following special tools or equivalent designs from other than GM sources: a hydraulic press; a J-22919 differential inner bearing installer; hot tap water to heat the mechanical speedometer drive gear; a 250°F. oven to heat the electronic type of speedometer drive gear. Supply both new bolts (10) for attaching the ring gear to the differential carrier and a new speedometer drive gear before beginning work. Note also that if the transmission or clutch and differential case, differential carrier, or differential bearing assemblies have been replaced, new selective shims must be installed to provide proper bearing preload, according to "Selecting and Installing New Differential Selective Shims" below.**

6. If the transaxle uses a mechanical speedometer drive gear (which is made of nylon), preheat it in hot tap water for five minutes. If it uses an electronic speedometer drive gear (made of steel), preheat it in an oven at 250°F. for 120 minutes before installing it. Install the drive gear. Allow it to cool before proceeding.

7. Install the 2 differential bearings, using the press and the Inner Bearing Installer so the bearings will not be damaged.

8. Install the side differential gears and their 2 thrust washers. Install the pinion gears and their 2 washers onto the cross-differential pin. Install the pin and its retaining capscrew with its lockwasher. Torque the capscrew to 84 inch lbs.

9. Install the ring gear onto the differential carrier with the chamfer on the inside diameter facing the carrier. Install the 10 new mounting bolts, and torque them to 61 ft. lbs. If the parts mentioned in the note above have been replaced, perform "Selecting and Installing New Differential Selective Shims" below.

SELECTING AND INSTALLING NEW DIFFERENTIAL SELECTIVE SHIMS

➡ **To perform this procedure, you will need the following GM special tools or equivalent designs from other sources: J-8092 universal drive handle; J-26935 shim selection set; J-26938 and J-8092 axle seal and bearing race installer.**

1. Install the seven spacers (J-26935-13) into the inner side of the transmission case and slide the long attaching bolts through from the outside.

2. Install the bearing race directly over the differential bearing on the clutch and differential housing side even though it will eventually be mounted in the clutch and differential housing. Then, install the J-26935-3 spacer over the bearing cup.

3. Bolt the clutch and differential housing over the spacers and torque the long through-bolts to 10 ft. lbs. Then, measure the width of the slot in the spacer (dimension **U**) with a feeler gauge. Use gauges of the dimensions for **U** shown in the chart. Use the largest gauge that does not bind in the slot. When you have determined the proper dimension, read down the list of dimensions and pick the one 2 sizes larger.

4. Remove the through bolts, separate the case halves, and remove the spacers. Install the selected shim of the proper size into the bore in the clutch and differential housing case.

5. Install the bearing race with the bearing race and axle seal installer. Install the axle seal with the same special tools.

Assembly of The Transaxle

ASSEMBLY OF THE GEARSHIFT RAILS AND SUPPORT COMPONENTS

➡ **To perform this procedure, you will need a hydraulic press, a J-35824 or equivalent output/input shaft support bearing installer, a J-36031 or equivalent retainer bolt hex socket, and a J-36182-1 or equivalent gear cluster a transmission case assembly/disassembly pallet, and petroleum jelly.**

1. Position the input and output shafts next to each other with corresponding gears in normal mesh. Then install the following parts:

a. The 1-2 shift rail

b. Install the lock pin in the end of the 1-2 shift rail, using petroleum jelly to retain it.

c. The 3-4 shift rail.

d. The 5th shift rail.

e. The Reverse shift rail.

f. The shift gate and disengage roller.

2. Position the entire gear cluster and shift rail assembly onto the assembly/disassembly pallet, aligning the shift rail and shaft pilots with the corresponding holes in the fixture.

3. Install the transmission case over the shafts, aligning the bearing bores with the shaft pilots. Install a new output shaft bearing, using the output shaft support bearing installer and the press. Install a new input shaft bearing in the same way.

4. Slide the shift rails so as to engage both 4th and reverse gears. Then, check that the output and input shaft bearings are still fully seated in the case.

5. Install new output and input shaft bearing retainers with the retainer bolt hex socket, torquing both to 50 ft. lbs. Then, shift both forks back to Neutral position. Turn the transmission case over and support it.

ASSEMBLY OF THE SHIFT SHAFT

1. Install the reverse shift lever. Install the forward shift lever and bias spring.

2. Assemble the four shift shaft rollers and 2 shift shaft pins into the shift shaft, using petroleum jelly to retain them in place. Then, slide the shift shaft assembly into the gearbox by gently tapping it with a light hammer, aligning the hole in the shaft with the hole in the shift lever. Install the shift lever retaining pin so its ends are even with the surface of the shift lever.

ASSEMBLY OF THE CLUTCH AND DIFFERENTIAL HOUSING

➡ **You will need a sealant equivalent to GM Part No. 1052942 to perform this procedure.**

1. Apply the sealant mentioned above to the outside of the bolt hole pattern in the flange of the gear case.

2. Position the differential assembly into the case. Then, install the output shaft bearing to the upper end of the output shaft, turning it so the small inside diameter of the bearing cage faces the clutch housing.

3. Install the magnet into the case.

4. Install the clutch housing onto the transmission case, and install the attaching bolts, torquing them to 15 ft. lbs.

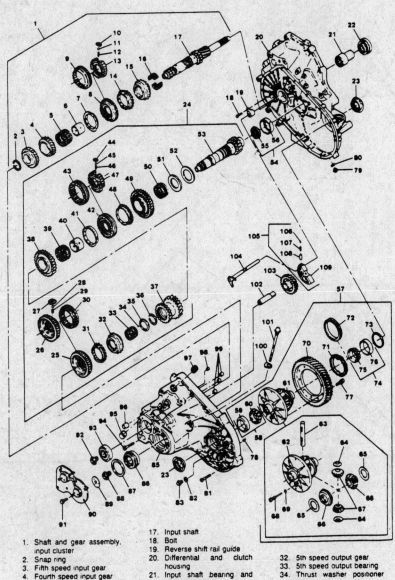

47. 1st/2nd synchronizer hub
48. 1st gear synchronizer blocking ring
49. 1st speed output gear
50. 1st speed output bearing
51. Thrust bearing
52. Thrust washer
53. Output shaft
54. Output shaft support bearing
55. Output bearing
56. Output bearing race
57. Differential and gear assembly
58. Differential bearing assembly
59. Differential bearing race
60. Differential bearing
61. Differential case assembly
62. Differential case
63. Differential cross pin
64. Pinion gear thrust washer
65. Side gear thrust washer
66. Differential side gear
67. Differential pinion gear
68. Pinion gear shaft bolt
69. Lockwasher
70. Differential ring gear
71. Speedometer output gear (mechanical speedometers)
72. Speedometer output gear (electronic speedometers)
73. Differential shim
74. Differential bearing assembly
75. Differential bearing
76. Differential bearing race
77. Differential ring gear bolt
78. Pin (2)
79. Oil drain plug
80. Washer
81. Transmission case bolt
82. Washer
83. Level check plug
84. (no designation)
85. Transmission case
86. Output gear bearing
87. Output gear shim
88. Output gear bearing retainer
89. Oil slinger washer
90. Transmission case end plate
91. Output gear bearing
92. Input gear retainer retainer
93. Input gear bearing
94. Reverse idler bolt
95. Detent lever bushing
96. Sliding sleeve bushing
97. Shift shaft needle bearing
98. Reverse shift rail bushing
99. Shift rail bushing (3)
100. Fluid level indicator washer
101. Fluid level indicator
102. Reverse idler shaft
103. Reverse idler gear
104. Reverse idler gear shift rail
105. Reverse idler gear bracket assembly
106. Reverse idler gear ball retaining bracket
107. Reverse idler gear spring bracket
108. Reverse idler gear detent bracket sleeve
109. Reverse idler gear bracket

1. Shaft and gear assembly, input cluster
2. Snap ring
3. Fifth speed input gear
4. Fourth speed input gear
5. Bearing cage
6. Needle race
7. Synchronizer ring blocker, fourth speed
8. Synchronizer assembly, fourth speed
9. Synchronizer sleeve, third and fourth speeds
10. Synchronizer key, third and fourth speeds
11. Synchronizer ball, third/fourth speeds (3)
12. Synchronizer spring, third/fourth speeds
13. Clutch hub, third/fourth speed synchronizer
14. Synchronizer ring, blocker, 3rd speed
15. Third speed input gear
16. Bearing cage (2)

17. Input shaft
18. Bolt
19. Reverse shift rail guide
20. Differential and clutch housing
21. Input shaft bearing and sleeve assembly
22. Clutch release bearing assembly
23. Drive axle oil seal
24. Output cluster shaft and gear assembly
25. Reverse output gear/5th speed synchronizer assembly
26. Reverse gear
27. 5th gear synchronizer key (3)
28. 5th speed synchronizer ball (3)
29. 5th speed synchronizer spring
30. 5th speed synchronizer sleeve
31. 5th gear synchronizer blocking ring

32. 5th speed output gear
33. 5th speed output bearing
34. Thrust washer positioner ball
35. Thrust washer
36. Snap ring
37. 3rd/4th speed cluster gear
38. 2nd speed output gear
39. 2nd speed output bearing
40. 2nd speed output bearing race
41. 2nd speed synchronizer blocking ring
42. 1st/2nd gear synchronizer assembly
43. 1st/2nd speed synchronizer sleeve
44. 1st/2nd speed synchronizer key
45. 1st/2nd speed synchronizer ball
46. 1st/2nd speed synchronizer spring

FIG. 24 Disassembled view of the transaxle — all except Isuzu 5-speed

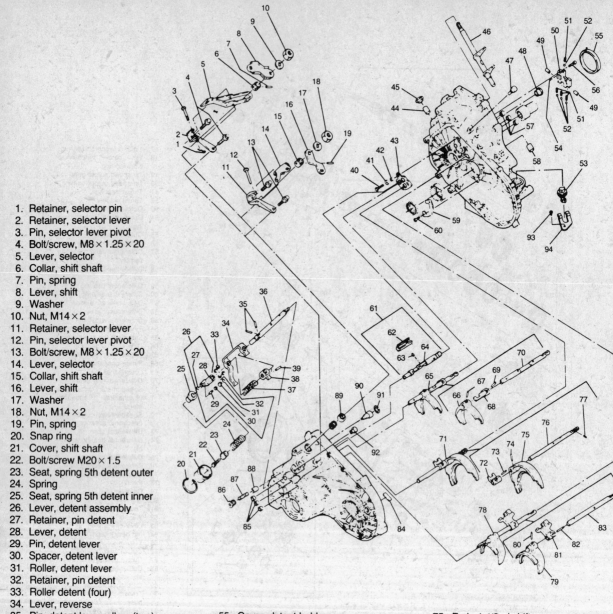

1. Retainer, selector pin
2. Retainer, selector lever
3. Pin, selector lever pivot
4. Bolt/screw, M8 × 1.25 × 20
5. Lever, selector
6. Collar, shift shaft
7. Pin, spring
8. Lever, shift
9. Washer
10. Nut, M14 × 2
11. Retainer, selector lever
12. Pin, selector lever pivot
13. Bolt/screw, M8 × 1.25 × 20
14. Lever, selector
15. Collar, shift shaft
16. Lever, shift
17. Washer
18. Nut, M14 × 2
19. Pin, spring
20. Snap ring
21. Cover, shift shaft
22. Bolt/screw M20 × 1.5
23. Seat, spring 5th detent outer
24. Spring
25. Seat, spring 5th detent inner
26. Lever, detent assembly
27. Retainer, pin detent
28. Lever, detent
29. Pin, detent lever
30. Spacer, detent lever
31. Roller, detent lever
32. Retainer, pin detent
33. Roller detent (four)
34. Lever, reverse
35. Pin, detent lever rollers (two)
36. Shaft, shift
37. Spring, 3rd/4th bias
38. Lever, shift
39. Pin, roll
40. Bolt/screw, M6 × 1 × 12 (three)
41. Washer, flat (three)
42. Spacer (three)
43. Plate, shift interlock
44. Bushing, outer clutch fork
45. Seal, clutch fork
46. Shaft, clutch fork
47. Breather assembly
48. Bushing, reverse shift rail
49. Pin, interlock (two)
50. Holder, detent
51. Spring, detent (four)
52. Ball, detent (four)
53. Speedo signal assembly
54. Pin, spring

55. Cover, detent holder
56. Bolt/screw, M6 × 1 × 30 (two)
57. Bushings, shift rail (three)
58. Bushing, inner clutch fork
59. Retainer, output bearing race
60. Bolt/screw, M6 × 1 × 12 (two)
61. Rail, reverse shift assembly
62. Shift gate, 5th/reverse
63. Roller, gear disengage
64. Shaft, reverse shift
65. Rail, 3rd/4th shift assembly
66. Fork, 3rd/4th shift shift
67. Pin, fork retainer
68. Lever, 3rd/4th select
69. Pin, lever retainer
70. Shaft, 3rd/4th shift
71. Rail, 1st/2nd shift assembly
72. Lever, 1st/2nd select
73. Pin, lever retainer
74. Pin, fork retainer

75. Fork, 1st/2nd shift
76. Shaft, 1st/2nd shift
77. Pin, lock
78. Rail, 5th shift assembly
79. Fork, 5th shift
80. Pin, fork retainer
81. Lever, 5th shift
82. Pin, lever retainer
83. Shaft, 5th shift
84. Magnet, clip collector
85. Plug, shift rail (three)
86. Bolt/screw, M2 × 1.5
87. Spring, sliding sleeve
88. Sleeve, sliding
89. Seal, shift shaft
90. Plug
91. Snap ring
92. Stud
93. Speedo signal assembly retainer
94. Bolt

FIG. 25 Disassembled view of the transaxle shift linkage — all except Isuzu 5-speed

SELECTING AND INSTALLING NEW OUTPUT SHAFT SUPPORT BEARING SELECTIVE SHIMS

➡ **To perform this procedure, you will need a J–2600–19 metric dial depth gauge or equivalent, an ordinary michrometer, and a sealer such as 1052942.**

1. First, inspect the output bearing to be sure the it is fully seated in its bore. Make sure the associated bearing retainer is properly torqued, breaking loose the bolts and retorquing, if necessary.

2. Use the depth dial gauge to measure the distance between the end plate mounting surface and outer race of the output shaft bearing. The arms of the gauge rest on the mounting surface and the actuating pin of the dial gauge rests on the race. Consult the chart and select the shim dimension ("A") closest to the gauge reading. Slip the shim into position.

3. Subtract the thickness of the shim (as shown in the chart) from the gauge reading found in the step above. Make sure the result does not exceed 0.03mm or, if shim thickness exceeds the measurement (so you get a minus value), the difference is not greater than 0.03mm. In other words, the upper surface of the shim can be as much as 0.03mm above or 0.03mm below the end plate mounting surface. If necessary, change the shim to the next thinner one to correct a dimension more than 0.03mm above the mounting surface; change it to the next thicker one to correct a dimension more than 0.03mm below the mounting surface.

INSTALLING THE TRANSMISSION CASE END PLATE

4. Install the oil slinger onto the upper surface of the bearing. Apply the sealer mentioned in the note above to the bolt hole pattern for the outside end plate. Then, install the end plate and the nine bolts, and torque the bolts to 15 ft. lbs.

INSTALLING THE SHIFT RAIL DETENT INTO THE CLUTCH AND DIFFERENTIAL HOUSING

1. Fill the breather hole in the case with petroleum jelly. Position the shift rails in neutral position in order to expose all the interlock notches. Position the reverse shift rail so that the detent ball sits in the notch on the rail and, at the same time, on the reverse bushing.

2. Install the reverse shift rail bushing. Then, install the four detent balls into the notches in the shift rails and retain them with petroleum jelly.

3. Install the 2 interlock pins and four springs into the bores of the detent holder.

4. Install the assembled detent holder. Work the balls into the spring pockets, using a small screwdriver. Pry the reverse rail upward to permit its detent ball to enter the spring pocket.

5. Now, use the screwdriver to gently pry the holder into a position which will cause the bolt holes to align with the threads in the detent holder assembly. On earlier models install the interlock plate.

6. If the transaxle uses the interlock plate, make sure the 3-4 shift rail protrudes fully through the center of the lock plate and that the 1-2 shift rail protrudes fully through the aperture in the outer edge. If the 1-2 rail does not protrude fully, the entire shift mechanism will be locked up when the unit is assembled. Then, install the interlock plate or holder mounting bolts and torque them to 84 inch lbs.

7. Install the protective cover by tapping it until it is seated in its bore in the transaxle case.

8. Apply a high temperature grease to its inside bore, and then install the clutch throwout bearing.

INSTALLING THE SHIFT SHAFT DETENT COMPONENTS INTO THE TRANSMISSION HOUSING

1. Install the inner spring seat followed by the 5th/Reverse bias spring. Hold this spring in position while installing the outer spring seat and then starting the fastening screw. Torque the screw to 84 inch lbs.

2. Install the protective cover so that its retaining ring is past the snapring groove and then install the snapring.

INSTALLING THE TRANSAXLE EXTERNALLY MOUNTED LINKAGE

Install the external linkage in reverse order of removal. Observe the following torques: bracket bolts 17 ft. lbs.; lever attaching nut 61 ft. lbs. (hold the lever against tightening torque); electronic speedometer sensor assembly retaining bolt 84 inch lbs. Replace the fluid level indicator washer.

Halfshaft

REMOVAL & INSTALLATION

1988–89

◆ SEE FIG. 26-27

The inner joint on the right side halfshaft uses a male spline that locks into the transaxle gears. The left side halfshaft uses a female spline that is installed over the stub shaft on the transaxle.

1. With the weight of the vehicle on the tires, loosen the hub nut.

2. Raise and support the vehicle.

3. Remove the hub nut.

4. Install boot protectors on the boots.

5. Remove the brake caliper with the line attached and support it (on a wire) out of the way; DO NOT allow the caliper to hang from the line.

6. Remove the brake rotor and caliper mounting bracket.

7. Remove the strut to steering knuckle bolts. Pull the steering knuckle out of the strut bracket.

8. Using the Halfshaft Removal tool No. J–33008 or equivalent and the Extension tool No. J–29794 or equivalent, remove the halfshafts from the transaxle and support them safely.

9. Using a Spindle Remover tool No. J–28733 or equivalent, remove the halfshaft from the hub and bearing.

10. To install, loosely place the halfshaft on the transaxle and in the hub and bearing.

11. Properly position the steering knuckle to the strut bracket and install the bolt. Torque the bolts to 133 ft. lbs.

12. Install the brake rotor, caliper bracket and caliper. Place a holding device in the rotor to prevent it from turning.

13. Install the hub nut and washer. Torque the nut to 71 ft. lbs.

14. Seat the halfshafts into the transaxle using a prybar on the groove on the inner retainer.

15. Verify that the shafts are seated by grasping the CV-joint and pulling outwards; DO NOT grasp the shaft. If the snapring is seated, the halfshaft will remain in place.

16. To complete the installation, reverse the removal procedures. When the vehicle is lowered with the weight on the wheels, final torque the hub nut to 191 ft. lbs.

1990–92

◆ SEE FIG. 27-29

1. Raise the car and suitably support.

2. Remove the wheel assembly.

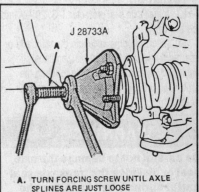

A. TURN FORCING SCREW UNTIL AXLE SPLINES ARE JUST LOOSE

FIG. 27 Removing the drive axle from the hub 1988–92

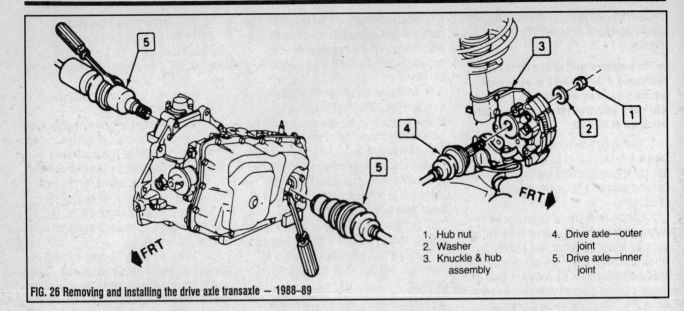

1. Hub nut
2. Washer
3. Knuckle & hub assembly
4. Drive axle—outer joint
5. Drive axle—inner joint

FIG. 26 Removing and installing the drive axle transaxle — 1988–89

3. Install drive seal protector J34754 or equivalent, on the outer joint.

4. Insert a drift into the into the caliper and rotor to prevent the rotor from turning.

4. Remove the shaft nut and washer.

5. Remove the lower ball joint cotter pin and nut and loosen the joint using tool J 38892 or equivalent. If removing the right axle, turn the wheel to the left, if removing the left axle, turn the wheel to the right.

6. Separate the joint, with a pry bar between the suspension support.

7. Disengage the axle from the hub and bearing using J 28733–A or equivalent.

8. Separate the hub and bearing assembly from the drive axle and move the strut and knuckle assembly rearward.

9. Disconnect the inner joint from the transaxle using tool J–28468 or J–33008

attached to J–29794 and J–2619–01 or from the intermediate shaft (V6 and 2.3L engines), if equipped.

To install:

10. Install axle seal protector J–37292–A into the transaxle.

11. Insert the drive axle into the transaxle or intermediate shaft (V6 and 2.3L engines), if equipped, by placing a suitable tool into the groove on the joint housing and tapping until seated.

❋❋ WARNING

Be careful not to damage the axle seal or dislodge the transaxle seal garter spring when installing the axle.

12. Verify that the drive axle is seated into the transaxle by grasping on the housing and pulling outward.

13. Install the drive axle into the hub and bearing assembly.

14. Install the lower ball joint to the knuckle. Tighten the ball joint to steering knuckle nut to 41 ft. lbs. (55 Nm) and install the cotter pin.

15. Install the washer and new drive shaft nut.

16. Insert a drift into the caliper and rotor to prevent the rotor from turning and tighten the drive shaft nut to 185 ft. lbs. (260 Nm).

17. Remove both J–37292–B and J–34754 seal protectors.

18. Install the tire and wheel assembly.

19. Lower the vehicle and connect the negative battery cable.

Intermediate Shaft

REMOVAL & INSTALLATION

1988–89

▶ SEE FIG. 30

1. Raise the car and suitably support.
2. Remove the wheel assembly.
3. Drain the transaxle.
4. Install the modified outer seal protector J–34754.
5. Remove the stabilizer shaft from the right control arm.
6. Remove the right ball joint from the knuckle.

7. Disconnect the drive axle from the intermediate axle shaft.

8. Remove the 2 housing to bracket bolts.

9. Remove the bottom bracket to engine bolt and loosen the top bolt, rotate the bracket out of the way.

10. Remove the 3 bolts holding the housing to the transaxle.

11. To install, place the intermediate shaft into position and lock the intermediate axle shaft into the transaxle.

12. Install the 3 bolts holding the housing to the transaxle and tighten to 18 ft. lbs.

15. Rotate the bracket into position and install the bottom bolt, tighten both bolts to 37 ft. lbs. (50 Nm).

16. Install the 2 housing to bracket bolts and tighten to 37 ft. lbs.

17. Coat the splines with chassis grease.

18. Connect the drive axle to the intermediate axle shaft.

19. Connect the right ball joint to the knuckle.

20. Install the stabilizer shaft to the right control arm.

21. Remove the modified outer seal protector J–34754.

22. Install the wheel.

23. Lower the car and fill the transaxle with the proper fluid.

1990

3.1L ENGINE

▶ SEE FIG. 31

1. Install engine support bar J–28467.
2. Raise the car and suitably support.
3. Remove the wheel assembly.
4. Drain the transaxle.

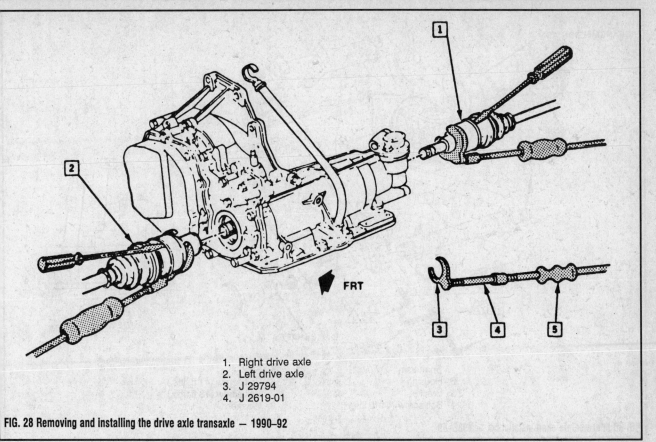

1. Right drive axle
2. Left drive axle
3. J 29794
4. J 2619-01

FIG. 28 Removing and installing the drive axle transaxle — 1990–92

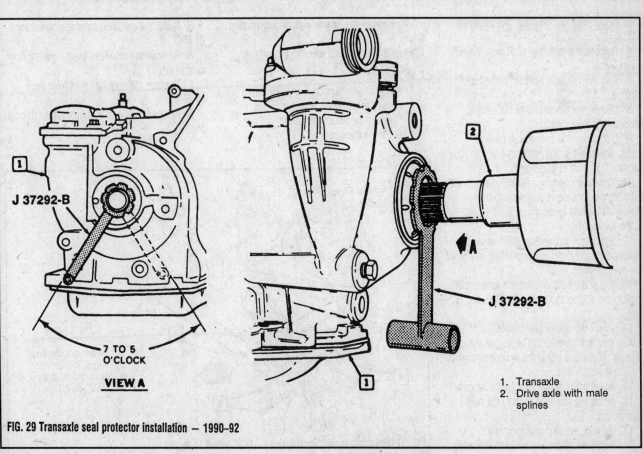

J 37292-B

7 TO 5
O'CLOCK

VIEW A

J 37292-B

1. Transaxle
2. Drive axle with male
   splines

FIG. 29 Transaxle seal protector installation — 1990–92

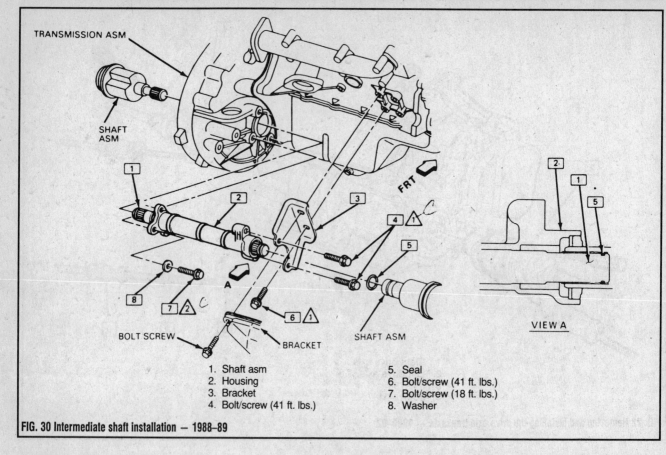

1. Shaft asm
2. Housing
3. Bracket
4. Bolt/screw (41 ft. lbs.)
5. Seal
6. Bolt/screw (41 ft. lbs.)
7. Bolt/screw (18 ft. lbs.)
8. Washer

FIG. 30 Intermediate shaft installation — 1988–89

5. Install the modified outer seal protector J–34754.

6. Remove the stabilizer shaft from the right control arm.

7. Remove the right ball joint from the knuckle.

8. Disconnect the drive axle from the intermediate axle shaft.

9. Disconnect the rear engine mount.

10. Remove the bolt retaining the intermediate shaft to the engine.

11. Carefully disengage the intermediate axle shaft from the transaxle and remove the intermediate shaft assembly.

To install:

12. Place the intermediate shaft assembly into position and lock the intermediate axle shaft into the transaxle.

13. Install the bolt retaining the intermediate shaft to the engine and tighten to 38 ft. lbs. (52 Nm).

14. Install the rear engine mount.

15. Coat the intermediate axle shaft with chassis grease and install the intermediate axle shaft to the drive axle.

16. Install the right ball joint to the knuckle.

17. Install the stabilizer shaft to the right control arm.

18. Remove the seal protector tool.

19. Install the wheel and lower the vehicle.

20. Remove the engine support bar holding fixture.

21. Fill the transaxle with the proper fluid.

2.3L ENGINE

1. Install engine support bar J–28467.

2. Raise the car and suitably support.

3. Remove the wheel assembly.

4. Drain the transaxle.

5. Install the modified outer seal protector J–34754.

6. Remove the stabilizer shaft from the right control arm.

7. Remove the right ball joint from the knuckle.

8. Remove the the rear engine mount through bolt.

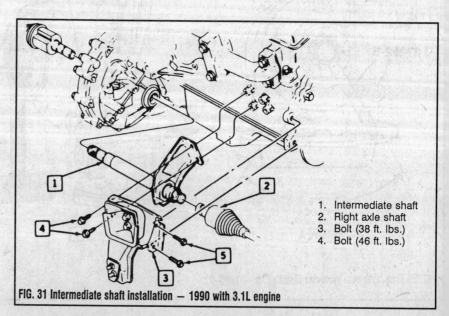

1. Intermediate shaft
2. Right axle shaft
3. Bolt (38 ft. lbs.)
4. Bolt (46 ft. lbs.)

FIG. 31 Intermediate shaft installation — 1990 with 3.1L engine

9. Disconnect the drive axle from the intermediate axle shaft.

10. Remove the bolt retaining the intermediate shaft to the engine.

11. Carefully disengage the intermediate axle shaft from the transaxle and remove the intermediate shaft assembly.

To install:

12. Place the intermediate shaft assembly into position and lock the intermediate axle shaft into the transaxle.

13. Install the bolt retaining the intermediate shaft to the engine and tighten to 38 ft. lbs. (52 Nm).

14. Coat the intermediate axle shaft with chassis grease and install the intermediate axle shaft to the drive axle.

15. Install the rear engine mount through bolt.

16. Install the right ball joint to the knuckle.

17. Install the stabilizer shaft to the right control arm.

18. Remove the seal protector tool.

19. Install the wheel and lower the vehicle.

20. Remove the engine support bar holding fixture.

21. Fill the transaxle with the proper fluid.

1991

▶ SEE FIG. 32-33

1. Install engine support bar J–28467.

2. Raise the car and suitably support.

3. Remove the wheel assembly.

4. Drain the transaxle.

5. Install the modified outer seal protector J–34754.

6. Remove the nut attaching the right stabilizer link to the stabilizer shaft.

7. Remove the right ball joint from the knuckle.

8. Disconnect the drive axle from the intermediate axle shaft and support the drive axle.

9. Disconnect the rear engine mount.

10. Remove the bolt retaining the intermediate shaft support bracket to the engine.

11. Carefully disengage the intermediate axle shaft from the transaxle and remove the intermediate shaft assembly.

To install:

12. Place the intermediate shaft assembly into position and lock the intermediate axle shaft into the transaxle.

13. Install the bolt retaining the intermediate shaft support bracket to the engine and tighten hand tight.

14. Install the rear engine mount.

15. Torque the intermediate shaft support bracket bolt to 37 ft. lbs. (50 Nm).

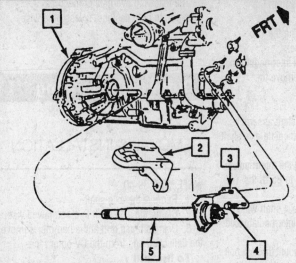

FIG. 32 Intermediate shaft installation — 1991–92 with Isuzu transaxle

1. Transaxle
2. Rear engine mount bracket
3. Intermediate shaft support bracket
4. Bolt
5. Intermediate shaft

16. Coat the intermediate axle shaft with chassis grease and install the intermediate axle shaft to the drive axle. Place a suitable tool into the groove on the joint housing and tap until seated.

❄ WARNING

Be careful not to damage the axle seal or dislodge the garter spring when installing.

17. Install the right ball joint to the knuckle. Tighten the nut to 26 ft. lbs. (35 Nm) plus a 60 degree rotation and install the cotter pin.

18. Install the nut attaching the stabilizer link to the stabilizer shaft. Tighten to 13 ft. lbs. (17 Nm) for all except GTZ models and 70 ft. lbs. (95 Nm) for GTZ models.

19. Remove the seal protector tool.

20. Install the wheel and lower the vehicle.

21. Remove the engine support bar holding fixture.

22. Fill the transaxle with the proper fluid.

1992

▶ SEE FIG. 32-33

1. Install engine support bar J–28467.

2. Raise the car and suitably support.

3. Remove the wheel assembly.

4. Drain the transaxle.

5. Install the modified outer seal protector J–34754.

6. Remove the stabilizer shaft from the right control arm.

7. Remove the right ball joint from the knuckle.

8. Remove the rear engine mount through bolt.

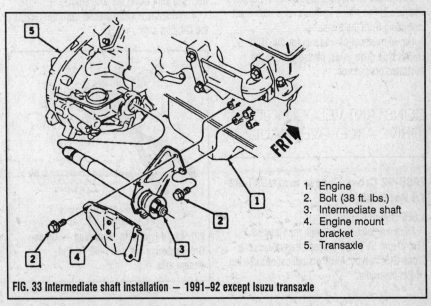

FIG. 33 Intermediate shaft installation — 1991–92 except Isuzu transaxle

1. Engine
2. Bolt (38 ft. lbs.)
3. Intermediate shaft
4. Engine mount bracket
5. Transaxle

9. Disconnect the drive axle from the intermediate axle shaft.

10. Remove the bolt retaining the intermediate shaft to the engine.

11. Carefully disengage the intermediate axle shaft from the transaxle and remove the intermediate shaft assembly.

To install:

12. Place the intermediate shaft assembly into position and lock the intermediate axle shaft into the transaxle.

13. Install the bolt retaining the intermediate shaft to the engine and tighten to 35 ft. lbs. (47 Nm).

14. Coat the intermediate axle shaft with chassis grease and install the intermediate axle shaft to the drive axle.

15. Install the rear engine mount through bolt.

16. Install the right ball joint to the knuckle.

17. Install the stabilizer shaft to the right control arm.

18. Remove the seal protector tool.

19. Install the wheel and lower the vehicle.

20. Remove the engine support bar holding fixture.

21. Fill the transaxle with the proper fluid.

CONSTANT VELOCITY JOINT (DRIVE AXLE) OVERHAUL

1988–90 Tri-Pot Design

♦ SEE FIGS. 34-36

All drive shafts except the left side inboard joint of the automatic transaxles incorporates a male spline and interlocks with the transaxle gears through the use of a barrel type snap rings. The left side inboard shaft

attachment on the automatic transaxle, utilizes a female spline which installs over a stub shaft protruding from the transaxle.

For all overhaul procedures for the 1988–90 Tri-Pot type drive axles, please refer to the illustrated procedures.

CONSTANT VELOCITY JOINT (DRIVE AXLE) OVERHAUL

1988–92 Cross Groove and 1991–92 Tri-Pot Design

♦ SEE FIGS. 37-56

The inner joint on cars with the HM-282, 5TM40 and NVT-550 5-speed transaxles, is a Cross-Groove type. All other applications use the Tri-Pot inner joint.

The following overhaul procedures incorporate both designs, unless otherwise noted.

Outer Deflector Ring

REMOVAL & INSTALLATION

♦ SEE FIGS. 39-40

1. Remove the axle shaft.

2. Clamp the axle shaft in a soft jawed vise.

3. Using a brass drift and a hammer, remove the deflecting ring from the CV outer race.

To install:

4. Position and square up the deflecting ring at press diameter of CV outer race.

5. Using a 3 in. (76mm) pipe coupling, M24×1.5 nut a fabricated sheet metal sleeve,tighten the nut until the deflector bottoms against the shoulder of the CV outer joint.

Outer Joint Seal

REMOVAL & INSTALLATION

♦ SEE FIGS. 41-43

1. Remove the large seal retaining clamp from the CV joint with a side cutter and discard.

2. Remove the small seal retaining clamp on the axle shaft with a side cutter and discard.

3. Separate the joint seal from the CV join race at large diameter and slide the seal away from the joint along the axle shaft.

4. Wipe the excess grease from the face of the CV joint inner race.

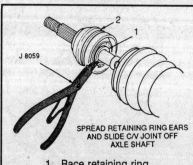

1. Race retaining ring
2. CV joint outer race

FIG. 41 CV joint axle separation — Cross-Groove design and 1991–92 Tri-Pot design axle

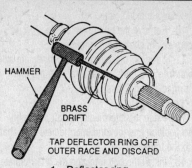

1. Deflector ring

FIG. 39 Outer deflector ring removal — Cross-Groove design and 1991–92 Tri-Pot design axle

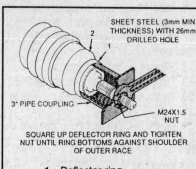

1. Deflector ring
2. CV joint outer race

FIG. 40 Outer deflector ring installation — Cross-Groove design and 1991–92 Tri-Pot design axle

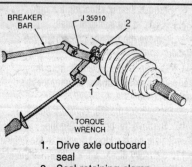

1. Drive axle outboard seal
2. Seal retaining clamp

FIG. 42 Seal retaining clamp installation — Cross-Groove design and 1991–92 Tri-Pot design axle

5. Spread the ears on the race retaining ring with snap ring pliers and remove the CV joint from the axle shaft.

6. Remove the seal from the axle shaft.

7. Disassemble the joint and flush the grease prior to installing a new seal.

To install:

8. Install the small retaining clamp on the neck of the new seal, but do not crimp.

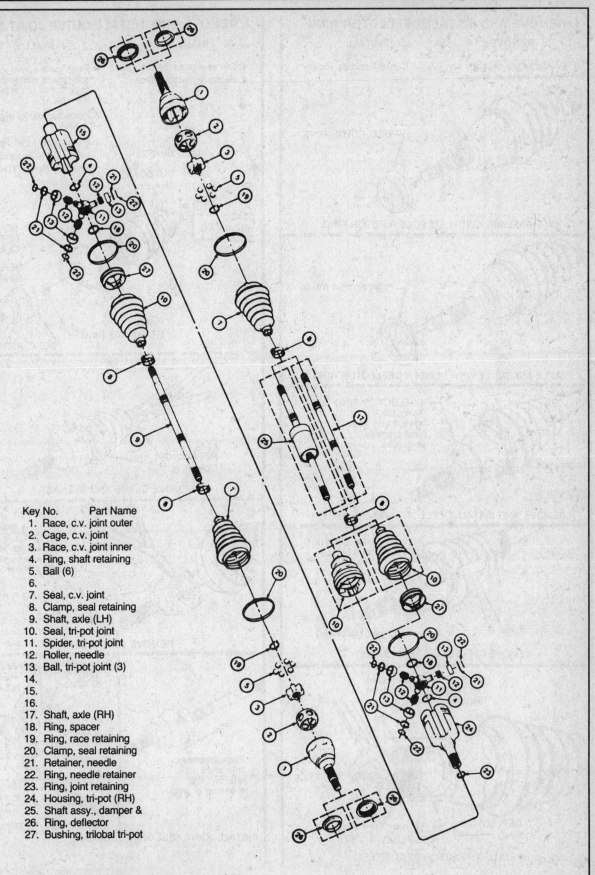

Key No.   Part Name
1. Race, c.v. joint outer
2. Cage, c.v. joint
3. Race, c.v. joint inner
4. Ring, shaft retaining
5. Ball (6)
6.
7. Seal, c.v. joint
8. Clamp, seal retaining
9. Shaft, axle (LH)
10. Seal, tri-pot joint
11. Spider, tri-pot joint
12. Roller, needle
13. Ball, tri-pot joint (3)
14.
15.
16.
17. Shaft, axle (RH)
18. Ring, spacer
19. Ring, race retaining
20. Clamp, seal retaining
21. Retainer, needle
22. Ring, needle retainer
23. Ring, joint retaining
24. Housing, tri-pot (RH)
25. Shaft assy., damper &
26. Ring, deflector
27. Bushing, trilobal tri-pot

FIG. 34 Disassembled view of the Tri-Pot design drive axle — 1988–90

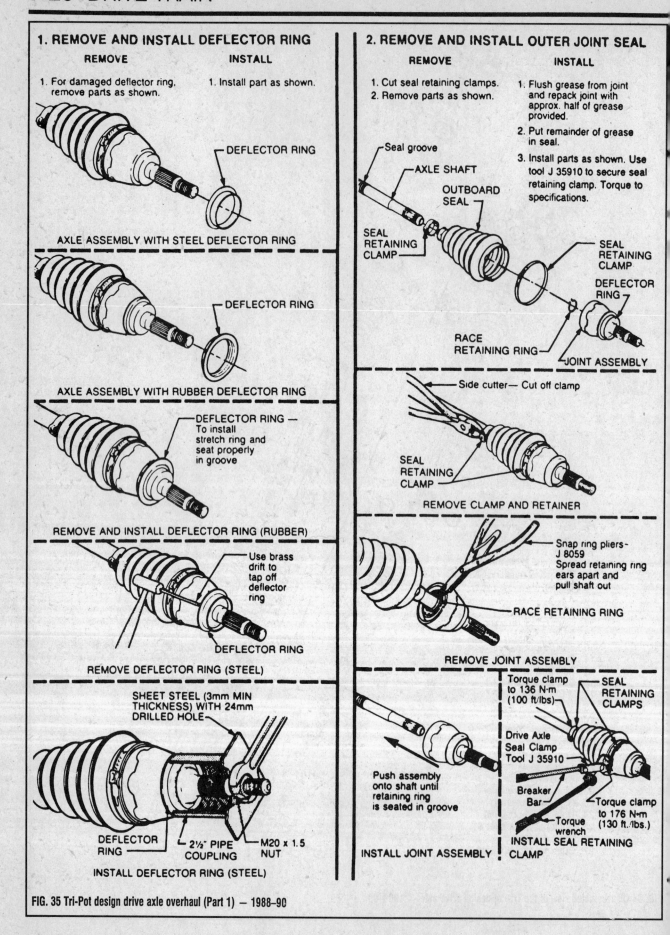

1. REMOVE AND INSTALL DEFLECTOR RING

REMOVE

1. For damaged deflector ring, remove parts as shown.

INSTALL

1. Install part as shown.

DEFLECTOR RING

AXLE ASSEMBLY WITH STEEL DEFLECTOR RING

DEFLECTOR RING

AXLE ASSEMBLY WITH RUBBER DEFLECTOR RING

DEFLECTOR RING — To install stretch ring and seat properly in groove

REMOVE AND INSTALL DEFLECTOR RING (RUBBER)

Use brass drift to tap off deflector ring

DEFLECTOR RING

REMOVE DEFLECTOR RING (STEEL)

SHEET STEEL (3mm MIN THICKNESS) WITH 24mm DRILLED HOLE

DEFLECTOR RING

2½" PIPE COUPLING

M20 x 1.5 NUT

INSTALL DEFLECTOR RING (STEEL)

2. REMOVE AND INSTALL OUTER JOINT SEAL

REMOVE

1. Cut seal retaining clamps.
2. Remove parts as shown.

INSTALL

1. Flush grease from joint and repack joint with approx. half of grease provided.
2. Put remainder of grease in seal.
3. Install parts as shown. Use tool J 35910 to secure seal retaining clamp. Torque to specifications.

Seal groove

AXLE SHAFT

OUTBOARD SEAL

SEAL RETAINING CLAMP

SEAL RETAINING CLAMP

DEFLECTOR RING

RACE RETAINING RING

JOINT ASSEMBLY

Side cutter— Cut off clamp

SEAL RETAINING CLAMP

REMOVE CLAMP AND RETAINER

Snap ring pliers— J 8059 Spread retaining ring ears apart and pull shaft out

RACE RETAINING RING

REMOVE JOINT ASSEMBLY

Push assembly onto shaft until retaining ring is seated in groove

INSTALL JOINT ASSEMBLY

Torque clamp to 136 N·m (100 ft/lbs)

SEAL RETAINING CLAMPS

Drive Axle Seal Clamp Tool J 35910

Breaker Bar

Torque clamp to 176 N·m (130 ft./lbs)

Torque wrench

INSTALL SEAL RETAINING CLAMP

FIG. 35 Tri-Pot design drive axle overhaul (Part 1) — 1988–90

3. DISASSEMBLE AND ASSEMBLE OUTER JOINT ASSEMBLY

REMOVE	INSTALL
1. Remove parts as shown.	1. Put a light coat of recommended grease on ball grooves of inner and outer races.
	2. Install parts as shown.
	NOTICE: Be sure retaining ring side of inner race faces axle shaft.
	3. Pack joint with recommended grease.

- BALLS (6)
- INNER RACE
- CAGE
- OUTER RACE

- OUTER RACE
- Remove ball
- INNER RACE
- CAGE
- Brass drift gently tap on cage until tilted enough to remove first ball. Remove other balls in similar manner.

DISASSEMBLE AND ASSEMBLE BALLS

- Pivot cage and inner race at 90° to center line of outer race with cage windows aligned with lands of outer race, lift out cage and inner race.
- CAGE
- Land
- Land
- Windows
- OUTER RACE

DISASSEMBLE AND ASSEMBLE CAGE AND INNER RACE TO OUTER RACE

- Rotate up and out of cage
- INNER RACE
- CAGE
- Land
- Cage window

DISASSEMBLE AND ASSEMBLE INNER RACE AND CAGE

4. REMOVE AND INSTALL INNER TRI-POT SEAL

REMOVE	INSTALL
1. Cut seal retaining clamps.	1. Flush grease from housing and repack housing with approx. half of grease furnished with new seal.
2. Remove parts as shown.	2. Put remainder of grease in seal.
	3. Refer to manufacturer's seal installation dimension prior to crimping clamps. Use tool J 35910 to secure seal retaining clamps. Torque to specifications.

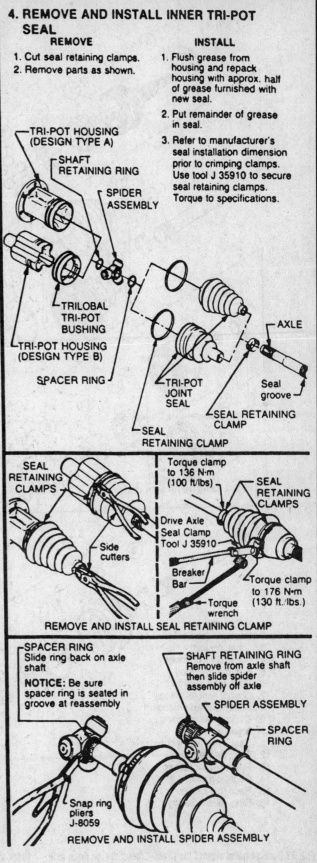

- TRI-POT HOUSING (DESIGN TYPE A)
- SHAFT RETAINING RING
- SPIDER ASSEMBLY
- TRILOBAL TRI-POT BUSHING
- TRI-POT HOUSING (DESIGN TYPE B)
- SPACER RING
- SEAL RETAINING CLAMP
- TRI-POT JOINT SEAL
- SEAL RETAINING CLAMP
- AXLE
- Seal groove

- SEAL RETAINING CLAMPS
- Side cutters
- Torque clamp to 136 N·m (100 ft/lbs)
- SEAL RETAINING CLAMPS
- Drive Axle Seal Clamp Tool J 35910
- Breaker Bar
- Torque clamp to 176 N·m (130 ft./lbs.)
- Torque wrench

REMOVE AND INSTALL SEAL RETAINING CLAMP

- SPACER RING — Slide ring back on axle shaft
- **NOTICE:** Be sure spacer ring is seated in groove at reassembly
- Snap ring pliers J-8059
- SHAFT RETAINING RING Remove from axle shaft then slide spider assembly off axle
- SPIDER ASSEMBLY
- SPACER RING

REMOVE AND INSTALL SPIDER ASSEMBLY

FIG. 36 Tri-Pot design drive axle overhaul (Part 2) — 1988–90

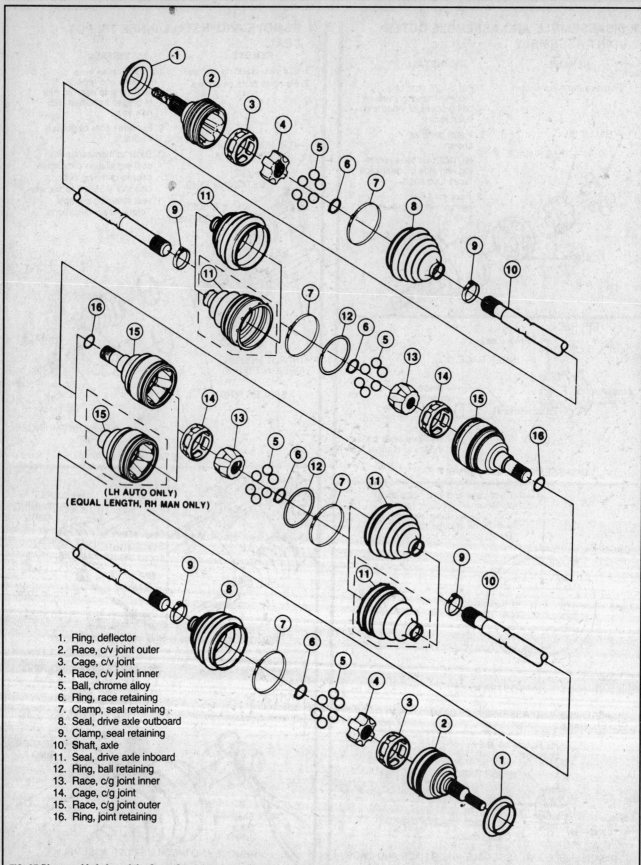

1. Ring, deflector
2. Race, c/v joint outer
3. Cage, c/v joint
4. Race, c/v joint inner
5. Ball, chrome alloy
6. Ring, race retaining
7. Clamp, seal retaining
8. Seal, drive axle outboard
9. Clamp, seal retaining
10. Shaft, axle
11. Seal, drive axle inboard
12. Ring, ball retaining
13. Race, c/g joint inner
14. Cage, c/g joint
15. Race, c/g joint outer
16. Ring, joint retaining

(LH AUTO ONLY)
(EQUAL LENGTH, RH MAN ONLY)

FIG. 37 Disassembled view of the Cross-Groove design drive axle — 1988–92

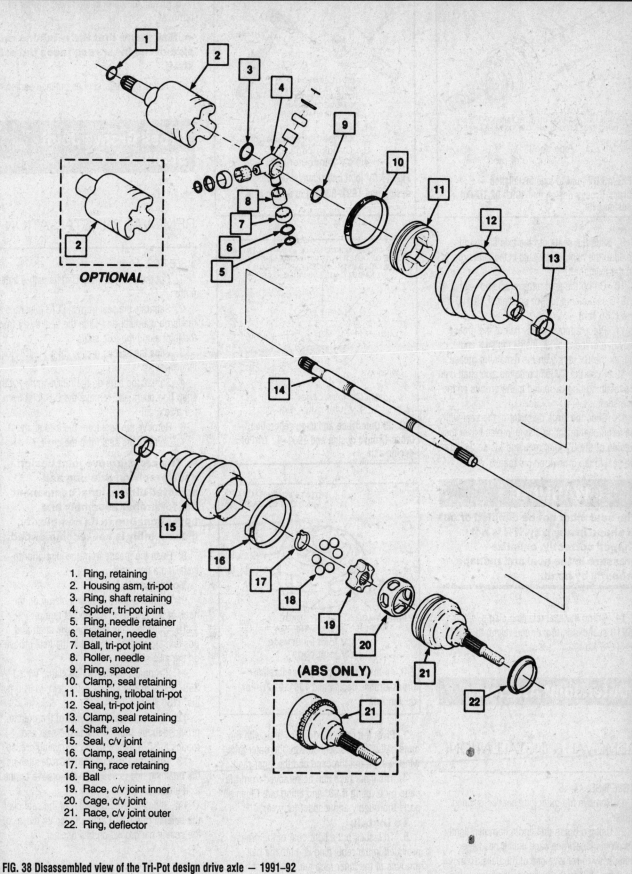

OPTIONAL

(ABS ONLY)

1. Ring, retaining
2. Housing asm, tri-pot
3. Ring, shaft retaining
4. Spider, tri-pot joint
5. Ring, needle retainer
6. Retainer, needle
7. Ball, tri-pot joint
8. Roller, needle
9. Ring, spacer
10. Clamp, seal retaining
11. Bushing, trilobal tri-pot
12. Seal, tri-pot joint
13. Clamp, seal retaining
14. Shaft, axle
15. Seal, c/v joint
16. Clamp, seal retaining
17. Ring, race retaining
18. Ball
19. Race, c/v joint inner
20. Cage, c/v joint
21. Race, c/v joint outer
22. Ring, deflector

FIG. 38 Disassembled view of the Tri-Pot design drive axle — 1991–92

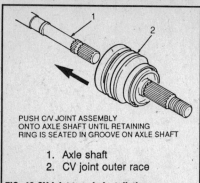

PUSH C/V JOINT ASSEMBLY
ONTO AXLE SHAFT UNTIL RETAINING
RING IS SEATED IN GROOVE ON AXLE SHAFT

1. Axle shaft
2. CV joint outer race

FIG. 43 CV joint to axle installation — Cross-Groove design and 1991–92 Tri-Pot design axle

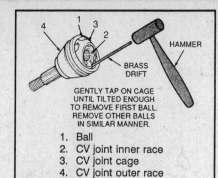

HAMMER

BRASS DRIFT

GENTLY TAP ON CAGE
UNTIL TILTED ENOUGH
TO REMOVE FIRST BALL.
REMOVE OTHER BALLS
IN SIMILAR MANNER.

1. Ball
2. CV joint inner race
3. CV joint cage
4. CV joint outer race

FIG. 44 CV joint ball removal — Cross-Groove design and 1991–92 Tri-Pot design axle

6. Install the parts in the reverse order of removal.

➡ **Make sure that the retaining ring side of the inner race faces the axle shaft.**

7. Install the outer seal as outlined earlier.

Cross Groove Joint Seal

REMOVAL & INSTALLATION

◆ SEE FIGS. 47-50

1. Cut the seal retaining clamps with a side cutter.

2. Separate the seal from the C/G joint race at the large diameter and slide the seal away from the joint along the axle shaft.

3. Wipe the excess grease from the C/G joint inner race.

4. Spread the ears on the retaining ring with snap ring pliers and remove the C/G joint from the axle shaft.

5. Remove the seal from the axle shaft.

6. Remove the seal from the axle shaft.

7. Remove the seal from the shaft.

➡ **The cross-groove joint design uses precision grinding and selected dimensional component fits for proper assembly and operation. Due to its complexity, disassembly is not recommended.**

8. Flush the grease from the joint prior to installing a new seal.

To install:

9. Install the small retaining clamp on the neck of the new seal, but do not crimp.

10. Slide the seal onto the axle shaft and position the neck of the seal in the seal groove on the axle shaft.

11. Crimp the seal retaining clamp with J 35910 seal clamp tool or equivalent, to 100 ft. lbs. (136 Nm).

12. Place approximately half of the grease provided in the seal kit, inside the seal and repack the C/G joint with the remaining grease.

13. Push the C/G joint onto the axle shaft until the retaining ring is seated in the groove on the axle shaft.

14. Slide the large diameter of the seal over the outside of the C/G joint and locate the lip of the seal in the groove on ball retainer.

9. Slide the seal onto the axle shaft and position the neck of the seal in the seal groove on the axle shaft.

10. Crimp the seal retaining clamp with J 35910 seal clamp tool or equivalent, to 100 ft. lbs. (136 Nm).

11. Place approximately half of the grease provided in the seal kit, inside the seal and repack the CV joint with the remaining grease.

12. Push the CV joint onto the axle shaft until the retaining ring is seated in the groove on the axle shaft.

13. Slide the large diameter of the seal with the large seal retaining clamp in place over the outside of the CV joint race and locate the lip of the seal in the groove on the race.

❊❊ WARNING

The seal must not be dimpled or out of shape in any way. If it is not shaped correctly, equalize pressure in the seal and reshape properly by hand.

14. Crimp the seal retaining clamp with J 35910 seal clamp tool or equivalent, to 130 ft. lbs. (176 Nm).

Outer Joint Assembly

REMOVAL & INSTALLATION

◆ SEE FIGS. 44-46

1. Remove the outer joint seal as outlined earlier.

2. Using a brass drift and a hammer, lightly tap on the inner race cage until it has tilted sufficiently to remove one of the balls. Remove the other balls in the same manner.

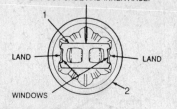

PIVOT CAGE AND INNER RACE AT 90° TO CENTER
LINE OF OUTER RACE WITH CAGE WINDOWS
ALIGNED WITH LANDS OF OUTER RACE.
LIFT OUT CAGE AND INNER RACE.

LAND

LAND

WINDOWS

1. CV joint cage
2. CV joint outer race

FIG. 45 Outer race and cage separation — Cross-Groove design and 1991–92 Tri-Pot design axle

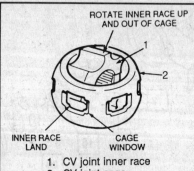

ROTATE INNER RACE UP
AND OUT OF CAGE

INNER RACE LAND

CAGE WINDOW

1. CV joint inner race
2. CV joint cage

FIG. 46 Inner race and cage separation — Cross-Groove design and 1991–92 Tri-Pot design axle

3. Pivot the cage 90 degrees and, with the cage ball windows aligned with the outer joint windows, lift out the cage and the inner race.

4. The inner race can be removed from the cage by pivoting it 90° and lifting out. Clean all parts thoroughly and inspect for wear.

To install:

5. To install, put a light coat of the grease provided in the rebuilding kit onto the ball grooves of the inner race and outer joint.

✳ WARNING

The seal must not be dimpled or out of shape in any way. If it is not shaped correctly, equalize pressure in the seal and reshape properly by hand.

15. Crimp the seal retaining clamp with J 35910 seal clamp tool or equivalent, to 130 ft. lbs. (176 Nm).

Inner Tri-Pot Seal

REMOVAL & INSTALLATION

◆ SEE FIGS. 51-56

1. Remove the larger seal retaining clamp from the tri-pot joint with a side cutter and discard.

✳ WARNING

Do not cut through the seal and damage the sealing surface of the tri-pot outer housing and trilobal bushing.

2. Remove the small seal retaining clamp from the axle shaft with a side cutter and discard.

3. Separate the seal from the trilobal tri-pot bushing at the large diameter and slide the seal away from the joint along the axle shaft.

4. Remove the tri-pot housing from the spider and shaft.

5. Spread the spacer ring with snap ring pliers and slide the spacer ring and tri-pot spider back on the axle shaft.

6. Remove the shaft retaining ring from the groove on the axle shaft and slide the spider assembly off of the shaft.

7. Check the tri-pot balls and needle rollers for damage or wear.

➡ **Use care when handling the spider assembly as the tri-pot balls and rollers may separate from the spider trunnions.**

8. Remove the trilobal tri-pot bushing from the tri-pot housing.

9. Remove the spacer ring and seal from the axle shaft.

10. Flush the grease from the tri-pot housing.

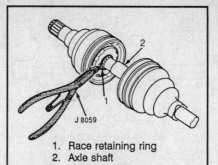

1. Race retaining ring
2. Axle shaft

FIG. 47 CG joint and axle separation — Cross-Groove design axle

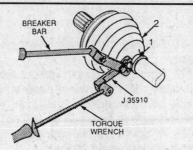

1. Seal retaining clamp
2. Drive axle inboard seal

FIG. 48 Seal retaining clamp installation — Cross-Groove design axle

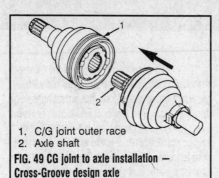

1. C/G joint outer race
2. Axle shaft

FIG. 49 CG joint to axle installation — Cross-Groove design axle

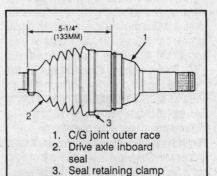

1. C/G joint outer race
2. Drive axle inboard seal
3. Seal retaining clamp

FIG. 50 CG joint seal installation measurement — Cross-Groove design axle

To install:

11. Install the small retaining clamp on the neck of the new seal, but do not crimp.

12. Slide the seal onto the axle shaft and position the neck of the seal in the seal groove on the axle shaft.

13. Crimp the seal retaining clamp with J 35910 seal clamp tool or equivalent, to 100 ft. lbs. (136 Nm).

14. Install the spacer ring on the axle shaft and beyond the 2nd groove.

15. Slide the tri-pot spider assembly against the spacer ring on the shaft.

➡ **Make sure the counterbored face of the tri-pot spider faces the end of the shaft.**

16. Install the shaft retaining ring in the groove of the axle shaft with the snap ring pliers.

17. Slide the tri-pot spider towards the end of the shaft and reseat the spacer ring in the groove on the shaft.

18. Place approximately half of the grease provided in the seal kit, inside the seal and repack the tri-pot housing with the remaining grease.

19. Install the trilobal tri-pot bushing to the tri-pot housing.

20. Position the larger clamp on the seal.

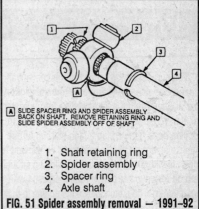

A SLIDE SPACER RING AND SPIDER ASSEMBLY BACK ON SHAFT. REMOVE RETAINING RING AND SLIDE SPIDER ASSEMBLY OFF OF SHAFT

1. Shaft retaining ring
2. Spider assembly
3. Spacer ring
4. Axle shaft

FIG. 51 Spider assembly removal — 1991–92 Tri-Pot design axle

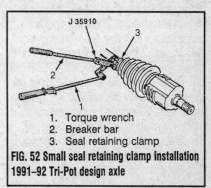

1. Torque wrench
2. Breaker bar
3. Seal retaining clamp

FIG. 52 Small seal retaining clamp installation 1991–92 Tri-Pot design axle

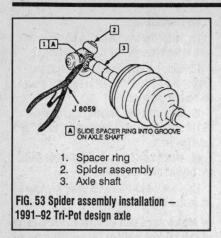

1. Spacer ring
2. Spider assembly
3. Axle shaft

FIG. 53 Spider assembly installation — 1991–92 Tri-Pot design axle

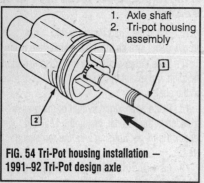

1. Axle shaft
2. Tri-pot housing assembly

FIG. 54 Tri-Pot housing installation — 1991–92 Tri-Pot design axle

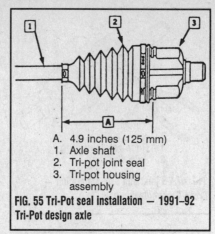

A. 4.9 inches (125 mm)
1. Axle shaft
2. Tri-pot joint seal
3. Tri-pot housing assembly

FIG. 55 Tri-Pot seal installation — 1991–92 Tri-Pot design axle

21. Slide the tri-pot housing over the tri-pot spider.

22. Slide the large diameter of the seal, with the larger clamp in place, over the outside of the trilobal bushing and locate the lip of the seal in the bushing groove.

23. Position the tri-pot assembly at the proper vehicle dimension as shown.

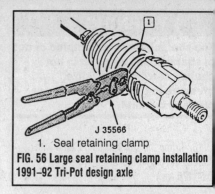

1. Seal retaining clamp

FIG. 56 Large seal retaining clamp installation 1991–92 Tri-Pot design axle

✷✷ WARNING

The seal must not be dimpled or out of shape in any way. If it is not shaped correctly, equalize pressure by carefully inserting a thin flat blunt tool (no sharp edges) between the large seal opening and the bushing and reshape properly by hand.

24. Crimp the seal retaining clamp with J 35566 seal clamp tool or equivalent.

CLUTCH

The purpose of the clutch is to disconnect and connect engine power from the transmission. A car at rest requires a lot of engine torque to get all that weight moving. An internal combustion engine does not develop a high starting torque (unlike steam engines), so it must be allowed to operate without any load until it builds up enough torque to move the car. Torque increases with engine rpm. The clutch allows the engine to build up torque by physically disconnecting the engine from the transmission, relieving the engine of any load or resistance. The transfer of engine power to the transmission (the load) must be smooth and gradual; if it weren't, drive line components would wear out or break quickly. This gradual power transfer is made possible by gradually releasing the clutch pedal. The clutch disc and pressure plate are the connecting link between the engine and transmission. When the clutch pedal is released, the disc and plate contact each other (clutch engagement), physically joining the engine and transmission. When the pedal is pushed in, the disc and plate separate (the clutch is disengaged), disconnecting the engine from the transmission.

The clutch assembly consists of the flywheel, the clutch disc, the clutch pressure plate, the throwout bearing and fork, the actuating linkage and the pedal. The flywheel and clutch pressure plate (driving members) are connected to the engine crankshaft and rotate with it. The clutch disc is located between the flywheel and pressure plate, and splined to the transmission shaft. A driving member is one that is attached to the engine and transfers engine power to a driven member (clutch disc) on the transmission shaft. A driving member (pressure plate) rotates (drives) a driven member (clutch disc) on contact and, in so doing, turns the transmission shaft. There is a circular diaphragm spring within the pressure plate cover (transmission side). In a relaxed state (when the clutch pedal is fully released), this spring is convex; that is, it is dished outward toward the transmission. Pushing in the clutch pedal actuates an attached linkage rod. Connected to the other end of this rod is the throwout bearing fork. The throwout bearing is attached to the fork. When the clutch

pedal is depressed, the clutch linkage pushes the fork and bearing forward to contact the diaphragm spring of the pressure plate. The outer edges of the spring are secured to the pressure plate and are pivoted on rings so that when the center of the spring is compressed by the throwout bearing, the outer edges bow outward and, by so doing, pull the pressure plate in the same direction — away from the clutch disc. This action separates the disc from the plate, disengaging the clutch and allowing the transmission to be shifted into another gear. A coil type clutch return spring attached to the clutch pedal arm permits full release of the pedal. Releasing the pedal pulls the throwout bearing away from the diaphragm spring resulting in a reversal of spring position. As bearing pressure is gradually released from the spring center, the outer edges of the spring bow outward, pushing the pressure plate into closer contact with the clutch disc. As the disc and plate move closer together, friction between the 2 increases and slippage is reduced until, when full spring pressure is applied (by fully releasing the pedal), The speed of the disc and plate are the same. This stops all slipping, creating a direct connection between the plate and disc which results in the transfer of power from the engine to the transmission. The clutch disc is now rotating with the pressure plate at engine speed and, because it is splined to the transmission shaft, the shaft now turns at the same engine speed. Understanding clutch operation can be rather difficult at first; if you're still confused after reading this, consider the following analogy. The action of the diaphragm spring can be compared to that of an oil can bottom. The bottom of an oil can is shaped very much like the clutch diaphragm spring and pushing in on the can bottom and then releasing it produces a similar effect. As mentioned earlier, the clutch pedal return spring permits full release of the pedal and reduces linkage slack due to wear. As the linkage wears, clutch free-pedal travel will increase and free-travel will decrease as the clutch wears. Free-travel is actually throwout bearing lash.

The diaphragm spring type clutches used are available in 2 different designs: flat diaphragm springs or bent spring. The bent fingers are bent back to create a centrifugal boost ensuring quick re-engagement at higher engine speeds. This design enables pressure plate load to increase as the clutch disc wears and makes low pedal effort possible even with a heavy-duty clutch. The throwout bearing used with the bent finger design is 1¼ in. (31.75mm) long and is shorter than the bearing used with the flat finger design. These bearings are not interchangeable. If the longer bearing is used with the bent finger clutch, free-pedal travel will not exist. This results in clutch slippage and rapid wear.

The transmission varies the gear ratio between the engine and rear wheels. It can be shifted to change engine speed as driving conditions and loads change. The transmission allows disengaging and reversing power from the engine to the wheels.

Adjustment

No adjustment of the clutch linkage or pedal position is required.

Clutch Start Switch

REMOVAL & INSTALLATION

▶ SEE FIG. 57
1. Disconnect the negative terminal from the battery.

2. Locate the switch on the clutch pedal support.
3. Disconnect the electrical connector from the switch and remove the switch by removing the nut from the stud.

To install:
4. Install the switch on the stud and tighten the retaining nut to 53 inch lbs. (6 Nm).
5. Connect the electrical harness to the switch.
6. Connect the negative battery cable and verify that the starter engages only when the clutch is fully engaged.

Clutch Master and Slave (Actuator) Cylinder

A hydraulic clutch mechanism is used on all clutch equipped vehicles. This mechanism uses a clutch master cylinder with a remote reservoir and a slave cylinder connected to the master cylinder. Whenever the system is disconnected for repair or replacement, the clutch system must be bled to insure proper operation.

REMOVAL & INSTALLATION

1988–89 All Engines
1990–92 With 2.2L Engine

▶ SEE FIG. 58 & 60
The clutch master and slave cylinders are removed from the vehicle as an assembly. After installation the clutch hydraulic system must be bled.
1. Disconnect the negative terminal from the battery.
2. From inside the vehicle, remove the hush panel.

➡ **If equipped with a 2.8L engine, remove the air cleaner assembly.**

3. Disconnect the clutch master cylinder push rod from the clutch master cylinder.
4. From the front of the dash, remove the trim cover.
5. Remove the clutch master cylinder-to-clutch pedal bracket nuts and the remote reservoir-to-chassis screws.
6. Remove the slave cylinder-to-transaxle nuts and the slave cylinder.
7. Remove the hydraulic system (as a unit) from the vehicle.

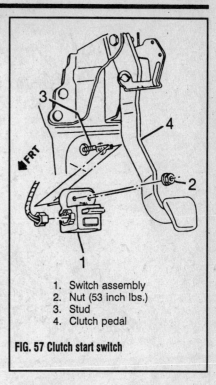

1. Switch assembly
2. Nut (53 inch lbs.)
3. Stud
4. Clutch pedal

FIG. 57 Clutch start switch

To install:
8. Install the slave cylinder-to-transaxle support, align the push rod to the clutch fork outer lever pocket. Torque the slave cylinder-to-transaxle support nuts to 16 ft. lbs. (22 Nm).

➡ **If installing a new clutch hydraulic system, DO NOT break the push rod plastic retainer; the straps will break on the first pedal application.**

9. Install the master cylinder-to-clutch pedal bracket. Torque the nuts evenly (to prevent damaging the master cylinder) to 15–20 ft. lbs. and reverse the removal procedures. Remove the pedal restrictor from the push rod. Lubricate the push rod bushing on the clutch pedal; if the bushing is cracked or worn, replace it.
10. If equipped with cruise control, check the switch adjustment at the clutch pedal bracket.

➡ **When adjusting the cruise control switch, do not exert more than 20 lbs. of upward force on the clutch pedal pad for damage to the master cylinder push rod retaining rod can result.**

11. Depress the clutch pedal several times to break the plastic retaining straps; DO NOT remove the plastic button from the end of the push rod.
12. To complete the installation, reverse the removal procedures. If necessary, bleed the clutch hydraulic system.

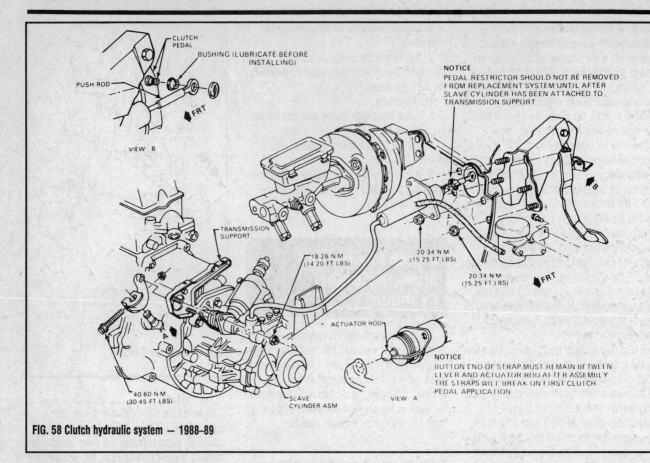

FIG. 58 Clutch hydraulic system — 1988–89

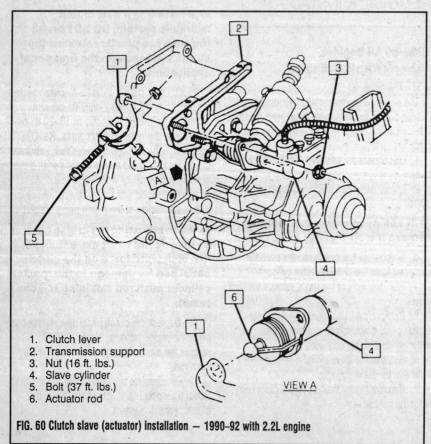

1. Clutch lever
2. Transmission support
3. Nut (16 ft. lbs.)
4. Slave cylinder
5. Bolt (37 ft. lbs.)
6. Actuator rod

FIG. 60 Clutch slave (actuator) installation — 1990–92 with 2.2L engine

1992 2.3L and 3.1L Engines

◆ SEE FIG. 59

The clutch master and slave cylinders are removed from the vehicle as an assembly. After installation the clutch hydraulic system must be bled.

1. Disconnect the negative terminal from the battery.
2. From inside the vehicle, remove the hush panel.
3. Remove the air cleaner duct assembly.
4. Disconnect the left fender brace.
5. Remove the battery.
6. Disconnect the M.A.T. sensor lead at the air cleaner.
7. Disconnect the Mass Air Flow sensor lead.
8. Remove the PCV pipe retaining clamp at the air intake duct.
9. Remove the clamp retaining the air intake duct to the throttle body.
10. Remove the Mass Air Flow sensor.
11. Remove the air cleaner bracket mounting bolts at the battery tray.
12. Remove the air cleaner, Mass Air Flow sensor and the air intake duct as an assembly.
13. Disconnect the electrical lead at the washer bottle, remove the attaching bolts and remove the bottle.

14. Disconnect the cruise control mounting bracket retaining nuts from the strut tower, if equipped.

15. Disconnect the clutch master cylinder push rod from the clutch pedal.

16. From the front of the dash, remove the trim cover, if so equipped.

17. Remove the clutch master cylinder retaining nuts at the dash.

18. Remove the actuator cylinder-to-transaxle nuts.

19. Remove the hydraulic system (as a unit) from the vehicle.

To Install:

20. Install the actuator cylinder-to-transaxle support, align the push rod to the clutch fork outer lever pocket. Torque the slave cylinder-to-transaxle support nuts to 16 ft. lbs. (22 Nm).

※※ WARNING

If installing a new clutch hydraulic system, DO NOT break the push rod plastic retainer; the straps will break on the first pedal application.

21. Install the master cylinder to the front of the dash. Torque the nuts evenly (to prevent damaging the master cylinder) to 16 ft. lbs. (22 Nm). Remove the pedal restrictor from the push rod. Lubricate the push rod bushing on the clutch pedal; if the bushing is cracked or worn, replace it.

22. If equipped with cruise control, check the switch adjustment at the clutch pedal bracket.

When adjusting the cruise control switch, do not exert more than 20 lbs. of upward force on the clutch pedal pad for damage to the master cylinder push rod retaining rod can result.

23. Depress the clutch pedal several times to break the plastic retaining straps; DO NOT remove the plastic button from the end of the push rod.

24. Install the washer bottle and connect the electrical lead.

25. Install the air cleaner, Mass Air Flow sensor and the air intake duct as an assembly.

26. Install the air cleaner bracket mounting bolts at the battery tray.

27. Install the Mass Air Flow sensor.

28. Install the clamp retaining the air intake duct to the throttle body.

29. Install the PCV pipe retaining clamp at the air intake duct.

30. Connect the Mass Air Flow sensor lead.

31. Connect the M.A.T. sensor lead at the air cleaner.

32. Install the battery.

33. Connect the left fender brace.

34. Install the air cleaner duct assembly.

35. From inside the vehicle, install the hush panel.

36. Connect the negative terminal from the battery.

Master Cylinder

REMOVAL & INSTALLATION

1990–91 With 2.3 and 3.1L Engines

▶ SEE FIG. 61

1. Disconnect the negative terminal from the battery.

2. From inside the vehicle, remove the hush panel.

3. Disconnect the clutch master cylinder push rod from the clutch master cylinder.

4. From the front of the dash, remove the trim cover.

5. Remove the air cleaner assembly.

6. Remove the clutch master cylinder-to-clutch pedal bracket nuts and the remote reservoir-to-chassis screws.

7. Disconnect the quick connect fitting on the hydraulic line and remove the master cylinder from the vehicle.

To install:

8. Connect the quick connect fitting on the hydraulic line and install the master cylinder to the vehicle.

9. With the master cylinder installed to the front of the dash tighten the retaining nuts to 20 ft. lbs. (27 Nm). Install the reservoir mounting screws.

10. Remove the pedal restrictor from the push rod on the new replacement. Lubricate the push rod bushing on the clutch pedal; if the bushing is cracked or worn, replace it.

11. If equipped with cruise control, check the switch adjustment at the clutch pedal bracket.

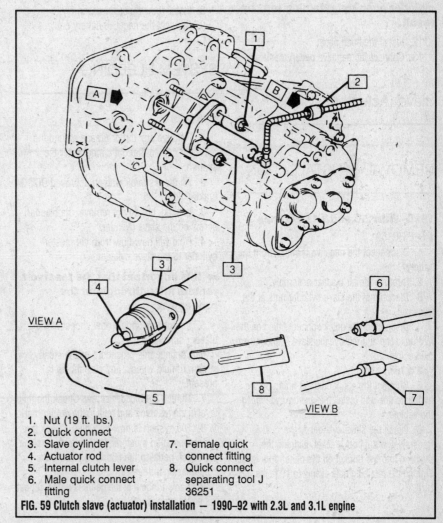

1. Nut (19 ft. lbs.)
2. Quick connect
3. Slave cylinder
4. Actuator rod
5. Internal clutch lever
6. Male quick connect fitting
7. Female quick connect fitting
8. Quick connect separating tool J 36251

FIG. 59 Clutch slave (actuator) installation — 1990–92 with 2.3L and 3.1L engine

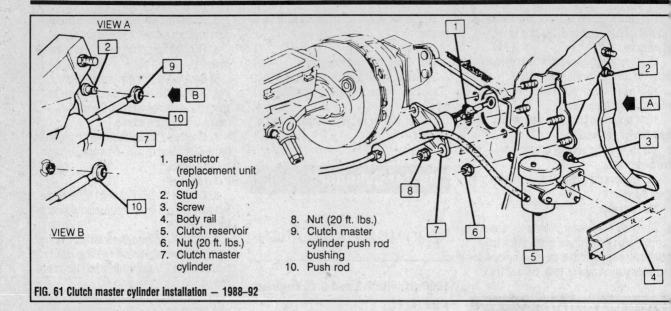

FIG. 61 Clutch master cylinder installation — 1988–92

VIEW A

VIEW B

1. Restrictor (replacement unit only)
2. Stud
3. Screw
4. Body rail
5. Clutch reservoir
6. Nut (20 ft. lbs.)
7. Clutch master cylinder
8. Nut (20 ft. lbs.)
9. Clutch master cylinder push rod bushing
10. Push rod

➡ **When adjusting the cruise control switch, do not exert more than 20 lbs. of upward force on the clutch pedal pad for damage to the master cylinder push rod retaining rod can result.**

12. Install the hush panel.
13. Connect the negative battery cable.

Slave (Actuator) Cylinder

REMOVAL & INSTALLATION

1990– With 2.3 and 3.1L Engines

◆ SEE FIG. 59

1. Disconnect the negative terminal from the battery.
2. Remove the air cleaner assembly.
3. Disconnect the slave cylinder nuts at the transaxle.
4. Disconnect the quick connect fitting on the hydraulic line and remove the slave cylinder from the vehicle.

To install:

5. Connect the quick connect fitting on the hydraulic line and install the master cylinder to the vehicle.
6. Install the slave cylinder to the transmission support bracket, aligning the pushrod into the pocket on the clutch fork lever. Tighten the retaining nuts evenly to 19 ft. lbs. (25 Nm).

7. Depress the clutch pedal several times to break the plastic retaining straps; DO NOT remove the plastic button from the end of the push rod.
8. Install the air cleaner assembly.
9. Connect the negative battery cable.

SYSTEM BLEEDING

1988–89

1. Remove any dirt or grease around the reservoir cap so that dirt cannot enter the system.
2. Fill the reservoir with an approved DOT 3 brake fluid.
3. Loosen, but do not remove, the bleeder screw on the slave cylinder.
4. Fluid will now flow from the master cylinder to the slave cylinder.

➡ **It is important that the reservoir remain filled throughout the procedure.**

5. Air bubbles should now appear at the bleeder screw.
6. Continue this procedure until a steady stream of fluid without any air bubbles is present.
7. Tighten the bleeder screw. Check the fluid level in the reservoir and refill to the proper mark.
8. The system is now fully bled. Check the clutch operation by starting the engine, pushing the clutch pedal to the floor and placing the transmission in reverse.
9. If any grinding of the gears is noted, repeat the entire procedure.

➡ **Never under any circumstances reuse fluid that has been in the system. The fluid may be contaminated with dirt and moisture.**

1990–92

1. Disconnect the slave cylinder from the transaxle.
2. Loosen the master cylinder mounting attaching nuts. Do not remove the master cylinder.
3. Remove any dirt or grease around the reservoir cap so dirt cannot enter the system. Fi the reservoir with an approved DOT 3 brake fluid.
4. Depress the hydraulic actuator cylinder pushrod approximately 0.787 in. (20.0mm) int the slave cylinder bore and hold.
5. install the diaphragm and cap on the reservoir while holding the slave cylinder pushrod.
6. Release the slave cylinder pushrod.
7. Hold the slave cylinder vertically with the pushrod end facing the ground.

➡ **The slave cylinder should be lower than the master cylinder.**

8. Press the pushrod into the slave cylinder bore with short 0.390 in. (10.0mm) strokes.
9. Observe the reservoir for air bubbles. Continue until air bubbles no longer enter the reservoir.
10. Connect the slave cylinder to the transaxle.
11. Tighten the master cylinder attaching nuts.
12. Top-up the clutch master cylinder reservoir.

13. To test the system, start the engine and push the clutch pedal to the floor. Wait 10 seconds and select reverse gear. There should be no gear clash. If clash is present, air may still be present in the system. Repeat bleeding procedure.

Clutch Assembly

✳✳✳ CAUTION

The clutch driven disc contains asbestos, which has been determined to be a cancer causing agent. Never clean clutch surfaces with compressed air! Avoid inhaling any dust from any clutch surface! When cleaning clutch surfaces, use a commercially available brake cleaning fluid.

REMOVAL & INSTALLATION

◆ SEE FIG. 62-67

1. Disconnect the negative terminal from the battery.
2. From inside the vehicle, remove the hush panel.
3. Disconnect the clutch master cylinder push rod from the clutch pedal.
4. Refer to the "Transaxle, Removal and Installation" procedures in this section and remove the transaxle.

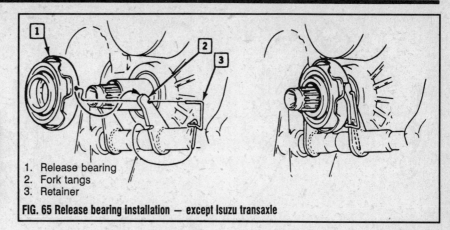

1. Release bearing
2. Fork tangs
3. Retainer

FIG. 65 Release bearing installation — except Isuzu transaxle

5. With the transaxle removed, matchmark the pressure plate and flywheel assembly to insure proper balance during reassembly.
6. Loosen the pressure plate-to-flywheel bolts (one turn at a time) until the spring pressure is removed.
7. Support the pressure plate and remove the bolts.
8. Remove the pressure plate and disc assembly; be sure to note the flywheel side of the clutch disc.
9. Clean and inspect the clutch assembly, flywheel, release bearing, clutch fork and pivot shaft for signs of wear. Replace any necessary parts.

To install:

10. Position the clutch disc and pressure plate in the appropriate position, align the "Heavy Side" of the flywheel assembly stamped with an **X** with the clutch cover "Light Side" marked with paint. Support the assembly with Alignment tool No. J-290742 or equivalent.

➡ **The clutch disc is installed with the damper springs offset towards the transaxle. Stamped letters on the clutch disc identify "Flywheel Side". Make sure the clutch disc is facing the same direction it was when removed. If the same pressure plate is being reused, align the marks made during the removal.**

11. Install the pressure plate to flywheel retaining bolts. Tighten them gradually and evenly as follows:

1988–90
Tighten the pressure plate-to-flywheel bolts to 15 ft. lbs. (20 Nm)

1991–92
a. Install and lightly seat bolts 1, 2, 3 then 4, 5, 6.

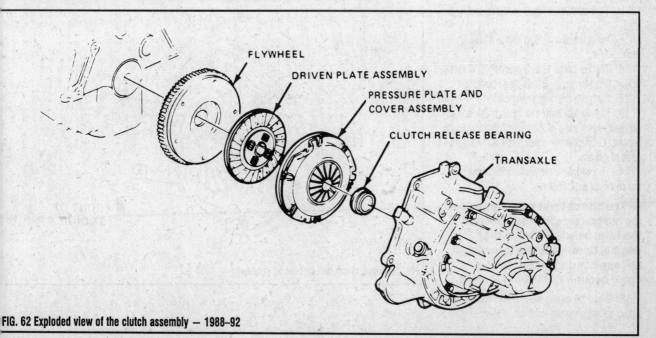

FLYWHEEL

DRIVEN PLATE ASSEMBLY

PRESSURE PLATE AND COVER ASSEMBLY

CLUTCH RELEASE BEARING

TRANSAXLE

FIG. 62 Exploded view of the clutch assembly — 1988–92

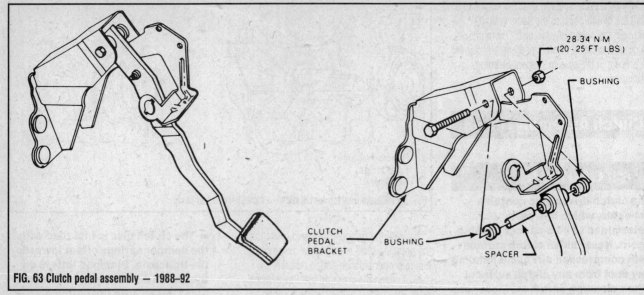

FIG. 63 Clutch pedal assembly — 1988–92

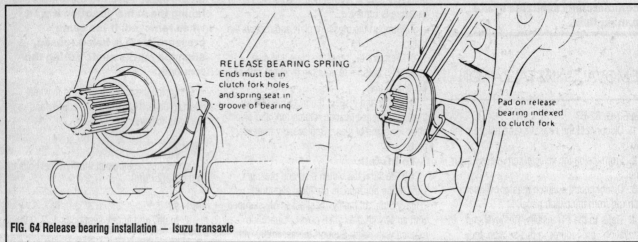

FIG. 64 Release bearing installation — Isuzu transaxle

b. Torque bolts 1, 2, 3 to 12 ft. lbs. (16 Nm).

c. Torque bolts 4, 5, 6 to 12 ft. lbs. (16 Nm).

d. Torque bolts 1, 2, 3 then 4, 5, 6 to 15 ft. lbs. (20 Mm) plus 30 degree rotation.

12. Remove the alignment tool.

13. Lightly lubricate the clutch fork ends. Fill the recess ends of the release bearing with grease. Lubricate the input shaft with a light coat of grease.

14. To complete the installation, reverse the removal procedures.

➡ **The clutch lever must not be moved towards the flywheel until the transaxle is bolted to the engine. Damage to the transaxle, release bearing and clutch fork could occur if this is not followed.**

15. Bleed the clutch system and check the clutch operation when finished.

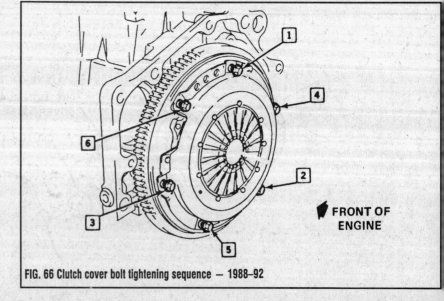

FIG. 66 Clutch cover bolt tightening sequence — 1988–92

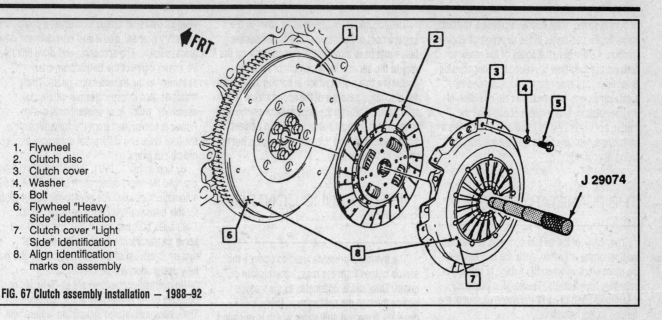

1. Flywheel
2. Clutch disc
3. Clutch cover
4. Washer
5. Bolt
6. Flywheel "Heavy Side" identification
7. Clutch cover "Light Side" identification
8. Align identification marks on assembly

J 29074

FIG. 67 Clutch assembly installation — 1988–92

AUTOMATIC TRANSAXLE

Understanding Automatic Transmissions

The automatic transmission allows engine torque and power to be transmitted to the drive wheels within a narrow range of engine operating speeds. The transmission will allow the engine to turn fast enough to produce plenty of power and torque at very low speeds, while keeping it at a sensible rpm at high vehicle speeds. The transmission performs this job entirely without driver assistance. The transmission uses a light fluid as the medium for the transmission of power. This fluid also works in the operation of various hydraulic control circuits and as a lubricant. Because the transmission fluid performs all of these three functions, trouble within the unit can easily travel from one part to another. For this reason, and because of the complexity and unusual operating principles of the transmission, a very sound understanding of the basic principles of operation will simplify troubleshooting.

THE TORQUE CONVERTER

The torque converter replaces the conventional clutch. It has three functions:

1. It allows the engine to idle with the vehicle at a standstill, even with the transmission in gear.
2. It allows the transmission to shift from range to range smoothly, without requiring that the driver close the throttle during the shift.
3. It multiplies engine torque to an increasing extent as vehicle speed drops and throttle opening is increased. This has the effect of making the transmission more responsive and reduces the amount of shifting required.

The torque converter is a metal case which is shaped like a sphere that has been flattened on opposite sides. It is bolted to the rear end of the engine's crankshaft. Generally, the entire metal case rotates at engine speed and serves as the engine's flywheel.

The case contains three sets of blades. One set is attached directly to the case. This set forms the torus or pump. Another set is directly connected to the output shaft, and forms the turbine. The third set is mounted on a hub which, in turn, is mounted on a stationary shaft through a one-way clutch. This third set is known as the stator.

A pump, which is driven by the converter hub at engine speed, keeps the torque converter full of transmission fluid at all times. Fluid flows continuously through the unit to provide cooling.

Under low speed acceleration, the torque converter functions as follows:

The torus is turning faster than the turbine. It picks up fluid at the center of the converter and, through centrifugal force, slings it outward.

Since the outer edge of the converter moves faster than the portions at the center, the fluid picks up speed.

The fluid then enters the outer edge of the turbine blades. It then travels back toward the center of the converter case along the turbine blades. In impinging upon the turbine blades, the fluid loses the energy picked up in the torus.

If the fluid were now to immediately be returned directly into the torus, both halves of the converter would have to turn at approximately the same speed at all times, and torque input and output would both be the same.

In flowing through the torus and turbine, the fluid picks up 2 types of flow, or flow in 2 separate directions. It flows through the turbine blades, and it spins with the engine. The stator, whose blades are stationary when the vehicle is being accelerated at low speeds, converts one type of flow into another. Instead of allowing the fluid to flow straight back into the torus, the stator's curved blades turn the fluid almost 90° toward the direction of rotation of the engine. Thus the fluid does not flow as fast toward the torus, but is already spinning when the torus picks it up. This has the effect of allowing the torus to turn much faster than the turbine. This difference in speed may be compared to the difference in speed between the smaller and larger gears in any gear train. The result is that engine power output is higher, and engine torque is multiplied.

As the speed of the turbine increases, the fluid spins faster and faster in the direction of engine rotation. As a result, the ability of the stator to redirect the fluid flow is reduced. Under cruising conditions, the stator is eventually forced to rotate on its one-way clutch in the direction of engine rotation. Under these conditions, the torque converter begins to behave almost like a solid shaft, with the torus and turbine speeds being almost equal.

THE PLANETARY GEARBOX

The ability of the torque converter to multiply engine torque is limited. Also, the unit tends to be more efficient when the turbine is rotating at relatively high speeds. Therefore, a planetary gearbox is used to carry the power output of the turbine to the halfshafts.

Planetary gears function very similarly to conventional transmission gears. However, their construction is different in that three elements make up one gear system, and, in that all three elements are different from one another. The three elements are: an outer gear that is shaped like a hoop, with teeth cut into the inner surface; a sun gear, mounted on a shaft and located at the very center of the outer gear; and a set of three planet gears, held by pins in a ring-like planet carrier, meshing with both the sun gear and the outer gear. Either the outer gear or the sun gear may be held stationary, providing more than one possible torque multiplication factor for each set of gears. Also, if all three gears are forced to rotate at the same speed, the gearset forms, in effect, a solid shaft.

Most modern automatics use the planetary gears to provide either a single reduction ratio of about 1.8:1, or 2 reduction gears: a low of about 2.5:1, and an intermediate of about 1.5:1. Bands and clutches are used to hold various portions of the gearsets to the transmission case or to the shaft on which they are mounted. Shifting is accomplished, then, by changing the portion of each planetary gearset which is held to the transmission case or to the shaft.

THE SERVOS AND ACCUMULATORS

The servos are hydraulic pistons and cylinders. They resemble the hydraulic actuators used on many familiar machines, such as bulldozers. Hydraulic fluid enters the cylinder, under pressure, and forces the piston to move to engage the band or clutches.

The accumulators are used to cushion the engagement of the servos. The transmission fluid must pass through the accumulator on the way to the servo. The accumulator housing contains a thin piston which is sprung away from the discharge passage of the accumulator. When fluid passes through the accumulator on the way to the servo, it must move the piston against spring pressure, and this action smooths out the action of the servo.

THE HYDRAULIC CONTROL SYSTEM

The hydraulic pressure used to operate the servos comes from the main transmission oil pump. This fluid is channeled to the various servos through the shift valves. There is generally a manual shift valve which is operated by the transmission selector lever and an automatic shift valve for each automatic upshift the transmission provides: i.e., 2-speed automatics have a low/high shift valve, while 3-speeds have a 1-2 valve, and a 2-3 valve.

There are 2 pressures which effect the operation of these valves. One is the governor pressure which is affected by vehicle speed. The other is the modulator pressure which is affected by intake manifold vacuum or throttle position. Governor pressure rises with an increase in vehicle speed, and modulator pressure rises as the throttle is opened wider. By responding to these 2 pressures, the shift valves cause the upshift points to be delayed with increased throttle opening to make the best use of the engine's power output.

Most transmissions also make use of an auxiliary circuit for downshifting. This circuit may be actuated by the throttle linkage or the vacuum line which actuates the modulator, or by a cable or solenoid. It applies pressure to a special downshift surface on the shift valve or valves.

The transmission modulator also governs the line pressure, used to actuate the servos. In this way, the clutches and bands will be actuated with a force matching the torque output of the engine.

Identification

All of the Corsica/Beretta cars use the Turbo Hydra-Matic 125C automatic transaxle as optional equipment. This is a fully automatic unit of conventional design, incorporating a four element hydraulic torque converter, a compound planetary gear set, and a dual sprocket and drive link assembly. The sprockets and drive link (Hy-Vo chain) connect the torque converter assembly to the transmission gears. The transaxle also incorporates the differential assembly, which is of conventional design. Power is transmitted from the transmission to the final drive and differential assembly through helical cut gears.

By September 1, 1991, Hydra-Matic will have changed the name designation of the THM 125C automatic transaxle. The new name designation for this transaxle will be Hydra-Matic 3T40. Transaxles built between 1989 and 1990 will serve as transitional years in which a dual system, made up of the old designation and the new designation will be in effect.

No overhaul procedures are given in this book because of the complexity of the transaxle. Transaxle removal and installation, adjustment, and halfshaft removal, installation, and overhaul procedures are covered.

Adjustments

The transaxle has only one band, with no provision for periodic adjustment. Throttle valve cable, Park/Lock cable and back-up light switch adjustments are found below. Pan removal, fluid and filter changes are covered in Section 1.

THROTTLE VALVE (TV) CABLE ADJUSTMENT

▶ SEE FIG. 68

Setting of the TV cable must be done by rotating the throttle lever at the carburetor or throttle body. Do not use the accelerator pedal to rotate the throttle lever.

1. With the engine off, depress and hold the reset tab at the engine end of the TV cable.
2. Move the slider until it stops against the fitting.
3. Release the rest tab.
4. Rotate the throttle lever to its full travel.

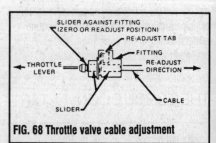

FIG. 68 Throttle valve cable adjustment

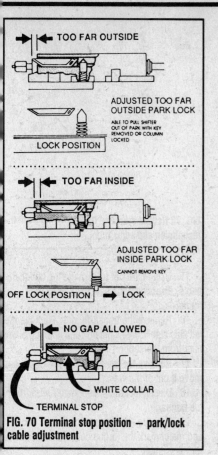

FIG. 70 Terminal stop position — park/lock cable adjustment

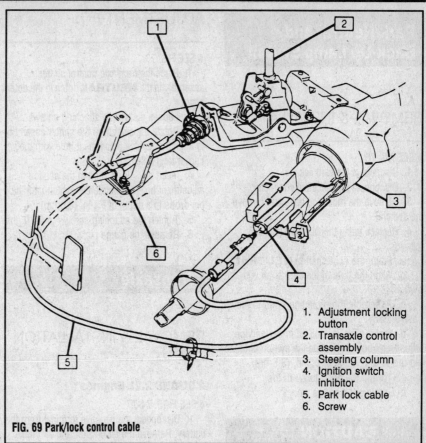

FIG. 69 Park/lock control cable

1. Adjustment locking button
2. Transaxle control assembly
3. Steering column
4. Ignition switch inhibitor
5. Park lock cable
6. Screw

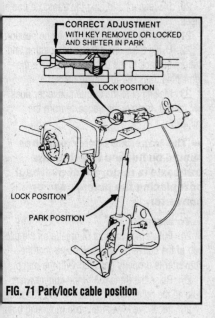

FIG. 71 Park/lock cable position

5. The slider must move (ratchet) toward the lever when the lever is rotated to its full travel position.

6. Recheck after the engine is hot and road test the vehicle.

PARK/LOCK CABLE ADJUSTMENT

♦ SEE FIGS. 69-72

1. Place the floor shift lever in the **PARK** position.
2. Turn the column lock cylinder to the **LOCK** position.
3. Unseat the body housing lock from the body housing.
4. With the body housing still attached to the shift control mounting bracket, adjust the outer cable conduit to obtain proper location for the white plastic housing in the ignition switch.

   a. There must be no gap between the metal terminal stop and the protruding end of the white plastic collar.

   b. The white plastic collar must either be flush or recessed approximately 0.04 inch (1 mm) within the ignition park lock housing.

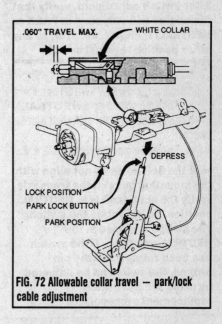

FIG. 72 Allowable collar travel — park/lock cable adjustment

5. While holding the outer cable conduit in position, seat the body housing lock in the body housing.
6. Check for proper operation.

Park/Neutral And Back-Up Lamp Switch

REMOVAL & INSTALLATION

♦ SEE FIG. 73

1. Disconnect the shift linkage.
2. Disconnect the electrical connector.
3. Remove the mounting bolts and remove the switch.
4. Replace using the OLD SWITCH as follows:

   a. Place the shift shaft in **NEUTRAL**.

   b. Align the flats of the shift shaft with the switch.

   c. Assemble the mounting bolts to the case loosely.

   d. Insert a $\frac{3}{32}$ in. drill bit in the service adjustment hole and rotate the switch until the pin drops to a depth of $\frac{9}{64}$ in. (3.6mm).

   e. Torque the bolts to 22 ft. lbs.

   f. Remove the gauge pin.

> ❄❄ **CAUTION**
>
> After switch adjustment, verify that the engine will only start in PARK or NEUTRAL. If engine will start in any other position readjust switch.

5. Replace using a NEW SWITCH as follows:

   a. Place the shift shaft in **NEUTRAL**.

   b. Align the flats of the shift shaft with the switch.

   c. Torque the mounting bolts to 22 ft. lbs.

➡ If the bolt holes do not align with the mounting boss on the transaxle, verify the shift shaft is in NEUTRAL position, do not rotate the switch. The switch is pinned in the NEUTRAL position. If the switch has been rotated and the pin broken, the switch an be adjusted by using the Old Switch replacement procedure.

> ❄❄ **CAUTION**
>
> After switch installation, verify that the engine will only start in PARK or NEUTRAL. If engine will start in any other position readjust the switch using the replacement of the Old Switch procedure.

ADJUSTMENT

♦ SEE FIG. 73

1. Place the transaxle control shifter assembly in the **NEUTRAL** notch in the detent plate.
2. Loosen the switch attaching screws.
3. Rotate the switch on the shifter assembly to align the service adjustment hole with the carrier tang hole.
4. Insert a $\frac{3}{32}$ in. drill bit in the service adjustment hole and rotate the switch until the pin drops to a depth of $\frac{9}{64}$ in. (3.6mm).
5. Tighten the attaching screws to 22 ft. lbs.
6. Remove the gauge pin.

Transaxle

REMOVAL & INSTALLATION

2.0L AND 2.2L Engines

♦ SEE FIGS. 74-77

1. Disconnect the negative terminal from the battery. Remove the air cleaner and air intake assembly.
2. Disconnect the T.V. cable from the throttle lever and the transaxle.
3. Remove the fluid level indicator and the filler tube.
4. Using the Engine Support Fixture tool No. J–28467 or equivalent and the Adapter tool No. J–35953 or equivalent, install them onto the engine.
5. Remove the wiring harness-to-transaxle nut.
6. Label and disconnect the electrical connectors for the speed sensor, TCC connector and the neutral safety/backup light switch.
7. Disconnect the shift linkage from the transaxle.
8. Remove the top 2 transaxle-to-engine bolts, the transaxle mount and bracket assembly.
9. Disconnect the rubber hose that runs from the transaxle to the vent pipe.
10. Raise and support the front of the vehicle.
11. Remove the front wheels and tire assemblies.
12. Disconnect the shift linkage and bracket from the transaxle.
13. Remove the left side splash shield.
14. Using a modified Drive Axle Seal Protector tool No. J–34754 or equivalent, install one on each drive axle to protect the seal from damage and the joint from possible failure.

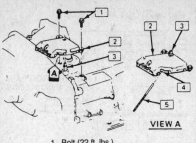

1. Bolt (22 ft. lbs.)
2. Switch asm.
3. Trans. shaft
4. Service adjustment hole
5. 3/32 inch drill bit

FIG. 73 Neutral start and back-up lamp switch installation and adjustment.

15. Using care not to damage the halfshaft boots, disconnect the halfshafts from the transaxle.
16. Remove the transaxle strut. Remove the left side stabilizer link pin bolt and bushing clamp nuts from the support.
17. Remove the left frame support bolts and move it out of the way.
18. Disconnect the speedometer wire from the transaxle.
19. Remove the transaxle converter cover and matchmark the torque converter-to-flywheel for reassembly.
20. Disconnect and plug the transaxle cooler pipes.
21. Remove the transaxle-to-engine support.
22. Using a transmission jack, position and secure the jack to the transaxle. Remove the remaining transaxle-to-engine bolts.
23. Making sure the torque converter does not fall out, remove the transaxle from the vehicle.

➡ **The transaxle cooler and lines should be flushed any time the transaxle is removed for overhaul or replacing the pump, case or converter.**

To install:

24. Put a small amount of grease on the pilot hub of the converter and make sure that the converter is properly engaged with the pump.
25. Raise the transaxle to the engine while guiding the right side halfshaft into the transaxle.
26. Install the lower transaxle mounting bolts and remove the jack.
27. Align the converter with the marks made previously on the flywheel and install the bolts hand tight.
28. Torque the converter bolts to 46 ft. lbs.; retorque the first bolt after the others.
29. Install the transaxle converter cover.
30. Install the speedometer wire connector.

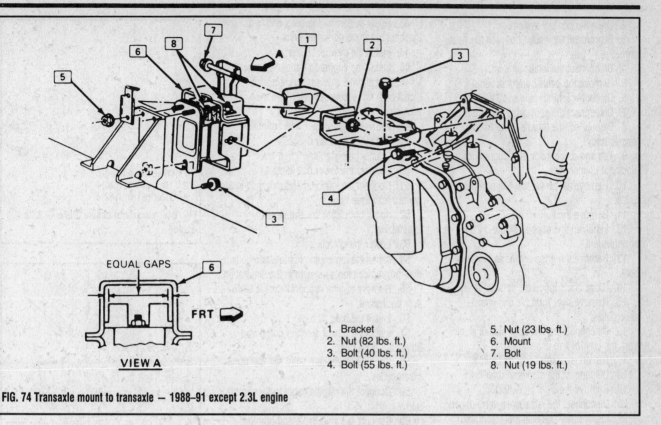

1. Bracket
2. Nut (82 lbs. ft.)
3. Bolt (40 lbs. ft.)
4. Bolt (55 lbs. ft.)
5. Nut (23 lbs. ft.)
6. Mount
7. Bolt
8. Nut (19 lbs. ft.)

FIG. 74 Transaxle mount to transaxle — 1988–91 except 2.3L engine

31. Position the L.H. drive axle shaft into the transaxle.
32. Install the left frame support assembly.
33. Install the left stabilizer shaft frame bushing nuts.
34. Install the left stabilizer bar link pin bolt.
35. Install the transaxle strut.
36. Seat the drive axles in the transaxle.
37. Remove the drive axle seal protectors.
38. Install the splash shield.
39. Install the shift linkage bracket to the transaxle.

40. Install both wheel and tire assemblies.
41. Lower the car and install the upper engine to transaxle bolts.
42. Install the shift linkage to the transaxle.
43. Install the speed sensor, TCC connector and the Park/Neutral and back-up switch wiring connectors.
44. Install the wiring harness and nut securing it to the transaxle.
45. Remove the engine support fixture.
46. Install the fluid level indicator and fill tube.

47. Install the T.V cable at the transaxle and throttle lever.
48. Install the rubber hoses to the transaxle vent pipe.
49. Install the air cleaner assembly and the air intake duct.
50. Install the negative battery cable.
51. Fill with fluid and check for leaks.

2.3L Engine

▶ SEE FIGS. 83-85
1. Disconnect the negative battery cable.

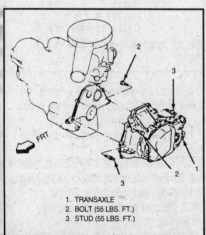

1. TRANSAXLE
2. BOLT (55 LBS. FT.)
3. STUD (55 LBS. FT.)

FIG. 75 Transaxle to engine bolts — 1988–92 except 1990 with the 2.2L and 1990–92 with the 2.3L engine

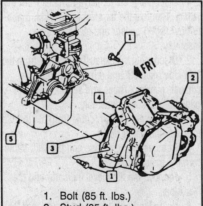

1. Bolt (85 ft. lbs.)
2. Stud (85 ft. lbs.)
3. Transaxle assembly
4. Bracket
5. Engine

FIG. 76 Transaxle to engine bolts — 1990 with the 2.2L engine

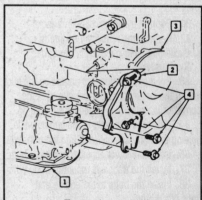

1. Transaxle assembly
2. Brace
3. Engine assembly
4. Bolt (32 ft. lbs.)

FIG. 77 Transaxle to engine brace — 2.3L and 2.2L engine

2. Drain the cooling system.

3. Disconnect the heater hoses at the heater core.

4. Disconnect the intake air duct.

5. Remove the cable control cover.

6. Disconnect the throttle and TV cable.

7. Disconnect the shift cable and bracket.

8. Disconnect the throttle cable from the throttle body.

9. Tag and disconnect all vacuum lines and electrical connections.

10. Remove the power steering pump and set aside.

11. Remove the fluid fill tube.

12. Install engine support fixture J 28467–A or equivalent.

13. Remove the 4 top engine to transaxle bolts.

14. Raise and support the vehicle safely.

15. Remove both front tire and wheel assemblies.

16. Disconnect the left inner splash shield from the control arm assembly.

17. Disconnect both lower ball joints.

18. Disconnect the stabilizer shaft links.

19. Remove the front air deflector.

20. Disconnect the left suspension support.

21. Install drive axle seal protectors and remove both drive axles.

22. Disconnect the engine to transaxle brace.

23. Remove the flywheel cover.

24. Remove the flywheel to torque converter bolts.

25. Disconnect the transaxle cooler pipes.

26. Disconnect the ground wires from the engine to transaxle bolt.

27. Disconnect the cooler pipe brace.

28. Disconnect the exhaust brace.

29. Remove the bolts from the engine and transaxle mount.

30. Remove the transaxle mount to body bolts.

31. Support the transaxle with a jack.

32. Remove the remaining engine to transaxle bolts and remove the transaxle.

To Install:

33. Put a small amount of grease on the pilot hub of the converter and make sure that the converter is properly engaged with the pump.

34. Raise the transaxle to the engine while guiding the right side halfshaft into the transaxle.

35. Install the lower engine to transaxle bolts.

37. Install the transaxle mount to body bolts.

38. Install the bolts to the engine and transaxle mount.

39. Connect the exhaust brace.

40. Connect the cooler pipe brace.

41. Connect the ground wires to the engine to transaxle bolt.

42. Connect the transaxle cooler pipes.

43. Apply sealant to the bolts and install the flywheel to torque converter bolts.

44. Install the flywheel cover.

45. Install the engine to transaxle brace.

46. Install drive axle seal protectors and install both drive axles, then remove the protectors.

47. Install the left suspension support.

48. Install the front air deflector.

49. Connect the stabilizer shaft links.

50. Connect the lower ball joints.

51. Connect the left inner splash shield to the control arm assembly.

52. Install both front tire and wheel assemblies.

53. Lower the vehicle.

54. Install the top engine to transaxle bolts to their proper location as shown in the illustration.

55. Remove engine support fixture J 28467–A or equivalent.

56. Install the fluid fill tube.

57. Install the power steering pump and adjust the drive belt.

58. Connect all vacuum lines and electrical connections.

59. Connect the throttle cable to the throttle body.

60. Connect the shift cable and bracket.

61. Connect the throttle and TV cable.

62. Install the cable control cover.

63. Connect the intake air duct.

64. Connect the heater hoses to the heater core.

65. Fill the cooling system.

66. Connect the negative battery cable.

67. Fill the transaxle.

68. Adjust the TV cable and shift linkage as necessary.

2.8L and 3.1L Engines

▶ SEE FIGS. 78-82

1. Disconnect the negative terminal from the battery. Remove the air cleaner, bracket, mass air flow (MAF) sensor and air tube as an assembly.

2. Disconnect the exhaust crossover from the right side manifold and remove the left side exhaust manifold. Raise and support the manifold/crossover assembly.

3. Disconnect the T.V. cable from the throttle lever and the transaxle.

4. Remove the vent hose and the shift cable from the transaxle.

5. Remove the fluid level indicator and the filler tube.

6. Using the Engine Support Fixture tool No. J–28467 or equivalent and the Adapter tool No. J–35953 or equivalent, install them on the engine.

7. Remove the wiring harness-to-transaxle nut.

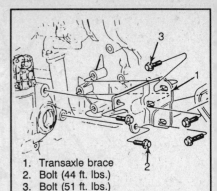

1. Transaxle brace
2. Bolt (44 ft. lbs.)
3. Bolt (51 ft. lbs.)

FIG. 84 Transaxle to engine brace — 2.3L engine

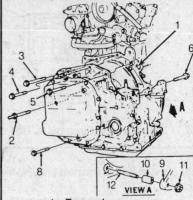

1. Transaxle
2. Stud (71 ft. lbs.) position 2
3. Bolt (71 ft. lbs.) position 3
4. Bolt (71 ft. lbs.) position 4
5. Bolt (71 ft. lbs.) position 5
6. Bolt (71 ft. lbs.)
7. Bolt (71 ft. lbs.)
8. Bolt (41 ft. lbs.)
9. Oil pan
10. Spacer
11. Nut (37- ft. lbs.)
12. Stud (115 inch lbs.)

FIG. 85 Transaxle to engine bolts — 2.3L engine

8. Label and disconnect the wires for the speed sensor, TCC connector and the neutral safety/backup light switch.

9. Remove the upper transaxle-to-engine bolts.

10. Remove the transaxle-to-mount through bolt, the transaxle mount bracket and the mount.

11. Raise and support the vehicle.

12. Remove the front wheel and tire assemblies.

13. Disconnect the shift cable bracket from the transaxle.

14. Remove the left side splash shield.

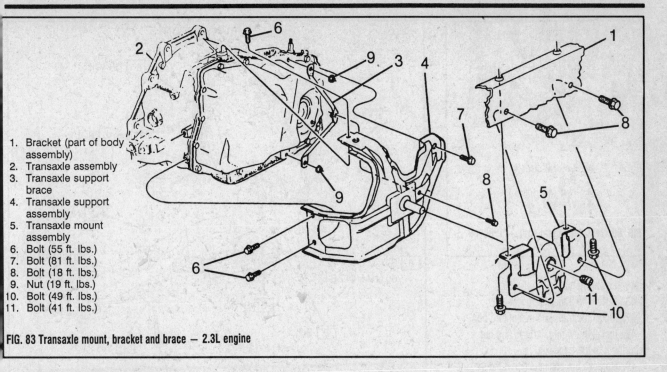

1. Bracket (part of body assembly)
2. Transaxle assembly
3. Transaxle support brace
4. Transaxle support assembly
5. Transaxle mount assembly
6. Bolt (55 ft. lbs.)
7. Bolt (81 ft. lbs.)
8. Bolt (18 ft. lbs.)
9. Nut (19 ft. lbs.)
10. Bolt (49 ft. lbs.)
11. Bolt (41 ft. lbs.)

FIG. 83 Transaxle mount, bracket and brace — 2.3L engine

15. Using a modified Drive Axle Seal Protector tool No. J–34754 or equivalent, install one on each drive axle to protect the seal from damage and the joint from possible failure.

16. Using care not to damage the halfshaft boots, disconnect the halfshafts from the transaxle.

17. Remove the torsional and lateral strut from the transaxle. Remove the left side stabilizer link pin bolt.

18. Remove the left frame support bolts and move it out of the way.

19. Disconnect the speedometer wire from the transaxle.

20. Remove the transaxle converter cover and matchmark the converter-to-flywheel for assembly.

21. Disconnect and plug the transaxle cooler pipes.

22. Remove the transaxle-to-engine support.

23. Using a transmission jack, position and secure it to the transaxle. Remove the remaining transaxle-to-engine bolts.

24. Make sure that the torque converter does not fall out and remove the transaxle from the vehicle.

➡ The transaxle cooler and lines should be flushed any time the transaxle is removed for overhaul, to replace the pump, case or converter.

To install:

25. Put a small amount of grease on the pilot hub of the converter and make sure that the converter is properly engaged with the pump.

26. Raise the transaxle to the engine while guiding the right side halfshaft into the transaxle.

27. Install the lower transaxle mounting bolts and remove the jack.

28. Install the cooler lines at the transmission.

29. Position the L.H. drive axle shaft into the transaxle.

30. Install the left frame support bolts.

31. Install the left stabilizer shaft bushing clamp nuts at the support.

32. Install the left stabilizer bar link pin bolt.

33. Seat the drive axles in the transaxle.

34. Remove the drive axle seal protectors.

35. Install the shift linkage bracket to the transaxle.

36. Install the speedometer wire connector.

37. Install the transaxle brace bolts.

38. Install the transaxle lateral strut.

39. Install the transaxle torsional strut.

40. Align the converter with the marks made previously on the flywheel and install the bolts hand tight.

41. Torque the converter bolts to 46 ft. lbs.; retorque the first bolt after the others.

42. Install the transaxle converter cover.

43. Install the splash shield.

44. Install both wheel and tire assemblies.

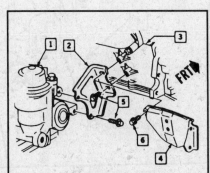

1. Transaxle assembly
2. Brace
3. Engine assembly
4. Bracket
5. Bolt (32 ft. lbs.)
6. Bolt (47 ft. lbs.)

FIG. 78 Transaxle to engine brace — 1988–91 2.8L and 3.1L engine

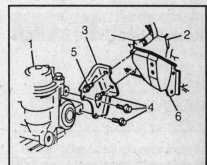

1. Transaxle assembly
2. Engine assembly
3. Brace
4. Bolt (37 ft. lbs.)
5. Bolt (38 ft. lbs.)
6. Bracket

FIG. 79 Transaxle to engine brace — 1992 3.1L engine

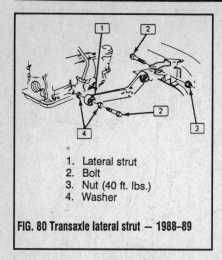

1. Lateral strut
2. Bolt
3. Nut (40 ft. lbs.)
4. Washer

FIG. 80 Transaxle lateral strut — 1988–89

45. Lower the car.

46. Install the transaxle mount.

47. Install the transaxle mount thru bolt.

48. Install the wiring harness and nut securing it to the transaxle.

49. Remove the engine support fixture.

50. Install the fluid level indicator and fill tube.

51. Install the neutral start and TCC connectors.

52. Install the shift cable.

53. Install the T.V. cable at the transaxle and throttle lever.

54. Install the rubber hoses to the transaxle vent pipe.

55. Install the L.H. exhaust manifold bolts and exhaust crossover bolts.

56. Install the air cleaner mounting bracket, MAF sensor and air tube as an assembly.

57. Install the negative battery cable.

58. Fill with fluid and check for leaks.

Halfshaft

REMOVAL, INSTALLATION AND OVERHAUL

The procedures for the automatic transaxle half-shafts are the same as those outlined earlier for the manual transaxle.

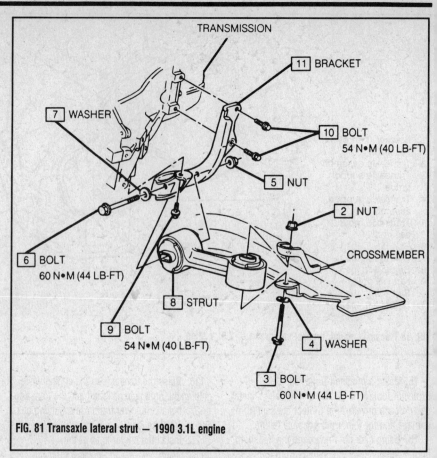

FIG. 81 Transaxle lateral strut — 1990 3.1L engine

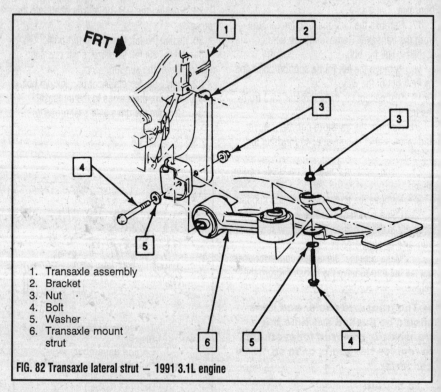

1. Transaxle assembly
2. Bracket
3. Nut
4. Bolt
5. Washer
6. Transaxle mount strut

FIG. 82 Transaxle lateral strut — 1991 3.1L engine

TORQUE SPECIFICATIONS

Component	U.S.	Metric
Manual Transaxle		
Transaxle to engine bolts:	See illustrations	
Transaxle mounting bolts:	See illustrations	
Back-up light switch		
1988-90:	84 inch lbs.	9 Nm
1991-92:	24 inch lbs.	33 Nm
Drive axle intermediate shaft		
1988-89		
Shaft housing to engine:	18 ft. lbs.	25 Nm
Housing to bracket bolts:	37 ft. lbs.	50 Nm
1990		
Shaft to engine:	38 ft. lbs.	52 Nm
1991		
Shaft to engine:	37 ft. lbs.	50 Nm
1992		
Shaft to engine:	35 ft. lbs.	47 Nm
Tri-Pot design driveaxle		
1988-90		
Inner seal clamp:	130 ft. lbs.	176 Nm
Outer seal clamp:	130 ft. lbs.	176 Nm
Cross-Groove design driveaxle		
1988-92		
Inner seal clamp:	130 ft. lbs.	176 Nm
Outer seal clamp:	100 ft. lbs.	136 Nm
Clutch		
Clutch start switch:	53 inch lbs.	6 Nm
Slave (actuator) cylinder to transaxle		
1988-89 All engines:	16 ft. lbs.	22 Nm
1990-92 with 2.2L engine:	16 ft. lbs.	22 Nm
1990 with 2.3L and 3.1L engine:	19 ft. lbs.	25 Nm
Master cylinder retaining nuts:	20 ft. lbs.	27 Nm
Pressure plate to flywheel bolts		
1988-89:	15 ft. lbs.	20 Nm
1990-92 torque sequence		
a.Bolts 1, 2, 3:	12 ft. lbs.	16 Nm
b.Bolts 4, 5, 6:	12 ft. lbs.	16 Nm
c.Bolts 1, 2, 3:	15 ft. lbs. plus	20 Nm
30 degree rotation		
d.Bolts 4, 5, 6:	15 ft. lbs. plus	20 Nm
30 degree rotation		
Automatic transaxle		
Neutral and back-up switch:	22 ft. lbs.	
Transaxle to engine bolts:	See illustrations	
Transaxle mounting bolts:	see illustrations	

Troubleshooting Basic Clutch Problems

Problem	Cause
Excessive clutch noise	Throwout bearing noises are more audible at the lower end of pedal travel. The usual causes are: • Riding the clutch • Too little pedal free-play • Lack of bearing lubrication A bad clutch shaft pilot bearing will make a high pitched squeal, when the clutch is disengaged and the transmission is in gear or within the first 2″ of pedal travel. The bearing must be replaced. Noise from the clutch linkage is a clicking or snapping that can be heard or felt as the pedal is moved completely up or down. This usually requires lubrication. Transmitted engine noises are amplified by the clutch housing and heard in the passenger compartment. They are usually the result of insufficient pedal free-play and can be changed by manipulating the clutch pedal.
Clutch slips (the car does not move as it should when the clutch is engaged)	This is usually most noticeable when pulling away from a standing start. A severe test is to start the engine, apply the brakes, shift into high gear and SLOWLY release the clutch pedal. A healthy clutch will stall the engine. If it slips it may be due to: • A worn pressure plate or clutch plate • Oil soaked clutch plate • Insufficient pedal free-play
Clutch drags or fails to release	The clutch disc and some transmission gears spin briefly after clutch disengagement. Under normal conditions in average temperatures, 3 seconds is maximum spin-time. Failure to release properly can be caused by: • Too light transmission lubricant or low lubricant level • Improperly adjusted clutch linkage
Low clutch life	Low clutch life is usually a result of poor driving habits or heavy duty use. Riding the clutch, pulling heavy loads, holding the car on a grade with the clutch instead of the brakes and rapid clutch engagement all contribute to low clutch life.

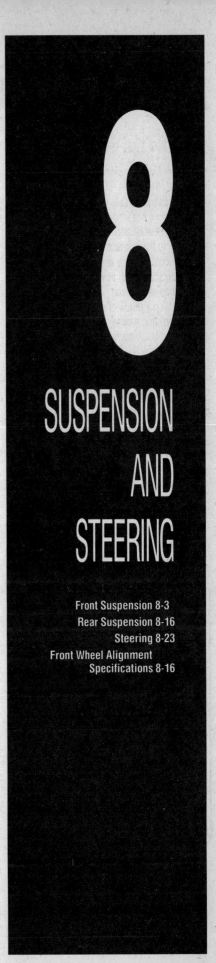

8

SUSPENSION AND STEERING

Wheels

REMOVAL & INSALLATION

♦ SEE FIG. 1

1. Raise the vehicle and support it safely.
2. Remove the wheel cover, if so equipped.
3. Mark the location of the tire and wheel assembly to the hub and remove the wheel nuts.
4. Remove the tire and wheel assembly.
5. If equipped with aluminum wheels, remove the hub cap as follows:

   a. Place a block of wood approximately 2 in. (51mm) in diameter with a squared off end against the back surface of the cap.

   b. Remove the cap with a sharp hammer blow on the block of wood.

❈❈ CAUTION

Never use oil or grease on the studs or nuts.

To install:

6. Install the hub cap on the aluminum wheel, if removed.
7. Install the tire and wheel aligning the marks made during removal.
8. Install the wheel nuts and tighten in sequence to 100 ft. lbs. (140 Nm).

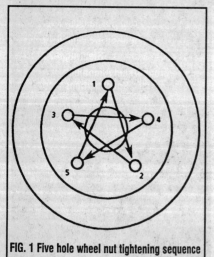

FIG. 1 Five hole wheel nut tightening sequence

➡ **The wheel nuts must be tightened in sequence and to the proper torque to avoid bending the wheel, brake drum or rotor.**

9. Install the wheel cover, if equipped.
10. Lower the vehicle.

INSPECTION

A wheel must be replaced if they are bent, dented, have excessive lateral or radial runout, leak air through welds, have elongated bolt holes, if the wheel nuts will not stay tight or if they are heavily rusted.

Replacement wheels must be equivalent to the original equipment wheels in load capacity, diameter, rim width, offset and mounting configuration. A wheel of improper size or type may affect wheel and bearing life, brake cooling, speedometer/odometer calibration, vehicle ground clearance and the tire clearance to the body and chassis.

Steel wheels can be identified by a 2 or 3 letter code stamped into the rim near the valve stem. Aluminum wheels have a code, part number and manufacturer ID cast into their back side.

Wheel Lug Studs

REPLACEMENT

♦ SEE FIGS. 1A-1B

1. Remove the front hub and bearing assembly.
2. Using tool J 6627–A, or equivalent, remove the stud from the hub and bearing assembly.

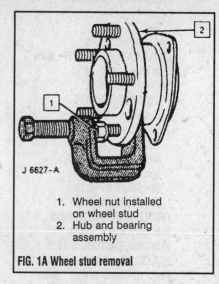

J 6627-A

1. Wheel nut installed on wheel stud
2. Hub and bearing assembly

FIG. 1A Wheel stud removal

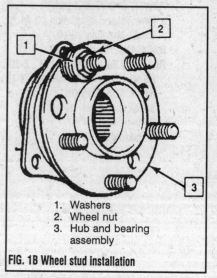

1. Washers
2. Wheel nut
3. Hub and bearing assembly

FIG. 1B Wheel stud installation

3. Install the new wheel stud into the hub and bearing assembly.
4. Install flat washers and the stud nut (flat side down) onto the wheel stud and tighten the wheel studs until it is fully seated.
6. Install the hub and bearing assembly.

FRONT SUSPENSION

The Corsica and Beretta use MacPherson strut front suspension designs. A MacPherson strut combines the functions of a shock absorber and an upper suspension member (upper arm) into 1 unit. The strut is surrounded by a coil spring, which provides normal front suspension functions.

The strut bolts to the body shell at its upper end, and to the steering knuckle at the lower end. The strut pivots with the steering knuckle by means of a sealed mounting assembly at the upper end which contains a preloaded, non-adjustable bearing.

The steering knuckle is connected to the chassis at the lower end by a conventional lower control arm, and pivots in the arm in a preloaded ball joint of standard design. The knuckle is fastened to the ball joint stud by means of a castellated nut and cotter pin.

Advantages of the MacPherson strut design, aside from its relative simplicity, include reduced weight and friction, minimal intrusion into the engine and passenger compartments, and ease of service.

✳ WARNING

When servicing suspension components always install drive axle boot protector J–33162, in order to prevent damage to the drive axle boot.

Springs and Shock Absorbers

TESTING

The function of the shock absorber is to dampen harsh spring movement and provide a means of dissipating the motion of the wheels so that the shocks encountered by the wheels are not totally transmitted to the body and, therefore, to you and your passengers. As the wheel moves up and down, the shock absorber shortens and lengthens, thereby imposing a restraint on movement by its hydraulic action.

A good way to see if your shock absorbers are functioning correctly is to push one corner of the car until it is moving up and down for almost the full suspension travel, then release it and watch its recovery. If the car bounces slightly about 1 more time and then comes to a rest, the shock is alright. If the car continues to bounce excessively, the shocks will probably require replacement.

MacPherson Struts

REMOVAL & INSTALLATION

1988–89

The struts retain the springs under tremendous pressure even when removed from the car. For these reasons, several expensive special tools and substantial specialized knowledge are required to safely and effectively work on these parts. We recommend that if spring or shock absorber repair work is required, you remove the strut or struts involved and take them to a repair facility which is fully equipped and familiar with the car.

1988–90

▶ SEE FIGS. 2 AND 5

1. Working under the hood, and unscrew the upper strut-to-body nuts.
2. Loosen the wheel nuts, raise and support the car and allow the suspension to hang free, then remove the wheel and tire.
3. Install a drive axle seal protective cover (J–33162).
4. Use a 2-armed puller and press the tie rod out of the strut bracket.
5. Remove both strut-to-steering knuckle bolts and carefully lift out the strut.
6. Installation is in the reverse order of removal. Torque the upper strut to body nuts to 18 ft.lbs. (25 Nm). Be sure that the flat sides of the strut-to-knuckle bolt heads are horizontal (see illustration) and torque to 133 ft. lbs. (180 Nm).

1991–92

▶ SEE FIGS. 3-4 AND 6

1. Working under the hood, and unscrew the upper strut-to-body nuts.

2. Loosen the wheel nuts, raise and support the car and allow the suspension to hang free:
    a. Place jack stands under the suspension supports.
    b. Lower the vehicle slightly so the weight of the vehicle rest on the suspension supports and not the control arms.
3. Remove the wheel and tire.

✳ WARNING

Care must be taken not to allow the tri-pot joints from being over extended when either end of the shaft is disconnected. Over extension could result in separation of the internal components.

4. Install modified inner drive drive axle seal protector J 34754, to prevent possible boot damage.
5. Remove the cotter pin and nut and separate the tie rod end from the strut assembly, using a 2-armed puller to press the tie rod out of the strut bracket.
6. Scribe the strut flange as follows:
    a. Using a sharp tool, scribe the knuckle along the lower outboard strut radius.
    b. Scribe the strut flange on the inboard side along the curve of the knuckle.
    c. Make a scribe mark across the strut/knuckle interface.
7. Remove the bolts attaching the strut to the knuckle assembly.

✳ WARNING

Care should be used to avoid chipping or scratching the spring coating. Damage to the coating could cause premature failure.

To install:
8. Place the strut into position and hand tighten the nuts attaching the top of the strut to the body.
9. Align the steering knuckle with the strut flange scribe marks and install the bolts and nuts and tighten to 133 ft. lbs. (180 Nm).
10. Install the tie rod end into the strut assembly and install the nut and cotter pin. Tighten the nut to 55 ft. lbs. (75 Nm).

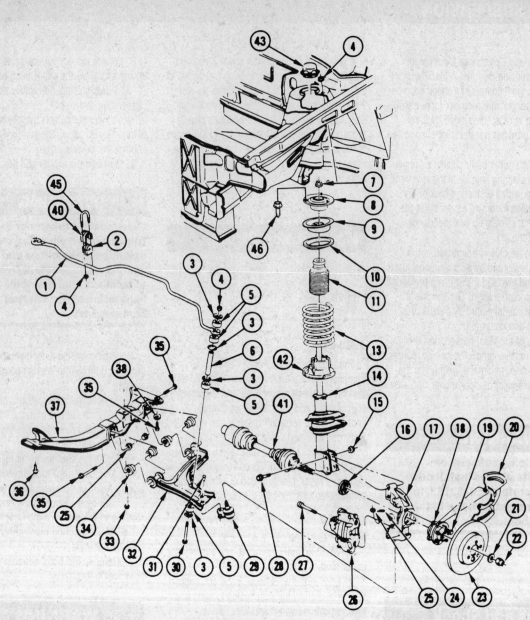

1. Shaft, frt stab
2. Insulator, frt stab shf
3. Washer, fl (.119 × .353)
4. Nut, hex (M8 × 1.25)
5. Grommet, frt stab shf link
6. Spacer, unit frt stab shf
7. Nut, frt susp strut
8. Mount, frt susp strut
9. Seat, frt spr
10. Insulator, frt spr
11. Bumper/shield, frt susp strut
13. Spring, frt coil
14. Absorber, w/strut, frt shk
    strut, frt shk-LH
15. Nut, hex (M16 × 2)

16. Seal, frt whl inr brg
17. Knuckle, strg
18. Bearing, frt whl
19. Bolt, frt disc brk sph shld
20. Shield, frt brk disc splash
21. Washer, frt susp reinf
22. Nut, frt whl dr shf
23. Disc, frt whl brk
24. Pin, cotter (3.2 × 25M)
25. Nut, hex lock (M12 × 1.75)
26. Caliper, frt brk
27. Bolt, frt brk caliper hsg ret
28. Bolt, screw frt susp strut
29. Ball joint, strg knu lwr cont arm
30. Bolt, hex (M8 × 1.25 × 170)

31. Rivet
32. Arm asm, frt lwr cont-RH
33. Bolt, screw frt susp supt
34. Bushing, strg knu lwr cont arm
35. Bolt, hex hd (M12 × 1.75 × 85)
36. Bolt, screw frt susp supt
37. Support, supt frt susp
38. Washer, frt
40. Clamp, frt stab shf
41. Shaft, axle frt whl dr
42. Insulator, frt spr lwr
43. Cover, frt susp strut mt
45. Bolt, "U" frt stab shaft insl clamp
46. Screw, M8 1¼ × 16

FIG. 2 Exploded view of the front suspension — 1988–90

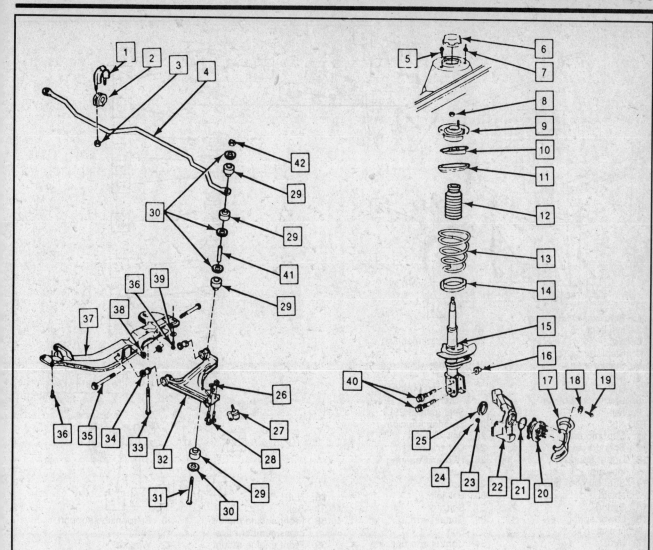

1. Stabilizer shaft clamp
2. Insulator
3. Nut
4. Stabilizer shaft
5. Bolt
6. Strut mount cover
7. Nut
8. Strut dampener shaft nut
9. Strut mount
10. Spring seat
11. Upper spring insulator
12. Strut bumper and shield
13. Spring
14. Lower spring insulator
15. Strut
16. Nut
17. Disc brake splash shield
18. Washer
19. Bolt
20. Hub and bearing assembly
21. Seal (part of 25)
22. Steering knuckle
23. Ball joint nut
24. Cotter pin
25. Hub and bearing seal
26. Nut
27. Ball joint
28. Bolt
29. Stabilizer link insulator
30. Washer
31. Bolt
32. Control arm
33. Bolt
34. Control arm bushing
35. Bolt
36. Bolt
37. Suspension support
38. Nut
39. Washer
40. Bolt
41. Spacer
42. Nut

FIG. 3 Exploded view of the front suspension — 1991-92 except model GTZ

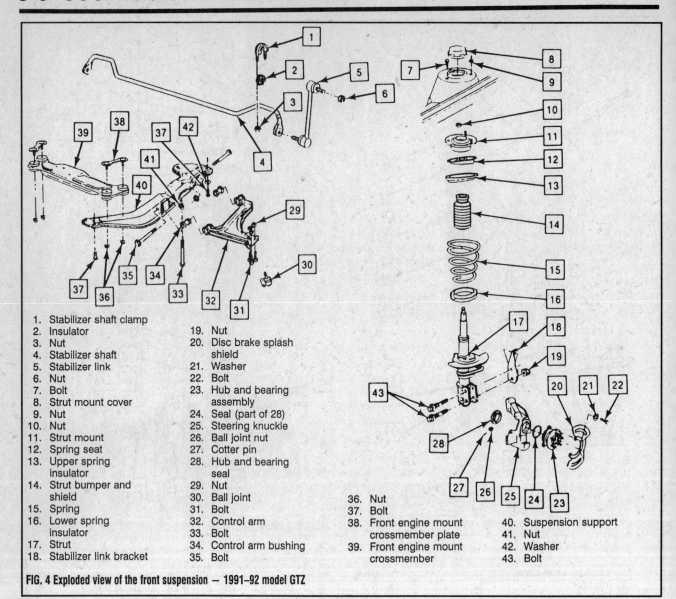

1. Stabilizer shaft clamp
2. Insulator
3. Nut
4. Stabilizer shaft
5. Stabilizer link
6. Nut
7. Bolt
8. Strut mount cover
9. Nut
10. Nut
11. Strut mount
12. Spring seat
13. Upper spring insulator
14. Strut bumper and shield
15. Spring
16. Lower spring insulator
17. Strut
18. Stabilizer link bracket
19. Nut
20. Disc brake splash shield
21. Washer
22. Bolt
23. Hub and bearing assembly
24. Seal (part of 28)
25. Steering knuckle
26. Ball joint nut
27. Cotter pin
28. Hub and bearing seal
29. Nut
30. Ball joint
31. Bolt
32. Control arm
33. Bolt
34. Control arm bushing
35. Bolt
36. Nut
37. Bolt
38. Front engine mount crossmember plate
39. Front engine mount crossmember
40. Suspension support
41. Nut
42. Washer
43. Bolt

FIG. 4 Exploded view of the front suspension — 1991–92 model GTZ

11. Torque the nuts and bolt attaching the top of the strut assembly to the body to 18 ft. lbs. (25 Nm).

12. Remove the modified drive axle seal protector.

13. Slightly raise the vehicle and remove the jack stands from under the suspension supports.

14. Install the tire and wheel assembly.

15. Check the front end alignment.

STRUT MODIFICATION

♦ SEE FIG. 7

This modification is made only if a camber adjustment is anticipated.

1. Place the strut in a vise. This step is not absolutely necessary; filing can be accomplished by disconnecting the strut from the steering knuckle.

2. File the holes in the outer flanges so as to enlarge the bottom holes until they match the slots already in the inner flanges.

3. Camber adjustment procedures are detailed later in this Section.

DISASSEMBLY

1988–90

♦ SEE FIGS. 8-9

✳✳ CAUTION

The coil springs are retained under considerable pressure. They can exert enough force to cause serious injury. Exercise extreme caution when disassembling the strut for coil spring removal.

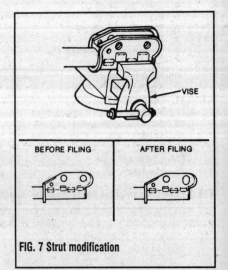

BEFORE FILING   AFTER FILING

FIG. 7 Strut modification

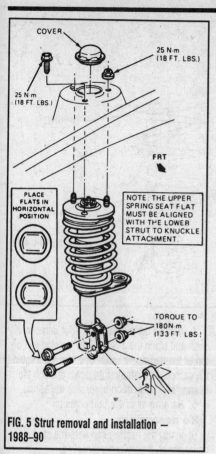

FIG. 5 Strut removal and installation — 1988–90

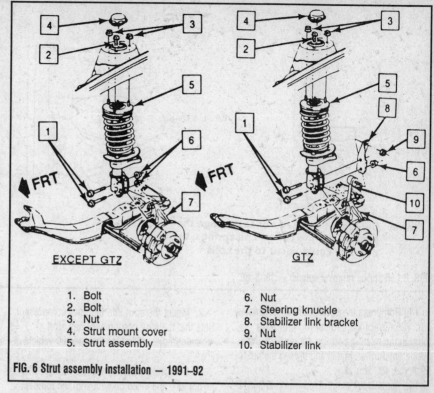

EXCEPT GTZ

GTZ

1. Bolt
2. Bolt
3. Nut
4. Strut mount cover
5. Strut assembly
6. Nut
7. Steering knuckle
8. Stabilizer link bracket
9. Nut
10. Stabilizer link

FIG. 6 Strut assembly installation — 1991–92

This procedure requires the use of a spring compressor and several other special tools. It cannot be performed without them. If you do not have access to these tools, DO NOT attempt to disassemble the strut.

1. Remove the strut assembly.

2. Clamp the spring compressor (J-26584) in a vise. Position the strut assembly in the bottom adapter of the compressor and install the special tool J26584-400 (see illustration). Be sure that the adapter captures the strut and that the locating pins are engaged.

3. Place the top adapter, J-26584-430, on the strut cap. Note that the adapter has drilled holes designating each specific car.

4. Using a 1 in. socket, turn the screw on top of the compressor clockwise until the top support flange contacts the adapters. Continue turning the screw until the coil spring is compressed approximately 1/2 in. (13mm) — 4 complete turns. Never bottom the spring or the strut damper rod.

5. Unscrew the nut from the strut damper shaft and place the J-34013-27 alignment rod on the top of the damper shaft. Use this rod to guide the damper shaft straight down through the spring cap while decompressing the spring.

6. Turn the compressor adjusting screw counterclockwise until the spring tension has been relieved. Remove the adapters and then remove the coil spring.

7. To install, clamp the strut compressor body J 26584 in a vise.

8. Position the strut assembly in the compressor using bottom adapter J-26584-400. Make sure the adapter captures the strut and the locating pins are engaged.

9. Position the spring on the strut. Make sure the spring is properly seated on the bottom of the spring plate.

10. Install all shields, bumpers and insulators on the spring seat.

11. Install the spring strut seat assembly on top of the spring and make sure they are centered together and aligned properly.

➡ The ends of the spring coil are to be located within 0 to 10 mm from the end of the groove in the upper insulator and 10 to 15 mm from the end of the groove in the lower insulator.

12. Place the top adapter, J-26584-430, on the strut cap. Lower the compressor to capture the cap. Pull up the damper rod to full extension and clamp in place with J-34013-20.

13. Insert alignment rod, J-34013-27 through the bearing and spring caps and position on top of the damper rod. Compress the spring and guide the damper rod through the bearing cap using the alignment rod during compression.

✳✳ WARNING

During compression of the spring be sure to use the guide rod to guide the shaft thru the exact center of the bearing. If the threads of the damper rod catch on the bearing cap and prevent the rod from passing cleanly thru the bearing, stop compressing immediately. Decompress the spring and begin again.

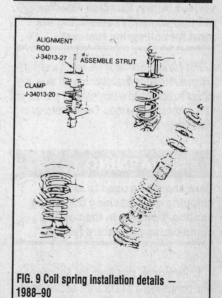

FIG. 9 Coil spring installation details — 1988–90

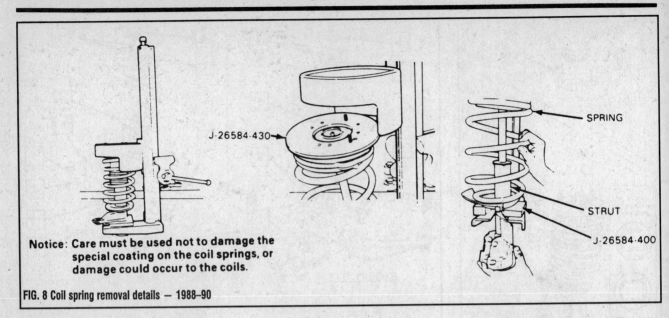

Notice: Care must be used not to damage the special coating on the coil springs, or damage could occur to the coils.

FIG. 8 Coil spring removal details — 1988–90

14. Compress the spring until approximately 1 in. (25mm) of the damper rod protrudes through the bearing cap. Do not compress the spring any further. Install and tighten the nut to 59 ft. lbs. (80 Nm).

15. Remove the damper rod clamp J–34013–20.

16. Back off the spring compressor and remove the strut assembly.

1991–92

◆ SEE FIGS. 10-11

※※ CAUTION

The coil springs are retained under considerable pressure. They can exert enough force to cause serious injury. Exercise extreme caution when disassembling the strut for coil spring removal.

This procedure requires the use of a spring compressor and several other special tools. It cannot be performed without them. If you do not have access to these tools, DO NOT attempt to disassemble the strut.

※※ WARNING

Care should be used to avoid chipping or scratching the spring coating. Damage to the coating could cause premature failure.

1. Remove the strut assembly. Mount the strut compressor J 34013 in the holding fixture J 3289–20.

2. Mount the strut into the strut compressor. Note that the strut compressor has strut mounting holes drilled for the specific vehicle line.

3. Compress the strut approximately ½ its height after the initial contact with the top cap.

➡ **Never bottom the spring or dampener rod.**

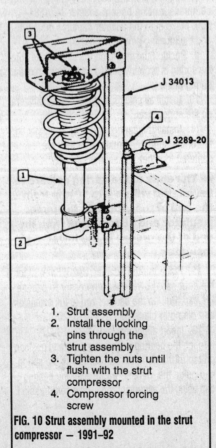

1. Strut assembly
2. Install the locking pins through the strut assembly
3. Tighten the nuts until flush with the strut compressor
4. Compressor forcing screw

FIG. 10 Strut assembly mounted in the strut compressor — 1991–92

4. remove the nut from the strut dampener shaft and place the J 34013–27 guiding rod on top of the dampener shaft. Use this rod to guide the dampener shaft straight down through the bearing cap while decompressing the spring.

5. Remove all of the components.

To assemble:

6. Install the bearing cap onto the strut compressor, if previously removed.

7. Mount the strut into the strut compressor using the bottom locking pin only. Extend the dampener shaft and install clamp J 34013–20 on the dampener shaft.

8. Install the spring over the dampener and swing the assembly up so that the upper locking pin can be installed. Install the upper insulator, shield bumper and upper spring seat. be sure the flat on the upper spring seat is facing in the proper direction. The spring seat flat should be

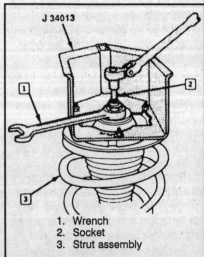

1. Wrench
2. Socket
3. Strut assembly

FIG. 11 Removing the dampener shaft nut — 1991–92

facing the same direction as the centerline of the strut assembly spindle.

9. Install the guiding rod and turn the forcing screw while the guiding rod centers the assembly. When the threads on the dampener shaft are visible, remove the guiding rod and install the nut. Use a crowfoot line wrench, while holding the dampener shaft with a socket and tighten the nut to 65 ft. lbs. (88 Nm).

10. Remove the clamp.

Ball Joints

INSPECTION

1. Raise and support the front of the car and let the suspension hang free.

2. Grasp the wheel at the top and the bottom and shake it in an in-and-out motion. Check for any horizontal movement of the steering knuckle relative to the lower control arm. Replace the ball joint if such movement is noted.

3. If the ball stud is disconnected from the steering knuckle and any looseness is detected, or if the ball stud can be twisted in its socket using finger pressure, replace the ball joint.

REMOVAL & INSTALLATION

Only 1 ball joint is used in each lower arm. The MacPherson strut design does not use an upper ball joint.

1988–90

▶ SEE FIG. 12

1. Loosen the wheel nuts, raise the car, and remove the wheel.

2. Use a 1/8 in. (3mm) drill bit to drill a hole through the center of each of the 3 ball joint rivets.

3. Use a 1/2 in. (13mm) drill bit to drill completely through the rivet.

4. Use a hammer and punch to remove the rivets. Drive them out from the bottom.

5. Use the special tool J–29330 or a ball joint removal tool to separate the ball joint from the steering knuckle (see illustration). Don't forget to remove the cotter pin.

6. Disconnect the stabilizer bar from the lower control arm. Remove the ball joint.

7. Install the new ball joint into the control arm with the 3 bolts supplied as shown and torque to 50 ft. lbs. Installation of the remaining components is in the reverse order of removal. Tighten the castellated nut on the ball joint to 55 ft. lbs. and use a new cotter pin. Check the toe setting and adjust as necessary.

1991–92

▶ SEE FIG. 12

1. Loosen the wheel nuts and safely raise the car.

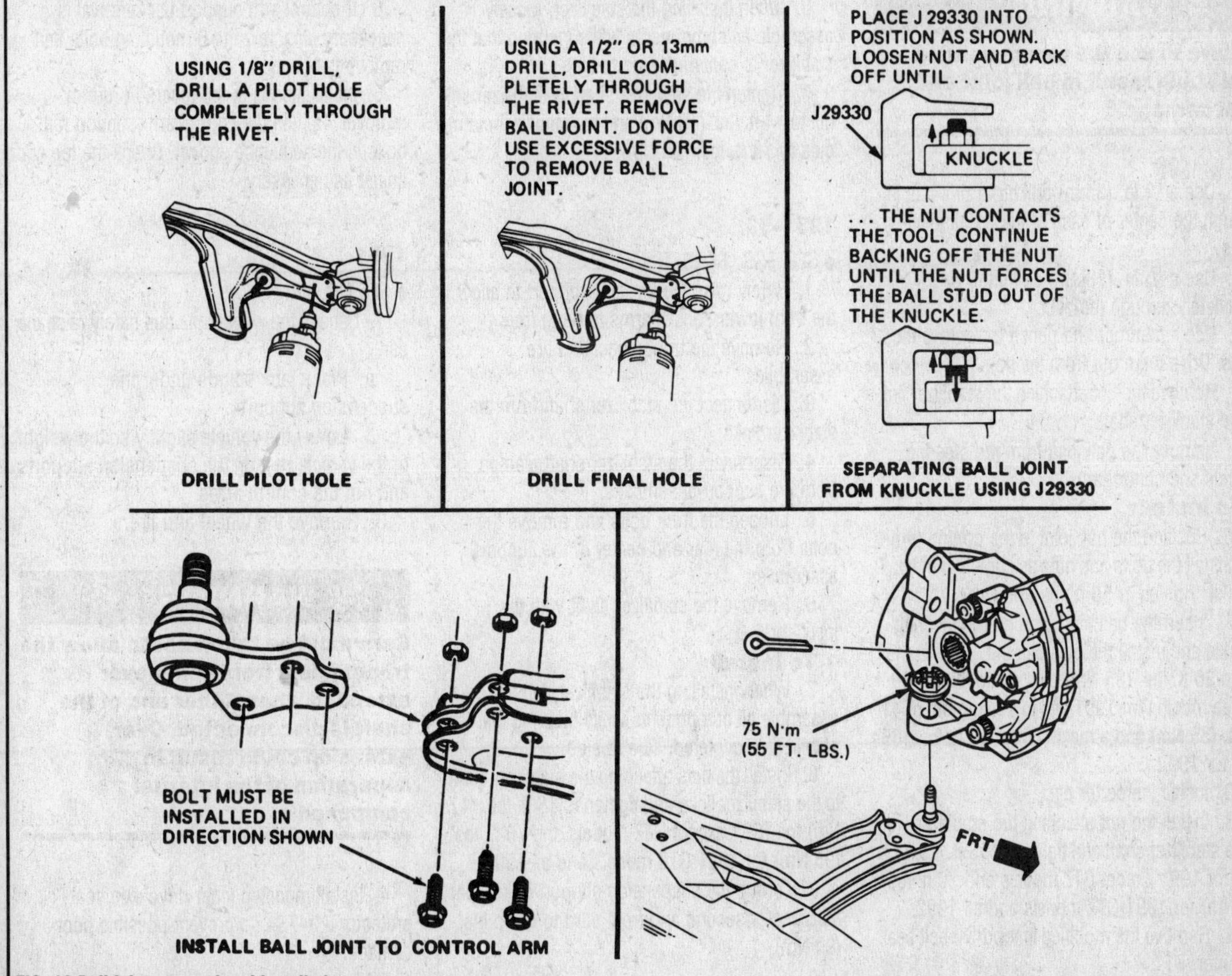

FIG. 12 Ball joint removal and installation

a. Place jack stands under the suspension supports.

b. Lower the vehicle slightly so the weight of the vehicle rest on the suspension supports and not the control arms.

2. Remove the wheel and tire.

※※ WARNING

Care must be taken not to allow the tri-pot joints from being over extended when either end of the shaft is disconnected. Over extension could result in separation of the internal components.

3. Install modified inner drive axle seal protector J 34754, to prevent possible boot damage.

4. Remove the cotter pin and nut from the ball joint and separate the ball joint from the steering knuckle, using tool J 29330 or equivalent.

※※ WARNING

Failure to use the recommended tool could result in ball joint and seal damage.

5. Use a 1/8 in. (3mm) drill bit to drill a hole through the center of each of the 3 ball joint rivets.

6. Use a 1/2 in. (13mm) drill bit to drill completely through the rivet.

7. Use a hammer and punch to remove the rivets. Drive them out from the bottom.

8. Remove the nut attaching the stabilizer link to the stabilizer shaft.

9. Remove the ball joint from the steering knuckle and control arm.

To install:

10. Position the ball joint to the control arm and install the bolts and nuts as shown in the ball joint kit. Tighten to 50 ft. lbs. (68 Nm).

11. Insert the ball stud through the steering knuckle and install the ball joint nut. Tighten the nut to 26 ft. lbs. (35 Nm) plus an additional 60 degree rotation for 1991 and to a minimum of 41 ft lbs. (55 Nm) and a maximum of 50 ft. lbs. (65 Nm) for 1992.

12. Install the cotter pin.

13. Install the nut attaching the stabilizer link to the stabilizer shaft and tighten to 13 ft. lbs. (17 Nm) for 1991 except GTZ models and 70 ft. lbs. (95 Nm) for 1991 GTZ models and all 1992.

14. Remove the modified inner drive belt seal protector.

15. Slightly raise the vehicle and remove the jack stands from under the suspension supports.

16. Install the tire and wheel assembly.

17. Check the front end alignment.

Stabilizer Bar

REMOVAL & INSTALLATION

1988–90

♦ SEE FIG. 13

1. Safely raise the car and support to allow the front lower control arms to hang free.

2. Remove the left front wheel and tire.

3. Disconnect the stabilizer shaft from the control arms.

4. Disconnect the stabilizer shaft from the support assemblies.

5. Loosen the front bolts and remove the bolts from the rear and center of the support assemblies.

6. When installing the stabilizer, loosely assemble all components while insuring that the stabilizer is centered, side to side.

7. Tighten the stabilizer shaft to stabilizer link nut to 14 ft. lbs. (18 Nm) and the stabilizer clamp nuts to 18 ft. lbs. (25 Nm).

1991–92

♦ SEE FIGS. 14-15

1. Safely raise the car and support to allow the front lower control arms to hang free.

2. Remove the front wheel and tire assemblies.

3. Disconnect the stabilizer shaft from the stabilizer links.

4. Disconnect the stabilizer shaft clamps from the support assemblies.

5. Loosen the front bolts and remove the bolts from the rear and center of the support assemblies.

6. Remove the stabilizer shaft with the insulators.

To install:

7. When installing the stabilizer, loosely assemble all components while insuring that the stabilizer is centered, side to side.

8. Install the nuts attaching the stabilizer shaft to the stabilizer links and tighten to 13 ft. lbs. (17 Nm) for 1991 except GTZ models and 70 ft. lbs. (95 Nm) for 1991 GTZ models and all 1992.

9. Torque the suspension support bolts; rear first, center second and front third to 66 ft. lbs. (90 Nm).

10. Torque the clamp nuts to 17 ft. lbs. (23 Nm).

11. Install the front wheel and tire assemblies.

12. Check the front wheel alignment.

Control Arm

REMOVAL & INSTALLATION

1988–90

♦ SEE FIG. 16

1. Raise and support the front of the car. Remove the wheel.

2. Disconnect the stabilizer bar from the control arm and/or support.

3. Separate the ball joint from the steering knuckle as previously detailed.

4. Remove the 2 control arm-to-support bolts and remove the control arm.

5. If control arm support bar removal is necessary, unscrew the 6 mounting bolts and remove the support.

6. Installation is in the reverse order of removal. Tighten the control arm support rail bolts in the sequence shown. Check the toe and adjust as necessary.

1991

♦ SEE FIG. 17

1. Loosen the wheel nuts and safely raise the car.

a. Place jack stands under the suspension supports.

b. Lower the vehicle slightly so the weight of the vehicle rest on the suspension supports and not the control arms.

3. Remove the wheel and tire.

※※ WARNING

Care must be taken not to allow the tri-pot joints from being over extended when either end of the shaft is disconnected. Over extension could result in separation of the internal components.

4. Install modified inner drive axle seal protector J 34754, to prevent possible boot damage.

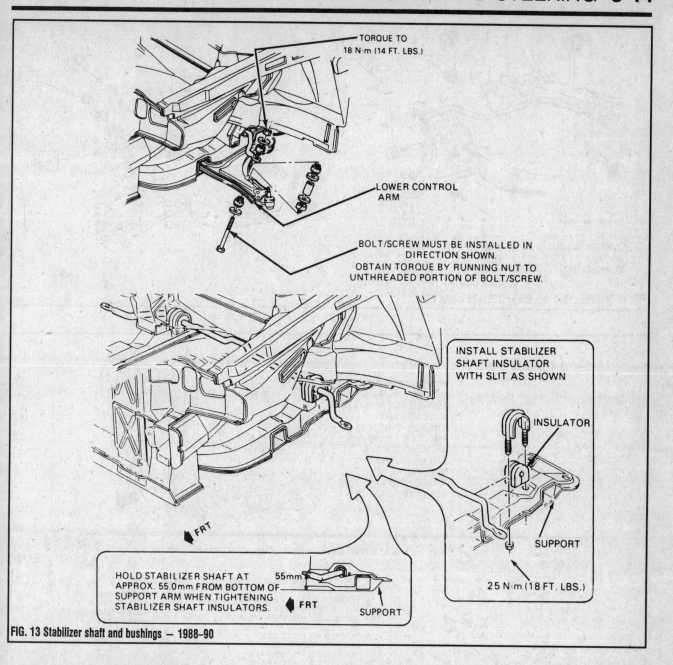

TORQUE TO
18 N·m (14 FT. LBS.)

LOWER CONTROL ARM

BOLT/SCREW MUST BE INSTALLED IN DIRECTION SHOWN.
OBTAIN TORQUE BY RUNNING NUT TO UNTHREADED PORTION OF BOLT/SCREW.

INSTALL STABILIZER SHAFT INSULATOR WITH SLIT AS SHOWN

INSULATOR

SUPPORT

25 N·m (18 FT. LBS.)

FRT

HOLD STABILIZER SHAFT AT APPROX. 55.0mm FROM BOTTOM OF SUPPORT ARM WHEN TIGHTENING STABILIZER SHAFT INSULATORS.

55mm

FRT

SUPPORT

FIG. 13 Stabilizer shaft and bushings — 1988–90

5. Remove the cotter pin and nut from the ball joint and separate the ball joint from the steering knuckle, using tool J 29330 or equivalent.

❊❊ WARNING

Failure to use the recommended tool could result in ball joint and seal damage.

6. On models equipped with the 2.3L engine only, install overhead engine support, J 28467–A or equivalent and remove the nuts attaching the front engine mount crossmember to the suspension support.

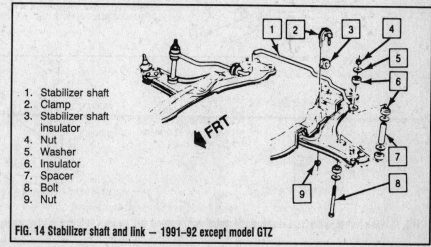

1. Stabilizer shaft
2. Clamp
3. Stabilizer shaft insulator
4. Nut
5. Washer
6. Insulator
7. Spacer
8. Bolt
9. Nut

FRT

FIG. 14 Stabilizer shaft and link — 1991–92 except model GTZ

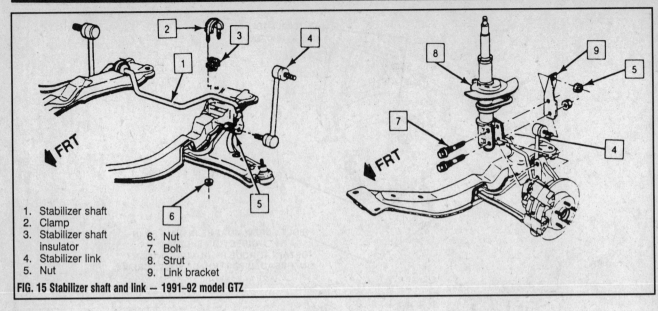

1. Stabilizer shaft
2. Clamp
3. Stabilizer shaft insulator
4. Stabilizer link
5. Nut
6. Nut
7. Bolt
8. Strut
9. Link bracket

FIG. 15 Stabilizer shaft and link — 1991–92 model GTZ

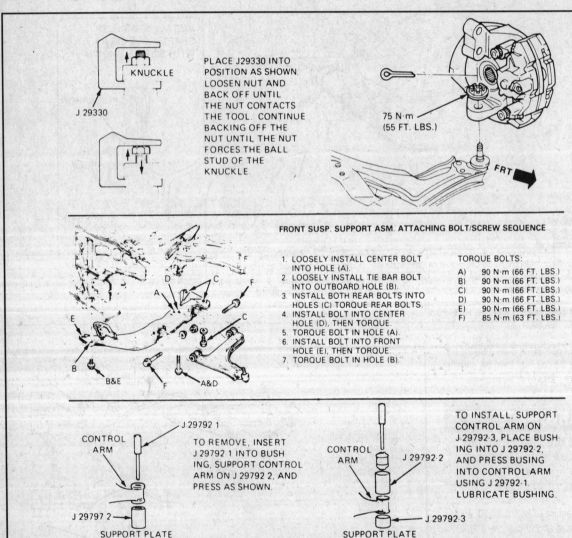

PLACE J29330 INTO POSITION AS SHOWN. LOOSEN NUT AND BACK OFF UNTIL THE NUT CONTACTS THE TOOL. CONTINUE BACKING OFF THE NUT UNTIL THE NUT FORCES THE BALL STUD OF THE KNUCKLE.

J 29330

KNUCKLE

75 N·m (55 FT. LBS.)

FRT

FRONT SUSP. SUPPORT ASM. ATTACHING BOLT/SCREW SEQUENCE

1. LOOSELY INSTALL CENTER BOLT INTO HOLE (A).
2. LOOSELY INSTALL TIE BAR BOLT INTO OUTBOARD HOLE (B).
3. INSTALL BOTH REAR BOLTS INTO HOLES (C) TORQUE REAR BOLTS.
4. INSTALL BOLT INTO CENTER HOLE (D), THEN TORQUE.
5. TORQUE BOLT IN HOLE (A).
6. INSTALL BOLT INTO FRONT HOLE (E), THEN TORQUE.
7. TORQUE BOLT IN HOLE (B).

TORQUE BOLTS:
A) 90 N·m (66 FT. LBS.)
B) 90 N·m (66 FT. LBS.)
C) 90 N·m (66 FT. LBS.)
D) 90 N·m (66 FT. LBS.)
E) 90 N·m (66 FT. LBS.)
F) 85 N·m (63 FT. LBS.)

CONTROL ARM

J 29792 1

TO REMOVE, INSERT J 29792 1 INTO BUSHING, SUPPORT CONTROL ARM ON J 29792 2, AND PRESS AS SHOWN.

J 29792 2

SUPPORT PLATE

CONTROL ARM

J 29792 2

TO INSTALL, SUPPORT CONTROL ARM ON J 29792 3, PLACE BUSHING INTO J 29792 2, AND PRESS BUSING INTO CONTROL ARM USING J 29792 1. LUBRICATE BUSHING.

J 29792 3

SUPPORT PLATE

FIG. 16 When installing the front suspension (control arm) support rail, be sure to follow the tightening sequence — 1988–90

7. Remove the bolts attaching the suspension support to the vehicle.

8. Remove the bolts attaching the control arm to the suspension support.

To install:

9. Position the control arm and loosely install the bolts attaching the control arm to the suspension support.

10. Place the suspension support into position, guiding the ball joint into the steering knuckle and loosely install the bolts.

11. Install the nuts attaching the stabilizer shaft clamp to the suspension support and tighten to 17 ft. lbs. (23 Nm).

12. On models equipped with the 2.3L engine only, install the nuts attaching the front engine mount crossmember to the suspension support and tighten to 30 ft. lbs. (40 Nm).

13. Install the nut attaching the ball joint to the steering knuckle and tighten to 26 ft. lbs. (35 Nm) plus a 60 degree rotation for 1991 and 41–50 ft. lbs. (55–65 Nm) for 1992.

14. Install the nuts attaching the stabilizer link to the stabilizer shaft and tighten to 13 ft. lbs. (17 Nm) for except GTZ models and 70 ft. lbs. (95 Nm) for GTZ models.

15. Remove the modified drive axle seal protector.

16. Slightly raise the vehicle and remove the jack stands from under the suspension supports.

17. Install the tire and wheel assembly.

18. On models equipped with the 2.3L engine only, remove the overhead engine support, J 28467–A or equivalent.

19. With the vehicle at curb height, torque the suspension support attaching bolts to; rear first, center second and front third to 66 ft. lbs. (90 Nm).

20. With the vehicle at curb height torque the control arm attaching bolts to 44 ft. lbs. (60 Nm) plus an additional 60 degree rotation.

21. Check the front end alignment.

1992

◆ SEE FIG. 18

1. Loosen the wheel nuts and safely raise the car.

   a. Place jack stands under the suspension supports.

   b. Lower the vehicle slightly so the weight of the vehicle rest on the suspension supports and not the control arms.

2. Remove the wheel and tire.

❋❋ WARNING

Care must be taken not to allow the tri-pot joints from being over extended when either end of the shaft is disconnected. Over extension could result in separation of the internal components.

3. Install modified inner drive axle seal protector J 34754, to prevent possible boot damge.

4. Remove the cotter pin and nut from the ball joint and separate the ball joint from the steering knuckle, using tool J 29330 or equivalent.

❋❋ WARNING

Failure to use the recommended tool could result in ball joint and seal damage.

5. Remove the bolts attaching the suspension support to the vehicle.

6. Remove the bolts attaching the control arm to the suspension support.

To install:

7. Position the control arm and loosely install the bolts attaching the control arm to the suspension support.

8. Place the suspension support into position, guiding the ball joint into the steering knuckle and loosely install the bolts.

9. Install the nuts attaching the stabilizer shaft clamp to the suspension support and tighten to 17 ft. lbs. (23 Nm).

10. Install the nut attaching the ball joint to the steering knuckle and tighten to 41–50 ft. lbs. (55–65 Nm).

11. Install the nuts attaching the stabilizer link

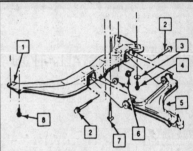

1. Suspension support
2. Bolt
3. Washer
4. Bolt (tighten 1st)
5. Control arm
6. Nut
7. Bolt (tighten 2nd)
8. Bolt (tighten 3rd)

FIG. 18 Control arm and suspension support mounting — 1992

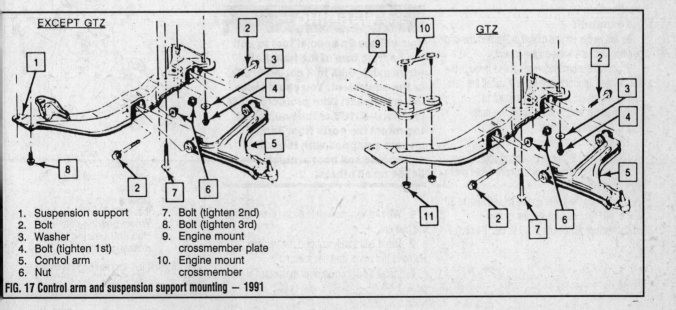

1. Suspension support
2. Bolt
3. Washer
4. Bolt (tighten 1st)
5. Control arm
6. Nut
7. Bolt (tighten 2nd)
8. Bolt (tighten 3rd)
9. Engine mount crossmember plate
10. Engine mount crossmember

FIG. 17 Control arm and suspension support mounting — 1991

to the stabilizer shaft and tighten to 70 ft. lbs. (95 Nm).

12. Remove the modified drive axle seal protector.

13. Slightly raise the vehicle and remove the jack stands from under the suspension supports.

14. Install the tire and wheel assembly.

15. With the vehicle at curb height, torque the suspension support attaching bolts to; center first to 66 ft. lbs. (90 Nm), front second to 65 ft. lbs. (88 Nm) and rear third to 65 ft. lbs. (88 Nm).

16. With the vehicle at curb height torque the control arm attaching bolts to 61 ft. lbs. (83 Nm).

17. Check the front end alignment.

Front Engine Mount Crossmember

REMOVAL & INSTALLATION

2.3L Engine

1991 ONLY

▶ SEE FIG. 19

1. Install overhead engine support, J 28467–A or equivalent.

2. Remove the front engine mount upper nut.

3. Raise the engine.

4. Raise the vehicle and support it safely.

5. Remove the front engine mount to crossmember nuts.

6. Remove the engine mount crossmember with the front engine mount.

7. Remove the engine mount from the crossmember.

To install:

8. Install the engine mount crossmember into position with the front engine mount.

9. Install the crossmember plates through the suspension supports and loosely install the nuts.

10. Install the front engine mount to crossmember and loosely install the nuts.

11. Lower the vehicle.

12. Lower the engine.

13. Remove the engine support tool.

14. Install the front engine mount upper nut to 55 ft. lbs. (75 Nm).

15. Torque the lower engine mount nuts to 30 ft. lbs. (40 Nm) and the engine mount crossmember plate nuts to 40 ft. lbs. 54 Nm).

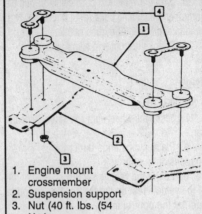

1. Engine mount crossmember
2. Suspension support
3. Nut (40 ft. lbs. (54 Nm)
4. Engine mount crossmember plate

FIG. 19 Front engine mount crossmember installation — 1991 with 2.3L engine

Wheel Bearings

The front wheel bearings are sealed, non-adjustable units which require no periodic attention. They are bolted to the steering knuckle by means of an integral flange.

Front Hub, Knuckle And Bearing

REMOVAL & INSTALLATION

▶ SEE FIG. 20-24

※※ WARNING

You will need a special tool to pull the bearing free of the halfshaft (drive axle), G.M. tool no. J-28733 or the equivalent. You should also use a halfshaft boot protector, G.M. tool no. J-33162 or the equivalent to protect the parts from damage on cars equipped with the 2.0L 4 cyl. engine and boot protector J-34754 on all others.

1. With the vehicle weight on the tires, loosen the hub nut.

2. Raise and safely support the vehicle. Remove the wheel and tire assembly.

3. Install a boot cover over the outer CV-joint boot.

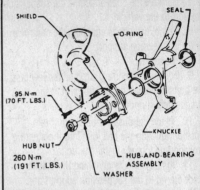

FIG. 20 Front hub and bearing assembly — 1988-90

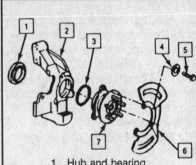

1. Hub and bearing assembly
2. Steering knuckle
3. Seal (part of 1)
4. Washer
5. Splash shield
6. Hub and bearing assembly

FIG. 21 Front hub and bearing assembly — 1991

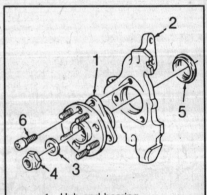

1. Hub and bearing assembly
2. Steering knuckle
3. Washer
4. Drive axle nut (192 ft. lbs. (260 Nm)
5. Wheel bearing seal
6. Hub and bearing retaining bolt

FIG. 22 Front hub and bearing assembly — 1992

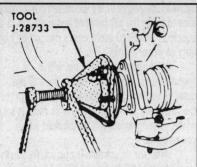

FIG. 23 Removing the front hub and bearing assembly — 1988–92

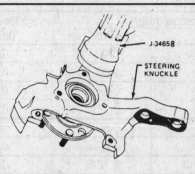

FIG. 24 Installation of the steering knuckle seal — 1988–92

4. Remove the hub nut. Remove the brake caliper and support it aside (on a wire); do not allow the caliper to hang on the brake line.

5. Remove the hub and bearing mounting bolts.

6. Remove the brake rotor splash shield.

7. Using a hub puller tool, press the hub and bearing from the halfshaft.

8. Disconnect the stabilizer link from the lower control arm.

9. Remove the cotter pin and the ball joint-to-knuckle attaching nut.

10. Disconnect the ball joint from the steering knuckle, using a ball joint separator tool.

11. Remove the halfshaft from the knuckle and support it aside.

12. Matchmark the strut in relationship to the knuckle, for alignment purposes and remove the strut-to-knuckle attaching nuts.

13. Remove the knuckle from the strut.

14. Using a brass drift, remove the inner knuckle seal.

To install:

15. Clean and inspect the steering knuckle bore and the bearing mating surfaces.

16. Using a seal driver tool, install it into the steering knuckle; be sure to lubricate the new seal and the bearing with a high temperature wheel bearing grease.

17. Connect the ball joint to the knuckle and install the ball joint-to-knuckle attaching nut, hand tight.

18. Position the knuckle to the strut and install the attaching bolts. Align the matchmarks and tighten the attaching bolts to 129 ft. lbs. (175 Nm) for 1988–90 and 133 ft. lbs. (180 Nm) for 1991–92. Tighten the ball joint-to-knuckle attaching nut to 55 ft. lbs (75 Nm) for 1988–90 and 26 ft. lbs. (35 Nm) plus 60 degree rotation for 1991–92.

19. Install a new O-ring between the bearing and knuckle assembly.

20. Install the splash shield, hub/bearing assembly, to the knuckle and install the attaching bolts. Tighten the attaching bolts to 67 ft. lbs. (90 Nm) for 1988–90 and 70 ft. lbs. (95 Nm) for 1991–92.

21. Remove the boot cover from the outer CV-joint boot and slide the halfshaft into the knuckle assembly.

22. Install the hub washer and attaching nut, (use and new nut) on the halfshaft. Tighten the attaching nut to a partial torque of 71 ft. lbs. (100 Nm), at this time.

23. Connect the stabilizer link to the lower control arm.

24. Install the brake rotor, caliper and the wheel/tire assembly.

25. Lower the vehicle and tighten the hub nut to 191 ft. lbs. (259 Nm).

Front End Alignment

▶ SEE FIG. 25

The toe setting is the only adjustment normally required on a Corsica/Beretta. However, in special circumstances, such as damage due to road hazard, collision, etc., camber may be adjusted after modifying the strut as detailed earlier in this Section. Caster is not adjustable.

CAMBER

Camber is the inward or outward tilt from the vertical, measured in degrees, of the front wheels at the top. An onward tilt gives the wheel positive camber; an inward tilt is called negative camber. Proper camber is critical to assure even tire wear.

1. Modify the suspension strut as detailed earlier.

2. Loosen the strut-to-knuckle bolts just enough to allow movement between the strut and the knuckle.

3. Grasp the top of the tire and move it in or out until the proper specification is obtained.

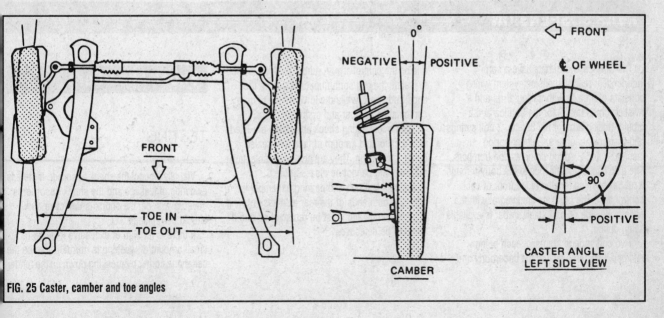

FIG. 25 Caster, camber and toe angles

4. Tighten both bolts just enough to hold the adjustment. Remove the wheels and tighten the bolts to the proper specifications.

5. Replace the wheels.

TOE

Toe is the amount, measured in a fraction of a millimeter, that the wheels are closer together at one end than the other. Toe-in means that the front wheels are closer together at the front than the rear; toe-out means the rear of the front wheels are closer together than the front.

Toe is adjusted by turning the tie rods. It must be checked after camber has been adjusted, but it can be adjusted without disturbing the camber setting. You can make this adjustment without special equipment if you make very careful measurements. The wheels must be straight ahead.

1. Toe can be determined by measuring the distance between the centers of the tire treads, at the front of the tire and at the rear. If the tread pattern makes this impossible, you can measure between the edges of the wheel rims, but make sure to move the car forward and measure in a couple of places to avoid errors caused by bent rims or wheel runout.

2. If the measurement is not within specifications, loosen the clamp bolts at the outer tie rod and rotate the adjuster to align the toe to specifications. Rotate the tie rods evenly, or the steering wheel will be crooked when you're done.

3. When the adjustment is correct, tighten the clamp bolts to 35 ft. lbs.

WHEEL ALIGNMENT SPECIFICATIONS

Years	Models	Caster (deg.)		Camber (deg.)		Toe-i
		Range	Pref.	Range	Pref.	(in.)
1988	Corsica	0.7P–2.7P	1.7P	0.3P–1.3P	0.8P	0
	Beretta	0.7P–2.7P	1.7P	0.3P–1.3P	0.8P	0
1989	Corsica	0.4P–1.9P	1.15P	0–1.2P①	0.6P②	0
	Beretta	0.4P–1.9P	1.15P	0–1.2P①	0.6P②	0
1990	Corsica	0.4P–1.9P	1.15P	0–1.2P①	0.6P②	0
	Beretta	0.4P–1.9P	1.15P	0–1.2P①	0.6P②	0
1991	Corsica	0.4P–1.9P	1.15P	0.6N–0.8P③	0.1P④	0
	Beretta	0.4P–1.9P	1.15P	0.6N–0.8P③	0.1P④	0
1992	Corsica	0.4P–1.9P	1.15P	0.6N–0.8P③	0.1P⑤	0
	Beretta	0.4P–1.9P	1.15P	0.6N–0.8P③	0.1P⑤	0
	Corsica	0.4P–1.9P	1.15P	0.8N–0.4P⑥	0.2N⑥	0
	Beretta	0.4P–1.9P	1.15P	0.8N–0.4P⑥	0.2N⑥	0

① With FE3 sport suspension: 0.8N–0.4P
② With FE3 sport suspension: 0.2N
③ GTZ: 0.8N–0.4P
④ GTZ: 0.2N
⑤ FE1 & F41 suspension options
⑥ FE2 & F37 suspension options

REAR SUSPENSION

The Corsica and Beretta have a semi-independent rear suspension system which consists of an axle with trailing arms and a twisting cross beam, for the Corsica and a tubular trailing arm for the Beretta, 2 coil springs and 2 shock absorbers, 2 upper spring insulators and 2 spring compression bumpers. The axle assembly attaches to the body through a rubber bushing located at the front of each control arm. The brackets are integral with the underbody side rails. A stabilizer bar is available as an option.

Two coil springs are used, each being retained between a seat in the underbody and one on the control arm. A rubber cushion is used to isolate the coil spring upper end from the underbody seat, while the lower end sits on a combination bumper and spring insulator.

The double acting shock absorbers are filled with a calibrated amount of fluid and sealed during production. They are non-adjustable, non-refillable and cannot be disassembled.

A single unit hub and bearing assembly is bolted to both ends of the rear axle assembly; it is a sealed unit and must be replaced as one if found to be defective.

Shock Absorbers

TESTING

Visually inspect the shock absorber. If there is evidence of leakage and the shock absorber is covered with oil, the shock is defective and should be replaced.

If there is no sign of excessive leakage (a small amount of weeping is normal) bounce the car at one corner by pressing down on the fender bumper and releasing. When you have the car ouncing as much as you can, release the fender r bumper. The car should stop bouncing after he first rebound. If the bouncing continues past he center point of the bounce more than once, he shock absorbers are worn and should be eplaced.

REMOVAL & INSTALLATION

SEE FIGS. 26-29

1. Open the trunk lid, remove the trim cover if resent, and remove the upper shock absorber ut.

→ Warning: ◊ Do not remove both hock absorbers at one time as uspending the rear axle at full ength could result in damage to he brake lines and hoses.

2. Raise the vehicle and support the rear axle ssembly to remove the weight from the shock bsorbers.

3. Remove the lower attaching bolt and emove the shock.

To install:

4. If new shock absorbers are being installed, epeatedly compress them while inverted and xtend them in their normal upright position. This ill purge them of air.

5. Install the shocks in the reverse order of emoval. Torque as follows:

a. Tighten the 2 upper outer nuts to 13 ft. s. (18 Nm).

b. Tighten the 1 upper center nut to 22 ft. s. (30 Nm).

c. For 1988 models, tighten the lower nount nut and bolt to 35 ft. lbs. (47 Nm) Corsica) and 43 ft. lbs. (58 Nm) (Beretta).

d. For 1989–90 models, tighten the lower nount nut and bolt to 35 ft. lbs. (47 Nm) Corsica) and 21 ft. lbs. (28 Nm) (Beretta).

e. For 1991–92 models, tighten the lower nount nut (Beretta) to 35 ft. lbs. (47 Nm) and he lower mount bolt (Corsica) to 35 ft. lbs. 47 Nm).

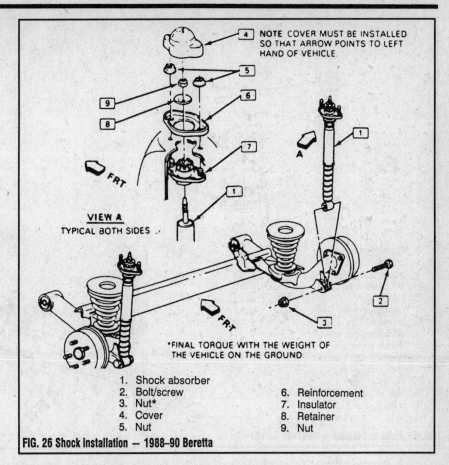

NOTE COVER MUST BE INSTALLED SO THAT ARROW POINTS TO LEFT HAND OF VEHICLE.

VIEW A
TYPICAL BOTH SIDES

*FINAL TORQUE WITH THE WEIGHT OF THE VEHICLE ON THE GROUND.

1. Shock absorber
2. Bolt/screw
3. Nut*
4. Cover
5. Nut
6. Reinforcement
7. Insulator
8. Retainer
9. Nut

FIG. 26 Shock installation — 1988–90 Beretta

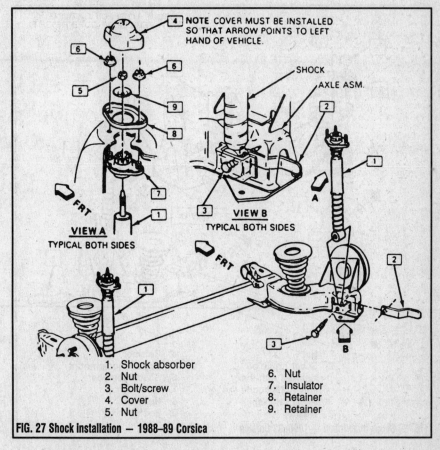

NOTE COVER MUST BE INSTALLED SO THAT ARROW POINTS TO LEFT HAND OF VEHICLE.

SHOCK
AXLE ASM.

VIEW B
TYPICAL BOTH SIDES

VIEW A
TYPICAL BOTH SIDES

1. Shock absorber
2. Nut
3. Bolt/screw
4. Cover
5. Nut
6. Nut
7. Insulator
8. Retainer
9. Retainer

FIG. 27 Shock installation — 1988–89 Corsica

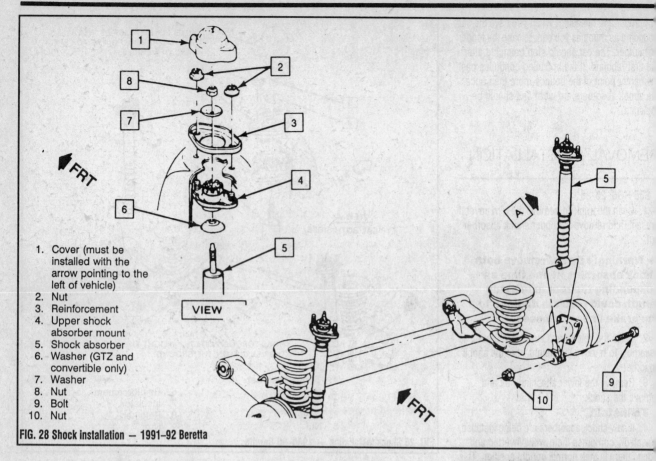

1. Cover (must be installed with the arrow pointing to the left of vehicle)
2. Nut
3. Reinforcement
4. Upper shock absorber mount
5. Shock absorber
6. Washer (GTZ and convertible only)
7. Washer
8. Nut
9. Bolt
10. Nut

FIG. 28 Shock installation — 1991–92 Beretta

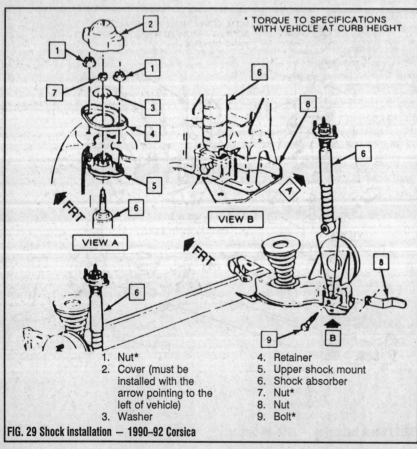

* TORQUE TO SPECIFICATIONS WITH VEHICLE AT CURB HEIGHT

1. Nut*	4. Retainer
2. Cover (must be installed with the arrow pointing to the left of vehicle)	5. Upper shock mount
	6. Shock absorber
	7. Nut*
	8. Nut
3. Washer	9. Bolt*

FIG. 29 Shock installation — 1990–92 Corsica

Springs

REMOVAL & INSTALLATION

◆ SEE FIG. 30

✱✱ CAUTION

The coil springs are under a considerable amount of tension. Be very careful when removing or installing them; they can exert enough force to cause very serious injuries.

1. Raise and support the car on a hoist. Do not use a twin-post hoist. The swing arc of the axle may cause it to slip from the hoist when the bolts are removed. If a suitable hoist is not available, raise and support the car on jackstands, and use a jack under the axle.

2. Support the axle with a jack that can be raised and lowered.

3. Remove the brake hose attaching brackets (right and left), allowing the hoses to hang freely. Do not disconnect the hoses.

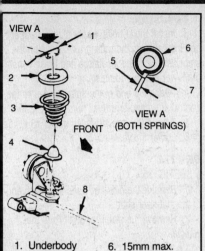

1. Underbody
2. Spring insulator
3. Spring
4. Compression bumper
5. Axle asm.
6. 15mm max. (.594")
7. Spring
8. Spring stop part of spring seat

FIG. 30 Typical rear coil spring installation

4. Remove both shock absorber lower attaching bolts from the axle.

5. Lower the axle. Remove the coil spring and insulator.

To install:

6. Position the spring and insulator in the seats and raise the axle. The ends of the upper coil of the spring must be must be positioned in the seat of the body and within the limits.

➡ **Install the upper insulators to the body with adhesive prior installing the spring.**

7. Connect the shocks to the rear axle and torque the bolts to the specifications noted in the shock absorber installation procedure. It will be necessary to bring the axle assembly to curb height prior to torquing bolts on the shocks.

8. Install the brake line brackets to the body.

9. Install the wheel.

10. Remove the jack stands and lower the vehicle.

Rear Hub and Bearing

REMOVAL & INSTALLATION

1988–90

▶ SEE FIG. 31

1. Loosen the wheel lug nuts. Raise and support the car and remove the wheel.

2. Remove the brake drum. Removal procedures are covered in the next Section, if needed.

❉❉ WARNING

Do not hammer on the brake drum to remove; damage to the bearing will result.

3. Remove the 4 hub and bearing retaining bolts and remove the assembly from the axle. The top rear attaching bolt will not clear the brake shoe when removing the hub and bearing assembly. Partially remove the hub and bearing assembly prior to removing this bolt.

To install:

4. Position the top attaching bolt in the hub and bearing assembly prior to the installation in the axle assembly.

5. Install the remaining hub and bearing bolts and torque to 38 ft. lbs. (52 Nm.).

6. Install the brake drum and wheel and tire assembly.

7. Lower the vehicle.

1991

▶ SEE FIG. 32

1. Loosen the wheel lug nuts. Raise and support the car and remove the wheel.

2. Remove the brake drum. Removal procedures are covered in the next Section, if needed.

❉❉ WARNING

Do not hammer on the brake drum to remove; damage to the bearing will result.

3. Remove the 4 hub and bearing retaining bolts (Corsica) or nuts (Beretta) and remove the assembly from the axle. The top rear attaching bolt will not clear the brake shoe when removing the hub and bearing assembly. Partially remove the hub and bearing assembly prior to removing this bolt.

To install:

4. Position the top attaching bolt in the hub and bearing assembly prior to the installation in the axle assembly, for the Corsica only.

5. Install the remaining hub and bearing bolt/nuts and torque to 38 ft. lbs. (52 Nm.).

6. Install the brake drum and wheel and tire assembly.

7. Lower the vehicle.

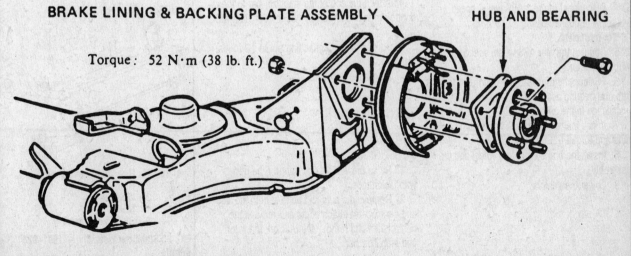

BRAKE LINING & BACKING PLATE ASSEMBLY   HUB AND BEARING

Torque: 52 N·m (38 lb. ft.)

FIG. 31 Rear hub and bearing assembly installation — 1988–90

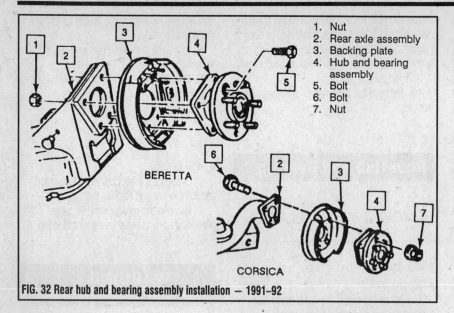

1. Nut
2. Rear axle assembly
3. Backing plate
4. Hub and bearing assembly
5. Bolt
6. Bolt
7. Nut

BERETTA

CORSICA

FIG. 32 Rear hub and bearing assembly installation — 1991–92

1992

♦ SEE FIG. 32

1. Loosen the wheel lug nuts. Raise and support the car and remove the wheel.

2. Remove the brake drum. Removal procedures are covered in the next Section 9, if needed.

❊❊❊ WARNING

Do not hammer on the brake drum to remove; damage to the bearing will result.

3. Remove the 4 hub and bearing retaining bolts/nuts and remove the assembly from the axle. The top rear attaching bolt/nut will not clear the brake shoe when removing the hub and bearing assembly. Partially remove the hub and bearing assembly prior to removing this bolt/nut.

4. Disconnect the rear ABS wheel speed sensor wire connector.

To install:

5. Connect the rear ABS wheel speed sensor wire connector.

6. Position the top attaching bolt/nut in the hub and bearing assembly prior to the installation in the axle assembly.

7. Install the remaining hub and bearing bolt/nuts and torque to 38 ft. lbs. (52 Nm.).

8. Install the brake drum and wheel and tire assembly.

9. Lower the vehicle.

Stabilizer Bar

REMOVAL & INSTALLATION

1988–90

♦ SEE FIG. 33-34

1. Raise the vehicle and support the body with jackstands.

2. Remove the nuts and bolts at both the axle and control arm attachments and remove the control arm and remove the bracket, insulator and stabilizer bar.

To install:

3. Install the U-bolts, upper clamp, spacer and insulators in the trailing axle. Position the stabilizer bar in the insulators and loosely install the lower clamp and nuts.

4. Attach the end of the stabilizer bar to the control arms and torque all nuts to 16. ft. lbs. (22 Nm).

5. Torque the axle attaching nut to 13 ft. lbs. (18 Nm).

6. Lower the vehicle.

1991–92

CORSICA

♦ SEE FIG. 33

1. Raise the vehicle and support the body with jackstands.

2. Remove the nuts and bolts at both the axle and control arm attachments and remove the control arm and remove the bracket, insulator and stabilizer bar.

To install:

3. Install the U-bolts, upper clamp, spacer and insulators in the trailing axle. Position the stabilizer bar in the insulators and loosely install the lower clamp and nuts.

4. Attach the end of the stabilizer bar to the control arms and torque all nuts to 16. ft. lbs.

5. Torque the axle attaching nut to 13 ft. lbs.

6. Lower the vehicle.

BERETTA

♦ SEE FIG. 35

1. Remove the nuts and bolts from both ends of the stabilizer shaft.

2. Remove the stabilizer shaft from the vehicle.

To install:

3. Position the stabilizer shaft and install retaining the nuts and bolts.

4. Tighten the nuts to 103 ft. lbs. (139 Nm).

Rear Axle/Control Arm

The control arms and axle are one unit. The axle structure itself maintains the geometrical relationship of the wheels relative to the body. The axle assembly attaches to the underbody through a rubber bushing located at the front of each control arm. Each control arm bolts to underbody brackets.

REMOVAL & INSTALLATION

1988–92

♦ SEE FIG. 36

1. Raise the vehicle and support the with jackstands under the control arms.

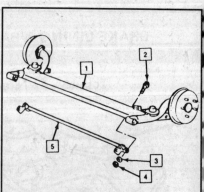

1. Rear axle assembly
2. Bolt
3. Washer
4. Nut
5. Stabilizer shaft

FIG. 35 Stabilizer assembly — 1991–92 Beretta

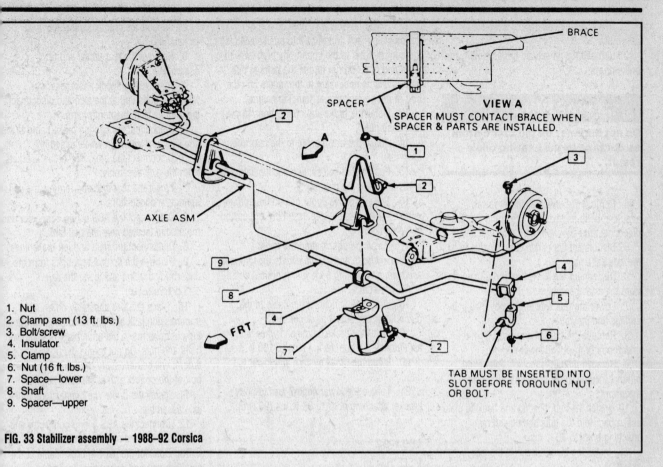

1. Nut
2. Clamp asm (13 ft. lbs.)
3. Bolt/screw
4. Insulator
5. Clamp
6. Nut (16 ft. lbs.)
7. Space—lower
8. Shaft
9. Spacer—upper

BRACE

SPACER

VIEW A
SPACER MUST CONTACT BRACE WHEN
SPACER & PARTS ARE INSTALLED.

AXLE ASM

FRT

TAB MUST BE INSERTED INTO
SLOT BEFORE TORQUING NUT,
OR BOLT.

FIG. 33 Stabilizer assembly — 1988–92 Corsica

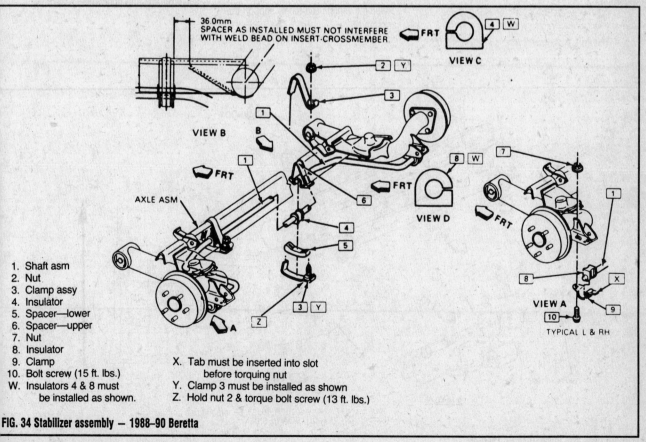

1. Shaft asm
2. Nut
3. Clamp assy
4. Insulator
5. Spacer—lower
6. Spacer—upper
7. Nut
8. Insulator
9. Clamp
10. Bolt screw (15 ft. lbs.)
W. Insulators 4 & 8 must
   be installed as shown.

X. Tab must be inserted into slot
   before torquing nut
Y. Clamp 3 must be installed as shown
Z. Hold nut 2 & torque bolt screw (13 ft. lbs.)

36.0mm
SPACER AS INSTALLED MUST NOT INTERFERE
WITH WELD BEAD ON INSERT-CROSSMEMBER.

FRT

VIEW C

VIEW B

FRT

AXLE ASM

FRT

VIEW D

FRT

VIEW A

TYPICAL L & RH

FIG. 34 Stabilizer assembly — 1988–90 Beretta

2. Remove the stabilizer bar from the axle assembly.

3. Remove the wheel and tire assembly and brake drum.

❈❈ WARNING

Do not hammer on the brake drum as damage to the bearing could result.

4. Remove the shock absorber lower attaching bolts and paddle nuts at the axle and disconnect the shocks from the control arm.

5. Disconnect the parking brake cable from the axle assembly.

6. Disconnect the brake line at the brackets from the axle assembly.

7. Lower the rear axle and remove the coil springs and insulators.

8. Remove the control arm bolts from the underbody bracket and lower the axle.

9. Remove the hub attaching bolts and remove the hub, bearing and backing plate assembly.

10. Install the hub, bearing and backing plate assembly. Hold the nuts and tighten the attaching bolts to 38 ft. lbs.

11. Install the stabilizer bar to the axle assembly.

12. Place the axle assembly on a transmission jack and raise into position. Attach the control arms to the underbody bracket with bolts and nuts. Do not torque the bolts at this time. It will be necessary to torque the bolt the bolt of the control arm at standing height.

13. Install the brake line connections to the axle assembly.

14. Attach the brake cable to the rear axle assembly.

15. Position the coil springs and insulators in seats and raise the rear axle.

16. The end of the upper coil on the springs must be parallel to the axle assembly and seated in the pocket.

17. Install the shock absorber lower attachment bolts and paddle nuts to the rear axle and torque the bolt to 35 ft. lbs. (Corsica) and 43 ft. lbs (Beretta).

18. Install the parking brake cable to the guide hook and adjust as necessary.

19. Install the brake drums and wheel and tire assemblies. Torque the lug nuts to 100 ft. lbs.

20. Bleed the brake system and lower the car.

21. Torque the lower control arm to body bracket attaching bolts to 66 ft. lbs (90 Nm).

1991–92

♦ SEE FIG. 36

1. Raise the vehicle and safely support the with jackstands.

2. Support the rear axle assembly with jackstands.

3. Remove the rear wheel and tire assemblies.

4. Remove the shock absorber lower attaching bolts and at the axle and disconnect the shocks from the control arm.

5. Disconnect the parking brake cable at the equalizer unit and right wheel assembly.

6. Disconnect the brake line at the brackets from the axle assembly.

7. Lower the rear axle and remove the coil springs and insulators.

8. Disconnect the ABS wiring connector and mount clip located near the fuel tank.

8. Disconnect the right and left brake lines.

9. Remove the control arm bolts from the underbody bracket and lower the axle.

To install:

10. Place the axle assembly on a transmission jack and raise into position. Attach the control arms to the underbody bracket with bolts and nuts. Do not torque the bolts at this time. It will be necessary to torque the bolt the bolt of the control arm at standing height.

11. Install the brake line connections to the axle assembly.

12. Connect the ABS wiring connector and mount clip located near the fuel tank.

13. Connect the parking brake cable at the equalizer unit and right wheel assembly.

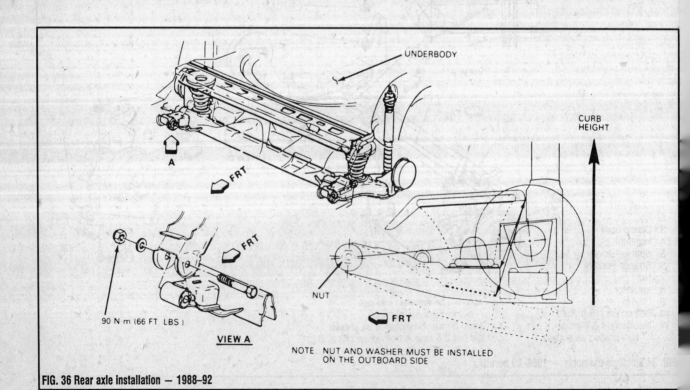

FIG. 36 Rear axle installation — 1988–92

14. Position the upper and lower insulators, using adhesive, and install the springs in the seats and raise the rear axle.

15. The end of the upper coil on the springs must be parallel to the axle assembly and seated in the pocket.

16. Install the shock absorber lower attachment bolts and nuts to the rear axle and torque the bolt to 35 ft. lbs. (47 Nm).

17. Install the right and left side brake line bracket mount bolts to the body and tighten to 8 ft. lbs. (11 Nm).

18. Install the wheel and tire assemblies. Torque the lug nuts to 100 ft. lbs.

19. Bleed the brake system and lower the car.

20. Torque the lower control arm to body bracket attaching bolts to 52 ft. lbs (70 Nm) plus an additional 120 degree rotation.

Rear Wheel Alignment

Rear wheel alignment is not adjustable.

STEERING

The power rack and pinion steering system has a rotary control valve which directs the hydraulic fluid to either side of the rack piston. The integral rack piston is attached to the rack and converts the hydraulic pressure into left or right linear motion. A vane-type constant displacement pump with integral reservoir provides hydraulic pressure. No in-car adjustments are necessary or possible on the system.

Steering Wheel

REMOVAL & INSTALLATION

1988–90

♦ SEE FIG. 37

1. Disconnect the negative terminal from the battery. Turn the steering wheel so the wheels are in the straight ahead position.

2. From the rear of the steering wheel, remove the horn cover-to-steering wheel screws. Disconnect the horn electrical connector from the steering wheel.

3. Remove the steering wheel-to-column retainer, nut, washer (if equipped) and damper assembly.

4. Using a marking tool, mark the steering wheel alignment with the steering shaft for realignment purposes.

5. Using the Steering Wheel Puller tool No. J-1859–03 or equivalent, press the steering wheel from the steering column.

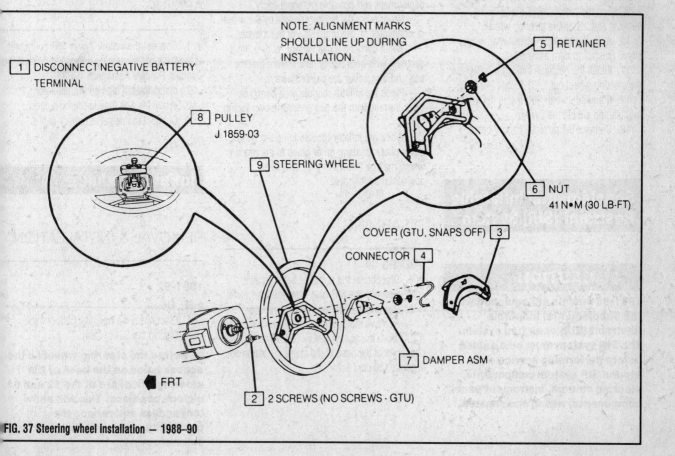

NOTE: ALIGNMENT MARKS SHOULD LINE UP DURING INSTALLATION.

1 DISCONNECT NEGATIVE BATTERY TERMINAL

8 PULLEY J 1859-03

9 STEERING WHEEL

5 RETAINER

6 NUT 41 N•M (30 LB-FT)

COVER (GTU, SNAPS OFF) 3

CONNECTOR 4

7 DAMPER ASM

◀ FRT

2 2 SCREWS (NO SCREWS - GTU)

FIG. 37 Steering wheel installation — 1988–90

6. To install, reverse the removal procedures. Torque the steering wheel nut to 30 ft. lbs. (41 Nm).

1991–92

➡ SEE FIG. 38

1. Disconnect the negative battery cable.

2. Disable the SIR system and remove the inflator module as outlined below.

3. Without SIR, remove the horn cover-to-steering wheel screws.

4. Disconnect the horn electrical connector from the steering wheel and remove the horn contact.

5. Remove the steering wheel-to-column retainer, nut, washer.

6. Mark the steering wheel alignment with the steering shaft for installation purposes.

7. Using a steering wheel puller, press the steering wheel from the steering column.

➡ **Under no circumstances should the steering wheel or shaft be hammered on. Sharp blows to the steering column could loosen the plastic injections which maintain column rigidity.**

To install:

8. If equipped with SIR, feed the coil assembly connector through the steering wheel.

9. Align the matchmarks made during removal and install the steering wheel.

10. Align the steering wheel with the turn signal cancelling cam assembly.

11. Install the hexagon locking nut. Tighten the steering wheel nut to 31 ft. lbs. (42 Nm).

12. If equipped with SIR, install the inflator module and enable the system.

13. Connect the negative battery cable.

Supplemental Inflatable Restraint (SIR) System

❋❋ CAUTION

1991–92 models are equipped with the Supplemental Inflatable Restraint (SIR) or air bag system. The SIR system must be disabled before performing service on or around SIR system components, steering column, instrument panel components, wiring and sensors.

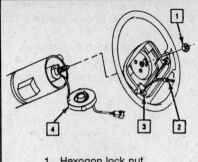

1. Hexagon lock nut
2. Horn contact
3. Horn contact switch
4. Coil assembly

FIG. 38 Steering wheel installation — 1991–92

Failure to follow safety and disabling procedures could result in accidental air bag deployment, possible personal injury and unnecessary SIR system repairs.

Precautions

Several precautions must be observed when handling the inflator module to avoid accidental deployment and possible personal injury.

• Never carry the inflator module by the wires or connector on the underside of the module.

• When carrying a live inflator module, hold securely with both hands, and ensure that the bag and trim cover are pointed away.

• Place the inflator module on a bench or other surface with the bag and trim cover facing up.

• When the inflator module is on the bench, never place anything on or close to the module which may be thrown in the event of an accidental deployment.

DISARMING

➡ SEE FIG. 39

1. Disconnect the negative battery cable.

2. Remove the SIR fuse from the fuse panel.

3. Remove the left side sound insulator.

4. Remove the Connector Positive Assurance (CPA) from the yellow 2-way SIR harness connector at the base of the steering column and separate the connector.

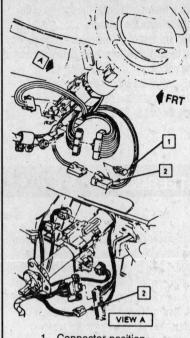

1. Connector position assurance (CPA)
2. Yellow two-way SIR harness connector

FIG. 39 Yellow two-way SIR harness connector — 1991–92

ARMING

1. Connect the yellow 2-way SIR connector at the base of the steering column and insert the Connect Positive Assurance (CPA).

2. Install the left side sound insulator.

3. Install the SIR fuse in the fuse panel.

4. Connect the negative battery cable.

Inflator Module

REMOVAL & INSTALLATION

1991–92

➡ SEE FIG. 40

1. Disconnect the negative battery cable.

2. Disarm the SIR system.

➡ **Rotate the steering wheel so the access holes on the back of the steering wheel are at the 12 and 6 o'clock positions. This will allow tool access and reduce the possibility of marring the steering column cover.**

3. Remove the 4 screws from the back of the inflator module.

4. Remove the inflator module from the steering wheel.

5. Remove the Connector Positive Assurance (CPA) from the inflator module electrical connector and disconnect the connector.

To install:

6. Connect the coil assembly connector. Install the CPA into the connector.

➡ **Ensure that no wires at the back of the inflator module are pinched when aligning the inflator module to the steering wheel.**

7. Install the inflator module and the 4 attaching bolts.

8. Arm the SIR system.

9. Connect the negative battery cable.

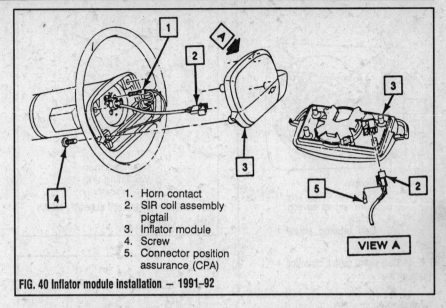

1. Horn contact
2. SIR coil assembly pigtail
3. Inflator module
4. Screw
5. Connector position assurance (CPA)

VIEW A

FIG. 40 Inflator module installation — 1991–92

CENTERING THE COIL ASSEMBLY

◆ SEE FIG. 41

In the event the coil becomes uncentered, perform the following:

1. With the steering wheel removed, remove the coil assembly from the steering column.

2. Hold the coil assembly with the clear bottom up in order to see the coil ribbon.

3. There are 2 styles of coils: one rotates clockwise and the other rotates counterclockwise.

4. While holding the coil assembly, depress the spring lock to rotate the hub in the direction of the arrow until it stops. The coil ribbon should be wound up snug against the center hub.

5. Rotate the coil hub in the opposite direction approximately 2¹/₂ turns.

6. Release the spring lock between the locking tabs adjacent to the arrow.

Turn Signal Switch

REMOVAL & INSTALLATION

1988–90

◆ SEE FIGS. 42-44

➡ **Tool No. J–35689–A or equivalent, is required to remove the terminals from the connector on the turn signal switch.**

1. Refer to the "Steering Wheel, Removal and Installation" in this section and remove the steering wheel.

2. Pull the turn signal canceling cam assembly from the steering shaft.

3. Remove the hazard warning knob-to-steering column screw and the knob.

➡ **Before removing the turn signal assembly, position the turn signal lever so the turn signal assembly-to-steering column screws can all be removed.**

4. Remove the column housing cover-to-column housing bowl screw and the cover.

➡ **If equipped with cruise control, disconnect the cruise control electrical connector.**

5. Remove the turn signal lever-to-pivot assembly screw and the lever; one screw is in the front and one is in the rear.

6. Using the Terminal Remover tool No. J-35689-A or equivalent, disconnect and label the wires "F" and "G" on the connector at the buzzer switch assembly from the turn signal switch electrical harness connector.

7. Remove the turn signal switch-to-steering column screws and the switch.

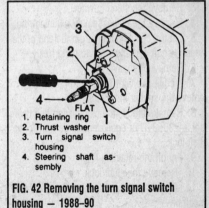

1. Retaining ring
2. Thrust washer
3. Turn signal switch housing
4. Steering shaft assembly

FIG. 42 Removing the turn signal switch housing — 1988–90

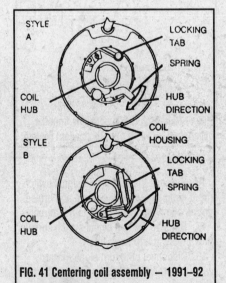

FIG. 41 Centering coil assembly — 1991–92

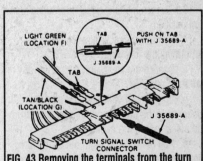

FIG. 43 Removing the terminals from the turn signal switch connector — 1988–90

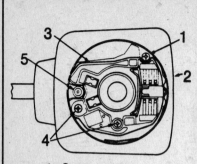

1. Screw
2. Housing cover
3. Turn signal switch
4. Screw
5. Self tapping screw

FIG. 44 Turn signal switch mounting — 1988–90

8. To install, reverse the removal procedures. Torque the turn signal switch-to-steering column screws to 35 inch lbs. and the steering wheel nut to 30 ft. lbs.

1991–92

♦ SEE FIGS. 45-52

1. Disable the SIR system. See Disarming procedure in this section.
2. Disconnect the negative battery cable.
3. Place the ignition to the LOCK position.
3. Remove the steering wheel.
4. Remove the coil assembly retaining ring.
5. Lift the coil assembly from the end of the steering shaft and allow coil to hang freely.
6. Remove the wave washer.
7. If equipped with a standard column, remove the spacer shaft lock.
8. Remove the shaft lock retaining ring using tool J–23653–C or equivalent, to compress the shaft lock.
9. Pry off the retaining ring.
10. Remove the shaft lock.
11. Remove the turn signal cancelling cam assembly.
12. Remove the upper bearing spring.
13. Position the turn signal lever to the right turn position.
14. Remove the multi-function lever by performing the following:
    a. Ensure the lever is in the center or **OFF** position.
    b. If equipped with cruise control, disconnect the cruise control connector from the steering column assembly.
    c. Pull the lever straight out of the turn signal switch.
15. Remove the hazard knob assembly.

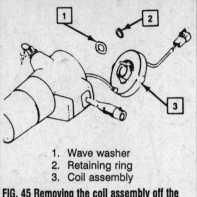

1. Wave washer
2. Retaining ring
3. Coil assembly

FIG. 45 Removing the coil assembly off the shaft — 1991–92

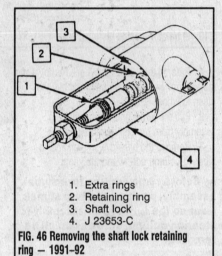

1. Extra rings
2. Retaining ring
3. Shaft lock
4. J 23653-C

FIG. 46 Removing the shaft lock retaining ring — 1991–92

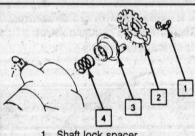

1. Shaft lock spacer
2. Shaft lock
3. Turn signal cancelling cam
4. Upper bearing spring

FIG. 47 Removing the components from the upper shaft — 1991–92 with standard column

16. Remove the screw and signal switch arm. If equipped with tilt column and cruise control, allow the switch arm to hang freely.
17. Remove the turn signal switch screws. Allow the switch to hang freely.
18. Disconnect the turn signal/hazard switch assembly terminal from the instrument panel harness.

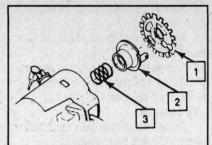

1. Shaft lock assembly
2. Turn signal cancelling cam
3. Upper bearing spring

FIG. 48 Removing the components from the upper shaft — 1991–92 with tilt column

19. If equipped with tilt column, disconnect the buzzer switch assembly terminals from the turn signal/hazard assembly connector. Remove the tan/black wire lead from cavity E and the light green wire from the cavity F.
20. Remove the upper steering column bolts.
21. Remove the wiring protector.
22. Connect a length of wire to the turn signal/hazard assembly terminal connector to aid in reassembly.
23. Gently pull the wire harness through the steering column housing shroud, steering column housing and lock assembly cover.
24. Disconnect the wire from the connector.

To install:

25. Connect the wire to the turn signal/hazard switch assembly connector.
26. Gently pull the connector through the steering column housing shroud, steering column housing and lock assembly cover.
27. Remove the wire.
28. Install the wiring protector.
29. If disconnected, connect the buzzer switch terminals to the turn signal/hazard switch assembly connector. Insert the tan/black wire lead into cavity E and the light green wire into cavity F.
30. Connect the turn signal/hazard switch assembly connector to the instrument panel harness.
31. Install the steering column support bracket bolts to the steering column. Tighten to 22 ft. lbs. (30 Nm).
32. Install the steering column upper support bolts. Tighten to 20 ft. lbs. (28 Nm).
33. Install the turn signal switch assembly and attaching screws. Tighten to 20 inch lbs. (2.3 Nm).
34. Install the hazard knob assembly.

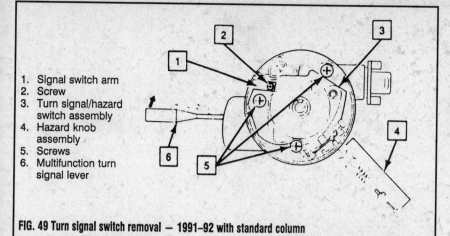

1. Signal switch arm
2. Screw
3. Turn signal/hazard switch assembly
4. Hazard knob assembly
5. Screws
6. Multifunction turn signal lever

FIG. 49 Turn signal switch removal — 1991–92 with standard column

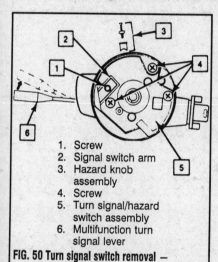

1. Screw
2. Signal switch arm
3. Hazard knob assembly
4. Screw
5. Turn signal/hazard switch assembly
6. Multifunction turn signal lever

FIG. 50 Turn signal switch removal — 1991–92 with tilt column

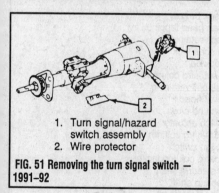

1. Turn signal/hazard switch assembly
2. Wire protector

FIG. 51 Removing the turn signal switch — 1991–92

35. Install the multi-function lever by performing the following:

a. Align the tab on the turn signal switch with the notch in the pivot of the turn signal switch.

b. Push the lever into the turn signal switch.

c. If equipped with cruise control, connect the connector to the steering column assembly.

36. Install the turn signal cancelling cam assembly. Lubricate with a synthetic grease.

37. Install the shaft lock.

38. Install the shaft lock retaining ring, lining up to block tooth on the shaft. Use tool J–23653–C to compress the shaft lock.

39. If equipped with a standard column, install the spacer shaft lock.

40. Install the wave washer.

41. Ensure the coil assembly is centered.

➡ **The coil assembly will become uncentered if the steering column is separated from the steering gear and is allowed to rotate or the centering spring is pushed down, letting the hub rotate while the coil is removed from the steering column.**

42. Install the coil assembly using the horn tower on the cancelling cam assembly inner ring and projections on the outer ring for alignment.

43. Install the coil assembly retaining ring. The ring must be firmly seated in the groove on the shaft. Gently pull the lower coil assembly wire to remove any wire kinks that may be inside the column.

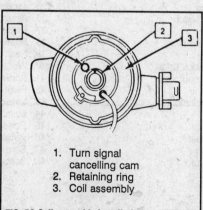

1. Turn signal cancelling cam
2. Retaining ring
3. Coil assembly

FIG. 52 Coil assembly installation — 1991–92

44. Install the steering wheel.
45. Enable the SIR system.
46. Connect the negative battery cable.

Ignition Switch and Dimmer Switch

REMOVAL & INSTALLATION

1988

◆ SEE FIGS. 53-59

1. Disconnect the negative battery cable.

2. If equipped with a column shift, place the transaxle selector in **P**.

3. Place the lock cylinder in the **ACC** position.

4. Remove the left side sound insulator panel.

5. Remove the steering column-to-support bolts. Gently lower the steering column onto the driver's seat.

6. Disconnect the dimmer and ignition switch connectors.

7. Remove the dimmer switch nut, bolt and disconnect the dimmer switch from the actuator rod.

8. Remove the switch.

To install:

9. Make sure the ignition lock cylinder is in the **ACC** position.

10. Insert the dimmer switch actuator rod into the hole in the dimmer switch.

11. Position the dimmer switch in place on the stud and install the retainer nut and screw. Do not tighten.

12. Position the dimmer switch so a click is heard when the turn signal lever is pulled. Tighten the nut and screw to 35 inch lbs. (4 Nm).

13. Raise the steering column into place and connect the dimmer switch and turn signal switch connectors.

14. Install the steering column-to-support screws and secure the steering column in place.

15. Install the left side lower trim panel.

16. Connect the negative battery cable.

1989–90

◆ SEE FIGS. 61-63

➡ **The manufacturer recommends that the steering column be removed from vehicle before performing this procedure.**

1. Disconnect the negative battery cable.

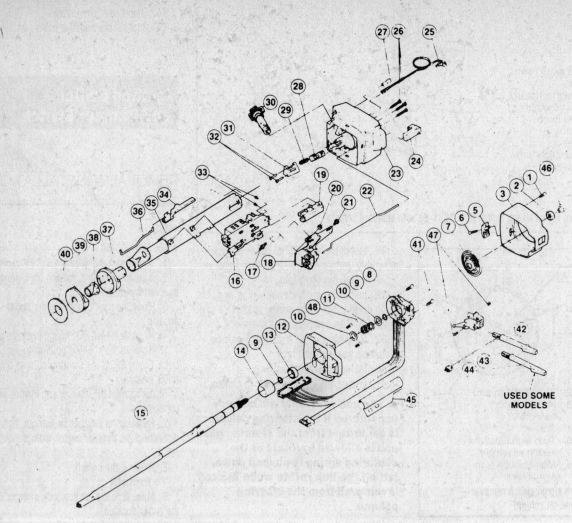

1. Screw, pan head cross recess
2. Nut, hexagon jam
3. Cover, column housing
4. Spacer, compression
5. Knob, hazard warning
6. Screw, ov, hd c/rec
7. Cam asm, turn sig cancel
8. Switch asm, turn signal
9. Ring, retaining
10. Washer, thrust
11. Spring, upper bearing
12. Housing, turn signal switch
13. Bearing asm
14. Spacer, strg column housing
15. Shaft asm, steering
16. Switch asm, column lock & ign
17. Stud, dimr & ign sw moutning
18. Switch asm, dimmer
19. Housing asm, ign sw inhibiter
20. Nut, hexagon
21. Screw, wsher hd
22. Rod, dimmer sw actuator
23. Bowl, steering column
24. Cap, dimmer switch rod
25. Switch asm, buzzer
26. Screw, pan head tapping
27. Screw, lock retaining
28. Bolt, strg shaft lock
29. Spring, lock bolt
30. Lock cyl set, strg column
31. Plate, lock bolt retaining
32. Screw, oval head
33. Screw, pan hd c/rec
34. Rack, switch actuator
35. Jacket asm, strg column
36. Actuator, ign switch
37. Bushing, strg column jacket
38. Bearing, steering shaft
39. Seal, steering shaft
40. Washer, seal retaining
41. Screw, pan head cross recess
42. Pivot asm, dimmer switch actuator
43. Lever, T/S & cruise
44. Lever, turn signal
45. Portector, wiring
46. Retainer, steering wheel nut
47. Screw, C/S tapping
48. Screw, pan hd 6-lobed soc tap

FIG. 53 Standard column with park lock — 1988

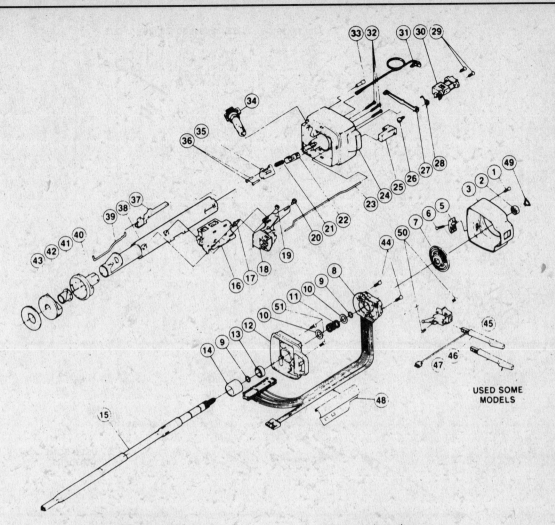

1. Screw, pan head cross recess
2. Nut, hexagon jam
3. Cover, column housing
4. Spacer, compression
5. Knob, hazard warning
6. Screw, ov, hd c/rec
7. Cam asm, turn signal
8. Switch asm, turn signal
9. Ring, retaining
10. Washer, thrust
11. Spring, upper bearing
12. Housing, turn signal switch
13. Bearing asm
14. Spacer, strg column housing
15. Shaft asm, steering
16. Switch asm, ignition
17. Stud, dimr & ign sw moutning
18. Switch asm, dimmer
19. Nut, hexagon
20. Screw, washer hd
21. Spring, lock bolt
22. Bolt, strg shaft lock
23. Rod, dimmer sw actuator
24. Bowl, steering column
25. Cap, dimmer switch rod
26. Bolt, key release lever
27. Lever, key release
28. Spring, key release lever
29. Screw, pan head tapping
30. Bracket, tilt lever & shoe
31. Switch asm, buzzer
32. Screw, pan head tapping
33. Screw lock retaining
34. Lock cyl set, strg column
35. Plate, lock bolt retaining
36. Screw, oval head
37. Rack, switch actuator
38. Jacket asm, strg column
39. Actuator, ign switch
40. Bushing, strg column jacket
41. Bearing, steering shaft
42. Seal, steering shaft
43. Washer, seal retaining
44. Screw, pan head cross recess
45. Pivot asm, dimmer switch actuator
46. Lever, T/S & cruise
47. Lever, turn signal
48. Protector, wiring
49. Retainer, steering wheel nut
50. Screw, C/S tapping
51. Screw, pan hd 6-lobed soc tap

FIG. 54 Standard column with key release — 1988

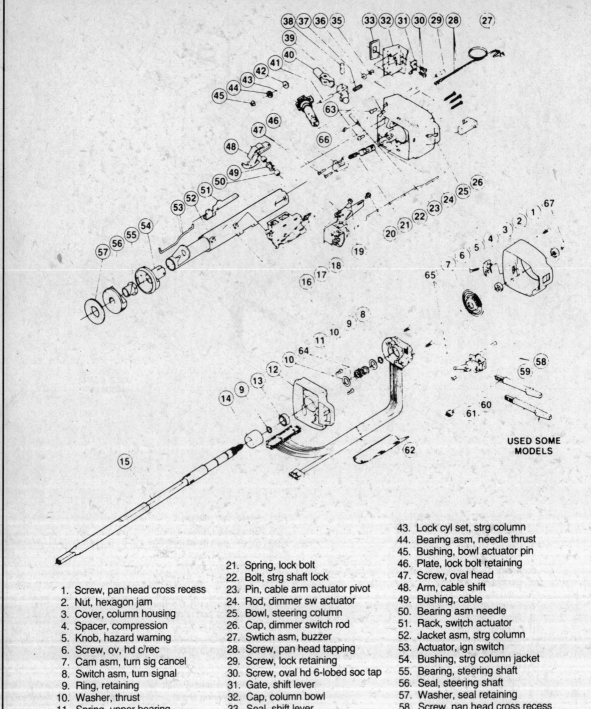

43. Lock cyl set, strg column
44. Bearing asm, needle thrust
45. Bushing, bowl actuator pin
46. Plate, lock bolt retaining
47. Screw, oval head
48. Arm, cable shift
49. Bushing, cable
50. Bearing asm needle
51. Rack, switch actuator
52. Jacket asm, strg column
53. Actuator, ign switch
54. Bushing, strg column jacket
55. Bearing, steering shaft
56. Seal, steering shaft
57. Washer, seal retaining
58. Screw, pan head cross recess
59. Pivot asm, dimmer switch actuator
60. Lever, T/S & cruise
61. Lever, turn signal
62. Protector, wiring
63. Screw, pan hd 6-lobed soc tap
64. Screw, pan hd 6-lobed soc tap
65. Screw, C/S tapping
66. Ring, retaining
67. Retainer, steering wheel nut

21. Spring, lock bolt
22. Bolt, strg shaft lock
23. Pin, cable arm actuator pivot
24. Rod, dimmer sw actuator
25. Bowl, steering column
26. Cap, dimmer switch rod
27. Swtich asm, buzzer
28. Screw, pan head tapping
29. Screw, lock retaining
30. Screw, oval hd 6-lobed soc tap
31. Gate, shift lever
32. Cap, column bowl
33. Seal, shift lever
34. This number not used
35. Bushing, cap actuator pin
36. Spacer, shfit lever clevis
37. Spring, shift lever
38. Pin, shift lever clevis pivot
39. Actuator asm, cable arm
40. Clevis, shift lever
41. Pin, cable arm actuator pivot
42. Race, bearing asm thrust

1. Screw, pan head cross recess
2. Nut, hexagon jam
3. Cover, column housing
4. Spacer, compression
5. Knob, hazard warning
6. Screw, ov, hd c/rec
7. Cam asm, turn sig cancel
8. Switch asm, turn signal
9. Ring, retaining
10. Washer, thrust
11. Spring, upper bearing
12. Housing, turn signal switch
13. Bearing asm
14. Spacer, strg column housing
15. Shaft asm, steering
16. Switch asm, ignition
17. Stud, dimr & ign sw mounting
18. Switch asm, dimmer
19. Nut, hexagon
20. Screw, washer hd

FIG. 55 Standard column with column shift and automatic transaxle — 1988

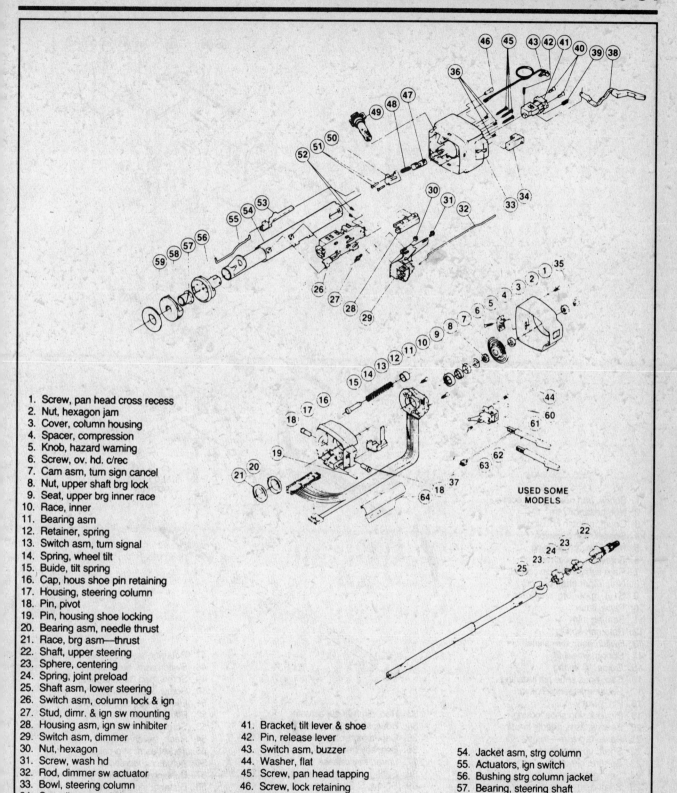

1. Screw, pan head cross recess
2. Nut, hexagon jam
3. Cover, column housing
4. Spacer, compression
5. Knob, hazard warning
6. Screw, ov. hd. c/rec
7. Cam asm, turn sign cancel
8. Nut, upper shaft brg lock
9. Seat, upper brg inner race
10. Race, inner
11. Bearing asm
12. Retainer, spring
13. Switch asm, turn signal
14. Spring, wheel tilt
15. Buide, tilt spring
16. Cap, hous shoe pin retaining
17. Housing, steering column
18. Pin, pivot
19. Pin, housing shoe locking
20. Bearing asm, needle thrust
21. Race, brg asm—thrust
22. Shaft, upper steering
23. Sphere, centering
24. Spring, joint preload
25. Shaft asm, lower steering
26. Switch asm, column lock & ign
27. Stud, dimr. & ign sw mounting
28. Housing asm, ign sw inhibiter
29. Switch asm, dimmer
30. Nut, hexagon
31. Screw, wash hd
32. Rod, dimmer sw actuator
33. Bowl, steering column
34. Cap, dimmer switch rod
35. Retainer, steering wheel nut
36. Bumper, column tilt
37. Screw, C/S tapping
38. Lever, shoe release
39. Spring, release lever
40. Screw, pan head cross recess

41. Bracket, tilt lever & shoe
42. Pin, release lever
43. Switch asm, buzzer
44. Washer, flat
45. Screw, pan head tapping
46. Screw, lock retaining
47. Bolt, strg shaft lock
48. Spring, lock bolt
49. Lock cyc set, strg column
50. Plate, lock bolt retaining
51. Screw, oval head
52. Screw, pan hd c/rec
53. Rack, switch actuator

54. Jacket asm, strg column
55. Actuators, ign switch
56. Bushing strg column jacket
57. Bearing, steering shaft
58. Seal, steering shaft
59. Washer, seal retaining
60. Screw, pan head cross recess
61. Pivot asm, dimmer switch actuator
62. Lever, T/S & cruise
63. Lever, turn signal
64. Protector, wiring

FIG. 56 Tilt column with park lock — 1988

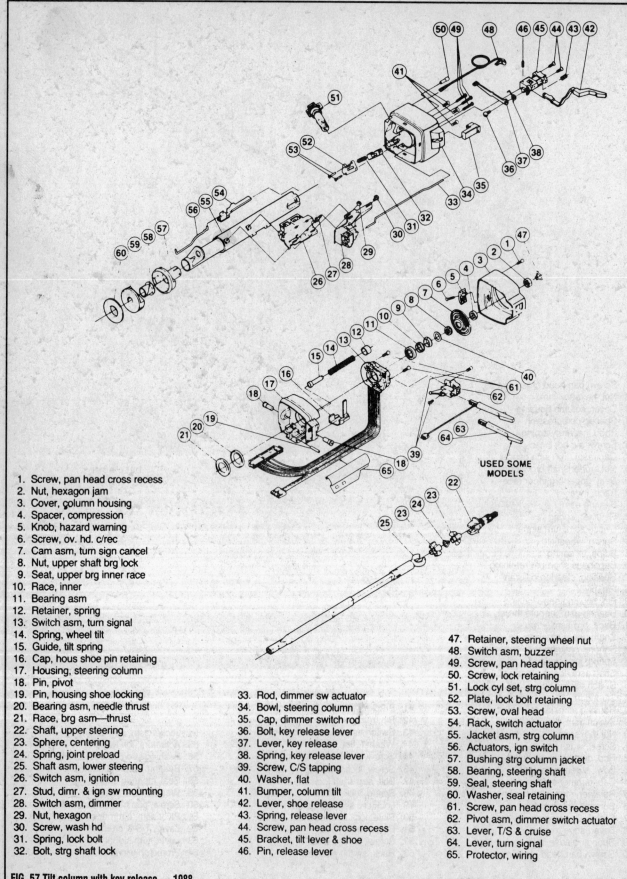

1. Screw, pan head cross recess
2. Nut, hexagon jam
3. Cover, column housing
4. Spacer, compression
5. Knob, hazard warning
6. Screw, ov. hd. c/rec
7. Cam asm, turn sign cancel
8. Nut, upper shaft brg lock
9. Seat, upper brg inner race
10. Race, inner
11. Bearing asm
12. Retainer, spring
13. Switch asm, turn signal
14. Spring, wheel tilt
15. Guide, tilt spring
16. Cap, hous shoe pin retaining
17. Housing, steering column
18. Pin, pivot
19. Pin, housing shoe locking
20. Bearing asm, needle thrust
21. Race, brg asm—thrust
22. Shaft, upper steering
23. Sphere, centering
24. Spring, joint preload
25. Shaft asm, lower steering
26. Switch asm, ignition
27. Stud, dimr. & ign sw mounting
28. Switch asm, dimmer
29. Nut, hexagon
30. Screw, wash hd
31. Spring, lock bolt
32. Bolt, strg shaft lock

33. Rod, dimmer sw actuator
34. Bowl, steering column
35. Cap, dimmer switch rod
36. Bolt, key release lever
37. Lever, key release
38. Spring, key release lever
39. Screw, C/S tapping
40. Washer, flat
41. Bumper, column tilt
42. Lever, shoe release
43. Spring, release lever
44. Screw, pan head cross recess
45. Bracket, tilt lever & shoe
46. Pin, release lever

47. Retainer, steering wheel nut
48. Switch asm, buzzer
49. Screw, pan head tapping
50. Screw, lock retaining
51. Lock cyl set, strg column
52. Plate, lock bolt retaining
53. Screw, oval head
54. Rack, switch actuator
55. Jacket asm, strg column
56. Actuators, ign switch
57. Bushing strg column jacket
58. Bearing, steering shaft
59. Seal, steering shaft
60. Washer, seal retaining
61. Screw, pan head cross recess
62. Pivot asm, dimmer switch actuator
63. Lever, T/S & cruise
64. Lever, turn signal
65. Protector, wiring

FIG. 57 Tilt column with key release — 1988

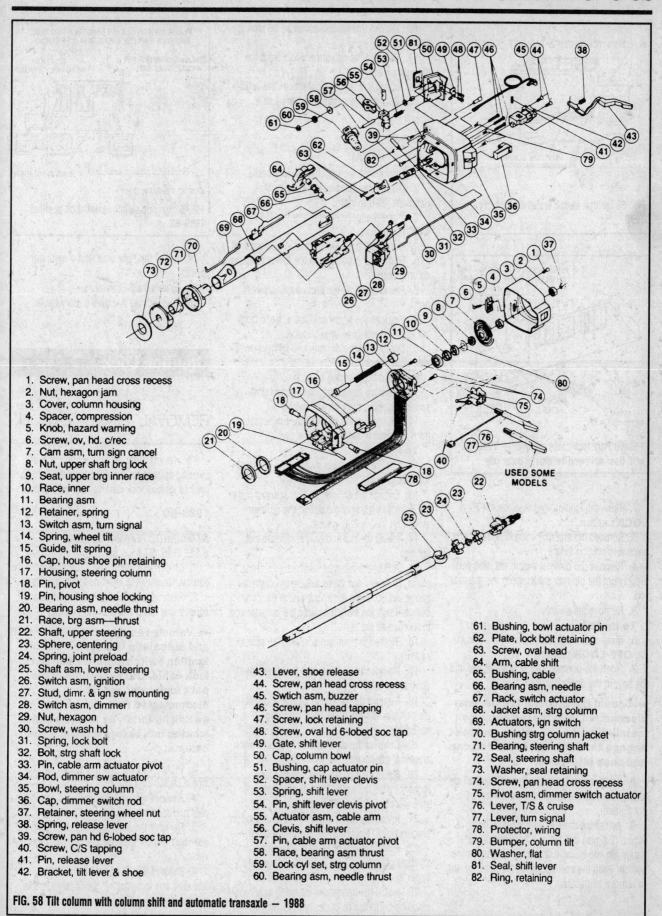

1. Screw, pan head cross recess
2. Nut, hexagon jam
3. Cover, column housing
4. Spacer, compression
5. Knob, hazard warning
6. Screw, ov, hd. c/rec
7. Cam asm, turn sign cancel
8. Nut, upper shaft brg lock
9. Seat, upper brg inner race
10. Race, inner
11. Bearing asm
12. Retainer, spring
13. Switch asm, turn signal
14. Spring, wheel tilt
15. Guide, tilt spring
16. Cap, hous shoe pin retaining
17. Housing, steering column
18. Pin, pivot
19. Pin, housing shoe locking
20. Bearing asm, needle thrust
21. Race, brg asm—thrust
22. Shaft, upper steering
23. Sphere, centering
24. Spring, joint preload
25. Shaft asm, lower steering
26. Switch asm, ignition
27. Stud, dimr. & ign sw mounting
28. Switch asm, dimmer
29. Nut, hexagon
30. Screw, wash hd
31. Spring, lock bolt
32. Bolt, strg shaft lock
33. Pin, cable arm actuator pivot
34. Rod, dimmer sw actuator
35. Bowl, steering column
36. Cap, dimmer switch rod
37. Retainer, steering wheel nut
38. Spring, release lever
39. Screw, pan hd 6-lobed soc tap
40. Screw, C/S tapping
41. Pin, release lever
42. Bracket, tilt lever & shoe

43. Lever, shoe release
44. Screw, pan head cross recess
45. Swtich asm, buzzer
46. Screw, pan head tapping
47. Screw, lock retaining
48. Screw, oval hd 6-lobed soc tap
49. Gate, shift lever
50. Cap, column bowl
51. Bushing, cap actuator pin
52. Spacer, shift lever clevis
53. Spring, shift lever
54. Pin, shift lever clevis pivot
55. Actuator asm, cable arm
56. Clevis, shift lever
57. Pin, cable arm actuator pivot
58. Race, bearing asm thrust
59. Lock cyl set, strg column
60. Bearing asm, needle thrust

61. Bushing, bowl actuator pin
62. Plate, lock bolt retaining
63. Screw, oval head
64. Arm, cable shift
65. Bushing, cable
66. Bearing asm, needle
67. Rack, switch actuator
68. Jacket asm, strg column
69. Actuators, ign switch
70. Bushing strg column jacket
71. Bearing, steering shaft
72. Seal, steering shaft
73. Washer, seal retaining
74. Screw, pan head cross recess
75. Pivot asm, dimmer switch actuator
76. Lever, T/S & cruise
77. Lever, turn signal
78. Protector, wiring
79. Bumper, column tilt
80. Washer, flat
81. Seal, shift lever
82. Ring, retaining

USED SOME MODELS

FIG. 58 Tilt column with column shift and automatic transaxle — 1988

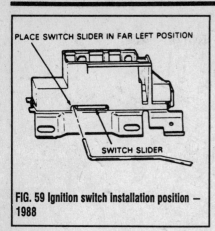

FIG. 59 Ignition switch installation position — 1988

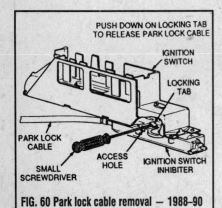

FIG. 60 Park lock cable removal — 1988–90 with floor shift and automatic transaxle

2. Place the ignition switch in the **OFF-LOCK** position.

3. Remove the steering column and place in a suitable holding fixture.

4. Remove the dimmer switch nut, bolt and disconnect the dimmer switch from the actuator rod.

5. Remove the switch.

To install:

6. Make sure the ignition lock cylinder is in the **OFF-LOCK** position.

7. Insert the dimmer switch actuator rod into the hole in the dimmer switch.

➡ **Should the actuator rod become disengaged from the rod cap, upon installation the tab on the rod must engage the wide slot in the rod cap and snap into place.**

8. Position the dimmer switch in place on the stud and install the retainer nut and screw. Do not tighten.

9. Adjust the dimmer switch by inserting a $\frac{1}{32}$ in. (0.8mm) drill bit or a 2.34mm diameter gauge pin into the adjustment hole in the dimmer switch. Push the switch against the actuator rod to remove all the lash.

10. Tighten the nut and screw to 35 inch lbs. (4 Nm).

11. Remove the adjustment tool from the dimmer switch.

12. Install the steering column in the vehicle.

13. Connect the negative battery cable.

1991–92

➡ SEE FIGS. 63-65

1. Disconnect the negative battery cable.

2. Disable the Supplemental Inflatable Restraint (SIR) system.

3. Place the ignition switch in the **OFF-LOCK** position.

4. Remove the left side sound insulator panel.

5. Remove the bolts from the lower steering column support.

6. Remove the flange and coupling pinch bolt.

7. Remove the upper and lower bolts from the upper steering column support.

8. Disconnect the dimmer and ignition switch electrical connectors.

9. Lower the steering column.

10. Remove the hexagonal nut and bolt/screw attaching the dimmer switch.

11. Disengage the dimmer switch actuator from the switch and remove the switch.

To install:

12. Ensure the ignition switch is in the **OFF-LOCK** position.

13. Engage the dimmer switch actuator rod in the dimmer switch and position the dimmer switch on the mounting stud.

14. Install the nut and bolt/screw. Do not tighten.

15. Adjust the dimmer switch by inserting a $\frac{1}{32}$ in. (0.8mm) drill bit or a 2.34mm diameter gauge pin into the adjustment hole in the dimmer switch. Push the switch against the actuator rod to remove all the lash.

16. Tighten the nut and screw to 35 inch lbs. (4 Nm).

17. Remove the adjustment tool from the dimmer switch.

18. Support the steering column and install the column into the flange and coupling assembly.

19. Connect the dimmer and ignition switch electrical connectors.

20. Raise the column into position and loosely install the lower bolts to the upper steering column support bracket.

21. Install the lower steering column support bracket bolts. Tighten to 22 ft. lbs. (30 Nm).

22. Install the upper bolts to the upper steering column support bracket. Tighten the upper and lower bolts to 21 ft. lbs. (28 Nm).

23. Install the flange and coupling assembly pinch bolt. Tighten to 30 ft. lbs. (41 Nm).

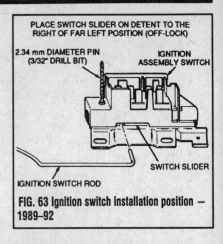

FIG. 63 Ignition switch installation position — 1989–92

24. Install the right side sound insulator panel.

25. Enable the SIR system.

26. Connect the negative battery cable.

Ignition Lock

REMOVAL & INSTALLATION

The manufacturer recommends that the steering column be removed from the vehicle prior to ignition lock removal and installation.

1988–90

STANDARD STEERING COLUMN

➡ SEE FIGS. 53-55 & 60

1. Disconnect the negative terminal from the battery. Remove the left-side lower trim panel.

2. Remove the steering column-to-support screws and lower the steering column.

➡ **Vehicles equipped with floor shift and automatic transaxles use an ignition switch inhibiter and park lock cable. On these models the park lock cable must be disconnected from the ignition switch inhibiter, by releasing the locking tab, before removing the column.**

3. Disconnect the dimmer switch and turn signal switch connectors.

4. Remove the wiring harness-to-firewall nuts and steering column.

5. Remove the steering column-to-steering gear bolt and the steering column from the vehicle.

6. Refer to the "Combination Switch, Removal and Installation" procedures in this section and remove the combination switch.

1. Retainer
2. Hexagon jam nut
3. Pan head screw
4. Column housing cover
5. Hazard warning knob
6. Screw
7. Turn signal cancelling cam
8. Screw
9. Turn signal switch
10. Retaining ring
11. Thrust washer
12. Upper bearing spring
13. Screw
14. Turn signal switch housing
15. Bearing assembly
16. Spacer
17. Wiring protector
18. Actuator
19. Screw
20. Steering shaft
21. Buzzer switch
22. Dimmer switch rod cap
23. Lock retaining screw
24. Steering column bowl and jacket assembly
25. Lock cylinder set
26. Steering shaft lock bolt
27. Lock bolt spring
28. Lock bolt retaining plate
29. Oval head screw
30. Switch actuator rack
31. Ignition switch actuator
32. Bushing
33. Pan head tapping screw
34. Bracket
35. Key release lever spring (Floor shift M/T trans. only)
36. Key release lever (Floor shift M/T trans. only)
37. Key release lever bolt (Floor shift M/T trans. only)
38. Dimmer switch actuator rod
39. Washer head screw
40. Hexagon nut
41. Dimmer switch assembly
42. Dimmer switch mounting stud
43. Ignition switch

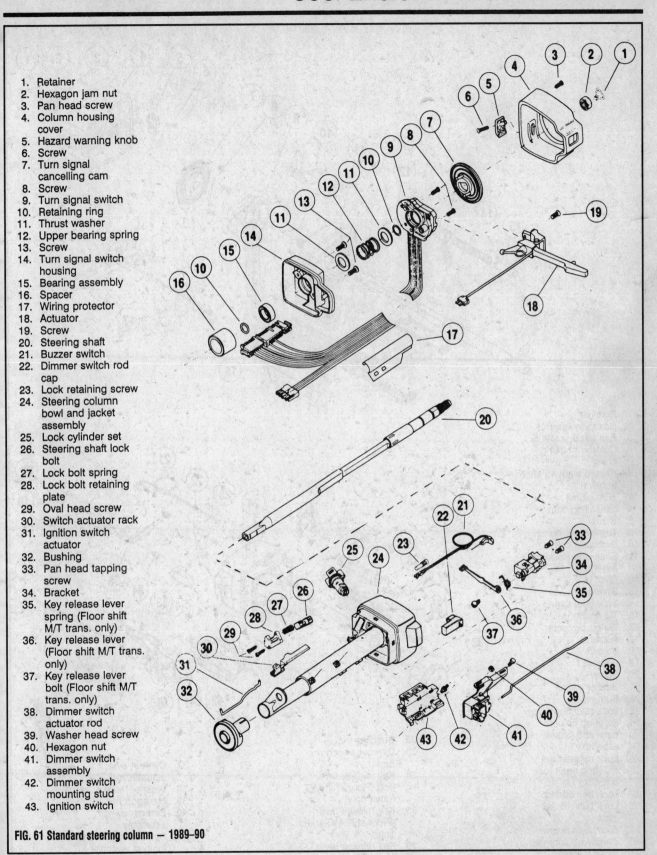

FIG. 61 Standard steering column — 1989–90

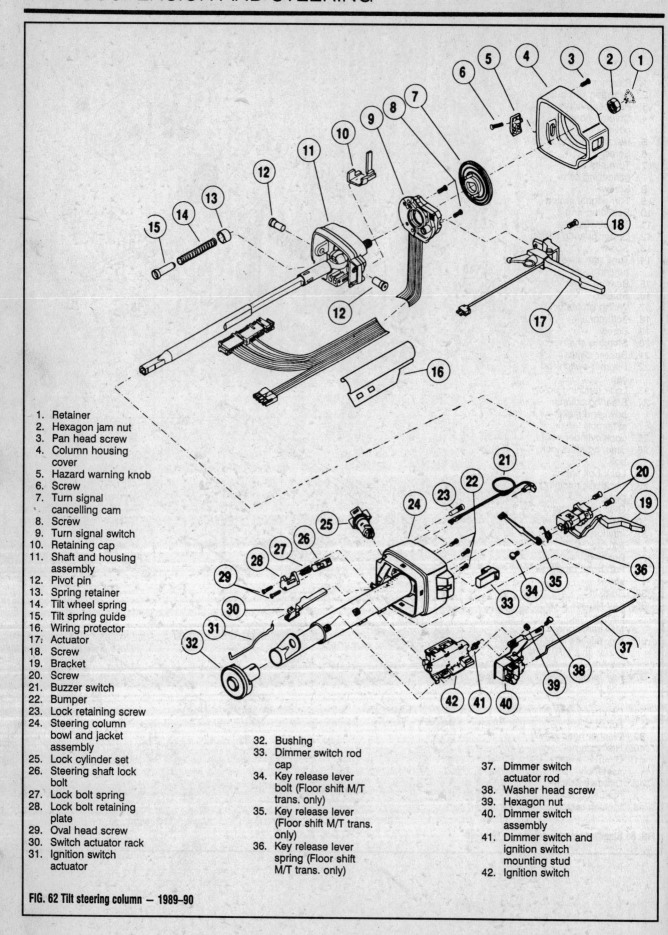

1. Retainer
2. Hexagon jam nut
3. Pan head screw
4. Column housing
   cover
5. Hazard warning knob
6. Screw
7. Turn signal
   cancelling cam
8. Screw
9. Turn signal switch
10. Retaining cap
11. Shaft and housing
    assembly
12. Pivot pin
13. Spring retainer
14. Tilt wheel spring
15. Tilt spring guide
16. Wiring protector
17. Actuator
18. Screw
19. Bracket
20. Screw
21. Buzzer switch
22. Bumper
23. Lock retaining screw
24. Steering column
    bowl and jacket
    assembly
25. Lock cylinder set
26. Steering shaft lock
    bolt
27. Lock bolt spring
28. Lock bolt retaining
    plate
29. Oval head screw
30. Switch actuator rack
31. Ignition switch
    actuator

32. Bushing
33. Dimmer switch rod
    cap
34. Key release lever
    bolt (Floor shift M/T
    trans. only)
35. Key release lever
    (Floor shift M/T trans.
    only)
36. Key release lever
    spring (Floor shift
    M/T trans. only)

37. Dimmer switch
    actuator rod
38. Washer head screw
39. Hexagon nut
40. Dimmer switch
    assembly
41. Dimmer switch and
    ignition switch
    mounting stud
42. Ignition switch

FIG. 62 Tilt steering column – 1989–90

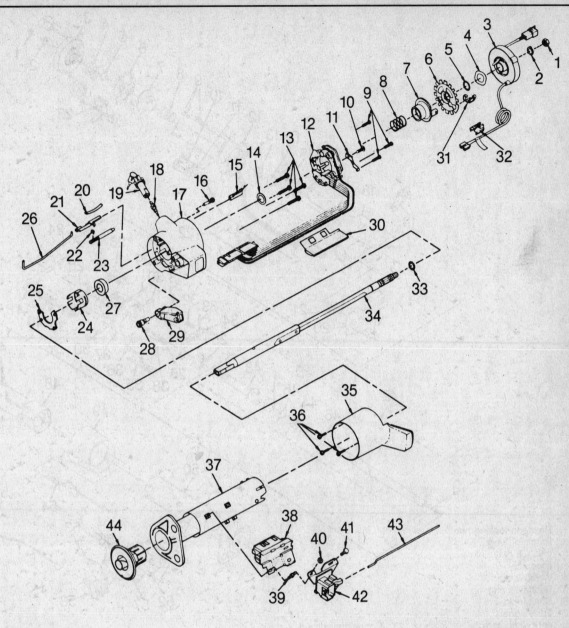

1. Hexagon locking nut
2. Retaining ring
3. Inflation restraint coil assembly
4. Wave washer
5. Retaining ring
6. Shaft lock
7. Turn signal cancelling cam
8. Upper bearing spring
9. Screw
10. Screw
11. Signal switch arm
12. Turn signal switch
13. Screw
14. Thrust washer
15. Buzzer switch
16. Lock retaining screw
17. Steering column housing
18. Switch actuator sector
19. Lock cylinder set
20. Rack preload spring
21. Switch actuator rack
22. Spring thrust washer
23. Lock bolt
24. Bearing retainer bushing
25. Upper bearing retainer
26. Switch actuator rod
27. Bearing assembly
28. Pivot pin
29. Pivot assembly
30. Wiring protector
31. Shaft lock spacer
32. Connector shroud
33. Retaining ring
34. Steering column shaft assembly
35. Floor shift bowl
36. Screw
37. Steering column jacket assembly
38. Ignition switch
39. Dimmer switch and ignition switch mounting stud
40. Hex nut
41. Screw
42. Dimmer switch assembly
43. Dimmer switch rod
44. Bushing

FIG. 64 Standard steering column — 1991–92

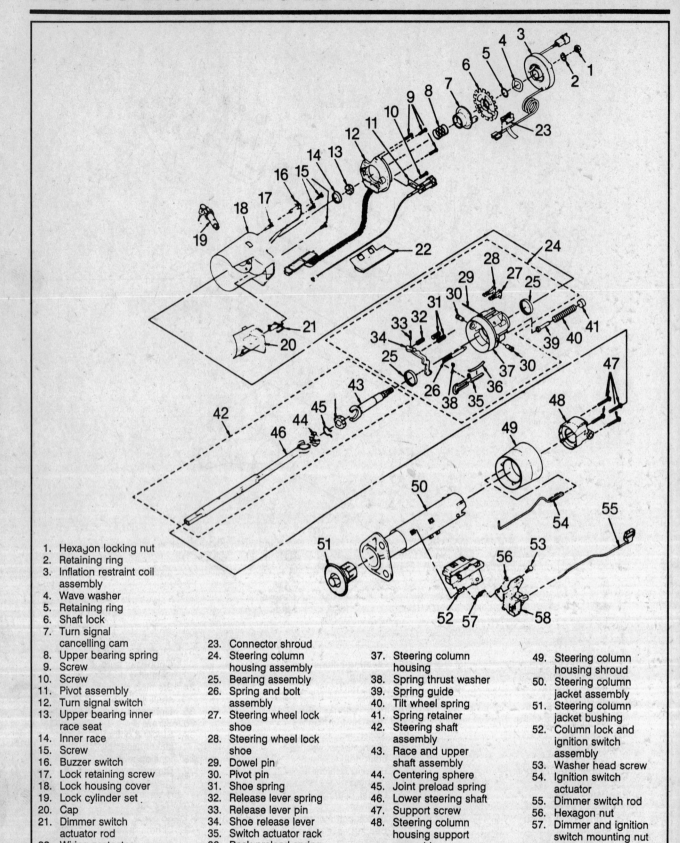

1. Hexagon locking nut
2. Retaining ring
3. Inflation restraint coil assembly
4. Wave washer
5. Retaining ring
6. Shaft lock
7. Turn signal cancelling cam
8. Upper bearing spring
9. Screw
10. Screw
11. Pivot assembly
12. Turn signal switch
13. Upper bearing inner race seat
14. Inner race
15. Screw
16. Buzzer switch
17. Lock retaining screw
18. Lock housing cover
19. Lock cylinder set
20. Cap
21. Dimmer switch actuator rod
22. Wiring protector

23. Connector shroud
24. Steering column housing assembly
25. Bearing assembly
26. Spring and bolt assembly
27. Steering wheel lock shoe
28. Steering wheel lock shoe
29. Dowel pin
30. Pivot pin
31. Shoe spring
32. Release lever spring
33. Release lever pin
34. Shoe release lever
35. Switch actuator rack
36. Rack preload spring

37. Steering column housing
38. Spring thrust washer
39. Spring guide
40. Tilt wheel spring
41. Spring retainer
42. Steering shaft assembly
43. Race and upper shaft assembly
44. Centering sphere
45. Joint preload spring
46. Lower steering shaft
47. Support screw
48. Steering column housing support assembly

49. Steering column housing shroud
50. Steering column jacket assembly
51. Steering column jacket bushing
52. Column lock and ignition switch assembly
53. Washer head screw
54. Ignition switch actuator
55. Dimmer switch rod
56. Hexagon nut
57. Dimmer and ignition switch mounting nut
58. Dimmer switch

FIG. 65 Tilt steering column — 1991–92

7. Place the lock cylinder in the RUN position.

8. Remove the steering shaft assembly and turn signal switch housing as an assembly.

9. Using the Terminal Remover tool No. J-35689–A or equivalent, disconnect and label the wires "F" and "G" on the connector at the buzzer switch assembly from the turn signal switch electrical harness connector.

10. Place the lock cylinder in the RUN position and remove the buzzer switch.

11. Place the lock cylinder in the ACCESSORY position. Remove the lock cylinder retaining screw and the lock cylinder.

12. Remove the dimmer switch nut/bolt, the dimmer switch and actuator rod.

13. Remove the dimmer switch mounting stud (the mounting nut was mounted to it).

14. Remove the ignition switch-to-steering column screws and the ignition switch.

15. Remove the lock bolt screws and the lock bolt.

16. Remove the switch actuator rack and ignition switch.

17. Remove the steering shaft lock and spring.

18. Observe the following torques when installing. Torque the steering lock screw to 27 inch lbs., the dimmer switch stud to 35 inch lbs., the turn signal switch housing screws to 88 inch lbs., the turn signal switch screws to 35 inch lbs. and the steering wheel lock nut to 30 ft. lbs.

19. To install the lock bolt, lubricate it with lithium grease and install the lock bolt, spring and retaining plate.

20. Lubricate the teeth on the switch actuator rack. Install the rack and the ignition switch through the opening in the steering bolt until it rests on the retaining plate.

21. Install the steering column lock cylinder set by holding the barrel of the lock cylinder, insert the key and turn it to the ACCESSORY position.

22. Install the lock set in the steering column while holding the rack against the lock plate.

23. Install the lock retaining screw. Insert the key in the lock cylinder and turn the lock cylinder to the START position and the rack will extend.

24. Center the slotted holes on the ignition switch mounting plate and install the ignition switch mounting screw and nut.

25. Install the dimmer switch and actuator rod into the center slot on the switch mounting plate.

26. Install the buzzer switch and turn the lock cylinder to the RUN position. Push the switch in until it is bottomed out with the plastic tab that covers the lock retaining screw.

27. Install the steering shaft and turn signal housing as an assembly.

28. Install the turn signal switch. To complete the installation, reverse the removal procedures.

TILT STEERING COLUMN
♦ SEE FIG. 56-60

1. Disconnect the negative terminal from the battery. Tilt the column up as far as it will go and remove the left-side lower trim panel.

2. Remove the steering column-to-support screws and lower the steering column.

➡ **Vehicles equipped with floor shift and automatic transaxles use an ignition switch inhibiter and park lock cable. On these models the park lock cable must be disconnected from the ignition switch inhibiter, by releasing the locking tab, before removing the column.**

3. Disconnect the dimmer switch and turn signal switch connectors.

4. Remove the wiring harness-to-firewall nuts and steering column.

5. Remove the steering column-to-steering gear bolt and the steering column from the vehicle.

6. Refer to the "Combination Switch, Removal and Installation" procedures in this section and remove the combination switch.

7. Using a flat type pry blade, position it in the square opening of the spring retainer, push downward (to the left) to release the spring retainer. Remove the wheel tilt spring.

8. Remove the spring retainer, the tilt spring and the tilt spring guide.

9. Remove the shoe pin retaining cap. Using the Pivot Pin Removal tool No. J-21854–01 or equivalent, remove the 2 pivot pins.

10. Place the lock cylinder in the RUN position.

11. Pull the shoe release lever and release the steering column housing.

12. Remove the column housing, the steering shaft assembly and turn signal switch housing as an assembly.

13. Using the Terminal Remover tool No. J-35689–A or equivalent, disconnect and label the wires "F" and "G" on the connector at the buzzer switch assembly from the turn signal switch electrical harness connector.

14. Place the lock cylinder in the RUN position and remove the buzzer switch.

15. Place the lock cylinder in the ACCESSORY position. Remove the lock cylinder retaining screw and the lock cylinder.

16. Remove the dimmer switch nut/bolt, the dimmer switch and actuator rod.

17. Remove the dimmer switch mounting stud (the mounting nut was mounted to it).

18. Remove the ignition switch-to-steering column screws and the ignition switch.

19. Remove the lock bolt screws and the lock bolt.

20. Remove the switch actuator rack and ignition switch.

21. Remove the steering shaft lock and spring.

22. Observe the following torques when installing. Torque the steering lock screw to 27 inch lbs., the dimmer switch stud to 35 inch lbs., the turn signal switch housing screws to 88 inch lbs., the turn signal switch screws to 35 inch lbs. and the steering wheel lock nut to 30 ft. lbs.

23. To install the lock bolt, lubricate it with lithium grease and install the lock bolt, spring and retaining plate.

24. Lubricate the teeth on the switch actuator rack. Install the rack and the ignition switch through the opening in the steering bolt until it rests on the retaining plate.

25. Install the steering column lock cylinder set by holding the barrel of the lock cylinder, insert the key and turn the key to the ACCESSORY position.

26. Install the lock set in the steering column while holding the rack against the lock plate.

27. Install the lock retaining screw. Insert the key in the lock cylinder. Turn the lock cylinder to the START position and the rack will extend.

28. Center the slotted holes on the ignition switch mounting plate. Install the ignition switch mounting screw and nut.

29. Install the dimmer switch and actuator rod into the center slot on the switch mounting plate.

30. Install the buzzer switch and turn the lock cylinder to the RUN position. Push the switch in until it is bottomed out with the plastic tab that covers the lock retaining screw.

31. Install the steering shaft and turn signal housing as an assembly.

32. Install the turn signal switch. To complete the installation, reverse the removal procedures.

1991-92
♦ SEE FIGS. 64-65

1. Disconnect the negative battery cable.

2. Disable the SIR system as outlined earlier in this section.

3. Remove the steering wheel.

4. Remove the coil assembly retaining ring.

5. Lift the coil assembly from the end of the steering shaft and allow coil to hang freely.

6. Remove the wave washer.

7. If equipped with a standard column, remove the spacer shaft lock.

8. Remove the shaft lock retaining ring using tool J-23653–C or equivalent, to compress the shaft lock.

9. Pry off the retaining ring.

10. Remove the shaft lock.

11. Remove the turn signal cancelling cam assembly.

12. Remove the upper bearing spring.

13. Position the turn signal lever to the right turn position.

14. Remove the multi-function lever by performing the following:

  a. Ensure the lever is in the center or **OFF** position.

  b. If equipped with cruise control, disconnect the cruise control connector from the steering column assembly.

  c. Pull the lever straight out of the turn signal switch.

15. Remove the hazard knob assembly.

16. Remove the screw and signal switch arm. If equipped with tilt column and cruise control, allow the switch arm to hang freely.

17. Remove the turn signal switch screws. Allow the switch to hang freely.

18. Disconnect the turn signal/hazard switch assembly terminal from the instrument panel harness.

19. If equipped with tilt column, disconnect the buzzer switch assembly terminals from the turn signal/hazard assembly connector. Remove the tan/black wire lead from cavity E and the light green wire from the cavity F.

20. Remove the upper steering column bolts.

21. Remove the wiring protector.

22. Connect a length of wire to the turn signal/hazard assembly terminal connector to aid in reassembly.

23. Gently pull the wire harness through the steering column housing shroud, steering column housing and lock assembly cover.

24. Disconnect the wire from the connector.

25. Ensure the lock cylinder is in the **LOCK** position. Remove the lock cylinder attaching screw.

26. Remove the lock cylinder.

To install:

27. Install the lock cylinder and attaching screw. Tighten to 40 inch lbs. (4 Nm).

28. Turn the ignition key to the **RUN** position.

29. Install the buzzer switch.

30. Connect the wire to the turn signal/hazard switch assembly connector.

31. Gently pull the connector through the steering column housing shroud, steering column housing and lock assembly cover.

32. Remove the wire.

33. Install the wiring protector.

34. If disconnected, connect the buzzer switch terminals to the turn signal/hazard switch assembly connector. Insert the tan/black wire lead into cavity E and the light green wire into cavity F.

35. Connect the turn signal/hazard switch assembly connector to the instrument panel harness.

36. Install the steering column support bracket bolts to the steering column. Tighten to 22 ft. lbs. (30 Nm).

37. Install the steering column upper support bolts. Tighten to 20 ft. lbs. (28 Nm).

38. Install the turn signal switch assembly and attaching screws. Tighten to 20 inch lbs. (2 Nm).

39. Install the hazard knob assembly.

40. Install the multi-function lever by performing the following:

  a. Align the tab on the turn signal switch with the notch in the pivot of the turn signal switch.

  b. Push the lever into the turn signal switch.

  c. If equipped with cruise control, connect the connector to the steering column assembly.

41. Install the turn signal cancelling cam assembly. Lubricate with a synthetic grease.

42. Install the shaft lock.

43. Install the shaft lock retaining ring, lining up to block tooth on the shaft. Use tool J–23653–C to compress the shaft lock.

44. If equipped with a standard column, install the spacer shaft lock.

45. Install the wave washer.

46. Ensure the coil assembly is centered.

➡ **The coil assembly will become uncentered if the steering column is separated from the steering gear and is allowed to rotate or the centering spring is pushed down, letting the hub rotate while the coil is removed from the steering column.**

47. Install the coil assembly using the horn tower on the cancelling cam assembly inner ring and projections on the outer ring for alignment.

48. Install the coil assembly retaining ring. The ring must be firmly seated in the groove on the shaft. Gently pull the lower coil assembly wire to remove any wire kinks that may be inside the column.

49. Install the steering wheel.

50. Enable the SIR system as outlined earlier in this section.

51. Connect the negative battery cable.

Steering Column

REMOVAL & INSTALLATION

1988–90

♦ SEE FIG. 66

1. Disconnect the negative terminal from the battery. Remove the left-side lower trim panel.

2. Remove the 4 upper steering column mounting bolts. Lower the steering column onto the seat.

3. Disconnect the dimmer switch and turn signal switch electrical connectors.

4. Remove the wiring harness-to-firewall/steering column nuts.

➡ **If the vehicle is equipped with a Park Lock, the Park Lock cable must be disconnected by pressing the locking tab at the ignition switch inhibiter before removing the column from the vehicle.**

5. Push the seal away from the rag joint and remove the 2 lower steering column-to-steering rack bolts and the steering column from the vehicle.

To install:

6. Insert the steering shaft into the rag coupling, raise the column into position and loose assemble the 2 capsule bolts.

7. Install and torque to 22 ft. lbs. (30 Nm), the lower shackle bolt. this positions the column in the fore-aft direction.

8. Torque the 2 capsule bolts to 20 ft. lbs. (27 Nm).

9. Install and torque the coupling pinch bolt to 29 ft. lbs. (40 Nm).

10. Pull the seal over the end of the column. The seal is retained by the lip of the bushing.

➡ **Make the electrical connections before the column is inserted into the rag coupling or after installation of the 3 attaching bolts. In no case should the column be supported by only the rag joint. Torque values and sequences are shown in the illustration.**

1991

♦ SEE FIG. 67

1. Disable the SIR system as outlined earlier in this section.

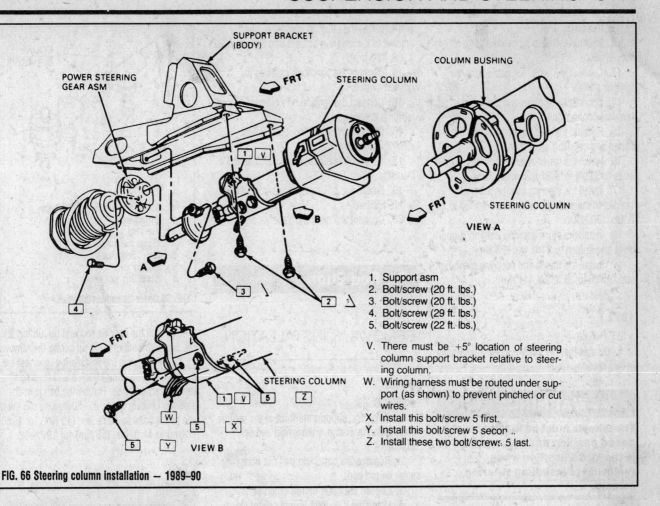

FIG. 66 Steering column installation — 1989–90

1. Support asm
2. Bolt/screw (20 ft. lbs.)
3. Bolt/screw (20 ft. lbs.)
4. Bolt/screw (29 ft. lbs.)
5. Bolt/screw (22 ft. lbs.)

V. There must be +5° location of steering column support bracket relative to steering column.
W. Wiring harness must be routed under support (as shown) to prevent pinched or cut wires.
X. Install this bolt/screw 5 first.
Y. Install this bolt/screw 5 secon...
Z. Install these two bolt/screws 5 last.

❈❈ WARNING

The wheels must be in the straight ahead position and the key must be in the LOCK position when removing or installing steering column.

2. Disconnect the negative battery cable.

3. Disconnect the hazard/turn signal switch electrical connection.

4. Disconnect the cruise control electrical connection.

5. Remove the steering column support bracket bolts from the column.

6. Remove the flange and coupling pinch bolt.

7. Remove the upper steering column support bolts.

8. Remove the lower steering column support bolts.

9. Disconnect the ignition and dimmer switch terminal connections.

10. Disconnect the park lock cable from the ignition switch.

11. Remove the steering column assembly.

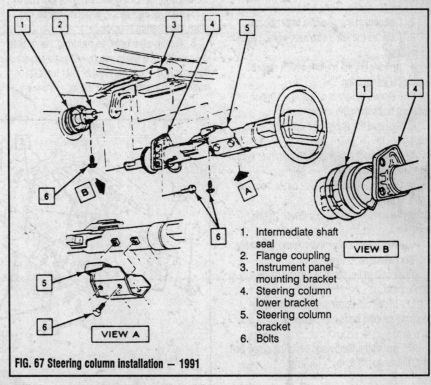

1. Intermediate shaft seal
2. Flange coupling
3. Instrument panel mounting bracket
4. Steering column lower bracket
5. Steering column bracket
6. Bolts

FIG. 67 Steering column installation — 1991

To install:

12. Position the steering column assembly in the vehicle.

13. Connect the park lock cable from the ignition switch.

14. Connect the ignition and dimmer switch terminal connections.

15. Position the steering column into the flange and coupling assembly.

16. Install the lower steering column support bolts and tighten to 21 ft. lbs. (28 Nm)

17. Install the steering column support bracket to the steering column and tighten to 22 ft. lbs. (30 Nm).

18. Install the upper steering column support bolts and tighten to 21 ft. lbs. (28 Nm)

19. Install the flange and coupling pinch bolt and tighten to 30 ft. lbs. (41 Nm)

1992

▶ SEE FIG. 68

1. Disable the SIR system as outlined earlier in this section.

⁑ WARNING

The wheels must be in the straight ahead position and the key must be in the LOCK position when removing or installing steering column.

2. Disconnect the negative battery cable.

3. Remove the left instrument panel sound insulator.

4. Disconnect the multi-function switch electrical connection.

5. Remove the steering column support bracket bolts from the column.

6. Remove the flange and coupling pinch bolt.

7. Disconnect the ignition and dimmer switch terminal connections.

8. Disconnect the park lock cable from the ignition switch.

9. Remove the upper and lower steering column support bolts.

10. Remove the steering column assembly.

To install:

11. Position the steering column assembly in the vehicle.

12. Install the upper and lower steering column support bolts and tighten to 20 ft. lbs. (26 Nm)

13. Install the flange and coupling pinch bolt and tighten to 29 ft. lbs. (40 Nm)

14. Install the steering column support bracket to the steering column and tighten to 22 ft. lbs. (30 Nm).

15. Connect the park lock cable to the ignition switch.

16. Connect the ignition and dimmer switch terminal connections.

17. Connect the multi-function switch electrical connection.

18. Install the left instrument panel sound insulator.

19. Enable the SIR system as outlined earlier in this section.

20. Connect the negative battery cable.

Tie Rod Ends

REMOVAL & INSTALLATION

Outer

▶ SEE FIG. 69

1. Raise and support the front of the vehicle on jackstands. Remove the wheel and tire assembly.

2. Remove the cotter pin and nut from the outer tie rod end.

3. Loosen the outer tie rod pinch bolts.

4. Using the Ball Joint Remover tool No. J-24319-01 or equivalent, separate the tie rod from the steering knuckle.

5. Remove the outer tie rod from the adjuster by counting the exact number of turns required to remove it. This will allow proper installation without having to reset the toe in.

6. Install the new tie rod end by turning it in the same amount of turns as during the removal.

7. To complete the installation, connect the tie rod to the steering knuckle and reverse the removal procedures. Torque the ball joint-to-steering knuckle nut to 35–50 ft. lbs. and the tie rod pinch bolts to 35 ft. lbs. (46 Nm) for 1988–90 and to 41 ft. lbs. (55 Nm) for 1991–92.

Inner

▶ SEE FIG. 70

1. Remove the inner tie rod end lock plate bolt. If both inner tie rods are being replaced, discard the used lock plate.

2. Slide the inner tie rod out from between the plate and the steering rack.

3. Reinstall the lock plate bolt to insure proper tie rod-to-steering gear realignment.

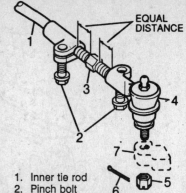

1. Inner tie rod
2. Pinch bolt
3. Tie rod adjuster
4. Outer tie rod
5. Hex lock nut
6. Cotter pin
7. Steering knuckle

FIG. 69 Outer tie rod installation

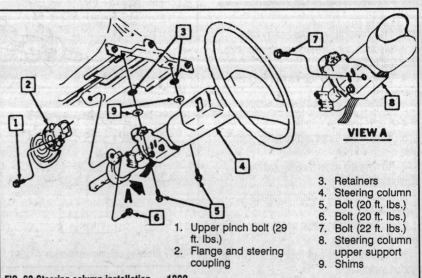

1. Upper pinch bolt (29 ft. lbs.)
2. Flange and steering coupling

3. Retainers
4. Steering column
5. Bolt (20 ft. lbs.)
6. Bolt (20 ft. lbs.)
7. Bolt (22 ft. lbs.)
8. Steering column upper support
9. Shims

FIG. 68 Steering column installation — 1992

4. Remove the cotter pin and nut from the outer tie rod end.

5. Using the Ball Joint Remover tool No. J–24319–01 or equivalent, separate the tie rod from the steering knuckle.

6. Remove the inner and outer tie rod assembly from the vehicle.

7. Note the position of the inner and outer tie rods in relation to each other. Place the assembly in a vise and loosen the adjuster pinch bolts.

8. Remove the outer tie rod from the adjuster by counting the exact number of turns required to remove it. This will allow proper installation without having to reset the toe in.

9. To install, place the new inner tie rod in the vise and install the outer tie rod end and adjuster the same amount of turns as when removing it.

10. Check the alignment between the inner and outer tie rods is the same as during removal.

11. To complete the installation, use a new lock plate and reverse the removal procedures. Torque the inner tie rod-to-lock plate bolts to 65 ft. lbs. (90 Nm).

Rack And Pinion Assembly

REMOVAL & INSTALLATION

▶ SEE FIGS. 71-72

✳✳ WARNING

On 1991–92 models, the wheels of the vehicle must be in the straight ahead position and the ignition switch in the LOCK position before disconnecting the flange and coupling assembly from the steering column or the rack and pinion steering gear. Failure to do so may cause the supplemental inflatable restraint (SIR) coil assembly to become uncentered, which will damage the SIR coil assembly.

1. From inside the vehicle, remove the left-side lower sound insulator.

2. Remove the upper steering shaft-to-steering rack coupling pinch bolt.

3. Place a drain pan under the steering gear and disconnect the pressure lines from the steering gear.

4. Raise and support the front of the vehicle.

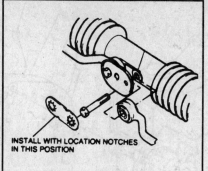

FIG. 70 Inner tie rod installation

INSTALL WITH LOCATION NOTCHES IN THIS POSITION

5. Remove both front wheel and tire assemblies.

6. Using the Ball Joint Remover tool No. J–24319–01 or equivalent, disconnect the tie rod ends from the steering knuckles.

7. Lower the vehicle.

8. Remove both steering gear-to-chassis clamps.

9. Slide the steering gear forward and remove the lower steering shaft-to-steering rack coupling pinch bolt.

10. From the firewall, disconnect the coupling and seal from the steering gear.

11. Raise and support the front of the vehicle.

12. Through the left-wheel opening, remove the steering gear with the tie rods.

➡ If the studs were removed with the mounting clamps, reinstall the

studs into the cowl panel and tighten to the studs are fully seated against the dash panel. The torque should not exceed 15 ft. lbs. (20 Nm). After a second use of the stud a thread locking compound should be used.

To install:

13. Install the rack and pinion through the left wheel opening.

14. Install the dash seal on the rack and pinion assembly.

15. Move the rack and pinion assembly forward and install the coupling lower pinch bolt and tighten to 30 ft. lbs. (41 Nm).

16. Install the gear inlet and outlet pipes to the steering gear and tighten to 19 ft. lbs. (26 Nm).

17. Hand tighten the camp nuts, then tighten the left side clamp nuts first to 22 ft. lbs. (30 Nm), then tighten the right side clamp nuts to 22 ft. lbs. (30 Nm).

18. Raise and safely support the vehicle.

19. Install the tie rod ends to the struts and install the cotter pins after torquing the nuts to 34 ft. lbs. (47 Nm).

20. Install the wheel and tire assemblies.

21. Lower the vehicle and install the steering column upper pinch bolt to 30 ft. lbs. (41 Nm).

22. Refill power steering pump reservoir and bleed the power steering system.

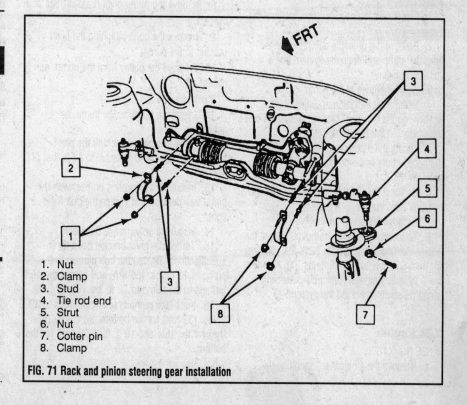

1. Nut
2. Clamp
3. Stud
4. Tie rod end
5. Strut
6. Nut
7. Cotter pin
8. Clamp

FIG. 71 Rack and pinion steering gear installation

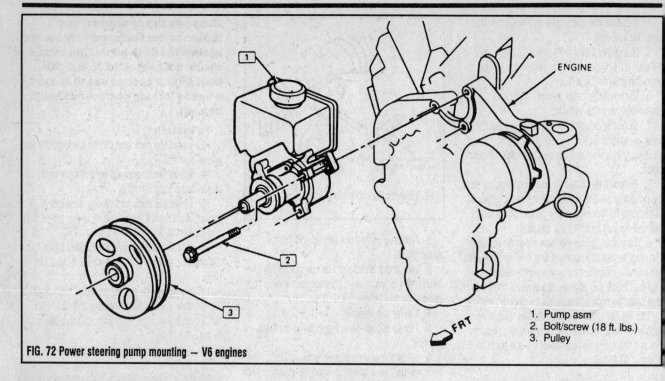

FIG. 72 Power steering pump mounting — V6 engines

1. Pump asm
2. Bolt/screw (18 ft. lbs.)
3. Pulley

Power Steering Pump

REMOVAL & INSTALLATION

All Except 2.3L Engine

♦ SEE FIGS. 72-73

1. Disconnect the negative terminal from the battery.
2. Remove the pressure and return hoses from the pump and drain the system into a suitable container.
3. Cap the fittings at the pump.
4. Using a 12 in. (305mm) adjustable wrench, on the tensioner casting, loosen the belt tensioner. Lift the belt off the pulley.
5. Locate the 3 pump attaching bolts through the access hole in the pulley and remove the bolts.
6. On the 2.0L and 2.2L engine, remove the one bolt from the rear of the pump.
7. Remove the pump assembly.
8. To install, reverse the removal. Torque the power steering pump bolts to 22 ft. lbs. (30 Nm) for the V6 engine and to 18 ft. lbs. (25 Nm) for the 4 cylinder engines. Refill power steering pump reservoir and bleed the system.

2.3L Engine

♦ SEE FIG. 74-75

1. Remove the air cleaner assembly.

2. Disconnect the power brake booster line.
3. Remove the poly groove drive belt.
4. Disconnect the electrical connector from the idle speed power steering pressure switch.
5. Remove the pump bracket bolts and bracket.
6. Remove the hose clamp and return hose.
7. Remove the attaching bolt and remove the pressure pipe to the pump.
8. Remove the pump pivot bracket bolts and bracket.
9. Remove the bolts attaching the pivot bracket to the pump.
10. Remove the pulley from the pump, as necessary.

To Install:

11. Install the pulley to the pump, as necessary.
12. Install the bolts attaching the pivot bracket to the pump and torque to 23 ft. lbs. (31 Nm).
13. Install the pump pivot bracket with the pump into position and tighten the bolt hand tight.
14. Install the poly groove drive belt.
15. Torque the pivot bracket bolts to specifications. Tighten the bolt closest to the pump to 19 ft. lbs. (26 Nm) and tighten the bolt furthest to the pump to 72 ft. lbs. (98 Nm).
16. Install the pump bracket and bolts to 39 ft. lbs. (53 Nm) for the bottom, 39 ft. lbs. (53 Nm) for the stud and 19 ft. lbs. (26 Nm) for the bottom.

17. Install the pressure pipe to the pump and tighten to 18 ft. lbs. (25 Nm).
18. Install the bolt attaching the pressure pipe to the pump and tighten to 23 ft. lbs. (31 Nm).
19. Install the return hose and clamp.
20. Install the air cleaner assembly.
21. Bleed the system.

Bleeding the System

➡ Automatic transmission fluid is NOT compatible with the seals and hoses of the power steering system. Under no circumstances should automatic transmission be used in place of power steering fluid in this system.

1. With the engine turned OFF, turn the wheels all the way to the left.
2. Fill the reservoir with power steering fluid until the level is at the COLD mark on the reservoir.
3. Start and operate the engine at fast idle for 15 seconds. Turn the engine OFF.
4. Recheck the fluid level and fill it to the COLD mark.
5. Start the engine and bleed the system by turning the wheels in both directions slowly to the stops.
6. Stop the engine and check the fluid. Fluid that still has air in it will be a light tan color.
7. Repeat this procedure until all air is removed from the system.

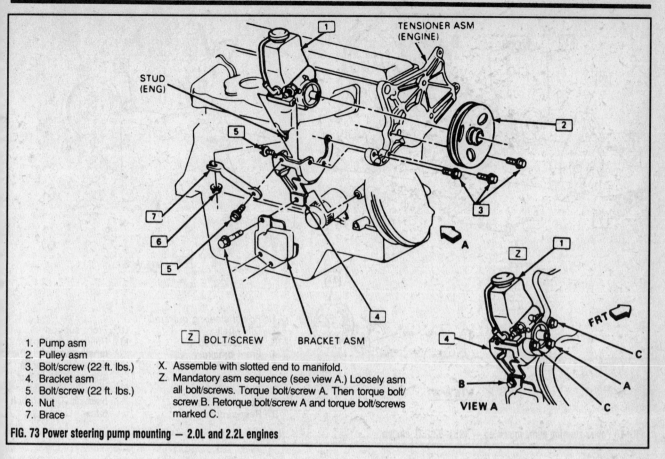

1. Pump asm
2. Pulley asm
3. Bolt/screw (22 ft. lbs.)
4. Bracket asm
5. Bolt/screw (22 ft. lbs.)
6. Nut
7. Brace

X. Assemble with slotted end to manifold.
Z. Mandatory asm sequence (see view A.) Loosely asm all bolt/screws. Torque bolt/screw A. Then torque bolt/screw B. Retorque bolt/screw A and torque bolt/screws marked C.

FIG. 73 Power steering pump mounting — 2.0L and 2.2L engines

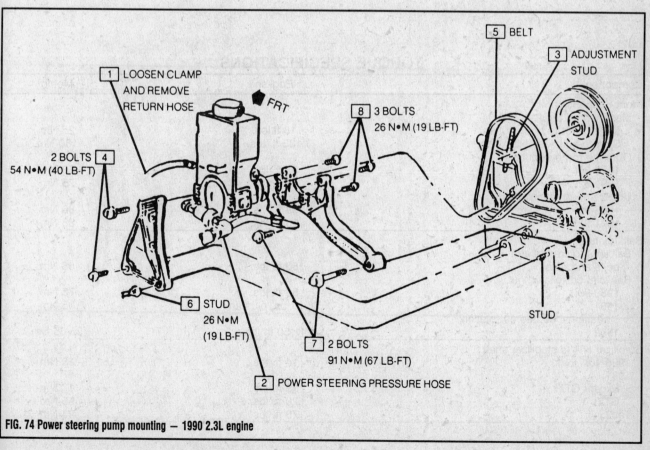

FIG. 74 Power steering pump mounting — 1990 2.3L engine

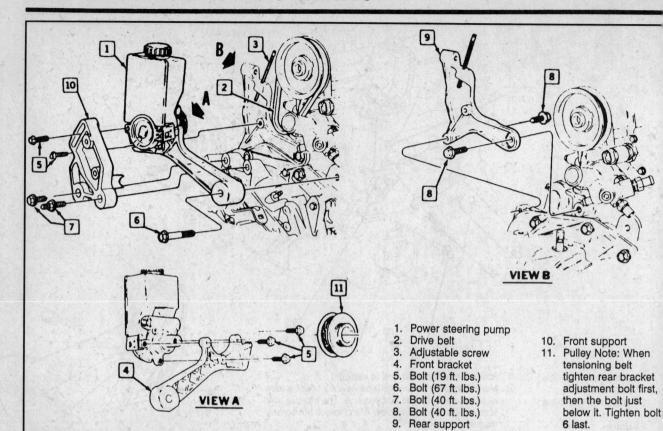

1. Power steering pump
2. Drive belt
3. Adjustable screw
4. Front bracket
5. Bolt (19 ft. lbs.)
6. Bolt (67 ft. lbs.)
7. Bolt (40 ft. lbs.)
8. Bolt (40 ft. lbs.)
9. Rear support
10. Front support
11. Pulley Note: When tensioning belt tighten rear bracket adjustment bolt first, then the bolt just below it. Tighten bolt 6 last.

FIG. 75 Power steering pump mounting — 1991–92 2.3L engine

TORQUE SPECIFICATIONS

Component	English	Metric
Front Suspension		
MacPherson Strut		
Upper strut to body nuts:	18 ft.lbs.	25 Nm
Strut-to-knuckle bolts:	133 ft. lbs.	180 Nm
Outer tie rod end nuts		
1988-90:	35 ft. lbs.	50 Nm
1991-92:	55 ft. lbs.	75 Nm
Upper spring retaining nut		
1988-90:	59 ft. lbs.	80 Nm
1991-92:	65 ft. lbs.	88 Nm
Ball Joints		
Ball joint to control arm		
bolts and nuts:	50 ft. lbs.	68 Nm
Ball joint castellated nut		
1988-90:	55 ft. lbs.	75 Nm
1991:	26 ft. lbs. plus an	35 Nm
additional 60 degree rotation		
1992:	41-50 ft. lbs.	55-65 Nm
Stabilizer link to stabilizer shaft		
1988-90:	14 ft. lbs.	18 Nm
1991		
Except GTZ:	13 ft. lbs.	17 Nm
GTZ:	70 ft. lbs.	95 Nm
1992:	70 ft. lbs.	95 Nm

TORQUE SPECIFICATIONS

Component	U.S.	Metric
Control arm and suspension support bolts		
1988-90:	See text	
1991		
Rear 1st:	66 ft. lbs.	90 Nm
Center 2nd:	66 ft. lbs.	90 Nm
Front 3rd:	66 ft. lbs.	90 Nm
1992		
Center 1st:	66 ft. lbs.	90 Nm
Front 2nd:	65 ft. lbs.	88 Nm
Rear 3rd:	65 ft. lbs.	88 Nm
Front engine mount crossmember		
1991 2.3L engine only		
Front engine mount upper nut:	55 ft. lbs.	75 Nm
Lower engine mount nuts:	30 ft. lbs.	40 Nm
Crossmember plate nuts:	40 ft. lbs.	54 Mm
Rear Suspension		
Shock Absorbers		
2 upper outer nuts:	13 ft. lbs.	18 Nm
1 upper center nut:	22 ft. lbs.	30 Nm
Lower mount nut and bolt		
1988		
Corsica:	35 ft. lbs.	47 Nm
Beretta:	43 ft. lbs.	58 Nm
1989-90		
Corsica:	35 ft. lbs.	47 Nm
Beretta:	21 ft. lbs.	28 Nm
1991-92		
Corsica:	35 ft. lbs.	47 Nm
Beretta:	35 ft. lbs.	47 Nm
Rear hub and bearing bolts/nuts:	38 ft. lbs.	52 Nm
Stabilizer bar		
1988-90		
Stabilizer to control arms:	16 ft lbs.	22 Nm
Stabilizer to axle:	13 ft lbs.	18 Nm
1991-92 Corsica		
Stabilizer to control arms:	16 ft lbs.	22 Nm
Stabilizer to axle:	13 ft lbs.	18 Nm
1991-92 Beretta		
Stabilizer retaining nuts:	103 ft lbs.	139 Nm
Rear axle assembly		
Control arm to body bracket		
1988-90:	66 ft. lbs.	90 Nm
1991-92:	52 ft. lbs.	70 Nm
plus 120 degree rotation		
Steering		
Steering wheel retaining nut		
1988-90:	30 ft. lbs.	41 Nm
1991-92:	31 ft. lbs.	42 Nm
Turn signal switch to column		
1988-90:	35 inch lbs.	4 Nm
1991-92:	20 inch lbs.	2.3 Nm
Ignition and dimmer switch nut:	35 inch lbs.	4 Nm

TORQUE SPECIFICATIONS

Component	Metric	U.S.
Steering column		
1988-90		
Lower shackle bolt:	22 ft. lbs.	30 Nm
Two capsule bolts:	20 ft. lbs.	27 Nm
Coupling pinch bolt:	29 ft. lbs.	40 Nm
1991		
Column support bracket:	22 ft. lbs.	30 Nm
Two upper support bolts:	21 ft. lbs.	28 Nm
Coupling pinch bolt	30 ft. lbs.	41 Nm
1992		
Column support bracket:	22 ft. lbs.	30 Nm
Two upper support bolts:	20 ft. lbs.	26 Nm
Coupling pinch bolt:	29 ft. lbs.	40 Nm
Outer tie rod end		
Ball joint to knuckle nut:	35-55 ft lbs.	
Tie rod pinch bolts		
1988-90:	35 ft. lbs.	46 Nm
1991-92:	41 ft. lbs.	55 Nm
Inner tie rod to lock plate:	65 ft. lbs.	90 Nm
Power steering pump attaching bolts		
2.0L and 2.2L engines:	18 ft. lbs.	25 Nm
2.8L and 3.1L engines:	22 ft. lbs.	30 Nm
2.3L engine		
Bracket bolts (Bottom):	39 ft. lbs.	53 Nm
Bracket bolts (Front):	19 ft. lbs.	26 Nm
Bracket bolts (Rear):	72 ft. lbs.	98 Nm
Bracket bolts (Top):	19 ft. lbs.	26 Nm
Bracket stud (Stud):	39 ft. lbs.	53 Nm

Troubleshooting the Power Steering Pump

Problem	Cause	Solution
Chirp noise in steering pump	• Loose belt	• Adjust belt tension to specification
Belt squeal (particularly noticeable at full wheel travel and stand still parking)	• Loose belt	• Adjust belt tension to specification
Growl noise in steering pump	• Excessive back pressure in hoses or steering gear caused by restriction	• Locate restriction and correct. Replace part if necessary.
Growl noise in steering pump (particularly noticeable at stand still parking)	• Scored pressure plates, thrust plate or rotor • Extreme wear of cam ring	• Replace parts and flush system • Replace parts
Groan noise in steering pump	• Low oil level • Air in the oil. Poor pressure hose connection.	• Fill reservoir to proper level • Tighten connector to specified torque. Bleed system by operating steering from right to left—full turn.
Rattle noise in steering pump	• Vanes not installed properly • Vanes sticking in rotor slots	• Install properly • Free up by removing burrs, varnish, or dirt
Swish noise in steering pump	• Defective flow control valve	• Replace part
Whine noise in steering pump	• Pump shaft bearing scored	• Replace housing and shaft. Flush system.
Hard steering or lack of assist	• Loose pump belt • Low oil level in reservoir **NOTE:** Low oil level will also result in excessive pump noise • Steering gear to column misalignment • Lower coupling flange rubbing against steering gear adjuster plug • Tires not properly inflated	• Adjust belt tension to specification • Fill to proper level. If excessively low, check all lines and joints for evidence of external leakage. Tighten loose connectors. • Align steering column • Loosen pinch bolt and assemble properly • Inflate to recommended pressure
Foaming milky power steering fluid, low fluid level and possible low pressure	• Air in the fluid, and loss of fluid due to internal pump leakage causing overflow	• Check for leaks and correct. Bleed system. Extremely cold temperatures will cause system aeriation should the oil level be low. If oil level is correct and pump still foams, remove pump from vehicle and separate reservoir from body. Check welsh plug and body for cracks. If plug is loose or body is cracked, replace body.

Troubleshooting the Power Steering Pump (cont.)

Problem	Cause	Solution
Low pump pressure	• Flow control valve stuck or inoperative • Pressure plate not flat against cam ring	• Remove burrs or dirt or replace. Flush system. • Correct
Momentary increase in effort when turning wheel fast to right or left	• Low oil level in pump • Pump belt slipping • High internal leakage	• Add power steering fluid as required • Tighten or replace belt • Check pump pressure. (See pressure test)
Steering wheel surges or jerks when turning with engine running especially during parking	• Low oil level • Loose pump belt • Steering linkage hitting engine oil pan at full turn • Insufficient pump pressure	• Fill as required • Adjust tension to specification • Correct clearance • Check pump pressure. (See pressure test). Replace flow control valve if defective.
Steering wheel surges or jerks when turning with engine running especially during parking (cont.)	• Sticking flow control valve	• Inspect for varnish or damage, replace if necessary
Excessive wheel kickback or loose steering	• Air in system	• Add oil to pump reservoir and bleed by operating steering. Check hose connectors for proper torque and adjust as required.
Low pump pressure	• Extreme wear of cam ring • Scored pressure plate, thrust plate, or rotor • Vanes not installed properly • Vanes sticking in rotor slots • Cracked or broken thrust or pressure plate	• Replace parts. Flush system. • Replace parts. Flush system. • Install properly • Freeup by removing burrs, varnish, or dirt • Replace part

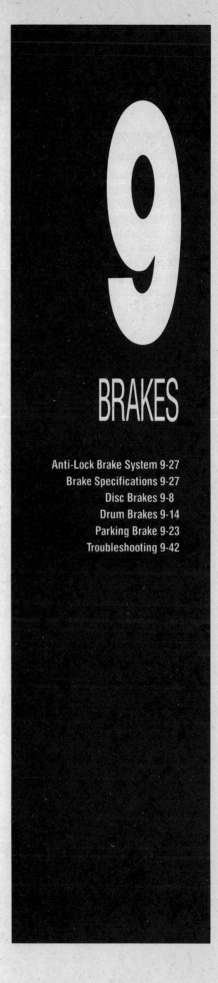

9

BRAKES

THE BRAKE SYSTEM

Hydraulic System

The hydraulic system is used to actuate the brakes. The system transports the power required to force the frictional surfaces of the braking system together from the pedal to the individual braking units at each wheel. A hydraulic system is used for three reasons. First, fluid under pressure can be carried to all parts of the automobile by small hoses, some of which are flexible, without taking up a significant amount of room or posing routing problems. Second, liquid is non-compressible; a hydraulic system can transport force without modifying or reducing that force. Third, a great mechanical advantage can be given to the brake pedal end of the system, and the foot pressure required to actuate the brakes can be reduced by making the surface area of the master cylinder pistons smaller than that of any of the pistons in the wheel cylinders or calipers.

The master cylinder consists of a fluid reservoir and a double cylinder and piston assembly. Double type master cylinders are designed to separate the front and rear braking systems hydraulically in case of a leak.

Steel lines carry the brake fluid to a point on the vehicle's frame near each of the vehicle's wheels. The fluid is then carried to the slave cylinders by flexible tubes in order to allow for suspension and steering movements.

In drum brake systems, the slave cylinders are called wheel cylinders. Each wheel cylinder contains two pistons, one at either end, which push outward in opposite directions. In disc brake systems, the slave cylinders are part of the calipers. One or four cylinders are used to force the brake pads against the disc, but all cylinders contain one piston only. All slave cylinder pistons employ some type of seal, usually made of rubber, to minimize the leakage of fluid around the piston. A rubber dust boot seals the outer end of the cylinder against dust and dirt. The boot fits around the outer end of the piston on disc brake calipers, and around the brake actuating rod on wheel cylinders.

The hydraulic system operates as follows: When at rest, the entire system, from the pistons in the master cylinder to those in the wheel cylinders or calipers, is full of brake fluid. Upon application of the brake pedal, fluid trapped in front of the master cylinder pistons is forced through the lines to the slave cylinders. Here, it forces the pistons outward, in the case of drum brakes, and inward toward the disc, in the case

of disc brakes. The motion of the pistons is opposed by return springs mounted outside the cylinders in drum brakes, and by internal springs or spring seals in disc brakes.

Upon release of the brake pedal, a spring located inside the master cylinder immediately returns the master cylinder pistons to the normal position. The pistons contain check valves and the master cylinder has compensating ports drilled in it. These are uncovered as the pistons reach their normal position. The piston check valves allow fluid to flow toward the wheel cylinders or calipers as the pistons withdraw. Then, as the return springs force the brake pads or shoes into the released position, the excess fluid returns to the master cylinder fluid reservoir through the compensation ports. It is during the time the pedal is in the released position that any fluid that has leaked out of the system will be replaced through the compensating ports.

Dual circuit master cylinders employ two pistons, located one behind the other, in the same cylinder. The primary piston is actuated directly by mechanical linkage from the brake pedal. The secondary piston is actuated by fluid trapped between the two pistons. If a leak develops in front of the secondary piston, it moves forward until it bottoms against the front of the master cylinder, and the fluid trapped between the pistons will operate the rear brakes. If the rear brakes develop a leak, the primary piston will move forward until direct contact with the secondary piston takes place, and it will force the secondary piston to actuate the front brakes. In either case, the brake pedal moves farther when the brakes are applied, and less braking power is available.

All dual-circuit systems use a distributor switch to warn the driver when only half of the brake system is operational. This switch is located in a valve body which is mounted on the master cylinder. A hydraulic piston receives pressure from both circuits, each circuit's pressure being applied to one end of the piston. When the pressures are in balance, the piston remains stationary. When one circuit has a leak, however, the greater pressure in that circuit during application of the brakes will push the piston to one side, closing the distributor switch and activating the brake warning light.

In disc brake systems, this valve body also contains a metering valve and, in some cases, a proportioning valve. The metering valve keeps pressure from traveling to the disc brakes on the front wheels until the brake shoes on the rear

wheels have contacted the drums, ensuring that the front brakes will never be used alone. The proportioning valve throttles the pressure to the rear brakes so as to avoid rear wheel lock-up during very hard braking.

These valves may be tested by removing the lines to the front and rear brake systems and installing special brake pressure testing gauges. Front and rear system pressures are then compared as the pedal is gradually depressed. Specifications vary with the manufacturer and design of the brake system.

Brake system warning lights may be tested by depressing the brake pedal and holding it while opening one of the wheel cylinder bleeder screws. If this does not cause the light to go on substitute a new lamp, make continuity checks, and, finally, replace the switch as necessary.

The hydraulic system may be checked for leaks by applying pressure to the pedal gradually and steadily. If the pedal sinks very slowly to the floor, the system has a leak. This is not to be confused with a springy or spongy feel due to the compression of air within the lines. If the system leaks, there will be a gradual change in the position of the pedal with a constant pressure.

Check for leaks along all lines and at wheel cylinders. If no external leaks are apparent, the problem is inside the master cylinder.

Disc Brakes

Instead of the traditional expanding brakes that press outward against a circular drum, disc brake systems utilize a cast iron disc with brake pads positioned on either side of it. Braking effect is achieved in a manner similar to the way you would squeeze a spinning phonograph record between your fingers. The disc (rotor) is a one-piece casting with cooling fins between the two braking surfaces. This enables air to circulate between the braking surfaces making them less sensitive to heat buildup and more resistant to fade. Dirt and water do not affect braking action since contaminants are thrown off by the centrifugal action of the rotor or scraped off by the pads. Also, the equal clamping action of the two brake pads tends to ensure uniform, straight line stops. All disc brakes are inherently self-adjusting.

Drum Brakes

Drum brakes employ two brake shoes mounted on a stationary backing plate. These shoes are positioned inside a circular cast iron drum which rotates with the wheel assembly. The shoes are held in place by springs; this allows them to slide toward the drums (when they are applied) while keeping the linings and drums in alignment. The shoes are actuated by a wheel cylinder which is mounted at the top of the backing plate. When the brakes are applied, hydraulic pressure forces the wheel cylinder's two actuating links outward. Since these links bear directly against the top of the brake shoes, the tops of the shoes are then forced outward against the inner side of the drum. This action forces the bottoms of the two shoes to contact the brake drum by rotating the entire assembly slightly (known as servo action). When pressure within the wheel cylinder is relaxed, return springs pull the shoes back away from the drum.

The drum brakes are designed to self-adjust during application when the car is moving in reverse. This motion causes both shoes to rotate very slightly with the drum, rocking an adjusting lever, thereby causing rotation of the adjusting screw by means of an actuating lever.

Power Brake Boosters

Power brakes operate just as standard brake systems except in the actuation of the master cylinder pistons. A vacuum diaphragm is located on the front of the master cylinder and assists the driver in applying the brakes, reducing both the effort and travel he must put into moving the brake pedal.

The vacuum diaphragm housing is connected to the intake manifold by a vacuum hose. A check valve is placed at the point where the hose enters the diaphragm housing, so that during periods of low manifold vacuum brake assist vacuum will not be lost.

Depressing the brake pedal closes off the vacuum source and allows atmospheric pressure to enter on one side of the diaphragm. This causes the master cylinder pistons to move and apply the brakes. When the brake pedal is released, vacuum is applied to both sides of the diaphragm, and return springs return the diaphragm and master cylinder pistons to the released position. If the vacuum fails, the brake pedal rod will butt against the end of the master cylinder actuating rod, and direct mechanical application will occur as the pedal is depressed.

The hydraulic and mechanical problems that apply to conventional brake systems also apply to power brakes, and should be checked for if the following tests do not reveal the problem.

Test for a system vacuum leak as described below:

1. Operate the engine at idle with the transaxle in Neutral without touching the brake pedal for at least one minute.

2. Turn off the engine, and wait one minute.

3. Test for the presence of assist vacuum by depressing the brake pedal and releasing it several times. Light application will produce less and less pedal travel, if vacuum was present. If there is no vacuum, air is leaking into the system somewhere.

4. Test for system operation as follows:

   a. Pump the brake pedal (with engine off) until the supply vacuum is entirely gone.

   b. Put a light, steady pressure on the pedal.

   c. Start the engine, and operate it at idle with the transaxle in Neutral. If the system is operating, the brake pedal should fall toward the floor if constant pressure is maintained on the pedal.

Power brake systems may be tested for hydraulic leaks just as ordinary systems are tested, except that the engine should be idling with the transaxle in Neutral throughout the test.

BRAKE SYSTEM

The Corsica and Beretta have a diagonally split hydraulic system. This differs from conventional practice in that the left front and right rear brakes are on one hydraulic circuit, and the right front and left rear are on the other.

A diagonally split system necessitates the use of a special master cylinder design. The master cylinder incorporates the functions of a standard tandem master cylinder, plus a warning light switch and proportioning valves. Additionally, the master cylinder is designed with a quick take-up feature which provides a large volume of fluid to the brakes at low pressure when the brakes are initially applied. The low pressure fluid acts to quickly fill the large displacement requirements of the system.

The front disc brakes are single piston sliding caliper units. Fluid pressure acts equally against the piston and the bottom of the piston bore in the caliper. This forces the piston outward until the pad contacts the rotor. The force on the caliper bore forces the caliper to slide over,

carrying the other pad into contact with the other side of the rotor. The disc brakes are self-adjusting.

On the 1988–92 Corsica and the 1992 Beretta the rear drum brakes are conventional duo-servo units. A dual piston wheel cylinder, mounted to the top of the backing plate, actuates both brake shoes. Wheel cylinder force to the shoes is supplemented by the tendency of the shoes to wrap into the drum (servo action). An actuating link, pivot and lever serve to automatically engage the adjuster as the brakes are applied when the car is moving in reverse. Provisions for manual adjustment are also provided. The rear brakes also serve as the parking brakes; linkage is mechanical.

On the 1988–91 Beretta, the rear drum brakes are the leading-trailing design. In the leading-trailing drum brake, the return springs hold both shoes against the wheel cylinder at the top and against the fixed anchor at the bottom. When the brakes are applied, the wheel cylinder moves both sides out to contact the drum. This brakes are self adjusting and it is normal with this

design for the forward shoe to wear faster than the rear shoe.

Vacuum boost is a standard. The booster is a conventional tandem vacuum unit.

Anti-lock brakes are standard on all 1992 models.

Adjustments

DISK BRAKES

The front disc brakes are inherently self-adjusting. No adjustments are either necessary or possible.

DRUM BRAKES

♦ SEE FIGS. 1-2

On the Corsica the drum brakes are designed to self-adjust when applied with the car moving

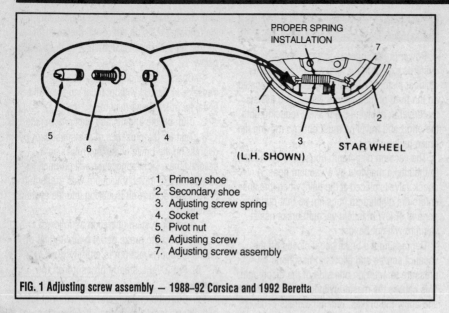

1. Primary shoe
2. Secondary shoe
3. Adjusting screw spring
4. Socket
5. Pivot nut
6. Adjusting screw
7. Adjusting screw assembly

FIG. 1 Adjusting screw assembly — 1988–92 Corsica and 1992 Beretta

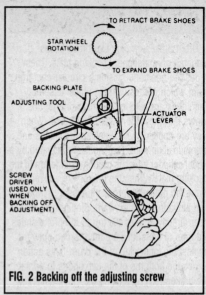

FIG. 2 Backing off the adjusting screw

in reverse. On the Beretta the drum brakes self-adjust during normal service. Both drum brake systems can also be adjusted manually however, and should be whenever the linings are replaced.

1. Raise and support the vehicle safely.
2. Remove the tire and wheel assembly.
3. Mark the relationship of the wheel to the axle flange and remove the brake drum.
4. Measure the drum inside diameter using tool J 2177–A, or equivalent.
5. Turn the star wheel, and adjust the shoe and lining diameter to be 0.050 in. (1.27mm) for 1987–90 or 0.030 in. (0.76mm) for 1991–92.
6. Install the drums and wheels aligning the previous marks.
7. Lower the vehicle.
8. Tighten the wheel nuts to 100 ft. lbs.
9. Make several alternate forward and reserve stops applying firm force to the brake pedal until ample pedal reserve is built up.

Stoplight Switch

REMOVAL & INSTALLATION

♦ SEE FIG. 3
1. Disconnect the negative terminal from the battery.
2. Remove the lower left trim panel. Locate the stoplight switch on the brake pedal support.
3. Disconnect the electrical connector from the switch and remove the switch by twisting it out of the tubular retaining clip.

4. Using a new retaining clip, install the switch and connect the electrical connector.
5. To adjust the switch, pull back on the brake pedal, push the switch through the retaining clip noting the "clicks"; repeat this procedure until no more "clicks" can be heard.
6. Connect the negative battery cable and check the switch operation.

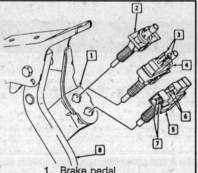

1. Brake pedal mounting bracket
2. Cruise control release valve (manual transaxle only)
3. Torque converter clutch terminals
4. TCC and cruse control release switch/valve (automatic transaxle only)
5. Stoplamp switch
6. Cruise control release switch terminals
7. Stop lamp switch terminals
8. Brake pedal assembly

FIG. 3 Stop light switch installation

Brake Pedal

REMOVAL & INSTALLATION

♦ SEE FIG. 4
1. removing the lower steering column panel.
2. Remove the brake pedal bracket.
3. Remove the pushrod front the brake pedal.
4. Remove the pivot bolt and bushing and remove the brake pedal.

To install:
5. Reinstall the brake pedal, bushing and pivot bolt and tighten the bolt to 25 ft. lbs. (34 Nm).
6. Install the pushrod to brake pedal.
7. Install the brake pedal bracket.
8. Install the lower steering column panel.

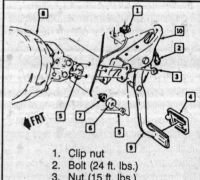

1. Clip nut
2. Bolt (24 ft. lbs.)
3. Nut (15 ft. lbs.)
4. Pedal cover
5. Booster push rod
6. Washer
7. Retainer
8. Vacuum booster
9. Brake pedal
10. Bracket

FIG. 4 Brake pedal mounting

Master Cylinder

REMOVAL & INSTALLATION

1988–91

▶ SEE FIG. 5

1. Disconnect the electrical connector from the fluid level sensor.

2. Disconnect and cap the four (4) brake lines on the master cylinder.

3. Remove the master cylinder-to-power booster nuts and the master cylinder with the reservoir attached.

To install:

4. Position the master cylinder and tighen the retaining nuts to 20 ft. lbs. (27 Nm). and the brake lines-to-master cylinder to 13–15 ft. lbs. (17–20 Nm).

5. Connect the fluid level electrical sensor wires.

6. Refill the reservoir with an approved DOT 3 brake fluid and bleed the brake system.

1992

▶ SEE FIG. 6

1. Disconnect the electrical connector from the fluid level sensor.

2. Disconnect the electrical connectors from both solenoids.

3. Disconnect the 3-pin and 6 pin motor pack electrical connectors.

4. Disconnect and cap the four (4) brake lines on the master cylinder and modulator.

5. Remove the master cylinder-to-power

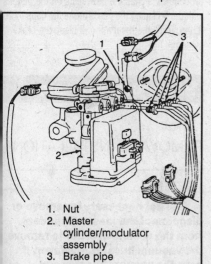

1. Nut
2. Master cylinder/modulator assembly
3. Brake pipe

FIG. 6 Master cylinder installation — 1992

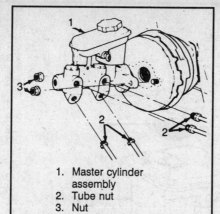

1. Master cylinder assembly
2. Tube nut
3. Nut

FIG. 5 Master cylinder installation — 1988–91

booster nuts and remove the master cylinder and modulator assembly.

To install:

6. Position the master cylinder and tighen the retaining nuts to 20 ft. lbs. (27 Nm). and the brake lines-to-master cylinder and modulator to 15 ft. lbs. (20 Nm).

7. Connect the fluid level electrical sensor wires.

8. Connect the electrical connectors to both solenoids.

9. Connect the 3-pin and 6 pin motor pack electrical connectors.

10. Refill the reservoir with an approved DOT 3 brake fluid and bleed the brake system.

OVERHAUL

▶ SEE FIG. 7

This is a tedious, time consuming job. You can save yourself a lot of trouble by buying a rebuilt master cylinder from your dealer or parts supply house. The small difference in price between a rebuilding kit and a rebuilt part usually makes it more economical, in terms of time and work, to buy the rebuilt part.

1. Remove the master cylinder.

2. Remove the reservoir cover and drain the fluid.

3. Unbolt the proportioners and failure warning switch from the side of the master cylinder body. Discard the O-rings found under the proportioners. Use new ones on installation. There may or may not be an O-ring under the original equipment failure warning switch. If there is, discard it. In either case, use an O-ring upon assembly.

4. Clamp the master cylinder body in a vise, taking care not to crush it. Depress the primary piston with a wooden dowel and remove the lock ring with a pair of snapring pliers.

5. The primary and secondary pistons can be removed by applying compressed air into one of the outlets at the end of the cylinder and plugging the other three outlets. The primary piston must be replaced as an assembly if the seals are bad. The secondary piston seals are replaceable. Install these new seals with the lips facing outwards.

6. Inspect the bore for corrosion. If any corrosion is evident, the master cylinder body must be replaced. Do not attempt to polish the bore with crocus cloth, sandpaper, or anything else. The body is aluminum; polishing the bore won't work.

7. To remove the failure warning switch piston assembly, remove the allen head plug from the end of the bore and withdraw the assembly with a pair of needlenose pliers. The switch piston assembly seals are replaceable.

8. The reservoir can be removed from the master cylinder body if necessary. Clamp the body in a vise by its mounting flange. Use a prey bar to remove the reservoir. If the reservoir is removed, remove the reservoir grommets and discard them. The quick take-up valves under the grommets are accessible after the retaining snaprings are removed. Use snapring pliers; no other tool will work.

9. Clean all parts in denatured alcohol and allow to air dry. Do not use anything else to clean, and do not wipe dry with a rag, which will leave bits of lint behind. Inspect all parts for corrosion or wear. Generally, it is best to replace all rubber parts whenever the master cylinder is disassembled, and replace any metal part which shows any sign whatsoever of wear or corrosion.

10. Lubricate all parts with clean brake fluid before assembly.

11. Install the quick take-up valves into the master cylinder body and secure with the snaprings. Make sure the snaprings are properly seated in their grooves. Lubricate the new reservoir grommets with clean brake fluid and press them into the master cylinder.

12. Install the reservoir into the grommets by placing the reservoir on its lid and pressing the master cylinder body down onto it with a rocking motion.

13. Lubricate the switch piston assembly with clean brake fluid. Install new O-rings and retainers on the piston. Install the piston assembly into the master cylinder and secure with the plug, using a new O-ring on the plug. Torque is 80–140 inch lbs. (5–16 Nm.).

14. Assemble the new secondary piston

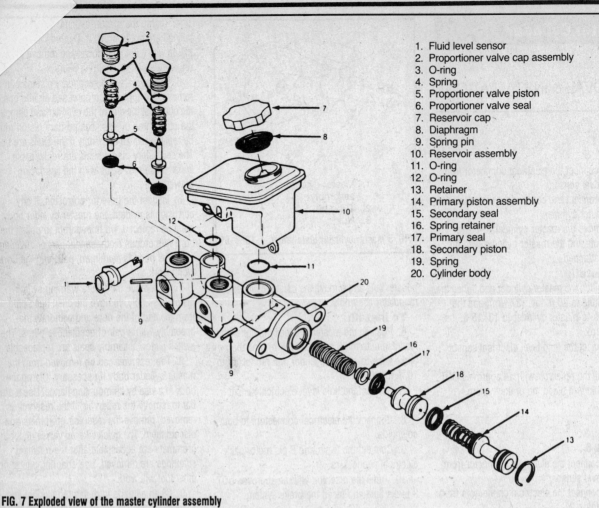

1. Fluid level sensor
2. Proportioner valve cap assembly
3. O-ring
4. Spring
5. Proportioner valve piston
6. Proportioner valve seal
7. Reservoir cap
8. Diaphragm
9. Spring pin
10. Reservoir assembly
11. O-ring
12. O-ring
13. Retainer
14. Primary piston assembly
15. Secondary seal
16. Spring retainer
17. Primary seal
18. Secondary piston
19. Spring
20. Cylinder body

FIG. 7 Exploded view of the master cylinder assembly

seals onto the piston. Lubricate the parts with clean brake fluid, then install the spring, spring retainer and secondary piston into the cylinder. Install the primary piston, depress, and install the lock ring.

15. Install new O-rings on the proportioners and the failure warning switch. Install the proportioners and torque to 18–30 ft. lbs. (25–40 Nm.). Install the failure warning switch and torque to 15–50 inch lbs. (2–6 Nm.).

16. Clamp the master cylinder body upright into a vise by one of the mounting flanges. Fill the reservoir with fresh brake fluid. Pump the piston with a dowel until fluid squirts from the outlet ports. Continue pumping until the expelled fluid is free of air bubbles.

17. Install the master cylinder, and bleed the brakes. Check the brake system for proper operation. Do not move the car until a hard brake pedal is obtained and the brake system has been thoroughly checked for soundness.

Proportioning Valve

REMOVAL & INSTALLATION

▶ SEE FIG. 7

➡ **It may be necessary to remove the reservoir in order to remove the proportioning valve. If the reservoir is removed, bleed the brake system when finished.**

1. Remove the proportioning valve cap on the master cylinder.

2. Remove and discard the O-rings.

3. Remove the springs, the proportioning valve pistons and the seals from the valves.

4. Inspect the valves for corrosion or abnormal wear; to replace, if necessary.

5. Clean all parts in denatured alcohol and dry them with air before reassembling.

To install:

6. To install, use new O-rings (coated with silicone grease) and reverse the removal procedures. Install the new seals on the pistons with the lip facing the cap. Torque the caps to 20 ft. lbs. Refill the reservoir and bleed the brake system.

Power Brake Booster

REMOVAL & INSTALLATION

▶ SEE FIG. 8

➡ **It is not necessary to remove or disconnect the master cylinder from the vehicle in order to remove the vacuum booster. However, if both the vacuum booster and master cylinder are to be removed, remove the master cylinder first as described earlier.**

1. Refer to the "Master Cylinder, Removal and Installation" procedures in this section and remove the master cylinder. Move the master cylinder forward just enough to clear the studs on the vacuum booster. This will flex the pipes slightly. Be carefull not to bend or distort the brake pipes.

➡ **Place the master cylinder in an upright position to prevent fluid loss.**

2. It may be necessary on some models to remove the left lower trim panel inside the vehicle, then disconnect the brake pedal-to-booster push rod from the brake pedal.

3. Disconnect the vacuum line from the booster.

4. Remove the brake booster mounting nuts and the booster.

To install:

5. To install, reverse the removal procedures.

➡ **When installing the push rod to the brake pedal, tilt the entire vacuum booster push rod onto the clevis pin without putting undue side pressure on the push rod.**

6. Torque the master cylinder-to-power booster to 20 ft. lbs. (28 Nm) and the power booster mounting nuts to 20 ft. lbs. (28 Nm). Bleed the brake system.

Brake Hose

REMOVAL & INSTALLATION

Front

◆ SEE FIG. 9-10

1. Raise and support the car safely.
2. Remove the tire and wheel.
3. Clean the dirt from both hose end fittings.
4. Remove the brake pipe from the hose.
5. Remove the brake hose from the caliper and discard the two copper gaskets on either side of the fitting block.
6. Install the hose using new copper gaskets.
7. Check that the hose doesn't rub in extreme left and right turn conditions.
8. Fill and maintain the brake fluid level in the reservoir and bleed the brake system.

Rear

◆ SEE FIG. 11-12

1. Raise and support the car safely.

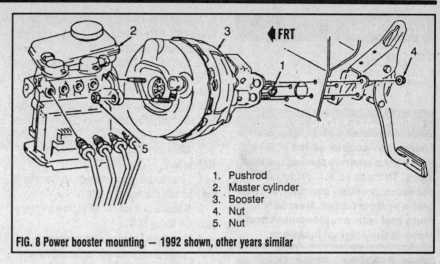

1. Pushrod
2. Master cylinder
3. Booster
4. Nut
5. Nut

FIG. 8 Power booster mounting — 1992 shown, other years similar

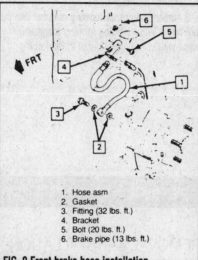

1. Hose asm
2. Gasket
3. Fitting (32 lbs. ft.)
4. Bracket
5. Bolt (20 lbs. ft.)
6. Brake pipe (13 lbs. ft.)

FIG. 9 Front brake hose installation — 1988–91

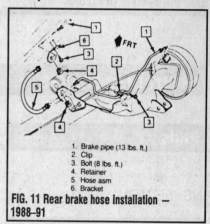

2. Clean the dirt from both hose end fittings.

3. With the aid of a backup wrench, disconnect the brake pipe fitting on both ends of the brake hose.

4. Remove the retaining clips from both ends.

5. After installing the hose fill and maintain the brake fluid level in the reservoir and bleed the brake system.

1. Brake pipe (13 lbs. ft.)
2. Clip
3. Bolt (8 lbs. ft.)
4. Retainer
5. Hose asm
6. Bracket

FIG. 11 Rear brake hose installation — 1988–91

VIEW A

1. Bleeder screw cap
2. Bracket screw
3. Bracket
4. Caliper assembly
5. Brake hose screw
6. Washer
7. Brake hose

FIG. 10 Front brake hose installation — 1992

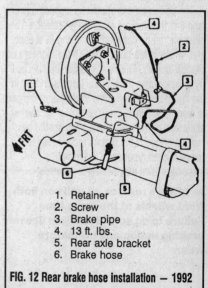

1. Retainer
2. Screw
3. Brake pipe
4. 13 ft. lbs.
5. Rear axle bracket
6. Brake hose

FIG. 12 Rear brake hose installation — 1992

Brake Pipe

REPLACEMENT

✻ CAUTION

Always use double walled steel brake pipe when replacing brake pipes. The use od any other pipe is not recommended and may cause brake system failure. Carefully route and retain replacement brake pipes in the original locations.

✻ WARNING

The following procedure requires the use of a J 29803–A ISO flaring tool, or its equivalent. Do not use single lap flaring tools. Double lap flaring tools must be used to produce a flare strong enough to hold the system pressure.

1. Obtain the recommended pipe and steel fitting nuts of the correct size. Outside deameter of pipe is used to specify size.

2. Cut pipe to length with a pipe cutter. Do not force the cutter, advance the tool only a small amount per turn of the tool. Correct length of pipe may be determined by measuring old pipe using a string and adding 1/8 in. (3mm) for each ISO flare.

3. Make sure fittings are installed before starting flare.

4. Chamfer the inside and outside diameter of the pipe with the deburing tool.

5. Remove all traces of lubricant from brake pipe and flaring tool.

6. Clamp the flaring tool body in vise.

7. Select the correct size collet and forming mandrel for pipe size used.

8. Insert the proper forming mandrel into the tool body. While holding forming mandrel in place with your finger, thread in the forcing screw until it makes contact and begins to move the forming mandrel. When contact is made, turn the forcing screw back one complete turn.

9. Slide the clamping nut over the brake pipe and insert the prepared brake pipe into the correct collet. Leave approximately 0.750 inch (19 mm) of tubing extending out the collet. Insert the assembly into the tool body. The brake pipe end must contact the face of the forming mandrel.

10. Tighten the clamping nut into the tool body very tight or the pipe may push out.

11. Wrench tighten the forcing screw in until it bottoms. Do not over tighten the forcing screw or the flare may become over-sized.

12. Back the clamping nut out of the tool body and disassemble the clamping nut and collet assembly. The flare is now ready for use.

13. Bend pipe assembly to match old pipe. Clearance of 0.750 inch (19 mm) must be maintained to all moving or vibrating parts.

FRONT DISC BRAKES

Pads

INSPECTION

The pad thickness should be inspected every time that the tires are removed for rotation. The outer pad an be checked by looking in at each end, which is the point at which the highest rate of wear occurs. The inner pad can be checked by looking down through the inspection hole in the top of the caliper. If the thickness of the pad is worn to within 1/32 in. (0.8mm) of the rivet at either end of the pad, all the pads should be replaced. This is the factory recommended measurement; your state's automobile inspection laws may not agree with this.

➡ **Always replace all pads on both front wheels at the same time. Failure to do so will result in uneven braking action and premature wear.**

REMOVAL & INSTALLATION

1988–91
◆ SEE FIGS. 13-21

✻ CAUTION

Brake shoes contain asbestos, which has been determined to be a cancer causing agent. Never clean the brake surfaces with compressed air! Avoid inhaling any dust from any brake surface! When cleaning brake surfaces, use a commercially available brake cleaning fluid.

1. Siphon 2/3 of the brake fluid from the master cylinder reservoir. Loosen the wheel lug nuts and raise the car. Remove the wheel and reinstall two wheel nuts to retain the rotor.

2. Position a 12 in. (305mm) adjustable pliers over the inboard brake shoe tab and the inboard caliper housing so that the caliper piston bottoms in its bore.

✻ WARNING

If you haven't removed some brake fluid from the master cylinder, it will overflow when the piston is retracted.

3. Remove the allen head caliper mounting bolts. Inspect the bolts for corrosion, and replace as necessary.

4. Remove the caliper from the steering knuckle and suspend it from the body of the car with a length of wire. Do not allow the caliper to hang by its hose.

5. Use a 12 in. (305mm) adjustable pliers to straighten the bent over shoe tabs and remove the outboard shoe and lining.

6. Remove the inboard shoe and lining.

7. Remove the rubber bushings from the mounting bolt holes.

8. Install new bushings and lubricate with a light coating of silicone grease before installation. These bushings must always be replaced when the pads are replaced. They are usually included in the pad replacement kits.

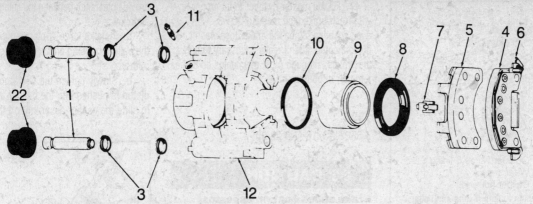

1. Mounting bolt and sleeve assembly
3. Bushing
4. Outboard shoe & lining
5. Inboard shoe & lining
6. Wear sensor
7. She retainer spring
8. Boot
9. Piston
10. Piston seal
11. Bleeder valve
12. Caliper housing
22. Boot

FIG. 13 Exploded view of the caliper assembly — 1988–91

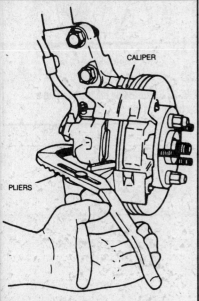

FIG. 14 Use pliers to compress the piston — 1988–91

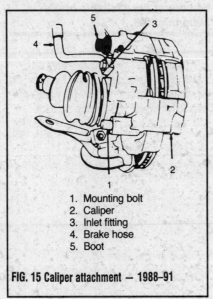

1. Mounting bolt
2. Caliper
3. Inlet fitting
4. Brake hose
5. Boot

FIG. 15 Caliper attachment — 1988–91

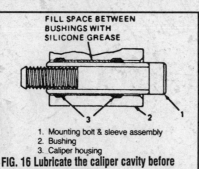

FILL SPACE BETWEEN BUSHINGS WITH SILICONE GREASE

1. Mounting bolt & sleeve assembly
2. Bushing
3. Caliper housing

FIG. 16 Lubricate the caliper cavity before reassembly — 1988–92

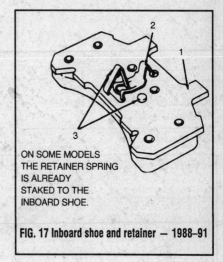

ON SOME MODELS THE RETAINER SPRING IS ALREADY STAKED TO THE INBOARD SHOE.

FIG. 17 Inboard shoe and retainer — 1988–91

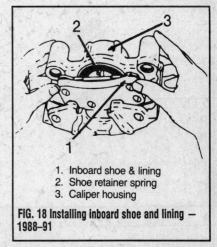

1. Inboard shoe & lining
2. Shoe retainer spring
3. Caliper housing

FIG. 18 Installing inboard shoe and lining — 1988–91

9. Install the retainer spring on the inboard pad. A new spring should be included in the pad replacement. On some models the spring is already staked to the inboard shoe.

10. Install the inboard shoe by snaping the retainer spring into the piston ID. The shoe must lay flat against the piston.

11. Install the outboard pad into the caliper with the wear sensor at the leading edge of the shoe during forward wheel rotation. The back of the shoe must lay flat against the caliper.

12. Install the caliper and tighten the mounting bolts to 38 ft. lbs. Install the boots securely.

13. Apply the brake pedal at least three times to seat the linings.

14. Pry on the outboard shoe with a large flat bladed tool between the outboard shoe flange and the hat section of the rotor. Keep the tool wedged in place for the following step.

15. Have an assistant apply moderate force on the brake pedal and clinch the outboard shoe tabs. The outboard shoe should be locked tightly in position.

16. Install the wheel and lower the car.

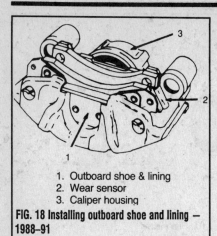

1. Outboard shoe & lining
2. Wear sensor
3. Caliper housing

FIG. 18 Installing outboard shoe and lining — 1988-91

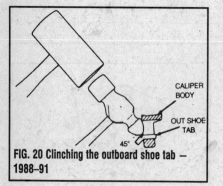

FIG. 20 Clinching the outboard shoe tab — 1988-91

17. Fill the master cylinder to its proper level with fresh brake fluid meeting DOT 3 specifications. Since the brake hose wasn't disconnected, it isn't really necessary to bleed the brakes, although most mechanics do this as a matter of course.

1992

▶ SEE FIGS. 16 AND 22-30

❈❈ CAUTION

Brake shoes contain asbestos, which has been determined to be a cancer causing agent. Never clean the brake surfaces with compressed air! Avoid inhaling any dust from any brake surface! When cleaning brake surfaces, use a commercially available brake cleaning fluid.

1. Siphon ⅔ of the brake fluid from the master cylinder reservoir. Loosen the wheel lug nuts and raise the car. Remove the wheel and reinstall two wheel nuts to retain the rotor.
2. Push the piston into the caliper bore to provide clearance between the linings and rotors as follows:

a. Install a large C-clamp over the top of the caliper housing and against the back of the outboard shoe.

b. Slowly tighten the C-clamp until the piston is pushed into the caliper bore enough to slide the caliper assembly off the rotor.

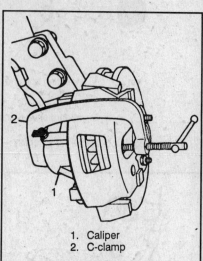

1. Caliper
2. C-clamp

FIG. 23 Compressing the piston using a C-clamp — 1992

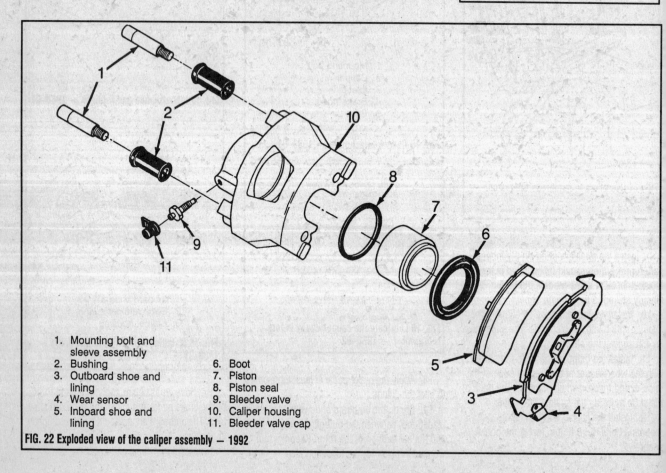

1. Mounting bolt and sleeve assembly
2. Bushing
3. Outboard shoe and lining
4. Wear sensor
5. Inboard shoe and lining
6. Boot
7. Piston
8. Piston seal
9. Bleeder valve
10. Caliper housing
11. Bleeder valve cap

FIG. 22 Exploded view of the caliper assembly — 1992

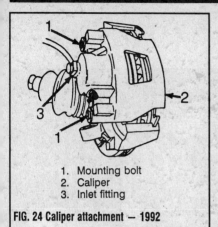

1. Mounting bolt
2. Caliper
3. Inlet fitting

FIG. 24 Caliper attachment — 1992

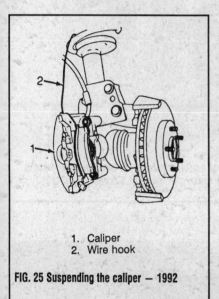

1. Caliper
2. Wire hook

FIG. 25 Suspending the caliper — 1992

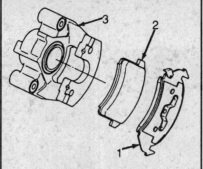

1. Outboard shoe and lining
2. Inboard shoe and lining
3. Caliper housing

FIG. 26 Shoe and lining assembly — 1992

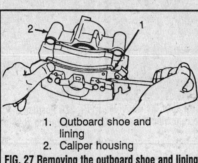

1. Outboard shoe and lining
2. Caliper housing

FIG. 27 Removing the outboard shoe and lining assembly — 1992

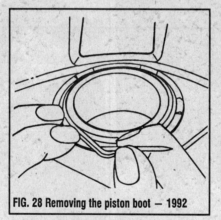

FIG. 28 Removing the piston boot — 1992

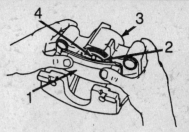

1. Inboard shoe and lining
2. Piston
3. Caliper housing
4. Shoe retainer spring

FIG. 29 Installing inboard shoe and lining — 1992

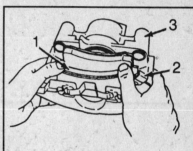

1. Outboard shoe and lining
2. Wear sensor
3. Caliper housing

FIG. 30 Installing outboard shoe and lining — 1992

Caliper

REMOVAL & INSTALLATION

> ❊ **CAUTION**
>
> **Brake shoes contain asbestos, which has been determined to be a cancer causing agent. Never clean the brake surfaces with compressed air! Avoid inhaling any dust from any brake surface! When cleaning brake surfaces, use a commercially available brake cleaning fluid.**

1. Follow Steps 1, 2 and 3 of the pad replacement procedure.

2. Before removing the caliper mounting bolts, remove the bolt holding the brake hose to the caliper.

3. Remove the mounting bolts and sleeve assemblies and remove the caliper from the rotor and knuckle. Suspend the caliper from the strut using a wire hook.

4. Use a suitable prying tool and disengage the buttons on the shoe from the holes in the caliper housing.

5. Remove the inboard shoe and lining.

To install:

6. Place the C-clamp over the caliper housing and into the piston. Carefully tighten the piston into the caliper bore.

7. After bottoming the piston, lift the inner edge of the boot and press out any trapped air. the boot must lay flat.

8. Install the inboard shoe by snaping the retainer spring into the piston.

9. Install the outboard pad into the caliper with the wear sensor at the leading edge of the shoe during forward wheel rotation. The back of the shoe must lay flat against the caliper.

10. Install the caliper and tighten the mounting bolts to 38 ft. lbs. (51 Nm). Install the boots securely.

11. Apply the brake pedal at least three times to seat the linings.

12. Install the wheel and lower the car.

13. Fill the master cylinder to its proper level with fresh brake fluid meeting DOT 3 specifications. Since the brake hose wasn't disconnected, it isn't really necessary to bleed the brakes, although most mechanics do this as a matter of course.

FIG. 22A The front disc brake and rotor assembly shown after the wheel is removed. Reinstall 2 lugnuts to retain the rotor before removing the caliper assembly–1992 shown

FIG. 22B Position a drip pan below, and spray the brake assembly with a brake cleaning solution, to remove all traces of a asbestos dust–1992 shown

FIG. 22C Install a C-clamp as shown to compress the piston into the caliper bore–1992 shown

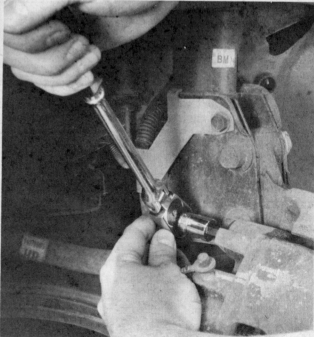

FIG. 22D Using a suitable tool, remove the two allen head caliper mounting bolts–1992 shown

3. Remove the caliper mounting bolts. Inspect them for corrosion and replace them if necessary.

4. With the pads installed as outlined in pad replacement, install the caliper and mounting bolts and torque to 38 ft. lbs. (51 Nm). The brake hose fitting should be tightened to 33 ft. lbs.

OVERHAUL

▶ SEE FIGS. 13 AND 21-22

1. Remove the caliper.
2. Remove the pads.
3. Place some cloths or a slat of wood in front of the piston. Remove the piston by applying compressed air to the fluid inlet fitting. Use just enough air pressure to ease the piston from the bore.

❊❊ CAUTION

Do not try to catch the piston with your fingers, which can result in serious injury.

---

4. Remove the piston boot with a suitable pry tool, working carefully so that the piston bore is not scratched.
5. Remove the bleeder screw.
6. Inspect the piston for scoring, nicks, corrosion, wear, etc., and damaged or worn chrome plating. Replace the piston if any defects are found.
7. Remove the piston seal from the caliper bore groove using a piece of pointed wood or plastic. Do not use a screwdriver, which will damage the bore. Inspect the caliper bore for nicks, corrosion, and so on. Very light wear can

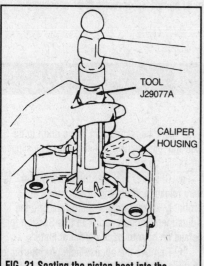

FIG. 21 Seating the piston boot into the housing — 1988-92

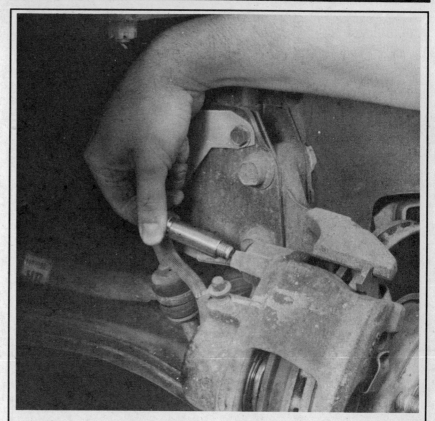

FIG. 22E Remove the mounting bolt and sleeve assembly from the caliper–1992 shown

FIG. 22F Remove the caliper from the rotor and suspend from the strut assembly using a metal coat hanger or equivalent–1992 shown

FIG. 22G Remove the inboard shoe and lining–1992 shown

11. Install the bleeder screw, tightening to 80–140 inch lbs. (9–16 Nm.). Do not overtighten.

12. Install the pads, install the caliper, and bleed the brakes.

Disc (Rotor)

REMOVAL & INSTALLATION

1. Remove the caliper.
2. Remove the rotor.
3. To install, reposition the rotor and install the caliper and pads as outlined earlier.

INSPECTION

1. Check the rotor surface for wear or scoring. Deep scoring, grooves or rust pitting can be removed by refacing, a job to be referred to your local machine shop or garage. Minimum thickness is stamped on the rotor (21.08 mm). If the rotor will be thinner than this after refinishing, it must be replaced.

2. Check the rotor parallelism (thickness variation); it must vary less than 0.01mm measured at four or more points around the circumference. Make all measurements at the same distance in from the edge of the rotor. Refinish the rotor if it fails to meet this specification.

3. Measure the disc runout with a dial indicator. If runout exceeds 0.10mm, and the wheel bearings are OK (if runout is being measured with the disc on the car), the rotor must be refaced or replaced as necessary.

be cleaned up with crocus cloth. Use finger pressure to rub the crocus cloth around the circumference of the bore; do not slide it in and out. More extensive wear or corrosion warrants replacement of the part.

8. Clean any parts which are to be reused in denatured alcohol. Dry them with compressed air or allow to air dry. Don't wipe the parts dry with a cloth, which will leave behind bits of lint.

9. Lubricate the new seal, provided in the repair kit, with clean brake fluid. Install the seal in its groove, making sure it is fully seated and not twisted.

10. Install the new dust boot on the piston. Lubricate the bore of the caliper with clean brake fluid and insert the piston into its bore. Position the boot in the caliper housing and seat with a seal driver of the appropriate size, or G.M. tool No. J–29077A.

REAR DRUM BRAKES

Brake Drums

REMOVAL & INSTALLATION

◆ SEE FIGS. 1-2 AND 31

1. Loosen the wheel lug nuts. Raise and support the car. Mark the relationship of the wheel to the axle and remove the wheel.

✳✳ CAUTION

Brake shoes contain asbestos, which has been determined to be a cancer causing agent. Never clean the brake surfaces with compressed air! Avoid inhaling any dust from any brake surface! When cleaning brake surfaces, use a commercially available brake cleaning fluid.

2. Mark the relationship of the drum to the axle and remove the drum. If it cannot be slipped off easily, try the following:

a. Check to see that the parking brake is fully released. If so, the brake shoes are probably locked against the drum. See the Adjustment section earlier in this Section for details on how to back off the adjuster.

b. Remove the access hole plug from the backing plate and insert a suitable tool through the hole to push the parking brake lever off its stop. This will allow the shoe linings to retract slightly.

c. Insert a punch tool through the hole at the bottom of the splash shield. Tap gently on the tool to loosen the drum.

d. Use a rubber mallet to tap gently on the outer rim of the drum.

3. To install, reposition the drum making sure to align the matchmarks made during removal. Lug nut torque is 100 ft. lbs.

INSPECTION

1. After removing the brake drum, wipe out the accumulated dust with a damp cloth.

❊❊ CAUTION

Do not blow the brake dust out of the drums with compressed air or lung power. Brake linings contain asbestos, a known cancer causing substance. Dispose of the cloth used to clean the parts after use.

2. Inspect the drums for cracks, deep grooves, roughness, scoring, or out-of-roundness. Replace any drum which is cracked; do not try to weld it up.

3. Smooth any slight scores by polishing the friction surface with fine emery cloth. Heavy or extensive scoring will cause excessive lining wear and should be removed from the drum through resurfacing, a job to be referred to your local machine shop or garage. The maximum finished diameter of the drums is 200.64mm. The drum must be replaced if the diameter is 201.40mm or greater.

Brake Shoes

INSPECTION

After removing the brake drum, inspect the brake shoes. If the lining is worn down to within $\frac{1}{32}$ in. (0.8mm) of a rivet, the shoes must be replaced.

➡ **This figure may disagree with your state's automobile inspection laws.**

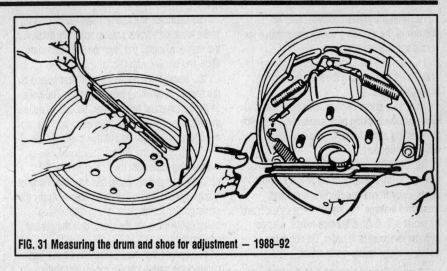

FIG. 31 Measuring the drum and shoe for adjustment — 1988–92

If the brake lining is soaked with brake fluid or grease, it must be replaced. If this is the case, the brake drum should be sanded with crocus cloth to remove all traces of brake fluid, and the wheel cylinders should be rebuilt. Clean all grit from the friction surface of the drum before replacing it.

If the lining is chipped, cracked, or otherwise damaged, it must be replaced with a new lining.

➡ **Always replace the brake linings in sets of two on both ends of the axle. Never replace just one shoe, or both shoes on one side and not the other. It is a good idea to replace one set at a time so that you always have an example to refer to if you get confused during reassembly.**

Check the condition of the shoes, retracting springs, and holddown springs for signs of overheating. If the shoes or springs have a slight blue color, this indicates overheating and replacement of the shoes and springs is recommended. The wheel cylinders should be rebuilt as a precaution against future problems.

REMOVAL & INSTALLATION

❊❊ CAUTION

Brake shoes contain asbestos, which has been determined to be a cancer causing agent. Never clean the brake surfaces with compressed air! Avoid inhaling any dust from any brake surface! When cleaning brake surfaces, use a commercially available brake cleaning fluid.

1988–92 Corsica and 1992 Beretta

➤SEE FIGS. 32 AND 32A–33

1. Loosen the lug nuts on the wheel to be serviced, raise and support the car, and remove the wheel and brake drum.

➡ **It is not really necessary to remove the hub and wheel bearing assembly from the axle, but it does make the job easier. If you can work with the hub and bearing assembly in place, skip down to Step 3.**

2. Remove the four hub and bearing assembly retaining bolts and remove the assembly from the axle.

3. Remove the return springs from the shoes with a pair of needle nose pliers. There are also special brake spring pliers for this job.

4. Remove the holddown springs by gripping them with a pair of pliers, then pressing down and turning 90°. There are special tools to grab and turn these parts, but pliers work fairly well.

5. Remove the shoe holddown pins from behind the brake backing plate. They will simply slide out once the holddown spring tension is relieved.

6. Lift up the actuator lever for the self-adjusting mechanism and remove the actuating link. Remove the actuator lever, pivot, and the pivot return spring.

7. Spread the shoes apart to clear the wheel cylinder pistons and remove the parking brake strut and spring.

8. If the hub and bearing assembly is still in place, spread the shoes far enough apart to clear it.

9. Disconnect the parking brake cable from the lever. Remove the shoes, still connected by their adjusting screw spring, from the car.

10. With the shoes removed, note the position of the adjusting spring and remove the spring and adjusting screw.

11. Remove the C-clip from the parking brake lever and remove the lever from the secondary shoe.

12. Use a damp cloth to remove all dirt and dust from the backing plate and brake parts. See the warning about brake dust in the drum removal procedure.

13. Check the wheel cylinders by carefully pulling the lower edges of the wheel cylinder boots away from the cylinders. If there is excessive leakage, the inside of the cylinder will be moist with fluid. If leakage exists, a wheel cylinder overhaul is in order. Do not delay, because brake failure could result.

➡ **A small amount of fluid will be present to act as a lubricant for the wheel cylinder pistons. Fluid spilling from the boot center hole, after the piston is removed, indicates cup leakage and the necessity for cylinder overhaul.**

14. Check the backing plate attaching bolts to make sure that they are tight. Use fine emery cloth to clean all rust and dirt from the shoe contact surfaces on the plate.

15. Lubricate the fulcrum end of the parking brake lever with brake grease specially made for the purpose. Install the lever on the secondary shoe and secure with C-clip.

16. Install the adjusting screw and spring on the shoes, connecting them together. The coils of the spring must not be over the star wheel on the adjuster. The left and right hand springs are not interchangeable. Do not mix them up.

17. Lubricate the shoe contact surfaces on the backing plate with the brake grease. Be certain when you are using this stuff that none of it actually gets on the linings or drums. Apply the same grease to the point where the parking brake cable contacts the plate. Use the grease sparingly.

18. Spread the shoe assemblies apart and connect the parking brake cable. Install the shoes on the backing plate, engaging the shoes at the top temporarily with the wheel cylinder pistons. Make sure that the star wheel on the adjuster is lined up with the adjusting hole in the backing plate, if the hole is back there.

19. Spread the shoes apart slightly and install the parking brake strut and spring. Make sure that the end of the strut without the spring engages the parking brake lever. The end with the spring engages the primary shoe (the one with the shorter lining).

20. Install the actuator pivot, lever and return spring. Install the actuating link in the shoe retainer. Lift up the actuator lever and hook the link into the lever.

21. Install the holddown pins through the back of the plate, install the lever pivots and holddown springs. Install the shoe return springs with a pair of pliers. Be very careful not to stretch or otherwise distort these springs.

22. Take a look at everything. Make sure the linings are in the right place, the self-adjusting mechanism is correctly installed, and the parking brake parts are all hooked up. If in doubt, remove the other wheel and take a look at that one for comparison.

23. Measure the width of the linings, then measure the inside width of the drum. Adjust the linings by means of the adjuster so that the drum will fit onto the linings.

24. Install the hub and bearing assembly onto the axle if removed. Tighten the retaining bolts to 38 ft. lbs. (51 Nm).

25. Install the drum and wheel tightening the lug nuts to 100 ft. lbs. Adjust the brakes using the procedure given earlier in this Section. Be sure to install a rubber hole cover in the knock-out hole after the adjustment is complete. Adjust the parking brake.

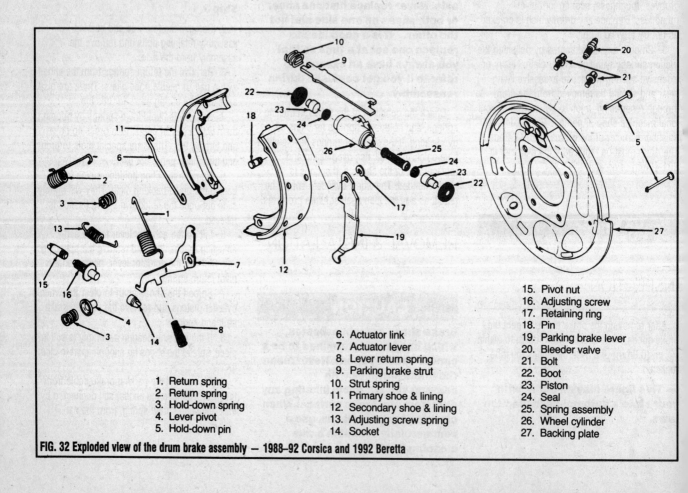

1. Return spring
2. Return spring
3. Hold-down spring
4. Lever pivot
5. Hold-down pin
6. Actuator link
7. Actuator lever
8. Lever return spring
9. Parking brake strut
10. Strut spring
11. Primary shoe & lining
12. Secondary shoe & lining
13. Adjusting screw spring
14. Socket
15. Pivot nut
16. Adjusting screw
17. Retaining ring
18. Pin
19. Parking brake lever
20. Bleeder valve
21. Bolt
22. Boot
23. Piston
24. Seal
25. Spring assembly
26. Wheel cylinder
27. Backing plate

FIG. 32 Exploded view of the drum brake assembly — 1988–92 Corsica and 1992 Beretta

FIG. 32A Removing the brake drum–1988–92 Corsica and 1992 Beretta

FIG. 32B Position a drip pan below, and spray the brake assembly with a brake cleaning solution, to remove all traces of a asbestos dust–1992 shown

FIG. 32C Using a special brake tool to remove the return springs–1988–92 Corsica and 1992 Beretta

FIG. 32D Unhook the return springs and remove–1988–92 Corsica and 1992 Beretta

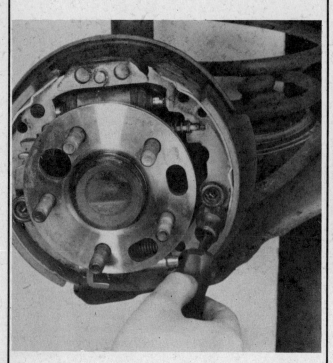

FIG. 32E Removing the holddown springs, using a special brake tool–1988–92 Corsica and 1992 Beretta

FIG. 32F Remove the shoe holddown pins from behind the brake backing plate–1988–92 Corsica and 1992 Beretta

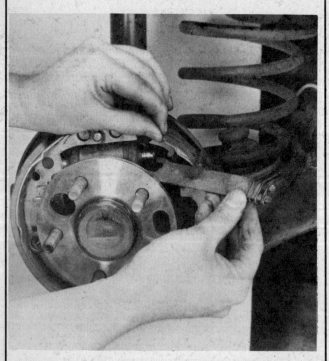

FIG. 32G Remove the parking brake strut–1988–92 Corsica and 1992 Beretta

FIG. 32H Remove the actuator lever and lever return spring–1988–92 Corsica and 1992 Beretta

FIG. 32I Pull apart and remove the brake shoe assemblies—1988–92 Corsica and 1992 Beretta

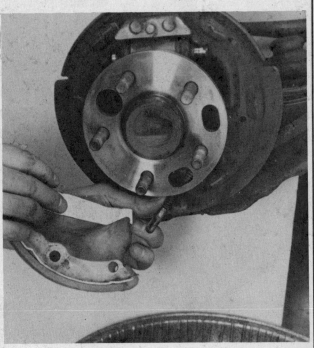

FIG. 32J Unhook the parking brake lever from the cable—1988–92 Corsica and 1992 Beretta

FIG. 32K Remove the parking barke lever to shoe retaining clip—1988–92 Corsica and 1992 Beretta

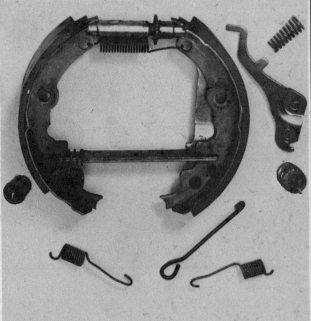

FIG. 32L Exploded view of the rear brake parts—1988–92 Corsica and 1992 Beretta

FIG. 32M Apply brake grease to the backing plate contact surfaces—1988–92 Corsica and 1992 Beretta

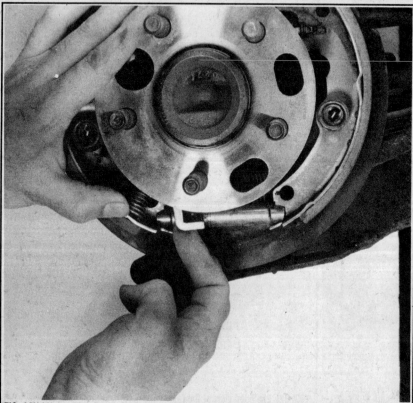

FIG. 32N Lift up on the actuator lever and hook the link into the lever—1988–92 Corsica and 1992 Beretta

26. Lower the car and check the pedal for any sponginess or lack of a hard feel. Check the braking action and the parking brake. The brakes must not be applied severely immediately after installation. They should be used moderately for the first 200 miles of city driving or 1000 miles of highway driving, to allow the linings to conform to the shape of the drum.

1988–91 Beretta

◆ SEE FIG. 33

1. Loosen the lug nuts on the wheel to be serviced, raise and support the car, and remove the wheel and brake drum. (See drum removal above).

➡ **It is not really necessary to remove the hub and wheel bearing assembly from the axle, but it does make the job easier. If you can work with the hub and bearing assembly in place, skip down to Step 3.**

2. Remove the four hub and bearing assembly retaining bolts and remove the assembly from the axle.

3. Remove the actuator and return spring from the shoes with a pair of needle nose pliers. There are also special brake spring pliers for this job.

4. Remove the spring connecting link, adjuster actuator and spring washer.

5. Remove the hold down springs by gripping them with a pair of pliers, then pressing down and turning 90°. There are special tools to grab and turn these parts, but pliers work fairly well.

6. Remove the shoe holddown pins from behind the brake backing plate. They will simply slide out once the holddown spring tension is relieved.

7. Disconnect the parking brake cable and remove the shoe and lining assemblies.

8. Remove the adjusting screw assembly and the lower return spring.

9. Remove the retaining ring, pin, spring washer and park brake lever from the shoe and lining.

10. Use a damp cloth to remove all dirt and dust from the backing plate and brake parts. See the warning about brake dust in the drum removal procedure.

11. Check the wheel cylinders by carefully pulling the lower edges of the wheel cylinder boots away from the cylinders. If there is excessive leakage, the inside of the cylinder will be moist with fluid. If leakage exists, a wheel cylinder overhaul is in order. Do not delay, because brake failure could result.

➡ **A small amount of fluid will be present to act as a lubricant for the wheel cylinder pistons. Fluid spilling from the boot center hole, after the piston is removed, indicates cup leakage and the necessity for cylinder overhaul.**

12. Check the backing plate attaching bolts to make sure that they are tight. Use fine emery cloth to clean all rust and dirt from the shoe contact surfaces on the plate.

13. Lubricate the fulcrum end of the parking brake lever with brake grease specially made for the purpose. Also lubricate the adjusting screw threads, inside diameter of the socket and the socket face. Install the adjuster spring clip in the same position as when removed.

14. Install the lower return spring between the shoe and linings.

❈❈ WARNING

Do not over-stretch the lower return spring more than 3.88 in. (98.5mm) or it will be damaged.

15. Connect the parking brake cable to the adjuster shoe then install both shoe and lining assemblies with the hold down springs and pins.

FIG. 320 Install the brake return springs using a pair of pliers or a suitable brake tool–1988–92 Corsica and 1992 Beretta

FIG. 33 Exploded view of the drum brake assembly — 1988–91 Beretta

1. Actuator spring
2. Upper return spring
3. Spring connecting link
4. Adjuster actuator
5. Spring washer
6. Lower return spring
7. Hold-down spring assembly
8. Hold-down pin
9. Adjuster shoe & lining
10. Shoe & lining
11. Adjuster socket
12. Spring clip
13. Adjuster nut
14. Adjuster screw
15. Retaining ring
16. Pin
17. Spring washer
18. Park brake lever
19. Screw & lockwasher
20. Boot
21. Piston
22. Seal
23. Spring assembly
24. Bleeder valve
25. Wheel cylinder
26. Bleeder valve cap
27. Backing plate assembly
32. Access hole plug
33. Adjuster pin

The lower return spring should be positioned under the anchor plate.

→ **The adjuster shoe and lining is the one in which the adjuster pin was installed in the shoe web. Also, the adjuster shoe and lining is to the front of the car on the L.H. brake assembly or to the rear of the car on the R.H. brake assembly.**

16. Install the adjuster screw assembly between between the two shoe and lining assemblies and position to the backing plate.

→ **Proper installation of the adjusting screw is with the adjuster screw engaging the notch in the adjuster shoe and the spring clip pointing towards the backing plate.**

17. Install the spring washer with the concave side against the web of the adjuster shoe and lining.

18. Install the adjuster actuator so that the top leg engages the notch in the adjuster screw.

19. Install the spring connecting link and hold in place.

20. Install the upper return spring by inserting the angled hook end of the spring through the park brake lever and the shoe and lining. Grasp the long straight section of the spring with suitable pliers and pull the spring straight across and then down to hook into the crook on the spring connecting link.

※ WARNING

Do not over-stretch the upper return spring more than 5.49 in. (139.5mm) or it will be damaged.

21. Install the actuator spring with suitable pliers.

22. Take a look at everything. Make sure the linings are in the right place, the self-adjusting mechanism is correctly installed, and the parking brake parts are all hooked up. If in doubt, remove the other wheel and take a look at that one for comparison.

23. Measure the width of the linings, then measure the inside width of the drum. Adjust the linings by means of the adjuster so that the drum will fit onto the linings.

24. Install the hub and bearing assembly onto the axle if removed. Tighten the retaining bolts to 38 ft. lbs.

25. Install the drum and wheel tightening the lug nuts to 100 ft. lbs. Adjust the brakes using the procedure given earlier in this Section. Make sure the parking brake lever is on its stop.(See drum removal). Be sure to install a rubber hole cover in the knock-out hole after the adjustment is complete. Adjust the parking brake.

26. Lower the car and check the pedal for any sponginess or lack of a hard feel. Check the braking action and the parking brake. The brakes must not be applied severely immediately after installation. They should be used moderately for the first 200 miles of city driving or 1000 miles of highway driving, to allow the linings to conform to the shape of the drum.

Wheel Cylinders

REMOVAL & INSTALLATION

※※ CAUTION

Brake shoes contain asbestos, which has been determined to be a cancer causing agent. Never clean the brake surfaces with compressed air! Avoid inhaling any dust from any brake surface! When cleaning brake surfaces, use a commercially available brake cleaning fluid.

1988-91 Beretta

◆ SEE FIG. 33

1. Raise and support the rear of the vehicle on jackstands. Remove the tire and brake drum. Remove the brake shoes and attaching hardware.

2. Clean any dirt from around the wheel cylinder.

3. Disconnect and plug the brake line from the wheel cylinder.

4. Remove the wheel cylinder-to-backing plate bolt and lockwasher.

5. Remove the wheel cylinder.

6. To install, apply a liquid gasket to the shoulder of the wheel cylinder that faces the backing plate and reverse the removal procedures. Torque the wheel cylinder-to-backing plate bolt to 106 inch lbs. (12 Nm) and the brake line-to-wheel cylinder to 13 ft. lbs. (17 Nm). Bleed the brake system. Inspect the brake operation.

1988-92 Corsica and 1992 Beretta

◆ SEE FIG. 32

1. Raise and support the rear of the vehicle on jackstands. Remove the tire and brake drum.

2. Clean any dirt from around the wheel cylinder.

3. Disconnect and plug the brake line from the wheel cylinder.

4. Remove the wheel cylinder bolts using a #6 Torx socket.

5. Remove the wheel cylinder.

6. To install, position the wheel assembly and hold in place with a wooden block between the cylinder and axle flange.

7. Install the wheel cylinder bolts using a # 6 Torx socket and tighten to 15 ft. lbs. (20 Nm).

8. Install the inlet tube nut and torque to 13 ft. lbs. (17 Nm).

9. Bleed the brake system. Inspect the brake operation.

Bleeding

→ **For vehicles equipped with anti-lock brakes, please refer to the bleeding procedure in that section.**

The purpose of bleeding the brakes is to expel air trapped in the hydraulic system. The system must be bled whenever the pedal feels spongy, indicating that compressible air has entered the system. It must also be bled whenever the system has been opened or repaired. You will need a helper for this job.

※※ CAUTION

Never reuse brake fluid which has been bled from the brake system.

1. The sequence for bleeding is right rear, left front, left rear and right front. If the car has power brakes, remove the vacuum by applying the brakes several times. Do not run the engine while bleeding the brakes.

2. Clean all the bleeder screws. You may want to give each one a shot of penetrating solvent to loosen it up; seizure is a common problem with bleeder screws, which then break off, sometimes requiring replacement of the part to which they are attached.

3. Fill the master cylinder with DOT 3 brake fluid.

☀☀ WARNING

Brake fluid absorbs moisture from the air. Don't leave the master cylinder or the fluid container uncovered any longer than necessary. Be careful handling the fluid; it eats paint.

Check the level of the fluid often when bleeding, and refill the reservoirs as necessary. Don't let them run dry, or you will have to repeat the process.

4. Attach a length of clear vinyl tubing to the bleeder screw on the wheel cylinder. Insert the other end of the tube into a clear, clean jar half filled with brake fluid.

5. Have your assistant slowly depress the brake pedal. As this is done, open the bleeder screw 1/3–1/2 of a turn, and allow the fluid to run through the tube. Then close the bleeder screw before the pedal reaches the end of its travel. Have your assistant slowly release the pedal. Repeat this process until no air bubbles appear in the expelled fluid.

6. Repeat the procedure on the other three brakes, checking the level of fluid in the master cylinder reservoir often.

After you're done, there should be no sponginess in the brake pedal feel. If there is, either there is still air in the line, in which case the process should be repeated, or there is a leak somewhere, which of course must be corrected before the car is moved.

Backing Plate

REMOVAL & INSTALLATION

♦ SEE FIGS. 31-32
1. Raise and support the vehicle safely.

FIG. 33A Bleeding the front brakes–1992 Corsica shown, all models similar

2. Remove all the brake components as outlined earlier.
3. Remove the inlet tube and nut from the wheel cylinder.
4. Disconnect the parking brake cable from the backing plate.
5. Remove the hub and bearing assembly bolts as outlined in Section 8 and remove the backing plate.

To install:
6. Install the backing plate to the axle assembly.

7. Install the hub and bearing assembly bolts as outlined in Section 8.
8. Connect the parking brake cable to the backing plate.
9. Install the inlet tube and nut to the wheel cylinder and tighten the nuts to 12 ft. lbs. 17 Nm).
10. Install all the brake components as outlined earlier.
11. Blled the brake system and lower the vehicle.

PARKING BRAKE

Cable

ADJUSTMENT

1988–92 Corsica and 1992 Beretta
1. Adjust the brakes as described earlier.

2. If the vehicle is equipped with a hand parking brake, apply the parking brake lever exactly 5 clicks. If the vehicle has a foot operated parking brake, depress the parking barke pedal 2 rachet clicks.
3. Raise and support the rear of the vehicle on jackstands.

➡ **Make sure the equalizer nut groove is liberally lubricated with grease.**

4. Tighten the adjusting nut until the right rear wheel can just be turned rearward using two hands but is locked when forward rotation is attempted.
5. Release the parking brake and check to see if both wheels turn freely in either direction by hand.
6. Lower the vehicle.

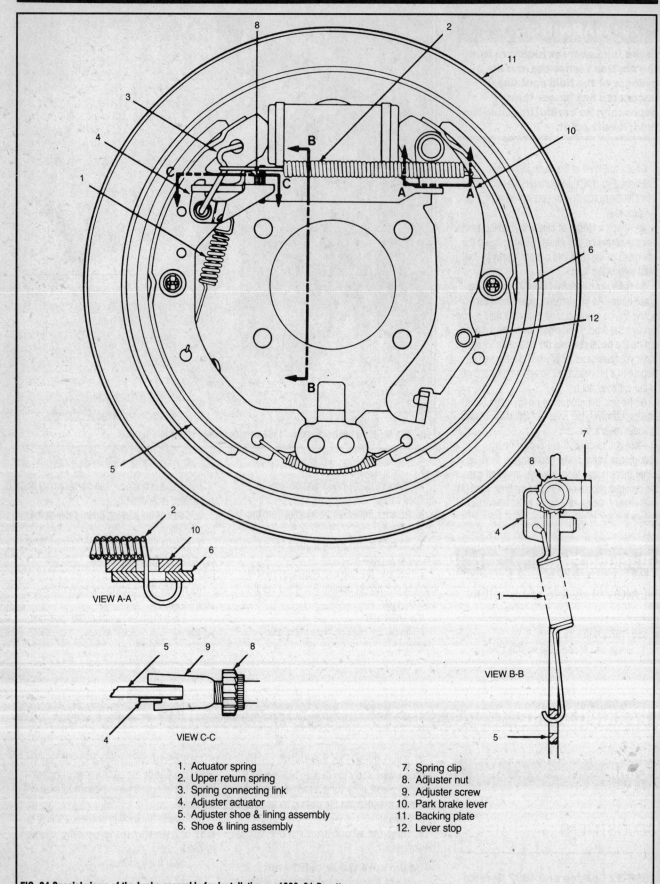

VIEW A-A

VIEW C-C

VIEW B-B

1. Actuator spring
2. Upper return spring
3. Spring connecting link
4. Adjuster actuator
5. Adjuster shoe & lining assembly
6. Shoe & lining assembly
7. Spring clip
8. Adjuster nut
9. Adjuster screw
10. Park brake lever
11. Backing plate
12. Lever stop

FIG. 34 Special views of the brake assembly for installation — 1988–91 Beretta

1988–91 Beretta

▶ SEE FIG. 35

1. Adjust the brakes as described earlier.

2. Apply and release the parking brake 6 times to 10 clicks. Release the parking brake.

➡ **Check to see that both rear wheels turn freely.**

3. Check the parking brake pedal assembly for full release by turning the ignition to **ON** and inspecting the BRAKE warning lamp. The lamp should be off. If the Brake lamp is on and the brake appears to be released, operate the pedal release lever and pull downward on the front parking brake cable to remove the slack from the assembly.

4. Apply the parking brake to 4 clicks.

5. Raise and support the rear of the vehicle on jackstands.

6. Locate the access hole in the backing plate and adjust the parking brake cable until a 1/8 in. (3mm) drill bit can be inserted between the the brake shoe webbing and the parking brake lever.

7. Check to make sure that a 1/4 in. (6mm) drill bit will NOT fit in the same position.

8. Release the parking brake and check to see if both wheels turn freely by hand.

9. Lower the vehicle.

REMOVAL & INSTALLATION

Front Cable

1. Raise and support the vehicle on jackstands.

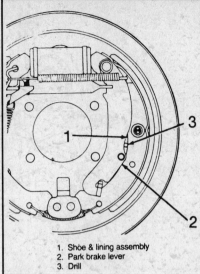

1. Shoe & lining assembly
2. Park brake lever
3. Drill

FIG. 35 Parking brake adjustment — 1988–91 Beretta

2. Loosen, but do not remove, the equalizer nut to remove the cable.

3. Disconnect the cable from the equalizer and right rear cable.

4. Remove the hand grip from the parking brake lever inside the vehicle.

5. Remove the console.

6. Disconnect the cable from the parking brake lever.

7. Remove the nut holding the cable to the floor.

8. Remove the exhaust hanger bracket mounting nuts.

9. Remove the catalytic converter shield.

10. Remove the cable.

11. To install, Lubricate the cable and reverse the removal procedures. Adjust the parking brake.

Rear Cable

1988–89

▶ SEE FIG. 36

1. Raise and support the vehicle on jackstands.

2. Loosen the equalizer nut until the cable tension is released. Must be separated from the threaded rod, if removing the left cable.

3. Disconnect the right side cable button from the connector.

4. Disconnect the conduit end of the cable from the bracket on the axle.

5. Remove the tire and the brake drum.

6. Disconnect the cable from the parking brake lever attached to the brake shoes.

7. Remove the conduit end from the brake shoe backing plate.

8. To install, lubricate the cable and reverse the removal procedures. Adjust the parking brake.

1990–91

▶ SEE FIG. 37

1. Raise and support the vehicle on jackstands.

2. Loosen the equalizer nut until the cable tension is released. Must be separated from the threaded rod, if removing the right cable.

3. Disconnect the left side cable button from the connector.

4. Disconnect the conduit end of the cable from the bracket on the axle.

5. Remove the tire and the brake drum.

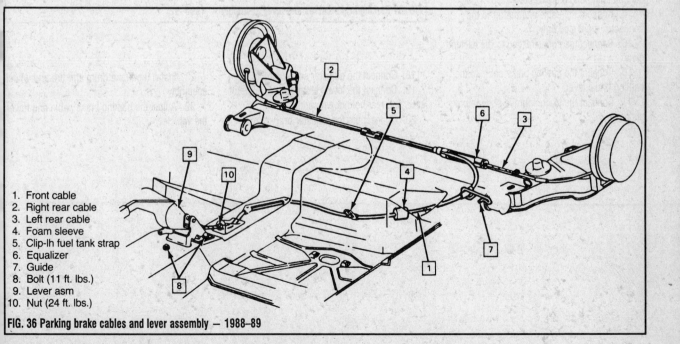

1. Front cable
2. Right rear cable
3. Left rear cable
4. Foam sleeve
5. Clip-lh fuel tank strap
6. Equalizer
7. Guide
8. Bolt (11 ft. lbs.)
9. Lever asm
10. Nut (24 ft. lbs.)

FIG. 36 Parking brake cables and lever assembly — 1988–89

6. Disconnect the cable from the parking brake lever attached to the brake shoes.

7. Remove the conduit end from the brake shoe backing plate.

8. To install, lubricate the cable and reverse the removal procedures. Adjust the parking brake.

1992

▶ SEE FIG. 37

1. Raise and support the vehicle on jackstands.

2. Loosen the equalizer nut until the cable tension is released. Must be separated from the threaded rod, if removing the left cable.

3. Remove the tire and the brake drum.

4. Insert a screwdriver between the brake shoe and the top part of the brake adjuster bracket.

5. Push the bracket to the front and release the top adjuster bracket rod.

6. Disconnect the hold down the spring, actuator lever and lever return spring.

7. Disconnect the adjuster screw spring.

8. Disconnect the top rear brake shoe return spring.

9. Disconnect the parking brake cable from the parking brake lever.

10. Disconnect the conduit fitting from the backing plate while depressing the conduit fitting retaining tangs.

11. Disconnect the cable end button from the connector, right side only.

12. Disconnect the conduit fitting from the axle bracket while depressing the conduit fitting retaining tangs.

To install:

13. Connect the conduit retaining tangs and conduit fitting into the axle bracket.

14. Connect the cable end button to the connector, right side only.

15. Connect the conduit fitting to the backing plate.

16. Connect the parking brake cable to the parking brake lever.

17. Connect the top rear brake shoe return spring.

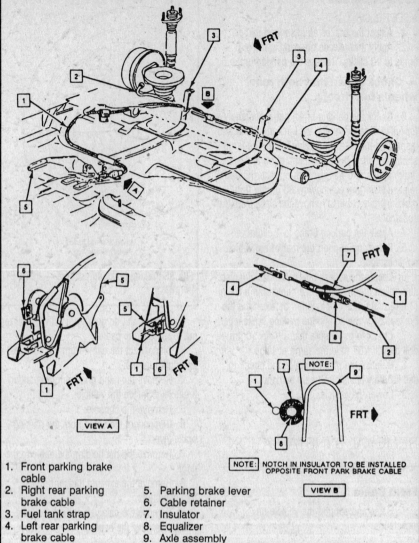

VIEW A

VIEW B

1. Front parking brake cable
2. Right rear parking brake cable
3. Fuel tank strap
4. Left rear parking brake cable
5. Parking brake lever
6. Cable retainer
7. Insulator
8. Equalizer
9. Axle assembly

NOTE: NOTCH IN INSULATOR TO BE INSTALLED OPPOSITE FRONT PARK BRAKE CABLE

FIG. 37 Parking brake cables and lever assembly — 1990–92

18. Connect the adjuster screw spring.

19. Connect the lever return spring, actuator lever, and rear hold down spring.

20. Connect the top adjuster bracket rod.

21. Install the brake drum and tire and wheel assembly.

22. Adjust the parking brake cable and lower the vehicle.

BRAKE SPECIFICATIONS

(All specifications in inches)

Years	Model	Master Cyl. Bore	Brake Disc			Orig. Inside Dia.	Brake Drum			Wheel Cyl. or CaliperBore	
			Original Thickness	Minimum Thickness	Maximum Run-out		Max. Wear Limit	Maximum Machine O/S		Front	Rear
988	Corsica	0.945	0.885	0.830	0.004	7.879	7.929	7.899		NA	0.625
	Beretta	0.945	0.885	0.830	0.004	7.879	7.929	7.899		NA	0.748
989	Corsica	0.945	0.885	0.830	0.004	7.879	7.929	7.899		NA	0.625
	Beretta	0.945	0.885	0.830	0.004	7.879	7.929	7.899		NA	0.748
990	Corsica	0.875	0.885	0.830	0.004	7.879	7.929	7.899		NA	0.625
	Beretta	0.875	0.885	0.830	0.004	7.879	7.929	7.899		NA	0.748
991	Corsica	0.875	0.885	0.830	0.004	7.879	7.929	7.899		NA	0.625
	Beretta	0.875	0.885	0.830	0.004	7.879	7.929	7.899		NA	0.748
992	Corsica	0.875	0.885	0.830	0.004	7.879	7.929	7.899		NA	0.625
	Beretta	0.875	0.885	0.830	0.004	7.879	7.929	7.899		NA	0.748

ANTI-LOCK BRAKE SYSTEM

DESCRIPTION

ABS-VI has been designed to improve the controllability and steerability of a vehicle during braking that would cause one or more wheels to lock. ABS-VI accomplishes this objective by controlling the hydraulic pressure applied to each wheel brake.

BASIC KNOWLEDGE REQUIRED

Before using this section, it is important that you have a basic knowledge of the following items. Without this basic knowledge, it will be difficult to use the diagnostic procedures contained in this section.

Basic Electrical Circuits — You should understand the basic theory of electricity and know the meaning of voltage, current (amps) and resistance (ohms). You should understand what happens in a circuit with an open or shorted wire. You should be able to read and understand a wiring diagram.

Use Of Circuit Testing Tools — You should know how to use a test light and how to use jumper wires to bypass components to test circuits. You should be familiar with the High Impedance Multimeter (DVM) J 34029–A. You should be able to measure voltage, resistance and current and be familiar with the meter controls and how to use them correctly.

ONBOARD DIAGNOSTICS

The ABS-VI contains sophisticated onboard diagnostics that, when accessed with a bidirectional "Scan" tool, are disigned to identify the source of any system fault as specifically as possible, including whether or not the fault is intermittent. There are 58 diagnostic fault codes to assist the service technician with diagnosis. The last diagnostic fault code to occur is specifically identified, and specific ABS data is stored at the time of this fault, also, the first five codes set. Additionally, using a bidirectional "Scan" tool, each input and output can be monitored, thus enabling fault confirmation and repair verification. Manual control of components and automated functional tests are also available when using a GM approved "Scan" tool. Details of many of these functions are contained in the following sections.

ENHANCED DIAGNOSTICS

Enhanced Diagnostic Information, found in the CODE HISTORY function of the bidirectional "Scan" tool, is designed to provide the service technician with specific fault occurrence information. For each of the first five (5) and the very last diagnostic fault codes stored, data is stored to identify the specific fault code number, the number of failure occurrences, and the

number of drive cycles since the failure first and last occurred (a drive cycle occurs when the ignition is turned "ON" and the vehicle is driven faster than 10 mph). However, if a fault is present, the drive cycle counter will increment by turning the ignition "ON" and "OFF". These first five (5) diagnostic fault codes are also stored in the order of occurrence. The order in which the first 5 faults occurred can be useful in determining if a previous fault is linked to the most recent faults, such as an intermittent wheel speed sensor which later becomes completely open.

During difficult diagnosis situations, this information can be used to identify fault occurrence trends. Does the fault occur more frequently now than it did during the last time when it only failed 1 out of 35 drive cycles? Did the fault only occur once over a large number of drive cycles, indication an unusual condition present when the fault occurred? Does the fault occur infrequently over a large number of drive cycles, indication special diagnosis techniques may be required to identify the source of the fault?

If a fault occurred 1 out of 20 drive cycles, the fault is intermittent and has not reoccurred for 19 drive cycles. This fault may be difficult or impossible to duplicate and may have been caused by a severe vehicle impact (large pot hole, speed bump at high speed, etc.) that momentarily opened an electrical connector or caused unusual vehicle suspension movement.

Problem resolution is unlikely, and the problem may never reoccur (check diagnostic aids proved for that code). If the fault occurred 3 out of 15 drive cycles, the odds of finding the cause are still not good, but you know how often it occurs and you can determine whether or not the fault is becoming more frequent based on an additional or past occurances visit if the source of the problem can not or could not be found. If the fault occurred 10 out of 20 drive cycles, the odds of finding the cause are very good, as the fault may be easily reproduced.

By using the additional fault data, you can also determine if a failure is randomly intermittent or if it has not reoccurred for long periods of time due to weather changes or a repair prior to this visit. Say a diagnostic fault code occurred 10 of 20 drive cycles but has not reoccurred for 10 drive cycles. This means the failure occurred 10 of 10 drive cycles but has not reoccurred since. A significant environmental change or a repair occurred 10 drive cycles ago. A repair may not be necessary if a recent repair can be confirmed. If no repair was made, the service can focus on diagnosis techniques used to locate difficult to recreate problems.

DIAGNOSTIC PROCESS

When servicing the ABS-VI, the following steps should be followed in order. Failure to follow thest steps may result in the loss of important diagnostic data and may lead to difficult and time consuming diagnosis procedures.

1. Using a bidirectional "Scan" tool, read all current and history diagnostic codes. Be certain to note which codes are current diagnostic code failures. DO NOT CLEAR CODES unless directed to do so.

2. Using a bidirectional "Scan" tool, read the CODE HISTORY data. Note the diagnostic fault codes stored and their frequency of failure. Specifically note the last failure that occurred and the conditions present when this failure occurred. This "last failure" should be the starting point for diagnosis and repair.

3. Perform a vehicle preliminary diagnosis inspection. This should include:

   a. Inspection of the compact master cylinder for proper brake fluid level.

   b. Inspection of the ABS hydraulic modulator for any leaks or wiring damage.

   c. Inspection of brake components at all four (4) wheels. Verify no drag exists. Also verify proper brake apply operation.

   d. Inspection for worn or damaged wheel bearings that allow a wheel to "wobble."

e. Inspection of the wheel speed sensors and their wiring. Verify correct air gap range, solid sensor attachment, undamaged sensor toothed ring, and undamaged wiring, especially at vehicle attachment points.

   f. Verify proper outer CV joint alignment and operation.

   g. Verify tires meet legal tread depth requirements.

4. If no codes are present, or mechanical component failure codes are present, perform the automated modulator test using the Tech 1 or T-100 to isolate the cause of the problem. If the failure is intermittent and not reproducible, test drive the vehicle while using the automatic snapshot feature of the bidirectional "Scan" tool.

Perform normal acceleration, stopping, and turning maneuvers. If this does not reproduce the failure, perform an ABS stop, on a low coefficient surface such as gravel, from approximately 30–50 mph (48–80 km/h) while triggering on any ABS code. If the failure is still not reproducible, use the enhanced diagnostic information found in CODE HISTORY to determine whether or not this failure should be further diagnosed.

5. Once all system failures have been corrected, clear the ABS codes.

The Tech 1 and T-100, when plugged into the ALDL connector, becomes part of the vehicle's electronic system. The Tech 1 and T-100 can also perform the following functions on components linked by the Serial Data Link (SDL):

- Display ABS data
- Display and clear ABS trouble codes
- Control ABS components
- Perform extensive ABS diagnosis
- Provide diagnostic testing for "Intermittent" ABS conditions.

Each test mode has specific diagnosis capabilities which depend upon various keystrokes. In general, five (5) keys control sequencing: "YES," "NO," "EXIT," "UP" arrow and "DOWN" arrow. The FO through F9 keys select operating modes, perform functions within an operating mode, or enter trouble code or model year designations.

In general, the Tech 1 has five (5) test modes for diagnosing the antilock brake system. The five (5) test modes are as follows:

MODE FO: DATA LIST — In this test mode, the Tech 1 continuously monitors wheel speed data, brake switch status and other inputs and outputs.

MODE F1: CODE HISTORY — In this mode, fault code history data is displayed. This data includes how many ignition cycles since the fault code occurred, along with other ABS information. The first five (5) and last fault codes set are included in the ABS history data.

MODE F2: TROUBLE CODES — In this test mode, trouble codes stored by the EBCM, both current ignition cycle and history, may be displayed or cleared.

MODE F3: ABS SNAPSHOT — In this test mode, the Tech 1 captures ABS data before and after a fault occurrence or a forced manual trigger.

MODE F4: ABS TESTS — In this test mode, the Tech 1 performs hydraulic modulator functional tests to assist in problem isolation during troubleshooting. Included here is manual control of the motors which is used prior to bleeding the brake system.

Press F7 to covert from English to metric.

DISPLAYING CODES

Diagnostic fault codes can only be read through the use of a bidirectional "Scan" tool. There are no provisions for "Flash Code" diagnostics.

CLEARING CODES

The trouble codes in EBCM memory are erased in one of two ways:

1. Tech 1 "Clear Codes" selection.
2. Ignition cycle default.

These two methods are detailed below. Be sure to verify proper system operation and absence of codes when clearing procedure is completed.

The EBCM will not permit code clearing until all of the codes have been displayed. Also, codes cannot be cleared by unplugging the EBCM, disconnecting the battery cables, or turning the ignition "OFF" (except on an ignition cycle default).

Tech 1 "Clear Codes" Method

Select F2 for trouble codes. After codes have been viewed completely, Tech 1 will ask, "CLEAR ABS CODES"; ANSWER "yes." Tech 1 will then read, "DISPLAY CODE HIST. DATA"? "LOST" IF CODES CLEARED. "NO" TO CLEAR CODES. Answer "NO" and codes will be cleared.

Ignition Cycle Default

If no diagnostic fault code occurs for 100 drive cycles (a drive cycle occurs when the ignition is turned "ON" and the vehicle is driven faster than 10 mph), any existing fault codes are cleared from the EBCM memory.

INTERMITTENT FAILURES

As with most electronic systems, intermittent failures may be difficult to accurately diagnose. The following is a method to try to isolate an intermittent failure especially wheel speed circuitry failures.

If an ABS fault occurs, the "ABS" warning light indicator will be "ON" during the ignition cycle in which the fault was detected. If it is an intermittent problem which seems to have corrected itself ("ABS" warning light "OFF"), a history trouble code will be stored. Also stored will be the history data of the code at the time the fault occurred. The Tech 1 must be used to read ABS history data.

INTERMITTENTS AND POOR CONNECTIONS

Most intermittents are caused by faulty electrical connections or wiring, although occassionally a sticking relay or solenoid can be a problem. Some items to check are:

1. Poor mating of connector halves, or terminals not fully seated in the connector body (backed out).

2. Dirt or corrosion on the terminals. The terminals must be clean and free of any foreign material which could impede proper terminal contact.

3. Damaged connector body, exposing the terminals to moisture and dirt, as well as not maintaining proper terminal orientation with the component or mating connector.

4. Improperly formed or damaged terminals. All connector terminals in problem circuits sdhould be checked carefully to ensure good contact tension. Use a corresponding mating terminal to check for proper tension. Refer to "Checking Terminal Contact" in this section for the specific procedure.

5. The J 35616–A Connector Test Adapter Kit must be used whenever a diagnostic procedure requests checking or probing a terminal. Using the adapter will ensure that no damage to the terminal will occur, as well as giving an idea of whether contact tension is sufficient. If contact tension seems incorrect, refer to "Checking Terminal Contact" in this section for specifics.

6. Poor terminal-to-wire connection. Checking this requires removing the terminal from the connector body. Some conditions which fall under this description are poor crimps, poor solder joints, crimping over wire insulation rather than the wire itself, corrosion in the wire-to-terminal contact area, etc.

7. Wire insulation which is rubbed through, causing an intermittent short as the bare area touches other wiring or parts of the vehicle.

8. Wiring broken inside the insulation. This condition could cause a continuity check to show a good circuit, but if only 1 or 2 strands of a multi-strand type wire are intact, resistance could be far too high.

Checking Terminal Contact

When diagnosing an electrical system that uses Metri-Pack 150/280/480/630 series terminals (refer to Terminal Repair Kit J 38125–A instruction manual J 38125–4 for terminal identification), it is important to check terminal contact between a connector and component, or between inline connectors, before replacing a suspect component.

Frequently, a diagnostic chart leads to a step that reads "Check for poor connection". Mating terminals must be inspected to ensure good terminal contact. A poor connection between the male and female terminal at a connector may be the result of contamination or deformation.

Contamination is caused by the connector halves being improperly connected, a missing or damaged connector seal, or damage to the connector itself, exposing the terminals to moisture and dirt. Contamination, usually in underhood or underbody connectors, leads to terminal corrosion, causing an open circuit or an intermittently open circuit.

Deformation is caused by probing the mating side of a connector terminal without the proper adapter, improperly joining the connector halves or repeatedly separating and joining the connector halves. Deformation, usually to the female terminal contact tang, can result in poor terminal contact causing an open or intermittently open circuit.

Follow the procedure below to check terminal contact.

1. Separate the connector halves. Refer to Terminal Repair Kit J 38125–A instruction manual J 38125–4, if available.

2. Inspect the connector halves for contamination. Contamination will result in a white or green buildup within the connector body or between terminals, causing high terminal resistance, intermittent contact or an open circuit. An underhood or underbody connector that shows signs of contamination should be replaced in its entirety: terminals, seals, and connector body.

3. Using an equivalent male terminal from the Terminal Repair Kit J 38125–A, check the retention force of the female terminal in question by inserting and removing the male terminal to the female terminal in the connector body. Good terminal contact will require a certain amount of force to separate the terminals.

4. Using an equivalent female terminal from the Terminal Repair Kit J 38125–A, compare the retention force of this terminal to the female terminal in question by joining and separating the male terminal to the female terminal in question. If the retention force is significantly different between the two female terminals, replace the female terminal in question, using a terminal from Terminal Repair Kit J 38125–A.

Anti-Lock Brake System Service

Precaution

Failure to observe the following precautions may result in system damage.

• Before performing electric arc welding on the vehicle, disconnect the Electronic Brake Control Module (EBCM) and the hydraulic modulator connectors.

• When performing painting work on the vehicle, do not expose the Electronic Brake Control Module (EBCM) to temperatures in excess of 185°F (85°C) for longer than 2 hrs. The system may be exposed to temperatures up to 200°F (95°C) for less than 15 min.

• Never disconnect or connect the Electronic Brake Control Module (EBCM) or hydraulic modulator connectors with the ignition switch ON.

• Never disassemble any component of the Anti-Lock Brake System (ABS) which is designated non-serviceable; the component must be replaced as an assembly.

• When filling the master cylinder, always use Delco Supreme 11 brake fluid or equivalent, which meets DOT-3 specifications; petroleum base fluid will destroy the rubber parts.

Electrical Connectors

♦ SEE FIG. 38

Some ABS-VI components are equipped with electrical connectors using a Connector Position Assurance (CPA) lock.

1. Remove the lock before separating the electrical connectors.

2. Be careful not to damage the locking pin during removal.

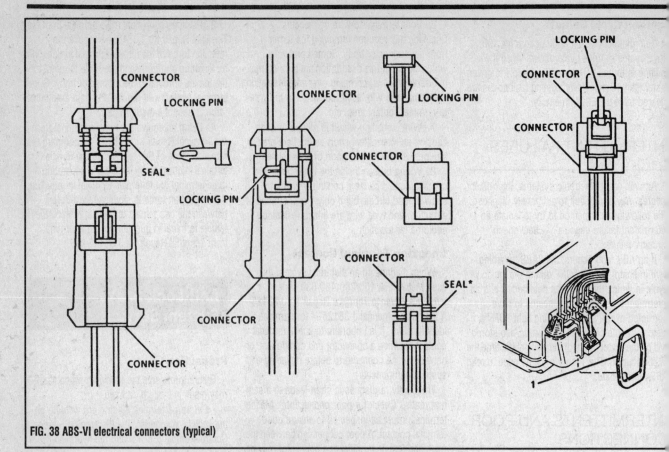

FIG. 38 ABS-VI electrical connectors (typical)

3. Make sure that the rubber connector seal is in place on the connector before and after connection.

4. Always install the lock after ther connection is made.

ABS Hydraulic Modulator Assembly Bleeder Valves

REMOVAL & INSTALLATION

♦ SEE FIG. 39

1. Remove the bleeder valve or valves.

2. Install the bleeeder valve and tighten to 65 inch lbs. (7 Nm).

Fluid Level Sensor

REMOVAL & INSTALLATION

♦ SEE FIG. 40

1. Disconnect the electrical connection from the fluid level sensor.

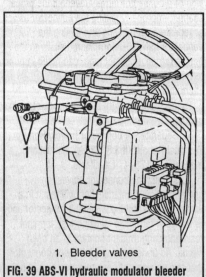

1. Bleeder valves

FIG. 39 ABS-VI hydraulic modulator bleeder locations

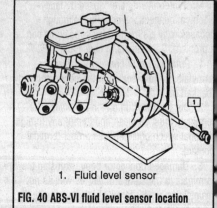

1. Fluid level sensor

FIG. 40 ABS-VI fluid level sensor location

2. Remove the fluid level sensor using needle nose pliers to compress the switch locking tabs at the inboard side of the master cylinder.

To install:

3. Insert the fluid level sensor unit until the locking tabs snap in place.

4. Connect the electrical connector to the sensor.

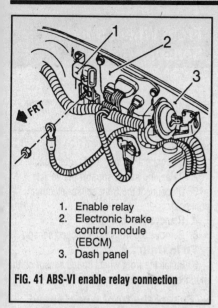

1. Enable relay
2. Electronic brake control module (EBCM)
3. Dash panel

FIG. 41 ABS-VI enable relay connection

Enable Relay

REMOVAL & INSTALLATION

♦ SEE FIG. 41

1. Disconnect the electrical connection.
2. Release the retainer on the bracket and slide the relay off the bracket.

To install:

3. Slide the relay onto the bracket and make sure the retainer kocks the relay to the bracket.
4. Connect the electrical connection.

ABS Lamp Driver Module

♦ SEE FIG. 42

1. Disconnect the negative battery cable.
2. Remove the right side lower sound insulator panel.
3. Slide the glove box all the way out or remove it completely.
4. The lamp driver module is above the cruise control module taped to the instrument panel harness and is light green in color.
5. Open the connector and slide the circuit board out of the connector.

To install:

6. Install the circuit board to the connector.
7. Reposition the connector to the instrument panel harness and make sure it is retaped in place.

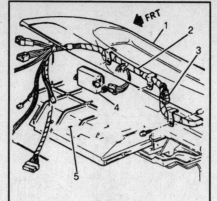

1. Instrument panel
2. Instrument panel harness
3. ABS-lamp driver module
4. Cruise control module
5. Glove box

FIG. 42 ABS-VI lamp driver module

8. Slide the glove box back into the dash or reinstall the screws, if removed.
9. Install the right side lower sound insulator panel.
10. Connect the negative battery cable.

ABS Hydraulic Modulator Assembly

REMOVAL & INSTALLATION

♦ SEE FIG. 43

❄ CAUTION

To avoid personal injury, use the Tech I Scan tool to relieve the gear tension in the hydraulic modulator. This procedure must be performed prior to removal of the brake control and motor assembly.

1. Disconnect the negative battery cable.
2. Disconnect the 2 solenoid electrical connectors and the fluid level sensor connector.
3. Disconnect the 6-pin and 3-pin motor pack electrical connectors.
4. Wrap a shop towel around the hydraulic brake lines and disconnect the 4 brake lines from the modulator.

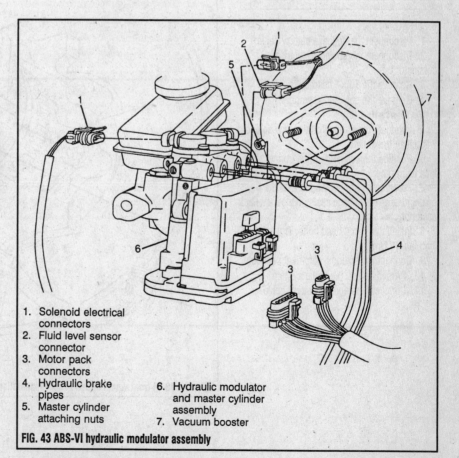

1. Solenoid electrical connectors
2. Fluid level sensor connector
3. Motor pack connectors
4. Hydraulic brake pipes
5. Master cylinder attaching nuts
6. Hydraulic modulator and master cylinder assembly
7. Vacuum booster

FIG. 43 ABS-VI hydraulic modulator assembly

➡ **Cap the disconnected lines to prevent the loss of fluid and the entry of moisture and contaminants.**

5. Remove the 2 nuts attaching the ABS hydraulic modulator assembly to the vacuum booster.

6. Remove the ABS hydraulic modulator assembly from the vehicle.

To install:

7. Install the ABS hydraulic modulator assembly to the vehicle. Install the 2 attaching nuts and tighten to 20 ft. lbs. (27 Nm).

8. Connect the 4 brake pipes to the modulator assembly. Tighten to 13 ft. lbs. (17 Nm).

9. Connect the 6-pin and 3-pin electrical connectors and the fluid level sensor connector.

10. Properly bleed the system.

11. Connect the negative battery cable.

Hydraulic Modulator Solenoid Assembly

1. Solenoid electrical connectors
2. Torx® head bolts
3. Solenoid assembly
4. ABS hydraulic modulator

FIG. 44 ABS-VI hydraulic modulator solenoid assembly

REMOVAL & INSTALLATION

◆ SEE FIG. 44

1. Disconnect the negative battery cable.

2. Disconnect the solenoid electrical connector.

3. Remove the Torx® head bolts.

4. Remove the solenoid assembly.

To install:

5. Lubricate the O-rings on the new solenoid with clean brake fluid.

6. Position the solenoid so the connectors face each other.

7. Press down firmly by hand until the solenoid assembly flange seats on the modulator assembly.

8. Install the Torx® head bolts. Tighten to 39 inch lbs. (5 Nm).

9. Connect the solenoid electrical connector.

10. Properly bleed the brake system.

11. Connect the negative battery cable.

Front Wheel Speed Sensor

REMOVAL & INSTALLATION

◆ SEE FIG. 45–45A

1. Disconnect the negative battery cable.

2. Raise and safely support the vehicle.

3. Disconnect the front sensor electrical connector.

4. Remove the Torx® bolt.

5. Remove the front wheel speed sensor.

To install:

6. Install the front wheel speed sensor on the mounting bracket.

➡ **Ensure the front wheel speed sensor is properly aligned and lays flat against the bracket bosses.**

7. Install the Torx® bolt. Tighten to 106 inch lbs. (12 Nm).

8. Connect the front sensor electrical connector.

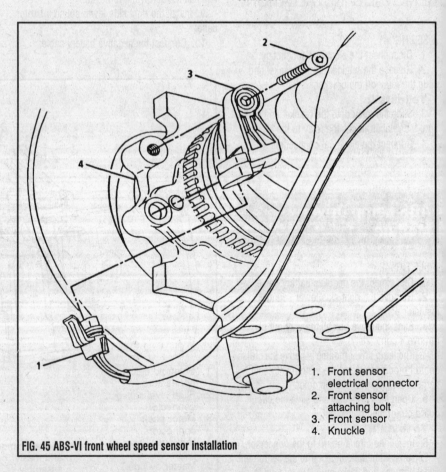

1. Front sensor electrical connector
2. Front sensor attaching bolt
3. Front sensor
4. Knuckle

FIG. 45 ABS-VI front wheel speed sensor installation

9. Lower the vehicle.
10. Connect the negative battery cable.

Rear Wheel Bearing And Speed Sensor Assembly

REMOVAL & INSTALLATION

SEE FIG. 46–46A

► The rear integral wheel bearing and sensor assembly must be replaced as a unit.

1. Disconnect the negative battery cable.
2. Raise and safely support the vehicle.
3. Remove the rear wheel.
4. Remove the brake drum.
5. Disconnect the rear sensor electrical connector.
6. Remove the bolts and nuts attaching the rear wheel bearing and speed sensor assembly to the backing plate.

► With the rear wheel bearing and speed sensor attaching bolts and nuts removed, the drum brake assembly is supported only by the brake line connection. To avoid bending or damage to the brake line, do not bump or exert force on the assembly.

7. Remove the rear wheel bearing and speed sensor assembly.

To install:

8. Install the rear wheel bearing and speed sensor assembly by aligning the bolt hoses in the wheel bearing and speed sensor assembly, drum brake assembly and rear suspension bracket. Install the attaching bolts and nuts. Tighten to 38 ft. lbs. (52 Nm).

9. Connect the rear speed sensor electrical connector.
10. Install the brake drum.
11. Install the rear wheel.
12. Lower the vehicle.
13. Connect the negative battery cable.

FIG. 45A Front wheel sensor–1992 Corsica shown, all models similar

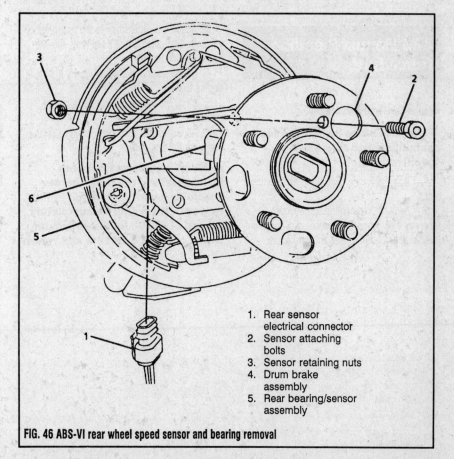

1. Rear sensor electrical connector
2. Sensor attaching bolts
3. Sensor retaining nuts
4. Drum brake assembly
5. Rear bearing/sensor assembly

FIG. 46 ABS-VI rear wheel speed sensor and bearing removal

FIG. 46A Rear wheel sensor—1992 Corsica shown, all models similar

ABS Manual Bleeding Procedure

Brake Control Assembly

➡ Only use brake fluid from a sealed container which meets DOT 3 specifications.

1. Clean the area around the master cylinder cap.
2. Check fluid level in master cylinder reservoir and top-up, as necessary. Check fluid level frequently during bleeding procedure.

3. Attach a bleeder hose to the rear bleeder valve on the brake control assembly. Slowly open the bleeder valve.
4. Depress the brake pedal slowly until fluid begins to flow.
5. Close the valve and release the brake pedal.
6. Repeat for the front bleeder valve on the brake control assembly.

➡ When fluid flows from both bleeder valves, the brake control assembly is sufficiently full of fluid. However, it may not be completely purged of air. Bleed the individual wheel calipers/cylinders and return

to the control assembly to purge the remaining air.

Wheel Calipers/Cylinders

➡ Prior to bleeding the rear brakes the rear displacement cylinder must be returned to the top-most position. This can be accomplished using the Tech I Scan tool or T-100 (CAMS), by entering the manual control function and applying the rear motor.

If a Tech I or T-100 are unavailable bleed the front brakes. Ensure the pedal is firm. Carefully drive the vehicle to a speed above 4 mph to cause the ABS system to initialize. This will return the rear displacement cylinder to the top-most position.

1. Clean the area around the master cylinder cap.
2. Check fluid level in master cylinder reservoir and top-up, as necessary. Check fluid level frequently during bleeding procedure.
3. Raise and safely support the vehicle.
4. Attach a bleeder hose to the bleeder valve of the right rear wheel and submerge the opposite hose in a clean container partially filled with brake fluid.
5. Open the bleeder valve.
6. Slowly depress the brake pedal.
7. Close the bleeder valve and release the brake pedal.
8. Wait 5 seconds.
9. Repeat Steps 5–8 until the pedal begins to feel firm and no air bubbles appear in the bleeder hose.
10. Repeat Steps 5–9, until the pedal is firm and no air bubbles appear in the brake hose, for the remaining wheels in the following order:
    a. left rear
    b. right front
    c. left front.
11. Lower the vehicle.

DIAGNOSTIC PROCESS
(Page 2 of 3)

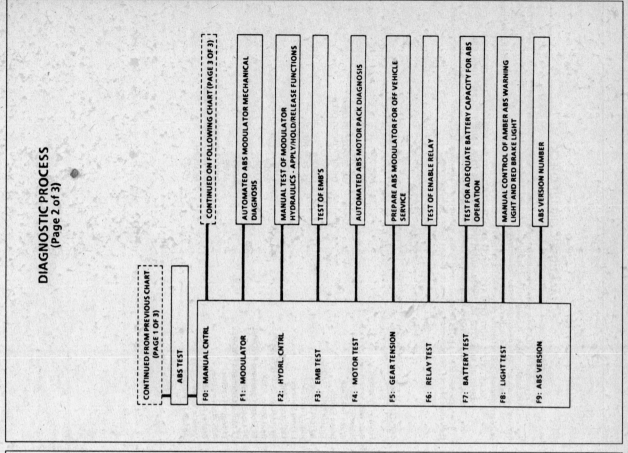

CONTINUED FROM PREVIOUS CHART (PAGE 1 OF 3)

ABS TEST

- F0: MANUAL CNTRL — CONTINUED ON FOLLOWING CHART (PAGE 3 OF 3)
- F1: MODULATOR — AUTOMATED ABS MODULATOR MECHANICAL DIAGNOSIS
- F2: HYDRL. CNTRL — MANUAL TEST OF MODULATOR HYDRAULICS - APPLY/HOLD/RELEASE FUNCTIONS
- F3: EMB TEST — TEST OF EMB'S
- F4: MOTOR TEST — AUTOMATED ABS MOTOR PACK DIAGNOSIS
- F5: GEAR TENSION — PREPARE ABS MODULATOR FOR OFF VEHICLE SERVICE
- F6: RELAY TEST — TEST OF ENABLE RELAY
- F7: BATTERY TEST — TEST FOR ADEQUATE BATTERY CAPACITY FOR ABS OPERATION
- F8: LIGHT TEST — MANUAL CONTROL OF AMBER ABS WARNING LIGHT AND RED BRAKE LIGHT
- F9: ABS VERSION — ABS VERSION NUMBER

DIAGNOSTIC PROCESS
(Page 1 of 3)

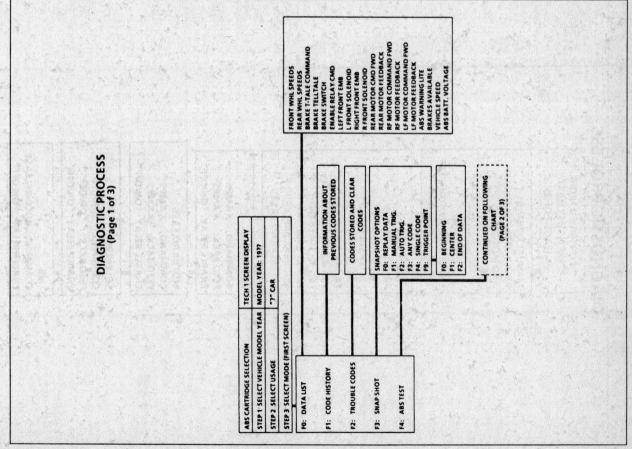

ABS CARTRIDGE SELECTION	TECH 1 SCREEN DISPLAY
STEP 1 SELECT VEHICLE MODEL YEAR	MODEL YEAR: 19??
STEP 2 SELECT USAGE	"?" CAR
STEP 3 SELECT MODE (FIRST SCREEN)	

- F0: DATA LIST — FRONT WHL SPEEDS / REAR WHL SPEEDS / BRAKE T-TALE COMMAND / BRAKE TELLTALE / BRAKE SWITCH / ENABLE RELAY CMD / L FRONT EMB / RIGHT FRONT EMB / L. FRONT SOLENOID / R. FRONT SOLENOID / REAR MOTOR CMD FWD / REAR MOTOR FEEDBACK / RF MOTOR COMMAND FWD / LF MOTOR COMMAND FWD / RF MOTOR FEEDBACK / LF MOTOR FEEDBACK / ABS WARNING LITE / BRAKES AVAILABLE / VEHICLE SPEED / ABS BATT. VOLTAGE
- F1: CODE HISTORY — INFORMATION ABOUT PREVIOUS CODES STORED
- F2: TROUBLE CODES — CODES STORED AND CLEAR CODES
- F3: SNAP SHOT — SNAPSHOT OPTIONS
  - F0: REPLAY DATA
  - F1: MANUAL TRIG.
  - F2: AUTO TRIG.
  - F3: ANY CODE
  - F4: SINGLE CODE
  - F9: TRIGGER POINT
    - F0: BEGINNING
    - F1: CENTER
    - F2: END OF DATA
- F4: ABS TEST — CONTINUED ON FOLLOWING CHART (PAGE 2 OF 3)

DIAGNOSTIC CIRCUIT CHECK

The Diagnostic Circuit Check is an organized approach to identifying a problem created by an Antilock Brake System (ABS) malfunction. It must be the starting point for any ABS complaint diagnosis, because it directs the Service Technician to the next logical step in diagnosing the complaint.

The "Scan" Data listed in the table may be used after completing the Diagnostic Circuit Check and finding the on-board diagnostics functioning properly and no trouble codes displayed.

A "SCAN" TOOL THAT DISPLAYS FAULTY DATA SHOULD NOT BE USED, AND THE PROBLEM SHOULD BE REPORTED TO THE MANUFACTURER. THE USE OF A FAULTY "SCAN" TOOL CAN RESULT IN MISDIAGNOSIS AND UNNECESSARY PARTS REPLACEMENT.

Only the parameters listed below are used in this manual for diagnosing. If a "Scan" reads other parameters, the values are not recommended by General Motors for use in diagnosing.

"SCAN" DATA

"SCAN" Position	Units Displayed
Front WHL Speeds	MPH/KPH
Rear WHL Speeds	MPH/KPH
Brake T-TALE CMD	ON/OFF
Brake Tell-TALE	ON/OFF/CIRCUIT OPEN
Brake Switch	ON/OFF/CIRCUIT OPEN
Enable Relay CMD	ON/OFF
R Front Solenoid	ON/OFF
Right Front EMB	RELEASE/HOLD
L Front Solenoid	ON/OFF
Left Front EMB	RELEASE/HOLD
Rear Motor CMD FWD/REV	AMPS
RF Motor Command FWD/REV	AMPS
RF Motor Feedbac	AMPS
LF Motor Command FWD/REV	AMPS
LF Motor Feedbac	AMPS
ABS Warning Lite	ON/OFF/FLASHING
Brakes Available	ANTILOCK/BASE BRAKES
Vehicle Speed	MPH/KPH
ABS BATT Voltage	VOLTS

DIAGNOSTIC PROCESS

CONTINUED FROM PREVIOUS CHART (PAGE 2 OF 3)

MANUAL CONTROL
RELAY, EMB, SOLENOIDS AND MOTORS

↑ = TURN "ON"
↓ = TURN "OFF"
ENTER = RELAY "ON/OFF"
YES TO CONTINUE

SELECT
F0: LF APPLY
F1: LF RELEASE
F2: LF SOLENOID
F3: LF EMB
F4: RF APPLY
F5: RF RELEASE
F6: RF SOLENOID
F7: RF EMB
F8: REAR APPLY
F9: REAR RELEASE

MOTOR APPLY
COMMAND: X AMPS
FEED BACK: X AMPS
ENABLE RELAY: "ON/OFF"

MOTOR RELEASE
COMMAND: X AMPS
FEED BACK: X AMPS
ENABLE RELAY: "ON/OFF"

SOLENOID
COMMAND: "ON/OFF"
FEED BACK: "ON/OFF"
ENABLE RELAY: "ON/OFF"

EMB
COMMAND: HOLD/RELEASE
ENABLE RELAY: "ON/OFF"

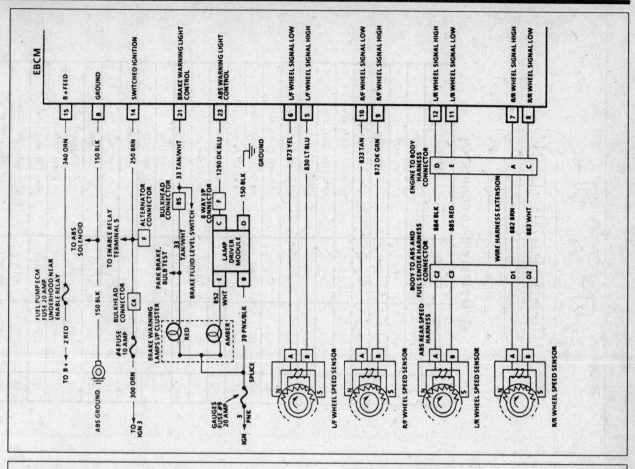

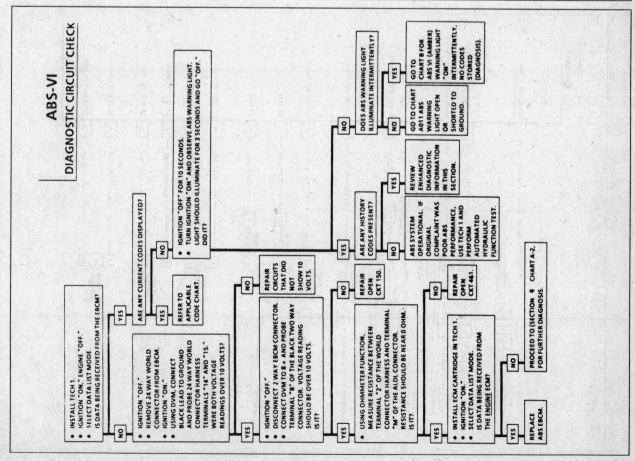

EBCM 24 PIN WORLD CONNECTOR

PIN	CIRCUIT NO.	COLOR	CIRCUIT
1	799	TAN/WHT	NOT USED
2	461	ORN	SERIAL DATA LINE
3	OPEN		NOT USED
4	1289	LT BLU/BLK	R/F ABS SOLENOID
5	830	LT BLU	L/F WHEEL SIGNAL HIGH
6	873	YEL	L/F WHEEL SIGNAL LOW
7	882	BRN	R/R WHEEL SIGNAL HIGH
8	883	WHT	R/R WHEEL SIGNAL LOW
9	872	DK GRN	R/F WHEEL SIGNAL HIGH
10	833	TAN	R/F WHEEL SIGNAL LOW
11	885	RED	L/R WHEEL SIGNAL LOW
12	884	BLK	L/R WHEEL SIGNAL HIGH
13	20	LT BLU	BRAKE SWITCH INPUT
14	250	BRN	SWITCH IGNITION
15	340	ORN	B + FEED
16	OPEN		NOT USED
17	OPEN		NOT USED
18	VENT TUBE	BLK	VENT TUBE
19	1286	LT GRN	L/F EMB
20	1287	GRY	R/F EMB
21	33	TAN/WHT	BRAKE TELLTALE
22	879	PPL/WHT	ENABLE RELAY CONTROL
23	1290	DK BLU	ABS WARNING LIGHT CONTROL
24	1288	DK GRN/YEL	L/F ABS SOLENOID

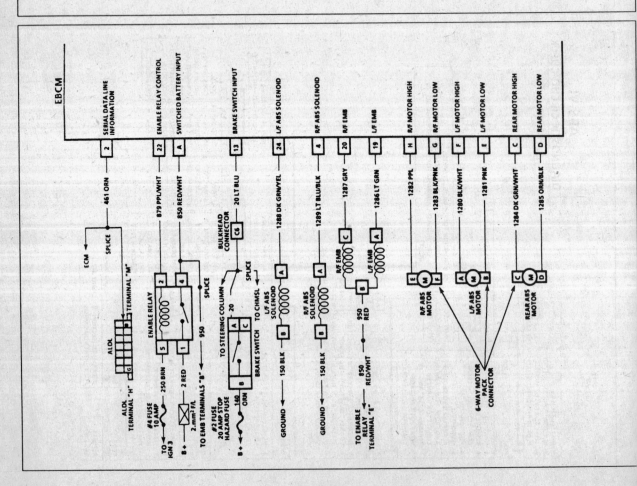

ABS SYMPTOM AND TROUBLE CODE TABLE

CHART	SYMPTOM
A	ABS (Amber) Warning Light "ON" Constantly, No Codes Stored
B	ABS (Amber) Warning Light "ON" Intermittently, No Codes Stored

TROUBLE CODE	DESCRIPTION
A011	ABS Warning Light Circuit Open or Shorted to Ground
A013	ABS Warning Light Circuit Shorted to Battery
A014	Enable Relay Contacts Or Fuse Open
A015	Enable Relay Contacts Shorted to Battery
A016	Enable Relay Coil Circuit Open
A017	Enable Relay Coil Circuit Shorted to Ground
A018	Enable Relay Coil Circuit Shorted to Battery
A021	Left Front Wheel Speed = 0 (1 of 2)
A022	Right Front Wheel Speed = 0 (1 of 2)
A023	Left Rear Wheel Speed = 0 (1 of 2)
A024	Right Rear Wheel Speed = 0 (1 of 2)
A025	Left Front Excessive Wheel Speed Variation (1 of 2)
A026	Right Front Excessive Wheel Speed Variation (1 of 2)
A027	Left Rear Excessive Wheel Speed Variation (1 of 2)
A028	Right Rear Excessive Wheel Speed Variation (1 of 2)
A031	Two Wheel Speeds = 0 (1 of 2) (Non-Tubular Rear Axle)
A036	Two Wheel Speeds = 0 (1 of 2) (Tubular Rear Axle)
A037	Low System Voltage
A038	High System Voltage
A041	Left Front EMB Will Not Hold Motor
A042	Right Front EMB Will Not Hold Motor
A044	Rear Axle ESB Will Not Hold Motor
A045	Left Front Channel Will Not Move
A046	Right Front Channel Will Not Move
A047	Rear Axle Channel Will Not Move
A048	Left Front Motor Free Spins
A051	Right Front Motor Free Spins
A052	Rear Axle Motor Free Spins
A053	Left Front Channel in Release Too Long
A054	Right Front Channel In Release Too Long
A055	Rear Axle Channel in Release Too Long
A056	Motor Driver Fault Detected
A057	Left Front Motor Circuit Open
A058	Left Front Motor Circuit Shorted to Ground
A061	Left Front Motor Circuit Shorted to Battery or Motor Shorted
A062	Right Front Motor Circuit Open
A063	Right Front Motor Circuit Shorted to Ground
	Right Front Motor Circuit Shorted to Battery or Motor Shorted

6 WAY EBCM CONNECTOR

PIN	CIRCUIT NO.	COLOR	CIRCUIT
C	1284	DK GRN/WHT	REAR MOTOR HIGH
D	1285	ORN/BLK	REAR MOTOR LOW
E	1281	PNK	L/F MOTOR LOW
F	1280	BLK/WHT	L/F MOTOR HIGH
G	1283	BLK/PNK	R/F MOTOR LOW
H	1282	PPL	R/F MOTOR HIGH

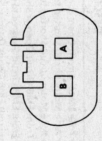

2 WAY EBCM CONNECTOR

PIN	CIRCUIT NO.	COLOR	CIRCUIT
A	850	RED/WHT	SWITCHED BATTERY INPUT
B	150	BLK	GROUND

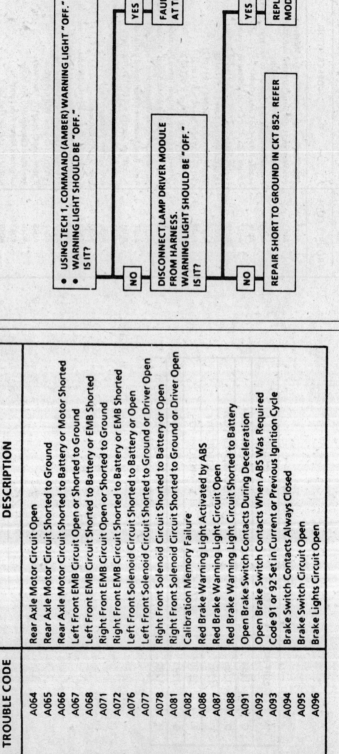

CHART A
ABS (AMBER) WARNING LIGHT "ON" CONSTANTLY, NO CODES STORED

- USING TECH 1, COMMAND (AMBER) WARNING LIGHT "OFF."
- WARNING LIGHT SHOULD BE "OFF."

IS IT?

NO → DISCONNECT LAMP DRIVER MODULE FROM HARNESS. WARNING LIGHT SHOULD BE "OFF." IS IT?

YES → FAULT IS NOT PRESENT AT THIS TIME.

NO → REPAIR SHORT TO GROUND IN CKT 852. REFER

YES → REPLACE LAMP DRIVER MODULE ASSEMBLY.

ABS SYMPTOM AND TROUBLE CODE TABLE

TROUBLE CODE	DESCRIPTION
A064	Rear Axle Motor Circuit Open
A065	Rear Axle Motor Circuit Shorted to Ground
A066	Rear Axle Motor Circuit Shorted to Battery or Motor Shorted
A067	Left Front EMB Circuit Open or Shorted to Ground
A068	Left Front EMB Circuit Shorted to Battery or EMB Shorted
A071	Right Front EMB Circuit Open or Shorted to Ground
A072	Right Front EMB Circuit Shorted to Battery or EMB Shorted
A076	Left Front Solenoid Circuit Shorted to Battery or Open
A077	Left Front Solenoid Circuit Shorted to Ground or Driver Open
A078	Right Front Solenoid Circuit Shorted to Battery or Open
A081	Right Front Solenoid Circuit Shorted to Ground or Driver Open
A082	Calibration Memory Failure
A086	Red Brake Warning Light Activated by ABS
A087	Red Brake Warning Light Circuit Open
A088	Red Brake Warning Light Circuit Shorted to Battery
A091	Open Brake Switch Contacts During Deceleration
A092	Open Brake Switch Contacts When ABS Was Required
A093	Code 91 or 92 Set in Current or Previous Ignition Cycle
A094	Brake Switch Contacts Always Closed
A095	Brake Switch Circuit Open
A096	Brake Lights Circuit Open

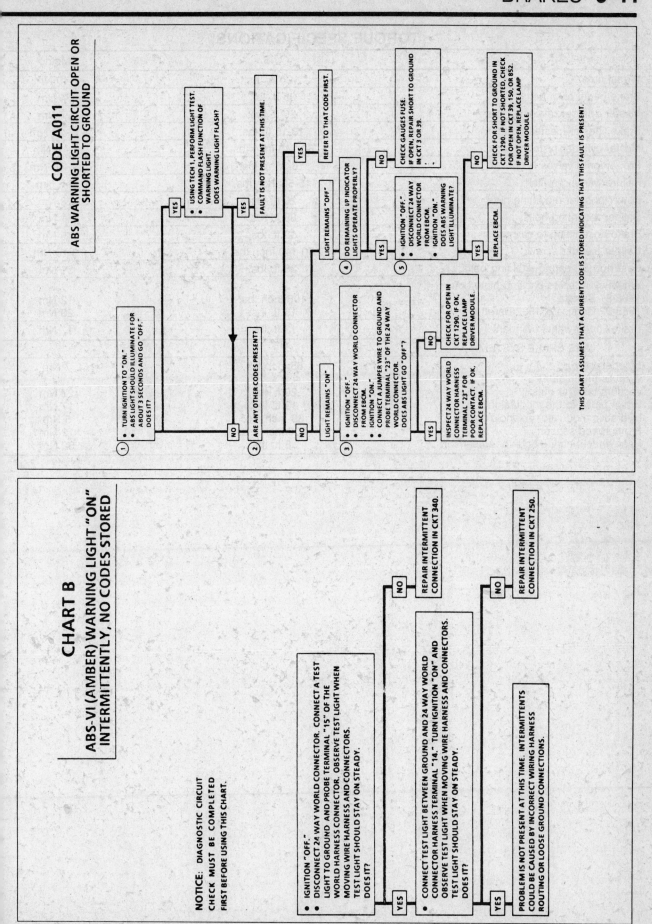

CODE A011
ABS WARNING LIGHT CIRCUIT OPEN OR SHORTED TO GROUND

1. TURN IGNITION TO "ON."
   - ABS LIGHT SHOULD ILLUMINATE FOR ABOUT 3 SECONDS AND GO "OFF." DOES IT?

YES → USING TECH 1, PERFORM LIGHT TEST. COMMAND FLASH FUNCTION OF WARNING LIGHT. DOES WARNING LIGHT FLASH?
YES → FAULT IS NOT PRESENT AT THIS TIME.

2. ARE ANY OTHER CODES PRESENT?

YES → REFER TO THAT CODE FIRST.

3. - IGNITION "OFF."
   - DISCONNECT 24 WAY WORLD CONNECTOR FROM EBCM.
   - IGNITION "ON."
   - CONNECT A JUMPER WIRE TO GROUND AND PROBE TERMINAL "23" OF THE 24 WAY WORLD CONNECTOR. DOES ABS LIGHT GO "OFF"?

LIGHT REMAINS "ON"
LIGHT REMAINS "OFF"

YES → INSPECT 24 WAY WORLD CONNECTOR HARNESS TERMINAL "23" FOR POOR CONTACT. IF OK, REPLACE EBCM.
NO → CHECK FOR OPEN IN CKT 1290. IF OK, REPLACE LAMP DRIVER MODULE.

4. DO REMAINING UP INDICATOR LIGHTS OPERATE PROPERLY?

NO → CHECK GAUGES FUSE. IF OPEN, REPAIR SHORT TO GROUND IN CKT 3 OR 39.

5. - IGNITION "OFF."
   - DISCONNECT 24 WAY WORLD CONNECTOR FROM EBCM.
   - IGNITION "ON."
   - DOES ABS WARNING LIGHT ILLUMINATE?

YES → REPLACE EBCM.
NO → CHECK FOR SHORT TO GROUND IN CKT 1290. IF NOT SHORTED, CHECK FOR OPEN IN CKT 39, 150, OR 852. IF NOT OPEN, REPLACE LAMP DRIVER MODULE.

THIS CHART ASSUMES THAT A CURRENT CODE IS STORED INDICATING THAT THIS FAULT IS PRESENT.

CHART B
ABS-VI (AMBER) WARNING LIGHT "ON" INTERMITTENTLY, NO CODES STORED

NOTICE: DIAGNOSTIC CIRCUIT CHECK MUST BE COMPLETED FIRST BEFORE USING THIS CHART.

- IGNITION "OFF."
- DISCONNECT 24 WAY WORLD CONNECTOR. CONNECT A TEST LIGHT TO GROUND AND PROBE TERMINAL "15" OF THE WORLD HARNESS CONNECTOR. OBSERVE TEST LIGHT WHEN MOVING WIRE HARNESS AND CONNECTORS. TEST LIGHT SHOULD STAY ON STEADY. DOES IT?

YES → - CONNECT TEST LIGHT BETWEEN GROUND AND 24 WAY WORLD CONNECTOR HARNESS TERMINAL "14." TURN IGNITION "ON" AND OBSERVE TEST LIGHT WHEN MOVING WIRE HARNESS AND CONNECTORS. TEST LIGHT SHOULD STAY ON STEADY. DOES IT?

YES → PROBLEM IS NOT PRESENT AT THIS TIME. INTERMITTENTS COULD BE CAUSED BY INCORRECT WIRING HARNESS ROUTING OR LOOSE GROUND CONNECTIONS.

NO → REPAIR INTERMITTENT CONNECTION IN CKT 250.

NO → REPAIR INTERMITTENT CONNECTION IN CKT 340.

TORQUE SPECIFICATIONS

Component	U.S.	Metric
Wheel nuts:	100 ft. lbs.	140 Nm
Brake pedal pivot bolt:	25 ft. lbs.	34 Nm
Master cylinder retaining nuts:	20 ft. lbs.	27 Nm
Brake lines-to-master cylinder:	13-15 ft. lbs.	17-20 Nm
Master cylinder piston plug:	80-140 inch lbs.	5-16 Nm
Proportioner valves:	18-30 ft. lbs.	25-40 Nm
Failure warning switch:	15-50 inch lbs.	2-6 Nm
Power booster mounting nuts:	20 ft. lbs.	28 Nm
Caliper mounting bolts:	38 ft. lbs.	51 Nm
Brake hose fitting to caliper:	33 ft. lbs.	45 Nm
Caliper bleeder screw:	80-140 inch lbs.	9-16 Nm
Rear hub & bearing retaining bolts:	38 ft. lbs.	51 Nm
Wheel cylinder- to-backing plate bolt		
1988-91 Beretta:	106 inch lbs.	12 Nm
1988-92 Corsica & 1992 Beretta:	15 ft. lbs.	20 Nm
Brake line-to-wheel cylinder:	13 ft. lbs.	17 Nm
ABS BRAKE SYSTEM		
Bleeder valve:	65 inch lbs.	7 Nm
ydraulic modulator to		
vacuum booster nuts:	20 ft. lbs.	27 Nm
Brake pipes to the modulator:	13 ft. lbs.	17 Nm
Hydraulic modulator solenoid bolts:	39 inch lbs.	5 Nm
Front speed sensor:	106 inch lbs.	12 Nm
Rear wheel bearing and speed sensor:	38 ft. lbs.	52 Nm

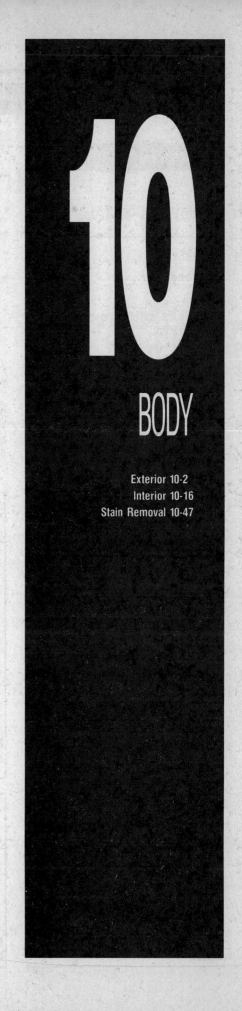

10

BODY

EXTERIOR

Doors

REMOVAL & INSTALLATION

▶ SEE FIGS. 1-3

Front and Rear

1988–90

1. Mark the location of the upper and lower door hinge strap.
2. Remove the trim panel.
3. Remove the armrest support brackets.
4. Remove the water deflector.
5. Disconnect all the electrical connections to the door electrical components.
6. Remove the rubber conduit from the door.
7. While the door is supported, remove the (4) nuts and and (4) screws.
8. Remove the door with the aid of a helper.
9. To install, position the door to the body with the aid of a helper and install the four nuts.
10. Check for proper alignment of the door to body and the lock to the striker. Loosen the nuts and align if necessary. Tighten the nuts and screws to 15—20 ft. lbs. (20—28 Nm).
11. Install the wiring harness.
12. Install the rubber conduit.
13. Connect all the door electrical components.
14. Install the water deflector.
15. Install the armrest support brackets.
16. Install the trim panel.

1991–92

1. Mark the location of the upper and lower door hinge strap.
2. Remove the trim panel.
3. Remove the hanger plates which are riveted to the door inner panel (see trim panel removal in this section).
4. Remove the water deflector.
5. Disconnect all the electrical connections to the door electrical components.
6. Remove the rubber conduit from the door.
7. Remove the check link screw.
8. While the door is supported, remove the door side hinge to door nuts.
9. Remove the door with the aid of a helper.
10. To install, position the door to the body with the aid of a helper and install the four nuts.
11. Check for proper alignment of the door to body and the lock to the striker. Loosen the nuts and align if necessary. Tighten the nuts to 18 ft. lbs. (24 Nm) and the check link screw to 18 ft. lbs. (24 Nm).
12. Install the wiring harness.
13. Install the rubber conduit.
14. Connect all the door electrical components.
15. Install the water deflector.
16. Install the hanger plates.
17. Install the trim panel.

ADJUSTMENT

The hinges are bolted to the door and to the body. The door side hinges have elongated holes which allow for some up and down and in and out adjustment by loosening the nuts. The nuts are torqued to 15—20 ft. lbs. A floating cage plate inside the door also allows for adjustment. There is no fore and aft adjustment provision.

Hood

REMOVAL & INSTALLATION

▶ SEE FIGS. 4-9

1. Raise the hood and install protective coverings over the fender areas.

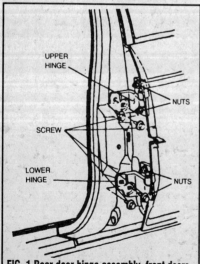

FIG. 1 Rear door hinge assembly, front doors similar

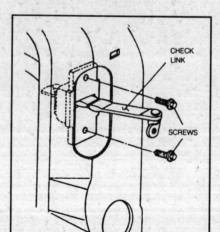

FIG. 2 Installing the door check link to the door, rear door shown, front door similar

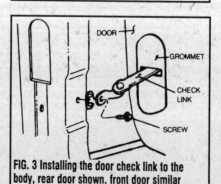

FIG. 3 Installing the door check link to the body, rear door shown, front door similar

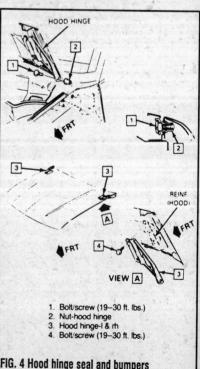

1. Bolt/screw (19–30 ft. lbs.)
2. Nut-hood hinge
3. Hood hinge-l & rh
4. Bolt/screw (19–30 ft. lbs.)

FIG. 4 Hood hinge seal and bumpers

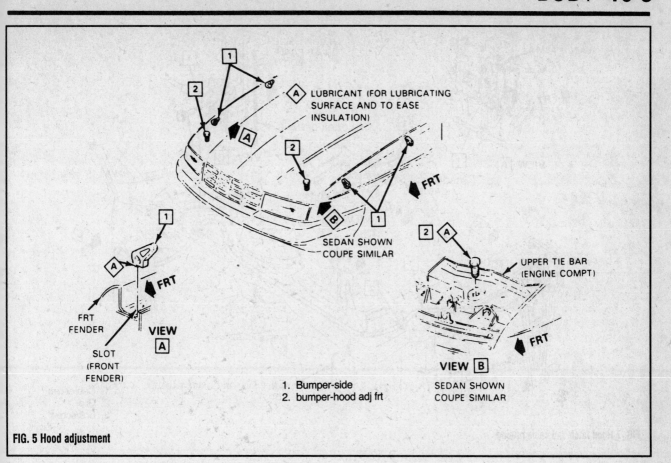

A LUBRICANT (FOR LUBRICATING SURFACE AND TO EASE INSULATION)

SEDAN SHOWN
COUPE SIMILAR

FRT FENDER

SLOT (FRONT FENDER)

VIEW A

FRT

UPPER TIE BAR (ENGINE COMPT)

VIEW B

SEDAN SHOWN
COUPE SIMILAR

1. Bumper-side
2. bumper-hood adj frt

FIG. 5 Hood adjustment

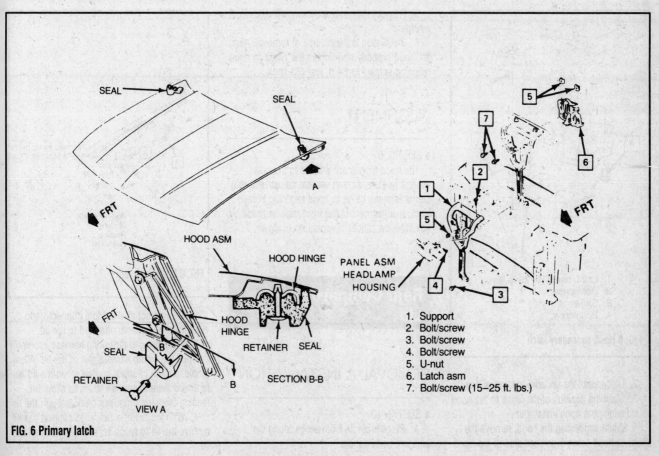

SEAL

SEAL

FRT

HOOD ASM

HOOD HINGE

HOOD HINGE

RETAINER   SEAL

SECTION B-B

SEAL

RETAINER

VIEW A

PANEL ASM HEADLAMP HOUSING

FRT

1. Support
2. Bolt/screw
3. Bolt/screw
4. Bolt/screw
5. U-nut
6. Latch asm
7. Bolt/screw (15–25 ft. lbs.)

FIG. 6 Primary latch

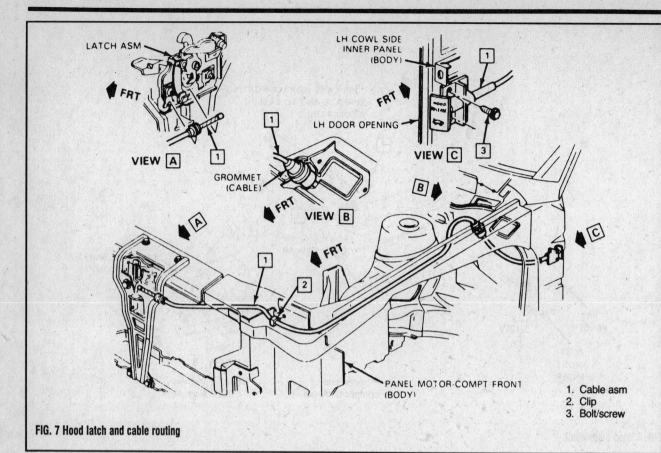

FIG. 7 Hood latch and cable routing

1. Cable asm
2. Clip
3. Bolt/screw

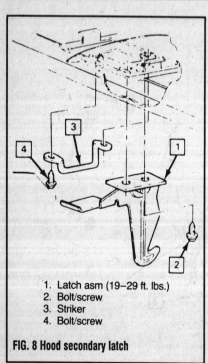

1. Latch asm (19–29 ft. lbs.)
2. Bolt/screw
3. Striker
4. Bolt/screw

FIG. 8 Hood secondary latch

2. Disconnect the underhood lamp wiring.

3. Mark the position of the hinge to the hood to aid alignment upon installation.

4. While supporting the hood, remove the hinge to hood screws on each side of the hood.

5. Remove the hood assembly with the aid of a helper.

6. Installation is the reverse of removal. Align the hood properly and tighten the hinge to hood retaining screws to 24 ft. lbs. (33 Nm).

ALIGNMENT

◆ SEE FIG. 5

The hood hinges are welded to the cowl assembly. Fore, aft and vertical adjustment may be made at the hinge to hood retaining screws. Vertical adjustment at the front may be made by adjusting the rubber bumpers up or down.

Rear Compartment Lid

REMOVAL & INSTALLATION

◆ SEE FIG. 10

1. Place protective coverings along the adjacent body panels.

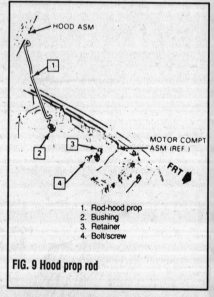

1. Rod-hood prop
2. Bushing
3. Retainer
4. Bolt/screw

FIG. 9 Hood prop rod

2. Disconnect all electrical connectors to electrical components attached to the lid.

3. Tie a string to the wiring harness assembly and pull the wiring harness out of the lid. Allow ample amount of string so that when the lid is removed there is enough string to allow for feeding the wiring harness back through the lid.

4. With the aid of a helper to support the lid, remove the lid to hinge screws and remove the lid.

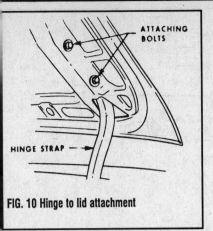

FIG. 10 Hinge to lid attachment

5. To install, with the aid of a helper, locate the lid to hinges, install the screws and tighten to 21 ft. lbs. 29 Nm).

6. Pull the string through the lid until the wiring harness is within the lid and attach the wiring connectors to the electrical components.

ALIGNMENT

Front to Rear, Up and Down (At Front Corners)

1. Loosen the screws.

2. Align as necessary and tighten the screws.

Up And Down Adjustment (At Rear Corners)

1. Loosen the rubber bumpers to raise the lid.
2. Tighten the rubber bumpers to the lower lid.

Side to Side Adjustment

1. Remove the rear seat cushion and back.
2. Remove the quarter trim panels.
3. Remove the center high mounted stop lamp.
4. Remove the rear seat-to-back window foundation assembly.
5. Loosen the hinge-to-body screws and adjust the lid as necessary.
6. Reinsatll all previously removed parts.

Lift Window (Hatchback)

REMOVAL & INSTALLATION

4-Door Hatchback

◆ SEE FIGS. 11-16
1. Remove the lift window upper and side finish mouldings.

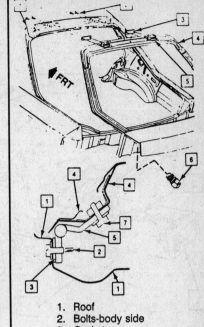

1. Roof
2. Bolts-body side
3. Gasket
4. Lift window
5. Hinge
6. Bumper
7. Bolt-lift window side

FIG. 13 Lift window hinges — Corsica Hatchback

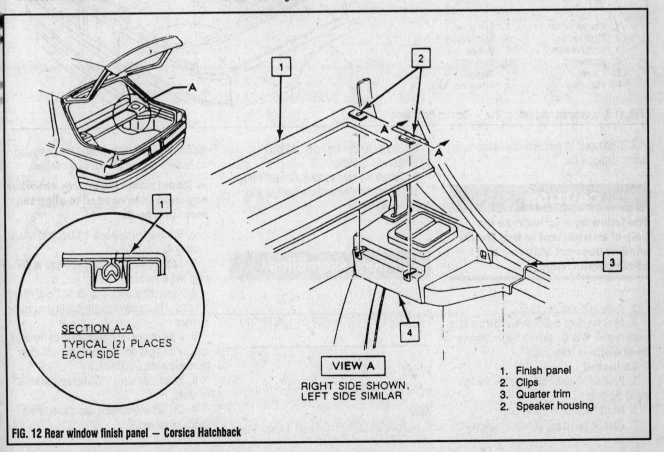

SECTION A-A
TYPICAL (2) PLACES EACH SIDE

VIEW A
RIGHT SIDE SHOWN. LEFT SIDE SIMILAR

1. Finish panel
2. Clips
3. Quarter trim
2. Speaker housing

FIG. 12 Rear window finish panel — Corsica Hatchback

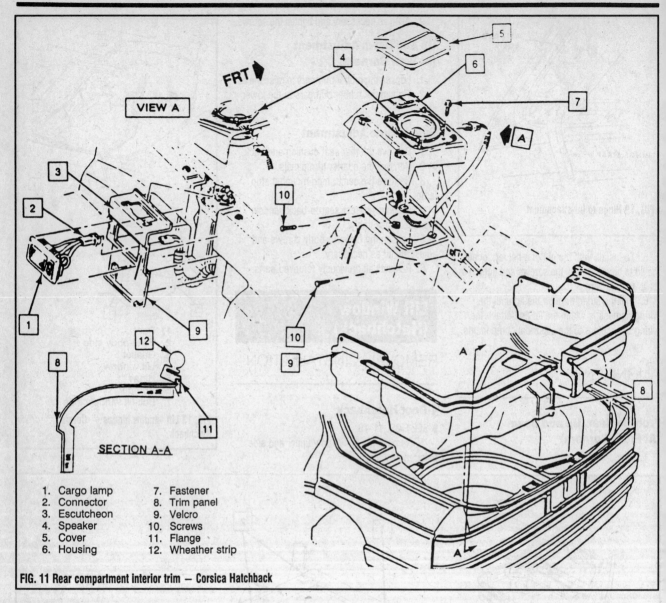

1. Cargo lamp
2. Connector
3. Escutcheon
4. Speaker
5. Cover
6. Housing
7. Fastener
8. Trim panel
9. Velcro
10. Screws
11. Flange
12. Wheather strip

FIG. 11 Rear compartment interior trim — Corsica Hatchback

2. Disconnect all electrical connectors to lamps, defogger etc.

> ※ **CAUTION**
> **The following step requires the help of an assistant so that the lift window does not fall down and cause personal injury.**

3. Remove the strut rod clips.
4. Mark the hinge outline on the lid if the lid is being reused. With the aid of a helper, remove the lift window to hinge bolts.

To Install
5. Position the lid on the hinge and loosely install the bolts.
6. Install the strut on the lid side.
7. Position the lid and align with mark or fit to opening.

8. Slightly tighten the bolts and check alignment and operation.
9. Torque the bolts to 19 ft. lbs. (25 Nm).
10. Install the electrical connections and finish mouldings.

Bumper Assemblies

REMOVAL & INSTALLATION

Front
▶ SEE FIGS. 17-21

1988
1. Place a jack under the front bumper before removing the bolts to prevent it from dropping down when the bumper bolts are removed.

➡ **Do not rotate the energy absorber any more than needed to align the mounting holes.**

2. Remove the right and left fascia to header panel bolts.
3. Remove the fascia to fender nuts in the right and left side.
4. Remove the bumper bolts on the right and left side at the energy absorbers and remove the bumper.
5. If the energy absorbers are to be replaced, remove the bolts and nuts from the unit, then remove the unit and the shims.
6. Install the energy absorber and shims if removed.
7. Check the dimension and add/subtract shims as needed.

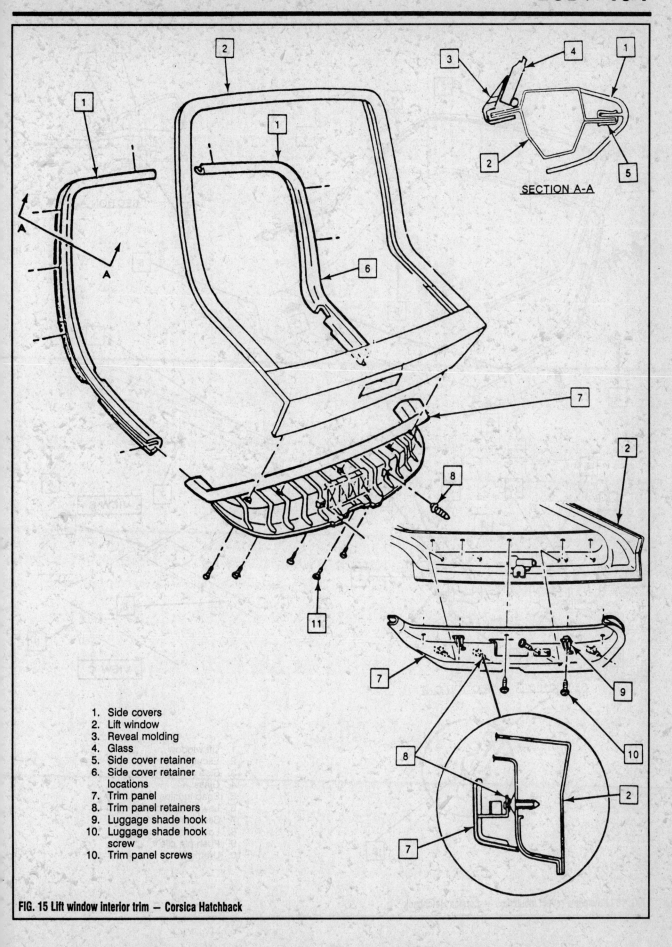

SECTION A-A

1. Side covers
2. Lift window
3. Reveal molding
4. Glass
5. Side cover retainer
6. Side cover retainer locations
7. Trim panel
8. Trim panel retainers
9. Luggage shade hook
10. Luggage shade hook screw
10. Trim panel screws

FIG. 15 Lift window interior trim — Corsica Hatchback

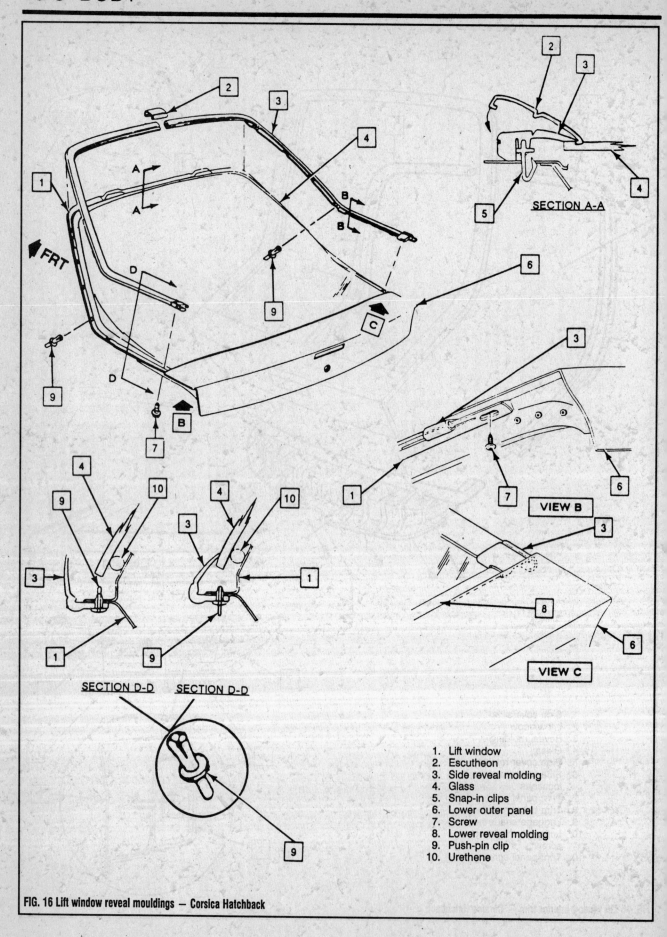

FIG. 16 Lift window reveal mouldings — Corsica Hatchback

SECTION A-A

VIEW B

VIEW C

SECTION D-D   SECTION D-D

FRT

1. Lift window
2. Escutcheon
3. Side reveal molding
4. Glass
5. Snap-in clips
6. Lower outer panel
7. Screw
8. Lower reveal molding
9. Push-pin clip
10. Urethene

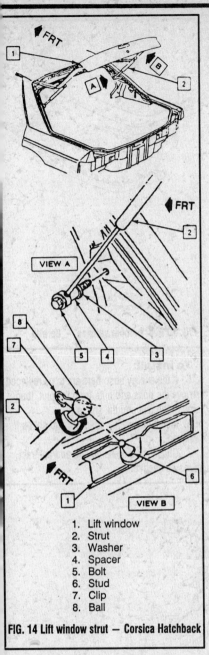

1. Lift window
2. Strut
3. Washer
4. Spacer
5. Bolt
6. Stud
7. Clip
8. Ball

FIG. 14 Lift window strut — Corsica Hatchback

➡ **Do not rotate the energy absorber any more than needed to align the mounting holes.**

2. Remove the headlights and the front grille.

3. Remove the lower air deflector(s) on 1990–92 Beretta styles.

4. Remove the side marker, parking and fog light sockets, if equipped.

5. Remove the 3 bolts from each side that attach the fascia to the wheelhouse.

6. Remove the 3 bolts from each side that attach the fascia to the fender.

7. Remove the 4 nuts on each side that attach the energy absorber to the plate assembly and remove the bumper.

To install:

8. Position the assembly on jack stands and install the bolts on the plate on the energy absorber.

9. Support the bumper to prevent rotation of the energy absorbers.

10. Install the nuts at the bumper to energy absorber brackets but do not tighten. Install the fascia to fender and wheelhouse bolts.

11. Install the fascia to fender bolts.

12. Install the fascia to wheelhouse bolts.

13. Check for proper clearance and add shims, if necessary.

➡ **If adjustment is necessary to align the bumper, loosen the energy absorber mounting bolts and position as required (holes are slotted). Adjustment from side to side can be made by loosening the bumper bracket bolts. Tighten all bolts securely.**

14. Tighten the bumper bar to energy absorber bolts to (18–25 ft. lbs. (24–34 Nm).

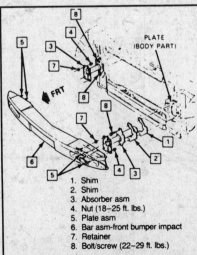

1. Shim
2. Shim
3. Absorber asm
4. Nut (18–25 ft. lbs.)
5. Plate asm
6. Bar asm-front bumper impact
7. Retainer
8. Bolt/screw (22–29 ft. lbs.)

FIG. 17 Front bumper bar and energy absorber installation

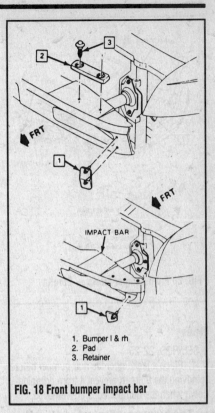

1. Bumper l & rh
2. Pad
3. Retainer

FIG. 18 Front bumper impact bar

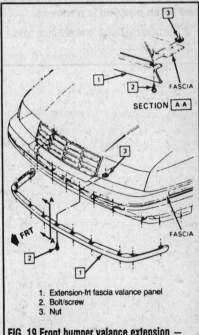

1. Extension-frt fascia valance panel
2. Bolt/screw
3. Nut

FIG. 19 Front bumper valance extension — Corsica

15. Install the side marker, parking and fog light sockets, if equipped.

16. Install the lower air deflector(s) on 1990–92 Beretta styles.

17. Install the headlights and the front grille.

8. Support the bumper to prevent rotation of the energy absorbers.

9. Install the bolts at the bumper to energy absorber brackets, and fascia to fender nuts, and fascia to fender panel bolts.

10. If adjustment is required to align bumper, loosen the energy absorber mounting bolts and position as required (holes are slotted). Adjustment side to side can be made by loosening the bumper bracket bolts. Torque all bolts and nuts.

1989–92

1. Place a jack under the front bumper before removing the bolts to prevent it from dropping down when the bumper bolts are removed.

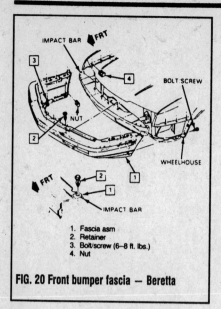

FIG. 20 Front bumper fascia — Beretta

1. Fascia asm
2. Retainer
3. Bolt/screw (6–8 ft. lbs.)
4. Nut

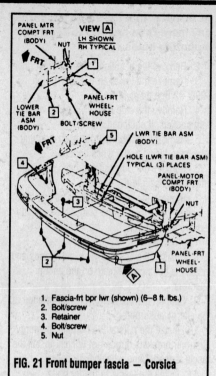

FIG. 21 Front bumper fascia — Corsica

1. Fascia-frt bpr lwr (shown) (6–8 ft. lbs.)
2. Bolt/screw
3. Retainer
4. Bolt/screw
5. Nut

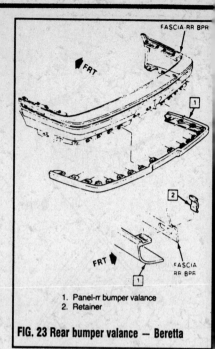

FIG. 23 Rear bumper valance — Beretta

1. Panel-rr bumper valance
2. Retainer

Rear

♦ SEE FIGS. 22-25

1. Place a jack under the rear bumper before removing the bolts to prevent it from dropping down when the bumper bolts are removed.

➡ **The bumper will pivot on the other end when one end is removed.**

2. Remove the fasica to wheelhouse bolts. There are 3 on each side.

3. Remove the sidemarker lamps and sockets, by removing the Torx screw at the front of the lamp.

4. Remove the bumper bolts on the right and left side and remove the bumper.

To Install:

5. If the energy absorbers are to be replaced, remove the bolts and nuts from the unit, then remove the unit and the shims.

6. Install the energy absorber and shims if removed.

7. Check the dimension and add/subtract shims as needed.

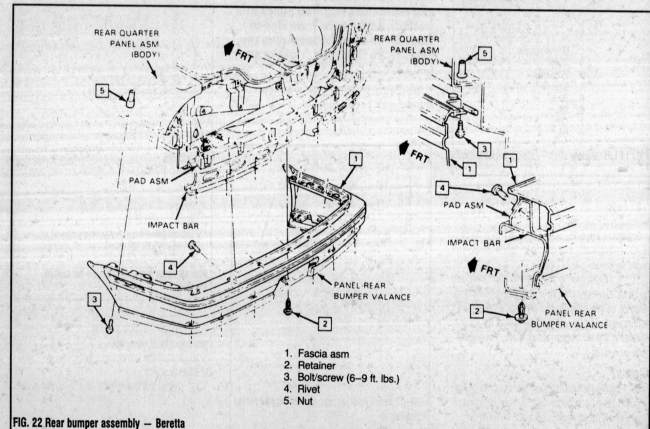

1. Fascia asm
2. Retainer
3. Bolt/screw (6–9 ft. lbs.)
4. Rivet
5. Nut

FIG. 22 Rear bumper assembly — Beretta

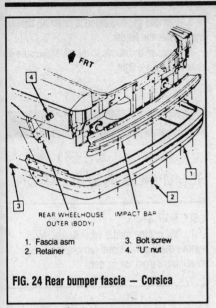

1. Fascia asm
2. Retainer
3. Bolt screw
4. "U" nut

FIG. 24 Rear bumper fascia — Corsica

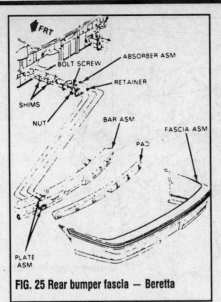

FIG. 25 Rear bumper fascia — Beretta

5. On the Beretta, install the lower retainer.

6. On the GTZ, press in the grille to engage the clip at the lower corners.

7. On the standard Beretta and Corsica install the bolts and tighten to 17 inch lbs. (1.9 Nm).

8. Install the radiator air baffle.

9. Install the bolts from the radiator air baffle to the grille and tighten to 17 inch lbs. (1.9 Nm). Three on the Beretta and five on the Corsica.

Outside Mirrors

REMOVAL & INSTALLATION

♦ SEE FIG. 29

The door outside mirrors are stud mounted to the door filler. The mirror glass face may be replaced by placing a piece of tape over the glass then breaking the mirror face. Adhesive back mirror faces are available. Left side flat and right side convex mirror faces must be replaced with the same type mirror face when surfaced.

1. Remove the door trim panel.
2. Remove the upper trim panel.
3. Remove the sound absorber.
4. Remove the (3) nuts.
5. Remove the control cable from the upper trim panel.
6. Remove the filler and mirror.
7. To install, place the filler over the studs on the mirror.

8. Support the bumper to prevent rotation of the energy absorbers.

9. Install the bolts at the bumper to energy absorber brackets, and end cap to fender nuts and bolts.

10. If adjustment is required to align bumper, loosen the energy absorber mounting bolts and position as required (holes are slotted). Adjustment side to side can be made by loosening the bumper bracket bolts. Torque all bolts and nuts to 21 ft. lbs. (29 Nm)

8. Remove the bolts at the baffles located at the radiator support.

9. Transfer the headlamps and grille.

10. Reverse the above to install.

1990–92

1. Remove the radiator air baffle.

2. Remove the bolts from the lower front corners to the headlamp housing panel on the standard Beretta and Corsica.

3. On the GTZ, ppull the top of the grille forward for access to the lower retainer screw and remove the grille.

To install:

4. Position the grille to the headlamp housing panel.

Front End Panel And Grille

REMOVAL & INSTALLATION

♦ SEE FIGS. 26-28

1988–89

1. Open the hood.

2. Remove the headlamp bezel screws.

3. Remove the bolt at each fender to front end panel at the upper corner at the headlamp.

4. Remove the screw at each turn signal housing and remove the housing.

5. Remove the bolt from the front end panel to the radiator support located below the turn signal housing area.

6. Remove the nut at the inner fender panel.

7. Remove the nuts attaching the bumper end cap to the panel at each side.

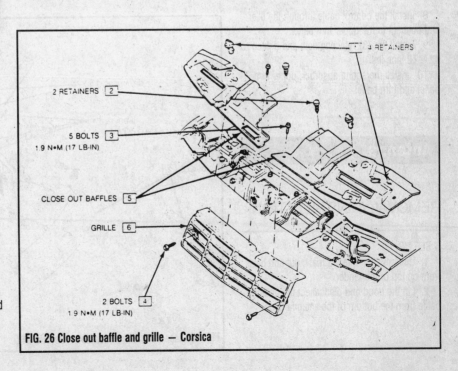

FIG. 26 Close out baffle and grille — Corsica

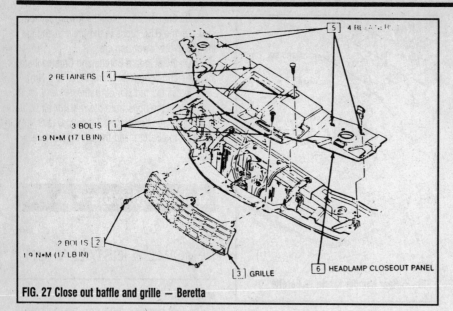

FIG. 27 Close out baffle and grille — Beretta

2 RETAINERS [4]

3 BOLTS [1]
1 9 N•M (17 LB IN)

2 BOLTS [2]
1 9 N•M (17 LB IN)

[3] GRILLE

[5] 4 RETAINERS

[6] HEADLAMP CLOSEOUT PANEL

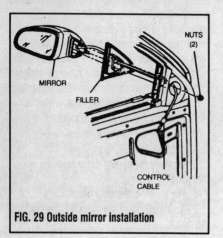

FIG. 29 Outside mirror installation

MIRROR

FILLER

NUTS (2)

CONTROL CABLE

8. Install the control cable through the filler and connect to the upper trim panel.

9. Install the (3) retaining nuts and tighten to 42–72 inch lbs.

10. Install the sound absorber, upper trim panel and trim panel.

Antenna

REMOVAL & INSTALLATION

♦ SEE FIG. 30

1. Unscrew the antenna mast, nut and bezel from on top of the fender.

2. Lift the hood and disconnect the antenna cable from the bottom of the antenna base.

3. Remove the two antenna retaining screws from inside the fender.

4. Reverse the above to install. Make sure all connections are tight.

Fenders

REMOVAL & INSTALLATION

♦ SEE FIGS. 31-33

1. Drill out the fender wheelhouse rivets, remove the 6 screws and remove the wheelhouse from the fender.

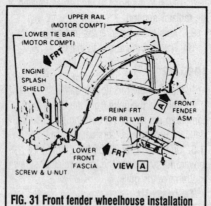

FIG. 31 Front fender wheelhouse installation

UPPER RAIL (MOTOR COMPT)

LOWER TIE BAR (MOTOR COMPT)

ENGINE SPLASH SHIELD

REINF FRT FDR RR LWR

FRONT FENDER ASM

LOWER FRONT FASCIA

SCREW & U-NUT

VIEW [A]

FRT

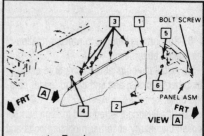

1. Fender
2. Bolt/screw 3-4 ft. lbs.
3. Bolt/screw 13-18 ft. lbs.
4. Bolt/screw 6-8 ft. lbs.
5. Key/bolt
6. U-nut

FIG. 33 Front fender assembly installation and bolt torques

BOLT SCREW

PANEL ASM

VIEW [A]

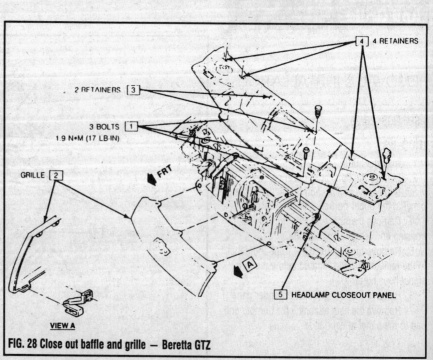

FIG. 28 Close out baffle and grille — Beretta GTZ

[4] 4 RETAINERS

2 RETAINERS [3]

3 BOLTS [1]
1 9 N•M (17 LB IN)

GRILLE [2]

FRT

[5] HEADLAMP CLOSEOUT PANEL

VIEW A

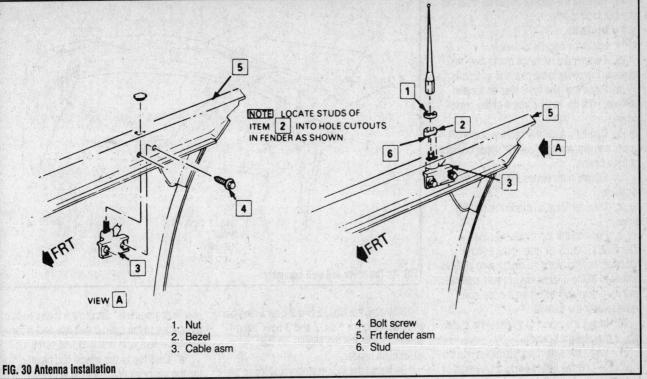

1. Nut
2. Bezel
3. Cable asm
4. Bolt screw
5. Frt fender asm
6. Stud

FIG. 30 Antenna installation

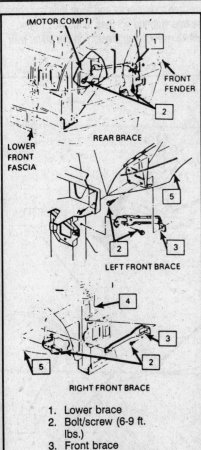

1. Lower brace
2. Bolt/screw (6-9 ft. lbs.)
3. Front brace
4. Motor compartment foot panel
5. Front fender

FIG. 32 Front fender braces

2. Remove the headlights and headlight housing.

3. Disconnect the fender braces.

4. Remove the hood assembly.

5. Remove the fender attaching bolts and remove the fender.

To Install:

6. Position the fender to the engine compartment upper side rail and bumper fascia.

7. Install the fender attaching bolts, but do not tighten.

8. Maintain a uniform gap spacing to the door and hood and tighten the bolts to the specifications as noted in the illustration.

9. Install the fender braces.

10. Install the headlight housing and headlights.

11. Install the wheelhouse.

Convertible Tops

TOP REPLACEMENT

▶ SEE FIGS. 34-38

1. Remove the quarter and rear belt mouldings.

2. Remove the front rail and No. 1 bow seal and retainers.

3. Remove the welt assembly and top cover from the No. 1 bow.

4. Remove the screws from the eyelets and springs from the rear of each side retention cable and pull the cable towards the front to remove.

5. Remove the screws and brackets from the lower end of each rear retention cable and pull the cables through the listing pockets from the upper end.

6. Remove the screws securing the cover's listing pocket and bar to the No. 2 bow and remove the listing bar.

7. Remove the screws securing the cover's listing pocket and bar to the No. 3 bow and remove the listing bar.

8. Remove the staples at the top of the No. 3 bow, securing the backlite, noting the location and spacing of the staples before removal.

9. Remove the top cover from the rear belt tacking strip, noting the location and spacing of the staples before removal.

➡ **Mark the location of the backlite outer panels along the balance of the rear belt tacking strip.**

10. Disconnect the ground and lead wires from the rear defogger.

11. Disconnect the zipper holding the backlight to the top cover at the top of the daylight opening.

12. Remove the screws holding the 2 straps to the No. 4 bow.

13. Remove the backlite assembly from the rear belt tacking strip.

To install:

14. Install the backlite assembly.

15. Transfer the reference marks from the removed top cover to the new one as follows:

a. Place the new top cover on a clean surface, with the inner surface of the cover down.

b. Carefully align the backlite opening upper corners and rear quarter upper corners of both covers.

c. Secure both covers together at these locations.

d. Transfer location marks for tacking strips.

e. Position the top cover over the framework, top cover may require some lateral stretching along the rear bow to achieve proper fit of the quarter flaps to rear side rails and to remove fullness from the top cover valance over the backlite.

16. Install the zipper to the backlite at the top of the daylight opening.

17. Install the side retention cables into the top cover side rail listing pockets. A length of welding rod or equivalent wire can be used to pull the cable through the side rail listing pocket.

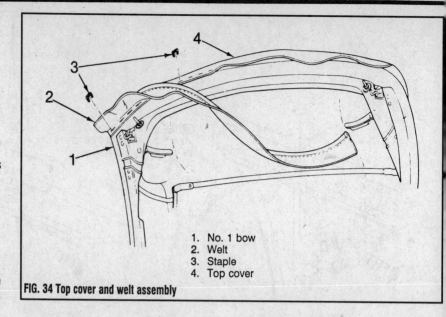

1. No. 1 bow
2. Welt
3. Staple
4. Top cover

FIG. 34 Top cover and welt assembly

18. Install the Nos. 2 and 3 bow listing bar and pocket to the Nos. 2 and 3 bow using screws. Raise the top slightly off the windshield header.

19. Install the side retention cables to the springs and eyelets on the rear rails and screws.

20. Install the rear retention cables into the rear listing pockets. Secure the lower ends of the cables to the quarter belt line and inner reinforcement with brackets and screws.

a. Lock top to the windshield header. Pull the top cover straight forward at the seams to desired top fullness and align thee top cover seams with the notches in the No. 1 bow. While maintaining tension on the cover over

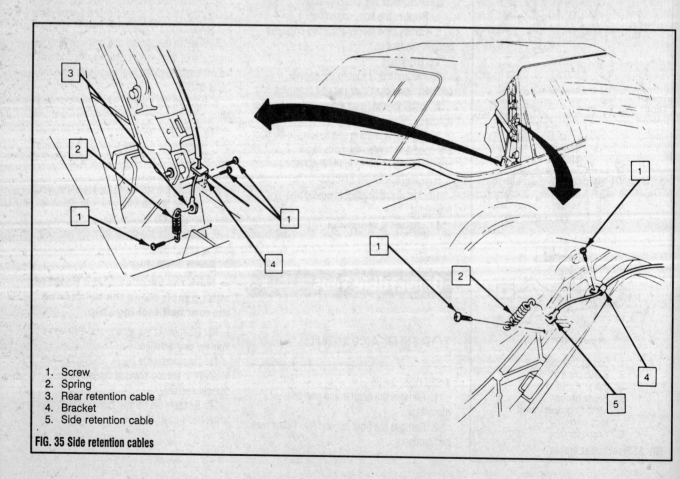

1. Screw
2. Spring
3. Rear retention cable
4. Bracket
5. Side retention cable

FIG. 35 Side retention cables

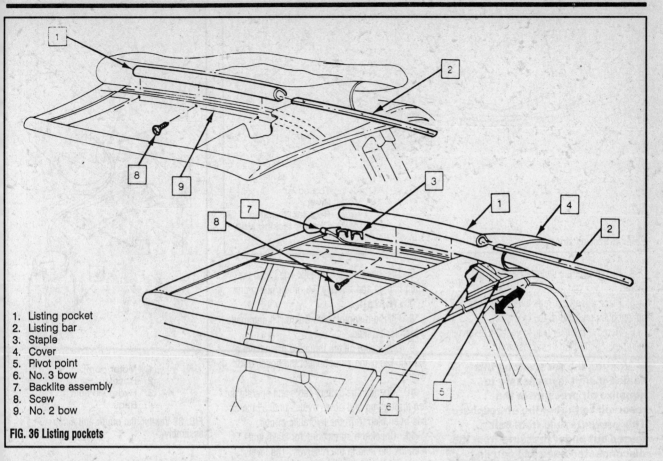

1. Listing pocket
2. Listing bar
3. Staple
4. Cover
5. Pivot point
6. No. 3 bow
7. Backlite assembly
8. Scew
9. No. 2 bow

FIG. 36 Listing pockets

top of the No. 1 bow, make a pencil mark on the cover outer surface along the forward edge of the No. 1 bow.

b. Raise the top off the header to a suitable working height.

21. Install the cover to the No. 1 bow using staples after pulling 1/4 in. (6mm) past the reference mark.

22. Trim excess material.

a. Raise the top and lock to the windshield header. Check the appearance of the top trim.

b. If additional tension is needed on the top cover, pull the cover farther forward.

c. Staple and recheck top for proper appearance.

23. Install the welt assembly to the No. 1 bow using staples.

24. Install the front rail and the No. 1 bow seal retainers using attaching screws.

25. Apply weatherstrip adhesive to the retainer inner surface. Attach the front rail and No. 1 bow seal assembly to the front rail inner retainer and across the No. 1 bow. Lock the top to the windshield header.

26. Install the top cover to the belt tacking strips starting at the rear rail and working rearward. Apply downward pressure to the top cover at each point of the staple installation.

27. Pierce holes in the top cover and backite assembly along the tacking strip for belt molding attaching studs.

28. Install the back belt and quarter belt moldings.

➡ **When complete, the folding top cover should be free from wrinkles and draws. Claen up the top material and vehicle as required.**

MOTOR/PUMP REPLACEMENT

◆ SEE FIG. 39

1. Operate the folding top to the full up position.

2. Disconnect the negative battery cable.

3. Remove the rear seat cushion and rear seatback to gain access to the motor/pump unit.

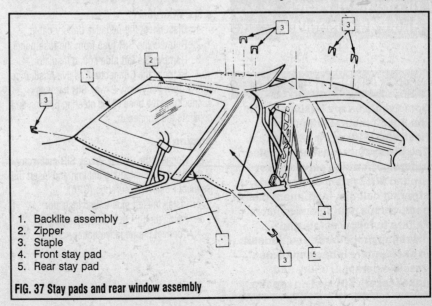

1. Backlite assembly
2. Zipper
3. Staple
4. Front stay pad
5. Rear stay pad

FIG. 37 Stay pads and rear window assembly

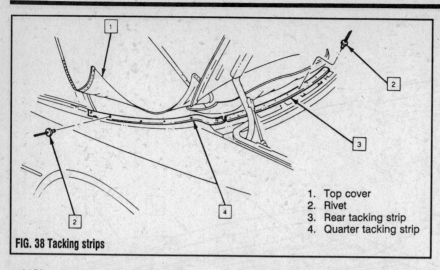

1. Top cover
2. Rivet
3. Rear tacking strip
4. Quarter tacking strip

FIG. 38 Tacking strips

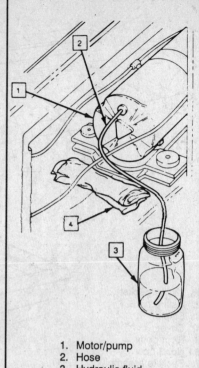

1. Motor/pump
2. Hose
3. Hydraulic fluid
4. Rags

FIG. 39 Venting the motor and pump assembly

4. Disconnect the wiring harness at the motor.

5. Place absorbant rags below the hose connections and end of the reservoir.

6. Remove the filler plug to vent the reservoir; then replace the plug in the reservoir.

➡ Venting the reservoir on this sealed-in unit is necessary to equalize air pressure in the reservoir to that of the atmosphere. This prevents fluid from being forced out under pressure from the disconnected lines and causing damage to the trim or body finish.

7. Disconnect the hydraulic lines, cap the open fittings and remove the motor/pump unit.

To install:

8. Fill the reservoir with Dexron®II automatic transmission fluid.

9. Make sure all the threaded parts have a seal ring in place and connect the hoses and wiring.

10. Connect the battery cable and operate the top through up and down cycles until all the air has been bled from the hydraulic circuit.

11. Check the conections for leaks and recheck the fluid in the reservoir. The level should be even with the fill hole.

12. Install the rear seat back and cushion.

INTERIOR

Instrument Panel and Pad Assembly

✳ CAUTION

Some vehicles are equipped with the Supplemental Inflatable Restraint (SIR) or air bag system. The SIR system must be disabled before performing service on or around SIR system components, steering column, instrument panel components, wiring and sensors. Failure to follow safety and disabling procedures could result in accidental air bag deployment, possible personal injury and unnecessary SIR system repairs.

Air Bag Disarming

▶ SEE FIGS. 40-41

1. Disconnect the negative battery cable.
2. Remove the SIR fuse from the fuse panel.
3. Remove the left side sound insulator.
4. Remove the Connector Positive Assurance (CPA) from the yellow 2-way SIR harness connector at the base of the steering column and separate the connector.

Arming

1. Connect the yellow 2-way SIR connector at the base of the steering column and insert the Connect Positive Assurance (CPA).
2. Install the left side sound insulator.
3. Install the SIR fuse in the fuse panel.
4. Connect the negative battery cable.

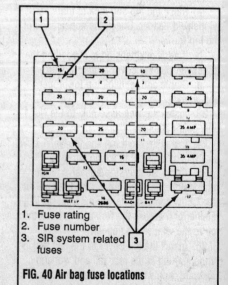

1. Fuse rating
2. Fuse number
3. SIR system related fuses

FIG. 40 Air bag fuse locations

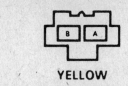

YELLOW

FIG. 41 Yellow 2-way air bag connector at the steering column

REMOVAL & INSTALLATION

1988–90

♦ SEE FIGS. 42-44

➡ **The instrument panel can be removed with some of its components left in place. Unless removal is necessary for component service, leave as much in place as possible. It may be easier to remove later on a workbench.**

1. Disconnect the negative battery cable.
2. Remove the cluster assembly.
3. Disconnect the electrical connectors from the steering column.
4. Remove the accessory center.
5. Remove the right sound insulator.
6. Remove the right instrument panel compartment.
7. Disconnect the electrical connectors behind the passenger,s side of the instrument panel by reaching through the glove compartment opening.
8. Disconnect the antenna by reaching through the glove compartment opening.
9. Remove the left compartment.
10. Disconnect the electrical connectors from the fuse block by reaching through the left compartment opening.
11. Remove the defroster grille.
12. Remove the speaker covers by prying gently with a suitable tool to release them from the 2 spring clips.
13. Reach under the driver's side of the instrument panel and remove the cover from the junction block.
14. From under the hood, remove the cover from the junction block on the driver's side of the cowl. Remove the 2 nuts from the junction block retainer and the 1 bolt from the center junction block retainer.
15. Remove the junction block from the cowl by reaching under the instrument panel.
16. Disconnect the electrical connector from the lower left side of the heater module.

17. Remove the 2 nuts holding the wiring harness and clutch neutral start switch at the cowl, on manual transaxle cars.
18. Remove the 2 bolts from the defroster opening.
19. Remove the 1 bolt from each speaker opening.
20. Remove the 1 bolt at the lower front on each side of the instrument panel.
21. Remove the instrument panel.

To install:

22. Position the instrument panel into the vehicle.
23. Install the 2 bolts at the lower front.
24. Install the 2 bolts through the speaker openings.
25. Install the 2 bolts through the defroster opening.
26. Install the 2 nuts holding the wiring harness to the cowl.
27. Connect the electrical connector to the lower left side of the heater module.
28. Install the junction block to the cowl by reaching under the instrument panel.
29. From under the hood, Install the 2 nuts from the junction block retainer and the 1 bolt from the center junction block retainer. Install the cover on the junction block.
30. Install the speaker covers by pressing into place.
31. Install the defroster grille.

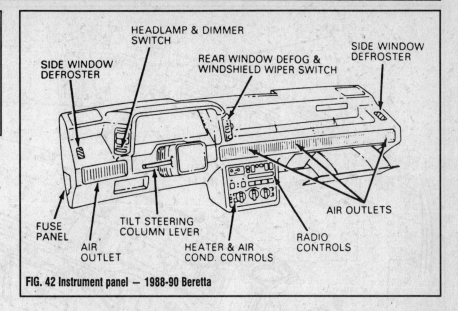

FIG. 42 Instrument panel — 1988-90 Beretta

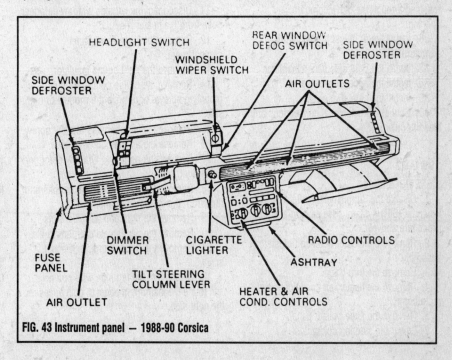

FIG. 43 Instrument panel — 1988-90 Corsica

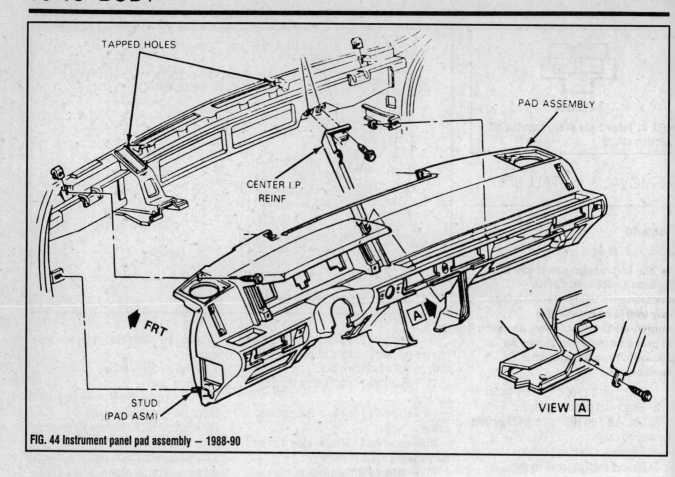

FIG. 44 Instrument panel pad assembly — 1988-90

32. Install the electrical connectors to the fuse block.

33. Install the left compartment.

34. Install the antenna lead.

35. Connect the electrical connectors behiind the passenger,s side of the instrument panel by reaching through the glove compartment opening.

36. Install the right instrument panel compartment.

37. Install the right side sound insulator.

38. Install the accessory center.

39. Install the cluster assembly.

40. Conncet the electrical connections at the steering column.

1991-92

▶ SEE FIGS. 45-46

1. Disable the Supplemental Inflatable Restraint (SIR) system. (See caution and procedure above).

2. Remove the cluster bezel and cluster assembly.

3. Remove the trim bezel.

4. Remove the heater, air conditioner and radio controls.

5. Remove the knee bolster panel.

6. Lower the steering column.

7. Disconnect the Assembly line Diagnostic Link (ALDL) connector.

8. Remove the convience center and bracket.

9. Remove the turn signal bracket.

10. Remove the left center brace bolt from the instrument panel.

11. Disconnect the left side window defogger hose from the heater module.

12. Remove the instrument panel compartment.

13. Remove the right sound insulator.

14. Remove the cruise control module mounting screws and move the module to one side.

15. Remove the wire harness retainer screw.

16. Remove the air distributor screws.

17. Remove the right side window defogger outlet duct.

18. Remove the right/center brace bolts and nuts from the instrument panel.

19. Remove the right and left pillar nuts.

20. Remove the windshield defroster grille.

21. Remove the upper instrument panel screws.

22. Disconnect the left side wire retainers and rotate the instrument panel to gain access to the right side.

23. Disconnect the cluster connection and wiring harness clips to the instrument panel.

24. Disconnect the knee bolster brace.

25. Disconnect the center wire harness retainer screws.

26. Disconnect the fuse block.

27. Disconnect the wire retainer on the right of the steering column.

28. Remove the instrument panel pad from the vehicle.

29. Disconnect the right and left window defogger outlets.

30. Disconnect the right and left defogger outlet nozzles.

31. Disconnect the left center air outlets.

32. Disconnect the right side outlet assembly (cup holder).

33. Remove the bracket from the right side of the instrument panel.

34. Remove the knee bolster reinforcement on the left side of the steering column.

35. Remove the pillar studs.

To install:

36. Install the pilar studs to the instrument panel.

34. Install the knee bolster reinforcement on the left side of the steering column.

35. Install the bracket on the right side of the instrument panel.

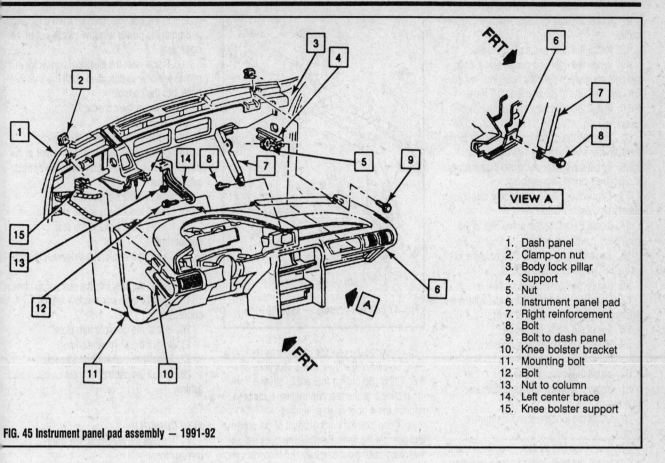

FIG. 45 Instrument panel pad assembly — 1991-92

VIEW A

1. Dash panel
2. Clamp-on nut
3. Body lock pillar
4. Support
5. Nut
6. Instrument panel pad
7. Right reinforcement
8. Bolt
9. Bolt to dash panel
10. Knee bolster bracket
11. Mounting bolt
12. Bolt
13. Nut to column
14. Left center brace
15. Knee bolster support

36. Connect the right side outlet assembly (cup holder).

37. Connect the left center air outlets.

38. Connect the right and left defogger outlet nozzles.

39. Connect the right and left window defogger outlets.

40. Position the air distributor and wire harness in an approximate location in the vehicle.

41. Position the instrument panel pad in approximate location in the vehicle.

42. Install the knee bolster bracket and bolts and tighten 58 inch lbs. (6.5 Nm).

43. Connect the cluster connection and wiring harness clips to the instrument panel.

44. Install the air distributor screws.

45. Connect the right side window defogger outlet nozzle to the instrument panel and duct to air distributor.

46. Locate the instrument panel assembly on the windshield lower frame and body hinge pillars.

➡ **Make sure the knee bracket interlocks with the U-shaped suport on the dash panel.**

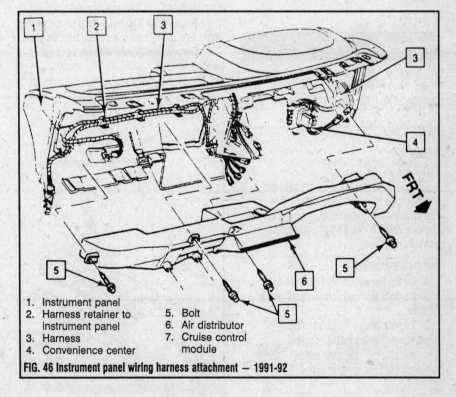

1. Instrument panel
2. Harness retainer to instrument panel
3. Harness
4. Convenience center
5. Bolt
6. Air distributor
7. Cruise control module

FIG. 46 Instrument panel wiring harness attachment — 1991-92

47. Install the screws to the windshield lower frame.

48. Install the nuts to the pillar studs.

49. Install the right and center brace, bolts and nuts and tighten the bolts to 58 inch lbs. (6.5 Nm) and the nuts to 89 inch lbs. (10 Nm).

50. Install the right wire harness retainer screw.

51. Position the cruise control module to the air distibutor and install the retaing screws.

52. Install the instrument panel compartment and lamp electrical connection.

53. Connect the left side window defogger duct to the heater module.

54. Install the left center brace bolt to the instrument panel pad.

55. Secure the turn signal flasher to the clip on the convenience center bracket.

56. Install the convenience center.

57. Raise the steering column and tighten the retaining bolts to 20 ft. lbs. (27 Nm).

58. Install the ALDL connector.

59. Position the knee bolster panel and tighten the screws to 13 inch lbs. (1.5 Nm).

60. Install the radio reciever.

61. Install the heater and air conditioner control.

62. Install the trim bezel and instrument cluster.

63. Enable the SIR system as outlined earler.

64. Install the right and left sound insulators.

Console

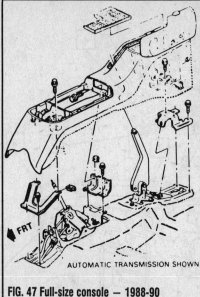

FIG. 47 Full-size console — 1988-90

REMOVAL & INSTALLATION

1988–90

◆ SEE FIG. 47-49

Full-size and mini consoles are available depending on the model and options. The full-size includes a storage compartment at the rear. The mini console has a small compartment located at the front.

FULL-SIZE CONSOLE

1. On the Beretta, remove the ashtray.

2. Remove the front compartment on the Corsica.

3. Remove the parking brake handle by removing the phillips retaining screw.

4. Remove the shift lever handle/knob by removing the Torx retaining screw.

5. Remove the console trimplate by removing the 2 screws at the front of the trim plate and then lifting and pulling forward to release from the retainers at the rear. On manual transaxles, remove the 4 boot retainer screws.

6. Open the rear compartment of the console and remove the liner. Remove the trunk release switch by pulling out carefully and disconnecting the electrical connector. Remove the 2 bolts from the bottom of the compartment.

7. Remove the 2 bolts from the center, in the upper rear of the area covered by the trim plate.

8. Remove the 2 bolts at the front of the console.

9. Lift the console, then lift from underneath and push the power window switch out of the console.

10. Disconnect the electrical connector at the power window switch, then push the switch back into the console.

11. Remove the console.

To install:

12. Install the console in the vehicle.

13. Connect the electrical connector at the power window switch, then plcae the console into position.

14. Install the 2 bolts at the front.

15. Install the 2 bolts at the center.

16. Install the 2 bolts in the rear compartment.

17. Install the trunk release connector and switch.

18. Install the liner into the rear compartment.

19. Install the power window switch connector.

20. Install the console trim plate.

21. Install the shift handle/knob.

22. Install the parking brake handle.

23. Install the ashtray or front compartment ashtray.

MINI CONSOLE

1. Remove the liner from the front compartment.

2. Remove the 2 screws from the front compartment.

3. Remove the Torx screw holding the shift handle/knob.

4. Remove 1 screw from each side of the rear of the console.

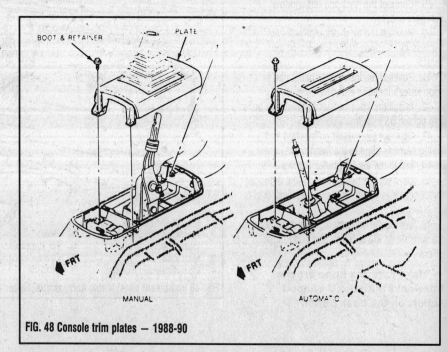

FIG. 48 Console trim plates — 1988-90

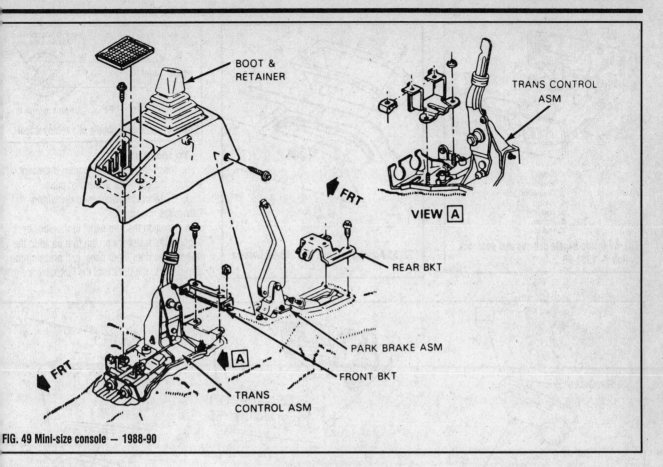

FIG. 49 Mini-size console — 1988-90

5. Remove the console.

6. On manual transaxles, remove the 4 boot retainer screws from inside the console.

To install:

7. Install the shifter boot or trim plate.

8. Install the console and 2 screws at the rear.

9. Install the Torx screw holding the shift handle/knob.

10. Install the 2 screws to the front compartment.

11. Install the liner.

Door Trim Panel

REMOVAL & INSTALLATION

1988-90

◆ SEE FIGS. 50-57

The armrest on the four door models is an integral part of the trim panel. The armrest on the two door models is retained by screws and inverted nuts fom the back side of the trim panel and requires trim panel removal.

On models equipped with power window switches make sure the ignition is in the off position to eliminate the possibility of accidently shorting out the switch with a metal tool.

1. Remove the door trim retaining screws on the two door models.

2. On the four door models, remove the armrest pull cups.

3. Remove the window regulator handle, if present.

4. Disconnect the switches if present.

5. Remove the trim panel using tool J—24595B or equivalent to disengage the fasteners on the trim panel from the holes in the door inner panel.

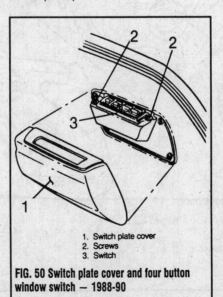

1. Switch plate cover
2. Screws
3. Switch

FIG. 50 Switch plate cover and four button window switch — 1988-90

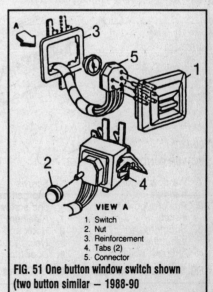

VIEW A
1. Switch
2. Nut
3. Reinforcement
4. Tabs (2)
5. Connector

FIG. 51 One button window switch shown (two button similar — 1988-90

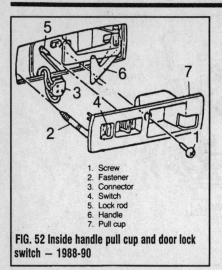

1. Screw
2. Fastener
3. Connector
4. Switch
5. Lock rod
6. Handle
7. Pull cup

FIG. 52 Inside handle pull cup and door lock switch — 1988-90

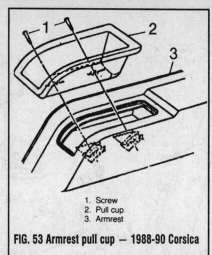

1. Screw
2. Pull cup
3. Armrest

FIG. 53 Armrest pull cup — 1988-90 Corsica

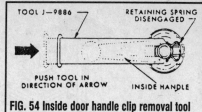

FIG. 54 Inside door handle clip removal tool

To install:

6. Insert the wiring harnesses, if present, through the openings in the trim panel.

7. Connect the switches to the wiring harnesses, if present.

8. Position the trim panel to the door by aligning the fasteners on the trim panel to the holes in the door inner panel and pressing the trim panel to the door until the fasteners are fully engaged.

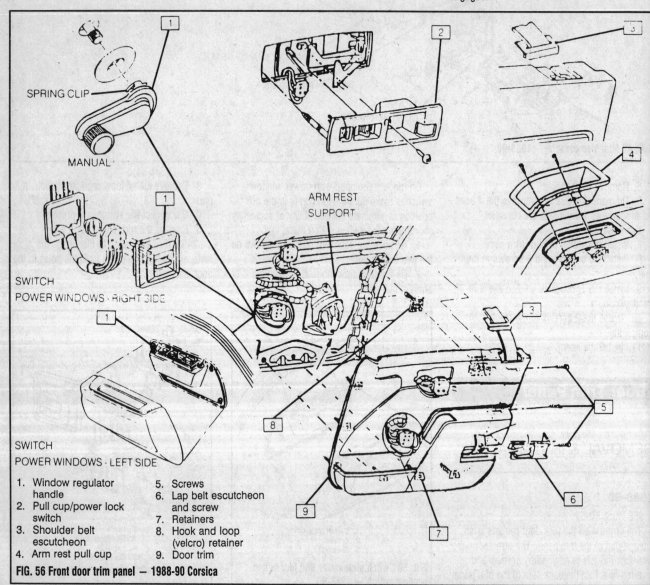

1. Window regulator handle
2. Pull cup/power lock switch
3. Shoulder belt escutcheon
4. Arm rest pull cup
5. Screws
6. Lap belt escutcheon and screw
7. Retainers
8. Hook and loop (velcro) retainer
9. Door trim

FIG. 56 Front door trim panel — 1988-90 Corsica

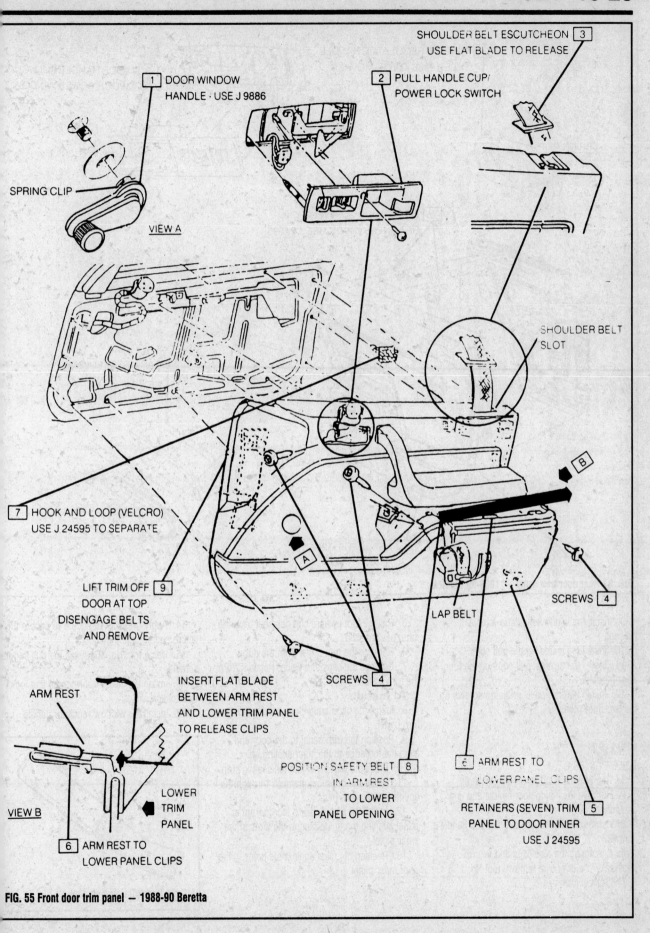

FIG. 55 Front door trim panel — 1988-90 Beretta

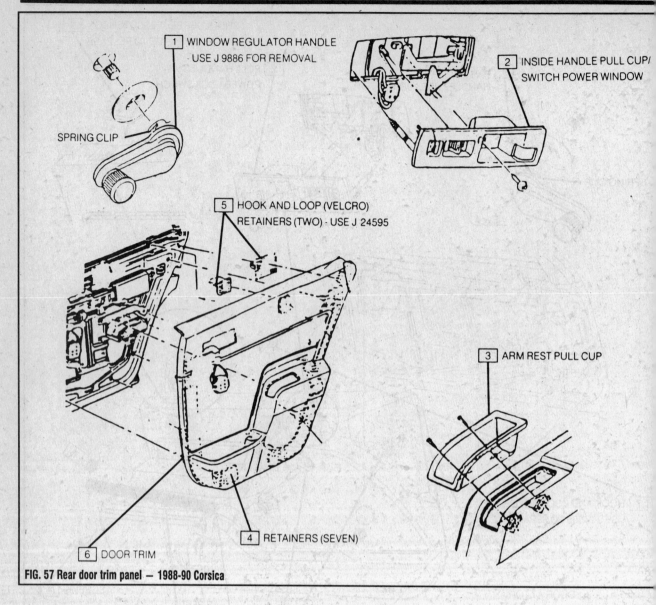

1 WINDOW REGULATOR HANDLE - USE J 9886 FOR REMOVAL

SPRING CLIP

2 INSIDE HANDLE PULL CUP/ SWITCH POWER WINDOW

5 HOOK AND LOOP (VELCRO) RETAINERS (TWO) - USE J 24595

3 ARM REST PULL CUP

4 RETAINERS (SEVEN)

6 DOOR TRIM

FIG. 57 Rear door trim panel — 1988-90 Corsica

9. Install the window regulator handle, if present.

10. Install the inside handle pull cups.

11. Install the armrest pull cups on the four door models.

12. Install the trim panel retaining screws on the two door models.

1991–92

▶ SEE FIGS. 58-62

1. Remove the window regulator handle.

2. Remove the inside door handle and lock escutcheon.

3. Using torx No. 30, remove the pull handle screws.

4. Disengage the nine clips and velcro retainer with a door trim removal tool No. J 38778, or equivalent.

5. Pull the trim upward and detach it from the inner sealing strip.

6. Remove the trim panel from the door.

7. Remove the clips and velcro rtetainer from the trim panel.

To Install:

8. Install the clips and velcro rtetainer to the trim panel.

9. Position the trim panel to the door and align the top edge to the inner sealing strip.

10. Press the trim panel into the sealing strip.

11. Route the door lock harness through the opening of the trim pad.

12. Install the trim panel to the door inner panel aligning the guide pins to the slots in the inner panel.

13. Position the clips against the holes in the door inner panel.

14. Apply pressure to secure to secure the velcro and engage the clips.

15. Using torx No. 30, install the pull handle screws.

16. Install the inside door handle and lock escutcheon.

17. Install the window regulator handle.

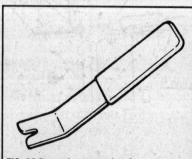

FIG. 62 Door trim removal tool

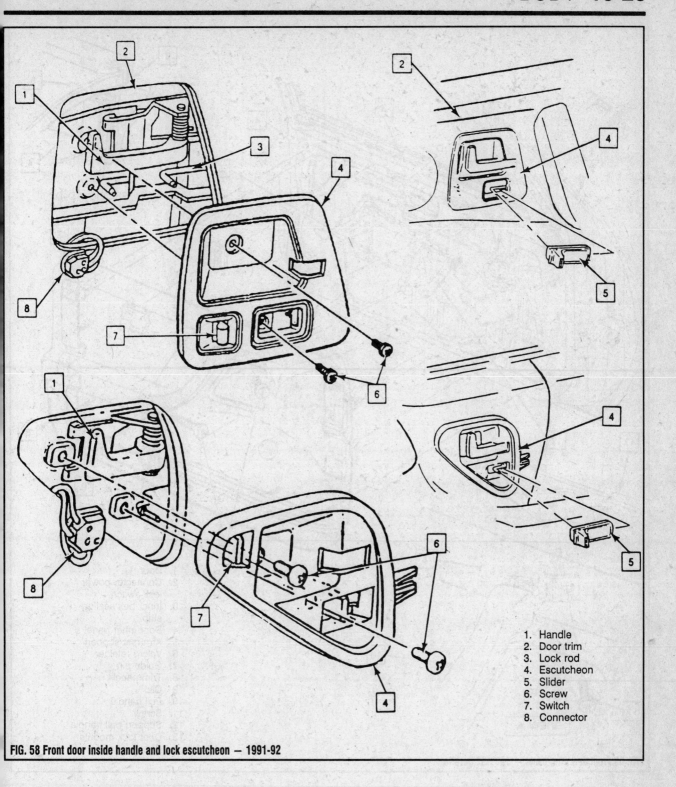

1. Handle
2. Door trim
3. Lock rod
4. Escutcheon
5. Slider
6. Screw
7. Switch
8. Connector

FIG. 58 Front door inside handle and lock escutcheon — 1991-92

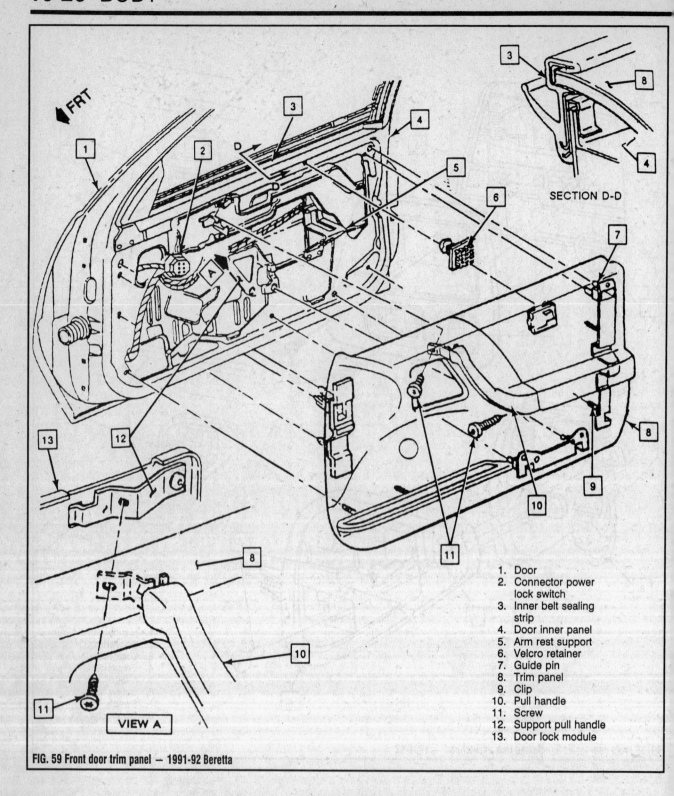

SECTION D-D

VIEW A

1. Door
2. Connector power lock switch
3. Inner belt sealing strip
4. Door inner panel
5. Arm rest support
6. Velcro retainer
7. Guide pin
8. Trim panel
9. Clip
10. Pull handle
11. Screw
12. Support pull handle
13. Door lock module

FIG. 59 Front door trim panel — 1991-92 Beretta

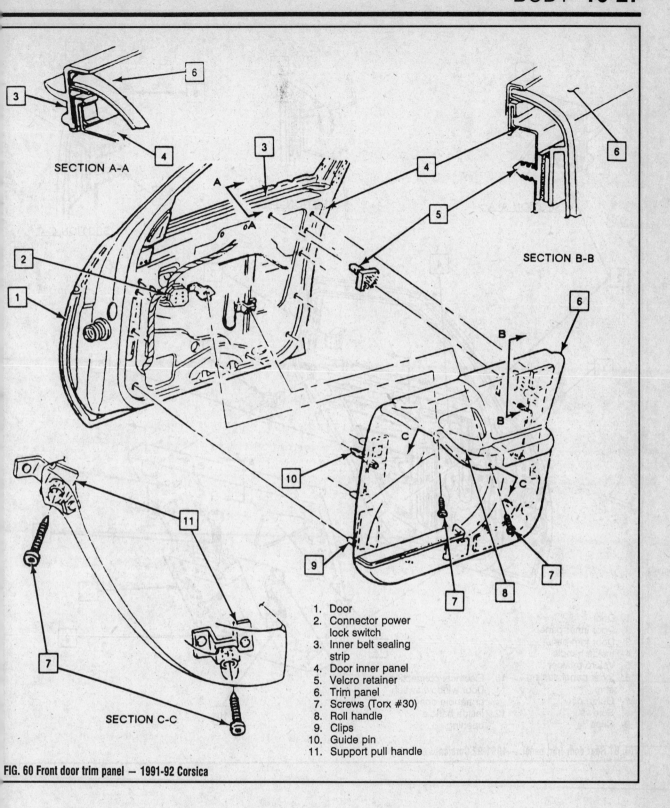

SECTION A-A

SECTION B-B

SECTION C-C

1. Door
2. Connector power
   lock switch
3. Inner belt sealing
   strip
4. Door inner panel
5. Velcro retainer
6. Trim panel
7. Screws (Torx #30)
8. Roll handle
9. Clips
10. Guide pin
11. Support pull handle

FIG. 60 Front door trim panel — 1991-92 Corsica

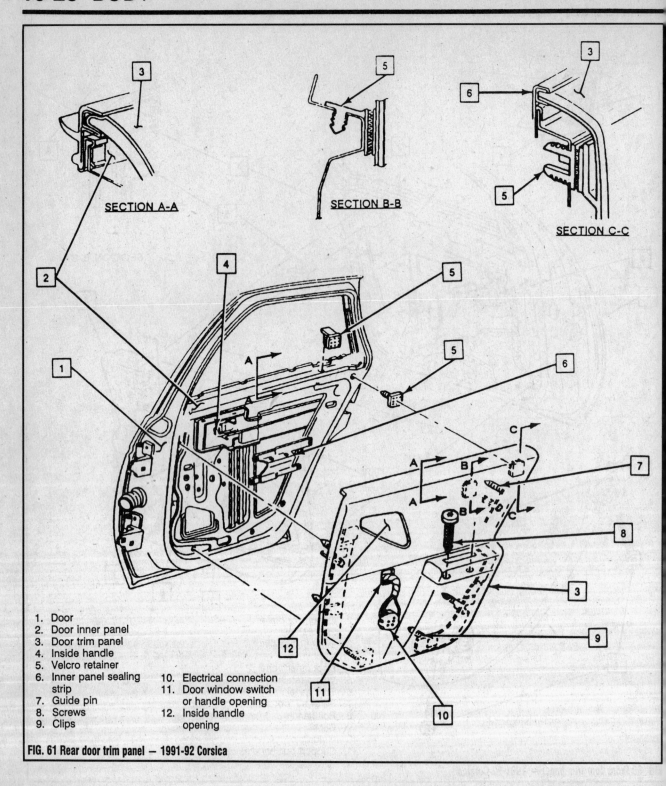

SECTION A-A

SECTION B-B

SECTION C-C

1. Door
2. Door inner panel
3. Door trim panel
4. Inside handle
5. Velcro retainer
6. Inner panel sealing
   strip
7. Guide pin
8. Screws
9. Clips

10. Electrical connection
11. Door window switch
    or handle opening
12. Inside handle
    opening

FIG. 61 Rear door trim panel — 1991-92 Corsica

Door Lock Module

REMOVAL & INSTALLATION

All of the parts are contained in one unit, a module asssembly. The entire module assembly is therefore removed when repair to any component is required except the power lock actuator and the inside handle which can be serviced on the vehicle.

Beretta

▶ SEE FIG. 63

1. Remove the trim panel as outlined earlier.
2. Loosen the water deflector.
3. Remove the front door lock pillar at the handle cover assembly.
4. Disconnect the lock cylinder at the lock rod.
5. Disconnect the outside handle at the lock rod.
6. Remove the lock retaining screws.
7. Remove the rivets by punching out the mandrel, then using a ³⁄₁₆ in. drill bit.
8. Disconnect the connector at the power lock system.
9. Remove the lock module assembly.

To install:

10. Place the lock module assembly in position through the access hole in the door inner panel. Align the module to the holes in the door facing.

➡ **While performing the next step the lock assembly must be held tightly against the door facing while tightening the screws. All screws must be driven at a 90° angle to the door facing to prevent cross threading or stripping of screws. It is also required to tighten the screws to 62 inch lbs. (7 Nm).**

11. Install and torque the retaining screws.
12. Install the connector to the power lock system.
13. Install new rivets using ³⁄₁₆ in. × ¹⁄₄ in. peel type rivets.
14. Connect the outside handle to the lock rod.
15. Connect the lock cylinder to the lock rod.
16. Check the lock system for proper operation.
17. Install the cover assembly.
18. Install the water deflector and the trim panel.

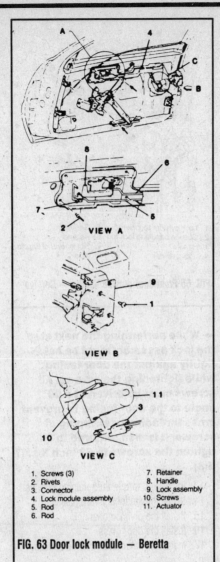

1. Screws (3)	7. Retainer
2. Rivets	8. Handle
3. Connector	9. Lock assembly
4. Lock module assembly	10. Screws
5. Rod	11. Actuator
6. Rod	

FIG. 63 Door lock module — Beretta

Corsica

FRONT

▶ SEE FIG. 64

1. Remove the trim panel as outlined earlier.
2. Loosen the water deflector.
3. Remove the front door lock pillar at the handle cover assembly.
4. Disconnect the lock cylinder at the lock rod.
5. Disconnect the outside handle at the lock rod.
6. Remove the lock retaining screws.
7. Remove the rivets by punching out the mandrel, then using a ³⁄₁₆ in. drill bit.
8. Disconnect the connector at the power lock system.
9. Remove the lock module assembly.

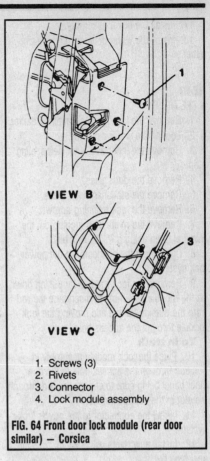

1. Screws (3)
2. Rivets
3. Connector
4. Lock module assembly

FIG. 64 Front door lock module (rear door similar) — Corsica

To install:

10. Place the lock module assembly in position through the access hole in the door inner panel. Align the module to the holes in the door facing.

➡ **While performing the next step the lock assembly must be held tightly against the door facing while tightening the screws. All screws must be driven at a 90° angle to the door facing to prevent cross threading or stripping of screws. It is also required to tighten the screws to 62 inch lbs. (7 Nm).**

11. Install and torque the retaining screws.
12. Install the connector to the power lock system.
13. Install new rivets using ³⁄₁₆ in. × ¹⁄₄ in. peel type rivets.

➡ **To reinstall rods, remove the rubber bumpers located on the door facing to ease rod installation.**

14. Connect the outside handle to the lock rod.
15. Connect the lock cylinder to the lock rod.
16. Check the lock system for proper operation.

17. Install the cover assembly.

18. Install the water deflector and the trim panel.

REAR

→ SEE FIG. 64

1. Remove the trim panel as outlined earlier.

2. Loosen the water deflector.

3. Remove the inner and outer belt sealing strip.

4. Remove the door glass.

5. Remove the stationary vent glass.

6. Remove the lock retaining screws.

7. Remove the rivets by punching out the mandrel, then using a ³⁄₁₆ in. drill bit.

8. Disconnect the connector at the power lock system.

9. Remove the lock module by pulling down on the module assembly to disengage the rod from the outside handle and moving the lock module through the access hole.

To install:

10. Place the lock module assembly in position through the access hole in the door inner panel being sure to engage the rod through the slot in the outside handle.

11. Install the connector to the power lock system.

12. Install new rivets using ³⁄₁₆ in. × ¹⁄₄ in. peel type rivets.

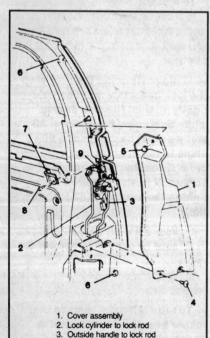

FIG. 65 Cover assembly-front door lock pillar at handle — Beretta

1. Cover assembly
2. Lock cylinder to lock rod
3. Outside handle to lock rod
4. Screws
5. Nut
6. Nuts
7. Anti-theft shield
8. Screw
9. Lock cylinder

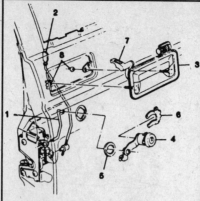

1. Lock cylinder to lock rod
2. Outside handle to lock rod
3. Handle
4. Lock cylinder
5. Gasket
6. Retainer
7. Slot in lever of handle
8. Nuts

FIG. 66 Front door outside handle — Corsica

→ **While performing the next step the lock assembly must be held tightly against the door facing while tightening the screws. All screws must be driven at a 90° angle to the door facing to prevent cross threading or stripping of screws. It is also required to tighten the screws to 62 inch lbs. (7 Nm).**

13. Install and torque the retaining screws.

14. Install the stationary vent glass.

15. Install the division channel.

16. Install the door glass.

17. Install the inner and outer belt sealing strip.

18. Check the lock system for proper operation.

19. Install the water deflector and the trim panel.

Door Lock assembly

REMOVAL & INSTALLATION

→ SEE FIG. 65-68

1. Remove the lock module assembly.

2. Disconnect all rods attached to the lock.

3. Remove the lock assembly from the module.

→ **A new service lock will have a block-out plug installed. Do not operate the lock or remove the plug until the lock is installed and the rod is connected to the lock.**

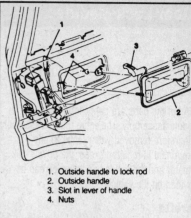

1. Outside handle to lock rod
2. Outside handle
3. Slot in lever of handle
4. Nuts

FIG. 67 Rear door outside handle — Corsica

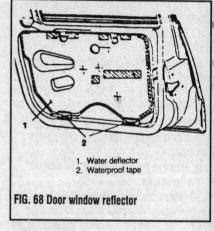

1. Water deflector
2. Waterproof tape

FIG. 68 Door window reflector

To install:

4. To install, attach the lock assembly to the module.

5. Connect all rods that were removed.

6. Install the lock module assembly.

Rear Compartment Lid and Lift Window Lock

REMOVAL & INSTALLATION

→ SEE FIG. 69, 69A-69B

1. On the Corsica sedan, remove the rivets using ¹⁄₄ in. (6mm) drill bit.

2. Remove the retaining screws on the Corsica hatchback and Beretta. On the Beretta the screws are located on the body end panel.

3. Remove the screws holding the release solenoid to the lock and remove the lock

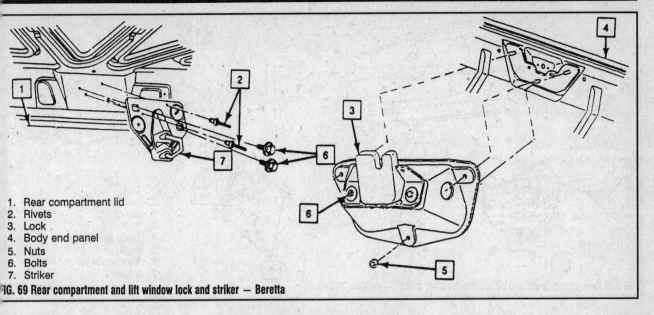

1. Rear compartment lid
2. Rivets
3. Lock
4. Body end panel
5. Nuts
6. Bolts
7. Striker

FIG. 69 Rear compartment and lift window lock and striker — Beretta

To Install:

4. Position the lock and install the screws on the Corsica sedan and Beretta and the nuts on the Corsica hatchback. Tighten the screws to 53 inch lbs. (6 Nm). and the nuts to 124 inch lbs. (14 Nm).

5. Install the screws holding the release solenoid to the lock and tighten to 53 inch lbs. (6 Nm).

Heater and A/C Ventilation Ducts

REMOVAL & INSTALLATION

◆ SEE FIG. 70

❈ CAUTION

Some vehicles are equipped with the Supplemental Inflatable Restraint (SIR) or air bag system. The SIR system must be disabled before performing service on or around SIR system components, steering column, instrument panel components, wiring and sensors. Failure to follow safety and disabling procedures could result in accidental air bag deployment, possible personal injury and unnecessary SIR system

repairs. Refer to Instrument Panel and Pad removal and installation, in this section, for disabling the SIR system.

1. Remove the instrument panel and pad assembly as outlined in this section.

2. Remove the air distribution assembly.

3. Separate the air ventilation ducts from the instrument panel and air distributor.

To Install:

4. Reconnect the ventilation ducts.

5. Install the air distribution system.

6. Install the instrument panel and pad assembly and enable the SIR system, as outlined in this section.

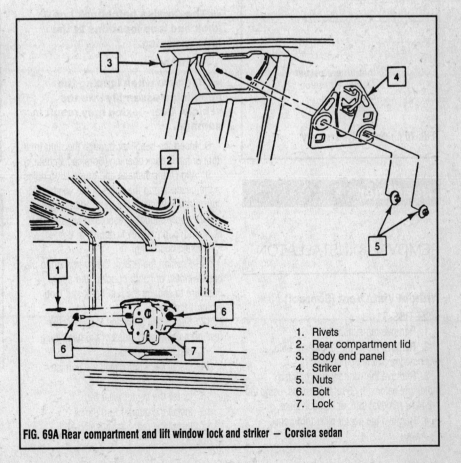

1. Rivets
2. Rear compartment lid
3. Body end panel
4. Striker
5. Nuts
6. Bolt
7. Lock

FIG. 69A Rear compartment and lift window lock and striker — Corsica sedan

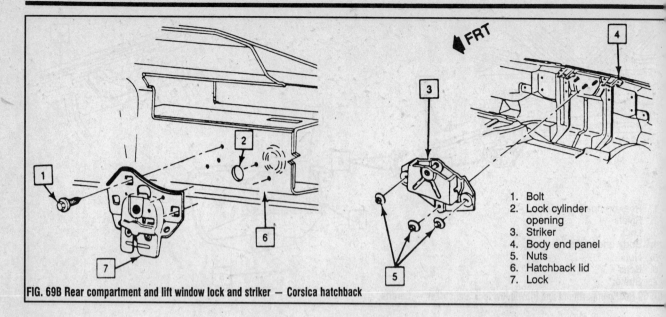

FIG. 69B Rear compartment and lift window lock and striker — Corsica hatchback

1. Bolt
2. Lock cylinder opening
3. Striker
4. Body end panel
5. Nuts
6. Hatchback lid
7. Lock

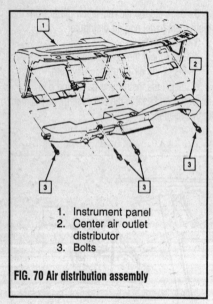

1. Instrument panel
2. Center air outlet distributor
3. Bolts

FIG. 70 Air distribution assembly

Headliner

REMOVAL & INSTALLATON

Without Vista Vent (Sunroof)

♦ SEE FIGS. 71-73

1. Remove the sunshades.
2. Remove the dome lamp lens, bulb, retainerclips and lamp housing.
3. Remove the window side garnish moldings, held on by 3 retaining clips, using tool J-24416 removal tool, or its equivqlent.
4. Remove the center pillar trim panel.

5. Remove the rear seat cushion and seatback.
6. Remove the quarter trim panel.
7. Using headliner removal tool J-2772, or its equivalent, loosen the headliner. Start at one end, insert the tool between of the hook and loop material and carefully separate the hook portion from the loop portion until the headlining is loose.

➡ **The Corsica hatchback has 4 hook and loop locations at the hatch opening.**

To install:

➡ **Use care when loading the headlining assembly into the vehicle. Over-flexing may result in damage.**

8. Insert the headliner through the right front door or hatch back opening (Corsica hatchback).
9. Align the sunshade and dome lamp holes in the headlining to the holes in the windshield upper frame. Position the mirror hareness.
10. Apply enough pressure to engage the hook and loop (velcro) fasteners at the windshield opemning.
11. Position the rear of the headlining to the back window or hatch opening and apply pressure to engage the rear hook and loop (velcro) fasteners.
12. Secure the hook and loop (velcro) fasteners along both sides of the headlining.
13. Install the sunshades.
14. Install the windshield side garnish moldings.
15. Install the center pillar trim.
16. Install the quarter trim panel.
17. Install the rear seat cushion and seatback.

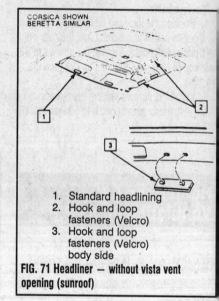

CORSICA SHOWN
BERETTA SIMILAR

1. Standard headlining
2. Hook and loop fasteners (Velcro)
3. Hook and loop fasteners (Velcro) body side

FIG. 71 Headliner — without vista vent opening (sunroof)

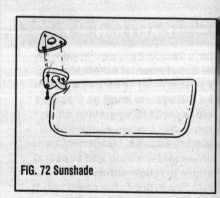

FIG. 72 Sunshade

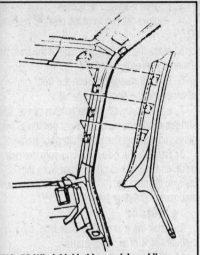

FIG. 73 Windshield side garnish molding installation

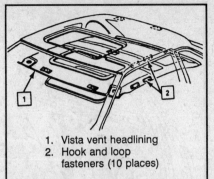

1. Vista vent headlining
2. Hook and loop fasteners (10 places)

FIG. 74 Headliner — with vista vent opening (sunroof)

With Vista Vent (Sunroof)

◆ SEE FIG. 74-75

1. Remove the vista vent glass assembly.
2. Remove the latch base.
3. Disengage the finishing lace from the vista vent headliner retainer.
4. Carefully separate the headliner from the retainer.
5. Remove the sunshades.
6. Remove the dome lamp lens, bulb, retainerclips and lamp housing.
7. Remove the window side garnish moldings, held on by 3 retaining clips, using tool J 24416 removal tool, or its equivalent.
8. Remove the center pillar trim panel.
9. Remove the rear seat cushion and seatback.
10. Remove the quarter trim panel.

To install:

➡ **Use care when loading the headlining assembly into the vehicle. Over-flexing may result in damage.**

11. Insert the headliner through the right front door or hatch back opening (Corsica hatchback).
12. Align the sunshade and dome lamp holes in the headlining to the holes in the windshield upper frame. Position the mirror hareness.
13. Apply enough pressure to engage the hook and loop (velcro) fasteners at the windshield opemning.
14. Position the rear of the headlining to the back window or hatch opening and apply pressure to engage the rear hook and loop (velcro) fasteners.
15. Secure the hook and loop (velcro) fasteners along both sides of the headlining.

16. Install the sunshades.
17. Install the windshield side garnish moldings.
18 Tuck the headlining around the entire periphery of vent opening into the retainer.
19. Position and insert the latch base.
20. Loacte the end of the lace at the left side of the base. Press the lace into the retainer and roll toward the corner.
21. Install the latch base and glass assembly.

Door Glass

REMOVAL & INSTALLATION

Front

1988–91

◆ SEE FIGS. 76-77

1. Remove the trim panel.
2. Remove the inner belt sealing strip and front upper bumper.
3. Loosen the water deflector.
4. Remove the two front run channel retaining screws and remove the channel.
5. Remove the front run channel retainer.
6. Remove the rear run channel retainer.
7. Disengage the lower sash channel with the glass in the half down position and rotate the glass and lift the glass up and inboard of the door frame.

To install:

8. Lower the glass into the door and engage the lower sash channel to regulator. Raise the glass to the full up position.
9. Install the rear run channel retainer.
10. Install the front run channel retainer.
11. Install the front run channel.
12. Install the inner belt sealing strip and front upper bumper.

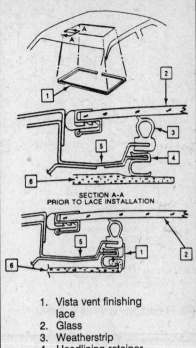

1. Vista vent finishing lace
2. Glass
3. Weatherstrip
4. Headlining retainer
5. Vista vent opening
6. Headlining assembly

FIG. 75 Headliner and finishing lace — with vista vent opening (sunroof)

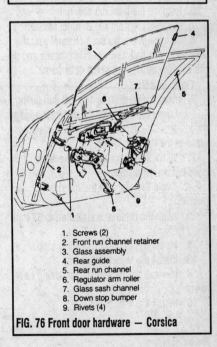

1. Screws (2)
2. Front run channel retainer
3. Glass assembly
4. Rear guide
5. Rear run channel
6. Regulator arm roller
7. Glass sash channel
8. Down stop bumper
9. Rivets (4)

FIG. 76 Front door hardware — Corsica

13. Install the channel screws and tighten to 80 – 106 inch lbs. (9–12 Nm
14. Install the water deflector and the trim panel.

1991–92

◆ SEE FIGS. 76-77

1. Remove the trim panel.

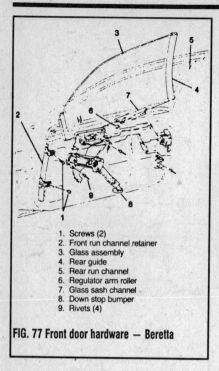

1. Screws (2)
2. Front run channel retainer
3. Glass assembly
4. Rear guide
5. Rear run channel
6. Regulator arm roller
7. Glass sash channel
8. Down stop bumper
9. Rivets (4)

FIG. 77 Front door hardware — Beretta

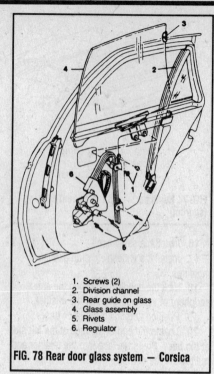

1. Screws (2)
2. Division channel
3. Rear guide on glass
4. Glass assembly
5. Rivets
6. Regulator

FIG. 78 Rear door glass system — Corsica

2. Remove the door armrest hanger plates by drilling out the rivet with a 3/16 in. drill.
3. Peel off the water deflector.
4. Remove the inner panel sealing strip.
5. Remove the rear run channel guide.
6. Remove the front run channel.
7. Remove the front run channel retainer.
8. Disengage the the sash channel with the window in the half down position, rotate and lift the window up and out of the door frame.

To install:

9. Install the front glass channel and guide.
10. Lower the glass into the door and engage the lower sash channel to regulator. Raise the glass to the full up position.
11. Install the front run channel retainer 2 bolts but do not tighten.
   a. Cycle the glass to the full down position.
   b. Align the retainer and tighten to 97 inch lbs. (11 Nm)
12. Install the inner belt sealing strip.
13. Install the water deflector.
14. Inwstall the hanger plates, using new rivets.
15. Install the trim panel.

Rear

1988–90

◆ SEE FIGS. 78-80
1. Remove the trim panel.
2. Remove the inner and outer belt sealing strip.

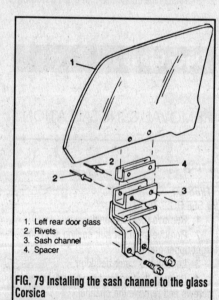

1. Left rear door glass
2. Rivets
3. Sash channel
4. Spacer

FIG. 79 Installing the sash channel to the glass Corsica

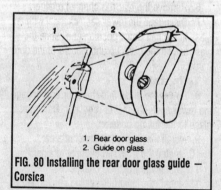

1. Rear door glass
2. Guide on glass

FIG. 80 Installing the rear door glass guide — Corsica

3. Loosen the water deflector.
4. Remove the two front run channel retainin screws.
5. Mask the the outboard side of the front ru channel with protective tape.
6. Place a wedge between the front run channel and the door outer panel.
7. Lower the glass to the bottom of the doo and remove the remove the front portion of the glass run channel from the front door frame.
8. Remove the glass, making sure the rear guide on the glass is disengaged from the division channel and lifting the glass upward an outboard of the door frame.

To install:

9. Install the glass to the door from the outboard side of the door frame.
10. Lower the glass to the bottom of the doo and install the front portion of the glass run channel to the front door frame.
11. Install the rear guide on the glass to the channel.
12. Install the two front run channel retaining screws.
13. Remove the wedge and masking tape.
14. Check the window for proper operation.
15. Install the water deflector.
16. Install the inner and outer belt sealing strip.
17. Install the trim panel.

1991–92

◆ SEE FIG. 78-80
1. Remove the trim panel.
2. Remove the inner and outer belt sealing strip.
3. Remove the door armrest hanger plates by drilling out the rivet with a 3/16 in. drill.
4. Loosen the water deflector.
5. Mask the the outboard side of the front run channel with protective tape.
6. Lower the glass to the bottom of the door and remove the remove the front portion of the glass from the run channel.
7. Remove the two front run channel retaining screws.
6. Place a wedge between the front run channel and the door outer panel.
7. Remove the glass, making sure the rear guide on the glass is disengaged from the division channel and lifting the glass upward and through the access created by wedging the division channel and door panel.

To install:

8. Install the glass to the door from the outboard side of the door frame.

9. Lower the glass to the bottom of the door and install the front portion of the glass run channel to the front door frame.

10. Install the rear guide on the glass to the channel.

11. Install the 2 regulator to sash retaining bolts and tighten to 75 inch lbs. (8.5 Nm).

12. Remove the wedge and masking tape.

13. Check the window for proper operation.

14. Install the water deflector.

15. Install the hager plate using new rivets.

16. Install the inner and outer belt sealing strip.

17. Install the trim panel.

Rear Door Vent Glass

REMOVAL & INSTALLATION

♦ SEE FIG. 81

1. Remove the trim panel as outlined earlier.

2. Loosen the water deflector.

3. Remove the inner belt sealing strip.

4. Place the rear door glass in the full-down position.

5. Remove the screws/bolts.

6. Move the division channel towards the front of the car and remove the vent glass.

To Install:

7. Install the vent glass to the channel.

8. Install the vent glass and channel to the door from the inboard of door frame.

9. Install all retaining screws/bolt.

10. Install the water deflector

11. Install the inner belt sealing strip.

12. Install the trim panel.

Window Regulator

REMOVAL & INSTALLATION

Front

♦ SEE FIG. 76-77

1. Tape the glass in the full up position.

2. Remove the trim panel.

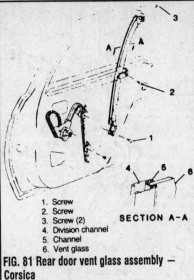

1. Screw
2. Screw
3. Screw (2)
4. Division channel
5. Channel
6. Vent glass

SECTION A-A

FIG. 81 Rear door vent glass assembly — Corsica

3. Remove the armrest support brackets or hanger plates. Drill out the hanger plate rivets using a ³⁄₁₆ in. drill.

4. Loosen the water deflector.

5. On all 1990–92 models, except 1990 Beretta, remove the lock module assembly as outlined earlier.

5. Drill out the four regulator retaining rivets using a ³⁄₁₆ in. drill bit.

6. Remove the regulator by disengaging the roller from the glass sash channel, disconnecting the electrical connector to the motor (power window systems) and removing the regulator through the door inner access hole.

❄ CAUTION

If you wish to remove the electric motor from the regulator, refer to the Electric Window Motor procedure. The regulator lift arm is under tension from the counterbalence spring and can cause personal injury if the sector gear is not locked in position.

To install:

7. Install the regualtor through the door inner access hole and attach the roller to the sash channel.

8. Connect the electrical connector to the motor (power window systems).

9. Install the rivets using ¹⁄₄ in. peel type.

10. On all 1990–92 models, except 1990 Beretta, install the lock module assembly as outlined earlier.

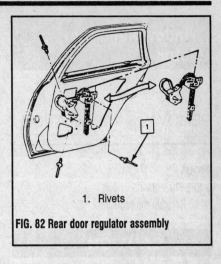

1. Rivets

FIG. 82 Rear door regulator assembly

11. Install the water deflector.

12. Install the armrest support brackets or hanger plates using new rivets.

13. Install the trim panel.

Rear

♦ SEE FIG. 82

1. Tape the glass in the full up position.

2. Remove the trim panel.

3. Remove the armrest support bracket or hanger plate, using a ³⁄₁₆ in. drill.

4. Loosen the water deflector.

5. Remove the 2 regulator to sash channel retaining screws.

6. Drill out the regulator retaining rivets using a ¹⁄₄ in. drill bit.

7. Remove the regualtor by disengaging the roller from the glass sash channel, disconnecting the electrical connector to the motor (power window systems) and removing the regulator through the door inner access hole.

To install:

8. Install the regualtor through the door inner access hole and attach the roller to the sash channel.

9. Connect the electrical connector to the motor (power window systems).

10. Install the regualtor to sash retaining screws.

11. Install the rivets using ¹⁄₄ in. peel type.

12. Install the water deflector.

13. Install the armrest support bracket or hanger plate, using new rivets.

14. Install the trim panel.

Window Regulator Motor

REMOVAL & INSTALLATION

Front

♦ SEE FIGS. 83-85

1. Remove the regulator.

❊❊ CAUTION

It is important to perform Step 2. The regulator lift arm is under tension from the counterbalance spring and can cause personal injury if the sector gear is not locked in position. Inspect the regulator for a counter balance spring. Some 1990–92 Corsica models do not use a a a counterbalance spring.

2. Drill a hole through the regulator sector gear and backplate and install a screw and nut to lock the sector gear in position. Do not drill the hole closer than $1/2$ in. (13mm) to the edge of the sector gear or backplate.

3. Drill out the rivets using a $3/16$ in. drill bit.

4. Remove the motor.

➡ **Depending on the position of the regulator, it may be necessary to remove portions of one of the remaining rivet later.**

To Install:

5. Attach the motor to the regulator using a $1/4$ in. × $31/32$ in. rivet.

6. Once at least 2 rivets are installed, remove the screw and nut locking the sector gear in the fixed position. Use an electric power source to rotate the regulator in the desired direction to provide access to the remaining rivet.

➡ **It may be necessary to to grind a portion off the corner of the sector gear on some models to provide space to remove the remaining rivet.**

7. Once the remaining rivet can be removed install a new one.

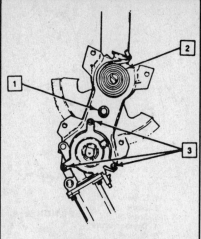

1. Bolt and washer securing sector gear to backplate
2. Counterbalance spring
3. Motor to regulator attaching rivets

FIG. 83 Secure the regulator sector gear to the regulator back plate

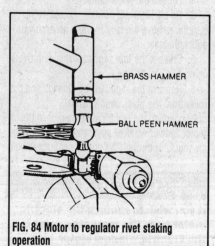

BRASS HAMMER

BALL PEEN HAMMER

FIG. 84 Motor to regulator rivet staking operation

8. Install the regulator and motor assembly to the door inner panel using $1/4$ in. × $1/2$ in. peel type rivet.

Rear

1. Remove the regulator.
2. Remove the motor by drilling out the rivets holding the motor to the actuator using a $1/4$ in. (6mm) drill bit.
3. Attach the motor to the regulator using a $1/4$ in. × $31/32$ in. rivet.
4. Install the regulator.

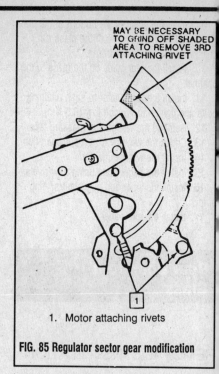

MAY BE NECESSARY TO GRIND OFF SHADED AREA TO REMOVE 3RD ATTACHING RIVET

1. Motor attaching rivets

FIG. 85 Regulator sector gear modification

Windshield and Rear Window Glass

REMOVAL & INSTALLATION

♦ SEE FIGS. 86-89

❊❊ CAUTION

Approved safety glasses and gloves should be worn when performing this procedure to reduce the chance of personal injury.

1. Remove the wiper arms and the blade.
2. Remove the cowl vent screen.
3. Reveal the moldings from around the windhield or back glass.
4. Remove the glass supports on the windshield.
5. Disconnect the rear window defogger electrical connection.

❊❊ WARNING

Disconnect by pulling the connector not the wire.

6. If the glass is to be reused, center mark glass position in the body opening with tape or grease pencil.

7. Mask off the area around the glass to protect painted surfaces and to aid in clean up after installation.

8. Using a razor or utility knife, make a preliminary cut around the entire perimeter of the glass, staying as close to the edge of glass as possible.

9. Using cold knife J 24402–A or equivalent, cut out windshield or back glass, keeping blade as close to edge of glass as possible. Remove glass.

➡ **Glass opening of any loose material. If glass is to be reinstalled, all urethane must be removed from glass.**

To install:

10. Replace the glass supports on the windshield. Position the glass in opening, apply a piece of masking tape over each edge of glass and adjacent body pillars. Slit tape vertically at the edge of the glass. During installation, tape on glass can be aligned with tape on the body to guide glass into desired position. If the glass is being reused, use center marks applied in step 5 to align glass to opening. Remove the glass.

➡ **Clean the surface of the glass to which adhesive will be applied (around edge of inside surface) by wiping with a clean, alcohol dampened cloth. Allow to air dry.**

11. Two primers are provided in the urethane adhesive kit GM P/N 9636067 or equivalent. The clear primer is used on the glass prior to the black primer. Apply the primer around the entire perimeter of glass edge and $1/4$ in. (6mm) inboard on inner surface. Allow the primer to dry five minutes.

12. Install the rear window reveal molding, use the black weatherstrip cement in the molding glass cavity at the corners and ends to secure the molding on the glass during installation.

13. Use J 24811–A sealant dispensing gun or equivalent to apply a smooth continuous bead of adhesive around the edge of glass where primed.

14. With the aid of a helper, lift the glass into the window opening. On back window installations it will be necessary to use suction cups to position the glass in opening. Windshield glass can be positioned without the aid of carrying devices. Carry the glass with one hand on inside of glass and one hand on outside. At the window opening, put glass in a horizontal position. While one man holds the glass in this

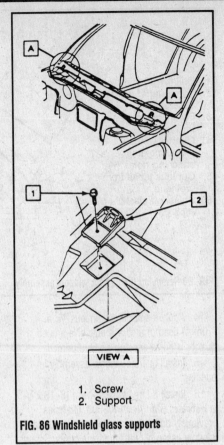

VIEW A

1. Screw
2. Support

FIG. 86 Windshield glass supports

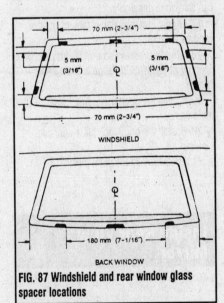

WINDSHIELD

BACK WINDOW

FIG. 87 Windshield and rear window glass spacer locations

position, the second man can reach one arm around the body pillar and support the glass while other man assumes same position.

15. With the glass centered in the opening, place glass on lower supports and use tape guides applied in step 1 to carefully place glass in proper position.

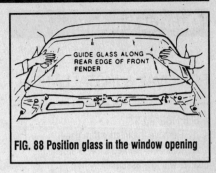

FIG. 88 Position glass in the window opening

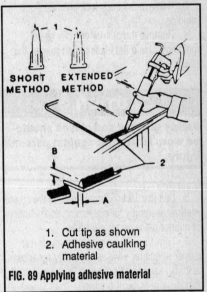

SHORT METHOD EXTENDED METHOD

1. Cut tip as shown
2. Adhesive caulking material

FIG. 89 Applying adhesive material

16. Press the glass firmly to wet-out and set adhesive. Use care to avoid excessive squeezeout which would cause an appearance problem. Using the small disposable brush or flat-bladed tool, paddle material around the edge of glass to ensure watertight seal. If necessary, paddle additional material to fill voids in seal.

17. Install the windshield upper reveal molding.

18. Watertest the vehicle at once using a soft spray. Use warm or hot water if available. Do not direct hard stream of water at fresh adhesive material. If any leaks are found, paddle in extra adhesive at leak point using a small disposable brush or flat-bladed tool. Water applied on the top of urethane adhesive, either during watertest or as a separate operation, will speed up the cure of the urethane.

19. Cowl vent screen.

20. Reveal the moldings.

21. Install the windshield wipers and blades.

24. Connect the rear window defogger wires.

25. On the windshield and back glass installation, the vehicle must remain at normal room temperature for 6 hours to complete the proper cure of adhesive.

Quarter Window

REMOVAL & INSTALLATION

♦ SEE FIGS. 90-91

1. Remove the interior trim panel.
2. Mask the painted surface around the quarter window assembly.
3. Remove the body lock pillar applique molding.
4. Remove the quarter window reveal moldings. Use a flat blade tool to release the clips.

✳✳ CAUTION

Safety glasses and gloves should be worn to protect against personal injury.

5. Drill five $\frac{1}{8}$ in. (3mm) holes in the quarter window assembly for positioning and retention of quarter glass on reinstallation.
6. Trim $\frac{1}{2}$ in. (13mm) off the lower rear corner of quarter window assembly for access to install service wire through urethane. Install service wire through urethane.
7. Disconnect the tabs on the front vertical lock pillar.
8. Using a hammer and sharp putty knife, cut off the plastic clips and trim off the excess urethane around the inside pinch-weld.
9. Insert a (0.020) service wire through the urethane at the lower rear corner of quarter window assembly.
10. Place a wire around quarter window assembly. Insert the other end of wire through urethane at the lower rear corner.
11. While holding one wire with locking pliers place other wire through the hole in center of wood dowel, 4 in. × $\frac{5}{8}$ in. (102mm × 16mm). Twist wire around wooden dowel and pull wire parallel to the glass to keep wire from pinch-weld flange, which may break the wire.
12. Apply outward pressure and remove the quarter window assembly.

➡ **Clean urethane from the quarter window assembly and pinch-weld flange.**

To install:

13. Two primers are provided in urethane kit GM P/N 9636067 or equivalent. Apply the clear primer first around quarter window assembly. Allow to dry. Then apply black primer over clear and black primer to pinch-weld flange. Allow the primer to dry 5 minutes.

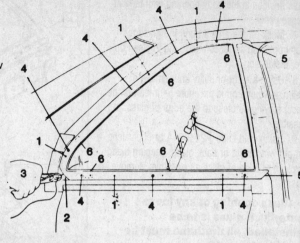

1. Drill five $\frac{1}{8}$ in. holes
2. Trim quarter window assembly
3. Feed cutting wire thru urethane
4. Quarter window reveal molding attaching holes (7)
5. Cut tabs loose from urethane
6. Chisel off plastic clips (6)

FIG. 90 Removing the quarter window assembly

14. Apply a smooth continuous $\frac{3}{8}$ in. (10mm) bead of urethane adhesive around quarter window assembly where primed.
15. Install quarter window assembly in opening.
16. Install 5 large washer head (8–18 x $\frac{3}{4}$ in.) screws GM P/N 11403606 into holes previously drilled to align and secure quarter window assembly until urethane cures. Screws can remain in assembly.
17. Apply urethane under tabs of quarter window assembly.
18. Paddle urethane around the inside quarter window at pinch-weld flange and clean off excess.
19. Install the quarter window reveal moldings.
20. Install the body lock pillar applique molding.
21. Install the interior trim panel.

Inside Rear View Mirror

REPLACEMENT

The rearview mirror head is attached to a support with a retaining screw. The support is secured to the windshield glass. This support is installed by the glass supplier using a plastic-polyvinyl butyl adhesive.

1. Locking pliers
2. Pull handle
3. Service wire

FIG. 91 Locating service wire for quarter window removal

Service replacement windshield glass has the mirror support bonded to the glass assembly.

Service kits are available to replace a detached mirror support or install a new part. Follow the manufacturer's instructions for replacement.

Seats

REMOVAL & INSTALLATION

♦ SEE FIGS. 92-94

The front seat assemblies are secured to the floor at 3 points. The center, front of the seat is bolted to an adjuster which in turn is secured by 2 bolts that thread into weld nuts in the floor pan. Two rollers at the rear of the seat which are an integral part of the seat, travel in guide tracks. The inboard track is secured to the side of the inner rocker panel and the outboard track secures to the side of the floor pan tunnel. Removal and installation of both front and rear seats are obvious upon inspection. When installing the seats and cushioins the following torque specifications should be used:

1988–90:

• Seat adjuster to floor pan bolts — 7–11 ft. lbs.

• Recliner to seat frame bolts — 15–21 ft. lbs.

• Seat adjuster to seat frame nut — 7–10 ft. lbs.

• Track guide to floor pan bolt — 7–10 ft. lbs.

1991–92:

• Seat adjuster to floor pan bolts — 26 ft. lbs. (36 Nm)

• Recliner to seat frame bolts — 18 ft. lbs. (24 Nm)

• Seat adjuster to seat frame nut — 21 ft. lbs. (29 Nm)

• Rear seat cushion to floor pan bolts — 11 ft. lbs. (15 Nm)

• Rear seat back anchor bolts — 31 ft. lbs. (42 Nm)

• Foldown rear seat back bolts — 18 ft. lbs. (25 Nm)

Seat Belts

REMOVAL & INSTALLATION

Precautions

When servicing safety belts refer to the following precautions:

1. Seat belts will be serviced as follows:

   a. Retractor portion(s) of the front and rear shoulder belt for outboard passenger and driver.

   b. Buckle portion of the front saet belt for outboard passenger and driver.

   c. Center rear belt and rear outer buckles are serviced separately.

2. Keep sharp edges and damaging objects away from the belts.

3. Avoid bending or damaging any portion of the belt buckle or latch plate.

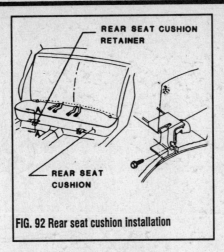

FIG. 92 Rear seat cushion installation

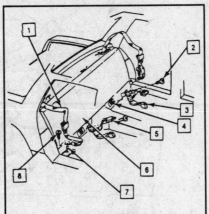

1. Outer belt
2. Bolt
3. Buckle-side belt
4. Seatback retainer
5. Center belt
6. Seatback
7. Spacer
8. Bolt

FIG. 93 Rear seatback installation — Beretta and Corsica sedan

4. Use correct seat belt anchor bolts and spacers. Tighten all safety belt anchor and retractor bolts to 31 ft. lbs. (42 Nm)

Front Door Passive Restraints

1988–90
♦ SEE FIGS. 95-96

1. Remove the front door trim panel and loosen the water deflector.
2. Remove the belt guide.
3. Remove the guide loop cover.
4. Remove the retractor screw.
5. Disconnect the electrical connector.
6. Disconnect the release cable.
7. Remove the retractor attaching nuts and remove the seat belt retractors.

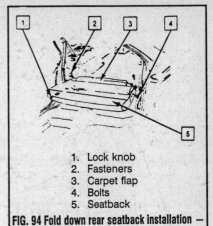

1. Lock knob
2. Fasteners
3. Carpet flap
4. Bolts
5. Seatback

FIG. 94 Fold down rear seatback installation — Corsica hatchback

To install:

8. Install the retractors and retainer nuts and tighten to 31 ft. lbs. (42 Nm).
9. Install the retractor screw.
10. Connect the electrical connector.
11. Install the guide loop and retainer nut and tighten to 17 ft. lbs. (23 Nm).
12. Close the door and check for correct operation.
13. Install the front door trim panel and the water deflector.

Driver and Passenger Retractor Side Belt Assemblies

1991–92
BERETTA
♦ SEE FIG. 97

1. Remove the anchor bolt.
2. Remove the guide cover, bolt and guide from the pillar.

➡ **On the convertible, remove the stationary bow lower trim panel to gain access to the guide.**

3. Remove the quarter trim panel
4. Remove the plug, bolt, washer and bushing safety belt to rocker panel.
5. Remove the bolt and retractor from the quarter panel.
5. Use a flat bladed tool and disengage the escutcheon from the trim panel.
6. Remove the belt assembly.

To install:

7. Insert the tab on the outboard side of the retractor into the key slot into the panel until seated.

➡ **The plastic casing on the retractor is color coded for identification. The right side is green and the left side is red.**

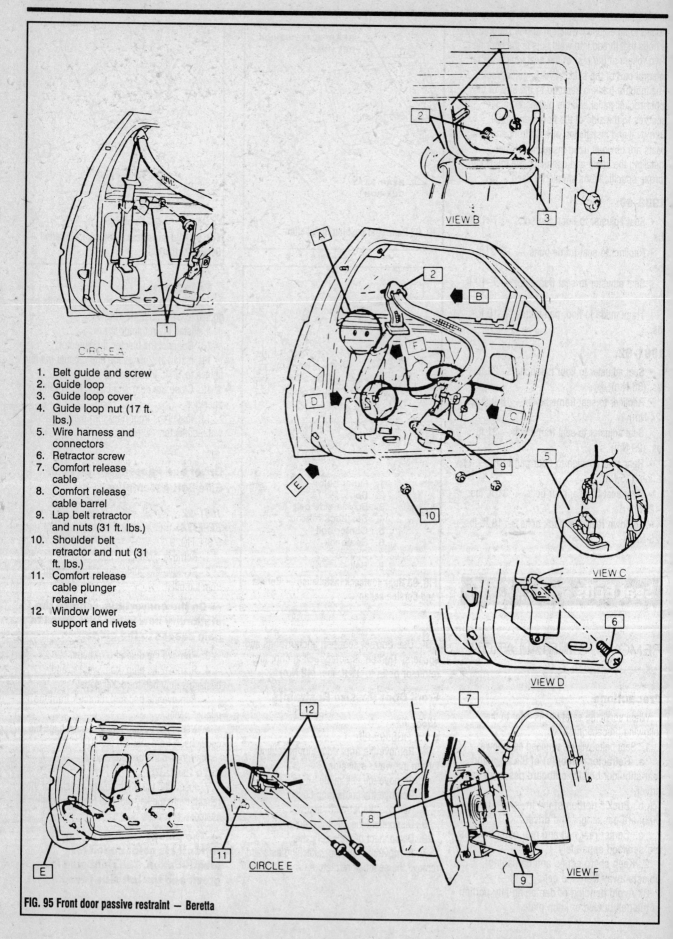

1. Belt guide and screw
2. Guide loop
3. Guide loop cover
4. Guide loop nut (17 ft. lbs.)
5. Wire harness and connectors
6. Retractor screw
7. Comfort release cable
8. Comfort release cable barrel
9. Lap belt retractor and nuts (31 ft. lbs.)
10. Shoulder belt retractor and nut (31 ft. lbs.)
11. Comfort release cable plunger retainer
12. Window lower support and rivets

FIG. 95 Front door passive restraint — Beretta

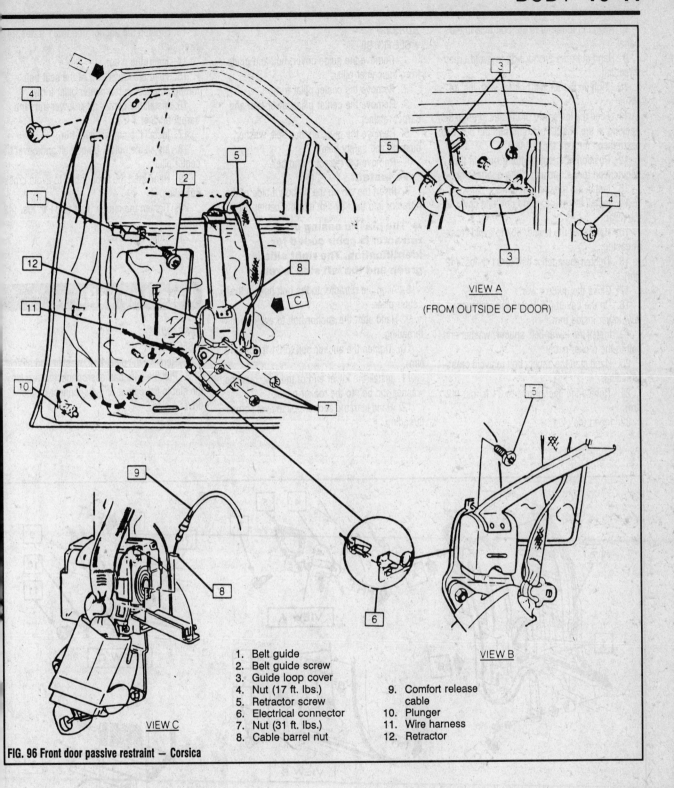

VIEW A
(FROM OUTSIDE OF DOOR)

VIEW B

VIEW C

1. Belt guide
2. Belt guide screw
3. Guide loop cover
4. Nut (17 ft. lbs.)
5. Retractor screw
6. Electrical connector
7. Nut (31 ft. lbs.)
8. Cable barrel nut
9. Comfort release cable
10. Plunger
11. Wire harness
12. Retractor

FIG. 96 Front door passive restraint — Corsica

8. Align the retractor to the bolt hole in the panel.

9. Hand start the anchor bolt to avoid cross-threading.

10. Tighten the anchor bolt to 31 ft. lbs. (42 Nm).

11. Feed the lower end of the belt through the opening in the quarter trim and pull the belt and escutcheon through the opening.

12. Position and engage the groove in the escutcheon to the opening in the quarter trim.

13. Install the quarter trim panel.

14. Install the guide, guide bolt and cover to the pillar.

15. Hand start the anchor bolt to avoid cross-threading.

16. Tighten the anchor bolt to 31 ft. lbs. (42 Nm).

17. Close the guide cover.

18. On the covertible, install the stationary bow lower inside trim.

19. Install the lower belt, spacer, washer and bolt to the rocker panel.

20. Hand start the anchor bolt to avoid cross-threading.

21. Tighten the anchor bolt to 31 ft. lbs. (42 Nm).

22. Insert the plug.

CORSICA

♦ SEE FIG. 98

1. Remove the guide cover, bolt and guide from the center pillar.

2. Remove the center pillar trim.

3. Remove the center pillar lower trim and carpet retainer.

5. Remove the plug, anchor bolt, washer, bushing and safety belt.

6. Remove the retractor and belt.

To Install:

7. Insert the tab on the outboard side of the retractor into the key slot into the center pillar.

➡ **The plastic casing on the retractor is color coded for identification. The right side is green and the left side is red.**

8. Align the retractor to the bolt hole in the center pillar.

9. Hand start the anchor bolt to avoid cross-threading.

10. Tighten the anchor bolt to 31 ft. lbs. (42 Nm).

11. Install the lower end of the belt, bushing, washer and bolt to the rocker panel.

12. Hand start the anchor bolt to avoid cross-threading.

13. Tighten the anchor bolt to 31 ft. lbs. (42 Nm).

14. Insert the plug.

15. Feed the lower end of the seat belt through the slot in the center pillar trim.

16. Install the center pillar lower trim and carpet retainer.

17. Install the center pillar trim.

18. Install the guide, guide bolt and cover the center pillar.

19. Hand start the anchor bolt to avoid cross threading.

20. Tighten the anchor bolt to 31 ft. lbs. (42 Nm).

21. Close the cover.

Inner Lap Belts

1988–90

♦ SEE FIG. 99

1. Remove the plug, bolt, washer and spacer.

2. Pull the wire harness connector through the slot in the carpet and disconnect on the driver's side.

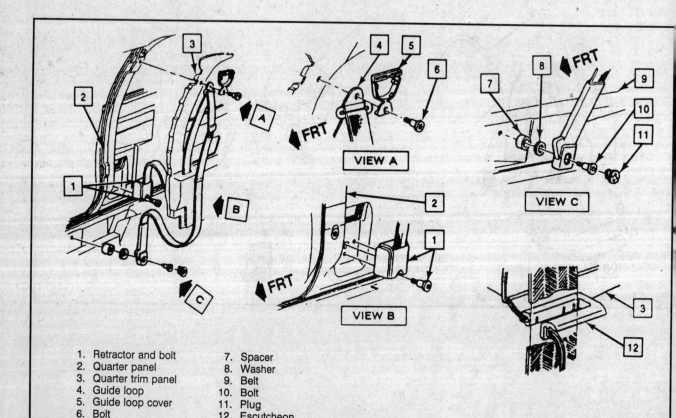

VIEW A

VIEW B

VIEW C

1. Retractor and bolt
2. Quarter panel
3. Quarter trim panel
4. Guide loop
5. Guide loop cover
6. Bolt
7. Spacer
8. Washer
9. Belt
10. Bolt
11. Plug
12. Escutcheon

FIG. 97 Front retractor, side shoulder belt — Beretta

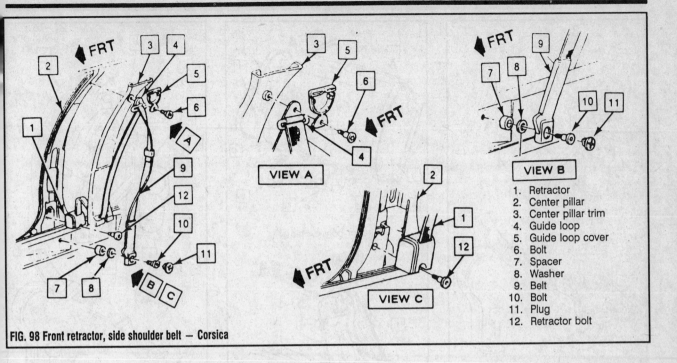

FIG. 98 Front retractor, side shoulder belt — Corsica

1. Retractor
2. Center pillar
3. Center pillar trim
4. Guide loop
5. Guide loop cover
6. Bolt
7. Spacer
8. Washer
9. Belt
10. Bolt
11. Plug
12. Retractor bolt

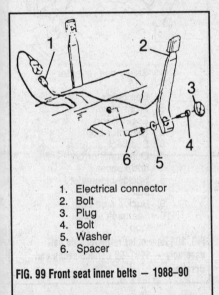

1. Electrical connector
2. Bolt
3. Plug
4. Bolt
5. Washer
6. Spacer

FIG. 99 Front seat inner belts — 1988–90

Front Seat Buckle Side Seat Belt Assemblies

1991–92
♦ SEE FIG. 100
1. Remove the plug, bolt, washer and spacer.
2. Pull the wire harness connector through the slot in the carpet and disconnect on the driver's side.

To install:
3. Connect the wire harness on the driver's side only.
4. Feed the connector and wire under the carpet through the slot in the carpet.
5. Install the spacer, washer, belt to the floor pan and align to the anchor hole in the floor.
6. Hand start the anchor bolts to avoid cross-threading.
7. Tighten the anchor bolts to 31 ft. lbs. (42 Nm).

Rear Seat Lap and Shoulder Belt Assembly

1988–90
CORSICA SEDAN AND BERETTA
♦ SEE FIG. 101
1. Remove the rear seat cushion.
2. Remove the bolt and buckle assembly.
3. Remove the seatback.
4. Remove the lower belt retaining bolt.
5. Remove the escutcheon trim.
6. Peel back the seat sound barrier assembly.

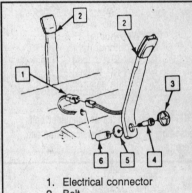

1. Electrical connector
2. Belt
3. Plug
4. Bolt
5. Washer
6. Spacer

FIG. 100 Front seat buckle-side seat belts — 1991–92

To install:
3. Hand start the anchor bolts to avoid cross-threading.
4. Connect the wire harness on the driver's side only.
5. Feed the connector and wire under the carpet through the slot in the carpet.
6. Install the spacer, washer, bolt and plug.
7. Tighten the anchor bolts to 31 ft. lbs. (42 Nm).

7. Remove the retractor bolt and thread the retractor web guide and belt assembly through the slot in the rear seat to the back window foundation assembly.
To install:
8. Thread the belt assembly through the slot in the rear seat to the back window foundation assembly. and engage the retractor webb guide to the foundation.
9. Tighten the retractor bolt to 31 ft. lbs. (42 Nm).
10. Install the escutcheon trim.
11. Install the seat sound barrier assembly.
12. Tighten the lower belt bolt to 31 ft. lbs. (42 Nm).

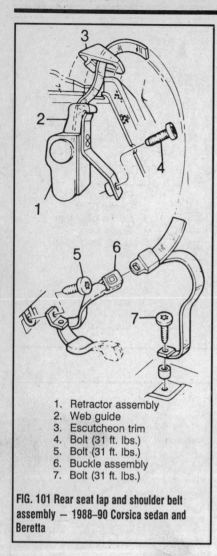

1. Retractor assembly
2. Web guide
3. Escutcheon trim
4. Bolt (31 ft. lbs.)
5. Bolt (31 ft. lbs.)
6. Buckle assembly
7. Bolt (31 ft. lbs.)

FIG. 101 Rear seat lap and shoulder belt assembly — 1988–90 Corsica sedan and Beretta

13. Install the seatback.
14. Install the bolt and buckle assembly and tighten the bolt to 31 ft. lbs. (42 Nm).
15. Install the seat cushion.

CORSICA HATCHBACK
▶ SEE FIG. 102

1. Remove the rear seat cushion and fold down seatback.
2. Remove the bolt and buckle assembly.
3. Remove the quarter trim panel.
4. Remove the outboard anchor bolt.
5. Remove the escutcheon trim bolt.
6. Remove the retractor bolt and retractor.

To install:

7. Position the retractor on the seatback support.
8. Hand start the retractor anchor bolt and the inner belt bolts to avoid cross-threading.
9. Tighten the anchor bolts to 31 ft. lbs. (42 Nm).

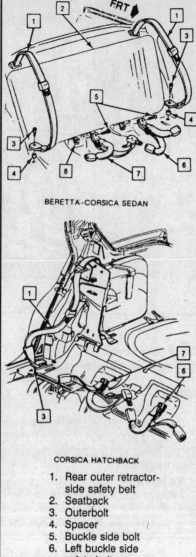

BERETTA-CORSICA SEDAN

CORSICA HATCHBACK

1. Rear outer retractor-side safety belt
2. Seatback
3. Outerbolt
4. Spacer
5. Buckle side bolt
6. Left buckle side safety belt
7. Right buckle side and center safety belt
8. Seatback anchor loop

FIG. 103 Rear seat center and outer buckle-side seat belt assembly — 1991–92

10. Install the escutcheon trim and hand start the guide anchor bolt to avoid cross-threading and tighten the anchor bolt to 31 ft. lbs. (42 Nm).
11. Install the outboard anchor bolt and tighten to 31 ft. lbs. (42 Nm).
12. Install the quarter trim.
13. Install the seatback and seat cushion.

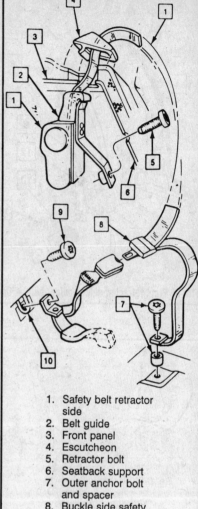

1. Safety belt retractor side
2. Belt guide
3. Front panel
4. Escutcheon
5. Retractor bolt
6. Seatback support
7. Outer anchor bolt and spacer
8. Buckle side safety belt
9. Buckle side bolt
10. Seatback anchor loop

FIG. 104 Rear outer retractor side belt assembly — 1991–92 Corsica sedan and Beretta

Rear Seat Center and Outer Buckle – Seat Belt Assemblies

1991–92
▶ SEE FIG. 103

1. Remove the rear seat cushion.
2. Remove the bolt from the right side combination outer buckle and center bolt.
3. Remove the bolt from the left buckle side.
4. remove the seat belts.

To install:

5. Install the seat belt to the floor pan on the Corsica hatchback and the rear seat back anchor loop on the Beretta and Corsica sedan.

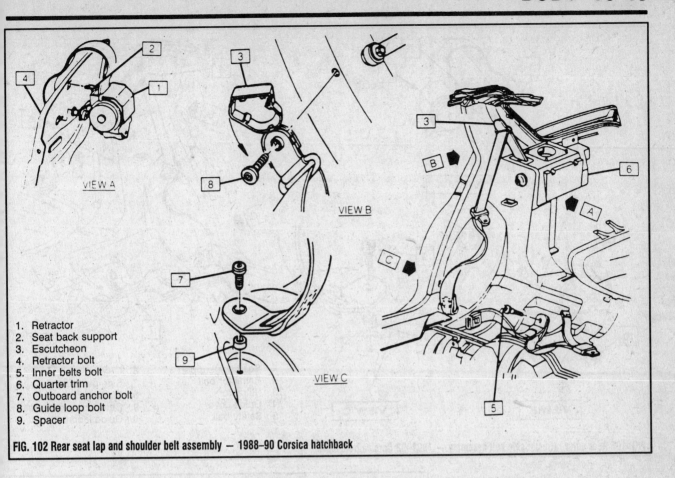

1. Retractor
2. Seat back support
3. Escutcheon
4. Retractor bolt
5. Inner belts bolt
6. Quarter trim
7. Outboard anchor bolt
8. Guide loop bolt
9. Spacer

FIG. 102 Rear seat lap and shoulder belt assembly — 1988–90 Corsica hatchback

6. Hand start the anchor bolts to avoid cross-threading.

7. Tighten the anchor bolts to 31 ft. lbs. (42 Nm).

8. Install the rear seat cushion.

Rear Outer Retractor Side Seat Belt

1991–92

CORSICA SEDAN AND BERETTA

▶ SEE FIG. 104

1. Remove the rear seat cushion and rear seatback.

2. Remove the rear quarter trim.

3. Remove the outboard anchor bolt and spacer.

4. Remove the escutcheon trim.

5. Peel back the seat sound barrier assembly.

6. Remove the retractor bolt from the seatabck support and lower the retractor into the rear compartment.

7. Feed the seat belt through the slot in the rear compartment front panel.

To install:

8. Feed the seat belt through the slot in the rear compartment front panel.

9. Align and engage the retractor webb guide to the seatback support.

10. Install and tighten the retractor bolt to 31 ft. lbs. (42 Nm).

11. Install the lower end of the belt to the outboard anchor plate in the floor pan.

12. Install the bolt and spacer.

13. Hand start the bolt to avoid cross-threading.

14. Tighten the anchor bolts to 31 ft. lbs. (42 Nm).

15. Install the escutcheon trim.

16. Install the seat sound barrier assembly.

17. Install the quarter trim panel.

18. Install the seatback and cushion.

CORSICA HATCHBACK

▶ SEE FIG. 105

1. Remove the rear seat cushion and fold down seatback.

2. Remove the bolt from the lower end of the belt outboard anchor.

3. Remove the quarter trim panel.

4. Lift the belt guide cover.

5. Remove the retractor bolt and retractor.

To install:

6. Position the retractor on the seatback support.

7. Hand start the retractor anchor bolt to avoid cross-threading.

8. Tighten the anchor bolts to 31 ft. lbs. (42 Nm).

9. Install the upper belt guide, cover and bolt to the pillar and hand start the anchor bolt to avoid cross-threading and tighten the anchor bolt to 31 ft. lbs. (42 Nm).

10. Install the lower end of the belt to outboard floor anchor.

11. Install the spacer and bolt and hand tighten, then tighten to 31 ft. lbs. (42 Nm).

12. Install the quarter trim.

13. Install the seatback and seat cushion.

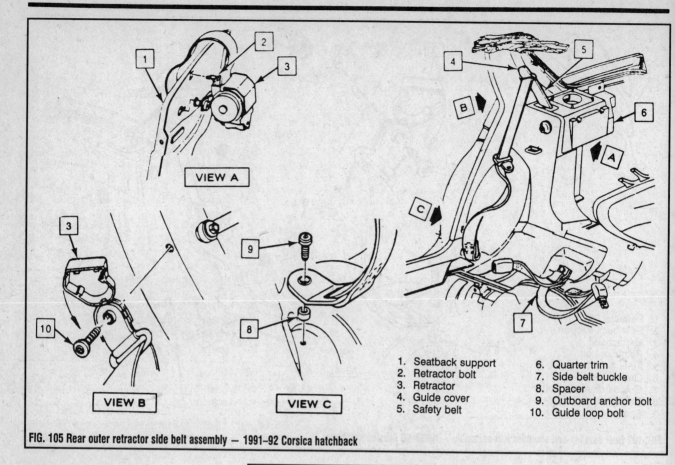

1. Seatback support
2. Retractor bolt
3. Retractor
4. Guide cover
5. Safety belt
6. Quarter trim
7. Side belt buckle
8. Spacer
9. Outboard anchor bolt
10. Guide loop bolt

FIG. 105 Rear outer retractor side belt assembly — 1991–92 Corsica hatchback

BERETTA CONVERTIBLES

► SEE FIG. 106

1. Remove the rear seat cushion and back.

2. Remove the quarter trim panel.

3. Remove the belt anchor bolt.

4. Remove the escutcheon screw.

5. Remove the retractor bolt and remove the belt assembly with retractor and escutcheon.

To install:

6. Make sure the belt is not twisted and install the belt assembly with retractor and escutcheon. Install the retractor bolt and tighten to 24 ft. lbs. (34 Nm).

7. Install the escutcheon screw.

8. Install and tighten the anchor bolt to 31 ft. lbs. (42 Nm).

9. Install the quarter trim.

10. Install the seatback and seat cushion.

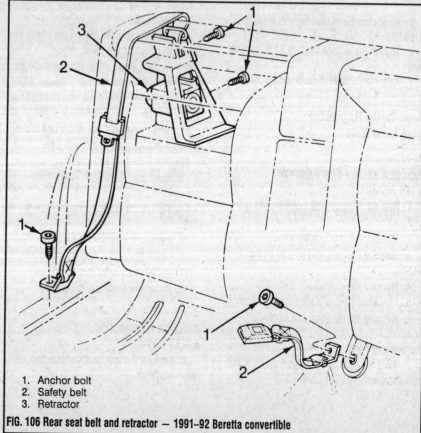

1. Anchor bolt
2. Safety belt
3. Retractor

FIG. 106 Rear seat belt and retractor — 1991–92 Beretta convertible

How to Remove Stains from Fabric Interior

For best results, spots and stains should be removed as soon as possible. Never use gasoline, lacquer thinner, acetone, nail polish remover or bleach. Use a 3' x 3" piece of cheesecloth. Squeeze most of the liquid from the fabric and wipe the stained fabric from the outside of the stain toward the center with a lifting motion. Turn the cheesecloth as soon as one side becomes soiled. When using water to remove a stain, be sure to wash the entire section after the spot has been removed to avoid water stains. Encrusted spots can be broken up with a dull knife and vacuumed before removing the stain.

Type of Stain	How to Remove It
Surface spots	Brush the spots out with a small hand brush or use a commercial preparation such as K2R to lift the stain.
Mildew	Clean around the mildew with warm suds. Rinse in cold water and soak the mildew area in a solution of 1 part table salt and 2 parts water. Wash with upholstery cleaner.
Water stains	Water stains in fabric materials can be removed with a solution made from 1 cup of table salt dissolved in 1 quart of water. Vigorously scrub the solution into the stain and rinse with clear water. Water stains in nylon or other synthetic fabrics should be removed with a commercial type spot remover.
Chewing gum, tar, crayons, shoe polish (greasy stains)	Do not use a cleaner that will soften gum or tar. Harden the deposit with an ice cube and scrape away as much as possible with a dull knife. Moisten the remainder with cleaning fluid and scrub clean.
Ice cream, candy	Most candy has a sugar base and can be removed with a cloth wrung out in warm water. Oily candy, after cleaning with warm water, should be cleaned with upholstery cleaner. Rinse with warm water and clean the remainder with cleaning fluid.
Wine, alcohol, egg, milk, soft drink (non-greasy stains)	Do not use soap. Scrub the stain with a cloth wrung out in warm water. Remove the remainder with cleaning fluid.
Grease, oil, lipstick, butter and related stains	Use a spot remover to avoid leaving a ring. Work from the outisde of the stain to the center and dry with a clean cloth when the spot is gone.
Headliners (cloth)	Mix a solution of warm water and foam upholstery cleaner to give thick suds. Use only foam—liquid may streak or spot. Clean the entire headliner in one operation using a circular motion with a natural sponge.
Headliner (vinyl)	Use a vinyl cleaner with a sponge and wipe clean with a dry cloth.
Seats and door panels	Mix 1 pint upholstery cleaner in 1 gallon of water. Do not soak the fabric around the buttons.
Leather or vinyl fabric	Use a multi-purpose cleaner full strength and a stiff brush. Let stand 2 minutes and scrub thoroughly. Wipe with a clean, soft rag.
Nylon or synthetic fabrics	For normal stains, use the same procedures you would for washing cloth upholstery. If the fabric is extremely dirty, use a multi-purpose cleaner full strength with a stiff scrub brush. Scrub thoroughly in all directions and wipe with a cotton towel or soft rag.

TORQUE SPECIFICATIONS

Component	U.S.	Metric
Doors		
Hinge to body		
1988-90:	15-20 ft. lbs.	20-28 Nm
1991-92:	18 ft. lbs.	24 Nm
Check link screws:	18 ft. lbs.	24 Nm
Lock module retaining screws:	62 inch lbs.	7 Nm
Front window channel retainer screws		
1988-90:	80-106 inch lbs.	9-12 Nm
1991-92:	97 inch lbs.	11 Nm
Rear regulator to sash bolts:	75 inch lbs.	8.5 Nm
Hood		
Hinge to hood bolts:	24 ft. lbs.	33 Nm
Rear compartment Lid		
Hinge to lid screws:	21 ft. lbs.	29 Nm
Lock retaining screws:	53 inch lbs.	6 Nm
Solenoid to lock screws:	53 inch lbs.	6 Nm
Hatchback lift window		
Hinge to lift window bolts:	19 ft. lbs.	25 Nm
Strut to body bolt:	30 ft. lbs.	40 Nm
Lock retaining nuts:	124 inch lbs.	14 Nm
Solenoid to lock screws:	53 inch lbs.	6 Nm
Bumpers		
Front bumper to absorber bolts:	18-25 ft. lbs.	24-34 Nm
Rear bumper to absorber bolts:	18-25 ft. lbs.	24-34 Nm
Seats		
1988-90		
Seat adjuster to floor pan bolts:	10 ft. lbs.	13 Nm
Recliner to seat frame bolts:	18 ft. lbs.	25 Nm
Seat adjuster to seat frame nut:	10 ft. lbs.	13 Nm
Track guide to floor pan bolt:	10 ft. lbs.	13 Nm
1991-92		
Seat adjuster to floor pan bolts:	26 ft. lbs.	36 Nm
Recliner to seat frame bolts:	18 ft. lbs.	24 Nm
Seat adjuster to seat frame nut:	21 ft. lbs.	29 Nm
Rear seat cushion to floor pan bolts:	11 ft. lbs.	15 Nm
Rear seat back anchor bolts:	31 ft. lbs.	42 Nm
Foldown rear seat back bolts:	18 ft. lbs.	25 Nm
Seat Belts		
Seat belt anchor and retractor bolts:	31 ft. lbs.	42 Nm

GLOSSARY

AIR/FUEL RATIO: The ratio of air to gasoline by weight in the fuel mixture drawn into the engine.

AIR INJECTION: One method of reducing harmful exhaust emissions by injecting air into each of the exhaust ports of an engine. The fresh air entering the hot exhaust manifold causes any remaining fuel to be burned before it can exit the tailpipe.

ALTERNATOR: A device used for converting mechanical energy into electrical energy.

AMMETER: An instrument, calibrated in amperes, used to measure the flow of an electrical current in a circuit. Ammeters are always connected in series with the circuit being tested.

AMPERE: The rate of flow of electrical current present when one volt of electrical pressure is applied against one ohm of electrical resistance.

ANALOG COMPUTER: Any microprocessor that uses similar (analogous) electrical signals to make its calculations.

ARMATURE: A laminated, soft iron core wrapped by a wire that converts electrical energy to mechanical energy as in a motor or relay. When rotated in a magnetic field, it changes mechanical energy into electrical energy as in a generator.

ATMOSPHERIC PRESSURE: The pressure on the Earth's surface caused by the weight of the air in the atmosphere. At sea level, this pressure is 14.7 psi at 32°F (101 kPa at 0°C).

ATOMIZATION: The breaking down of a liquid into a fine mist that can be suspended in air.

AXIAL PLAY: Movement parallel to a shaft or bearing bore.

BACKFIRE: The sudden combustion of gases in the intake or exhaust system that results in a loud explosion.

BACKLASH: The clearance or play between two parts, such as meshed gears.

BACKPRESSURE: Restrictions in the exhaust system that slow the exit of exhaust gases from the combustion chamber.

BAKELITE: A heat resistant, plastic insulator material commonly used in printed circuit boards and transistorized components.

BALL BEARING: A bearing made up of hardened inner and outer races between which hardened steel balls roll.

BALLAST RESISTOR: A resistor in the primary ignition circuit that lowers voltage after the engine is started to reduce wear on ignition components.

BEARING: A friction reducing, supportive device usually located between a stationary part and a moving part.

BIMETAL TEMPERATURE SENSOR: Any sensor or switch made of two dissimilar types of metal that bend when heated or cooled due to the different expansion rates of the alloys. These types of sensors usually function as an on/off switch.

BLOWBY: Combustion gases, composed of water vapor and unburned fuel, that leak past the piston rings into the crankcase during normal engine operation. These gases are removed by the PCV system to prevent the buildup of harmful acids in the crankcase.

BRAKE PAD: A brake shoe and lining assembly used with disc brakes.

BRAKE SHOE: The backing for the brake lining. The term is, however, usually applied to the assembly of the brake backing and lining.

BUSHING: A liner, usually removable, for a bearing; an anti-friction liner used in place of a bearing.

BYPASS: System used to bypass ballast resistor during engine cranking to increase voltage supplied to the coil.

CALIPER: A hydraulically activated device in a disc brake system, which is mounted straddling the brake rotor (disc). The caliper contains at least one piston and two brake pads. Hydraulic pressure on the piston(s) forces the pads against the rotor.

CAMSHAFT: A shaft in the engine on which are the lobes (cams) which operate the valves. The camshaft is driven by the crankshaft, via a belt, chain or gears, at one half the crankshaft speed.

CAPACITOR: A device which stores an electrical charge.

CARBON MONOXIDE (CO): A colorless, odorless gas given off as a normal byproduct of combustion. It is poisonous and extremely dangerous in confined areas, building up slowly to toxic levels without warning if adequate ventilation is not available.

CARBURETOR: A device, usually mounted on the intake manifold of an engine, which mixes the air and fuel in the proper proportion to allow even combustion.

CATALYTIC CONVERTER: A device installed in the exhaust system, like a muffler, that converts harmful byproducts of combustion into carbon dioxide and water vapor by means of a heat-producing chemical reaction.

CENTRIFUGAL ADVANCE: A mechanical method of advancing the spark timing by using fly weights in the distributor that react to centrifugal force generated by the distributor shaft rotation.

CHECK VALVE: Any one-way valve installed to permit the flow of air, fuel or vacuum in one direction only.

CHOKE: A device, usually a movable valve, placed in the intake path of a carburetor to restrict the flow of air.

CIRCUIT: Any unbroken path through which an electrical current can flow. Also used to describe fuel flow in some instances.

CIRCUIT BREAKER: A switch which protects an electrical circuit from overload by opening the circuit when the current flow exceeds a predetermined level. Some circuit breakers must be reset manually, while most reset automatically

COIL (IGNITION): A transformer in the ignition circuit which steps up the voltage provided to the spark plugs.

COMBINATION MANIFOLD: An assembly which includes both the intake and exhaust manifolds in one casting.

COMBINATION VALVE: A device used in some fuel systems that routes fuel vapors to a charcoal storage canister instead of venting them into the atmosphere. The valve relieves fuel tank pressure and allows fresh air into the tank as the fuel level drops to prevent a vapor lock situation.

COMPRESSION RATIO: The comparison of the total volume of the cylinder and combustion chamber with the piston at BDC and the piston at TDC.

CONDENSER: 1. An electrical device which acts to store an electrical charge, preventing voltage surges.
2. A radiator-like device in the air conditioning system in which refrigerant gas condenses into a liquid, giving off heat.

CONDUCTOR: Any material through which an electrical current can be transmitted easily.

CONTINUITY: Continuous or complete circuit. Can be checked with an ohmmeter.

COUNTERSHAFT: An intermediate shaft which is rotated by a mainshaft and transmits, in turn, that rotation to a working part.

CRANKCASE: The lower part of an engine in which the crankshaft and related parts operate.

CRANKSHAFT: The main driving shaft of an engine which receives reciprocating motion from the pistons and converts it to rotary motion.

CYLINDER: In an engine, the round hole in the engine block in which the piston(s) ride.

CYLINDER BLOCK: The main structural member of an engine in which is found the cylinders, crankshaft and other principal parts.

CYLINDER HEAD: The detachable portion of the engine, fastened, usually, to the top of the cylinder block, containing all or most of the combustion chambers. On overhead valve engines, it contains the valves and their operating parts. On overhead cam engines, it contains the camshaft as well.

DEAD CENTER: The extreme top or bottom of the piston stroke.

DETONATION: An unwanted explosion of the air/fuel mixture in the combustion chamber caused by excess heat and compression, advanced timing, or an overly lean mixture. Also referred to as "ping".

DIAPHRAGM: A thin, flexible wall separating two cavities, such as in a vacuum advance unit.

DIESELING: A condition in which hot spots in the combustion chamber cause the engine to run on after the key is turned off.

DIFFERENTIAL: A geared assembly which allows the transmission of motion between drive axles, giving one axle the ability to turn faster than the other.

DIODE: An electrical device that will allow current to flow in one direction only.

DISC BRAKE: A hydraulic braking assembly consisting of a brake disc, or rotor, mounted on an axle, and a caliper assembly containing, usually two brake pads which are activated by hydraulic pressure. The pads are forced against the sides of the disc, creating friction which slows the vehicle.

DISTRIBUTOR: A mechanically driven device on an engine which is responsible for electrically firing the spark plug at a predetermined point of the piston stroke.

DOWEL PIN: A pin, inserted in mating holes in two different parts allowing those parts to maintain a fixed relationship.

DRUM BRAKE: A braking system which consists of two brake shoes and one or two wheel cylinders, mounted on a fixed backing plate, and a brake drum, mounted on an axle, which revolves around the assembly. Hydraulic action applied to the wheel cylinders forces the shoes outward against the drum, creating friction, slowing the vehicle.

DWELL: The rate, measured in degrees of shaft rotation, at which an electrical circuit cycles on and off.

ELECTRONIC CONTROL UNIT (ECU): Ignition module, amplifier or igniter. See Module for definition.

ELECTRONIC IGNITION: A system in which the timing and firing of the spark plugs is controlled by an electronic control unit, usually called a module. These systems have no points or condenser.

ENDPLAY: The measured amount of axial movement in a shaft.

ENGINE: A device that converts heat into mechanical energy.

EXHAUST MANIFOLD: A set of cast passages or pipes which conduct exhaust gases from the engine.

FEELER GAUGE: A blade, usually metal, of precisely predetermined thickness, used to measure the clearance between two parts. These blades usually are available in sets of assorted thicknesses.

F-HEAD: An engine configuration in which the intake valves are in the cylinder head, while the camshaft and exhaust valves are located in the cylinder block. The camshaft operates the intake valves via lifters and pushrods, while it operates the exhaust valves directly.

FIRING ORDER: The order in which combustion occurs in the cylinders of an engine. Also the order in which spark is distributed to the plugs by the distributor.

FLATHEAD: An engine configuration in which the camshaft and all the valves are located in the cylinder block.

FLOODING: The presence of too much fuel in the intake manifold and combustion chamber which prevents the air/fuel mixture from firing, thereby causing a no-start situation.

FLYWHEEL: A disc shaped part bolted to the rear end of the crankshaft. Around the outer perimeter is affixed the ring gear. The starter drive engages the ring gear, turning the flywheel, which rotates the crankshaft, imparting the initial starting motion to the engine.

FOOT POUND (ft.lb. or sometimes, ft. lbs.): The amount of energy or work needed to raise an item weighing one pound, a distance of one foot.

FUSE: A protective device in a circuit which prevents circuit overload by breaking the circuit when a specific amperage is present. The device is constructed around a strip or wire of a lower amperage rating than the circuit it is designed to protect. When an amperage higher than that stamped on the fuse is present in the circuit, the strip or wire melts, opening the circuit.

GEAR RATIO: The ratio between the number of teeth on meshing gears.

GENERATOR: A device which converts mechanical energy into electrical energy.

HEAT RANGE: The measure of a spark plug's ability to dissipate heat from its firing end. The higher the heat range, the hotter the plug fires.

HUB: The center part of a wheel or gear.

HYDROCARBON (HC): Any chemical compound made up of hydrogen and carbon. A major pollutant formed by the engine as a byproduct of combustion.

HYDROMETER: An instrument used to measure the specific gravity of a solution.

INCH POUND (in.lb. or sometimes, in. lbs.): One twelfth of a foot pound.

INDUCTION: A means of transferring electrical energy in the form of a magnetic field. Principle used in the ignition coil to increase voltage.

INJECTION PUMP: A device, usually mechanically operated, which meters and delivers fuel under pressure to the fuel injector.

INJECTOR: A device which receives metered fuel under relatively low pressure and is activated to inject the fuel into the engine under relatively high pressure at a predetermined time.

INPUT SHAFT: The shaft to which torque is applied, usually carrying the driving gear or gears.

INTAKE MANIFOLD: A casting of passages or pipes used to conduct air or a fuel/air mixture to the cylinders.

JOURNAL: The bearing surface within which a shaft operates.

KEY: A small block usually fitted in a notch between a shaft and a hub to prevent slippage of the two parts.

MANIFOLD: A casting of passages or set of pipes which connect the cylinders to an inlet or outlet source.

MANIFOLD VACUUM: Low pressure in an engine intake manifold formed just below the throttle plates. Manifold vacuum is highest at idle and drops under acceleration.

MASTER CYLINDER: The primary fluid pressurizing device in a hydraulic system. In automotive use, it is found in brake and hydraulic clutch systems and is pedal activated, either directly or, in a power brake system, through the power booster.

MODULE: Electronic control unit, amplifier or igniter of solid state or integrated design which controls the current flow in the ignition primary circuit based on input from the pick-up coil. When the module opens the primary circuit, the high secondary voltage is induced in the coil.

NEEDLE BEARING: A bearing which consists of a number (usually a large number) of long, thin rollers.

OHM:(Ω) The unit used to measure the resistance of conductor to electrical flow. One ohm is the amount of resistance that limits current flow to one ampere in a circuit with one volt of pressure.

OHMMETER: An instrument used for measuring the resistance, in ohms, in an electrical circuit.

OUTPUT SHAFT: The shaft which transmits torque from a device, such as a transmission.

OVERDRIVE: A gear assembly which produces more shaft revolutions than that transmitted to it.

OVERHEAD CAMSHAFT (OHC): An engine configuration in which the camshaft is mounted on top of the cylinder head and operates the valves either directly or by means of rocker arms.

OVERHEAD VALVE (OHV): An engine configuration in which all of the valves are located in the cylinder head and the camshaft is located in the cylinder block. The camshaft operates the valves via lifters and pushrods.

OXIDES OF NITROGEN (NOx): Chemical compounds of nitrogen produced as a byproduct of combustion. They combine with hydrocarbons to produce smog.

OXYGEN SENSOR: Used with the feedback system to sense the presence of oxygen in the exhaust gas and signal the computer which can reference the voltage signal to an air/fuel ratio.

PINION: The smaller of two meshing gears.

PISTON RING: An open ended ring which fits into a groove on the outer diameter of the piston. Its chief function is to form a seal between the piston and cylinder wall. Most automotive pistons have three rings: two for compression sealing; one for oil sealing.

PRELOAD: A predetermined load placed on a bearing during assembly or by adjustment.

PRIMARY CIRCUIT: Is the low voltage side of the ignition system which consists of the ignition switch, ballast resistor or resistance wire, bypass, coil, electronic control unit and pick-up coil as well as the connecting wires and harnesses.

PRESS FIT: The mating of two parts under pressure, due to the inner diameter of one being smaller than the outer diameter of the other, or vice versa; an interference fit.

RACE: The surface on the inner or outer ring of a bearing on which the balls, needles or rollers move.

REGULATOR: A device which maintains the amperage and/or voltage levels of a circuit at predetermined values.

RELAY: A switch which automatically opens and/or closes a circuit.

RESISTANCE: The opposition to the flow of current through a circuit or electrical device, and is measured in ohms. Resistance is equal to the voltage divided by the amperage.

RESISTOR: A device, usually made of wire, which offers a preset amount of resistance in an electrical circuit.

RING GEAR: The name given to a ring-shaped gear attached to a differential case,or affixed to a flywheel or as part a planetary gear set.

ROLLER BEARING: A bearing made up of hardened inner and outer races between which hardened steel rollers move.

ROTOR: 1. The disc-shaped part of a disc brake assembly, upon which the brake pads bear; also called, brake disc.
2. The device mounted atop the distributor shaft, which passes current to the distributor cap tower contacts.

SECONDARY CIRCUIT: The high voltage side of the ignition system, usually above 20,000 volts. The secondary includes the ignition coil, coil wire, distributor cap and rotor, spark plug wires and spark plugs.

SENDING UNIT: A mechanical, electrical, hydraulic or electromagnetic device which transmits information to a gauge.

SENSOR: Any device designed to measure engine operating conditions or ambient pressures and temperatures. Usually electronic in nature and designed to send a voltage signal to an on-board computer, some sensors may operate as a simple on/off switch or they may provide a variable voltage signal (like a potentiometer) as conditions or measured parameters change.

SHIM: Spacers of precise, predetermined thickness used between parts to establish a proper working relationship.

SLAVE CYLINDER: In automotive use, a device in the hydraulic clutch system which is activated by hydraulic force, disengaging the clutch.

SOLENOID: A coil used to produce a magnetic field, the effect of which is to produce work.

SPARK PLUG: A device screwed into the combustion chamber of a spark ignition engine. The basic construction is a conductive core inside of a ceramic insulator, mounted in an outer conductive base. An electrical charge from the spark plug wire travels along the conductive core and jumps a preset air gap to a grounding point or points at the end of the conductive base. The resultant spark ignites the fuel/air mixture in the combustion chamber.

SPLINES: Ridges machined or cast onto the outer diameter of a shaft or inner diameter of a bore to enable parts to mate without rotation.

TACHOMETER: A device used to measure the rotary speed of an engine, shaft, gear, etc., usually in rotations per minute.

THERMOSTAT: A valve, located in the cooling system of an engine, which is closed when cold and opens gradually in response to engine heating, controlling the temperature of the coolant and rate of coolant flow.

TOP DEAD CENTER (TDC): The point at which the piston reaches the top of its travel on the compression stroke.

TORQUE: The twisting force applied to an object.

TORQUE CONVERTER: A turbine used to transmit power from a driving member to a driven member via hydraulic action, providing changes in drive ratio and torque. In automotive use, it links the driveplate at the rear of the engine to the automatic transmission.

TRANSDUCER: A device used to change a force into an electrical signal.

TRANSISTOR: A semi-conductor component which can be actuated by a small voltage to perform an electrical switching function.

TUNE-UP: A regular maintenance function, usually associated with the replacement and adjustment of parts and components in the electrical and fuel systems of a vehicle for the purpose of attaining optimum performance.

TURBOCHARGER: An exhaust driven pump which compresses intake air and forces it into the combustion chambers at higher than atmospheric pressures. The increased air pressure allows more fuel to be burned and results in increased horsepower being produced.

VACUUM ADVANCE: A device which advances the ignition timing in response to increased engine vacuum.

VACUUM GAUGE: An instrument used to measure the presence of vacuum in a chamber.

VALVE: A device which control the pressure, direction of flow or rate of flow of a liquid or gas.

VALVE CLEARANCE: The measured gap between the end of the valve stem and the rocker arm, cam lobe or follower that activates the valve.

VISCOSITY: The rating of a liquid's internal resistance to flow.

VOLTMETER: An instrument used for measuring electrical force in units called volts. Voltmeters are always connected parallel with the circuit being tested.

WHEEL CYLINDER: Found in the automotive drum brake assembly, it is a device, actuated by hydraulic pressure, which, through internal pistons, pushes the brake shoes outward against the drums.

MASTER

INDEX